Ruth Rendell

INSPECTOR WEXFORD

TED SMART

A TED SMART Publication

This edition first published by Cresset Editions
in 1993
an imprint of the Random House Group
20 Vauxhall Bridge Road
London SW1V 2SA

ISBN 0 09 182505 9

Jacket photograph by Tony Nutley

Typeset in Baskerville 11.5/13.5 by
Pure Tech Corporation, Pondicherry, India
Printed and bound in Great Britain by
Mackays of Chatham PLC, Chatham, Kent

From Doon With Death

The verses at the beginning of each chapter and the
inscriptions in Minna's books all appear in *The
Oxford Book of Victorian Verse*.

CONTENTS

For Don

From Doon With Death

You have broken my heart. There, I have written it. Not for you to read, Minna, for this letter will never be sent, never shrink and wither under your laughter, little lips prim and pleated, laughter like dulcimer music. . . .

Shall I tell you of the Muse who awaited me? I wanted you to walk beside me into her vaulted halls. There were the springs of Helicon! I would furnish you with the food of the soul, the bread that is prose and the wine that is poetry. Ah, the wine, Minna. . . . This is the rose-red blood of the troubadour!

Never shall I make that journey, Minna, for when I brought you the wine you returned to me the waters of indifference. I wrapped the bread in gold but you hid my loaves in the crock of contempt.

Truly you have broken my heart and dashed the wine-cup against the wall. . . .

CHAPTER ONE

Call once yet,
In a voice that she will know,
'Margaret, Margaret!'

Matthew Arnold, *The Forsaken Merman*

'I think you're getting things a bit out of proportion, Mr Parsons,' Burden said. He was tired and he'd been going to take his wife to the pictures. Besides, the first things he'd noticed when Parsons brought him into the room were the books in the rack by the fireplace. The titles were enough to give the most level-headed man the jitters, quite enough to make a man anxious where no ground for anxiety existed: *Palmer the Poisoner, The Trial of Madeleine Smith, Three Drowned Brides, Famous Trials, Notable British Trials.*

'Don't you think your reading has been preying on your mind?'

'I'm interested in crime,' Parsons said. 'It's a hobby of mine.'

'I can see that.' Burden wasn't going to sit down if he could avoid it. 'Look, you can't say your wife's actually missing. You've been home one and a half hours and she isn't here. That's all. She's probably gone to the pictures. As a matter of fact I'm on my way there now with my wife. I expect we'll meet her coming out.'

'Margaret wouldn't do that, Mr Burden. I know her and you don't. We've been married nearly six years and in all that time I've never come home to an empty house.'

'I'll tell you what I'll do. I'll drop in on my way back. But you can bet your bottom dollar she'll be home by then.' He

1

started moving towards the door. 'Look, get on to the station if you like. It won't do any harm.'

'No, I won't do that. It was just with you living down the road and being an inspector. . . .'

And being off duty, Burden thought. If I was a doctor instead of a policeman I'd be able to have private patients on the side. I bet he wouldn't be so keen on my services if there was any question of a fee.

Sitting in the half-empty dark cinema he thought: Well, it is funny. Normal ordinary wives as conventional as Mrs Parsons, wives who always have a meal ready for their husbands on the dot of six, don't suddenly go off without leaving a note.

'I thought you said this was a good film,' he whispered to his wife.

'Well, the critics liked it.'

'Oh, critics,' he said.

Another man, that could be it. But Mrs Parsons? Or it could be an accident. He'd been a bit remiss not getting Parsons to phone the station straight away.

'Look, love,' he said. 'I can't stand this. You stay and see the end. I've got to get back to Parsons.'

'I wish I'd married that reporter who was so keen on me.'

'You must be joking,' Burden said. 'He'd have stayed out all night putting the paper to bed. Or the editor's secretary.'

He charged up Tabard Road, then made himself stroll when he got to the Victorian house where Parsons lived. It was all in darkness, the curtains in the big bay downstairs undrawn. The step was whitened, the brass kerb above it polished. Mrs Parsons must have been a house-proud woman. Must have been? Why not, still was?

Parsons opened the door before he had a chance to knock. He still looked tidy, neatly dressed in an oldish suit, his tie knotted tight. But his face was greenish grey. It reminded Burden of a drowned face he had once seen on a mortuary

2

slab. They had put the glasses back on the spongy nose to help the girl who had come to identify him.

'She hasn't come back,' he said. His voice sounded as if he had a cold coming. But it was probably only fear.

'Let's have a cup of tea,' Burden said. 'Have a cup of tea and talk about it.'

'I keep thinking what could have happened to her. It's so open round here. I suppose it would be, being country.'

'It's those books you read,' Burden said. 'It's not healthy.' He looked again at the shiny paper covers. On the spine of one was a jumble of guns and knives against a blood-red background. 'Not for a layman,' he said. 'Can I use your phone?'

'It's in the front room.'

'I'll get on to the station. There might be something from the hospitals.'

The front room looked as if nobody ever sat in it. With some dismay he noted its polished shabbiness. So far he hadn't seen a stick of furniture that looked less than fifty years old. Burden went into all kinds of houses and he knew antique furniture when he saw it. But this wasn't antique and nobody could have chosen it because it was beautiful or rare. It was just old. Old enough to be cheap, Burden thought, and at the same time young enough not to be expensive. The kettle whistled and he heard Parsons fumbling with china in the kitchen. A cup crashed on the floor. It sounded as if they had kept the old concrete floor. It was enough to give anyone the creeps, he thought again, sitting in these high-ceilinged rooms, hearing unexplained inexplicable creaks from the stairs and the cupboard, reading about poison and hangings and blood.

'I've reported your wife as missing,' he said to Parsons. 'There's nothing from the hospitals.'

Parsons turned on the light in the back room and Burden followed him in. It must have a weak bulb under the parchment lampshade that hung from the centre of the ceiling.

About sixty watts, he thought. The shade forced all the light down, leaving the ceiling, with its plaster decorations of bulbous fruit, dark and in the corners blotched with deeper shadow. Parsons put the cups down on the side-board, a vast mahogany thing more like a fantastic wooden house than a piece of furniture, with its tiers and galleries and jutting beaded shelves. Burden sat down in a chair with wooden arms and seat of brown corduroy. The lino struck cold through the thick soles of his shoes.

'Have you any idea at all where your wife could have gone?'

'I've been trying to think. I've been racking my brains. I can't think of anywhere.'

'What about her friends? Her mother?'

'Her mother's dead. We haven't got any friends here. We only came here six months ago.'

Burden stirred his tea. Outside it had been close, humid. Here in this thick-walled dark place, he supposed, it must always feel like winter.

'Look,' he said, 'I don't like to say this, but somebody's bound to ask you. It might as well be me. Could she have gone out with some man? I'm sorry, but I had to ask.'

'Of course you had to ask. I know, it's all in here.' He tapped the bookcase. 'Just routine enquiries, isn't it? But you're wrong. Not Margaret. It's laughable.' He paused, not laughing. 'Margaret's a good woman. She's a lay preacher at the Wesleyan place down the road.'

No point in pursuing it, Burden thought. Others would ask him, probe into his private life whether he liked it or not, if she still hadn't got home when the last train came in and the last bus had rolled into Kingsmarkham garage.

'I suppose you've looked all over the house?' he asked. He had driven down this road twice a day for a year but he couldn't remember whether the house he was sitting in had two floors or three. His policeman's brain tried to reassemble the retinal photograph on his policeman's eye. A bay window at the bottom, two flat sash windows above it and – yes, two smaller ones above that under the slated eyelids of the roof. An ugly house, he thought, ugly and forbidding.

'I looked in the bedrooms,' Parsons said. He stopped pacing and hope coloured his cheeks. Fear whitened them again as he said: 'You think she might be up in the attics? Fainted or something?'

She would hardly still be there if she'd only fainted, Burden thought. A brain haemorrhage, yes, or some sort of accident. 'Obviously we ought to look,' he said. 'I took it for granted you'd looked.'

'I called out. We hardly ever go up there. The rooms aren't used.'

'Come on,' Burden said.

The light in the hall was even dimmer than the one in the dining-room. The little bulb shed a pallid glow on to a woven pinkish runner, on lino patterned to look like parquet in dark and lighter brown. Parsons went first and Burden followed him up the steep stairs. The house was biggish, but the materials which had been used to build it were poor and the workmanship unskilled. Four doors opened off the first landing and these were panelled but without beading and they looked flimsy. The flat rectangles of plywood in their frames reminded Burden of blind blocked-up windows on the sides of old houses.

'I've looked in the bedrooms,' Parsons said. 'Good heavens, she may be lying helpless up there!'

He pointed up the narrow uncarpeted flight and Burden noticed how he had said 'Good heavens!' and not 'God!' or 'My God!' as some men might have done.

'I've just remembered, there aren't any bulbs in the attic lights.' Parsons went into the front bedroom and unscrewed the bulb from the central lamp fitting. 'Mind how you go,' he said.

It was pitchy dark on the staircase. Burden flung open the door that faced him. By now he was certain they were going to find her sprawled on the floor and he wanted to get the discovery over as soon as possible. All the way up the stairs he'd been anticipating the look on Wexford's face when he told him she'd been there all along.

A dank coldness breathed out of the attic, a chill mingled with the smell of camphor. The room was partly furnished. Burden could just make out the shape of a bed. Parsons stumbled over to it and stood on the cotton counterpane to fit the bulb into the lamp socket. Like the ones downstairs it gave only an unsatisfactory light, which, streaming faintly through a shade punctured all over with tiny holes, patterned the ceiling and the distempered walls with yellowish dots. The window was uncurtained. A bright cold moon swam into the black square and disappeared again under the scalloped edge of a cloud.

'She's not in here,' Parsons said. His shoes had made dusty footprints on the white stuff that covered the bedstead like a shroud.

Burden lifted a corner of it and looked under the bed, the only piece of furniture in the room.

'Try the other room,' he said.

Once more Parsons went through the tedious, maddeningly slow motions of removing the light bulb. Now only the chill radiance from the window lit their way into the second attic. This was smaller and more crowded. Burden opened a cupboard and raised the lids from two trunks. He could see Parsons staring at him, thinking perhaps about what he called his hobby and about the things trunks could contain. But these were full of books, old books of the kind you sometimes see in stands outside second-hand shops.

The cupboard was empty and inside it the paper was peeling from the wall, but there were no spiders. Mrs Parsons was a house-proud woman.

'It's half past ten,' Burden said, squinting at his watch. 'The last train doesn't get in till one. She could be on that.'

Parsons said obstinately, 'She wouldn't go anywhere by train.'

They went downstairs again, pausing to restore the light bulb to the front bedroom. There was something sinister and creepy about the stair-well that could have been so easily dispelled, Burden thought, by white paint and stronger lights. As they descended he reflected momentarily on this woman and the life she lived here, going fussily about her chores, trying to bring a little smartness to the mud-coloured wood-work, the ugly ridged linoleum.

'I don't know what to do,' Parsons said.

Burden didn't want to go back into the little diningroom with the big furniture, the cold tea-dregs in their two cups. By now Jean would be back from the cinema.

'You could try phoning round her friends at the church,' he said, edging towards the front door. If Parsons only knew how many reports they got in of missing women and how few, how tiny a percentage, turned up dead in fields or chopped in trunks. . . .

'At this time of night?'

Parsons looked almost shocked, as if the habits of a lifetime, the rule that you never called on anyone after nine o'clock, mustn't be broken even in a crisis.

'Take a couple of aspirins and try to get some sleep,' Burden said. 'If anything comes up you can give me a ring. We've told the station. We can't do anything more. They'll let you know as soon as they hear.'

'What about tomorrow morning?'

If he'd been a woman, Burden thought, he'd beg me to stay. He'd cling to me and say, Don't leave me!

'I'll look in on my way to the station,' he said.

Parsons didn't shut the door until he was half-way up the street. He looked back once and saw the white bewildered face, the faint glow from the hall falling on to the brass step. Then, feeling helpless because he had brought the man no comfort, he raised his hand in a half-wave.

The streets were empty, still with the almost tangible

silence of the countryside at night. Perhaps she was at the station now, scuttling guiltily across the platform, down the wooden stairs, gathering together in her mind the threads of the alibi she had concocted. It would have to be good, Burden thought, remembering the man who waited on the knife edge that spanned hope and panic.

It was out of his way, but he went to the corner of Tabard Road and looked up the High Street. From here he could see right up to the beginning of the Stowerton Road where the last cars were leaving the forecourt of The Olive and Dove. The market place was empty, the only people to be seen a pair of lovers standing on the Kingsbrook Bridge. As he watched the Stowerton bus appeared between the Scotch pines on the horizon. It vanished again in the dip beyond the bridge. Hand in hand, the lovers ran to the stop in the centre of the market place as the bus pulled in close against the dismantled cattle stands. Nobody got off. Burden sighed and went home.

'She hasn't turned up,' he said to his wife.

'It *is* funny, you know, Mike. I should have said she was the last person to go off with some man.'

'Not much to look at?'

'I wouldn't say that exactly,' Jean said. 'She looked so – well, respectable. Flat-heeled shoes, no make-up, tidy sort of perm with hair-grips in it. You know what I mean. You must have seen her.'

'I may have done,' Burden said. 'It didn't register.'

'But I wouldn't call her plain. She's got a funny old-fashioned kind of face, the sort of face you see in family albums. You might not admire it, Mike, but you wouldn't forget her face.'

'Well, I've forgotten it,' Burden said. He dismissed Mrs Parsons to the back of his mind and they talked about the film.

CHAPTER TWO

One forenoon the she-bird crouched not on the nest,
Nor returned that afternoon, nor the next,
Nor ever appeared again.

Walt Whitman, *The Brown Bird*

Burden slept quickly, used to crises. Even here, a market town
he had expected to find dull after Brighton, the C.I.D. were
seldom idle.

The telephone rang at seven.

'Burden speaking.'

'This is Ronald Parsons. She hasn't come back. And, Mr
Burden – she hasn't taken a coat.'

It was the end of May and it had been a squally cold
month. A sharp breeze ruffled his bedroom curtains. He sat
up.

'Are you sure?' he asked.

'I couldn't sleep. I started going through her clothes and
I'm positive she hasn't taken a coat. She's only got three: a
raincoat, her winter coat and an old one she does the gardening in.'

Burden suggested a suit.

'She's only got one costume.' Parsons' use of the old-
fashioned word was in character. 'It's in her wardrobe. I think
she must have been wearing a cotton frock, her new one.' He
stopped and cleared his throat. 'She'd just made it,' he said.

'I'll get some things on,' Burden said. 'I'll pick you up in
half an hour and we'll go to the station together.'

Parsons had shaved and dressed. His small eyes were wide
with terror. The tea-cups they had used the night before had

9

just been washed and were draining on a homemade rack of wooden dowel rods. Burden marvelled at the ingrained habit of respectability that made this man, at a crisis in his life, spruce himself and put his house in order.

He tried to stop himself staring round the little hole of a kitchen, at the stone copper in the corner, the old gas stove on legs, the table with green American cloth tacked to its top. There was no washing machine, no refrigerator. Because of the peeling paint, the creeping red rust, it looked dirty. It was only by peering closely when Parsons' eyes were not on him that Burden could see it was in fact fanatically, pathetically, clean.

'Are you fit?' he asked. Parsons locked the back door with a huge key. His hand shook against crazed mottled tiles. 'You've got the photograph all right?'

'In my pocket.'

Passing the dining-room he noticed the books again. The titles leapt at him from red and yellow and black covers. Now that the morning had come and she was still missing Burden wondered fantastically if Tabard Road was to join Hilldrop Crescent and Rillington Place in the chronicle of sinister streets.

Would there one day be an account of the disappearance of Margaret Parsons under another such book-jacket with the face of his companion staring from the frontispiece? The face of a murderer is the face of an ordinary man. How much less terrifying if the killer wore the Mark of Cain for all the world to see! But Parsons? He could have killed her, he had been well instructed. His textbooks bore witness to that. Burden thought of the gulf between theory and practice. He shook off fantasy and followed Parsons to the front door.

Kingsmarkham was awake, beginning to bustle. The shops were still closed, but the buses had been running for two hours. Occasionally the sun shone in shafts of watery brilliance, then vanished again under clouds that were white and thick or bluish with rain. The bus queue stretched almost to the bridge; down towards the station men hurried, singly or in pairs, bowler-hatted, armed with cautious umbrellas, through long custom unintimidated by the hour-long commuting to London.

Burden pulled up at the junction and waited for an orange-painted tractor to pass along the major road.

'It all goes on,' Parsons said, 'as if nothing had happened.'

'Just as well.' Burden turned left. 'Helps you keep a sense of proportion.'

The police station stood appropriately at the approach to the town, a guarding bastion or a warning. It was new, white and square like a soap carton, and, rather pointlessly, Burden thought, banded and decorated here and there in a soap carton's colours. Against the tall ancient arcs of elms, only a few yards from the last Regency house, it flaunted its whiteness, its gloss, like a piece of gaudy litter in a pastoral glade.

Its completion and his transfer to Kingsmarkham had coincided, but sometimes the sight of it still shocked him. He watched for Parsons' reaction as they crossed the threshold. Would he show fear or just the ordinary citizen's caution? In fact, he seemed simply awed.

Not for the first time the place irritated Burden. People expected pitch pine and lino, green baize and echoing passages. These were at the same time more quelling to the felon, more comforting to the innocent. Here the marble and the tiles, irregularly mottled with a design like stirred oil, the peg-board for the notices, the great black counter that swept in a parabola across half the foyer, suggested that order and a harmony of pattern must reign above all things. It was as if the personal fate of the men and women who came through the swing doors mattered less than Chief Inspector Wexford's impeccable records.

He left Parsons dazed between a rubber plant and a chair shaped like the bowl of a spoon, a spongy spoon, cough-mixture red. It was absurd, he thought, knocking on Wexford's door, to build a concrete box of tricks like this amid the quiet crowded houses of the High Street. Wexford called him to come in and he pushed open the door.

'Mr Parsons is outside, sir.'

'All right.' Wexford looked at his watch. 'I'll see him now.'

He was taller than Burden, thick-set without being fat, fifty-two years old, the very prototype of an actor playing a top-brass policeman. Born up the road in Pomfret, living most of his life in this part of Sussex, he knew most people and he knew the district well enough for the map on the the buttercup-yellow wall to be regarded merely as a decoration.

Parsons came in nervously. He had a furtive cautious look, and there was something defiant about him as if he knew his pride would be wounded and was preparing to defend it.

'Very worrying for you,' Wexford said. He spoke without emphasizing any particular word, his voice level and strong. 'Inspector Burden tells me you haven't seen your wife since yesterday morning.'

'That's right.' He took the snapshot of his wife from his pocket and put it on Wexford's desk. 'That's her, that's Margaret.' He twitched his head at Burden. 'He said you'd want to see it.'

It showed a youngish woman in cotton blouse and dirndl skirt standing stiffly, her arms at her sides, in the Parsonses' garden. She was smiling an unnaturally broad smile straight into the sun and she looked flustered, rather short of breath, as if she had been called away from some mundane household task – the washing-up perhaps – had flung off her apron, dried her hands and run down the path to her husband, waiting with his box camera.

Her eyes were screwed up, her cheeks bunchy; she might really have been saying 'Cheese!' There was nothing here of the delicate cameo Jean's words had suggested.

Wexford looked at it and said, 'Is this the best you can do?'

Parsons covered the picture with his hand as if it had been desecrated.

He looked as if he might flare into rage, but all he said was:

'We're not in the habit of having studio portraits taken.'

'No passport?'

'I can't afford foreign holidays.'

Parsons had spoken bitterly. He glanced quickly at the venetian blinds, the scanty bit of haircord carpet, Wexford's chair with its mauve tweed seat, as if these were signs of a personal affluence rather than the furnishings supplied by a detached authority.

'I'd like a description of your wife, Mr Parsons,' Wexford said. 'Won't you sit down?'

Burden called young Gates in and set him tapping with one finger at the little grey typewriter.

Parsons sat down. He began speaking slowly, shamefacedly, as if he had been asked to uncover his wife's nakedness.

'She's got fair hair,' he said. 'Fair curly hair and very light blue eyes. She's pretty.' He looked at Wexford defiantly and Burden wondered if he realized the dowdy impression the photograph had given. 'I think she's pretty. She's got a high sort of forehead.' He touched his own low narrow one. 'She's not very tall, about five feet one or two.'

Wexford went on looking at the picture.

'Thin? Well built?'

Parsons shifted in his chair.

'Well built, I suppose.' An awkward flush tinged the pale face. 'She's thirty. She was thirty a few months ago, in March.'

'What was she wearing?'

'A green and white dress. Well, white with green flowers on it, and a yellow cardigan. Oh, and sandals. She never wears stockings in the summer.'

'Handbag?'

'She never carried a handbag. She doesn't smoke or use

make-up, you see. She wouldn't have any use for a handbag. Just her purse and her key.'

'Any distinguishing marks?'

'Appendicitis scar,' Parsons said, flushing again.

Gates ripped the sheet from the typewriter and Wexford looked at it.

'Tell me about yesterday morning, Mr Parsons,' he said. 'How did your wife seem? Excited? Worried?'

Parsons slapped his hands down on to his spread knees. It was a gesture of despair; despair and exasperation.

'She was the same as usual,' he said. 'I didn't notice anything. You see, she wasn't an emotional woman.' He looked down at his shoes and said again, 'She was the same as usual.'

'What did you talk about?'

'I don't know. The weather. We didn't talk much. I have to get off to work at half past eight – I work for the Southern Water Board at Stowerton. I said it was a nice day and she said yes, but it was too bright. It was bound to rain, too good to last. And she was right. It did rain, poured down all the morning.'

'And you went to work. How? Bus, train, car?'

'I don't have a car. . . .'

He looked as if he was about to enumerate all the other things he didn't have, so Wexford said quickly:

'Bus then?'

'I always catch the eight-thirty-seven from the market place. I said good-bye to her. She didn't come to the door. But that's nothing. She never did. She was washing up.'

'Did she say what she was going to do with herself during the day?'

'The usual things, I suppose, shopping and the house. You know the sort of things women do.' He paused, then said suddenly: 'Look, she wouldn't kill herself. Don't get any ideas like that. Margaret wouldn't kill herself. She's a religious woman.'

'All right, Mr Parsons. Try to keep calm and don't worry. We'll do everything we can to find her.'

Wexford considered, dissatisfaction in the lines of his face, and Parsons seemed to interpret this characteristically. He sprang to his feet, quivering.

'I know what you're thinking,' he shouted. 'You think I've done away with her. I know how your minds work. I've read it all up.'

Burden said quickly, trying to smooth things down. 'Mr Parsons is by way of being a student of crime, sir.'

'Crime?' Wexford raised his eyebrows. 'What crime?'

'We'll have a car to take you home,' Burden said. 'I should take the day off. Get your doctor to give you something so that you can sleep.'

Parsons went out jerkily, walking like a paraplegic, and from the window Burden watched him get into the car beside Gates. The shops were opening now and the fruiterer on the opposite side of the street was putting up his sunblind in anticipation of a fine day. If this had been an ordinary Wednesday, a normal weekday, Burden thought, Margaret Parsons might now have been kneeling in the sun, polishing that gleaming step, or opening the windows and letting some air into those musty rooms. Where was she, waking in the arms of her lover or lying in some more final resting place?

'She's bolted, Mike,' Wexford said. 'That's what my old father used to call a woman who eloped. A bolter. Still, better do the usual check-up. You can do it yourself since you knew her by sight.'

Burden picked up the photograph and put it in his pocket. He went first to the station but the ticket-collector and the booking clerks were sure Mrs Parsons hadn't been through.

But the woman serving at the bookstall recognized her at once from the picture.

'That's funny,' she said. 'Mrs Parsons always comes in to pay for her papers on Tuesdays. Yesterday was Tuesday but

I'm sure I never saw her. Wait a minute, my husband was on in the afternoon.' She called, 'George, here a sec.!'

The bookstall proprietor came round from the part of the shop that fronted on to the street. He opened his order book and ran a finger down the edge of one of the pages.

'No,' he said. 'She never came. There's two-and-two outstanding.' He looked curiously at Burden, greedy for explanations. 'Peculiar, that,' he said. 'She always pays up, regular as clockwork.'

Burden went back to the High Street to begin on the shops. He marched into the big supermarket and up to the check-out counter. The woman by the till was standing idly, lulled by background music. When Burden showed her the photograph she seemed to jerk back into life.

Yes, she knew Mrs Parsons by name as well as by sight. She was a regular customer and she had been in yesterday as usual.

'About half ten it was,' she said. 'Always the same time.'

'Did she talk to you? Can you remember what she said?'

'Now you are asking something. Wait a minute, I do remember. It's coming back to me. I said it was a problem to know what to give them, and she said, yes, you didn't seem to fancy salad, not when it was raining. She said she'd got some chops, she was going to do them in a batter, and I sort of looked at her things, the things she'd got in her basket. But she said, no, she'd got the chops on Monday.'

'Can you remember what she was wearing? A green cotton frock, yellow cardigan?'

'Oh, no, definitely not. All the customers were in raincoats yesterday morning. Wait a tic, that rings a bell. She said, "Golly, it's pouring." I remember because of the way she said "Golly", like a school-kid. She said, "I'll have to get something to put on my head," so I said, "Why not get one of our rain-hoods in the reduced line?" She said didn't it seem awful to have to buy a rain-hood in May? But she took one. I know

16

that for sure, because I had to check it separately. I'd already checked her goods.'

She left the counter and led Burden to a display of jumbled transparent scarves, pink, blue, apricot and white.

'They wouldn't actually keep the rain out,' she said confidingly. 'Not a downpour, if you know what I mean. But they're prettier than plastic. More glamorous. She had a pink one. I remarked on it. I said it went with her pink jumper.'

'Thank you very much,' Burden said. 'You've been most helpful.'

He checked at the shops between the supermarket and Tabard Road, but no one remembered seeing Mrs Parsons. In Tabard Road itself the neighbours seemed shocked and helpless. Mrs Johnson, Margaret Parsons' next-door neighbour, had seen her go out soon after ten and return at a quarter to eleven. Then, at about twelve, she thought it was, she had been in her kitchen and had seen Mrs Parsons go out into the garden and peg two pairs of socks on to the line. Half an hour later she had heard the Parsonses' front door open and close again softly. But this meant nothing. The milkman always came late, they had complained about it, and she might simply have put her hand out into the porch to take in the bottles.

There had been a sale at the auction rooms on the corner of Tabard Road the previous afternoon. Burden cursed to himself, for this meant that cars had been double parked along the street. Anyone looking out of her downstairs windows during the afternoon would have had her view of the opposite pavement blocked by this row of cars standing nose to tail.

He tried the bus garage, even rather wildly the car-hire firms, and drew a complete blank. Filled with foreboding, he went slowly back to the police station. Suicide now seemed utterly ruled out. You didn't chatter cheerfully about the chops you intended cooking for your husband's dinner if you intended to kill yourself, and you didn't go forth to meet your lover without a coat or a handbag.

Meanwhile Wexford had been through Parsons' house from the ugly little kitchen to the two attics. In a drawer of Mrs Parsons' dressing-table he found two winceyette nightdresses, oldish and faded but neatly folded, one printed cotton nightdress and a fourth, creased and worn perhaps for two nights, under the pillow nearest the wall on the double bed. His wife hadn't any more nightgowns, Parsons said, and her dressing-gown, made of blue woolly material with darker blue braiding, was still hanging on a hook behind the bedroom door. She hadn't a summer dressing-gown and the only pair of slippers she possessed Wexford found neatly packed heel to toe in a cupboard in the dining-room.

It looked as if Parsons had been right about the purse and the key. They were nowhere to be found. In the winter the house was heated solely by two open fires and the water by an immersion heater. Wexford set Gates to examining these fireplaces and to searching the dustbin, last emptied by Kingsmarkham Borough Council on Monday, but there was no trace of ash. A sheet of newspaper had been folded to cover the grate in the dining-room, and this, lightly sprinkled with soot, bore the date April 15th.

Parsons said he had given his wife five pounds house-keeping money on the previous Friday. As far as he knew she had no savings accumulated from previous weeks. Gates, searching the kitchen dresser, found two pound notes rolled up in a cocoa tin on one of the shelves. If Mrs Parsons had received only five pounds on Friday and out of this had bought food for her husband and herself for four or five days, leaving two pounds for the rest of the week, it was apparent that the missing purse could have contained at best a few shillings.

Wexford had hoped to find a diary, an address book or a letter which might give him some help. A brass letter-rack attached to the dining-room wall beside the fireplace contained only a coal bill, a circular from a firm fitting central-heating plant (had Mrs Parsons, after all, had her dreams?), two soap coupons and an estimate from a contractor for rendering and making good a damp patch on the kitchen wall.

'Your wife didn't have any family at all, Mr Parsons?' Wexford asked.

'Only me. We kept ourselves to ourselves. Margaret didn't...doesn't make friends easily. I was brought up in a children's home and when she lost her mother Margaret went to live with an aunt. But her aunt died when we were engaged.'

'Where was that, Mr Parsons? Where you met, I mean.'

'In London. Balham. Margaret was teaching in an infants' school and I had digs in her aunt's house.'

Wexford sighed. Balham! The net was widening. Still, you didn't travel forty miles without a coat or a handbag. He decided to abandon Balham for the time being.

'I suppose no one telephoned your wife on Monday night? Did she have any letters yesterday morning?'

'Nobody phoned, nobody came and there weren't any letters.' Parsons seemed proud of his empty life, as if it was evidence of respectability. 'We sat and talked. Margaret was knitting. I think I did a crossword puzzle part of the time.' He opened the cupboard where the slippers were and from the top shelf took a piece of blue knitting on four needles. 'I wonder if it will ever be finished,' he said. His fingers tightened on the ball of wool and he pressed the needles into the palm of his hand.

'Never fear,' Wexford said, hearty with false hope, 'we'll find her.'

'If you've finished in the bedrooms I think I'll go and lie down again. The doctor's given me something to make me sleep.'

Wexford sent for all his available men and set them to search the empty houses in Kingsmarkham and its environs, the fields that lay still unspoilt between the High Street and the Kingsbrook Road and, as afternoon came, the Kingsbrook itself. They postponed dragging operations until the shops had closed and the people dispersed, but even so a crowd gathered on the bridge and stood peering over the parapet at the wading men. Wexford, who hated this particular kind of ghoulishness, this lust for dreadful sights thinly disguised under a mask of shocked sympathy, glowered at them and tried to persuade them to leave the bridge, but they drifted back in twos and threes. At last when dusk came, and the men had waded far to the north and the south of the town, he called off the search.

Meanwhile Ronald Parsons, dosed with sodium amytal, had fallen asleep on his lumpy mattress. For the first time in six months dust had begun to settle on the dressing-table, the iron mantelpiece and the linoed floor.

CHAPTER THREE

Ere her limbs frigidly
Stiffen too rigidly,
Decently, kindly,
Smooth and compose them,
And her eyes, close them,
Staring so blindly!

Thomas Hood, *The Bridge of Sighs*

On Thursday morning a baker's roundsman, new to his job, called at a farm owned by a man called Prewett on the main Kingsmarkham-to-Pomfret road. There was no one about, so he left a large white loaf and a small brown one on a window-ledge and went back to where he had parked his van, leaving the gate open behind him.

Presently a cow nudged against the gate and pushed it wide open. The rest of the herd, about a dozen of them, followed and meandered down the lane. Fortunately for Mr Prewett (for the road to which they were heading was dere-stricted) their attention was distracted by some clumps of sow thistles on the edge of a small wood. One by one they lumbered across the grass verge, munched at the thistles, and gradually, slowly, penetrated into the thickets. The briars were thick and the wood dim. There were no more thistles, no more wet succulent grass. Trapped and bewildered, they stood still, lowing hopefully.

It was in this wood that Prewett's cowman found them and Mrs Parsons' body at half past one.

By two Wexford and Burden had arrived in Burden's car, while Bryant and Gates brought Dr Crocker and two men with cameras. Prewett and the cowman, Bysouth, primed with knowledge from television serials, had touched nothing, and Margaret Parsons lay as Bysouth had found her, a bundle of damp cotton with a yellow cardigan pulled over her head.

Burden pushed aside the branches to make an arch and he and Wexford came close until they were standing over her. Mrs Parsons was lying against the trunk of a hawthorn tree perhaps eight feet high. The boughs, growing outwards and downwards like the spokes of an umbrella, made an almost enclosed igloo-shaped tent.

Wexford bent down and lifted the cardigan gently. The new dress had a neckline cut lowish at the back. On the skin, running from throat to nape to throat, was a purple circle like a thin ribbon. Burden gazed and the blue eyes seemed to stare back at him. An old-fashioned face, Jean had said, a face you wouldn't forget. But he would forget in time, as he forgot them all. Nobody said anything. The body was photographed from various angles and the doctor examined the neck and the swollen face. Then he closed the eyes and Margaret Parsons looked at them no more.

'Ah, well,' Wexford said. 'Ah, well.' He shook his head slowly. There was, after all, nothing else to say.

After a moment he knelt down and felt among the dead leaves. In the cavern of thin bending branches it was close and unpleasant, but quite scentless. Wexford lifted the arms and turned the body over, looking for a purse and a key. Burden watched him pick something up. It was a used matchstick, half burnt away.

They came out of the hawthorn tent into comparative light and Wexford said to Bysouth:

'How long have these cows been in here?'

'Be three hour or more, sir.'

Wexford gave Burden a significant look. The wood was badly trampled and the few naked patches of ground were boggy with cattle dung. A marathon wrestling match could have taken place in that wood before breakfast, but Prewett's cows would have obliterated all traces of it by lunchtime; a wrestling match or a struggle between a killer and a terrified woman. Wexford set Bryant and Gates to searching among the maze of gnat-ridden brambles while he and Burden went back to the car with the farmer.

Mr Prewett was what is known as a gentleman farmer and his well-polished riding boots, now somewhat spattered, did no more than pay service to his calling. The leather patches on the elbows of his tobacco-coloured waisted jacket had been stitched there by a bespoke tailor.

'Who uses the lane, sir?'

'I have a Jersey herd pastured on the other side of the Pomfret road,' Prewett said. He had a county rather than a country accent. 'Bysouth takes them over in the morning and back in the afternoon by way of the lane. Then there is the occasional tractor, you know.'

'What about courting couples?'

'A stray car,' Prewett said distastefully. 'Of course this is a private road. Just as private in fact, Chief Inspector, as your own garage drive, but nobody respects privacy these days. I don't think any of the local lads and lasses come up here on foot. The fields are much more – well, salubrious, shall we say? We do get cars up here. You could stick a car under those overhanging branches and anyone could pass quite close to it at night without even seeing it was there.'

'I was wondering if you'd noticed any unfamiliar tyre marks between now and Tuesday, sir?'

'Oh, come!' Prewett waved a not very horny hand up towards the entrance to the lane and Burden saw what he meant. The lane was all tyre marks; in fact it was the tyre marks that made it into a road. 'The tractors go in and out, the cattle trample it. . . .'

'But you have a car, sir. With all this coming and going it's odd nobody saw anything unusual.'

'You must remember it's simply used for coming and going. No one hangs about here. My people have all got a job of work to do. They're good lads and they get on with it. In any case you'll have to discount my wife and myself. We've been in London from Monday until this morning and we mostly use the front entrance anyway. The lane's a short cut, Chief Inspector. It's fine for tractors but my own vehicle gets bogged down.' He stopped, then added sharply, 'When I'm in town I don't care to be taken for a horny-handed son of toil.'

Wexford examined the lane for himself and found only a morass of deeply rutted trenches zig-zagged with the tread marks of tractor tyres and deep round holes made by hoofs. He decided to postpone talking to Prewett's four men and the girl agricultural student until the time of Mrs Parsons' death had been fixed.

Burden went back to Kingsmarkham to break the news to Parsons because he knew him. Parsons opened the door numbly, moving like a sleep-walker. When Burden told him, standing stiffly in the dining-room with the dreadful books, he said nothing, but closed his eyes and swayed.

'I'll fetch Mrs Johnson,' Burden said. 'I'll get her to make you some tea.'

Parsons just nodded. He turned his back and stared out of the window. With something like horror Burden saw that the two pairs of socks were still pegged to the line.

'I'd like to be alone for a bit.'

'Just the same, I'll tell her. She can come in later.'

The widower shuffled his feet in khaki-coloured slippers.

'All right,' he said. 'And thanks. You're very good.'

Back at the station Wexford was sitting at his desk looking at the burnt matchstick. He said musingly:

'You know, Mike, it looks as if someone struck this to get a good look at her. That means after dark. Someone held it until it almost burnt his fingers.'

'Bysouth?'

24

Wexford shook his head.

'It was light, light enough to see – everything. No, whoever struck that match wanted to make sure he hadn't left anything incriminating behind him.' He slipped the piece of charred wood into an envelope. 'How did Parsons take it?' he asked.

'Difficult to say. It's always a shock, even if you're expecting it. He's so doped up on what the doctor's giving him he didn't seem to take it in.'

'Crocker's doing the post-mortem now. Inquest at ten on Saturday.'

'Can Crocker fix the time of death, sir?'

'Some time on Tuesday. I could have told him that. She must have been killed between half twelve and – what time did you say Parsons rang you on Tuesday night?'

'Exactly half past seven. We were going to the pictures and I was keeping an eye on the time.'

'Between half twelve and seven-thirty, then.'

'That brings me to my theory, sir.'

'Let's have it. I haven't got one.'

'Well, Parsons said he got home at six but no one saw him. The first anyone knew he was in the house was when he phoned me at half past seven. . . .'

'Okay, I'm listening. Just stick your head out of the door and get Martin to fetch us some tea.'

Burden shouted for tea and went on:

'Well, suppose Parsons killed her. As far as we know she doesn't know anyone else around here and, as you always say, the husband is the first suspect. Suppose Parsons made a date with his wife to meet him at Kingsmarkham bus garage.'

'What sort of a date?'

'He could have said they'd go and have a meal somewhere in Pomfret, or go for a walk, a picnic . . . anything.'

'What about the chops, Mike? She didn't have a date when she was talking to your supermarket woman.'

'They're on the phone. He could have telephoned her

during his lunch hour – it had begun to clear up by then – and asked her to pick up the bus at the garage at ten to six, suggested going into Pomfret for a meal. After all, maybe they make a habit of going out to eat. We've only got his word for what they did.'

Martin came in with the tea and Wexford, cup in hand, went over to the window and looked down into the High Street. The bright sun made him screw up his eyes and he pulled at the cord of the blind, half closing the slats.

'The Stowerton bus doesn't go to Pomfret,' he objected. 'Not the five-thirty-five. Kingsmarkham is the terminus.'

Burden took a sheet of paper out of his pocket.

'No, but the five-thirty-two does. Stowerton to Pomfret, via Forby and Kingsmarkham.' He concentrated on the figures he had written. 'Let me put it like this: Parsons phones his wife at lunchtime and asks her to meet the Stowerton bus that gets into Kingsmarkham at five-fifty, two minutes before the other bus, the one that goes into the garage. Now, he could have made that bus if he left a minute or two early.'

'You'll have to check that, Mike.'

'Anyway, Mrs P. catches the bus. It passes through Forby at six-one and reaches Pomfret at six-thirty. When they get to the nearest bus-stop to the wood by Prewett's farm Parsons says it's such a nice evening, let's get off and walk the rest of the way. . . .'

'It's a good mile this side of Pomfret. Still, they might be keen on country walks.'

'Parsons says he knows a short cut across the fields to Pomfret. . . .'

'Through a practically impenetrable dark wood, thistles, long wet grass?'

'I know, sir. I don't like that bit myself. But they might have seen something in the wood, a deer or a rabbit or something. Anyway, somehow or other Parsons gets her into that wood and strangles her.'

'Oh, marvellous! Mrs Parsons is going out to dinner in a fashionable country pub, but she doesn't object to plunging into the middle of a filthy wet wood after a rabbit. What's she going to do with it when she's caught it, eat it? Her old man follows her and when she's in the thickest part of the wood he says, "Stand still a minute, dear, while I get a bit of rope out of my pocket and strangle you!" God Almighty!'

'He might have killed her in the lane and dragged her body into the bushes. It's a dark lane and there's never anyone walking along the Pomfret road. He might have carried her – he's a big bloke and you wouldn't see the tracks after those cows had been all over it.'

'True.'

'The bus leaves Pomfret again at six-forty-one, gets to Forby at seven-nine, Kingsmarkham garage seven-twenty. That gives him about fifteen minutes in which to kill his wife and get back to the bus-stop on the other side of the Pomfret road. The bus gets there at about six-forty-six. He runs up Tabard Road and gets into his own house in five minutes, just in time to phone me at seven-thirty.'

Wexford sat down again in the little swivel chair with the purple cushion.

'He was taking an awful risk, Mike,' he said. 'He might easily have been seen. You'll have to check with the bus people. They can't pick up many passengers at the stop by Prewett's farm. What did he do with her purse and her key?'

'Chucked them in the bushes. There wasn't any point in hiding them, anyway. The thing is, I can't think of a motive.'

'Oh, motive,' Wexford said. 'Any husband's got a motive.'

'I haven't.' Burden was incensed. Someone knocked at the door and Bryant came in.

'I found this on the edge of the wood on the lane side, sir,' Bryant said. He was holding a small gilt cylinder in the tips of his gloved fingers.

'A lipstick,' Wexford said. He took it from Bryant, covering his fingers with a handkerchief, and upended it to expose a circular label on its base. ' "Arctic Sable," ' he read, 'and something that looks like eight-and-six written in violet ink. Anything else?'

'Nothing, sir.'

'All right, Bryant. You and Gates can get over to the Southern Water Board at Stowerton and find out exactly – and I mean precisely to the minute – what time Parsons left work on Tuesday evening.'

'This makes your theory look bloody silly, Mike,' he said when Bryant had gone. 'We'll get the fingerprint boys on it, but, I ask you, is it likely to be Mrs Parsons'? She doesn't take a handbag, she doesn't use make-up and she's as poor as a church mouse (dinner in Pomfret, my foot!), but she takes a lipstick with her in her purse or stuffed down her bosom – an eight-and-sixpenny lipstick, mark you – and when they get to the wood she sees a rabbit. She opens her purse to get out her shotgun, I presume, slings the lipstick into the ditch, runs after the rabbit, striking a match to show her the way, and, when she's in the middle of the wood, sits down and lets her old man strangle her!'

'You sent Bryant off to Stowerton.'

'He's got time on his hands.' Wexford paused, staring at the lipstick. 'By the way,' he said, 'I've checked on the Prewetts. There's no doubt they were in London. Mrs Prewett's mother's seriously ill, and according to University College Hospital they were at her bedside pretty well continuously from before lunch on Tuesday until late that night, and there on and off all day yesterday. The old girl rallied a bit last night and they left their hotel in the Tottenham Court Road after breakfast this morning. So that lets them out.'

He picked up the sheet of paper on which he had placed the Arctic Sable lipstick and held it out for Burden to see. The prints were smudged, but there was a clear one on its domed top.

'It's a new lipstick,' Wexford said. 'It's hardly been used. I want to find the owner of that lipstick, Mike. We'll go over to Prewett's again and talk to that land girl or whatever she calls herself.'

CHAPTER FOUR

Thou hast beauty bright and fair,
Manner noble, aspect free,
Eyes that are untouched by care;
What then do we ask of thee?

Bryan Waller Procter, *Hermione*

When Wexford had been told the prints on the lipstick definitely hadn't been made by Mrs Parsons they went back to the farm and questioned each of the men and the land girl (as Wexford called her in his old-fashioned vocabulary) separately. For all but one of them Tuesday afternoon had been busy and, in a very different way from murder, exciting.

Prewett had left the manager, John Draycott, in charge, and on Tuesday morning Draycott had gone to Stowerton market accompanied by a man called Edwards. They had taken a truck and used the front entrance to the farm. This was a long way round, but it was favoured because the lane to the Pomfret road was narrow and muddy and the week before the truck had got stuck in the ruts.

Bysouth and the man in charge of Prewett's pigs had remained alone at the farm, Miss Sweeting, the land girl, having had the day off on Tuesday to attend a lecture at Sewingbury Agricultural College. At half past twelve they had eaten their dinner in the kitchen, a meal cooked for them, as usual, by Mrs Creavey, who came up to the farm each day from Flagford to cook and clean. After dinner at a quarter past one the pig man, Traynor, had taken Bysouth with him to see a sow that was about to farrow.

At three Draycott and Edwards returned and the manager

began immediately on his accounts. Edwards, who included gardening among his duties, went to mow the front lawn. The man hadn't been constantly under his eye, Draycott told Wexford, but for the next hour he had been aware of the sound of the electric mower. At about half past three Draycott was interrupted by Traynor, who came in to tell him he was worried about the condition of the sow. Five piglets had been delivered, but she seemed to be in difficulties and Traynor wanted the manager's consent to call the vet. Draycott had gone to the sties, looked at the sow and talked for a few seconds to Bysouth, who was sitting beside her on a stool, before telephoning for the vet himself. The vet arrived by four and from then until five-thirty the manager, Edwards and Traynor had remained together. During this hour and a half, Traynor said, Bysouth had gone to fetch the cows in and put them in the milking shed. In order to do this he had had to pass the wood twice. Wexford questioned him closely, but he insisted that he had seen nothing out of the way. He had heard no untoward sound and there had been no cars either in the lane itself or parked on the Pomfret road. According to the other three men he had been even quicker than usual, a haste they attributed to his anxiety as to the outcome of the farrowing.

It was half past six before the whole litter of pigs had been delivered. The vet had gone into the kitchen to wash his hands and they had all had a cup of tea. At seven he left by the same way as he had come, the front entrance, giving a lift to Edwards, Traynor and Bysouth, who all lived in farm workers' cottages at a hamlet called Clusterwell, some two miles outside Flagford. During the Prewetts' absence Mrs Creavey was staying at the farm overnight. The manager performed his final round at eight and went home to his house about fifty yards down the Clusterwell road.

Wexford checked with the vet and decided that, apart from mystery story miracles, no one had had time to murder

Mrs Parsons and conceal her body in the wood. Only Bysouth had used the lane that passed the wood, and unless he had abandoned his charges dangerously near a derestricted road he was beyond suspicion. To be sure, Mrs Creavey had been alone and out of sight from three-thirty until six-thirty, but she was at least sixty, fat and notoriously arthritic.

Wexford tried to fix the time Bysouth had passed down and then up the lane, but the cowman didn't wear a watch and his life seemed to be governed by the sun. He protested vehemently that his mind had been on the sow's travail and that he had seen no one on the track, in the wood or walking in the fields.

Dorothy Sweeting was the only one of them who might remotely be supposed to have owned the Arctic Sable lipstick. But there is a particularly naked raw look about the face of a woman in an unpainted state when that woman habitually uses make-up. Dorothy Sweeting's face was sunburnt and shiny; it looked as if it had never been protected from the weather by cream and powder. The men were almost derisive when Wexford asked them if they had ever seen lipstick on her mouth.

'You didn't go to the farm all day, Miss Sweeting?'

Dorothy Sweeting laughed a lot. Now she laughed heartily. It seemed that to her the questioning was just like part of a serial or a detective story come to life.

'Not *to* it,' she said, 'but I went near it. Guilty, my lord!' Wexford didn't smile, so she went on: 'I went to see my auntie in Sewingbury after the lecture and it was such a lovely afternoon I got off the bus a mile this side of Pomfret and walked the rest of the way. Old Bysouth was bringing the cows in and I did just stop and have a chat with him.'

'What time would that have been?'

'Fiveish. It was the four-ten bus from Sewingbury.'

'All right, Miss Sweeting. Your prints will be destroyed after the check has been made.'

She roared with laughter. Looking at her big broad hands, her forearms like the village blacksmith's, Burden wondered what she intended to do with her life after she had qualified for whatever branch of bucolic craft she was studying.

'Hang on to them by all means,' she said. 'I'd like to take my place in the rogues' gallery.'

They drove back to Kingsmarkham along the quiet half-empty road. There was still an hour to go before the evening rush began. The sun had dimmed and the mackerel sky thickened until it looked like curds and whey. On the hedges that bordered the road the May blossom still lingered, touched now with brown as if it had been singed by fleeting fire.

Wexford led the way into the police station and they had Miss Sweeting's prints checked with the ones on the lipstick. As Wexford had expected, they didn't match. The student's big pitted fingertips were more like a man's than a woman's.

'I want to find the owner of that lipstick, Mike,' he said again. 'I want every chemist's shop in this place gone over with a small toothcomb. And you'd better do it yourself because it's not going to be easy.'

'Does it have to have any connection with Mrs Parsons, sir? Couldn't it have been dropped by someone going up the track?'

'Look, Mike, that lipstick wasn't by the road. It was right on the edge of the wood. Apart from the fact that they don't use the lane, Sweeting and Mrs Creavey don't wear lipstick and even if they did they wouldn't be likely to have one in a peculiar shade of pinkish brown like this. You know as well as I do, when a woman only uses lipstick on high days and holidays, for some reason or other, a sense of daring probably, she always picks a bright red. This is a filthy colour, the sort of thing a rich woman might buy if she'd already got a dozen lipsticks and wanted the latest shade for a gimmick.'

Burden knew Kingsmarkham well, but he got the local trade directory to check and found that there were seven chemists in Kingsmarkham High Street, three in side roads and one in a village which had now been absorbed as a suburb into Kingsmarkham itself. Bearing in mind what Wexford had said about a rich woman, he started on the High Street.

The supermarket had a cosmetics counter, but they kept only a limited stock of the more expensive brands. The assistant knew Mrs Parsons by name, having read that she was missing in a newspaper. She also knew her by sight and was agog. Burden didn't tell her the body had been found and he didn't waste any more time on questions when he learnt that, as far as the girl could remember, Mrs Parsons had bought only a tin of cheap talcum powder in the past month.

'That's a new line,' said the assistant in the next shop. 'It's only just come out. It comes in a range of fur shades, sort of soft and subtle, but we don't stock it. We wouldn't have the sale for it, you see.'

He walked up towards the Kingsbrook bridge past the Georgian house that was now the Youth Employment Bureau, past the Queen Anne house that was now a solicitor's office, and entered a newly opened shop in a block with maisonettes above it. It was bright and clean, with a dazzling stock of pots and jars and bottles of scent. They kept a large stock of the brand, he was told, but were still awaiting delivery of the fur range.

The waters of the brook had settled and cleared. Burden could see the flat round stones on the bottom. He leaned over the parapet and saw a fish jump. Then he went on, weaving his way between groups of schoolchildren, High School girls in panamas and scarlet blazers, avoiding prams and baskets on wheels. He had called at four shops before he found one that stocked the fur range. But they had only sold one and that in a colour called Mutation Mink, and they didn't put prices on their goods. The girl in the fifth shop, a queenly creature with hair like pineapple candy-floss, said that she was wearing Arctic Sable herself. She lived in a flat above the shop

and she went upstairs to fetch the lipstick. It was identical to
the one found in the wood except that it had no price written
on its base.

'It's a difficult shade to wear,' the girl said. 'We've sold a
couple in the other colours but that sort of brownish tint puts
the customers off.'

Now there were no more shops on this side of the High
Street, only a couple of big houses, the Methodist Church –
Mrs Parsons' church – standing back from the road behind a
sweep of gravel, a row of cottages, before the fields began. He
crossed the street at The Olive and Dove and went into a
chemist's shop between a florist's and an estate agent's. Burden
had sometimes bought shaving cream in this shop and he knew
the man who came out from the dispensary at the back. But
he shook his head at once. They didn't stock any cosmetics of
that make.

There were only two left: a little poky place with jars of
hair cream and toothbrushes in the window, and an elegant
emporium, double-fronted, with steps up to the door and a
bow window. The vendor of hair cream had never even heard
of Arctic Sable. He climbed up a short ladder and took from
a shelf a cardboard box of green plastic cylinders.

'Haven't sold a lipstick inside a fortnight,' he said.

Burden opened the door of the double-fronted shop and
stepped on to wine-coloured carpet. All the perfumes of Arabia
seemed to be assembled on the counters and the gilded tables.
Musk and ambergris and new-mown hay assaulted his nostrils.
Behind a pyramid of boxes, encrusted with glitter and bound
with ribbon, he could see the back of a girl's head, a girl with
short blonde curls wearing a primrose sweater. He coughed,
the girl turned and he saw that it was a young man.

'Isn't it a delightful shade?' the young man said. 'So young
and fresh and innocent. Oh, yes, definitely one of ours. I mark
everything with this.' And he picked up a purple ball-point
pen from beside the cash register.

'I don't suppose you could tell me who you sold this one to?'

'But I love probing and detecting! Let's be terribly thorough and have a real investigation.'

He opened a drawer with a knob made of cut glass and took out a tray of gilt lipsticks. There were several in each compartment.

'Let me see,' he said. 'Mutation Mink, three gone. I started off with a dozen of each shade. Trinidad Tiger – good heavens, nine gone! Rather a common sort of red, that one. Here we are, Arctic Sable, four gone. Now for my thinking cap.'

Burden said encouragingly that he was being most helpful.

'We do have a regular clientele, what you might call a segment of the affluent society. I don't want to sound snobbish, but I do rather eschew the cheaper lines. I remember now. Miss Clements from the estate agent's had one. No, she had two, one for herself and one for someone's birthday present. Mrs Darrell had another. I do recall that because she took Mutation Mink and changed her mind just as she was going out of the shop. She came back and changed it and while she was making up her mind someone else came in for a pale pink lipstick. Of course, Mrs Missal! She took one look – Mrs Darrell had tried the shade out on her wrist – and she said, "That is absolutely me!" Mrs Missal has exquisite taste because, whatever you may say, Arctic Sable is really intended for red-heads like her.'

'When was this?' Burden asked. 'When did you get the fur range in?'

'Just a tick.' He checked in a delivery book. 'Last Thursday, just a week ago. I sold the two to Miss Clements soon after they came in. Friday, I should say. I wasn't here on Saturday and Monday's always slack. Washing, you know. Tuesday's early closing and I know I didn't sell any yesterday. It must have been Tuesday morning.'

'You've been a great help,' Burden said.

'Not at all. You've brought a little sparkle into my worka-day world. By the by, Mrs Missal lives in that rather lovely bijou house opposite the Olive and Dove, and Mrs Darrell has the maisonette with the pink curtains in the new block in Queen Street.'

As luck had it, Miss Clements had both lipsticks in her handbag, her own partly used, and the other one she had bought for a present still wrapped in cellophane paper. As Burden left the estate agent's he glanced at his watch. Half past five. He had just made it before they all closed. He ran Mrs Darrell to earth in the maisonette next to her own. She was having tea with a friend, but she went down the spiral staircase at the back of the block and up the next one, coming back five minutes later with an untouched lipstick, Arctic Sable, marked eight-and-six in violet ink on its base.

The Stowerton-to-Pomfret bus was coming up the hill as he turned out of Queen Street and crossed the forecourt of The Olive and Dove. He checked with his watch and saw that it was gone ten to six. Maybe it had been late leaving Stowerton, maybe it often was. Damn those stupid women and their lipsticks, he thought; Parsons must have done it.

The lovely bijou house was a Queen Anne affair, much done up with white paint, wrought iron and window-boxes. The front door was yellow, flanked with blue lilies in stone urns. Burden struck the ship's bell with a copper clapper that hung on a length of cord. But, as he had expected, no one came. The garage, a converted coach-house, was empty and the doors stood open. He went down the steps again, crossed the road and walked up to the police station, wondering as he went how Bryant had got on with the Southern Water Board.

Wexford seemed pleased about the lipstick. They waited until Bryant had got back from Stowerton before going down to The Olive and Dove for dinner.

'It looks as if this clears Parsons,' Wexford said. 'He left the Water Board at five-thirty or a little after. Certainly not before. He couldn't have caught the five-thirty-two.'

'No,' Burden said reluctantly, 'and there isn't another till six-two.'

They went into the dining-room of The Olive and Dove and Wexford asked for a window table so that they could watch Mrs Missal's house.

By the time they had finished the roast lamb and started on the gooseberry tart the garage doors were still open and no one had come into or gone out of the house. Burden remained at the table while Wexford went to pay the bill, and just as he was getting up to follow him to the door he saw a blonde girl in a cotton dress enter the High Street from the Sewingbury Road. She walked past the Methodist Church, past the row of cottages, ran up the steps of Mrs Missal's house and let herself in at the front door.

'Come on, Mike,' Wexford said.

He banged at the bell with the clapper.

'Look at that bloody thing,' he said. 'I hate things like that.'

They waited a few seconds. Then the door was opened by the blonde girl.

'Mrs Missal?'

'Mrs Missal, Mr Missal, the children, all are out,' she said. She spoke with a strong foreign accent. 'All are gone to the sea.'

'We're police officers,' Wexford said. 'When do you expect Mrs Missal back?'

'Now is seven.' She glanced behind her at a black grandfather clock. 'Half past seven, eight. I don't know. You come back again in a little while. Then she come.'

'We'll wait, if you don't mind,' Wexford said.

They stepped over the threshold on to velvety blue carpet. It was a square hall, with a staircase running up from the centre at the back and branching at the tenth stair. Through an arch on the right-hand side of this staircase Burden saw a dining-room with a polished floor partly covered by Indian rugs in pale colours. At the far end of this room open french windows gave on to a wide and apparently endless garden. The hall was cool, smelling faintly of rare and subtle flowers.

'Would you mind telling me your name, miss, and what you're doing here?' Wexford asked.

'Inge Wolff. I am nanny for Dymphna and Priscilla.'

Dymphna! Burden thought, aghast. His own children were John and Pat.

'All right, Miss Wolff. If you'll just show us where we can sit down you can go and get on with your work.'

She opened a door on the left side of the hall and Wexford and Burden found themselves in a large drawing-room whose bow windows faced the street. The carpet was green, the chairs and a huge sofa covered in green linen patterned with pink and white rhododendrons. Real rhododendrons, saucer sized heads of blossom on long stems, were massed in two white vases. Burden had the feeling that when rhododendrons went out of season Mrs Missal would fill the vases with delphiniums and change the covers accordingly.

'No shortage of lolly,' Wexford said laconically when the girl had gone. 'This is the sort of set-up I had in mind when I said she might buy Arctic Sable for a gimmick.'

'Cigarette, sir?'

'Have you gone raving mad, Burden? Maybe you'd like to take your tie off. This is Sussex, not Mexico.'

Burden restored the packet and they sat in silence for ten minutes. Then he said, 'I bet she's got that lipstick in her handbag.'

'Look, Mike, four were sold, all marked in violet ink. Right? Miss Clements has two, Mrs Darrell has one. I have the fourth.'

'There could be a chemist in Stowerton or Pomfret or Sewingbury marking lipsticks in violet ink.'

RUTH RENDELL

'That's right, Mike. And if Mrs Missal can show me hers you're going straight over to Stowerton first thing in the morning and start on the shops over there.'

But Burden wasn't listening. His chair was facing the window and he craned his neck.

'Car's coming in now,' he said. 'Olive-green Mercedes, nineteen-sixty-two. Registration XPQ189Q.'

'All right, Mike, I don't want to buy it.'

As the wheels crunched on the drive and someone opened one of the nearside doors, Burden ducked his head.

'Blimey,' he said. 'She is something of a dish.'

A woman in white slacks stepped out of the car and strolled to the foot of the steps. The kingfisher-blue and darker-blue patterned silk scarf that held back her red hair matched her shirt. Burden thought she was beautiful, although her face was hard, as if the tanned skin was stretched on a steel frame. He was paid not to admire but to observe. For him the most significant thing about her was that her mouth was painted not brownish pink but a clear golden-red. He turned away from the window and heard her say loudly:

'I am sick to my stomach of bleeding kids! I bet you anything you like, Pete, that lousy little Inge isn't back yet.'

A key was turned in the front-door lock and Burden heard Inge Wolff running along the hall to meet her employers. One of the children was crying.

'Policemen? How many policemen? Oh, I don't believe it, Inge. Where's their car?'

'I suppose they want me, Helen. You know I'm always leaving the Merc outside without lights.'

In the drawing-room Wexford grinned.

The door opened suddenly, bouncing back from one of the flower-vases as if it had been kicked by a petulant foot. The red-haired woman came in first. She was wearing sunglasses with rhinestone frames, and although the sun had gone and the room was dim, she didn't bother to take them off. Her

40

husband was tall and big, his face bloated and already marked with purple veins. His long shirt-tails hung over his belly like a gross maternity smock. Burden winced at its design of bottles and glasses and plates on a scarlet and white checkerboard.

He and Wexford got up.

'Mrs Missal?'

'Yes, I'm Helen Missal. What the hell do you want?'

'We're police officers, Mrs Missal, making enquiries in connection with the disappearance of Mrs Margaret Parsons.'

Missal stared. His fat lips were already wet, but still he licked them.

'Won't you sit down,' he said. 'I can't imagine why you want to talk to my wife.'

'Neither can I,' Helen Missal said. 'What is this, a police state?'

'I hope not, Mrs Missal. I believe you bought a new lipstick on Tuesday morning?'

'So what? Is it a crime?'

'If you could just show me that lipstick, madam, I shall be quite satisfied and we won't take up any more of your time. I'm sure you must be tired after a day at the seaside.'

'You can say that again.' She smiled. Burden thought she suddenly seemed at the same time more wary and more friendly. 'Have you ever sat on a spearmint ice lolly?' She giggled and pointed to a very faint bluish-green stain on the seat of her trousers. 'Thank God for Inge! I don't want to see those little bastards again tonight.'

'Helen!' Missal said.

'The lipstick, Mrs Missal.'

'Oh, yes, the lipstick. Actually I did buy one, a filthy colour called Arctic something. I lost it in the cinema last night.'

'Are you quite sure you lost it in the cinema? Did you enquire about it? Ask the manager, for instance?'

'What, for an eight-and-sixpenny lipstick? Do I look that poor? I went to the cinema —'

41

'By yourself, madam?'

'Of course I went by myself.' Burden sensed a certain defensiveness, but the glasses masked her eyes. 'I went to the cinema and when I got back the lipstick wasn't in my bag.'

'Is this it?' Wexford held the lipstick out on his palm, and Mrs Missal extended long fingers with nails lacquered silver like armour-plating. 'I'm afraid I shall have to ask you to come down to the station with me and have your fingerprints taken.'

'Helen, what is this?' Missal put his hand on his wife's arm. She shook it off as if the fingers had left a dirty mark. 'I don't get it, Helen. Has someone pinched your lipstick, someone connected with this woman?'

She continued to look at the lipstick in her hand. Burden wondered if she realized she had already covered it with prints.

'I suppose it is mine,' she said slowly. 'All right, I admit it must be mine. Where did you find it, in the cinema?'

'No, Mrs Missal. It was found on the edge of a wood just off the Pomfret Road.'

'What?' Missal jumped up. He stared at Wexford, then at his wife. 'Take those damn' things off!' he shouted and twitched the sunglasses from her nose. Burden saw that her eyes were green, a very light bluish green flecked with gold. For a second he saw panic there; then she dropped her lids, the only shields that remained to her, and looked down into her lap.

'You went to the pictures,' Missal said. 'You said you went to the pictures. I don't get this about a wood and the Pomfret Road. What the hell's going on?'

Helen Missal said very slowly, as if she was inventing: 'Someone must have found my lipstick in the cinema. Then they must have dropped it. That's it. It's quite simple. I can't understand what all the fuss is about.'

'It so happens,' Wexford said, 'that Mrs Parsons was found strangled in that wood at half past one today.'

She shuddered and gripped the arms of her chair. Burden

thought she was making a supreme effort not to cry out. At last she said:

'It's obvious, isn't it? Your murderer, whoever he is, pinched my lipstick and then dropped it at the . . . the scene of the crime.'

'Except,' Wexford said, 'that Mrs Parsons died on Tuesday. I won't detain you any longer, madam. Not just at present. One more thing, though, have you a car of your own?'

'Yes, yes, I have. A red Dauphine. I keep it in the other garage with the entrance in the Kingsbrook Road. Why?'

'Yes, why?' Missal said. 'Why all this? We didn't even know this Mrs Parsons. You're not suggesting my wife . . .? My God, I wish someone would explain!'

Wexford looked from one to the other. Then he got up.

'I'd just like to have a look at the tyres, sir,' he said.

As he spoke light seemed suddenly to have dawned on Missal. He blushed an even darker brick red and his face crumpled like that of a baby about to cry. There was despair there, despair and the kind of pain Burden felt he should not look upon. Then Missal seemed to pull himself together. He said in a quiet reserved voice that seemed to cover a multitude of unspoken enquiries and accusations:

'I've no objection to your looking at my wife's car but I can't imagine what connection she has with this woman.'

'Neither can I, sir,' Wexford said cheerfully. 'That's what we shall want to find out. I'm as much in the dark as you are.'

'Oh, give him the garage key, Pete,' she said. 'I tell you I don't know any more. It's not my fault if my lipstick was stolen.'

'I'd give a lot to be able to hide behind those rhododendrons and hear what he says to her,' Wexford said as they walked up the Kingsbrook Road to Helen Missal's garage.

'And what she says to him,' Burden said. 'You think it's all right leaving them for the night, sir? She's bound to have a current passport.'

Wexford said innocently: 'I thought that might worry you, Mike, so I'm going to book a room at The Olive and Dove for the night. A little job for Martin. He'll have to sit up all night. My heart bleeds for him.'

The Missals' garden was large and roughly diamond-shaped. On the north side, the side where the angle of the diamond was oblique, the garden was bounded by the Kingsbrook, and on the other a hedge of tamarisk separated it from the Kingsbrook Road. Burden unlocked the cedarwood gates to the garage and made a note of the index number of Helen Missal's car. Its rear window was almost entirely filled by a toy tiger cub.

'I want a sample taken from those tyres, Mike,' Wexford said. 'We've got a sample from the lane by Prewett's farm. It's a bit of luck for us that the soil's practically solid cow dung.'

'Blimey,' Burden said, wincing as he got to his feet. He re-locked the doors. 'This is millionaires' row, all right.' He put the dried mud into an envelope and pointed towards the houses on the other side of the road: a turreted mansion, a ranch-style bungalow with two double garages and a new house built like a chalet with balconies of dark carved wood.

'Very nice if you can get it,' Wexford said. 'Come on. I'm going to get the car and have another word with Prewett, and, incidentally, the cinema manager. If you'll just drop that key in to Inge, or whatever she calls herself, you can get off home. I shall have to have a word with young Inge tomorrow.'

'When are you going to see Mrs Missal again, sir?'

'Unless I'm very much mistaken,' Wexford said, 'she'll come to me before I can get to her.'

CHAPTER FIVE

If she answer thee with No,
Wilt thou bow and let her go?

W. J. Linton, *Faint Heart*

Sergeant Camb was talking to someone on the telephone when
Wexford got to the station in the morning. He covered the
mouthpiece with his hand and said to the Chief Inspector:

'A Mrs Missal for you, sir. This is the third time she's
been on.'

'What does she want?'

'She says she must see you. It's very urgent.' Camb looked
embarrassed. 'She wants to know if you can go to her house.'

'She does, does she? Tell her if she wants me she'll have
to come here.' He opened the door of his office. 'Oh, and,
Sergeant Camb, you can tell her I won't be here after nine-
thirty.'

When he had opened the windows and made his desk
untidy – the way he liked it – he stuck his head out of the
door again and called for tea.

'Where's Martin?'

'Still at The Olive and Dove, sir.'

'God Almighty! Does he think he's on his holidays? Get
on to him and tell him he can get off home.'

It was a fine morning, June coming in like a lamb, and
from his desk Wexford could see the gardens of Bury Street
and the window-boxes of the Midland Bank full of blown
Kaiserskroon tulips. The spring flowers were passing, the
summer ones not yet in bud – except for rhododendrons. Just
as the first peals of the High School bell began to toll faintly

45

in the distance Sergeant Camb brought in the tea – and Mrs Missal.

'We'll have another cup, please.'

She had done her hair up this morning and left off her glasses. The organdie blouse and the pleated skirt made her look surprisingly demure, and Wexford wondered if she had abandoned her hostile manner with the raffish shirt and trousers.

'I'm afraid I've been rather a silly girl, Chief Inspector,' she said in a confiding voice.

Wexford took a clean piece of paper out of his drawer and began writing on it busily. He couldn't think of anything cogent to put down and as she couldn't see the paper from where she was sitting he just scribbled: *Missal, Parsons; Parsons, Missal.*

'You see I didn't tell you the entire truth.'

'No?' Wexford said.

'I don't mean I actually told lies. I mean I left bits out.'

'Oh, yes?'

'Well, the thing is, I didn't actually go to the pictures by myself. I went with a friend, a man friend.' She smiled as one sophisticate to another. 'There wasn't anything in it, but you know how stuffy husbands are.'

'I should,' Wexford said. 'I am one.'

'Yes, well, when I got home I couldn't find my new lipstick and I think I must have dropped it in my friend's car. Oh, tea for me. How terribly sweet!'

There was a knock at the door and Burden came in.

'Mrs Missal was just telling me about her visit to the cinema on Wednesday night,' Wexford said. He went on writing. By now he had filled half the sheet.

'It was a good picture, wasn't it, Mrs Missal? Unfortunately I had to leave half-way through.' Burden looked for a third tea-cup. 'What happened to that secret-agent character? Did he marry the blonde or the other one?'

'Oh, the other one,' Helen Missal said easily. 'The one who played the violin. She put the message into a sort of musical code and when they got back to London she played it over to M.I.5.'

'It's wonderful what they think of,' Burden said.

'Well, I won't keep you any longer, Mrs Missal. . . .'

'No, I must fly. I've got a hair appointment.'

'If you'll just let me have the name of your friend, the one you went to the cinema with. . . .'

Helen Missal looked from Wexford to Burden and back from Burden to Wexford. Wexford screwed up the piece of paper and threw it into the wastepaper basket.

'Oh, I couldn't do that. I mean, I couldn't get him involved.'

'I should think it over, madam. Think it over while you're having your hair done.'

Burden held the door open for her and she walked out quickly without looking back.

'I've been talking to a neighbour of mine,' he said to Wexford, 'a Mrs Jones who lives at nine, Tabard Road. You know, she told us about the cars being parked in Tabard Road on Tuesday afternoon. Well, I asked her if she could remember any of the makes or the colours and she said she could remember one car, a bright red one with a tiger in the back. She didn't see the number. She was looking at them from sideways on, you see, and they were parked nose to tail.'

'How long was it there?'

'Mrs Jones didn't know. But she says she first saw it about three and it was there when the kids got home from school. Of course, she doesn't know if it was there all that time.'

'While Mrs Missal is having her hair done, Mike,' Wexford said, 'I am going to have a word with Inge. As Mrs Missal says, Thank God for Inge!'

There was a tin of polish and a couple of dusters on the dining-room floor and the Indian rugs were spread on the

RUTH RENDELL

crazy paving outside the windows. Inge Wolff, it seemed, had
duties apart from minding Dymphna and Priscilla.

'All I know I will tell you,' she said dramatically. 'What
matter if I get the push? Next week, anyhow, I go home to
Hanover.'

Maybe, Wexford thought, and, on the other hand, maybe
not. The way things were going Inge Wolff might be needed
in England for the next few months.

'On Monday Mrs Missal stay at home all the day. Just for
shopping in the morning she go out. Also Tuesday she go
shopping in the morning, for in the afternoon is closing of all
shops.'

'What about Tuesday afternoon, Miss Wolff?'

'Ah, Tuesday afternoon she go out. First we have our
dinner. One o'clock. I and Mrs Missal and the children. Ah,
next week, only think, no more children! After dinner I wash
up and she go up to her bedroom and lie down. When she
come down she say, "Inge, I go out with the car," and she
take the key and go down the garden to the garage.'

'What time would that be, Miss Wolff?'

'Three, half past two. I don't know.' She shrugged her
shoulders. 'Then she come back, five, six.'

'How about Wednesday?'

'Ah, Wednesday. I have half-day off. Very good. Dymphna
come home to dinner, go back to school. I go out. Mrs Missal
stay home with Priscilla. And when comes the evening she go
out, seven, half past seven. I don't know. In this house always
are comings and goings. It is like a game.'

Wexford showed her the snapshot of Mrs Parsons.

'Have you ever seen this woman, Miss Wolff? Did she ever
come here?'

'Hundreds of women like this in Kingsmarkham. All are
alike except rich ones. The ones that come here, they are not
like this.' She gave a derisive laugh. 'Oh, no, is funny. I laugh
to see this. None come here like this.'

When Wexford got back to the station Helen Missal was sitting in the entrance hall, her red hair done in elaborate scrolls on the top of her head.

'Been thinking things over, Mrs Missal?' He showed her into his office.

'About Wednesday night . . .'

'Frankly, Mrs Missal, I'm not very interested in Wednesday night. Now, Tuesday afternoon. . . .'

'Why Tuesday afternoon?'

Wexford put the photograph on his desk where she could see it. Then he dropped the lipstick on top of it. The little gilt cylinder rolled about on the shiny snapshot and came to rest.

'Mrs Parsons was killed on Tuesday afternoon,' he said patiently, 'and we found your lipstick a few yards from her body. So, you see, I'm not very interested in Wednesday night.'

'You can't think . . . Oh, my God! Look, Chief Inspector, I was here on Tuesday afternoon. I went to the pictures.'

'You must just about keep that place going, madam. What a pity you don't live in Pomfret. They had to close the cinema there for lack of custom.'

Helen Missal drew in her breath and let it out again in a deep sigh. She twisted her feet round the metal legs of the chair.

'I suppose I'll have to tell you about it,' she said. 'I mean, I'd better tell the truth.' She spoke as if this was always a last distasteful resort instead of a moral obligation.

'Perhaps it would be best, madam.'

'Well, you see, I only said I went to the pictures on Wednesday to have an alibi. Actually, I went out with a friend.' She smiled winningly. 'Who shall be nameless.'

'For the moment,' Wexford said, un-won.

'I was going out with this friend on Wednesday night, but I couldn't really tell my husband, could I? So I said I was going to the pictures. Actually we just drove around the lanes. Well, I had to see the film, didn't I? Because my husband always . . . I mean, he'd obviously ask me about it. So I went to see the film on Tuesday afternoon.'

'In your car, Mrs Missal? You only live about a hundred yards from the cinema.'

'I suppose you've been talking to that bloody little Inge. You see, I had to take the car so that she'd think I'd gone a long way. I mean, I couldn't have gone shopping because it was early closing and I never walk anywhere. She knows that. I thought if I didn't take the car she'd guess I'd gone to the pictures and then she'd think it funny me going again on Wednesday.'

'Servants have their drawbacks,' Wexford said.

'You're not kidding. Well, that's all there is to it. I took the car and stuck it in Tabard Road . . . Oh God, that's where that woman lived, isn't it? But I couldn't leave it in the High Street because . . .' Again she tried a softening smile. 'Because of your ridiculous rules about parking.'

Wexford snapped sharply:

'Did you know this woman, madam?'

'Oh, you made me jump! Let me see. Oh, no, I don't think so. She's not the sort of person I'd be likely to know, Chief Inspector.'

'Who did you go out with on Wednesday night when you lost your lipstick, Mrs Missal?'

The smiles, the girlish confidences, hadn't worked. She flung back her chair and shouted at him:

'I'm not going to tell you. I won't tell you. You can't make me! You can't keep me here.'

'You came of your own accord, madam,' Wexford said. He swung open the door, smiling genially. 'I'll just look in this evening when your husband's at home and we'll see if we can get everything cleared up.'

The Methodist minister hadn't been much help to Burden. He hadn't seen Mrs Parsons since Sunday and he'd been surprised when she didn't come to the social evening on Tuesday. No, she had made no close friends at the church and he couldn't recall hearing anyone use her Christian name.

Burden checked the bus times at the garage and found that the five-thirty-two had left Stowerton dead on time. Moreover, the conductress on the Kingsmarkham bus, the one that left Stowerton at five-thirty-five, remembered seeing Parsons. He had asked for change for a ten-shilling note and they were nearly in Kingsmarkham before she got enough silver to change it.

'Fun and games with Mrs Bloody Missal,' Wexford said when Burden walked in. 'She's one of those women who tell lies by the light of nature, a natural crook.'

'Where's the motive, sir?'

'Don't ask me. Maybe she was carrying on with Parsons, picked him up at his office on Tuesday afternoon and bribed the entire Southern Water Board to say he didn't leave till after five-thirty. Maybe she'd got another boy friend she goes out with on Wednesdays, one for every day of the week. Or maybe she and Parsons and Mr X, who shall be nameless (God Almighty!), were Russian agents and Mrs Parsons had defected to the West. It's all very wonderful, Mike, and it makes me spew!'

'We haven't even got the thing she was strangled with,' Burden said gloomily. 'Could a woman have done it?'

'Crocker seems to think so. If she was a strong young woman, always sitting about on her backside and feeding her face.'

'Like Mrs Missal.'

'We're going to get down there tonight, Mike, and have the whole thing out again in front of her old man. But not till tonight. I'm going to give her the rest of the day to sweat in. I've got the report from the lab and there's no cow dung on Mrs Missal's tyres. But she didn't have to use her own car. Her husband's a car dealer, got a saleroom in Stowerton.

Those people are always chopping and changing their cars. That's another thing we'll have to check up on. The inquest's tomorrow and I want to get somewhere before then.'

Burden drove his own car into Stowerton and pulled into the forecourt of Missal's saleroom. A man in overalls came out from the glass-walled office between the rows of petrol-pumps.

'Two and two shots, please,' Burden said. 'Mr Missal about?'

'He's out with a client.'

'That's a pity,' Burden said. 'I looked in on Tuesday afternoon and he wasn't here. . . .'

'Always in and out he is. In and out. I'll just give your windscreen a wipe over.'

'Maybe Mrs Missal?'

'Haven't seen her inside three months. Back in March was the last time. She come in to lend the Merc and bashed the grid in. Women drivers!'

'Had a row, did they? That sounds like Pete.'

'You're not joking. He said, never again. Not the Merc or any of the cars.

'Well, well,' Burden said. He gave the man a shilling; more would have looked suspicious. 'Marriage is a battlefield when all's said and done.'

'I'll tell him you came in.'

Burden switched on the ignition and put the car in gear.

'Don't trouble,' he said. 'I'm seeing him tonight.'

He drove towards the exit and braked sharply to avoid a yellow convertible that swung sharply in from Maryfield Road. An elderly man was at the wheel; beside him, Peter Missal.

'There he is, if you want to catch him,' the pump attendant shouted.

Burden parked his own car and pushed open the swing doors. He waited beside a Mini-car revolving smoothly on a scarlet roundabout. Outside he could see Missal talking to the

52

driver of the convertible. Apparently the deal was off, for the other man left on foot and Missal came into the saleroom.

'What now?' he said to Burden. 'I don't like being hounded at my place of business.'

'I won't keep you,' Burden said. 'I'm just checking up on Tuesday afternoon. No doubt you were here all day. In and out, that is.'

'It's no business of yours where I was.' Missal flicked a speck of dust from the Mini's wing as it circled past. 'As a matter of fact I went into Kingsmarkham to see a client. And that's all I'm telling you. I respect personal privacy and it's a pity you don't do the same.'

'In a murder case, sir, one's private life isn't always one's own affair. Your wife doesn't seem to have grasped that either.' He went towards the door.

'My wife . . .' Missal followed him and, looking to either side of him to make sure there was no one about, hissed in an angry half-whisper: 'You can take that heap of scrap metal off my drive-in. It's causing an obstruction.'

CHAPTER SIX

Who was her father?
Who was her mother?
Had she a sister?
Had she a brother?
Or, was there a dearer one
Still, and a nearer one
Yet, than all other?

Thomas Hood, *The Bridge of Sighs*

The murder books had been taken away and the top shelf of the bookcase was empty. If Parsons was innocent, a truly bereaved husband, Burden thought, how dreadfully their covers must have screamed at him when he came into the shabby dining-room this morning. Or had he removed them because they had served their purpose?

'Chief Inspector,' Parsons said, 'I must know. Was she . . .? Had she . . .? Was she just strangled or was there anything else?' He had aged in the past days or else he was a consummate actor.

'You can set your mind at rest on that score,' Wexford said quickly. 'Your wife was certainly strangled, but I can assure you she wasn't interfered with in any other way.' He stared at the dull green curtains, the lino that was frayed at the skirting board, and said impersonally, 'There was no sexual assault.'

'Thank God!' Parsons spoke as if he thought there was still a God in some nonconformist heaven and as if he was really thanking Him. 'I couldn't bear it if there had been. I couldn't go on living. It would just about have killed Margaret.' He realized what he had said and put his head in his hands.

Wexford waited until the hands came down and the tearless eyes were once more fixed on his own.

'Mr Parsons, I can tell you that as far as we know there was no struggle. It looks as if your wife was sleeping until just before she was killed. There would have been just a momentary shock, a second's pain – and then nothing.'

Parsons mumbled, turning away his face so that they could catch only the last words, '. . . For though they be punished in the sight of man, yet is their hope full of immortality.'

Wexford got up and went over to the bookcase. He didn't say anything about the missing library of crime, but he took a book out of one of the lower shelves.

'I see this is a guide to the Kingsmarkham district.' He opened it and Burden glimpsed a coloured photograph of the market place. 'It isn't a new book.'

'My wife lived here – well, not here. In Flagford it was – for a couple of years after the end of the war. Her uncle was stationed with the R.A.F. at Flagford and her aunt had a cottage in the village.'

'Tell me about your wife's life.'

'She was born in Balham,' Parsons said. He winced, avoiding the Christian name. 'Her mother and father died when she was a child and she went to live with this aunt. When she was about sixteen she came to live in Flagford, but she didn't like it. Her uncle died – he wasn't killed or anything – he died of heart disease, and her aunt went back to Balham. My wife went to college in London and started teaching. Then we got married. That's all.'

'Mr. Parsons, you told me on Wednesday your wife would have taken her front-door key with her. How many keys did you have between you?'

'Just the two.' Parsons took a plain Yale key from his pocket and held it up to Wexford. 'Mine and – and Margaret's. She kept hers on a ring. The ring has a silver chain with a horseshoe charm on the end of it.' He added simply in a calm voice: 'I gave it to her when we came here. The purse is a brown one, brown plastic with a gilt clip.'

'I want to know if your wife was in the habit of going to Prewett's farm. Did you know the Prewetts or any of the farm workers? There's a girl there called Dorothy Sweeting. Did your wife ever mention her?'

But Parsons had never even heard of the farm until his wife's body had been found there. She hadn't cared much for the country or for country walks and the name Sweeting meant nothing.

'Do you know anyone called Missal?'

'Missal? No, I don't think so.'

'A tall good-looking woman with red hair. Lives in a house opposite The Olive and Dove. Her husband's a car dealer. Big bloke with a big green car.'

'We don't . . . we didn't know anyone like that.' His face twisted and he put up a hand to hide his eyes. 'They're a lot of snobs round here. We didn't belong and we should never have come.' His voice died to a whisper. 'If we'd stayed in London,' he said, 'she might still be alive.'

'Why *did* you come, Mr Parsons?'

'It's cheaper living in the country, or you think it's cheaper till you try it.'

'So your coming here didn't have anything to do with the fact that your wife once lived in Flagford?'

'Margaret didn't want to come here, but the job came up. Beggars can't be choosers. She had to work when we were in London. I thought she'd find some peace here.' He coughed and the sound tailed away into a sob. 'And she did, didn't she?'

'I believe there are some books in your attic, Mr Parsons. I'd like to have a good look through them.'

'You can have them,' Parsons said. 'I never want to see another book as long as I live. But there's nothing in them. She never looked at them.'

The dark staircases were familiar now and with familiarity

they had lost much of that sinister quality Burden had felt on his first visit. The sun showed up the new dust and in its gentle light the house seemed no longer like the scene of a crime but just a shabby relic. It was very close and Wexford opened the attic window. He blew a film of dust from the surface of the bigger trunk and opened its lid. It was crammed with books and he took the top ones out. They were novels: two by Rhoda Broughton, *Evelina* in the Everyman's Library and Mrs Craik's *John Halifax, Gentleman*. Their fly-leaves were bare and nothing fluttered from the pages when he shook them. Underneath were two bundles of school stories, among them what looked like the complete works of Angela Brazil. Wexford dumped them on the floor and lifted out a stack of expensive-looking volumes, some bound in suède, others in scented leather or watered silk.

The first one he opened was covered in pale green suède, its pages edged with gold. On the fly-leaf someone had printed carefully in ink:

> *If love were what the rose is,*
> *And I were like the leaf,*
> *Our lives would grow together*
> *In sad or singing weather . . .*

And underneath:

Rather sentimental, Minna, but you know what I mean. Happy, happy birthday. All my love, Doon. March 21st, 1950.

Burden looked over Wexford's shoulder.

'Who's Minna?'

'We'll have to ask Parsons,' Wexford said. 'Could be second-hand. It looks expensive. I wonder why she didn't keep it downstairs. God knows, this place needs brightening up.'

'And who's Doon?' Burden asked.

'You're supposed to be a detective. Well, detect.' He put the book on the floor and picked up the next one. This was the *Oxford Book of Victorian Verse*, still in its black and pearl-grey jacket, and Doon had printed another message inside. Wexford read it aloud in an unemotional voice.

'*I know you have set your heart on this, Minna, and I was so happy when I went to Foyle's and found it waiting for me. Joyeux Noel, Doon, Christmas, 1950.*' The next book was even more splendid, red watered silk and black leather. 'Let's have a look at number three,' Wexford said. '*The Poems of Christina Rossetti*. Very nice, gilt lettering and all. What's Doon got to say this time? *An un-birthday present, Minna dear, from Doon who wishes you happy for ever and ever. June 1950.* I wonder if Mrs P. bought the lot cheap from this Minna.'

'I suppose Minna could *be* Mrs P., a sort of nickname.'

'It had just crossed my mind,' Wexford said sarcastically. 'They're such good books, Mike, not the sort of things anyone would give to a church sale, and church sales seem to have been about Mrs Parsons' mark. Look at this lot: *Omar Khayyám*; Whitman's *Leaves of Grass*; William Morris. Unless I'm much mistaken that *Omar Khayyám* cost three or four pounds. And there's another one here, the *Verses of Walter Savage Landor*. It's an old-fashioned kind of book and the leaves haven't even been cut.' He read the message on the fly-leaf aloud:

'*I promise to bring back with me*
What thou with transport will receive,
The only proper gift for thee.
Of which no mortal shall bereave.

'*Rather apt, don't you think, Minna? Love from Doon. March 21st, 1951.*'

'It wasn't very apt, was it? And Minna, whoever she is, didn't receive it with transport. She didn't even cut the pages. I'm going to have another word with Parsons, Mike, and then we're going to have all this lot carted down to the station. This attic is giving me the creeps.'

But Parsons didn't know who Minna was and he looked surprised when Wexford mentioned the date, March 21st.

'I never heard anyone call her Minna,' he said distastefully, as if the name was an insult to her memory. 'My wife never spoke about a friend called Doon. I've never even seen those books properly. Margaret and I lived in the house her aunt left her till we moved here and those books have always been in the trunk. We just brought them with us with the furniture. I can't make it out about the date – Margaret's birthday was March 21st.'

'It could mean nothing, it could mean everything,' Wexford said when they were out in the car. 'Doon talks about Foyle's, and Foyle's, in case you don't know, my provincial friend, is in London in the Charing Cross Road.'

'But Mrs P. was sixteen in 1949 and she stayed two years in Flagford. She must have been living only about five miles from here when Doon gave her those books.'

'True. He could have lived here too and gone up to London for the day. I wonder why he printed the messages, Mike. Why didn't he write them? And why did Mrs P. hide the books as if she was ashamed of them?'

'They'd make a better impression on the casual caller than *The Brides in the Bath* or whatever it is,' Burden said. 'This Doon was certainly gone on her.'

Wexford took Mrs Parsons' photograph out of his pocket. Incredible that this woman had ever inspired a passion or fired a line of verse!

'Happy for ever and ever,' he said softly. 'But love isn't what the rose is. I wonder if love could be a dark and tangled wood, a cord twisted and pulled tighter on a meek neck?'

'A cord?' Burden said. 'Why not a scarf, that pink nylon thing? It's not in the house.'

59

'Could be. You can bet your life that scarf is with the purse and the key. Plenty of women have been strangled with a nylon stocking, Mike. Why not a nylon scarf?'

He had brought the Swinburne and the Christina Rossetti with him. It wasn't much to go on, Burden reflected, a bundle of old books and an elusive boy. Doon, he thought, Doon. If Minna was anything to go by Doon was bound to be a pseudonym too. Doon wouldn't be a boy any more but a man of thirty or thirty-five, a married man with children, perhaps, who had forgotten all about his old love. Burden wondered where Doon was now. Lost, absorbed perhaps into the great labyrinth of London, or still living a mile or two away. . . . His heart sank when he recalled the new factory estate at Stowerton, the mazy lanes of Pomfret with a solitary cottage every two hundred yards, and to the north, Sewingbury, where road after road of post-war detached houses pushed outwards like rays from the nucleus of the ancient town. Apart from these, there was Kingmarkham itself and the daughter villages, Flagford, Forby. . . .

'I don't suppose that Missal bloke could be Doon,' he said hopefully.

'If he is,' Wexford said, 'he's changed one hell of a lot.'

The river of my years has been sluggish, Minna, flowing slowly to a sea of peace, Ah, long ago how I yearned for the torrent of life!

Then yesternight, yestere'en, Minna, I saw you. Not as I have so often in my dreams, but in life. I followed you, looking for lilies where you trod. . . . I saw the gold band on your finger, the shackle of an importunate love, and I cried aloud in my heart, I, I, too have known the terrors of the night!

But withal my feast has ever been the feast of the spirit and to that other dweller in my gates my flesh has been as an unlit candle in a fast-sealed casket. The light in my soul has guttered, shrinking in the harsh wind. But though the casket be atrophied and the flame past resuscitation, yet the wick of the spirit cries, hungering for the hand that holds the taper of companionship, the torch of sweet confidence, the spark of friends reunited.

I shall see you tomorrow and we shall ride together along the silver streets of our youth. Fear not, for reason shall sit upon my bridle and gentle moderation within my reins. Will all not be well, Minna, will all not be pleasant as the warm sun on the faces of little children?

CHAPTER SEVEN

When she shall unwind
All those wiles she wound about me....

Francis Thompson, *The Mistress of Vision*

A black Jaguar, not new but well tended, was parked outside the Missals' house when Wexford and Burden turned in at the gate at seven o'clock. The wheels only were soiled, their hub-caps spattered with dried mud.

'I know that car,' Wexford said. 'I know it but I can't place it. Must be getting old.'

'Friends for cocktails,' Burden said sententiously.

'I could do with a spot of gracious living myself,' Wexford grumbled. He rang the ship's bell.

Perhaps Mrs Missal had forgotten they were coming or Inge hadn't been primed. She looked surprised yet spitefully pleased. Like her employer's, her hair was done up on top of her head, but with less success. In her left hand she held a canister of paprika.

'All are in,' she said. 'Two come for dinner. What a man! I tell you it is a waste to have men like him buried in the English countryside. Mrs Missal say, "Inge, you must make lasagna." All will be Italian, paprika, pasta, pimentoes.... Ach, it is just a game!'

'All right, Miss Wolff. We'd like to see Mrs Missal.'

'I show you.' She giggled, opened the drawing-room door and announced with some serendipity, 'Here are the policemen!'

Four people were sitting in the flowered armchairs and there were four glasses of pale dry sherry on the coffee-table.

For a moment nobody moved or said anything, but Helen Missal flushed deeply. Then she turned to the man who sat between her and her husband, parted her lips and closed them again.

So that's the character Inge was going on about in the hall, Burden thought. Quadrant! No wonder Wexford recognized the car.

'Good evening, Mr Quadrant,' Wexford said, indicating by a slight edge to his voice that he was surprised to see him in this company.

'Good evening, Chief Inspector, Inspector Burden.'

Burden had long known him as a solicitor he often saw in Kingsmarkham magistrates' court, long known and inexplicably disliked. He nodded to Quadrant and to the woman, presumably Quadrant's wife, who occupied the fourth armchair. They were somewhat alike, these two, both thin and dark with straight noses and curved red lips. Quadrant had the features of a grandee in an El Greco portrait, a grandee or a monk, but as far as Burden knew he was an Englishman. The Latin lips might have first drawn breath in a Cornish town and Quadrant be the descendant of an Armada mariner. His wife was beautifully dressed with the careless elegance of the very rich. Burden thought she made Helen Missal's blue shift look like something from a chainstore sale. Her fingers were heavily be-ringed, vulgarly so, if the stones were false, but Burden didn't think they were false.

'I'm afraid we're intruding again, sir,' Wexford said to Missal, his eyes lingering on Quadrant. 'I'd just like to have a talk with your wife, if you don't mind.'

Missal stood up, his face working with impotent rage. In his light-weight silver-grey suit he looked fatter than ever. Then Quadrant did a strange thing. He took a cigarette out of the box on the table, put it in his mouth and lit the cork tip. Fascinated, Burden watched him choke and drop the cigarette into an ashtray.

'I'm sick and tired of all this,' Missal shouted. 'We can't

even have a quiet evening with our friends without being hounded. I'm sick of it. My wife has given you her explanation and that ought to be enough.'

'This is a murder enquiry, sir,' Wexford said.

'We were just going to have dinner.' Helen Missal spoke sulkily. She smoothed her blue skirt and fidgeted with a string of ivory beads. 'I suppose we'd better go into your study, Pete. Inge'll be in and out of the dining-room. God! God damn it all, why can't you leave me in peace?' She turned to Quadrant's wife and said: 'Will you excuse me a moment, Fabia, darling? That is, if you can bear to stay and eat with the criminal classes.'

'You're sure you don't want Douglas to go with you?' Fabia Quadrant sounded amused, and Burden wondered if the Missals had warned them of the impending visit, suggested perhaps that this was to enquire into some parking offence. 'As your solicitor, I mean,' she said. But Wexford had mentioned murder and when he lit that cigarette Quadrant had been frightened.

'Don't be long,' Missal said.

They went into the study and Wexford closed the door.

'I want my lipstick back,' Helen Missal said, 'and I want my dinner.'

Unmoved, Wexford said, 'And I want to know who you went out with when you lost your lipstick, madam.'

'It was just a friend,' she said. She looked coyly up at Wexford, whining like a little girl asking permission to have a playmate to tea. 'Aren't I allowed to have any friends?'

'Mrs Missal, if you continue to refuse to tell me this man's name I shall have no alternative but to question your husband.'

Burden was becoming used to her sudden changes of mood, but still he was not quite prepared for this burst of violence.

'You nasty low-down bastard!' she said.

'I'm not much affected by that sort of abuse, madam. You see, I'm accustomed to moving in circles where such language is among the terms of reference. His name, please. This is a murder enquiry.'

'Well, if you must know it was Douglas Quadrant.'

And that, Burden thought, accounts for the choking act in the other room.

'Inspector Burden,' Wexford said, 'will you just take Mr Quadrant into the dining-room (never mind about Miss Wolff's dinner) and ask him for his version of what happened on Wednesday night? Or was it Tuesday afternoon, Mrs Missal?'

Burden went out and Wexford said with a little sigh, 'Very well, madam, now I'd like to hear about Wednesday night all over again.'

'What's that fellow going to say in front of my husband?'

'Inspector Burden is a very discreet officer. Provided I find everything satisfactory I've no doubt you can convince your husband that Mr Quadrant was consulted simply in his capacity as your solicitor.'

This was the line Burden took when he went back into the drawing-room.

'Is there some difficulty about Mrs Missal, then, Inspector?' Fabia Quadrant asked. She might have been asking some minion if he had attended to the wants of a guest. 'I expect my husband can sort it out.'

Quadrant got up lazily. Burden was surprised that he offered no resistance. They went into the dining-room and Burden pulled out two chairs from the side of the table. It was laid with place mats, tall smoky purple glasses, knives and forks in Swedish steel and napkins folded into the shape of water-lilies.

'A man must live,' Quadrant said easily when Burden asked him about his drive with Helen Missal. 'Mrs Missal is perfectly happily married. So am I. We just like to do a little dangerous living together from time to time. A drive, a drink . . . No harm done and everyone the happier for it.' He was being disarmingly frank.

Burden wondered why. It didn't seem to tie up with his manner when they had first arrived. Everyone the happier for it? Missal didn't look happy . . . and the woman with the rings? She had her money to console her. But what had all this to do with Mrs Parsons?

'We drove to the lane,' Quadrant said, 'parked the car and stood on the edge of the wood to have a cigarette. You know how smoky it gets inside a car, Inspector.' Burden was to be brought in as another man of the world. 'I'm afraid I know nothing about the lipstick. Mrs Missal is rather a happy-go-lucky girl. She tends to be careless about unconsidered trifles.' He smiled. 'Perhaps that's what I like about her.'

Had he seen him? Part of the time, yes, but he certainly hadn't had Quadrant under his eye all day.

'I suppose all this did happen on Wednesday,' Burden said, 'not Tuesday afternoon?'

'Now, come, Inspector. I was in court all day Tuesday. You saw me yourself.'

'We'd like to have a look at your car tyres, sir.' But as he said it Burden knew it was hopeless. Quadrant admitted visiting the lane on Wednesday.

In the study Wexford was getting much the same story from Helen Missal.

'We didn't go into the wood,' she said. 'We just stood under the trees. I took my handbag with me because it had got quite a bit of money in it and I think I must have dropped my lipstick when I opened the bag to get my hanky out.'

'You never went out of sight of the car?'

The net was spread and she fell in it.

'We never went out of sight of the car,' she said. 'We just stood under the trees and talked.'

'What a nervous person you must be, Mrs Missal, nervous and extremely cautious. You had Mr Quadrant with you and you were in sight of the car, but you were afraid someone might try to steal your handbag under your very eyes.'

She was frightened now and Wexford was sure she hadn't told him everything.

'Well, that's how it happened. I can't be expected to account for everything I do.'

'I'm afraid you can, madam. I suppose you've kept your cinema ticket?'

'Oh, my God! Can't you give me any peace? Of course I don't keep cinema tickets.'

'You don't show much foresight, madam. It would have been prudent to have kept it in case your husband wanted to see it. Perhaps you'll have a look for that ticket and when you've found it I'd like you to bring it down to the station. The tickets are numbered and it will be simple to determine whether yours was issued on Tuesday or Wednesday.'

Quadrant was waiting for him in the dining-room, standing by the sideboard now and reading the labels on two bottles of white wine. Burden still sat at the table.

'Ah, Chief Inspector,' Quadrant said in the tone he used for melting the hearts of lay magistrates. ' "What a tangled web we weave when first we practise to deceive"!'

'I wish you could convince Mrs Missal of the truth of that maxim, sir. Very unfortunate for you that you happened to choose that particular lane for your ... your talk with her on Wednesday night.'

'May I assure you, Chief Inspector, that it was merely a matter of misfortune.' He continued to look at the bottles of Barsac, misted and ice-cold. 'Had I been aware of the presence of Mrs Parsons' body in the wood I should naturally have come straight to you. In my position, my peculiar position, I always take it upon myself to give every possible assistance to you good people.'

'It is a peculiar position, isn't it, sir? What I should call a stroke of malignant fate.'

In the drawing-room Missal and Mrs Quadrant were sitting in silence. They looked, Burden thought, as if they had little in common. Helen Missal and the solicitor filed in, smiling brightly, as if they had all been playing some party game. The

67

charade had been acted, the word discovered. Now they could all have their dinner.

'Perhaps we can all have our dinner now,' Missal said.

Wexford looked at him.

'I believe you were in Kingsmarkham on Tuesday afternoon, Mr Missal? Perhaps you'll be good enough to tell me where you were exactly and if anyone saw you.'

'No, I won't,' Missal said. 'I'm damned if I do. You send your henchman —'

'Oh, Peter,' Fabia Quadrant interrupted. 'Henchman! What a word.'

Burden stood woodenly, waiting.

'You send your underling to show me up in front of my clients and my staff. You persecute my wife. I'm damned if I tell you what I do with every minute of my time!'

'Well, I had to,' Helen Missal said. She seemed pleased with herself, delighted that the focus of attention had shifted from herself to her husband.

'I'd like a sample from your car tyres,' Wexford said, and Burden wondered despairingly if they were going to have to scrape mud from the wheels of every car in Kingsmarkham.

'The Merc's in the garage,' Missal said. 'Make yourself at home. You do inside, so why not make free with the grounds? Maybe you'd like to borrow the lawn for the police sports.'

Fabia Quadrant smiled slightly and her husband pursed his lips and looked down. But Helen Missal didn't laugh. She glanced quickly at Quadrant and Burden thought she gave the ghost of a shiver. Then she lifted her glass and drained the sherry at a single gulp.

Wexford sat at his desk, doodling on a piece of paper. It was time to go home, long past time, but they still had the events of the day, the stray remarks, the evasive answers, to sift through and discuss. Burden saw that the Chief Inspector was writing, apparently aimlessly, the pair of names he had scribbled that morning when Mrs Missal had first come to him: *Missal, Parsons; Parsons, Missal.*

'But what's the connection, Mike? There must be a connection.' Wexford sighed and drew a thick black line through the names. 'You know, sometimes I wish this *was* Mexico. Then we could keep a crate of hooch in here. Tequila or some damn' thing. This everlasting tea is making me spew.'

'Quadrant and Mrs Missal . . .' Burden began slowly.

'They're having a real humdingin' affair,' Wexford interrupted, 'knocking it off in the back of his Jag.'

Burden was shocked.

'A woman like that?' he said. 'Why wouldn't they go to an hotel?'

'The best bedroom at The Olive and Dove? Be your age. He can't go near her place because of Inge and she can't go to his because of his wife.'

'Where does he live?'

'You know where Mrs Missal keeps her car? Well, up on the other side, on the corner of what our brothers in the uniformed branch call the junction with the Upper Kingsbrook Road. That place with the turrets. She couldn't go there because of darling Fabia. My guess is they went to that lane because Dougie Q. knows it well, takes all his bits of stuff there. It's quiet, it's dark and it's nasty. Just the job for him and Mrs M. When they've had their fun and games in the back of the car they go into the wood. . . .'

'Perhaps Mrs Missal saw a rabbit, sir,' Burden said innocently.

'Oh, for God's sake!' Wexford roared. 'I don't know why they went into the wood, but Mrs Missal might well fancy having a bit more under the bushes in God's sweet air. Maybe they saw the body. . . .'

'Quadrant would have come to us.'

'Not if Mrs Missal persuaded him not to, not if she said it would mean her Peter and his Fabia finding out about them.

She got to work on him and our courteous Dougie, whom ne'er the word of No woman heard speak – I *can* read, Mike – our courteous Dougie agrees to say nothing about it.'

Burden looked puzzled. Finally he said: 'Quadrant was scared, sir. He was scared stiff when we came in.'

'I suppose he guessed it was going to come out. His wife was there. That's quite natural.'

'Then wouldn't you have expected him to have been more cagey about it all? But he wasn't. He was almost too open about it.'

'Perhaps,' Wexford said, 'he wasn't scared we were going to ask about it. He was scared of *what* we were going to ask.'

'Or of what Mrs Missal might say.'

'Whatever it was, we didn't ask it or she gave the right answer. The right answer from his point of view, I mean.'

'I asked him about Tuesday. He said he was in court all day. Says I saw him there. I did, too, off and on.'

Wexford groaned. 'Likewise,' he said. 'I saw him but I wasn't keeping a watch on him and that makes a mighty lot of difference. I was up in Court One. He was defending in that drunk driving case downstairs. Let me think. They adjourned at one, went back at two.'

'We went into the Carousel for lunch. . . .'

'So did he. I saw him. But we went upstairs, Mike. He may have done too. I don't know. He was back in court by two and he didn't have the car. He walks when he's that near home.'

'Missal could do with taking a leaf out of his book,' Burden said. 'Get his weight down. He's a nasty piece of work, sir. Henchman!' he added in disgust.

'Underling, Mike,' Wexford grinned.

'What's stopping him telling us where he was on Tuesday?'

'God knows, but those tyres were as clean as a whistle.'

'He could have left the car on the Pomfret Road.'

'True.'

'I suppose Mrs Missal could have got some idea into her head that Quadrant was carrying on with Mrs P. —'

Wexford had begun to look fretful. 'Oh, come off it,' he said. 'Dougie Q. and Mrs P.? He's been knocking it off on the side for years. It's common knowledge. But have you seen the sort of things his taste runs to? I tell you, on Saturday mornings the High Street is littered with his discards, consoling themselves for their broken maidenheads or their broken marriages by showing off their new Mini-Minors. Mrs P. just wasn't his style. Anyway, Mrs Missal wouldn't have done murder for him. He was just a different way of passing a dull evening, one degree up on the telly.'

'I thought it was only men who looked at it that way.' Burden was always startled by his chief's occasional outbursts of graphic frankness. Wexford, who was always intuitive, sometimes even lyrical, could also be coarse. 'She was risking a lot for a casual affair.'

'You want to buck your ideas up, Mike,' Wexford snapped. 'Minna's *Oxford Book of Victorian Verse* is just about your mark. I'm going to lend it to you for your bedtime reading.'

Burden took the book and flicked through the pages: Walter Savage Landor, Coventry Patmore, Caroline Elizabeth Sarah Norton. . . . The names seemed to come from far away, the poets long dust. What possible connection could they have with dead, draggled Minna, with the strident Missals? Love, sin, pain – these were the words that sprang from almost every verse. After Quadrant's flippancies they sounded like ridiculous anachronisms.

'A connecting link, Mike,' Wexford said. 'That's what we want, a connection.'

But there was none to be found that night. Wexford took three of the other books ('Just in case our Mr Doon underlined anything or put in any fancy little ticks') and they walked out into the evening air. Beyond the bridge Quadrant's car still waited.

CHAPTER EIGHT

One of my cousins long ago,
A little thing the mirror said. . . .

James Thomson, *In the Room*

A bird was singing outside Wexford's office window; a black-
bird, Burden supposed. He had always rather liked listening
to it until one day Wexford said it sang the opening bars of
'The Thunder and Lightning Polka', and after that its daily
reiteration annoyed him. He wanted it to go on with the tune
or else vary a note or two. Besides, this morning he had had
enough of blackbirds and larks and nightingales, enough of
castle-bound maidens dying young and anaemic swains seren-
ading them with lute and tabor. He had sat up half the night
reading the Oxford Book and he was by no means convinced
that it had had anything to do with Mrs Parsons' death.

It was going to be a beautiful day, too beautiful for an
inquest. When Burden walked in Wexford was already at his
desk, turning the pages of the suède-covered Swinburne. The
rest of the Doon books had been removed from the house in
Tabard Road and dumped on Wexford's filing cabinet.

'Did you get anything, sir?' Burden asked.

'Not so's you'd notice,' Wexford said, 'but I did have an
idea. I'll tell you about it when you've read the report from
Balham. It's just come in.'

The report was typed on a couple of sheets of foolscap.
Burden sat down and began to go through it:

Margaret Iris Parsons (he read) was born Margaret Iris
Godfrey to Arthur Godfrey, male nurse, and his wife, Iris
Drusilla Godfrey, at 213 Holderness Road, Balham, on March

21st, 1933. Margaret Godfrey attended Holderness Road Infants' School from 1938 until 1940 and Holderness Road Junior School from 1940 until 1944. Both parents killed as a result of enemy action, Balham, 1942, after which Margaret resided with her maternal aunt and legal guardian, Mrs Ethel Mary Ives, wife of Leading Aircraftman Geoffrey Ives, a member of the regular Air Force, at 42 St John's Road, Balham. At this time the household included Anne Mary Ives, daughter of the above, birth registered at Balham, February 1st, 1932.

Leading Aircraftman Ives was transferred to Flagford, Sussex, R.A.F. Station during September 1949 (date not known). Mrs Ives, Anne Ives and Margaret Godfrey left Balham at this time, Mrs Ives having let her house in St John's Road, and took up residence in Flagford.

On the death of Geoffrey Ives from coronary thrombosis (Sewingbury R.A.F. Hospital, July 1951) Mrs Ives, her daughter and Margaret Godfrey returned to Balham and lived together at 42 St John's Road. From September 1951 until July 1953 Margaret Godfrey was a student at Albert Lake Training College for Women, Stoke Newington, London.

On August 15th, 1952, Anne Ives married Private Wilbur Stobart Katz, U.S. Army, at Balham Methodist Chapel, and left the United Kingdom for the United States with Private Katz in October 1952 (date not known).

Margaret Godfrey joined staff of Holderness Road Infants' School, Balham, September 1953.

Ronald Parsons (clerk) aged twenty-seven, became a lodger at 42 St John's Road, in April 1954. Death of Mrs Ethel Ives from cancer (Guy's Hospital, London), registered at Balham by Margaret Godfrey, May 1957. Margaret Godfrey and Ronald Parsons married at Balham Methodist Chapel, August 1957, and took up residence at 42 St John's Road, the house having been left jointly to Mrs Parsons and Mrs Wilbur Katz under the will of Mrs Ives.

42 St. John's Road was purchased compulsorily by Balham Council, November 1962, whereupon Mr and Mrs Parsons removed to Kingsmarkham, Sussex, Mrs Parsons having resigned from the staff of Holderness Road School.

(Refs: Registrar of Births and Deaths, Balham; Rev. Albert Derwent, Minister, Methodist Chapel, Balham; Royal Air Force Records; United States Air Force Records; London County Council Education Dept.; Guy's Hospital; Balham Borough Council.)

'I wonder where Mrs Wilbur Katz is now?' Burden said.

'You got any cousins in America, Mike?' Wexford asked in a quiet, deceptively gentle voice.

'I believe I have.'

'So've I and so have half the people I've ever met. But nobody ever does know where they are or even if they're alive or dead.'

'You said you'd had an idea, sir?'

Wexford picked up the report and stabbed at the second paragraph with his thick forefinger.

'It came to me in the night,' he said, 'in the interval between Whitman and Rossetti – sound like a couple of gangsters, don't they? Sweet Christ, Mike I ought to have thought of it before! Parsons said his wife came here when she was sixteen and even then it didn't click. I assumed, backwoods copper that I am, that Mrs Parsons had left school by then. But, Mike, she was a teacher, she went to a training college. When she was in Flagford she must have gone to school! I reckon they came to Flagford just after she'd taken her School Cert., or whatever they call it these days, and when she got here she went right on going to school.'

'There are only two girls' schools around here,' Burden said. 'The Kingsmarkham County High and that convent place in Sewingbury. St Catherine's.

'Well, she wouldn't have gone there. She was a Methodist and, as far as we know, her aunt was too. Her daughter got married in a Methodist chapel at any rate. It's just our luck that's it's Saturday and the school's shut.

'I want you to root out the head – you can dip out on the inquest, I'll be there. The head's a Miss Fowler and she lives in York Road. See what you can dig up. They must keep records. What we want is a list of the girls who were in Margaret Godfrey's class between September 1949 and July 1951.'

'It'll be a job tracing them, sir.'

'I know that, Mike, but somehow or other we've got to have a break. This just might be it. We know all about Margaret Parsons' life in Balham, and by the look of it it was mighty dull. Only two sensational things ever happened to her as far as I can see. Love and death, Mike, love and death. The thing is they both happened here in my district. Somebody loved her here and when she came back somebody killed her. One of those girls may remember a boy friend, a possessive boy friend with a long memory.'

'I wish,' Burden said, 'I wish some decent public-spirited cop-loving citizen would walk in here and just tell us he knew Mrs P., just tell us he'd taken her out in 1950 or even seen her in a shop last week.' He brooded for a second over the Balham report. 'They were an unhealthy lot, weren't they, sir? Cancer, coronary thrombosis . . .'

Wexford said slowly: 'When Parsons was telling us a bit of his wife's history I did just wonder why he said, "Her uncle died, he wasn't killed." It's a small point, but I see it now. Her parents *were* killed, but not in the way we mean when we talk about killing.'

After he had gone across the courthouse behind the police station Burden telephoned Miss Fowler. A deep cultured voice answered, carefully enunciating the name of the exchange and the number. Burden began to explain but Miss Fowler interrupted him. Yes, Margaret had been at the High School, although she could scarcely remember her from that time.

75

However, she had seen her recently in Kingsmarkham and had recognized her as the murdered woman from a newspaper photograph.

'Honestly, Inspector,' she said, 'what a very shocking thing!' She spoke as if the killing had offended rather than distressed her, or, Burden thought, as if the education meted out at her school should automatically have exempted any pupil from falling victim to a murderer.

He apologized for troubling her and asked if she could let him have the list Wexford wanted.

'I'll just give our school secretary, Mrs Mortlock, a ring,' Miss Fowler said. 'I'll get her to nip along to school and have a look through the records. If you could call on me about lunchtime, Inspector?'

Burden said he was most grateful.

'Not at all. It's no trouble,' Miss Fowler said. 'Honestly.'

The inquest was over in half an hour and Dr Crocker's evidence occupied ten minutes of that time. Death, he said, was caused by strangulation by means of a ligature; a scarf possibly or a piece of cloth. Mrs Parsons' body was otherwise unbruised and there had been no sexual assault. She had been a healthy woman, slightly overweight for her height. In his evidence Wexford gave his opinion that it was impossible to say whether or not there had been a struggle as the wood had been heavily trampled by Prewett's cows. The doctor was recalled and said that he had found a few superficial scratches on the dead woman's legs. These were so slight that he would not care to say whether they had been made before or after death.

A verdict was returned of murder by person or persons unknown.

Ronald Parsons had sat quietly throughout the inquest, twisting a handkerchief in his lap. He kept his head bowed as the coroner offered some perfunctory expressions of sympathy and indicated that he heard only by a slight movement, a tiny nod. He seemed so stunned with misery that Wexford was surprised when he caught up with him as he was crossing the flagged courtyard and touched him on the sleeve.

Without preamble he said, 'A letter came for Margaret this morning.'

'What d'you mean, a letter?' Wexford stopped. He had seen some of Mrs Parsons' letters; advertisements and coal bills.

'From her cousin in the States,' Parsons said. He took a deep breath and shivered in the warm sun.

Looking at him, Wexford realized that he was no longer stupefied. Some fresh bitterness was affecting him.

'I opened it.'

He spoke with a kind of guilt. She was dead and they had plundered her possessions. Now even her letters, letters posthumously received, were to be picked over, their words dissected as meticulously as her own body had been examined and exposed.

'I don't know . . . I can't think,' he said, 'but there's something in it about someone called Doon.'

'Have you got it with you?' Wexford asked sharply.

'In my pocket.'

'We'll go into my office.'

If Parsons noticed his wife's books spread about the room he gave no sign. He sat down and handed an envelope to Wexford. On the flap, just beneath the ragged slit Parsons had made, was a handwritten address: *From Mrs Wilbur S. Katz, 1183 Sunflower Park, Slate City, Colorado, U.S.A.*

'That would be Miss Anne Ives,' Wexford said. 'Did your wife correspond with her regularly?'

Parsons looked surprised at the name.

'Not to say regularly,' he said. 'She'd write once or twice a year. I've never met Mrs Katz.'

'Did your wife write to her recently, since you came here?'

'I wouldn't know, Chief Inspector. To tell you the truth,

I didn't care for what I knew of Mrs Katz. She used to write and tell Margaret all about the things she'd got – cars, washing machines, that sort of thing . . . I don't know whether it upset Margaret. She'd been very fond of her cousin and she never said she minded hearing about all those things. But I made it plain what I thought and she stopped showing me the letters.'

'Mr Parsons, I understand Mrs Ives' house was left jointly to your wife and Mrs Katz. Surely —?'

Parsons interrupted bitterly: 'We bought our share off her, Chief Inspector. Every penny of seven hundred pounds we paid – through a bank in London. My wife had to work full-time so that we could do it, and when we'd paid the lot, just paid off the lot, the council bought the place off us for nine hundred. They had a sort of order.'

'A compulsory-purchase order,' Wexford said. 'I see.' He stuck his head round the door. 'Sergeant Camb! Tea, please, and an extra cup. I'll just read that letter, if you don't mind, Mr Parsons.'

It was written on thin blue paper and Mrs Katz had found plenty to tell her cousin. The first two pages were entirely taken up with an account of a holiday Mr and Mrs Katz and their three children had spent in Florida; Mrs Katz's new car; a barbecue her husband had bought her. Mr and Mrs Parsons were invited to come to Slate City for a holiday. Wexford began to see what Parsons had meant.

The last page was more interesting.

Gee, Meg (Mrs Katz had written), *I sure was amazed to see you and Ron had moved to Kingsmarkham. I'll bet that was Ron's idea, not yours. And you have met up with Doon again, have you? I sure would like to know who Doon is. You've got to tell me, not keep dropping hints.*

Still, I can't see why you should be scared of Doon. What of, for the Lord's sake? There was never anything in that. (You know what I mean, Meg.) I can't believe Doon is still keen. You always had a

*suspicious mind!!! But if meeting Doon means trips in the car and a
few free meals I wouldn't be too scrupulous.*

*When are you and Ron going to get a car of your own? Wil says
he just doesn't know how you make out . . .*

There was some more in the same vein, sprinkled with
exclamation marks and heavily underlined. The letter ended:

*. . . Regards to Ron and remind him there's a big welcome wait-
ing for you both in Sunflower Park whenever you feel like hitting
Colorado, U.S.A. Love from Nan. Greg, Joanna and Kim send hugs to
their Auntie Meg.*

'This could be very important, Mr Parsons,' Wexford said. 'I'd
like to hang on to it.'

Parsons got up, leaving his tea untasted.

'I wish it hadn't come,' he said. 'I wanted to remember
Margaret as I knew her. I thought she was different. Now I
know she was just like the rest, carrying on with another man
for what she could get out of him.'

Wexford said quietly: 'I'm afraid it looks like that. Tell me,
didn't you have any idea that your wife might be going out
with this man, this Doon? It looks very much as if Doon knew
her when she lived in Flagford and took up with her again
when she came back. She must have gone to school here, Mr
Parsons. Didn't you know that?'

Did Parsons look furtive, or was it just a desire to hold on
to some remnants of his private life, his marriage broken both
by infidelity and by death, that made him flush and fidget?

'She wasn't happy in Flagford. She didn't want to talk
about it and I stopped asking her. I reckon it was because
they were such a lot of snobs. I respected her reticence, Chief
Inspector.'

'Did she talk to you about her boy friends?'

'That was a closed book,' Parsons said, 'a closed book for

both of us. I didn't *want* to know, you see.' He walked to the window and peered out as if it was night instead of bright day. 'We weren't those kind of people. We weren't the kind of people who have love affairs.' He stopped, remembering the letter. 'I can't believe it. I can't believe that of Margaret. She was a good woman, Chief Inspector, a good loving woman. I can't help thinking that Katz woman was making up a lot of things that just weren't true, making them up out of her own head.'

'We shall know a bit more when we hear from Colorado,' Wexford said. 'I'm hoping to get hold of the last letter your wife wrote to Mrs Katz. There's no reason why it shouldn't be made available to you.'

'Thank you for nothing,' Parsons said. He hesitated, touched the green cover of Swinburne's verses and walked quickly from the room.

It was some sort of a break, Wexford thought, some sort of a break at last. He picked up the telephone and told the switchboard girl he wanted to make a call to the United States. This had been a strange woman, he reflected as he waited, a strange secretive woman leading a double life. To her husband and the unobservant world she had been a sensible prudent housewife in sandals and a cotton frock, an infants' teacher who polished the front step with Brasso and went to church socials. But someone, someone generous and romantic and passionate, had been tantalized and maddened by her for twelve long years.

CHAPTER NINE

Sometimes a troop of damsels glad . . .

Tennyson, *The Lady of Shalott*

Miss Fowler's was an unacademic bookless flat. Burden, who was aware of his own failing of cataloguing people in types, had tried not to expect old-maidishness. But this was what he found. The room into which Miss Fowler showed him was full of hand-made things. The cushion covers had been carefully embroidered, the amateurish water-colours obviously executed with patience, the ceramics bold. It looked as if Miss Fowler could hardly bear to reject the gift of an old scholar, but the collection was neither restful nor pleasing.

'Poor, poor Margaret,' she said. Burden sat down and Miss Fowler perched herself in a rocking chair opposite him, her feet on a petit-point footstool. 'What a very shocking thing all this is! That poor man too. I've got the list you wanted.'

Burden glanced at the neatly typed row of names.

'Tell me about her,' he said.

Miss Fowler laughed self-consciously, then bit her lip as if she thought this was no occasion for laughter.

'Honestly, Inspector,' she said, 'I can't remember. You see, there are so many girls . . . Of course, we don't forget them all, but naturally it's the ones who achieve something, get Firsts or find really spectacular posts, those are the ones we remember. Hers wasn't a very distinguished year. There was plenty of promise, but none of it came to very much. I saw her, you know, after she came back.'

'Here? In Kingsmarkham?'

'It must have been about a month ago.' She took a packet

of Weights from the mantelpiece, offered one to Burden, and puffed bravely at her own as he held a match to it.

They never really grow up, he thought.

'I was in the High Street,' she went on. 'It was just after school and she was coming out of a shop. She said, "Good afternoon, Miss Fowler." Honestly, I hadn't the faintest idea who she was. Then she said she was Margaret Godfrey. You see, they expect you to remember them, Inspector.'

'Then how did you . . .?'

'How did I connect her with Mrs Parsons? When I saw the photograph. You know, I felt sorry we hadn't talked, but I'm always seeing old girls, but I honestly couldn't tell you who they are or their ages, come to that. They might be eighteen or thirty. You know how it is, you can't tell the ages of people younger than yourself.' She looked up at Burden and smiled. 'But you *are* young,' she said.

Again he returned to the list. The names were in alphabetical order. He read aloud slowly, waiting for Miss Fowler's reactions:

'*Lyn Annesley, Joan Bertram, Clare Clarke, Wendy Ditcham, Margaret Dolan, Margaret Godfrey, Mary Henshaw, Jillian Ingram, Anne Kelly, Helen Laird, Marjorie Miller, Hilda Pensteman, Janet Probyn, Fabia Rogers, Deirdre Sachs, Diana Stevens, Winifred Thomas, Gwen Williams, Yvonne Young.*'

Under the names Mrs Morpeth had written with an air of triumph: *Miss Clare Clarke is a member of the High School teaching staff!!!*

'I'd like to talk to Miss Clarke,' he said.

'She lives at Nectarine Cottage down the first lane on the left on the Stowerton Road,' Miss Fowler said.

Burden said slowly, 'Fabia is a very unusual name.'

Miss Fowler shrugged. She patted her stiffly waved grey hair. 'Not a particularly unusual type,' she said. 'Just one of those very promising people I was telling you about who never amounted to much. She lives here somewhere. She and her husband are quite well known in what I believe are called social circles. Helen Laird was another one. Very lovely, very self-confident. Always in trouble. Boys, you know. Honestly, so silly! I thought she'd go on the stage, but she didn't, she just got married. And then Miss Clarke, of course . . .'

Burden had the impression she had been about to include Miss Clarke among the failures, but that loyalty to her staff prevented her. He didn't pursue it. She had given him a more disturbing lead.

'What did you say happened to Helen Laird?'

'I really know nothing, Inspector. Mrs Morpeth said something about her having married a car salesman. Such a waste!' She stubbed out her cigarette into an ashtray that was daubed with poster paint and obviously home-baked. When she went on her voice sounded faintly sad. 'They leave, you know, and we forget them, and then about fifteen years later a little tot turns up in the first form and you think, I've seen that face before somewhere! Of course you have – her mother's.'

Dymphna and Priscilla, Burden thought, nearly sure. Not long now, and Dymphna's face, the same red hair perhaps, would revive in Miss Fowler's memory some long-lost chord.

'Still,' she said, as if reading his thoughts, 'there's a limit to everything and I retire in two years' time.'

He thanked her for the list and left. As soon as he got to the station Wexford showed him the Katz letter.

'It all points to Doon being the killer, sir,' Burden said, 'whoever he is. What do we do now, wait to hear from Colorado?'

'No, Mike, we'll have to press on. Clearly Mrs Katz doesn't know who Doon is and the best we can hope for is to get some of the background from her and the last letter Mrs P. sent her before she died. Doon is probably going to turn out to be a boy friend Mrs P. had when she was at school here. Let's hope she didn't have too many.'

'I've been wondering about that,' Burden said, 'because honestly – as Miss Fowler would say – those messages in Minna's books don't look like the work of a boy at all, not unless he was a very mature boy. They're too polished, too smooth. Doon could be an older man who got interested in her.'

'I thought of that,' Wexford said, 'and I've been checking up on Prewett and his men. Prewett bought that farm in 1949 when he was twenty-eight. He's an educated person and quite capable of writing those messages, but he was in London on Tuesday. There's no doubt about it, unless he was involved in a conspiracy with two doctors, an eminent heart specialist, a sister, God knows how many nurses and his own wife.

'Draycott's only been in the district two years and he was in Australia from 1947 to 1953. Bysouth can scarcely write his own name, let alone dig up suitable bits of poetry to send to a lady love, and much the same goes for Traynor. Edwards was in the Army throughout 1950 and 1951, and Dorothy Sweeting can't possibly know what was going on in Minna's love life twelve years ago. She was only seven.'

'Then it looks as if we'll have to ferret out what we can from the list,' Burden said. 'I think you'll be interested when you see some of the names, sir.'

Wexford took the list and when he came to Helen Laird and Fabia Rogers he swore fiercely. Burden had pencilled in *Missal* and *Quadrant*, following each surname with a question mark.

'Somebody's trying to be clever,' Wexford said, 'and that I won't have. Rogers. Her people are old man Rogers and his missus at Pomfret Hall. They're loaded. All made out of paint. There's no reason why she should have told us she knew Mrs P. When we talked to Dougie this Doon angle didn't seem that important. But Mrs Missal . . . Not know Mrs P. indeed, and they were in the same class!'

He had grown red with anger. Burden knew how he hated being taken for a ride.

'I was going to forget all about that cinema ticket, Mike, but now I'm not so sure. I'm going to have it all out again with Mrs Missal now.' He stabbed at the list. 'While I'm gone you can start contacting these women.'

'It would have to be a girls' school,' Burden grumbled. 'Women change their names, men don't.'

'Can't be helped,' Wexford said snappily. 'Mr Griswold's been on twice already since the inquest, breathing down my neck.'

Griswold was the Chief Constable. Burden saw what Wexford meant.

'You know him, Mike. The least hint of difficulty and he's screaming for the Yard,' Wexford said, and went out, leaving Burden with the list and the letter.

Before embarking on his womanhunt Burden read the letter again. It surprised him because it gave an insight into Mrs Parsons' character, revealing a side he had not really previously suspected. She was turning out to be a lot less pure than anyone had thought.

. . . *If meeting Doon means rides in the car and a few free meals I wouldn't be too scrupulous*, Mrs Katz had written. But at the same time she didn't know who Doon was. Mrs Parsons had been strangely secretive, enigmatic, hiding the identity of a boy friend from a cousin who had also been an intimate friend.

A strange woman, Burden thought, and a strange boy friend. It was a funny sort of relationship she had with this Doon, he said to himself. Mrs Katz says, *I can't see why you should be scared*, and later, on, *there was never anything in that*. What did she mean, anything in that? But Mrs P. was *scared*. What of, sexual advances? Mrs Katz says she had a suspicious mind. Fair enough, he reflected. Any virtuous woman would be scared and suspicious of a man who paid her a lot of attention. But at the same time there was never anything in it. Mrs P. mustn't be too scrupulous.

Burden groped vainly. The letter, like its recipient, was a

puzzle. As he put it down and turned to the telephone he was certain of only two facts: Doon hadn't been making advances; he wanted something else, something that frightened Mrs Parsons but which was so innocuous in the estimation of her cousin that it would be showing excessive suspicion to be scrupulous about it. He shook his head like a man who has been flummoxed by an intricate riddle, and began to dial.

He tried Bertram first because there was no Annesley in the book – and, incidentally, no Pensteman and no Sachs. But the Mr Bertram who answered said he was over eighty and a bachelor. Next he rang the number of the only Ditchams he could find, but although he listened to the steady ringing past all reason, there was no reply.

Mrs Dolan's number was engaged. He waited five minutes and tried again. This time she answered. Yes, she was Margaret Dolan's mother, but Margaret was now Mrs Heath and had gone to live in Edinburgh. In any case, Margaret had never brought anyone called Godfrey to the house. Her particular friends had been Janet Probyn and Deirdre Sachs, and Mrs Dolan remembered them as having been a little shut-in clique on their own.

Mary Henshaw's mother was dead. Burden spoke to her father. His daughter was still in Kingsmarkham. Married? Burden asked. Mr Henshaw roared with laughter while Burden waited as patiently as he could. He recovered and said his daughter was indeed married. She was Mrs Hedley and she was in the county hospital.

'I'd like to talk to her,' Burden said.

'You can't do that,' Henshaw said, hugely amused. 'Not unless you put a white coat on. She's having a baby, her fourth. I thought you were them, bringing me the glad news.'

Through Mrs Ingram he was put on to Jillian Ingram, now Mrs Bloomfield. But she knew nothing of Margaret Parsons except that at school she had been pretty and prim, fond of reading, rather shy.

'Pretty, did you say?'

'Yes, she was pretty, attractive in a sort of way. Oh, I know, I've seen the papers. Looks don't necessarily last, you know.'

Burden knew, but still he was surprised.

Anne Kelly had gone to Australia, Marjorie Miller . .

'My daughter was killed in a car crash,' said a harsh voice, full of awakened pain. 'I should have thought the police of all people would know that.'

Burden sighed. Pensteman, Probyn, Rogers, Sachs . . . all were accounted for. In the local directory alone he found twenty-six Stevenses, forty Thomases, fifty-two Williamses, twelve Youngs.

To track them all down would take best part of the afternoon and evening. Clare Clarke might be able to help him. He closed the directory and set off for Nectarine Cottage.

The french windows were open when Inge Wolff let Wexford into the hall and he heard the screams of quarrelling children. He followed her across the lawn and at first saw nobody but the two little girls: the elder a sharp miniature fascimile of her mother, bright-eyed, red-headed; the younger fat and fair with a freckle-blotched face. They were fighting for possession of a swing-boat, a red and yellow fairground thing with a rabbit for a figurehead.

Inge rushed over to them, shouting.

'Are you little girls that play so, or rough boys? Here is one policeman come to lock you up!'

But the children only clung more tightly to the ropes, and Dymphna, who was standing up, began to kick her sister in the back.

'If he's a policeman,' she asked, 'where's his uniform?'

Someone laughed and Wexford turned sharply. Helen Missal was in a hammock slung between a mulberry tree and the wall of a summerhouse and she was drinking milkless tea from a glass. At first he could see only her face and a honey-coloured arm dangling over the edge of the canvas. Then, as he came closer, he saw that she was dressed for sunbathing. She wore only a bikini, an ice-white figure of eight and a triangle against her golden skin. Wexford was embarrassed and his embarrassment fanned his anger into rage.

'Not again!' she said. 'Now I know how the fox feels. He doesn't enjoy it.'

Missal was nowhere about, but from behind a dark green barrier of macrocarpa Wexford could hear the hum of a motor mower.

'Can we go indoors, Mrs Missal?'

She hesitated for a moment. Wexford thought she was listening, perhaps to the sounds from the other side of the hedge. The noise of the mower ceased, then, as she seemed to hold her breath, started again. She swung her legs over the hammock and he saw that her left ankle was encircled by a thin gold chain.

'I suppose so,' she said. 'I don't have any choice, do I?'

She went before him through the open doors, across the cool dining-room where Quadrant had looked on the wine, and into the rhododendron room. She sat down and said:

'Well, what is it now?'

There was something outrageous and at the same time spiteful about the way she spread her nakedness against the pink and green chintz. Wexford turned away his eyes. She was in her own home and he could hardly tell her to go and put some clothes on. Instead he took the photograph from his pocket and held it out to her.

'Why did you tell me you didn't know this woman?'

Fear left her eyes and they flared with surprise.

'I didn't know her.'

'You were at school with her, Mrs Missal.'

She snatched the photograph and stared at it.

'I was not.' Her hair fell over her shoulders, bright copper like a new penny. 'At least, I don't think I was. I mean, she

was years older than me by the look of this. She may have
been in the sixth when I was in the first form. I just wouldn't
know.'

Wexford said severely: 'Mrs Parsons was thirty, the same
age as yourself. Her maiden name was Godfrey.'

'I adore "maiden name". It's such a charitable way of
putting it, isn't it? All right, Chief Inspector, I do remember
now. But she's aged, she's differnt. . . .' Suddenly she smiled,
a smile of pure delighted triumph, and Wexford marvelled that
this woman was the same age as the pathetic dead thing they
had found in the wood.

'It's very unfortunate you couldn't remember on Thursday
evening, Mrs Missal. You've put yourself in a most unpleasant
light, firstly by deliberately lying to Inspector Burden and
myself and secondly by concealment of important facts. Mr
Quadrant will tell you that I'm quite within my rights if I
charge you with being an accessary —'

Helen Missal interrupted sulkily. 'Why pick on me? Fabia
knew her too, and . . . Oh, there must be lots and lots of other
people.'

'I'm asking you,' he said. 'Tell me about her.'

'If I do,' she said, 'will you promise to go away and not
come back?'

'Just tell me the truth, madam, and I will gladly go away.
I'm a very busy man.'

She crossed her legs and smoothed her knees. Helen
Missal's knees were like a little girl's, a little girl who has never
climbed a tree or missed a bath.

'I didn't like school,' she said confidingly. 'It was so
restricting, if you know what I mean. I just begged and begged
Daddy to take me away at the end of my first term in the
sixth —'

'Margaret Godfrey, Mrs Missal.'

'Oh, yes, Margaret Godfrey. Well, she was a sort of cipher
– isn't that a lovely word? I got it out of a book. A sort of

cipher. She was one of the fringe people, not very clever or nice-looking or anything.' She glanced once more at the picture. 'Margaret Godfrey. D'you know, I can hardly believe it. I should have said she was the last girl to get herself murdered.'

'And who would be the first, Mrs Missal?'

'Well, someone like me,' she said, and giggled.

'Who were her friends, the people she went around with?'

'Let me think. There was Anne Kelly and a feeble spotty bitch called Bertram and Diana Something...'

'That would be Diana Stevens.'

'My God, you know it all, don't you?'

'I meant boy friends.'

'I wouldn't know. I was rather busy in that direction myself.' She looked at him, pouting provocatively, and Wexford wondered, with the first flicker of pity he had felt for her, if her coyness would increase as her beauty declined until in age she became grotesque.

'Anne Kelly,' he said, 'Diana Stevens, a girl called Bertram. What about Clare Clarke, what about Mrs Quadrant? Would they remember?'

She had said that she hated school, but as she began to speak her voice was softer than he had ever known it and her expression gentler. For a moment he forgot his anger, her lies, the provocative costume she wore, and listened.

'It's funny,' she said, 'but thinking of those names has sort of brought it back to me. We used to sit in a kind of garden, a wild old place. Fabia and me and a girl called Clarke – I see her around sometimes – and Jill Ingram and that Kelly girl and – and Margaret Godfrey. We were supposed to be working but we didn't much. We used to talk about ... Oh, I don't know. ...'

'About your boy friends, Mrs Missal?' As soon as the words were out Wexford knew he had been obtuse.

'Oh, no,' she said sharply. 'You've got it wrong. Not then, not in the garden. It was a wilderness, an old pond, bushes, a seat. We used to talk about . . . well, about our dreams, what we wanted to do, what we were going to make of our lives.' She stopped and Wexford could see in a sudden flash of vision a wild green place, the girls with their books and hear with his mind's ear the laughter, the gasp of dizzy ambition. Then he almost jumped at the change in her voice. She whispered savagely, as if she had forgotten he was there: 'I wanted to act! They wouldn't let me, my father and my mother. They made me stay at home and it all went. It sort of dissolved into nothing.' She shook back her hair and smoothed with the tips of two fingers the creases that had appeared between her eyebrows. 'I met Pete,' she said, 'and we got married.' Her nose wrinkled. 'The story of my life.'

'You can't have everything,' Wexford said.

'No,' she said, 'I wasn't the only one. . . .'

She hesitated and Wexford held his breath. He had an intuitive conviction that he was about to hear something of enormous significance, something that would iron out the whole case, wrap it up and tie it ready to hand to Mr Griswold. The green eyes widened and lit up; then suddenly the incandescence died and they became almost opaque. Outside in the hall a floorboard squeaked and Wexford heard the squashy sound of a rubber sole on thick carpet. Helen Missal's face became quite white.

'Oh God!' she said. 'Please, please don't ask about the cinema ticket. Please don't!'

Wexford cursed inwardly as the door opened and Missal came in. He was sweating and there were damp patches on the underarms of his singlet. He stared at his wife and in his eyes was a strange mixture of disgust and concupiscence.

'Put something on,' he shouted. 'Go on, put some clothes on.'

She got up awkwardly and Wexford had the illusion that

her husband's words were scrawled across her body like the obscene scribble on a pin-up picture.

'I was sunbathing,' she said.

Missal wheeled round on Wexford.

'Come to see the peep-show, have you?' His face was crimson with exertion and with jealousy. 'What the copper saw.'

Wexford wanted to be angry, to match the other man's rage with his own colder kind, but he could feel only pity.

All he said was, 'Your wife has been able to help me.'

'I'll bet she has.' Missal held the door open and almost pushed her through. 'Been kind, has she? That's a speciality of hers, being kind to every Tom, Dick and Harry.' He fingered his wet shirt as if his body disgusted him. 'Go on,' he said, 'start on me now. What were you doing in Kingsmark-ham on Tuesday afternoon, Mr Missal? The name of the client, Mr Missal. Your car was seen in the Kingsbrook Road, Mr Missal. Well, go on. Don't you want to know?'

Wexford got up and walked a few paces towards the door. The heavy blossoms, pink, puce and white, brushed against his legs. Missal stood staring at him like an overfed, under-exercised dog longing to let out an uninhibited howl.

'Don't you want to know? Nobody saw me. I could have been strangling that woman. Don't you want to know what I was doing? Don't you?'

Wexford didn't look at him. He had seen too many men's souls stripped to relish an unnecessary spiritual skinning.

'I know what you were doing,' he said, skipping the name, the 'sir'. 'You told me yourself, just now in this room.' He opened the door. 'If not in so many words.'

Douglas Quadrant's house was much larger and far less pleas-ing to the eye than the Missals'. It stood on an eminence amid shrubby grounds some fifty feet back from the road. A huge cedar softened to some extent its austere aspect, but when he was half-way up the path Wexford recalled similar houses he had seen in the north of Scotland, granite-built, vaguely gothic and set at each end with steeple-roofed towers.

There was something odd about the garden, but it was a few minutes before he realized in what its strangeness consisted. The lawns were smooth, the shrubs conventionally chosen, but about it all was a sombre air. There were no flowers. Douglas Quadrant's garden presented a Monet-like landscape of grey and brown and many-shaded green.

After Mrs Missal's blue lilies, the rhododendrons real and artificial in her drawing-room, this stately drabness should have been restful. Instead it was hideously depressing. Undoubtedly no flowers could bloom because none had been planted, but the effect was rather that the soil was barren or the air inclement.

Wexford mounted the shallow flight of broad steps under the blank eyes of windows hung with olive and burgundy and pigeon grey, and pressed the bell. Presently the door was opened by a woman of about seventy dressed amazingly in a brown frock with a beige cap and apron. She was what was once known, Wexford thought, as 'an elderly body'. Here, he was sure, there would be no frivolous Teutonic blondes.

She in her turn looked as if she would designate him as 'a person', a creature not far removed from a tradesman, who should have known better than to present himself at the front door. He asked for Mrs Quadrant and produced his card.

'Madam is having her tea,' she said, unimpressed by Wexford's bulk, his air of justice incarnate. 'I'll see if she can speak to you.'

'Just tell her Chief Inspector Wexford would like a word with her.' Affected by the atmosphere, he added, 'If you please.'

He stepped over the threshold and into the hall. It was as big as a large room and, surprisingly enough, the tapestries of hunting scenes stretched on frames and attached to the walls did nothing to diminish its size. Again there was the same absence of colour, but not quite a total absence. Worked into the coats of the huntsmen, the palfreys of their mounts, Wexford caught the gleam of dull gold, ox-blood red and a hint of heraldic murrey.

The old woman looked defiantly at him as if she was prepared to argue it out, but as Wexford closed the front door firmly behind him someone called out:

'Who is it, Nanny?'

He recognized Mrs Quadrant's voice and remembered how the night before she had smiled at Missal's crude joke.

Nanny just got to the double doors before him. She opened them in a way he had only seen done in films and, incongruously, grotesquely, there rose before his eyes a shot, ridiculous and immensely funny, from a Marx Brothers picture. The vision fled and he entered the room.

Douglas and Fabia Quadrant were sitting alone at either end of a low table covered by a lace cloth. Tea had apparently only just been brought in because the book Mrs Quadrant had been reading was lying open and face-upwards on the arm of her chair. The soft old silver of the teapot, the cream jug and the sugar bowl was so brightly polished that it reflected her long hands against the sombre colours of the room. It was forty years since Wexford had seen a brass kettle like this one boiling gently over a spirit flame.

Quadrant was eating bread and butter, just plain bread and butter but crustless and cut thin as a wafer.

'This is an unexpected pleasure,' he said, rising to his feet. This time there were no clumsy incidents with cigarettes. He restored his cup almost gracefully to the table and waved Wexford into an armchair.

'Of course, you know my wife?' He was like a cat, Wexford thought, a slim detached tom-cat who purred by day and went out on the tiles at night. And this room, the silver, the china, the long wine-coloured curtains like blood transmuted into velvet! And amidst it all Mrs Quadrant, dark-haired, elegant in black, was feeding cream to her cat. But when the lamps were lit he stole away to take his feline pleasures under the bushes in the creeping dark.

'Tea, Chief Inspector?' She poured a driblet of water into the pot.

'Not for me, thank you.' She had come a long way, Wexford thought, since those days in the wilderness garden, or perhaps, even then, her gym tunic had been of a more expensive make, her hair more expertly cut than the other girls'. She's beautiful, he thought, but she looks old, much older than Helen Missal. No children, plenty of money, nothing to do all day but feed cream to a ranging cat. Did she mind his infidelity, did she even know about it? Wexford wondered curiously if the jealousy that had reddened Missal had blanched and aged Quadrant's wife.

'And what can I do for you?' Quadrant asked. 'I half expected a visit this morning. I gather from the newspapers that you aren't making a great deal of headway.' Lining himself up on the side of the law, he added, 'An elusive killer this time, am I right?'

'Things are sorting themselves out,' Wexford said heavily. 'As a matter of fact it was your wife I wanted to speak to.'

'To me?' Fabia Quadrant touched one of her platinum ear-rings and Wexford noticed that her wrists were thin and her arms already corded like a much older woman's. 'Oh, I see. Because I knew Margaret, you mean. We were never very close, Chief Inspector. There must be dozens of people who could tell you more about her than I can.'

Possibly, Wexford thought, if I only knew where to find them.

'I didn't see her at all after her family moved away from Flagford until just a few weeks ago. We met in the High Street and had coffee. We discovered we'd gone our separate ways and – well!'

And that, Wexford said to himself, contrasting Tabard Road with the house he was in, must be the understatement of the case. For a second, building his impressions as he always did in a series of pictures, he glimpsed that meeting: Mrs Quadrant with her rings, her elaborately straight hair, and Margaret Parsons awkward in the cardigan and sandals that had seemed so comfortable until she came upon her old companion. What had they in common, what had they talked about?

'What did she talk about, Mrs Quadrant?'

'Oh, the changes in the place, people we'd known at school, that sort of thing.' The governess and the lady of the manor. Wexford sighed within himself.

'Did you ever meet anyone called Anne Ives?'

'You mean Margaret's cousin? No, I never met her. She wasn't at school with us. She was a typist or a clerk or something.'

Just another of the hoi-polloi, Wexford thought, the despised majority, the bottom seventy-five per cent.

Quadrant sat listening, swinging one elegant leg. His wife's condescension seemed to amuse him. He finished his tea, crumpled his napkin and helped himself to a cigarette. Wexford watched him take a box of matches from his pocket and strike one. Matches! That was odd. Surely if he had behaved consistently Quadrant would have used a lighter, one of these table lighters that look like a Georgian teapot, Wexford thought, his imagination working. There had been a single matchstick beside Mrs Parsons' body, a single matchstick half burnt away. . . .

'Now, Margaret Godfrey's boy friends, Mrs Quadrant. Can you remember anyone at all?'

He leant forward, trying to impress her with the urgency of his question. A tiny flash of something that might have been malice or simply recollection darted into her eyes and was gone. Quadrant exhaled deeply.

'There was a boy,' she said.

'Try to remember, Mrs Quadrant.'

'I ought to remember,' she said, and Wexford was sure she could, certain she was only stalling for effect. 'It was like a theatre, a London theatre.'

'Palladium, Globe, Haymarket?' Quadrant was enjoying himself. 'Prince of Wales?'

Fabia Quadrant giggled softly. It was an unkind titter, sympathetic towards her husband, faintly hostile to the Chief Inspector. For all his infidelity Quadrant and his wife shared something, something stronger, Wexford guessed, than ordinary marital trust.

'I know, it was Drury. Dudley Drury. He used to live in Flagford.'

'Thank you, Mrs Quadrant. It had just crossed my mind that your husband might have known her.'

'I?' As he spoke the monosyllable Quadrant's voice was almost hysterically incredulous. Then he began to rock with laughter. It was a soundless cruel mirth that seemed to send an evil wind through the room. He made no noise, but Wexford felt scorn leap out of the laughing man like a springing animal, scorn and contempt and the wrath that is one of the deadly sins. 'I, know *her*? In that sort of way? I assure you, dear Chief Inspector, that I most emphatically knew her not!'

Sickened, Wexford turned away. Mrs Quadrant was looking down into her lap. It was as if she had withdrawn into a sort of shame.

'This Drury,' Wexford said, 'do you know if she ever called him Doon?'

Was it his imagination or was it simply coincidence that at that moment Quadrant's laughter was switched off like a wrenched tap?

'Doon?' his wife said. 'Oh, no, I never heard her call anyone Doon.'

She didn't get up when Wexford rose to go, but gave him a dismissive nod and reached for the book she had been reading. Quadrant let him out briskly, closing the door before he reached the bottom of the steps as if he had been selling brushes or reading the meter. Dougie Q! If there was ever a fellow who could strangle one woman and then make love to another a dozen yards away ... But why? Deep in thought, he walked down the Kingsbrook Road, crossed to the opposite side of the road and would have passed Helen Missal's garage unseeing but for the voice that hailed him.

'Did you see Douglas?' Her tone was wistful but she had cheered up since he had last seen her. The bikini had been changed for a printed silk dress, high-heeled shoes and a big hat.

The question was beneath Wexford's dignity.

'Mrs Quadrant was able to fill in a few gaps,' he said.

'Fabia was? You amaze me. She's very discreet. Just as well, Douglas being what he is.' For a moment her pretty face was swollen with sensuality. 'He's magnificent, isn't he? He's splendid.' Shaking herself, she drew her hand across the face and when she withdrew it Wexford saw that the lust had been wiped away. 'My Christ,' she said, once more cheerful and outrageous, 'some people don't know when they're well off!' She unlocked the garage doors, opened the boot of the red Dauphine and took out a pair of flatter shoes.

'I had the impression,' Wexford said, 'that there was something else you wanted to tell me.' He paused. 'When your husband interrupted us.'

'Perhaps there was and perhaps there wasn't. I don't think I will now.' The shoes changed, she danced up to the car and swung the door open.

'Off to the cinema?' Wexford asked.

She banged the door and switched on the ignition.

'Damn you!' Wexford heard her shout above the roar of the engine.

CHAPTER TEN

We were young, we were merry, we were very very wise,
And the door stood open at our feast. . . .

Mary Coleridge, Unwelcome

Nectarine Cottage lay in a damp hollow, a bramble-filled basin
behind the Stowerton Road. The approach down a winding path
was hazardous and Miss Clarke was taking no chances. Notices
pencilled on lined paper greeted Burden at intervals as he
descended. The first on the gate had commanded *Lift and push
hard*; the second, some ten feet down the path, *Mind barbed wire*.
Presently the brambles gave place to faint traces of cultivation.
This was of a strictly utilitarian kind, rows of sad cabbages among
the weeds, a splendid marrow plant protected from the thistles
by a home-made cloche. Someone had pinned a sheet of paper
to its roof, *Do not remove glass*. Evidently Miss Clarke had clumsy
friends or was the victim of trespassers. This Burden could
understand, for there was nothing to indicate habitation but the
vegetables and the notices, and the cottage only came into view
when he was almost upon it at the end of the path.

The door stood wide open and from within came rich
gurgling giggles. For a moment he thought that, although there
were no other houses in the lane, he had come to the wrong
place. He rapped on the door, the giggles rose to a gale and
someone called out:

'Is that you, Dodo? We'd almost given you up.'

Dodo might be a man or a woman, probably a woman.
Burden gave a very masculine cough.

'Oh, gosh, it isn't,' said the voice. 'I tell you what, Di. It
must be old Fanny Fowler's cop, a coughing cop.'

Burden felt uncommonly foolish. The voice seemed to come from behind a closed door at the end of the passage.

He called loudly, 'Inspector Burden, madam!'

The door was immediately flung open and a woman came out dressed like a Tyrolean peasant. Her fair hair was drawn tightly back and twisted round her head in plaits.

'Oh, gosh,' she said again. 'I didn't realize the front door was still open. I was only kidding about you being Miss Fowler's cop. She rang up and said you might come.'

'Miss Clarke?'

'Who else?' Burden thought she looked very odd, a grown woman dressed up as Humperdinck's Gretel. 'Come and pig it along with Di and me in the dungeon,' she said.

Burden followed her into the kitchen. *Mind the steps*, said another notice pinned to the door and he saw it just in time to stop himself crashing down the three steep steps to the slate-flagged floor. The kitchen was even nastier than Mrs Parsons' and much less clean. But outside the window the sun was shining and a red rose pressed against the diamond panes.

There was nothing odd about the woman Miss Clarke had called Di. It might have been Mrs Parsons' double sitting at the table eating toast, only this woman's hair was black and she wore glasses.

'Di Plunkett, Inspector Burden,' Clare Clarke said. 'Sit down, Inspector – not that stool. It's got fat on it – and have a cup of tea.'

Burden refused the tea and sat on a wooden chair that looked fairly clean.

'I've no objection if you talk while I eat,' said Miss Clarke, bursting once more into giggles. She peered at a tin of jam and said crossly to her companion: 'Confound it! South African. I know I shan't fancy it now.' She pouted and said dramatically, 'Ashes on my tongue!' But Burden noticed that she helped herself generously and spread the jam on to a doorstep of bread. With her mouth full she said to him: 'Fire away. I'm all ears.'

'All I really want to know is if you can tell me the names of any of Mrs Parsons' boy friends when she was Margaret Godfrey, when you knew her.'

Miss Clarke smacked her lips.

'You've come to the right shop,' she said. 'I've got a memory like an elephant.'

'You can say that again,' said Di Plunkett, 'and it's not only your memory.' They both laughed, Miss Clarke with great good humour.

'I remember Margaret Godfrey perfectly,' she said. 'Second-class brain, anaemic looks, personality both prim and dim. Still, *de mortuis* and all that jazz, you know. (Prang that fly, Di. There's a squeegy-weegy sprayer thing on the shelf behind your great bonce.) Not a very social type, Margaret, no community spirit. Went around with a female called Bertram, vanished now into the mists of obscurity. (Got him, Di!) Chummed up with one Fabia Rogers for a while – Fabia, forsooth! not to mention Diana Stevens of sinister memory —'

Miss or Mrs Plunkett broke in with a scream of laughter and waving the fly-killer made as if to fire a stream of liquid at Miss Clarke's head. Burden shifted his chair out of range.

Ducking and giggling, Clare Clarke went on: '... Now notorious in the Stowerton rural district as Mrs William Plunkett, one of this one-eyed burg's most illustrious sons!'

'You are a scream, Clare,' Mrs Plunkett gasped. 'Really, I envy those lucky members of the upper fourth. When I think of what we had to put up with —'

'What about boy friends, Miss Clarke?'

'*Cherchez l'homme*, eh? I said you'd come to the right shop. D'you remember, Di, when she went out with him the first time and we sat behind them in the pictures? Oh, gosh, I'll never forget that to my dying day.'

'Talk about sloppy,' said Mrs Plunkett. ' "Do you mind if I hold your hand, Margaret?" I thought you were going to burst a blood-vessel, Clare.'

'What was his name?' Burden was bored and at the same time angry. He thought the years had toughened him, but now the picture of the green and white bundle in the wood swam before his eyes; that and Parsons' face. He realized that of all the people they had interviewed he hadn't liked a single one. Was there no pity in any of them, no common mercy?

'What was his name?' he said again wearily.

'Dudley Drury. On my sacred oath, Dudley Drury.'

'What a name to go to bed with,' Mrs Plunkett said.

Clare Clarke whispered in her ear, but loud enough for Burden to hear: 'She never did! Not on your sweet life.'

Mrs Plunkett saw his face and looked a little ashamed. She said defensively in a belated effort to help:

'He's still around if you want to trace him. He lives down by Stowerton Station. Surely you don't think he killed Meg Godfrey?'

Clare Clarke said suddenly: 'She was quite pretty. He was very keen on her. She didn't look like that then, you know, not like that ghastly mockery in the paper. I think I've got a snap somewhere. All girls together.'

Burden had got what he wanted. Now he wanted to go. It was a bit late in the day for snaps. If they could have seen one on Thursday it might have helped but that was all.

'Thank you, Miss Clarke,' he said, 'Mrs Plunkett. Good afternoon.'

'Well, cheeri-bye. It's been nice meeting you.' She giggled. 'It's not often we see a man in here, is it, Di?'

Half-way down the overgrown path he stopped in his tracks. A woman in jodhpurs and open-necked shirt was coming up towards the cottage, whistling. It was Dorothy Sweeting.

Dodo, he thought. They'd mistaken him for someone called

Dodo and Dodo was Dorothy Sweeting. From long experience Burden knew that whatever may happen in detective fiction, coincidence is more common than conspiracy in real life.

'Good afternoon, Miss Sweeting.'

She grinned at him with cheerful innocence.

'Oh, hallo,' she said, 'fancy seeing you. I've just come from the farm. There's a blinking great crowd like a Cup Final in that wood. You ought to see them.'

Still not inured to man's inhuman curiosity, Burden sighed.

'You know that bush where they found her?' Dorothy Sweeting went on excitedly. 'Well, Jimmy Traynor's flogging twigs off it at a bob a time. I told Mr Prewett he ought to charge half a crown admittance.'

'I hope he's not thinking of taking your advice, miss,' Burden said in a repressive voice.

'There's nothing wrong in it. I knew a fellow who had a plane crash on his land and he turned a whole field into a car park he had so many sightseers.'

Burden flattened himself against the hedge to let her pass.

'Your tea will be getting cold, Miss Sweeting,' he said.

'Whatever next?' Wexford said. 'If we don't look sharp they'll have every stick in that wood uprooted and taken home for souvenirs.'

'Shall I have a couple of the lads go over there, sir?' Burden asked.

'You do that, and go and get the street directory. We'll go and see this Drury character together.'

'You aren't going to wait to hear from Colorado, then?'

'Drury's a big possibility, Mike. He could well be Doon. I can't help feeling that whatever Parsons says about his wife's chastity, when she came back here she met up with Doon again and succumbed to his charms. As to why he should have killed her – well, all I can say is, men *do* strangle women they're having affairs with, and Mrs P. may have accepted the car rides and the meals without being willing to pay for services rendered.

'The way I see it, Mike, Doon had been seeing Mrs P. and asked her out on Tuesday afternoon with a view to persuading her to become his mistress. They couldn't meet at her home because of the risks and Doon was going to pick her up on the Pomfret Road. She took the rain-hood with her because the weather had been wet and she didn't bank on being in the car all the time. Even if she didn't want Doon for her lover she wouldn't want him to see her with wet hair.'

The time factor was bothering Burden and he said so.

'If she was killed early in the afternoon, sir, why did Doon strike a match to look at her? And if she was killed later, why didn't she pay for her papers before she went out with him and why didn't she explain to Parsons that she was going to be late?'

Wexford shrugged. 'Search me,' he said. 'Dougie Q. uses matches, carries them in his pocket. So do most men. He's behaving in a very funny way, Mike. Sometimes he's co-operative, sometimes he's actively hostile. We haven't finished with him yet. Mrs Missal knows more than she's saying —'

'Then there's Missal himself,' Burden interrupted.

Wexford looked thoughtful. He rubbed his chin and said: 'I don't think there's any mystery about what he was doing on Tuesday. He's as jealous as hell of that wife of his and not without reason as we know. I'm willing to take a bet that he keeps tabs on her when he can. He probably suspects Quadrant and when she told him she was going out on Tuesday afternoon he nipped back to Kingsmarkham on the off-chance, watched her go out, satisfied himself that she didn't go to Quadrant's office and went back to Stowerton. He'd know she'd dress herself up to the nines if she was meeting Dougie. When he saw her go off in the car along the Kingsbrook Road in the same clothes she was wearing that morning he'd bank on her going shopping in Pomfret – they don't close on Tuesdays – and he'd be able to set his mind at rest. I'm certain that's what happened.'

'It sounds like him,' Burden agreed. 'It fits. Was Quadrant here twelve years ago, sir?'

'Oh, yes, lived here all his life, apart from three years at Cambridge and, anyway, he came down in 1949. Still, Mrs P. was hardly his style. I asked him if he knew her and he just laughed, but it was the way he laughed. I'm not kidding, Mike, it made my blood run cold.'

Burden looked at his chief with respect. It must have been quite a display, he thought, to chill Wexford.

'I suppose the others could have been just – well, playthings as it were, and Mrs P. a life-long love.'

'Christ!' Wexford roared. 'I should never have let you read that book. Playthings, life-long love! You make me puke. For pity's sake find out where Drury lives and we'll get over there.'

According to the directory, Drury, Dudley J. and Drury, Kathleen lived at 14 Sparta Grove, Stowerton. Burden knew it as a street of tiny pre-war semi-detached houses, not far from where Peter Missal had his garage. It was not the kind of background he had visualized for Doon. He and Wexford had a couple of rounds of sandwiches from the Carousel and got to Stowerton by seven.

Drury's house had a yellow front door with a lot of neatly tied climbing roses on the trellis round the porch. In the middle of the lawn was a small pond made from a plastic bath and on its rim stood a plaster gnome with a fishing rod. Someone had evidently been polishing the Ford Popular on the garage drive. As a vehicle for clandestine touring Mrs Katz would probably have despised it, but it was certainly shiny enough to have dazzled Margaret Parsons.

The door-knocker was a cast-iron lion's head with a ring in its mouth. Wexford banged it hard, but no one came, so he pushed open the side gate and they entered the back garden. On a vegetable plot by the rear fence a man was digging potatoes.

Wexford coughed and the man turned round. He had a red glistening face, and although it was warm, the cuffs of his long-sleeved shirt were buttoned. His sandy hair and the whiteness of his wrists confirmed Wexford's opinion that he was probably sensitive to sunburn. Not the sort of man, Burden thought, to be fond of poetry and send snippets of verse to the girl he loved, surely not the sort of man to buy expensive books and write delicate whimsical messages in their fly-leaves.

'Mr Drury?' Wexford asked quietly.

Drury looked startled, almost frightened, but this could simply be alarm at the invasion of his garden by two men much larger than himself. There was sweat on his upper lip, again probably only the result of manual toil.

'Who are you?'

It was a thin highish voice that sounded as if its development towards a greater resonance had been arrested in puberty.

'Chief Inspector Wexford, sir, and Inspector Burden. County Police.'

Drury had looked after his garden. Apart from a couple of square yards from which potatoes had been lifted, there were various freshly turned patches all over the flower-beds. He stuck the prongs of the fork into the ground and wiped his hands on his trousers.

'Is this something to do with Margaret?' he asked.

'I think we'd better go into the house, Mr Drury.'

He took them in through a pair of french windows, considerably less elegant than Mrs Missal's, and into a tiny room crowded with post-war utility furniture.

Someone had just eaten a solitary meal. The cloth was still on the table and the dirty plates had been half-heartedly stacked.

'My wife's away,' Drury said. 'She took the kids to the seaside this morning. What can I do for you?'

He sat down on a dining chair, offered another to Burden and, observant of protocol, left the only armchair to Wexford.

'Why did you ask if it was something to do with Margaret, Mr Drury?'

'I recognized her photograph in the paper. It gave me a bit of a turn. Then I went to a do at the chapel last night and they were all talking about it. It made me feel a bit queer, I can tell you, on account of me meeting Margaret through the chapel.'

That would have been Flagford Methodist Church, Burden reflected. He recalled a maroon-painted hut with a corrugated-iron roof on the north side of the village green.

Drury didn't look scared any longer, only sad. Burden was struck by his resemblance to Ronald Parsons, not only a physical likeness but a similarity of phrase and manner. As well as the undistinguished features, the thin sandy hair, this man had the same defensiveness, the same humdrum turn of speech. A muscle twitched at the corner of his mouth. Anyone less like Douglas Quadrant would have been difficult to imagine.

'Tell me about your relationship with Margaret Godfrey,' Wexford said.

Drury looked startled.

'It wasn't a relationship,' he said.

What did he think he was being accused of? Burden wondered.

'She was one of my girl friends. She was just a kid at school. I met her at chapel and took her out . . . what, a dozen times.'

'When did you first take her out, Mr Drury?'

'It's a long time ago. Twelve years, thirteen years . . . I can't remember.' He looked at his hands on which the crusts of earth were drying. 'Will you excuse me if I go and have a bit of a wash?'

He went out of the room. Through the open serving hatch

Burden saw him run the hot tap and swill his hands under it. Wexford moved out of Drury's line of vision and towards the bookcase. Among the Penguins and the *Reader's Digests* was a volume covered in navy-blue suède. Wexford took it out quickly, read the inscription and handed it to Burden.

It was the same printing, the same breathless loving style. Above the title – *The Picture of Dorian Gray* – Burden read:

Man cannot live on wine alone, Minna, but this is the very best bread and butter. Farewell. Doon, July, 1951.

CHAPTER ELEVEN

They out-talked thee, hissed thee, tore thee,
Better men fared thus before thee.

Matthew Arnold, *The Last Word*

Drury came back, smiling cautiously. He had rolled up his sleeves and his hands were pink. When he saw the book Wexford was holding the smile faded and he said aggressively:

'I think you're taking a liberty.'

'Where did you get this book, Mr Drury?'

Drury peered at the printing, looked at Wexford and blushed. The tic returned, pumping his chin.

'Oh dear,' he said, 'she gave it me. I'd forgotten I'd got it.'

Wexford had become stern. His thick lower lip stood out, giving him a prognathous look.

'Look here, she gave me that book when I was taking her out. It says July here and that's when it must have been. July, that's right.' The blush faded and he went white. He sat down heavily. 'You don't believe me, do you? My wife'll tell you. It's been there ever since we got married.'

'Why did Mrs Parsons give it to you, Mr Drury?'

'I'd been taking her out for a few weeks.' He stared at Wexford with eyes like a hare's caught in the beam of headlights. 'It was the summer of – I don't know. What does it say there? Fifty-one. We were in her aunt's house. A parcel came for Margaret and she opened it. She looked sort of mad and she just chucked it down, chucked it on the floor, you see, but I picked it up. I'd heard of it and I thought . . . well, I thought it was a smutty book if you must know, and I wanted to read

109

it. She said, "Here, you can have it, if you like." Something like that. I can't remember the details of what she said. It was a long time ago. Minna had got fed up with this Doon and I thought she was sort of ashamed of him . . . '

'Minna?'

'I started calling her Minna then because of the name in the book. What have I said? For God's sake, don't look at me like that!'

Wexford stuck the book in his pocket.

'When did you last see her?'

Drury picked at the cord that bound the seat of his chair. He began pulling out little shreds of red cotton. At last he said:

'She went away in the August. Her uncle had died . . . '

'No, no. I mean recently.'

'I saw her last week. That isn't a crime, is it, seeing somebody you used to know? I was in the car and I recognized her. She was in the High Street, in Kingsmarkham. I stopped for a minute and asked her how she was, that sort of thing . . . '

'Go on. I want all the details.'

'She said she was married and I said so was I. She said she'd come to live in Tabard Road and I said we must get together sometime with her husband and Kathleen. Kathleen's my wife. Anyway, I said I'd give her a ring, and that was all.'

'She told you her married name?'

'Of course she did. Why shouldn't she?'

'Mr Drury, you said you recognized her photograph. Didn't you recognize her name?'

'Her name, her face, what's the odds? I'm not in court. I can't watch every word I say.'

'Just tell the truth and you won't have to watch your words. Did you telephone her?'

'Of course I didn't. I was going to, but then I read she was dead.'

'Where were you on Tuesday between twelve-thirty and seven?'

'I was at work. I work in my uncle's hardware shop in Pomfret. Ask him, he'll tell you I was there all day.'

'What time does the shop close?'

'Half past five, but I always try to get away early on Tuesdays. Look, you won't believe me.'

'Try me, Mr Drury.'

'I know you won't believe me, but my wife'll tell you, my uncle'll tell you. I always go to Flagford on Tuesdays to collect my wife's vegetable order. There's a nursery there, see, on the Clusterwell Road. You have to get there by half five otherwise they're closed. Well, we were busy last Tuesday and I was late. I try to get away by five, but it was all of a quarter past. When I got to Spellman's there wasn't anybody about. I went round the back of the greenhouses and I called out, but they'd gone.'

'So you went home without the vegetables?'

'No, I didn't. Well, I did, but not straight away. I'd had a hard day and I was fed up about the place being closed, so I went into The Swan and had a drink. A girl served me. I've never seen her before. Look, does my wife have to know about that? I'm a Methodist, see? I'm a member of the chapel. I'm not supposed to drink.'

Burden drew in his breath. A murder enquiry and he was worrying about his clandestine pint!

'You drove to Flagford along the main Pomfret Road?'

'Yes, I did. I drove right past that wood where they found her.' Drury got up and fumbled in vain along the mantelpiece for cigarettes. 'But I never stopped. I drove straight to Flagford. I was in a hurry to get the order ... Look, Chief Inspector, I wouldn't have done anything to Minna. She was a nice kid. I was fond of her. I wouldn't do a thing like that, kill someone!'

'Who else called her Minna apart from you?'

'Only this Doon fellow as far as I know. She never told me his real name. I got the impression she was sort of ashamed of him. Goodness knows why. He was rich and he was clever too. She said he was clever.' He drew himself up and looked at them belligerently. 'She preferred me,' he said.

He got up suddenly and stared at the chair he had mutilated. Among the dirty plates was a milk bottle, half full, with yellow curds sticking to its rim. He tipped the bottle into an empty tea-cup and drank from it, slopping a puddle into the saucer.

'I should sit down if I were you,' Wexford said.

He went into the hall and beckoned to Burden. They stood close together in the narrow passage. The carpet was frayed by the kitchen door and one of Drury's children had scribbled on the wallpaper with a blue crayon.

'Get on to The Swan, Mike,' he said. He thought he heard Drury's chair shift and, remembering the open french windows, turned swiftly. But Drury was still sitting at the table, his head buried in his hands.

The walls were thin and he could hear Burden's voice in the front room, then a faint trill as the receiver went back into its rest. Burden's feet thumped across the floor, entered the hall and stopped. There was utter silence and Wexford edged out of the door, keeping his eye on Drury through the crack.

Burden was standing by the front door. On the wall at the foot of the narrow staircase was a coat-rack, a zig-zag metal affair with gaudily coloured knobs instead of hooks. A man's sports jacket and a child's plastic mac hung on two of the knobs and on the one nearest to the stairs was a transparent pink nylon hood.

'It won't take prints,' Wexford said. 'Get back on that phone, Mike. I shall want some help. Bryant and Gates should be coming on about now.'

He unhooked the hood, covered the diminutive hall in three strides, and showed his find to Drury.

'Where did you get this, Mr Drury?'

'It must be my wife's,' Drury said. Suddenly assertive, he added pugnaciously, 'It's no business of yours!'

'Mrs Parsons bought a hood like this one on Tuesday morning.' Wexford watched him crumple once more in sick despair. 'I want your permission to search this house, Drury. Make no mistake about it, I can get a warrant, but it'll take a little longer.'

Drury looked as if he was going to cry.

'Oh, do what you like,' he said. 'Only, can I have a cigarette? I've left mine in the kitchen.'

'Inspector Burden will get them when he comes off the phone,' Wexford said.

They began to search, and within half an hour were joined by Gates and Bryant. Then Wexford told Burden to contact Drury's uncle at Pomfret, Spellman's nursery and the manager of the supermarket.

'The girl at The Swan isn't on tonight,' Burden said, 'but she lives in Flagford at 3 Cross Roads Cottages. No phone. Her name's Janet Tipping.'

'We'll get Martin over there straight away. Try and get a phone number out of Drury where we can get hold of his wife. If she's not gone far away – Brighton or Eastbourne – you can get down there tonight. When I've turned the place over I'm going to have another word with Mrs Quadrant. She admits she was "friendly" with Mrs P. and she's practically the only person who does, apart from our friend in the next room.'

Burden stretched the pink scarf taut, testing its strength.

'You really think he's Doon?' he asked incredulously.

Wexford went on opening drawers, feeling among a mêlée of coloured pencils, Snap cards, reels of cotton, scraps of paper covered with children's scribble. Mrs Drury wasn't a tidy housewife and all the cupboards and drawers were in a mess.

'I don't know,' he said. 'At the moment it looks like it, but it leaves an awful lot of loose ends. It doesn't fit in with my fancies, Mike, and since we can't afford to go by fancies...'

He looked through every book in the house – there were not more than two or three dozen – but he found no more from Doon to Minna. There was no Victorian poetry and the only novels apart from *The Picture of Dorian Gray* were paperback thrillers.

On a hook in the kitchen cabinet Bryant found a bunch of keys. One fitted the front door lock, another the strong box in Drury's bedroom, two more the dining-room and front-room doors, and a fifth the garage. The ignition keys to Drury's car were in his jacket on the coat-rack and the key to the back door was in the lock. Wexford, looking for purses, found only one, a green and white plastic thing in the shape of a cat's face. It was empty and labelled on the inside: *Susan Mary Drury*. Drury's daughter had taken her savings with her to the seaside.

The loft was approached by a hatch in the landing ceiling. Wexford told Bryant to get Drury's steps from the garage and investigate this loft. He left Gates downstairs with Drury and went out to his car. On the way he scraped some dust from the tyres of the blue Ford.

A thin drizzle was falling. It was ten o'clock and dark for a midsummer evening. If Drury had killed her at half past five, he thought, it would still have been broad daylight, much too early to need the light of a match flame. It would have to be a match they had found. Of all the things to leave behind a matchstick was surely the least incriminating! And why hadn't she paid for her papers, what had she done with herself during the long hours between the time she left the house and the time she met Doon? But Drury was terribly frightened... Wexford too had observed the resemblance between him and Ronald Parsons. It was reasonable to suppose, he argued, that this type of personality attracted Margaret Parsons and that she had chosen her husband because he reminded her of her old lover.

He switched on his headlights, pulled the windscreen wiper button, and started back towards Kingsmarkham.

CHAPTER TWELVE

Were you and she whom I met at dinner last week,
With eyes and hair of the Ptolemy black?

Sir Edwin Arnold, *To a Pair of Egyptian Slippers*

The house looked forbidding at night. In Wexford's headlights the rough grey granite glittered and the leaves of the flowerless wistaria which clung to it showed up a livid yellowish green.

Someone was dining with the Quadrants. Wexford pulled up beside the black Daimler and went up the steps to the front door. He rang the bell several times; then the door was opened, smoothly, almost offensively slowly, by Quadrant himself.

For dining with Helen Missal he had worn a lounge suit. At home, with his wife and guests, he ascended to evening dress. But there was nothing vulgar about Quadrant, no fancy waistcoat, no flirtation with midnight blue. The dinner jacket was black and faultless, the shirt – Wexford liked to hit on an apt quotation himself when he could – 'whiter than new snow on a raven's back'.

He said nothing but seemed to stare right through Wexford at the shadowy garden beyond. There was an insolent majesty about him which the tapestries that framed his figure did nothing to dispel. Then Wexford told himself sharply that this man was, after all, only a provincial solicitor.

'I'd like another word with your wife, Mr Quadrant.'

'At this hour?'

Wexford looked at his watch and at the same time Quadrant lifted his own cuff – links of silver and onyx glinted in the muted lights – raised his eyebrow at the square platinum dial on his wrist and said:

'It's extremely inconvenient.' He made no move to let Wexford enter. 'My wife isn't a particularly strong woman and we do happen to have my parents-in-law dining with us ...'

Old man Rogers and his missus, Pomfret Hall, Wexford thought vulgarly. He stood stolidly, not smiling.

'Oh, very well,' Quadrant said, 'but keep it brief, will you?'

There was a faint movement in the hall behind him. A brown dress, a wisp of coffee-coloured stuff, appeared for an instant against the embroidered trees on the hangings, then Mrs Quadrant's nanny scuttled away.

'You'd better go into the library.' Quadrant showed him into a room furnished with blue leather chairs. 'I won't offer you a drink since you're on duty.' The words were a little offensive. Then Quadrant gave his quick cat-like smile. 'Excuse me,' he said, 'while I fetch my wife.' He turned with the slow graceful movement of a dance measure, paused briefly and closed the door behind him, shutting Wexford in.

So he wasn't going to let him bust in on any family party, Wexford thought. The man was nervous, hiding some nebulous fear in the manner of men of his kind, under a massive self-control.

As he waited he looked about him at the books. There were hundreds here, tier upon tier of them on every wall. Plenty of Victorian poetry and plenty of Victorian novels, but just as much verse from the seventeenth and eighteenth centuries. Wexford shrugged. Kingsmarkham was surrounded by such houses as this one, a bastion of affluence, houses with libraries, libraries with books ...

Fabia Quadrant came in almost soundlessly. Her long dress was black and he remembered that black was not a colour but just a total absorption of light. Her face was gay, a little hectic, and she greeted him cheerfully.

'Hallo again, Chief Inspector.'

'I won't keep you long, Mrs Quadrant.'

'Won't you sit down?'

'Thank you. Just for a moment.' He watched her sit down and fold her hands in her lap. The diamond on her left hand burned in the dark nest between her knees. 'I want you to tell me everything you can remember about Dudley Drury,' he said.

'Well, it was my last term at school,' she said. 'Margaret told me she'd got a boy friend – her first, perhaps. I don't know. It's only twelve years ago, Chief Inspector, but we weren't like the adolescents of today. It wasn't remarkable to be without a boy friend at eighteen. Do you understand?' She spoke clearly and slowly, as if she were instructing a child. Something about her manner angered Wexford and he wondered if she had ever had to hurry in her life, ever had to snatch a meal standing up or run to catch a train. 'It was a little unusual, perhaps, but not odd, not remarkable. Margaret didn't introduce me to her friend but I remember his name because it was like Drury Lane and I had never heard it before as a surname.'

Wexford tried to crush his impatience.

'What did she tell you about him, Mrs Quadrant?'

'Very little.' She paused and looked at him as if she was anxious not to betray a man in danger. 'There was only one thing. She said he was jealous, jealous to the point of fanaticism.'

'I see.'

'He didn't care for her to have any other friends. I had the impression that he was very emotional and possessive.'

Traits you would hardly understand, Wexford thought, or would you? He remembered Quadrant's inconstancies and wondered again. Her voice, uncharacteristically sharp and censorious, interrupted his reverie.

'He was very upset that she was moving back to London. She said he was in a terrible state, his life wouldn't be worth living without her. You can imagine the sort of thing.'

'But he'd only known her a few weeks.'

'I'm simply telling you what she said, Chief Inspector.' She smiled as if she was an immense distance from Drury and

118

Margaret Godfrey, light years, an infinity of space. 'She didn't seem to care. Margaret wasn't a sensitive person.'

Soft footsteps sounded in the hall and behind Wexford the door opened.

'Oh, there you are,' Fabia Quadrant said. 'Chief Inspector Wexford and I have been talking about young love. It all seems to me rather like the expense of spirit in a waste of shame.'

But that wasn't young love, Wexford thought, trying to place the quotation. It was much more like what he had seen on Helen Missal's face that afternoon.

'Just one small point, Mrs Quadrant,' he said. 'Mrs Parsons seems to have been interested in Victorian poetry during the two years she lived in Flagford. I've wondered if there was any special significance behind that.'

'Nothing sinister, if that's what you mean,' she said. 'Nineteenth-century verse was part of the Advanced English syllabus for Higher School Certificate when we took it in 1951. I believe they call it "A" Levels now.'

Then Quadrant did a strange thing. Crossing the library between Wexford and his wife, he took a book out of the shelves. He put his hand on it without hesitation. Wexford had the impression he could have picked it out blindfold or in the dark.

'Oh, Douglas,' Mrs Quadrant said, 'he doesn't want to see that.'

'Look.'

Wexford looked and read from an ornate label that had been pasted inside the cover:

Presented to Fabia Rogers for distinguished results in Higher School Certificate, 1951.

In his job it didn't do to be at a loss for words, but now he could find no phrase to foster the pride on Quadrant's dark face, or mitigate the embarrassment on his wife's.

'I'll be going now,' he said at last.

Quadrant put the book back abruptly and took his wife's arm. She rested her fingers firmly on his jacket sleeve. Suddenly they seemed very close, but, for all that, it was a strangely sexless communion. Brother and sister, Wexford thought, a Ptolemy and a Cleopatra.

'Good night, Mrs Quadrant. You've been most co-operative. I apologize for troubling you . . .' He looked again at his watch. 'At this hour,' he said, savouring Quadrant's enmity.

'No trouble, Chief Inspector.' She laughed deprecatingly, confidently, as if she was really a happy wife with a devoted husband.

Together they showed him out. Quadrant was urbane, once more courteous, but the hand beneath the sleeve where his wife's fingers lay was clenched and the knuckles showed like white flints under the brown skin.

A bicycle was propped against the police-station wall, a bicycle with a basket, practical-looking lights and a bulging tool bag. Wexford walked into the foyer and almost collided with a fat fair woman wearing a leather windcheater over a dirndl skirt.

'I beg your pardon.'

'That's all right,' she said. 'No bones broken. I suppose you wouldn't be him, this Chief Inspector bod?'

Behind the desk the sergeant grinned slightly, changed the grin to a cough, and covered his mouth with his hand.

'I am Chief Inspector Wexford. Can I help you?'

She fished something out of her shoulder bag.

'Actually,' she said, 'I'm supposed to be helping you. One of your blokes came to my cottage. . . .'

'Miss Clarke,' Wexford said. 'Won't you come into my office?'

His hopes had suddenly risen unaccountably. It made a change for someone to come to him. Then they fell again when he saw what she had in her hand. It was only another photograph.

'I found it,' she said, 'among a lot of other junk. If you're sort of scouring the joint for people who knew Margaret it might help.'

The picture was an enlarged snapshot. It showed a dozen girls disposed in two rows and it was obviously not an official photograph.

'Di took it,' Miss Clarke said. 'Di Stevens that was. Best part of the sixth form are there.' She looked at him and made a face as if she was afraid that by bringing it she had done something silly. 'You can keep it if it's any use.'

Wexford put it in his pocket, intending to look at it later, although he doubted whether it would be needed now. As he was showing Miss Clarke out he met Sergeant Martin coming back from his interview with the manager of the supermarket. No records had been kept of the number of pink hoods sold during the week, only the total sale of hoods in all colours. The stock had come in on Monday and Saturday night twenty-six hoods had been sold. The manager thought that about twenty-five per cent of the stock had been pink and on a very rough estimate he guessed that about six pink ones had been sold.

Wexford sent Martin over to Flagford in search of Janet Tipping. Then he rang Drury's number. Burden answered. They hadn't found anything in the house. Mrs Drury was staying with her sister in Hastings, but the sister had no telephone.

'Martin'll have to get down there,' Wexford said. 'I can't spare you. What did Spellman say?'

'They closed at five-thirty sharp on Tuesday. Drury collected his wife's vegetable order on Wednesday.'

'What's he buying vegetables for, anyway? He grows them in the garden.'

'The order was for tomatoes, a cucumber and a marrow, sir.'

'That's fruit, not vegetables. Talking of gardening, I'm going to get some lights over to you and they can start digging. I reckon that purse and that key could be interred with Drury's potatoes.'

Dudley Drury was in a pitiful state when Wexford got back to Sparta Grove. He was pacing up and down but he looked weak at the knees.

'He's been sick, sir,' Gates said.

'Hard cheese,' Wexford said. 'What d'you think I am, a health visitor?'

The search of the house had been completed and the place looked a lot tidier than it had before they began. When the lighting equipment arrived Bryant and Gates started digging over the potato patch. White-faced, Drury watched from the dining-room windows as the clods of earth were lifted and turned. This man, Wexford thought, had once said life would be unlivable without Margaret Parsons. Had he really meant it would be unendurable, if another possessed her?

'I'd like you to come down to the station now, Drury.'

'Are you going to arrest me?'

'I'd just like to ask you a few more questions,' Wexford said. 'Just a few more questions.'

Meanwhile Burden had driven over to Pomfret, awakened the ironmonger and checked his nephew's alibi.

'Dud always gets off early on Tuesdays,' he grumbled. 'Gets earlier and earlier every week, it does. More like five than a quarter past.'

'So you'd say he left around five last Tuesday?'

'I wouldn't like to say five. Ten past, a quarter past. I was busy in the shop. Dud came in and said, "I'm off now, Uncle." I'd no call to go checking up on him, had I?'

'It might have been ten past or a quarter past?'

'It might have been twenty past for all I know.'

It was still raining softly. The main road was black and stickily gleaming. Whatever Miss Sweeting may have seen in the afternoon, the lane and the wood were deserted now. The top branches of the trees moved in the wind. Burden slowed down, thinking how strange it was that an uninteresting corner of the countryside should suddenly have become, because of the use to which someone had put it, a sinister and dreadful hiding place, the focal point of curious eyes and the goal, perhaps for years to come, of half the visitors to the neighbourhood. From henceforth Flagford Castle would take second place to Prewett's wood in the guide book of the ghoulish.

He met Martin on the forecourt of the police station. Janet Tipping couldn't be found. As usual on Saturday night she had gone out with her boy friend, and her mother had told Martin with a show of aggressive indifference that it was nothing for her to return as late as one or two o'clock. The cottage was dirty and the mother a slattern. She didn't know where her daughter was and, on being asked to hazard a guess, said that Janet and her friend had probably gone for a spin to the coast on his motor-bike.

Burden knocked on Wexford's door and the Chief Inspector shouted to him to come in.

Drury and Wexford sat facing each other.

'Let's go over Tuesday evening again,' Wexford was saying. Burden moved silently into one of the steel and tweed chairs. The clock on the wall, between the filing cabinet where Doon's books still lay and the map of Kingsmarkham, said that it wanted ten minutes to midnight.

'I left the shop at a quarter past five and I drove straight to Flagford. When I got to Spellman's they were closed so I went down the side and looked round the greenhouses. I called out a couple of times but they'd all gone. Look, I've told you all this.'

Wexford said quietly, 'All right, Drury. Let's say I've got a bad memory.'

Drury's voice had become very high and strained. He took out his handkerchief and wiped his forehead.

'I had a look round to see if the order was anywhere about, but it wasn't.' He cleared his throat. 'I was a bit fed-up on account of my wife wanting the vegetables for tea. I drove slowly through the village because I thought I might see Mr Spellman and get him to let me have the order, but I didn't see him.'

'Did you see anybody you know, anybody you used to know when you lived in Flagford?'

'There were some kids,' Drury said. 'I don't know who they were. Look, I've told you the rest. I went into The Swan and this girl served me. . . .'

'What did you have to drink?'

'A half of bitter.' He blushed. At the lie, Burden wondered, or at the breach of faith? 'The place was empty. I coughed and after a bit this girl came out from behind the back. I ordered the bitter and paid for it. She's bound to remember.'

'Don't worry, we'll ask her.'

'She didn't stay in the bar. I was all alone. When I'd finished my drink I went back to Spellman's to see if there was anyone about. I didn't see anyone and I went home.'

Drury jumped up and gripped the edge of the desk. Wexford's papers quivered and the telephone receiver rattled in its rest.

'Look,' he shouted, 'I've told you. I wouldn't have laid a finger on Margaret.'

'Sit down,' Wexford said and Drury crouched back, his face twitching. 'You were very jealous of her, weren't you?' His tone had become conversational, understanding. 'You didn't want her to have any friends but you.'

'That's not true.' He tried to shout but his voice was out of control. 'She was just a girl friend. I don't know what you mean, jealous. Of course I didn't want her going about with other boys when she was with me.'

'Were you her lover, Drury?'

'No, I was not.' He flushed again at the affront. 'You've got no business to ask me things like that. I was only eighteen.'

'You gave her a lot of presents, didn't you, a lot of books?'

'Doon gave her those books, not me. She'd finished with Doon when she came out with me. I never gave her anything. I couldn't afford it.'

'Where's Foyle's, Drury?'

'It's in London. It's a bookshop.'

'Did you ever buy any books there and give them to Margaret Godfrey?'

'I tell you I never gave her any books.'

'What about *The Picture of Dorian Gray?* You didn't give her that one. Why did you keep it? Because you thought it would shock her?'

Drury said dully, 'I've given you a specimen of my printing.'

'Printing changes a lot in twelve years. Tell me about the book.'

'I have told you. We were in her aunt's cottage and the book came in a parcel. She opened it and when she saw who'd sent it she said I could have it.'

At last they left him to sit in silence with the sergeant. Together they went outside.

'I've sent Drury's printing over to that handwriting bloke in St Mary's Road,' Wexford said. 'But printing, Mike, and twelve years ago! It looks as if whoever printed those inscriptions did so because his handwriting was poor or difficult to read. Drury's writing is very round and clear. I got the feeling he doesn't write much and his writing's never matured.'

'He's the only person we've talked to who called Mrs P. Minna,' Burden said, 'and who knew about Doon. He had one of those hood things in his house and while it could be one of the other five it could be Mrs P.'s. If he left his uncle's at five-ten or five-fifteen even he could have been at Prewett's by twenty past and by then Bysouth had had those cows in for nearly half an hour.'

The telephones had been silent for a long time now, an

unusually long time for the busy police station. What had happened to the call they had been awaiting since lunchtime? Wexford seemed to read his thoughts almost uncannily.

'We ought to hear from Colorado any minute,' he said. 'Calculating roughly that they're about seven hours behind us in time, suppose Mrs Katz was out for the day, she'd be getting home just about now. It's half past twelve here and that makes it between five and six in the West of the United States. Mrs Katz has got little kids. I reckon she and her family have been out for the day and they haven't been able to get hold of her. But she ought to be coming home about now and I hope they won't be too long.'

Burden jumped as the bell pealed. He lifted the receiver and gave it to Wexford. As soon as he spoke Burden could tell it was just another bit of negative evidence.

'Yes,' Wexford said. 'Yes, thank you very much. I see. Can't be helped. . . . Yes, good night.'

He turned back to Burden. 'That was Egham, the handwriting fellow. He says Drury could have printed those inscriptions. There's no question of the printing being disguised, but he says it was very mature for a boy of eighteen and if it's Drury's he would have expected a much greater development than Drury's present specimen shows.

'Moreover, there's another point in his favour. I took a sample from the treads of his tyres and although they haven't finished with it, the lab boys are pretty certain that car hadn't been parked in a muddy lane since it was new. The stuff I got was mostly sand and dust. Let's have some tea, Mike.'

Burden cocked his thumb at the door.

'A cup for him, sir?'

'My God, yes,' Wexford said. 'How many times do I have to tell you? This isn't Mexico.'

CHAPTER THIRTEEN

And I am sometimes proud and sometimes meek,
And sometimes I remember days of old . . .

Christina Rossetti, *Aloof*

Margaret Godfrey was one of five girls on the stone seat and she sat in the middle of the row. Those who stood behind rested their hands on the shoulders of the seated. Wexford counted twelve faces. The snapshot Diana Stevens had taken was very sharp and clear and the likenesses, even after so long, were good. He re-created in his mind the face he had seen on the damp ground, then stared with awakened curiosity at the face in the sun.

The others were all smiling, all but Margaret Godfrey, and her face was in repose. The white forehead was very high, the eyes wide and expressionless; her lips were folded, the corners tilted very slightly upwards, and she was looking at the camera very much as the Gioconda had looked at Leonardo. Secrecy vied with something else in those serene features. This girl, Wexford thought, looked as if she had undergone an experience most of her fellows could never have fathomed, and it had marked her not with suffering or shame but simply with smug tranquillity.

The gym tunic was an incongruity. She could have worn a high-necked dress with puffy sleeves. Her hair, soft then, not crimped and waved as it had been later, skimmed her cheekbones and lay across her temples in two shining arcs.

Wexford glanced across to the silent Drury, now sitting some five yards from him. Then, screening it once more with his hands, he looked long at the photograph. When

Burden came in he was still gazing and his tea had grown cold.

It was almost three o'clock.

'Miss Tipping is here,' Burden said.

Wexford came out of the sunny garden, covered the snapshot with a file and said:

'Let's have her in, then.'

Janet Tipping was a plump healthy-looking girl with a cone of lacquered hair above a stupid suspicious face. When she saw Drury her expression, vacuous and uncomprehending, was unaltered.

'Well, I can't say,' she said. 'I mean, it was a long time ago.'

Not twelve years, Burden thought, only four days.

'I could have served him. I mean, I serve hundreds of fellows with bitter. . . .' Drury stared at her, round-eyed, as if he was trying to drive recognition into her dim, tired consciousness. 'Look here,' she said, 'I don't want to get anybody hung.'

She came closer, peering, in the manner of one attracted by a monstrosity in a museum. Then she retreated, shaking her head.

'You must remember me,' Drury shouted. 'You've got to remember. I'll do anything, I'll give you anything if you'll only remember. You don't realize, this means everything to me. . . .'

'Oh, do me a favour,' the girl said, frightened now. 'I've racked my brains and I don't remember.' She looked at Wexford and said, 'Can I go now?'

The telephone rang as Burden showed her out. He lifted the receiver and handed it to Wexford.

'Yes . . . yes, of course I want her brought back,' Wexford said. 'That was Martin,' he said to Burden outside. 'Mrs Drury said she bought that rain-hood on Monday afternoon.'

'That doesn't necessarily mean —' Burden began.

'No, and Drury got in after six-thirty on Tuesday. She remembers because she was waiting for the tomatoes. She wanted to put them in a salad for their tea. If he wasn't killing Mrs P., Mike, that was a hell of a long drink he had. For an innocent man he's practically crazy with terror.'

Again Burden said, 'That doesn't necessarily mean —'

'I know, I know. Mrs Parsons liked them green and goosey, didn't she?'

'I suppose there wasn't anything in the garden, was there, sir?'

'Five nails, about a hundredweight of broken bricks and a Dinky Toy Rolls-Royce,' Wexford said. 'He ought to thank us. It won't need digging in the autumn.' He paused and added, 'If he's still here in the autumn.'

They went back into the office. Drury was sitting utterly immobile, his face lard-coloured like a peeled nut.

'That was a mighty long drink, Drury,' Wexford said. 'You didn't get home till after six-thirty.'

Drury mumbled, his lips scarcely moving: 'I wanted the order. I hung about. There's a lot of traffic about at six. I'm not used to drink and I didn't dare to drive for a bit. I wanted to find Mr Spellman.'

Half a pint, Burden thought, and he didn't dare to drive?

'When did you first resume your relationship with Mrs Parsons?'

'I tell you there wasn't a relationship. I never saw her for twelve years. Then I was driving through the High Street and I stopped and spoke to her. . . .'

'You were jealous of Mr Parsons, weren't you?'

'I never met Parsons.'

'You would have been jealous of anyone Mrs Parsons had married. You didn't have to see him. I suggest you'd been meeting Mrs Parsons, taking her out in your car. She got tired of it and threatened to tell your wife.'

'Ask my wife, ask her. She'll tell you I've never been unfaithful to her. I'm happily married.'

'Your wife's on her way here, Drury. We'll ask her.

Drury had jumped each time the telephone rang. Now as it sounded again after a long lull, a great shudder passed through him and he gave a little moan. Wexford, for hours on tenterhooks, only nodded to Burden.

'I'll take it outside,' he said.

Bryant's shorthand covered the sheet of paper in swift spidery hieroglyphics. Wexford had spoken to the Colorado police chief, but now as he stood behind Bryant he could hear nothing of that thick drawl through the headphones, only watch the words fall on to paper in a tangled code.

By four it had been transcribed. His face still phlegmatic, but to Burden vital with latent excitement, Wexford read the letter again. The dead words, now coldly typed on official paper, seemed still to have the force of life, a busy bustling life led by a woman in a country backwater. Here in the depths of the night, among the office furniture and the green steel filing cabinets, Mrs Parsons was for a moment – one of the few moments in the whole case – resurrected and become a real person. There was no drama in her words and only the whisper of a small tragedy, but because of her fate the letter was a dreadful document, the only existing recorded fragment of her inner life.

Dear Nan (Wexford read),

I can picture your surprise when you read my new address. Yes, we have come back here and are living a stone's throw from school and only a few miles from the dear old cottage. We had to sell auntie's house and lost quite a bit on it, so when Ron got the chance of a job out here we thought this might be the answer. It is supposed to be cheaper living in the country, but we have not noticed it yet, I can tell you.

In spite of what you all thought, I quite liked living in Flagford. It was only you-know-what that turned me off it. Believe me, Nan, I was really scared over that Doon business, so you can imagine I wasn't too pleased to run slap bang up against Doon again a couple of weeks after we moved in. Although I'm a lot older I still feel frightened and a bit revolted. I said it was better to let things rest but Doon will not have this. I must say it is quite pleasant to get a few rides in a nice comfortable car and get taken out for meals in hotels.

Believe me, Nan, it is as it has always been, just friendship. When Doon and I were younger I really don't think we knew it could be anything else. At least, I didn't. Of course the very thought disgusts me. Doon only wants companionship but it is a bit creepy.

So you are going to get another new car. I wish we could afford one but at present it is beyond our wildest dreams. I was sorry to hear about Kim having chicken pox so soon after measles. I suppose having a family has its drawbacks and its worries as well as its advantages. It does not look as if Ron and I will have the anxiety or the happiness now as I have not even had a false alarm for two years.

Still, I always say if you have a really happy marriage as we have, you should not need children to keep it together. Perhaps this is just sour grapes. Anyway, we are happy, and Ron seems much more relaxed now we are away from town. I never will understand, Nan, why people like Doon can't be content with what they have and not keep crying for the moon.

Well, I must close now. This is quite a big house really and not exactly filled with mod. cons.! Remember me to Wil and your offspring. Regards from Ron.

Love from Meg

A happy marriage? Could a marriage be happy, rocking uneasily on a sea of deceit and subterfuge? Burden put the letter down, then picked it up and read it again. Wexford told him of his conversation with the police chief and his face cleared a little.

'We'll never prove it,' Burden said.

'One thing, you can go and tell Drury Gates'll take him home now. If he wants to sue us I daresay Dougie Q. will be nothing loth to lend a hand. Only don't tell him that and don't let me see him. He's upsetting my liver.'

It was beginning to grow light. The sky was grey and misty and the streets were drying. Wexford, stiff and cramped with sitting, decided to leave his car and walk home.

He liked the dawn without usually being sufficiently strong-minded to seek it unless he must. It helped him to think. No one was about. The market place seemed much larger than it did by day and a shallow puddle lay in the gutter where the buses pulled in. On the bridge he met a dog, going purpose-fully about its mysterious business, trotting quickly, head high, as if making for some definite goal. Wexford stopped for a second and looked down into the water. The big grey figure stared back at him until the wind disturbed the surface and broke up the reflection.

Past Mrs Missal's house, past the cottages. . . . He was nearly home. On the Methodist church notice-board he could just make out the red-painted letters in the increasing light: 'God needs you for his friend.' Wexford came closer and read the words on another notice pinned beneath it. 'Mr R. Parsons invites all church members and friends to a service in memory of his wife, Margaret, who died so tragically this week, to be held here on Sunday at ten a.m.'

So today, for the first time since she had died, the house in Tabard Road would be empty. . . . No, Wexford thought, Parsons was at the inquest. But, then . . . His thoughts returned to certain events of the afternoon, to laughter shut off in full spate, to a book, a fierce transposition of emotion, to a woman dressed for an assignation.

'We'll never prove it,' Burden had said.

But they could go to Tabard Road in the morning, and they could try.

My demands were modest, Minna. I wanted so little, but a few hours out of the scores of hours that make a week, infinitesimal eddies in the great ocean of eternity.

I wanted to talk, Minna, to spread at your feet the pains

and sorrows, the anguish of a decade of despair. Time, I thought, time that planes out the rough edge of cruelty, that dulls the cutting blade of contempt, that trims the frayed fringe of criticism, time will have softened her eye and made tender her ear.

It was a quiet wood we went to, a lane where we had walked long ago, but you had forgotten the flowers we had gathered, the waxen diadem of the Traveller's Joy.

I talked softly, thinking you were pondering. All the while I thought you listening and at last I paused, hungry for your gentle praise, your love at last. Yes, Minna, love. Is that so bad, so evil, if it treads in the pure garments of companionship?

I gazed, I touched your hair. Your eyes were closed for you found dull sleep more salutary than my words and I knew it was too late. Too late for love, too late for friendship, too late for anything but death. . . .

CHAPTER FOURTEEN

Such closets to search, such alcoves to importune.

Robert Browning, *Love in a Life.*

Parsons was dressed in a dark suit. His black tie, not new and worn perhaps on previous mourning occasions, showed the shiny marks of a too-hot, inexpertly handled iron. Sewn to his left sleeve was a diamond-shaped patch of black cotton.

'We'd like to go over the house again,' Burden said, 'if you wouldn't mind leaving me the key.'

'I don't care what you do,' Parsons said. 'The minister's asked me to Sunday dinner. I shan't be back till this afternoon.' He began to clear his breakfast things from the table, putting the teapot, the marmalade jar away carefully in the places the dead woman had appointed for them. Burden watched him pick up the Sunday paper, unopened and unread, and tip his toast crusts on it before depositing it in a bucket beneath the sink. I'm selling this place as soon as I can,' he said.

'My wife thought of going along to the service,' Burden said.

Parsons kept his back turned to him. He poured water from a kettle over the single cup, the saucer, the plate.

'I'm glad,' he said. 'I thought people might like to come, people who won't be able to get along to the funeral tomorrow.' The sink was stained with brown now; crumbs and tea-leaves clung along a greasy tide-mark. 'I suppose you haven't got a lead yet? On the killer, I mean.' It was grotesque. Then Burden remembered what this man had read while his wife knitted.

'Not yet.'

He dried the crockery, then his hands, on the tea towel.

'It doesn't matter,' he said wearily. 'It won't bring her back.'

It was going to be a hot day, the first really hot day of the summer. In the High Street the heat was already making water mirages, lakes that sparkled and then vanished as Burden approached; in the road where actual water had lain the night before phantom water gleamed on the tar. Cars were beginning the nose-to-tail pilgrimage to the coast and at the junction Gates was directing the traffic, his arms flailing in blue shirt sleeves. Burden felt the weight of his own jacket.

Wexford was waiting for him in his office. In spite of the open windows the air was still.

'The air conditioning works better when they're shut,' Burden suggested.

Wexford walked up and down, sniffing the sunlight.

'It feels better this way,' he said. 'We'll wait till eleven. Then we'll go.'

They found the car Wexford had expected to see, parked discreetly in a lane off the Kingsbrook Road near where it joined the top end of Tabard Road.

'Thank God,' Wexford said almost piously. 'So far so good.

Parsons had given them the back-door key and they let themselves silently into the kitchen. Burden had thought this house would always be cold, but now, in the heat of the day, it felt stuffy and smelt of stale food and frowsty unwashed linen.

The silence was absolute. Wexford went into the hall, Burden following. They trod carefully lest the old boards should betray them. Parsons' jacket and raincoat hung on the hallstand, and on the little square table among a pile of circulars, a dirty handkerchief and a heap of slit envelopes, something gleamed. Burden came closer and stared, knowing better than to touch it. He pushed the other things aside and together they looked at a key with a horseshoe charm on the end of a silver chain.

'In here,' Wexford whispered, mouthing the words and making no sound.

Mrs Parsons' drawing-room was hot and dusty, but nothing was out of place. Wexford's searchers had replaced everything as they had found it, even to the vase of plastic roses that screened the grate. The sun, streaming through closed windows, showed a myriad dance of dust particles in its shafts. Otherwise all was still.

Wexford and Burden stood behind the door, waiting. It seemed like an age before anything happened at all. Then, when it did, Burden could hardly believe his eyes.

The bay window revealed a segment of deserted street, bright grey in the strong light and sharply cut by the short shadows of trees in the gardens opposite. There was no colour apart from this grey and sunlit green. Then, from the right-hand side, as if into a film shot, a woman appeared walking quickly. She was as gaudy as a kingfisher, a technicolor queen in orange and jade. Her hair, a shade darker than her shirt, swung across her face like heavy drapery. She pushed open the gate, her nails ten garnets on the peeling wood, and scuttled out of sight towards the back door. Helen Missal had come at last to her schoolfellow's house.

Wexford laid his finger unnecessarily to his lips. He gazed upwards at the ornate ceiling. From high above them came a faint footfall. Someone else had heard the high heels of their visitor.

Through the crack between the door and its frame, a quarter-inch-wide slit, Burden could see a knife-edge section of staircase. Up till now it had been empty, a vertical line of wallpaper above wooden banister. He felt the sweat start in his armpits. A stair squeaked and at the same moment a hinge gave a soft moan as the back door swung open.

Burden kept his eyes on the bright, sword-like line. He

tensed, scarcely daring to breathe, as the wallpaper and the wood were for a second obscured by a flash of black hair, dark cheek, white shirt shadowed with blue. Then, no more. He was not even certain where the two met, but it was not far from where he stood, and he felt rather than heard their meeting, so heavy and so desperate had the silence become.

Four people alone in the heat. Burden found himself praying that he could keep as still and at the same time as alert as Wexford. At last the heels tapped again. They had moved into the dining-room.

It was the man who spoke first and Burden had to strain to hear what he said. His voice was low and held under taut control.

'You should never have come here,' Douglas Quadrant said.

'I had to see you.' She spoke with loud urgency. 'You said you'd meet me yesterday, but you never came. You could have come, Douglas.'

'I couldn't get away. I was going to, but Wexford came.' His voice died away and the rest of the sentence went unheard.

'Afterwards you could. I know, I met him.'

In the drawing-room Wexford made a small movement of satisfaction as another loose end was tied.

'I thought . . .' They heard her give a nervous laugh, 'I thought I'd said too much. I almost did . . .'

'You shouldn't have said anything.'

'I didn't. I stopped myself. Douglas, you're hurting me!'

His reply was something savage, something they couldn't hear.

Helen Missal was taking no pains to keep her voice down and Burden wondered why one of them should show so much caution, the other hardly any.

'Why have you come here? What are you looking for?'

'You knew I would come. When you telephoned me last night and told me Parsons would be out, you knew it. . . .

137

They heard her moving about the room and Burden imagined the little straight nose curling in disgust, the fingers outstretched to the shabby cushions, drawing lines in the dust on the galleried sideboard. Her laughter, disdainful and quite humourless, was a surprise.

'Have you ever seen such a horrible house? Fancy, she lived here, she actually lived here. Little Meg Godfrey. . . .'

It was then that his control snapped and, caution forgotten, he shouted aloud.

'I hated her! My God, Helen, how I hated her! I never saw her, not till this week, but it was she who made my life what it was.' The ornaments on the tiered shelves rattled and Burden guessed that Quadrant was leaning against the sideboard, near enough for him to touch him but for the intervening wall. 'I didn't want her to die, but I'm glad she's dead!'

'Darling!' They heard nothing, but Burden knew as if he could see her that she was clinging to Quadrant now, her arms around his neck. 'Let's go away now. Please. There's nothing here for you.'

He had shaken her off violently. The little cry she gave told them that, and the slithering sound of a chair skidding across lino.

'I'm going back upstairs,' Quadrant said, 'and you must go. Now, Helen. You're as conspicuous in that get-up as . . .' They heard him pause, picking a metaphor, '. . . as a parrot in a dovecote.'

She seemed to stagger out, crippled both by her heels and his rejection. Burden, catching momentary sight of flame and blue through the door crack, made a tiny movement, but Wexford's fingers closed on his arm. Above them in the silent house someone was impatient with waiting. The books crashing to the floor two storeys up sounded like thunder when the storm is directly overhead.

Douglas Quadrant heard it too. He leapt for the stairs, but Wexford reached them first, and they confronted each other in the hall. Helen Missal screamed and flung her arm across her mouth.

'Oh God!' she cried, 'Why wouldn't you come when I told you?'

'No one is going anywhere, Mrs Missal,' Wexford said, 'except upstairs.' He picked up the key in his handkerchief.

Quadrant was immobile now, arm raised, for all the world, Burden thought, like a fencer in his white shirt, a hunter hunted and snared. His face was blank. He stared at Wexford for a moment and closed his eyes.

At last he said, 'Shall we go, then?'

They ascended slowly, Wexford leading, Burden at the rear. It was a ridiculous procession, Burden thought. Taking their time, hands to the banister, they were like a troop of house hunters with an order to view or relatives bidden upstairs to visit the bedridden.

At the first turn Wexford said:

'I think we will all go into the room where Minna kept her books, the books that Doon gave her. The case began here in this house and perhaps there will be some kind of poetic justice in ending it here. But the poetry books have gone, Mr Quadrant. As Mrs Missal said, there is nothing here for you.'

He said no more, but the sounds from above had grown louder. Then, as Wexford put his hand to the door of the little room where he and Burden had read the poetry aloud, a faint sigh came from the other side.

The attic floor was littered with books, some open and slammed face-downwards, others on their spines, their pages spread in fans and their covers ripped. One had come to rest against a wall as if it had been flung there and had fallen open at an illustration of a pigtailed girl with a hockey stick. Quadrant's wife knelt among the chaos, clutching a fistful of crumpled coloured paper.

When the door opened and she saw Wexford she seemed

to make an immense effort to behave as if this were her home, as if she was hunting in her own attic and the four who entered were unexpected guests. For a second Burden had the fantastic notion that she would attempt to shake hands. But no words came and her hands seemed paralysed. She began to back away from them and towards the window, gradually raising her arms and pressing her be-ringed fingers against her cheeks. As she moved her heels caught one of the scattered books, a girls' annual, and she stumbled, half falling across the larger of the two trunks. A star-shaped mark showed on her cheek-bone where a ring had dug into the flesh.

She lay where she had fallen until Quadrant stepped forward and lifted her against him. Then she moaned softly and turned her face, hiding it in his shoulder.

In the doorway Helen Missal stamped and said, 'I want to go home!'

'Will you close the door, Inspector Burden?' Wexford went to the tiny window and unlatched it as calmly as if he was in his own office. 'I think we'll have some air,' he said.

It was a tiny shoe-box of a room and khaki-coloured like the interior of a shoe-box. There was no breeze but the casement swung open to let in a more wholesome heat.

'I'm afraid there isn't much room,' Wexford said like an apologetic host. 'Inspector Burden and I will stand and you, Mrs Missal, can sit on the other trunk.'

To Burden's astonishment she obeyed him. He saw that she was keeping her eyes on the Chief Inspector's face like a subject under hypnosis. She had grown very white and suddenly looked much more than her actual age. The red hair might have been a wig bedizening a middle-aged woman.

Quadrant had been silent, nursing his wife as if she were a fractious child. Now he said with something of his former scorn:

'Sûreté methods, Chief Inspector? How very melodramatic.'

Wexford ignored him. He stood by the window, his face outlined against clear blue.

'I'm going to tell you a love story,' he said, 'the story of Doon and Minna.' Nobody moved but Quadrant. He reached for his jacket on the trunk where Helen Missal sat, took a gold case from the pocket and lit a cigarette with a match. 'When Margaret Godfrey first came here,' Wexford began, 'she was sixteen. She'd been brought up by old-fashioned people and as a result she appeared prim and shockable. Far from being the London girl come to startle the provinces, she was a suburban orphan thrown on the sophisticated county. Isn't that so, Mrs Missal?'

'You can put it that way if you like.'

'In order to hide her gaucheness she put on a curious manner, a manner compounded of secretiveness, remoteness, primness. To a lover these can make up a fascinating mixture. They fascinated Doon.

'Doon was rich and clever and good-looking. I don't doubt that for a time Minna – that's the name Doon gave her and I shall refer to her by it – Minna was bowled over. Doon could give her things she could never have afforded to buy and so for a time Doon could buy her love or rather her companionship; for this was a love of the mind and nothing physical entered into it.'

Quadrant smoked fiercely. He inhaled deeply and the cigarette end glowed.

'I have said Doon was clever,' Wexford went on. 'Perhaps I should add that brilliance of intellect doesn't always go with self-sufficiency. So it was with Doon. Success, the flowering of ambition, actual achievement depended in this case on close contact with the chosen one – Minna. But Minna was only waiting, biding her time. Because, you see . . .' He looked at the three people slowly and severally. '. . . You *know* that Doon, in spite of the wealth, the intellect, the good looks, had one insurmountable disadvantage, a disadvantage greater than any deformity, particularly to a woman of Minna's background, that no amount of time or changed circumstances could alter.'

Helen Missal nodded sharply, her eyes alight with memory. Leaning against her husband, Fabia Quadrant was crying softly.

'So when Dudley Drury came along she dropped Doon without a backward glance. All the expensive books Doon had given her she hid in a trunk and she never looked at them again. Drury was dull and ordinary – callow is the word, isn't it, Mrs Quadrant? Not passionate or possessive. Those are the adjectives I would apply to Doon. But Drury was without Doon's disadvantage, so Drury won.'

'She preferred me!' Burden remembered Drury's exultant cry in the middle of his interrogation.

Wexford continued:

'When Minna withdrew her love, or willingness to be loved, if you like, Doon's life was broken. To other people it had seemed just an adolescent crush, but it was real all right. At that moment, July 1951, a neurosis was set up which, though quiescent for years, flared again when she returned. With it came hope. They were no longer teenagers but mature. At last Minna might listen and befriend. But she didn't and so she had to die.'

Wexford stepped forward, coming closer to the seated man.

'So we come to you, Mr Quadrant.'

'If it wasn't for the fact that you're upsetting my wife,' Quadrant said, 'I should say that this is a splendid way of livening up a dull Sunday morning.' His voice was light and supercilious, but he flung his cigarette from him across the room and out of the open window past Burden's ear. 'Please go on.'

'When we discovered that Minna was missing – you knew we had. Your office is by the bridge and you must have seen us dragging the brook – you realized that the mud from that lane could be found in your car tyres. In order to cover yourself, for in your "peculiar position" (I quote) you knew our methods, and you had to take your car back to the lane on some legitimate pretext. It would hardly have been safe to go there during the day, but that evening you were meeting Mrs Missal —'

Helen Missal jumped up and cried, 'No, it isn't true!'

'Sit down,' Wexford said. 'Do you imagine she doesn't know about it? D'you think she didn't know about you and all the others?' He turned back to Quadrant. 'You're an arrogant man, Mr Quadrant,' he said, 'and you didn't in the least mind our knowing about your affair with Mrs Missal. If we ever connected you with the crime at all and examined your car, you could bluster a little but your reason for going to the lane was so obviously clandestine that any lies or evasions would be put down to that.

'But when you came to the wood you had to look and see, you had to make sure. I don't know what excuse you made for going into the wood . . .'

'He said he saw a Peeping Tom,' Helen Missal said bitterly.

'. . . but you did go in and because it was dark by then you struck a match to look more closely at the body. You were fascinated as well you might be and you held the match until it burnt down and Mrs Missal called out to you.

'Then you drove home. You had done what you came to do and with any luck nobody would ever connect you with Mrs Parsons. But later when I mentioned the name Doon to you – it was yesterday afternoon, wasn't it? – you remembered the books. Perhaps there were letters too – it was all so long ago. As soon as you knew Parsons would be out of the house you used the dead woman's missing key to get in, and so we found you searching for what Doon might have left behind.'

'It's all very plausible,' Quadrant said. He smoothed his wife's dishevelled hair and drew his arm more tightly around her. 'Of course, there isn't the remotest chance of your getting a conviction on that evidence, but we'll try it if you like.' He

spoke as if they were about to embark on some small strata-
gem, the means of getting home when the car has broken
down or a way of getting tactfully out of a party invitation.

'No, Mr Quadrant,' Wexford said, 'we won't waste our
time on it. You can go if you wish, but I'd prefer you to stay.
You see, Doon *loved* Minna, and although there might have
been hatred too, there would never have been contempt.
Yesterday afternoon when I asked you if you had ever known
her you laughed. That laughter was one of the few sincere
responses I got out of you and I knew then that although Doon
might have killed Minna, passion would never have turned
into ridicule.

'Moreover, at four o'clock this morning I learnt something
else. I read a letter and I knew then that you couldn't be
Doon and Drury couldn't be Doon. I learnt exactly what was
the nature of Doon's disadvantage.'

Burden knew what was coming but still he held his breath.

'Doon is a woman,' Wexford said.

CHAPTER FIFTEEN

Love not, love not! The thing you love may change,
The rosy lip may cease to smile on you;
The kindly beaming eye grow cold and strange;
The heart still warmly beat, yet not be true.

Caroline Norton, Love Not

He would have let them arrest him, would have gone with them, Burden thought, like a lamb. Now, assured of his immunity, his aplomb had gone and panic, the last emotion Burden would have associated with Quadrant, showed in his eyes.

His wife pulled herself away from him and sat up. During Wexford's long speeches she had been sobbing and her lips and eyelids were swollen. Her tears, perhaps because crying is a weakness of the young, made her look like a girl. She was wearing a yellow dress made of some expensive creaseless fabric that fell straight and smooth like a tunic. So far she had said nothing. Now she looked elated, breathless with unspoken words.

'When I knew that Doon was a woman,' Wexford said, 'almost everything fell into place. It explained so much of Mrs Parsons' secrecy, why she deceived her husband and yet could feel she wasn't deceiving him; why Drury thought she was ashamed of Doon; why in self-disgust she hid the books. . . .'

And why Mrs Katz, knowing Doon's sex but not her name, was so curious, Burden thought. It explained the letter that had puzzled them the day before. *I don't know why you should be scared. There was never anything in that.* . . . The cousin, the confidante, had known all along. For her it was no secret but a fact of which she had so long been aware that she had thought it unnecessary to tell the Colorado police chief until he had probed. Then it had come out as an artless postscript to the interview.

'Say, what is this?' he had said to Wexford. 'You figured it was a guy?'

Helen Missal had moved back into the shade. The trunk she sat on was against the wall and the sun made a brighter splash on her bright blue skirt, leaving her face in shadow. Her hands twitched in her lap and the window was reflected ten times in her mirror-like nails.

'Your behaviour was peculiar, Mrs Missal,' Wexford said. 'Firstly you lied to me in saying you didn't know Mrs Parsons. Perhaps you really didn't recognize her from the photograph. But with people like you it's so difficult to tell. You cry Wolf! so often that in the end we can only find out what actually happened from the conversation of others or by things you let slip accidentally.'

She gave him a savage glance.

'For God's sake give me one of those cigarettes, Douglas,' she said.

'I'd made up my mind that you were of no significance in this case,' Wexford went on, 'until something happened on Friday night. I came into your drawing-room and told your husband I wanted to speak to his wife. You were only annoyed but Mr Quadrant was terrified. He did something very awkward then and I could see that he was nervous. I assumed when you told me that you'd been out with him that he didn't want us to find out about it. But not a bit of it. He was almost embarrassingly forthcoming.

'So I thought and I thought and at last I realized that I'd been looking at that little scene from upside down. I remembered the exact words I'd used and who I'd been looking at . . . but we'll leave that now and pass on.

'Your old headmistress remembered you, Mrs Missal.

Everyone thought you'd go on the stage, she said. And you said the same thing. "I wanted to act!" you said. You weren't lying then. That was in 1951, the year Minna left Doon for Drury. I was working on the assumption that Doon was ambitious and her separation from Minna frustrated that ambition. If I was looking for a spoiled life I didn't have to go any further.

'In late adolescence Doon had been changed from a clever, passionate, hopeful girl into someone bitter and disillusioned. You fitted into that pattern. Your gaiety was really very brittle. Oh, yes, you had your affairs, but wasn't that consistent too? Wasn't that a way of consoling yourself for something real and true you couldn't have?'

She interrupted him then and shouted defiantly:

'So what?' She stood up and kicked one of the books so that it skimmed across the floor and struck the wall at Wexford's feet. 'You must be mad if you think I'm Doon. I wouldn't have a disgusting . . . a revolting thing like that for another woman!' Flinging back her shoulders, projecting her sex at them, she denied perversion as if it would show in some deformity of her body. 'I hate that sort of thing. It makes me feel sick! I hated it at school. I saw it all along, all the time . . .'

Wexford picked up the book she had kicked and took another from his pocket. The bloom on the pale green suède looked like dust.

'This was love,' he said quietly. Helen Missal breathed deeply. 'It wasn't disgusting or revolting. To Doon it was beautiful. Minna had only to listen and be gentle, only to be kind.' He looked out of the window as if engrossed by a flock of birds flying in leaf-shaped formation. 'Minna was only asked to go out with Doon, have lunch with her, drive around the lanes where they'd walked when they were young, listen when Doon talked about the dreams which never came to anything. Listen,' he said. 'It was like this.' His finger was in the book,

in its centre. He let it fall open at the marked page and began
to read:

> 'If love were what the rose is;
> And I were like the leaf,
> Our lives would grow together
> In sad or singing weather....'

Fabia Quadrant moved and spoke. Her voice seemed to
come from far away, adding to the stanza out of old memory:

> 'Blown fields or flowerful closes,
> Green pleasure or grey grief....'

They were the first words she had uttered. Her husband
seized her wrist, clamping his fingers to the thin bones. If he
had only dared, Burden thought, he would have covered her
mouth.

> 'If love were what the rose is,' she said,
> 'And I were like the leaf.'

She stopped on a high note, a child waiting for the
applause that should have come twelve years before and now
would never come. Wexford had listened, fanning himself
rhythmically with the book. He took the dream from her gently
and said:

'But Minna didn't listen. She was bored.' To the woman
who had capped his verse he said earnestly. 'She wasn't Minna
any more, you see. She was a housewife, an ex-teacher who
would have liked to talk about cooking and knitting patterns
with someone of her own kind.

'I'm sure you remember,' he said conversationally, 'how
close it got on Tuesday afternoon. It must have been very
warm in the car. Doon and Minna had had their lunch, a

much bigger lunch than Minna would have had here. . . . She was bored and she fell asleep.' His voice rose but not in anger. 'I don't say she deserved to die then, but she asked for death!'

Fabia Quadrant shook off her husband's hand and came towards Wexford. She moved with dignity to the only one who had ever understood. Her husband had protected her, Burden thought, her friends had recoiled, the one she loved had only been bored. Neither laughing nor flinching, a country police-man had understood.

'She did deserve to die! She did!' She took hold of the lapels of Wexford's coat and stroked the stuff. 'I loved her so. May I tell you about it because you understand? You see, I had only my letters.' Her face was pensive now, her voice soft and unsteady. 'No books to write.' She shook her head slowly, a child rejecting a hard lesson. 'No poems. But Douglas let me write my letters, didn't you, Douglas? He was so frightened . . . .' Emotion came bubbling up, flooding across her face till her cheeks burned, and the heat from the window bathed her.

'There was nothing to be frightened of!' The words were notes in a crescendo, the last a scream. 'If only they'd let me love her . . . love her, love her . . .' She took her hands away and tore them through the crest of hair. 'Love her, love her. . . .'

'Oh God!' Quadrant said, crouching on the trunk. 'Oh God!'

'Love her, love her . . . green pleasure or grey grief . . .' She fell against Wexford and gasped into his shoulder. He put his arm around her hard, forgetting the rules, and closed the window.

Still holding her, he said to Burden: 'You can take Mrs Missal away now. See she gets home all right.'

Helen Missal drooped, a battered flower. She kept her eyes down and Burden edged her through the door, out on to the landing and down the hot dark stair. Now was not the time, but he knew Wexford must soon begin:

'Fabia Quadrant, I must tell you that you are not obliged to say anything in answer to the charge but that anything you do say . . .'

The love story was ended and the last verse of the poem recited.

CHAPTER SIXTEEN

The truth is great and shall prevail.

Coventry Patmore, *Magna est Veritas*

Doon had written precisely a hundred and thirty-four letters to Minna. Not one had ever been sent or even left the Quadrants' library where, in the drawer of a writing-desk, Wexford found them that Sunday afternoon. They were wrapped in a pink scarf and beside them was a brown purse with a gilt clip. He had stood on this very spot the night before, all unknowing, his hand within inches of the scarf, the purse and these wild letters.

Scanning them quickly, Burden understood now why Doon had printed the inscriptions in Minna's books. The handwriting daunted him. It was spidery and difficult to decipher.

'Better take them away, I suppose,' he said. 'Are we going to have to read them all, sir?'

Wexford had looked more closely, sifting the significant from the more obviously insane.

'Only the first one and the last two, I fancy,' he said. 'Poor Quadrant. What a hell of a life! We'll take all this lot down to the office, Mike. I've got an uneasy feeling Nanny's listening outside the door.'

Outside, the heat and the bright light had robbed the house of character. It was like a steel engraving. Who would buy it, knowing what it had sheltered? It could become a school, Burden supposed, or an hotel or an old people's home. The aged might not care, chatting, reminiscing, watching television in the room where Fabia Quadrant had written to the woman she killed.

They crossed the lawn to their car.

' "Green pleasure and grey grief",' Wexford said. 'That just about sums this place up.'

He got into the passenger seat and they drove away.

At the police station they were all talking about it, loitering in the foyer. It was an excitement that had come just at the right moment, just when they were growing tired of remarking on the heat-wave. A murderer and a woman at that. . . . In Brighton it was one thing, Burden thought, but here! For Sergeant Camb it was making Sunday duty bearable; for green young Gates, who had almost decided to resign, it had tipped the scales in favour of his staying.

As Wexford came in, setting the doors swinging and creating a breeze out of the sultry air, they dispersed. It was as if each had suddenly been summoned to urgent business.

'Feeling the heat?' Wexford snapped. He banged into his office.

The windows had all been left open but not a paper on the desk had stirred.

'Blinds, Mike. Pull down the blinds!' Wexford threw his jacket on to a chair. 'Who in hell left the windows open? It upsets the air conditioning.'

Burden shrugged and pulled down the yellow slats. He could see that the gossip he hated had shaken Wexford into impatient rage. Tomorrow the whole town would seethe with speculation, with wisdom after the event. Somehow in the morning they were going to have to get her into the special court . . . But it was his day off. He brightened as he thought that he would take Jean to the sea.

Wexford had sat down and put the letters, thick as the manuscript of a long novel or an autobiography, Doon's autobiography, on the desk. It was shady in the office now, thin strips of light seeping through the blinds.

'D'you think he knew about it when he married her?' Burden asked. He began to sort through the letters, picking

152

here and there on a legible phrase. He read in a kind of embarrassed wonder, ' "Truly you have broken my heart and dashed the wine cup against the wall. . . ." '

Cooler now in temperature and temper, Wexford swivelled round in his purple chair.

'God knows,' he said. 'I reckon he always thought he was God's gift to women and marrying him would make her forget all about Minna.' He stabbed at one of the letters with his forefinger. 'I doubt whether the marriage was ever consummated.' Burden looked a little sick, but Wexford went on. ' "Even to that other dweller in my gates my flesh has been as an unlit candle. . . ." ' He looked at Burden. 'Et cetera, et cetera. All right, Mike, it is a bit repulsive.' If it had been less hot he would have brought his fist down on the desk. Fiercely he added, 'They're going to gobble it up at the Assizes.'

'It must have been terrible for Quadrant,' Burden said. 'Hence Mrs Missal and Co.'

'I was wrong about her. Mrs Missal, I mean. She was really gone on Quadrant, mad for him. When she realized who Mrs P. was and remembered what had happened at school, she thought Quadrant had killed her. Then, of course, she connected it with his behaviour in the wood. Can't you see her, Mike? . . .' Wexford was intent yet far away. 'Can't you imagine her thinking fast when I told her who Mrs P. was? She'd have remembered how Quadrant insisted on going to that lane, how he left her in the car and when he was gone a long time she followed him, saw the match flame under the bushes, called to him perhaps. I bet he was as white as a sheet when he got back to her.

'Then I talked to her yesterday and I caught her unawares. For a split second she was going to tell me about Fabia, about all her ambitions going to pot. She would have told me, too, only Missal came in. She telephoned Quadrant, then, in the five minutes it took me to get to his house and she went out to meet him. I asked her if she was going to the cinema! He didn't turn up. Coping with Fabia, probably. She phoned him again in the evening and told him she knew Fabia was Doon, knew she had had a schoolgirl crush on Mrs P. Then he must have said he wanted to get into Parsons' house and get hold of the books, just in case we'd overlooked them. Remember, he'd never seen them – he didn't know what was in them. Mrs Missal had seen the church notice-board. It's just by her house. She told Quadrant Parsons would be out. . . .'

'And Fabia had a key to Parsons' house,' Burden said. 'The key Mrs P. left in the car before she was killed.'

'Quadrant had to protect Fabia,' Wexford said. 'He couldn't be a husband but he could be a guardian. He had to make sure no one found out what things were really like for him and her. She was mad, Mike, really crazy, and his whole livelihood would have gone up in smoke if it was known. Besides, she had the money. It's only cat's meat what he makes out of his practice compared with what she's got.

'But it's no wonder he was always sneaking off in the evenings. Apart from the fact that he's obviously highly sexed, anything was preferable to listening to interminable stories about Minna. It must have been almost intolerable.'

He stopped for a moment, recalling his two visits to the house. How long had they been married? Nine years, ten? First the hints and the apologies; then the storms of passion, the memories that refused to be crushed, the bitter resentment of a chance infatuation that had warped a life.

With terrible finesse, worse than any clumsiness, Quadrant must have tried to break the spell. Wexford wrenched his thoughts away from those attempts, feeling again the convulsions of the woman in the attic, her heart beating against his chest.

Burden, whose knowledge of the Quadrants was less personal, sensed his chief's withdrawal. He said practically:

'Then Minna came back as Mrs P. Fabia met her and they went driving together in Quadrant's car. He didn't have it on Tuesday, but she did. When she got home on Tuesday night

Fabia told him she'd killed Mrs P. What he'd always been afraid of, that her mental state would lead to violence, had actually happened. His first thought must have been to keep her out of it. She told him where the body was and he thought of the car tyres.'

'Exactly,' Wexford said, caught up once more in circumstantial detail. 'Everything I said to him in Parsons' attic was true. He went to get fresh mud in the tyres and to look at the body. Not out of curiosity or sadism – although he must have felt sadistic towards Mrs P. and curious, by God! – but simply to satisfy himself that she *was* there. For all we know Fabia wasn't always lucid. Then Mrs Missal dropped her lipstick. She's what Quadrant calls a happy-go-lucky girl and that was just carelessness.

'He hoped we wouldn't get around to questioning Fabia, not for some time, at any rate. When I walked into Mrs Missal's drawing-room on Friday night —'

'You spoke to Missal,' Burden interrupted, 'but you were looking at Quadrant because we were both surprised to see him there. You said, "I'd like a word with your wife," and Quadrant thought you were speaking to him.'

'I was suspicious of him until yesterday afternoon,' Wexford said. 'Then when I asked him if he'd known Mrs P. and he laughed I knew he wasn't Doon. I said his laughter made me go cold and no wonder. There was a lot in that laugh, Mike. He'd seen Mrs P. dead and he'd seen her photograph in the paper. He must have felt pretty bitter when he thought of what it was that had driven his wife out of her mind and wrecked his marriage.'

'He said he'd never seen her alive,' Burden said. 'I wonder why not? I wonder why he didn't try to see her.'

Wexford reflected. He folded the scarf and put it away with the purse and the key. In the drawer his fingers touched something smooth and shiny.

'Perhaps he didn't dare,' he said. 'Perhaps he was afraid

of what he might do. . . .' He took the photograph out, but Burden was preoccupied, looking at another, the one Parsons had given them.

'They say love is blind,' Burden said. 'What did Fabia ever see in her?'

'She wasn't always like that,' Wexford said. 'Can't you imagine that a rich, clever, beautiful girl like Fabia was, might have found just the foil she was looking for in that . . .' He changed the pictures over, subtracting twelve years. 'Your pal, Miss Clarke, brought me this,' he said. It gave me a few ideas before we ever heard from Colorado.'

Margaret Godfrey was one of five girls on the stone seat and she sat in the middle of the row. Those who stood behind rested their hands on the shoulders of the seated. Burden counted twelve faces. The others were all smiling but her face was in repose. The white forehead was very high, the eyes wide and expressionless. Her lips were folded, the corners tilted very slightly upwards, and she was looking at the camera very much as the Gioconda had looked at Leonardo . . .

Burden picked out Helen Missal, her hair in outmoded sausage curls; Clare Clarke with plaits. All except Fabia Quadrant were staring at the camera. She stood behind the girl she had loved, looking down at a palm turned uppermost, at a hand dropping, pulled away from her own. She too was smiling but her brows had drawn together and the hand that had held and caressed hung barren against her friend's sleeve. Burden gazed, aware that chance had furnished them with a record of the first cloud on the face of love.

'Just one more thing,' he said. 'When you saw Mrs Quadrant yesterday you said she was reading. I wondered if . . . I wondered what the book was.'

Wexford grinned, breaking the mood. 'Science fiction,' he said. 'People are inconsistent.'

Then they pulled their chairs closer to the desk, spread the letters before them and began to read.

Some Lie
and
Some Die

*To my son, Simon Rendell, who goes to festivals,
and my cousin, Michael Richards, who wrote the song,
this book is dedicated with love and gratitude.*

CHAPTER ONE

'But why here? Why do they have to come here? There must be thousands of places all over this country where they could go without doing anyone any harm. The Highlands for instance. I don't see why they have to come here.'

Detective Inspector Michael Burden had made these remarks, or remarks very much like them, every day for the past month. But this time his voice held a note which had not been there before, a note of bitter bewilderment. The prospect had been bad enough. The reality was now unreeling itself some thirty feet below him in Kingsmarkham High Street and he opened the window to get a better – or a more devastating look.

'There must be thousands of them, all coming up from Station Road. And this is only a small percentage when you consider how many more will be using other means of transport. It's an invasion. God, there's a dirty-looking great big one coming now. You know what it reminds of? That poem my Pat was doing at school. Something about a pied piper. If "pied" means what I think it does, that customer's pied all right. You should see his coat.'

The only other occupant of the room had so far made no reply to this tirade. He was a big, heavy man, the inspector's senior by two decades, being at that time of life when people hesitated to describe him as middle-aged and considered 'elderly' as the more apt epithet. His face had never been handsome. Age and a very nearly total loss of hair had not improved its pouchy outlines, but an expression that was not so much easy-going as tolerant of everything but intolerance, redeemed it and made it almost attractive. He was sitting at his rosewood desk, trying to compose a directive on crime prevention, and now, giving an impatient shake of his head, he threw down his pen.

'Anyone not in the know,' said Chief Inspector Wexford, 'would think you were talking about rats.' He pushed back his chair and got up. 'A plague of rats,' he said. 'Why can't you expand your mind a bit? They're only a bunch of kids come to enjoy themselves.'

'You'll tell a different tale when we get car burning and shop-lifting and decent citizens beaten up and – and Hell's Angels.'

'Maybe. Wait till the time comes. Here, let me have a look.'

Burden shifted grudgingly from his point of vantage and allowed Wexford a few inches of window. It was early afternoon of a perfect summer's day, June the tenth. The High Street was busy as it always was on a Friday, cars pulling into and out of parking places, women pushing prams. Striped shop awnings were down to protect shoppers from an almost Mediterranean sun, and outside the Dragon workmen sat on benches drinking beer. But it was not these people who had attracted Burden's attention. They watched the influx as avidly as he and in some cases with as much hostility.

They were pouring across the road towards the bus stop by the Baptist church, a stream of boys and girls with packs on their backs and transistors swinging from their hands. Cars, which had pulled up at the zebra crossing to let them pass, hooted in protest, but they were as ineffectual as the waves of the Red Sea against the Children of Israel. On they came not thousands perhaps, but a couple of hundred, laughing and jostling each other, singing. One of them, a boy in a tee-shirt printed with the face of Che Guevara, poked out his tongue at an angry motorist and raised two fingers.

Mostly they wore jeans. Not long since they had been at school – some still were – and they had protested hotly at the enforced wearing of uniforms. And yet now they had their own, voluntarily assumed, the uniform of denims and shirts, long hair and, in some cases, bare feet. But there were those among them making a total bid for freedom from conventional clothes, the girl in red bikini top and dirty ankle-length satin skirt, her companion sweating but happy in black leather. Towering above the rest walked the boy Burden had particularly singled out. He was a magnificent tall Negro whose hair was a burnished black bush and who had covered his bronze body from neck to ankles in a black and white pony-skin coat.

'And that's only the beginning, sir,' said Burden when he thought Wexford had had time enough to take it all in.

'They'll be coming all night and all tomorrow. Why are you looking like that? As if you'd – well, lost something?'

'I have. My youth. I'd like to be one of them. I'd like to be swinging along out there, off to the pop festival. Wouldn't *you*?'

'No, frankly, I wouldn't. I'm sure I never would have. Those young people are going to cause a lot of trouble, make a hell of a noise and ruin the weekend for all those unfortunate citizens who live on the Sundays estate. Heaven help them, that's all I can say.' Like most people who make that remark, Burden had a lot more to say and said it, 'My parents brought me up to be considerate of the feelings of others and I'm very glad they did. A trip to the local hop on a Saturday night, maybe, and a few drinks, but to take over God knows how many acres of parkland just to indulge my tastes at the expense of others! I wouldn't have wanted it. I'd have thought I hadn't achieved enough to deserve it.'

Wexford made the noise the Victorians wrote as 'Pshaw!' 'Just because you're so bloody virtuous it doesn't mean there aren't going to be any more cakes and ale. I suppose you'll stop that boy of yours going up there?'

'I've told him he can go to Sundays tomorrow evening for two hours just to hear this Zeno Vedast, but he's got to be in by eleven. I'm not having him camp there. He's only just

fifteen. Zeno Vedast! That's not the name his godfathers and
godmothers gave him at his baptism, you can bet your life.
Jim Bloggs, more like. He comes from round here, they say.
Thank God he didn't stay. I don't understand this craze for
pop music. Why can't John play classical records?'

'Like his dad, eh? Sit at home getting a kick out of Mahler?
Oh, come off it, Mike.'

Burden said sulkily, 'Well, I admit pop music's not my
style. None of this is.'

'Your scene, Mike, your scene. Let's get the jargon right.
We're pigs and fuzz as it is. We don't have to be square as
well. Anyway, I'm sick of being an onlooker. Shall we get up
there?'

'What, now? We'll have to be there tomorrow when the
fighting and the burning starts.'

'I'm going now. You do as you like. Just one thing, Mike.
Remember the words of another Puritan – "Bethink ye, bethink ye, in the bowels of Christ, that ye may be mistaken."'

Where the Regency mansion now stands a house called Sun-
days has stood since the Norman Conquest. Why Sundays?
No one knows. Probably the name has nothing to do with the
Sabbath Day; probably – and this is the general belief – it
derives from the name of the man who built the first house,
Sir Geffroy Beauvoir de Saint Dieu.

Once the Sundays lands extended from Kingsmarkham to
Forby and beyond, but gradually fields and woodlands were
sold off, and now the house has only a small garden and a
park of a few acres. In the eyes of the preservationists Sundays
is irretrievably spoilt. Its tall cedars remain and its avenue of
hornbeams, the overgrown quarry is still untouched, but the
Italian garden is gone, Martin Silk, the present owner, grows
mushrooms in the orangery, and the view is ruined by the
newly built Sundays estate.

The Forby road skirts the park and bisects the estate. It is along here that the Forby bus runs four times a day, halting at the Sundays request stop which is outside the park gates. Wexford and Burden pulled in to a lay-by and watched the first of the young pilgrims tumble out of the two-thirty bus and hump their baggage over to the gates. These were open and on the lodge steps stood Martin Silk with half a dozen helpers ready to examine tickets. Wexford got out of the car and read the poster which was pasted over one of the gates: *The Sundays Scene, June 11th and 12th, Zeno Vadast, Betti Ho, The Verb To Be, Greatheart, The Acid, Emmanuel Ellerman.* As the busload went through and passed into the hornbeam avenue, he went up to Silk.

'Everything O.K., Mr Silk?'

Silk was a small man in late middle age with shoulder-length grey hair and the figure – at any rate, until you looked closely or saw him walk – of a boy of twenty. He was rich, eccentric, one of those people who cannot bear to relinquish their youth. 'Of course it's O.K.,' Silk said abruptly. He had no time for his own contemporaries. 'Everything will be fine if we're left alone.'

He stepped aside, turning on a big smile, to take tickets from half a dozen boys whose slogan-painted Dormobile, pink, orange and purple, had come to a stop by the lodge.

'Welcome, friends, to Sundays. Pitch your tents where you like. First come, first served. You can park the truck up by the house.'

Burden, who had joined them, watched the Dormobile career rather wildly up the avenue, music braying from its open windows.

'I hope you know what you're doing,' he said dourly. 'Beats me why you want to do it.'

'I want to do it, Inspector, because I love young people. I love their music. They've been hounded out of the Isle of Wight. No one wants them. I do. This festival is going to cost thousands and a good deal of it will come out of my pocket.

I've had to sell another bit of land to raise money and people can say what they like about that.'

Burden said hotly, 'The preservationists will have plenty to say, Mr Silk. The older residents don't want all this new building. Planning permission can be rescinded, you know.'

Seeing Silk's face grow red with anger, Wexford intervened.

'We all hope the festival's going to be a success. I know I do. I'm told Betti Ho's arriving in her own helicopter tomorrow afternoon. Is that a fact? When Silk, somewhat appeased, nodded, he went on: 'We want to keep the Hell's Angels out and try to keep trouble down to a minimum. Above all, we don't want violence, bikes set on fire and so on, the kind of thing they had at Weeley. I want to address the crowd before the concert starts, so maybe you'll allow me the use of your platform tomorrow evening. Shall we say six?'

'I don't mind as long as you don't antagonise people.' Silk greeted a group of girls, beaming on them, complimenting them on their ankle-length, vaguely Victorian gowns, approving the guitars which they wore slung from their shoulders. They giggled. At him, rather than with him, Wexford thought privately, but the encounter had the effect of putting Silk in a better temper. When the girls had wandered off into the park he said quite graciously to the policeman, 'D'you want to have a look round?'

'If you please,' said Wexford.

The encampment was to be sited on the left-hand side of the avenue where, under the limes and the cedars, a small herd of Friesians usually grazed. The cattle had been removed to pasture behind the house and the first of the tents were already up. In the midst of the park a stage had been erected, faced by arc-lamps. Wexford, who generally deplored armoured fences, was glad that Sundays park was enclosed by a spiked wall to keep what Burden called 'undesirable elements' out.

At only one point was the wall broken and this was at the side of the quarry, a deep semicircular fissure in the chalk at the Forby end. The two policemen walked up to the house, stood on the terrace and surveyed the scene.

A mobile shop selling soft drinks, crisps and chocolate had already been parked in the avenue, and a queue of hungry youth had formed alongside it. The stronger-minded were staking claims to desirable sites and banging in tent pegs. Through the gates came a thin but steady stream of new arrivals, on foot, in cars and on motor-cycles. Wexford jerked his head in the direction of the quarry and walked down the steps.

The lucky ones – those who had taken a day off work or missed a college lecture – had got there in the morning and established their camp. A boy in a Moroccan burnous was frying sausages over a calor-gas burner while his friends sat cross-legged beside him, entertaining him vocally and on a guitar. The Kingsbrook flows through Sundays park, dipping under the Forby Road and meandering between willows and alders close to the wall. It had already become a bathing place. Several campers were splashing about in the water, the girls in bras and panties, the boys in the black scants that serve as underpants or swimming trunks. Crossing the little wooden bridge, Burden looked the other way. He kept his eyes so determinedly averted that he almost fell over a couple who lay embraced in the long grass. Wexford laughed.

' "And thou," ' he said, ' "what needest with thy tribe's black tents who hast the red pavilion of my heart?" ' There's going to be a lot of that going on, Mike, so you'd best get used to it. Letts'll have to put a couple of men on that quarry if we don't want gate-crashers.'

'I don't know,' said Burden. 'You couldn't get a motorbike in that way.' He added viciously: 'Personally, I couldn't care less who gets in free to Silk's bloody festival as long as they don't make trouble.'

On the Sundays side the chalk slope fell away unwalled; on the other it was rather feebly protected by broken chestnut paling and barbed wire. Beyond the paling, beyond a narrow strip of grass, the gardens of three houses in The Pathway were visible. Each had a tall new fence with its own gate. Wexford looked down into the quarry. It was about twenty feet deep, its sides overgrown with brambles and honeysuckle and wild roses. The roses were in full bloom, thousands of flat shell-pink blossoms showing against the dark shrubby growth and the golden blaze of gorse. Here and there rose the slim silver trunks of birches. In the quarry depths was a little natural lawn of turf scattered with harebells. One of the flowers seemed to spiral up into the air, and then Wexford saw it was not a flower but a butterfly, a Chalkhill Blue, harebell-coloured, azure-winged.

'Pity they had to build those houses. It rather spoils things, doesn't it?'

Burden nodded. 'These days,' he said, 'I sometimes think you have to go about with your eyes half-closed or a permanent crick in your neck.'

'It'll still be lovely at night, though, especially if there's a moon. I'm looking forward to hearing Betti Ho. She sings those anti-pollution ballads, and if there's anything we do agree on, Mike, it's stopping pollution. You'll like Miss Ho. I must admit I want to hear this Vedast bloke do his stuff, too.'

'I get enough of him at home,' said Burden gloomily. 'John has his sickly love stuff churning out night and day.'

They turned back and walked along under the willows. A boy in the river splashed Wexford, wetting his trouser legs, and Burden shouted angrily at him, but Wexford only laughed.

CHAPTER TWO

'On the whole, they're behaving themselves very well.'

This remark was delivered by Inspector Burden on a note of incredulous astonishment as he and Wexford stood (in the words of Keats) on a little rounded hill, surveying from this eminence the *jeunesse dorée* beneath. It was Saturday night, late evening rather, the sky an inverted bowl of soft violet-blue in which the moon hung like a pearl, surrounded by bright galaxies. The light from these stars was as intense as it could be, but still insufficient, and the platform on which their own stars performed was dazzlingly illuminated, the clusters of arc-lamps like so many man-made moons.

The tents were empty, for their occupants sat or lay on the grass, blue now and pearling with dew, and the bright, bizarre clothes of this audience were muted by the moonlight, natural and artificial, to sombre tints of sapphire and smoke. And their hair was silvered, not by time but by night and the natural light of night-time. The calor-gas stoves had been extinguished, but some people had lit fires and from these arose slender spires, threads of blue melting into the deeper blue of the upper air. The whole encampment was blue-coloured, azure, jade where the parkland met the sky, tinted here and there like the plumage of a kingfisher, and the recumbent bodies of the *aficionados* were numberless dark blue shadows.

'How many, d'you reckon?' Wexford asked.

'Seventy or eighty thousand. They're not making much noise.'

'The moan of doves in immemorial elms
And murmuring of innumerable bees,'

169

quoted Wexford.

'Yes, maybe I shouldn't have thought of them as rats. They're more like bees, a swarm of bees.'

The soft buzz of conversation had broken out after Betti Ho had left the stage. Wexford couldn't sort out a single word from it, but from the concentrated intense atmosphere, the sense of total accord and quietly impassioned indignation, he knew they were speaking of the songs they had just heard and were agreeing with their sentiments.

The little Chinese girl, as pretty and delicate and clean as a flower, had sung of tides of filth, of poison, of encroaching doom. It had been strange to hear such things from such lips, strange in the clear purity of this night, and yet he knew, as they all knew, that the tides were there and the poison, the ugliness of waste and the squalor of indifference. She had been called back to sing once more their favourite, the ballad of the disappearing butterflies, and she had sung it through the blue plumes of their woodsmoke while the Kingsbrook chattered a soft accompaniment.

During the songs Burden had been seen to nod in vehement endorsement, but now he was darting quick glances here and there among the prone, murmuring crowd. At last he spotted his son with a group of other schoolboys, and he relaxed. But it was Wexford who noted the small additions John and his friends had made to their dress, the little tent they had put up, so that they would appear to conform with the crowd and not be stamped as mere local tyros, day boys and not experienced boarders.

Burden swatted at a gnat which had alighted on his wrist and at the same time caught sight of his watch.

'Vedast ought to be on soon,' he said. 'As soon as he's finished I'm going to collar John and send him straight home.'

'Spoilsport.'

The inspector was about to make a retort to this when the buzzing of the crowd suddenly increased in volume, rising to a roar of excited approval. People got up, stood, or moved nearer to the stage, the atmosphere seemed to grow tense.

'Here he comes,' said Wexford.

Zeno Vedast was announced by the disc jockey who was compèring the festival as one who needed no introductions, and when he advanced out of the shadows on to the platform the noise from the audience became one concentrated yell of joy. Rather different, Wexford thought wryly, from the chorus of 'Off, off, off . . .!' which had been their response to his own well-thought-out speech. He had been proud of that speech, tolerant and accommodating as it was, just a few words to assure them there would be no interference with their liberty, provided they behaved with restraint.

The police didn't want to spoil the festival, he had said, inserting a light joke; all they wanted was for the fans to be happy, to co-operate and not to annoy each other or the residents of Kingsmarkham. But it hadn't gone down at all well. He was a policeman and that was enough. 'Off, off, off,' they had shouted and 'Out, fuzz, out.' He hadn't been at all nervous but he had wondered what next. There hadn't been any next. Happily, law-abidingly, they were doing their own thing, listening to their own music in the blue and opalescent night.

Now they were roaring for Vedast and at him. The sound of their voices, their rhythmically clapping hands, their drumming feet, assailed him in a tide and seemed to wash over him as might a wave of floodwater. And he stood still in the white ambience, receiving the tide of tribute, his head bent, his bright hair hanging half over his face like a hood of silver cloth.

Then, suddenly, he flung back his head and held up one hand. The roar died, the clamour softened to a patter, dwindled into silence. Out of the silence a girl's voice called, 'Zeno, we love you!' He smiled. Someone came up to the stage and handed him a bulbous stringed instrument. He struck a single, low, pulsating note from it, a note which had an esoteric meaning for the crowd, for a gentle sigh arose from it, a murmur of satisfaction. They knew what he was going to sing first, that single note had told them and, after a rustle of contentment, a ripple of happiness that seemed to travel through all eighty thousand of them, they settled down to listen to what that note had betokened.

'It's called "Let-me-believe",' whispered Burden. 'John's got it on an L.P.' He added rather gloomily: 'We know it better than the National Anthem in our house.'

'I don't know it,' said Wexford.

Vedast struck the single note again and began immediately to sing. The song was about love; about, as far as Wexford could gather, a girl going to her lover's or her husband's house and not loving him enough or something and things going wrong. A not unfamiliar theme. Vedast sang in a clear low voice, face deadpan, but they didn't let him get beyond the first line. They roared and drummed again; again he stood silent with head bent; again he lifted his head and struck the note. This time they let him complete it, interrupting only with a buzzing murmur of appreciation when his voice rose an octave for the second verse.

> 'Remember me and my life-without-life,
> Come once more to be my wife,
> Come today before I grieve,
> Enter the web of let-me-believe . . .'

The melody was that of a folk-song, catchy, tuneful, melancholy, as befitted the lyric and the tender beauty of the night. And the voice suited it utterly, an untrained, clear tenor. Vedast seemed to have perfect pitch. His face was bony with a big nose and wide mobile mouth, the skin pallid in the moonlight, the eyes very pale in colour, perhaps a light hazel or a glaucous green. The long, almost skeletal, fingers drew not an accompaniment proper, not a tune, from the strings, but a series of isolated vibrant notes that seemed to twang into Wexford's brain and make his head swim.

> 'So come by, come nigh,
> come try and tell why
> some sigh, some cry,
> some lie and some die.'

When he had finished he waited for the tide to roar over him again, and it came, pounding from and through the crowd, a river of acclaim. He stood limply, bathing in the applause, until three musicians joined him on the stage and the first chords from their instruments cut into the tumult. Vedast sang another ballad, this time about children at a fair, and then another love-song. Although he hadn't gyrated or thrown himself about, his chest, bare and bead-hung, glistened with sweat. At the end of the third song he again stood almost limply, sensitively, as if his whole heart and soul were exposed to the audience, the clapping, the roaring, flagellating him. Why then, Wexford wondered, did he feel that, for all the man's intensity, his simplicity, his earnestness, the impression he gave was not one of sincerity? Perhaps it was just that he was getting old and cynical, inclined to suspect all entertainers of having one eye on the publicity and the other on the money.

But he hadn't thought that of Betti Ho. He had preferred her childlike bawling and her righteous anger. Still, he must be wrong. To judge from the noise the crowd was making as their idol left that stage, he was alone in his opinion, apart, of course, from Burden, who had been determined from the start to like nothing and who was already off in search of John.

'God, when I think of my own youth,' said Wexford as they strolled towards an open space where a van had arrived selling hot dogs. 'When I think of the prevalent attitude that it was somehow *wrong* to be young. We couldn't wait to be older so that we could compete with the old superior ruling people. They used to say, "You wouldn't understand at your age, you're too young." Now it's the young people who know everything, who make the fashions of speech and manners and clothes, and the old ones who are too old to understand.'

'Hum,' said Burden.

'We're two nations again now. Not so much the rich and the poor as the young and the old. Want a hot dog?'

'May as well.' Burden joined the queue, coldly disregarding the hostile glances he got, and bought two hot dogs from a boy in a striped apron. 'Thanks very much.'

'Thank *you*, dad,' said the boy.

Wexford laughed gleefully. 'You poor old dodderer,' he said. 'I hope your ancient teeth are up to eating this thing. How d'you like being contemporary?' He pushed through the queue towards a stand selling soft drinks. 'Excuse me!'

'Mind who you're shoving, grandad,' said a girl.

Now it was Burden's turn to laugh. 'Contemporary? We're three nations, young, old and middle and always will be. Shall we go and look at the quarry?'

There was to be no more live music for an hour. People had got down to cooking or buying their evening meals in earnest now. A strong smell of frying rose and little wisps of smoke. Already boys and girls could be seen dressed in red and yellow tee-shirts, stamped with the words 'Sundays Scene' on chest and sleeves. The arc-lamps' range wasn't great enough to reach the river, but as the night deepened, the moon had grown very bright. No one was bathing in the clear shallow water, but bathers had left evidence behind them, trunks and bras and jeans spread over the parapet of the bridge to dry.

They walked round the rim of the quarry, brambles catching at their ankles, the tiny, newly formed berries of the wayfarer's tree occasionally tapping their faces, berries which felt like ice-cold glass beads.

The place seemed to be entirely empty, but on the estate side the barbed wire had been cut and broken down. The twisted metal gleamed bright silver in the moonlight. Neither Wexford nor Burden could remember if the wire had been like that yesterday. It didn't seem important. They strolled along, not speaking, enjoying the loveliness of the night, the scent of meadowsweet, the gentle, keening music coming from far away.

Suddenly a gate opened in the fence of the last house in The Pathway and a man came out. He was a tall man with a hard, handsome face and he looked cross.

'Are you by any chance running this' – he sought for an appropriate word – 'this rave-up?'

'I beg your pardon?' said Wexford.

The man said rudely. 'You look too superannuated to be audience.'

'We're police officers. Is anything wrong?'

'*Wrong*? Yes, plenty's wrong. My name's Peveril. I live there.' He pointed back at the house whose garden gate he had come from. 'There's been an unholy racket going on for twenty-four hours now and the pace has hotted up revoltingly in the past three. I've been attempting to work, but that's quite impossible. What are you going to do about it?'

'Nothing, Mr Peveril, provided no one breaks the law.' Wexford put his head on one side. 'I can't hear anything at present, apart from a distant hum.'

'Then you must be going deaf. The trees muffle the noise down here. I don't know what use you think you're being here. You ought to hear it from my studio.'

'You were warned in plenty of time, sir. It'll all be over tomorrow. We did advise people who live near Sundays and who felt apprehensive about the festival to notify us of their intention and go away for the weekend.'

'Yes, and have their homes broken into by teenage layabouts. Experience ought to have taught me not to expect decency

175

from you people. You're not even in the thick of it.' Peveril
went back into his garden and banged the gate.

'We ought to have asked him if he'd seen any interlopers,'
said Burden, grinning.

'Everyone's an interloper to him.'

Wexford sniffed the air appreciatively. He lived in country
air, he was used to it. For years he had never troubled to
savour it, but he did now, not being sure how much longer it
would last. The night was bringing its humidity, little mists
lying low on the turf, wisps of whiteness drifting over the
quarry walls. A hare started from a tangle of dog roses, stared
at them briefly and fled across the wide silver meadow, gawky
legs flying.

'Listen,' Wexford whispered. 'The nightingale . . .'

But Burden wasn't listening. He had stopped to glance into
the brake from which the hare had come, had looked further
down, done a double take, and turned, his face red.

'Look at that! It really is a bit much. Apart from being –
well, disgusting, it happens to be against the law. This, after
all, is a public place.'

The couple hadn't been visible from the Sundays side.
They lay in a small declivity on the floor of the quarry where
the lawn dipped to form a grassy basin about the size of a
double bed. Burden had spoken in his normal voice, some
twenty feet above their heads, but the sound hadn't disturbed
the boy and girl, and Wexford recalled how Kinsey had said
that in these circumstances a gun could be fired in the vicinity
and the report pass unheard.

They were making love. They were both naked, eighteen
or nineteen years old, and of an absolute physical perfection.
Across the boy's long arched back the fern-like leaves of the
mountain ash which sheltered them scattered a lightly moving
pattern of feathery black shadows. They made no sound at all.
They were entirely engrossed in each other. And yet they
seemed at the same time to be one with their surroundings,

as if this setting had been made for them by some kindly god who had prepared it and waited yearningly for the lovers to come and make it complete.

The boy's hair was long, curly and golden, the girl's black and spread, her face cut crystal in the moonlight. Wexford watched them. He could not take his eyes away. There was nothing of voyeurism in the fascination they had for him and he felt no erotic stimulus. A cold atavistic chill invaded him, a kind of primeval awe. Bathed by the moonlight, enfolded by the violet night, they were Adam and Eve, Venus and Adonis, a man and woman alone at the beginning of the world. Silver flesh entwined, encanopied by an ever-moving, shivering embroidery of leaf shadows, they were so beautiful and their beauty so agonising, that Wexford felt enter into him that true panic, the pressure of procreating, urgent nature, that is the presence of the god.

He shivered. He whispered to Burden, as if parodying the other's words. 'Come away. This is a private place.'

They wouldn't have heard him if he had shouted, any more than they heard the sudden throb which thundered from the stage and then the thumping, yelling, screaming tumult as The Verb To Be broke into song.

CHAPTER THREE

There had been no trouble. A party of Hell's Angels had come to Sundays gates and been turned away. The walls were not high enough to keep them out but they kept out their bikes. A tent had caught fire. There was no question of arson. Someone had lit a fire too close to the canvas and Silk had housed the dispossessed owners in one of his spare bedrooms.

The singing went on most of the night, the keening swell, the thunderous roars of it, audible as far as away as Forby, and calls from outraged residents – Peveril among them – came steadily into Kingsmarkham police station. By dawn all was silent and most people asleep. The fires had been stamped out and the arc-lamps switched off as the sun came up to shine on Sundays through a golden haze.

The day promised to be less hot, but it was still very warm, warm enough for the campers to bathe in the Kingsbrook and queue up afterwards for ice-cream. By noon the vendors of food and drink and souvenirs had parked their vans all the way up the avenue. The canned music and the music made by little amateur groups ceased and Emmanuel Ellerman opened the second day of the concert with his hit song, 'High Tide'. The mist which had lain close to the ground at dawn had risen to lie as a blanket of cloud through which the sun gleamed palely. It was sultry and the atmosphere made people breathless.

Burden's son John had been allowed to return and hear Zeno Vedast sing for the last time. He kept out of his father's way, embarrassed in this society to have a policeman for a parent. Burden sniffed the air suspiciously as he and Wexford walked about the encampment.

'That smell is pot.'

'We've got enough to think about here without indulging in drug swoops,' said Wexford. 'The Chief Constable says to turn a blind eye unless we see anyone actually high and whooping about or jumping over the quarry because he's full of acid. I wish I could appreciate the noise those musicians are making but it's no good, I can't. I'm too bloody old. They've finished. I wonder who's next?'

'They all sound the same to me.' Burden kept looking for his son, fearing perhaps that he was being corrupted into taking drugs, making love or growing his hair. 'And they all look the same.'

'Do stop fretting about that boy of yours. That's not him you're looking at, anyway. I saw him go off to the hamburger stall just now. Hear that noise? That'll be Betti Ho's helicopter come to fetch her away.'

The bright yellow helicopter, like a gigantic insect in a horror film, hovered and spun and finally plopped into the field behind the house. The two policemen watched it come down and then joined the stream of people passing through the gate into the field. The Chinese singer wore a yellow dress – to match her aircraft? – and her black hair in a pigtail.

'What money she must get,' said Burden. 'I won't say *earn*.'

'She makes people think. She does a lot of good. I'd rather she had it than some of these politicians. There's your John, come to see the take-off. Now, don't go to him. Leave him alone. He's enjoying himself.'

'I wasn't going to. I'm not so daft I don't realise he doesn't want to know me here. There's Vedast. God, it's like the end of a state visit.'

Wexford didn't think it was much like that. A thousand or so of the fans had massed round the helicopter while Betti Ho stood in the midst of a circle of others, talking to Vedast who wore black jeans and whose chest was still bare. There was another girl with them and Vedast had his arm round her waist. Wexford moved closer to get a better look at her, for of all the striking, bizarre and strangely dressed people he had seen since Friday, she was the most fantastic.

She was nearly as tall as Vedast and good-looking in the flashy, highly coloured fashion of a beauty queen. It seemed to Wexford impossible that anyone could naturally possess so much hair, a frothy, bouffant mane of ice-blonde hair that bubbled all over her head and flowed nearly to her waist. Her figure was perfect. He told himself that it would need to be not to look ridiculous in skin-tight vest and hot pants of knitted string, principal-boy boots, thigh-high in gilt leather. From where he stood, twenty yards from her, he could see her eyelashes and see too that she wore tiny rainbow brilliants studded on to her eyelids.

'I wonder who that is?' he said to Burden.

'She's called Nell Tate,' said Burden surprisingly. 'Married to Vedast's road manager.'

'Looks as if she ought to be married to Vedast. How do *you* know, anyway?'

'How d'you think, sir? John told me. Sometimes I wish pop was an O Level subject, I can tell you.'

Wexford laughed. He could hardly take his eyes off the girl, and this was not because she attracted him or even because he admired her looks – he didn't. What intrigued him was contemplating for a moment the life her appearance advertised, a life and way of life utterly remote, he imagined, from anything he had ever known or, come to that, anything the majority of these fans had ever known. It was said that Vedast was a local boy made good. Where did she come from? What strange ladder had she climbed to find herself here and now the cynosure of so many eyes, embraced in public by the darling of the 'scene'?

Vedast withdrew his arm and kissed Betti Ho on both cheeks. It was the continental statesman's salute that has become the 'in' thing for a certain élite. Betti turned to Nell Tate and they too kissed. Then the Chinese girl climbed into her helicopter and the doors were closed.

'Things'll break up soon,' said Burden. 'What time is it?'

'Half four. The air's very heavy. Going to be a storm.'

'I wouldn't like to be in that thing in a storm.'

The aircraft buzzed and whirred and rose. Betti Ho leaned out and waved a yellow silk arm. The fans began to drift back towards Sundays park, drawn by the sound of amplified guitars. The Greatheart, a three-man group, had taken the stage. Burden, listening to them, began to show his first signs of approval since the beginning of the concert. The Greatheart made a speciality of singing parodies of wartime hits, but Burden didn't yet know they were parodies and a half-sentimental, half-suspicious smile twitched his lips.

Martin Silk was sitting on a camp-stool by the ashes of a dead fire talking to the boy in the magpie coat. It was too warm and humid to wear a jacket, let alone a fur coat, but the boy hadn't taken it off, as far as Wexford had noticed, since his arrival. Perhaps his dark bronze skin was accustomed to more tropical skies.

'Not a spot of trouble, you see,' said Silk, looking up.

'I wouldn't quite say that. There was that fire. Someone's reported a stolen bike and the bloke selling tee-shirts has had a hell of a lot pinched.'

'It's quite O.K. to nick things from *entrepreneurs*,' said the magpie boy in a mild, soft voice.

'In your philosophy, maybe. If and when it ever becomes the law of the land I'll go along with you.'

'It will, man, it will. Come the revolution.'

Wexford hadn't actually heard anyone speak seriously of the promised revolution as a foreseeable thing since he was himself a teenager in the early thirties. Apparently they were still on the same old kick. 'But then,' he said, 'there won't be any *entrepreneurs*, will there?'

The magpie boy made no reply but merely smiled very kindly. 'Louis,' said Silk proudly, 'is reading philosophy at the

University of the South. He has a remarkable political theory of his own. He is quite prepared to go to prison for his beliefs.'

'Well, he won't for his beliefs,' said Wexford. 'Not, that is, unless he breaches the peace with them.'

'Louis is the eldest son of a paramount chief. One day Louis Mbowele will be a name to be reckoned with in the emerging African states.'

'I shouldn't be at all surprised,' said Wexford sincerely. In his mind's eye he could see future headlines, blood, disaster, tyranny, and all well meant. 'Philosophy doctorate, political theory, British prison – he'll soon have all the qualifications. Good luck. Remember me when thou comest into thy kingdom.'

'Peace be with you,' said the African gravely.

Burden was standing with Superintendent Letts of the uniformed branch.

'Nearly all over, Reg,' said Letts.

'Yes. I don't want to be mean, but I'd like it soon to be over. All done and trouble-free.'

'Before the storm comes too. It'll be hell getting this lot off the park in a downpour.'

Above the roof of Sundays house the sky had deepened to indigo. And the house itself was bathed in livid light, that wan, spectral light that gleams under cloud canopies before a storm. The hornbeams in the avenue, stolid, conical trees, were too stocky to sway much in the rising breeze, but the low broom-like branches of the cedars had begun to sweep and sigh against the turf and, up by the house, the conifers shivered.

It was a hot wind, though, and when Zeno Vedast walked on to the stage he was still half-naked. He sang the 'Let-me-believe' ballad again to a silent crowd made tense by the stifling, thick air.

Wexford, who had once more wandered a little apart so that he was close by the scaffolding of the stage, found himself standing beside Nell Tate. Vedast was singing unaccompanied this time and she held his mandoline or ocarina or whatever it was. There was nothing exceptional in the fact that her eyes were fixed on the singer. So were seventy or eighty thousand other pairs of eyes. But whereas the rest showed enthusiasm, admiration, critical appreciation, hers were hungrily intense. Her gleaming mulberry-coloured lips were parted and she held her head slightly back in a yearning, swan-like curve. A little bored by the song, Wexford amused himself in watching her and then, suddenly, she turned and looked him full in the face.

He was shocked. Her expression was tragic, despairing, as if she had been and was for ever to be bitterly deprived of what she most wanted. Misery showed through the plastered biscuit make-up, the rosy blusher, the green and blue eyelid paint, and showed in spite of the absurd twinkling brilliants stuck about her eyes. He wondered why. She was older than he had thought at first but still only about twenty-eight. Was she in love with Vedast and unable to have him? That seemed improbable, for when Vedast had finished his first song he stepped over to the edge of the stage, squatted down and, in taking the stringed thing from Nell's hand, kissed her impulsively, but slowly and passionately, on the mouth. Vedast began singing again and now Wexford saw that she was looking calmer, the glittering lids closed briefly over her eyes.

'Is that the lot?' he asked, going back to Burden. 'I mean, is the concert over?'

Burden slipped unprotestingly into his role as pop expert, though a less likely or less enthusiastic authority could hardly have been found. 'Two more songs from The Greatheart,' he said, 'and then we can all go home. Some are going already. They only waited to hear the Naked Ape.'

'Fighting words, Mike, sacrilege. I thought he was rather good. There goes that pink and orange van. It's got graffiti all over it – did you see? – and someone's written on one of the doors. "This truck also available in paperback".'

The tents were coming down. Gas burners and kettles and tins of instant coffee were being thrust into kit bags, and a barefoot girl wandered vaguely about looking among the heaps of litter for the shoes she had discarded twenty-four hours before. The future leader of an emerging African state had abandoned polemics for the more prosaic pursuit of rolling up his sleeping bag. Martin Silk strolled among them, smiling with regal benignity at his young guests and rather malicious triumph at Wexford.

'You can't help feeling sorry for those Greatheart people, singing their guts out to an audience who couldn't care less. They must know they only stayed for Vedast.'

Wexford's words went unheard. 'There they are,' said Burden, 'that girl and her boy friend, the ones we saw last night. Coming straight from the quarry. Well, their little honeymoon's over. And they've had a row by the look of them or been bitten by something. It's always said there are adders on Sundays land.'

'You'd like that, wouldn't you?' Wexford snapped. 'That'd be a suitable retribution for doing what comes naturally in the Garden of Eden.' The girl and the boy showed no sign of having quarrelled, nor did either of them seem disabled. They were holding hands and running like Olympic sprinters. In a dirty and tattered version of the tee-shirt-jeans uniform, their long hair wind-blown, they had lost their primeval beauty of the night before. The magic and the wonder was all gone. They were just an ordinary young couple running, breathless and – frightened. Wexford took a step in their direction, suddenly concerned.

They stopped dead in front of him. The girl's face was white her breath laboured and choked. 'You're police, aren't you?' the boy said before Wexford could speak. 'Could you come, please? Come and see what...'

'In the quarry,' the girl said throatily. 'Oh, *please*. It was such a shock. There's a girl lying in the quarry and she's – she's dead. Ever so dead. Her face is – blood – horrible... Oh *God*!' She threw herself into the boy's arms and sobbed.

CHAPTER FOUR

She was screaming hysterically.

'You tell me,' Wexford said to the boy.

'We went to the quarry about ten minutes ago.' He talked jerkily, stammering. 'I – we – I'm with a party and Rosie's with a party and – and we shan't see each other again for a month. We wanted to be private but it's still daylight and we looked for somewhere we wouldn't be seen. Oh, Rosie, don't. Stop crying. Can't you *do something*?'

A crowd had gathered around them. Wexford spoke to a capable-looking girl. 'Take her into one of the tents and make some tea. Make it hot and strong. One of you others, find Mr Silk and see if he's got any brandy. Come along now. She'll tell you all about it. She'll want to.'

Rosie let forth a shriek. The other girl, justifying Wexford's faith in her, slapped one of the wet white cheeks. Rosie gagged and stared.

'That's better,' said Wexford. 'Into the tent with you. You'll be all right when you've had a hot drink.' He went back to the boy. 'What's your name?'

'Daniel. Daniel Somers.'

'You found a girl's body in the quarry?' Suddenly The Greatheart burst into song. 'God, I wish we could have a bit of hush. Where did you find it?'

'Under some bushes – well, sort of trees – on the side where the wire is.' Daniel shuddered, opening his eyes wide. 'There were – flies,' he said. 'Her face was all over blood and it was sort of dried and there were flies – *crawling.*'

'Come and show me.'

'Do I have to?'

'It won't take long.' Wexford said gently. 'You don't have to look at her again, only show us where she is.'

By now a fear that something had gone badly wrong had flurried the encampment on the side where they were standing, rumour 'stuffing the ears of men with false reports'. People came out of tents to stare, others raised themselves on one elbow from the ground, briefly deaf to The Greatheart. A low buzz of conversation broke out as boys and girls asked each other if this was the beginning of a drug swoop.

Daniel Somers, his face as white, his eyes as aghast as his girl friend's, seemed anxious now to get the whole thing over. He scrambled down the chalk slope and the policemen followed him in less gainly fashion. As yet there was nothing to see, nothing alarming. Under the louring grey sky, thick, purplish, not a blue rift showing, the quarry grass seemed a brighter, more livid green. Light, obliquely and strangely filtered under cloud rims, gave a vivid glow to the white faces of the wild roses and the silver undersides of birch leaves, lifting and shivering in the wind. On the little lawn the harebells shook like real bells ringing without sound.

Daniel hesitated a few feet from where a young birch grew out of a dense, man-high tangle of honeysuckle and dogwood. He shivered, himself near to hysteria.

'In there.' He pointed. 'I didn't touch her.'

Wexford nodded.

'You get back to Rosie now.'

The bushes had no thorns and were easily lifted. They surrounded the root of the tree like the fabric of a tent belling about its pole. Under them, half-curled around the root, lay the girl's body. It was somewhat in the position of a foetus, knees bent, arms folded so that the hands met under the chin.

Even Wexford's strong stomach lurched when he saw the face or what had been a face. It was a broken mass, encrusted with black blood and blacker flies which swarmed and buzzed sluggishly as the leafy covering was disturbed. Blood was in the hair too, streaking the yellow fibrous mass, matting it in places into hard knots. And blood was probably on the dark red dress, but its material, the colour of coagulated blood, had absorbed and negatived it.

The Greatheart were still performing.

'A girl's been murdered,' Wexford said to Silk. 'You must get this lot off the stage. Let me have a microphone.'

The crowd murmured angrily as the musicians broke off in the middle of a song and retreated. The murmur grew more menacing when Wexford appeared in their place. He held up one hand. It had no effect.

'Quiet please. I must have quiet.'

'Off, off, off!' they shouted.

All right. They could have it straight and see if that silenced them. 'A girl has been murdered,' he said, pitching his voice loud. 'Her body is in the quarry.' The voices died and he got the silence he wanted. 'Thank you. We don't yet know who she is. No one is to leave Sundays until I give permission. Understood?' They said nothing. He felt a deep pity for them, their festival spoiled, their eager young faces now cold and shocked. 'If anyone has missed a member of their party, a blonde girl in a red dress, will he or she please inform me?'

Silk behaved rather as if Wexford himself had killed the girl and put her in his quarry. 'Everything was going so well,' he moaned. 'Why did this have to happen? You'll see, it'll be another lever in the hands of the fuddy-duddies who want to suppress all free activity and gag young people. You see if I'm not right.' He gazed distractedly skywards at the grey massy clouds which had rolled out of the west.

Wexford turned from him to speak to a boy who touched his arm and said, 'There was a girl in our party who's disappeared. No one's seen her since this morning. We thought she'd gone home. She wasn't enjoying herself much.'

'How was she dressed?'

The boy considered and said, 'Jeans, I think, and a green top.'

'Fair hair? Mauve tights and shoes?'

'God, no. She's dark and she wasn't wearing anything like that.'

'It isn't she,' said Wexford.

The rain was coming. He had a brief nightmarish vision of rain descending in torrents on the encampment, turning the trodden grass into seas of mud, beating on the fragile tents. And all the while, throughout the night certainly, he and every policeman he could get hold of would have to interrogate wet, unhappy and perhaps panicky teenagers.

The photographers had come. He saw their car bumping over the hard turf and stop at the wooden bridge. Once she had been photographed, he could move her and perhaps begin the business of identification. He felt a dash of cold water on his hand as the first drops of rain fell.

'I've been wondering if we could get them all into the house,' said Silk.

Eighty thousand people into one house? On the other hand, it was a big house . . .

'Not possible. Don't think of it.'

Behind him a girl cleared her throat to attract his attention. Two girls stood there, one of them holding a black velvet coat.

'Yes?' he said quickly.

'We haven't seen our friend since last night. She left her coat in the tent and just went off. We can't find her or her boy friend, and I thought – we thought . . .'

'That she might be the girl we found? Describe her, please.'

'She's eighteen. Very dark hair, very pretty. She's wearing black jeans. Oh, it isn't her, is it? She's called Rosie and her boyfriend . . .'

'Is Daniel.' While the girl stared at him, round-eyed, marvelling at this omniscience, he said, 'Rosie's all right.' He pointed. 'She's over there, in that tent.'

'Thanks. God, we were really scared.'

How much more of this was there to be, he wondered,

before he had to say yes, yes, it sounds like her? Then he saw Dr Crocker, lean, trim and energetic, stalking towards him. The police doctor wore a white raincoat and carried an umbrella as well as his bag.

'I've been away for the weekend, Reg, taking your people's advice. I thought I was going to keep clear of all this. What's it about?'

'Didn't they tell you?'

'No, only that I was wanted.'

'There's a dead girl in the quarry.'

'Is there, by God? One of *them*?' Crocker pointed vaguely into the crowd.

'I don't know. Come and see.'

The rain was falling lightly, intermittently, the way rain does after a drought and before a deluge, as if each drop was being squeezed painfully out. Three police cars had succeeded in negotiating the rough ground and were parked at the quarry edge. In the quarry itself the photographers had completed their work, the undergrowth had been cut away and a tarpaulin canopy erected to screen the body from view. In spite of this, a crowd of boys and girls squatted or lolled all round the quarry, speculating among themselves, their eyes wide.

'Get back to your tents, the lot of you,' Wexford said. 'You'll get wet and you won't see anything.' Slowly, they began to move. 'Come on now. Ghoulishness is for ignorant old people. Your generation is supposed to be above this sort of thing.'

That did it. One or two of them grinned sheepishly. By the time Wexford and the doctor had scrambled down on to the little lawn – the harebells trodden to a mush – the sightseers had dispersed. Crocker knelt by the body and examined it.

'She's been dead at least five days.'

Wexford felt himself relax with relief.

'She was dead before the festival started,' said Crocker,

'and she wasn't a teenager. I'd say at least twenty-seven, maybe thirty.'

Under the canopy the flies were thick and noisy. Wexford rolled the body on to its side, revealing a large handbag of mauve patent leather which lay beneath it. Handbag, shoes and tights matched each other and clashed with the dark red dress. He opened the bag, spilling the contents on to a sheet of plastic. An envelope addressed to Miss Dawn Stonor, 23 Philimede Gardens, London, SW5, fell out. There was a letter inside it addressed from Lower Road, Kingsmarkham: *Dear Dawn, I will be glad to see you Monday but I suppose it will be one of your flying visits and you won't condesend to stop the night. Granma has had one of her bad turns but is all right again now. I got the mauve slacks and blouse from the cleaners that you left there and you can take it away with you. They charged 65p. which I will be glad of. See you Monday. Love, Mum.*

He noted the illiteracies, the badly formed writing. Something else in the letter struck in his mind, but he could think about that later. The main thing was that she had been easily and rapidly identified. 'Have the body removed,' he said to Sergeant Martin, 'and then I want the quarry searched.'

There was blood on his hand, fresh blood. How could that have come from a body five days dead? He looked again and saw that it hadn't. The blood was his own, flowing from a small wound near the base of his thumb.

'Broken glass everywhere,' he said wonderingly.

'Have you only just noticed?' Crocker gave a harsh, humourless laugh. 'You needn't bother to search for a weapon.'

They had come gaily and noisily, erupting from cars and trains and buses, arriving on a summer's day to hear music and bringing their own music with them. They left downcast, in silence, trudging through the rain. Most of them had had no more than a dozen hours of sleep throughout the weekend. Their faces were shocked and dirty and pale.

No one ran. There was no horseplay. They dismantled their wet tents, shouldered their baggage, leaving behind them greyish-white mountain ranges of rubbish. Moving towards the gates in long ragged files, they looked like refugees leaving a place of disaster. Daniel walked with Rosie, one arm embracing her, the other shouldering a rolled tent which bumped against his khaki pack. Louis Mbowele passed through the gates without looking up from the book he was reading. They chewed sweets, passed wine bottles from hand to hand in silence, indifferent in their saddened freemasonry as to who paid or who drank. Huddled together, they lit cigarettes, sheltering match flames from the downpour.

Lightning split the sky over Stowerton and the thunder rolled, grumbling in the west. From fast-travelling clouds, blue and black and roaring grey, the rain cascaded, sweeping people and their belongings into the avenue like so much debris buffeted by the tide. The cedars lifted their black arms, sleeved in spiky foliage, and slapped them, rattling up and down on what had been turf. It was turf no longer. Thousand upon thousand of strong young feet had shaved the grass to stubble, to final scorched aridity. The rain fell on to acres of brown desert.

Someone had abandoned a torn tent, a red canvas tent that bounded in the wind like a huge drowning butterfly until it became waterlogged and collapsed against the footings of the stage. The river began to fill, carrying with it as it plunged under the Forby Road a bobbing flotsam of paper, cans, transistor batteries and lost shoes.

CHAPTER FIVE

With the rain came a kind of false night, a streaming, early twilight. It drove everyone indoors, everyone, that is, but the departing young people who trudged through the downpour into Kingsmarkham. Soaked and shivering, the long processions came on towards the buses, towards the station. Some stayed behind on the Forby Road, hoping to hitch, doggedly resigned when cars passed without stopping, when motorists, put off by their draggled clothes and their long wet hair, rejected them.

They invaded the centre of the town, queueing for any bus that might come, forming dispirited lines that stretched the length of the High Street. A conglomeration of youth filled the centre, but the outskirts, the back streets, were deserted. In Lower Road where all the doors and windows were shut, every curtain drawn, rain drumming on rows of pavement-parked cars, it might have been the depths of winter. Only the roses in the front gardens of these squat red-brick council houses, the drooping foliage on cherry trees, showed that there should have been sunshine, that it was a June evening.

Number fifteen was a house just like its neighbours, a similar Dorothy Perkins trailing over the front door, its acid pink flowers clashing with ochreish red brick, similar white net curtains, draped crosswise like the bodice of a negligé, across its windows. A scaffolding of television aerials sprouted from its single chimney and juddered in the gale.

Wexford went slowly up the path. The rain was falling so heavily that he had to put up his umbrella even for this short distance from the car to the front door. He hated having to question the bereaved, hated himself for intruding on their grief and for feeling, if not showing, impatience when memories overcame them and tears silenced them. He knew now that Dawn Stonor had had no father. It was a woman in the barren country of deep middle age, alone and perhaps utterly broken, he had to interview. He tapped softly on the door.

Detective Polly Davies let him in.

'How is she, Polly?'

'She's O.K., sir. There wasn't much love lost between mother and daughter, as far as I can see. Dawn hadn't lived at home for ten years.'

Dreadful to feel relief at a lack of love . . . 'I'll talk to her now.'

Mrs Stonor had been driven to the mortuary and home again in a police car. Still wearing her coat, her red straw hat on the arm of her chair, she sat in the living room, drinking tea. She was a big, florid-faced woman of fifty-five with bad varicose veins, her swollen feet crushed into court shoes.

'Do you feel up to giving me some information, Mrs Stonor? I'm afraid this has been a bad shock for you.'

'What d'you want to know?' She spoke abruptly in a shrill, harsh voice. 'I can't tell you why she was in that quarry. Made a proper mess of her, didn't he?'

Wexford wasn't shocked. He knew that in most people there is something sado-masochistic, and even the newly-bereaved have an apparently ghoulish need to dwell with pleasurable horror on the injuries inflicted on dead relatives. Whether or not they express these feelings depends on their degree of cultivated repression rather than on grief.

'Who was "he", Mrs Stonor?'

She shrugged. 'Some man. There was always some man.'

'What did she do for a living?'

'Waitress in a club. Place called the Townsman up in London, up West somewhere. I never went there.' Mrs Stonor gave him a lowering, aggressive look. 'It's for men. The girls get themselves up in daft costumes like bathing suits with skirts, showing off all they've got. "Disgusting!" I said to her. "Don't you tell me about it, I don't want to know.' Her dad would have turned in his grave if he'd known what she did.'

'She came here on Monday?'

'That's right.' She took off her coat. He saw that she was heavily built, rigidly corseted. Her face was set in grim, peevish lines, and it was hard to tell whether it was more grim and peevish than usual. 'You wouldn't find a decent girl going to that quarry with a man,' she said. 'Had he done anything to her?'

The question was grotesque between people who had seen for themselves, but he knew what she meant. 'There was no sexual assault and intercourse hadn't taken place.'

She flushed darkly. He thought she was going to protest at his fairly blunt way of speaking but instead she rushed into an account of what he wanted to know. 'She came down by train, the one that gets in at half past eleven. I'd got her dinner for her, a bit of steak. She liked that.' The harsh voice wavered a little. 'She liked her bit of steak, did Dawn. Then we chatted a bit. We hadn't really got nothing in common any more.'

'Can you tell me what you talked about?'

'Nothing about *men*, if that's what you mean. She was fed-up on account of some little kid in the train had wiped his sticky fingers down her dress. It was a new dress, one of them minis, and it showed all her legs. I said she'd have to change it and she did.'

'She put on the dark red dress she was found in?'

'No, she never. That wasn't hers. I don't know where that come from. There was a mauve thing she had here as I'd fetched from the cleaners for her – they call them trousers suits – and she put that on. She was wearing mauve shoes so it looked all right. Well, like I said, we chatted a bit and she went up to see her gran – that's my mother as lives with me – and then Dawn went off to catch the four-fifteen train. Left here just before four.'

Wexford looked thoughtful. 'You thought she was going straight back to London?'

'Of course I did. She said so. She said, I've got to be in the club by seven. She took the blue dress with her in a bag and she said she'd have to run not to miss her train.'

'Two more things, Mrs Stonor, and then I'll leave you in peace. I'd like you to describe the trouser suit, if you would.'

'Very showy, it was. More like pyjamas than something you'd wear in the street. There was slacks, sort of flared, and a kind of tunic. It was mauve nylon stuff with a bit of darker mauve round the sleeves and the bottom of the tunic. Dawn liked to dress flashy.'

'Have you a photograph of her?'

Mrs Stonor gave him a suspicious glare. 'What, got up in them clothes?'

'No. Any photograph.'

'There was a photo she sent me for Christmas. Funny idea giving your mum a photo of yourself for Christmas, I thought. You can have that if you like.'

The photograph, a studio portrait, was brought. It had never been framed and, from its pristine condition, Wexford supposed that it had never been shown with pride to Mrs Stonor's friends but kept since its arrival in a drawer. Dawn had been a heavy-featured, rather coarse-looking girl, who wore thick make-up. The blonde hair was piled into puffs and ringlets, a massy structure reminding him of the head-dresses of eighteenth-century belles or perhaps of actresses playing such parts. She wore a blue silk evening gown, very low-cut and showing a great deal of fleshy bosom and shoulder.

Mrs Stonor eyed it irritably, peevishly, and Wexford could see that it would have been a disappointing gift for a mother of her type. Dawn had been twenty-eight. To have met with maternal favour, the picture should have shown not only a daughter but grandchildren, a wedding ring on those stiffly posed fingers, and behind the group the outline of a semi-detached house, well-kept-up and bought on a mortgage.

He felt a stirring of pity for this mother who was a mother no longer, a flash of sympathy which was dissipated at once when she said as he was leaving:

'About that trouser suit . . .'

'Yes?'

'It was more or less new. She only bought it back in the winter. I mean, I know a lady who'd give me five pounds for that.'

Wexford gave her a narrow glance. He tried not to show his distaste.

'We don't know what's become of it, Mrs Stonor. Perhaps the lady would like the shoes and the bag. You can have them in due course.'

The exodus continued. By now it was dark, a windswept, starless night, the rain falling relentlessly. Wexford drove back to the Sundays estate where, on both sides of the Forby road, police cars cruised along the streets or stood parked in lakes of trembling black water. Presently Burden found him and got into the car beside him.

'Well? Anything startling?'

'Nothing much, sir. Nobody remembers seeing a girl in a red dress down here during the week. But last Monday afternoon one woman from Sundays Grove, a Mrs Lorna Clarke, says she saw a blonde girl, answering Dawn's description, but wearing a . . .'

'Mauve trouser suit?'

'That's right! So it was her? I thought it must be from Mrs Clarke talking about mauve shoes and a mauve bag. Where did the red dress come from then?'

Wexford shook his head. 'It's beginning to look as if she died on Monday. She left her mother's house just before four that afternoon. When and where did your Mrs Clarke see her?'

'She got off the five-twenty-five bus from Kingsmarkham. Mrs Clarke saw her get off the bus and cross the road towards The Pathway. A few minutes later someone else saw her in The Pathway.'

'Which backs on to the quarry. Go on.'

'There are only five houses in The Pathway, two bungalows and three proper houses. If you remember, they didn't do any more buildings down there. People made a fuss about it and the ministry reversed the decision to grant planning permission. She was next seen by a woman who lives in the last house.'

'Not the wife of that bloke who came out making a to-do on Saturday night?'

Burden nodded. 'A Mrs Peveril, sir. They're both at home all day. He's a graphic designer, works at home. His wife says she saw a blonde girl in mauve go down the road at five-thirty and enter the public footpath that goes across the fields to Stowerton. She gave a very detailed description of the trouser suit, the shoes and the bag. But, of course, I couldn't be sure it was Dawn. I couldn't understand her being dressed in mauve. Mrs Peveril says the girl was holding a brown carrier bag.'

'Mm-hm. It certainly was Dawn. She changed out of a blue dress into the mauve thing and it was obviously the blue one she was carrying in the bag. She seems to have gone in for a lot of clothes changing, doesn't she? I wonder why. No other help from The Pathway?'

'No one else saw her. Each of the bungalows has only one occupant and they were both out at the relevant time. Miss Mowler's a retired district nurse and she was out on Monday till eight. Dunsand – he's a lecturer at the University of the South, philosophy or something – didn't get home from work till after half past six. I can't find anyone else who saw her on Monday or at any other time. My guess is she picked up some bloke and made a date to meet him between Sundays and Stowerton that evening.'

'Ye-es. I expect that's it. She left her mother at four and she must have caught the five-twelve bus. There are only two buses going to Forby in the afternoon, as you know. What did she do in that spare hour and ten minutes? We'll have to find out if anyone saw her in the High Street. There's the London angle too, but I've already got wheels moving there.'

'D'you want to see Mrs Peveril?'

'Not now, Mike. I doubt if we can make much progress tonight. I'll let them finish the house-to-house. They may get something more. She may have been seen later. I don't want to speculate at this stage.'

Burden left the car and, throwing his raincoat over his head, plunged off through the rain. Wexford turned the car, moving off in low gear through the torrents, the steady downpour, glancing once at Sundays where the last dispirited stragglers were leaving the park.

CHAPTER SIX

By the morning it had been established that Mrs Margaret Peveril of number five, The Pathway, was very probably the last person to have seen Dawn Stonor alive. On Monday, June sixth, Dawn had entered the pathfields at five-thirty and disappeared. By nine Wexford and Burden were back in The Pathway. By nine also an emergency interview room had been set up in the Baptist church hall where Sergeant Martin and a team of detectives waited to talk to anyone who might have seen Dawn on the previous Monday afternoon. The photograph had been blown up to poster size ready to jog memories, and another photograph prepared, this time of Polly Davies wearing a blonde wig and dressed in clothes resembling as nearly as possible Mrs Stonor's description of the mauve suit.

The rain had stopped during the night and the town and its environs looked washed, battered, wrung out to dry. All the summer warmth had gone with the storm, leaving a cloud-splashed sourly blue sky, a high sharp wind and mid-winter temperatures.

At Sundays Martin Silk was burning litter, the accumulated detritus of eighty thousand people's weekend. A row of fires blazed just behind the wall and the wind blew acrid white smoke in clouds over the Sundays estate, the Forby road and the barren brown plain of the park. Silk's little herd of Friesians had returned to their pasture. They stood in a huddle under the cedars, bewildered by the smoke.

The Pathway was shaped like an arm with bent elbow, its shoulder the junction with the Forby road, its wrist and hand − or perhaps its one pointing finger − a footpath which ran through hilly meadows and copses to Stowerton. Three houses and two bungalows had been built along this arm, but in its crook there were only open fields. The bungalows were identical, rather large pink plastered bungalows with red tiled roofs and detached garages. They stood 'in their gardens', as estate agents put it, meaning that there are sections of garden at the sides as well as at front and back. Some twenty feet separated one from the other, and a further twenty feet down stood a two-storey house. Similar building materials had been used for this house and the two dwellings on the upper arm, red brick, white stone, cedarwood, but they varied in size and in design. All had sparse lawns and flower-beds planted with unhappy-looking annuals.

'The Peverils came in first,' said Burden. 'Their place was finished in January. Miss Mowler and Dunsand both moved in in March. He came from Myringham, Miss Mowler from the town here and the Peverils from Brighton. The Robinsons retired here from London, moving in in April, and the Streets came here from up north last month.'

'Do they all have garden gates opening on to that bit of land between them and the quarry?' asked Wexford.

'Only the Peverils and the two bungalows. There was going to be a path made at the back, but someone got the planning authority to veto that.'

'We'll go and have a word with your Mrs Peveril.'

She was a very nervous woman, breathless with nerves. Wexford thought she was in her late thirties. Her hair-style and her clothes were fussy but not in any of the current modes. She dressed evidently in a somewhat modified version of the style of her youth, full, longish skirt, stilt heels. He sized her up immediately as belonging to a distinct and not uncommon type, the sheltered and conservative woman who, childless and exclusively dependent on her husband for all emotional needs, tends to be suspicious of other men and of the outside world. Such women will go to almost any lengths to preserve their security and their absolute domestic quietude, so Wexford was

rather surprised that Mrs Peveril had volunteered any information about a murder victim.

'All that smoke,' she said querulously, leading them into
an over-neat living room. 'Isn't it dreadful? I shan't be able
to get my washing out for hours. It was bad enough having
that ghastly racket over the weekend – I didn't get a wink of
sleep. The noise was frightful. I'm not surprised someone got
murdered.'

'The murder,' said Wexford, 'happened several days before
the festival started.'

'Did it?' Mrs Peveril looked unconvinced. 'When I heard
someone had been killed I said to my husband, they took too
many of those drugs they all take and someone went too far.
D'you mind not sitting on that cushion? I've just put a fresh
cover on it.'

Wexford moved on to a leather-seated and apparently
invulnerable chair. 'I believe you saw the girl?'

'Oh, yes, I saw her. There's no doubt about that.' She
gave a short nervous laugh. 'I don't know many people round
here except my friend on the other side of the estate, but I
knew that girl wasn't local. The people round here don't dress
like that.'

'What made you notice her?'

'If you're going to ask me a lot of questions I'd like my
husband to be present. I'll just call him. He's working but he
won't mind stopping for a bit. I might say – well, the wrong
thing if he wasn't here. I'll just call him.'

Wexford shrugged. In a manner of speaking, the 'wrong'
thing could easily be the thing he wanted her to say. But she
had asked for her husband as some people ask for their lawyers
and probably with less need. He saw no reason to refuse his
permission and he got up, smiling pleasantly, when Peveril
came in.

'You didn't see the girl yourself, Mr Peveril?'

'No, I was working.' Peveril was one of those men who

talk about work and working as if labour belongs exclusively to them, as if it is an arduous, exacting cross they must bear, while the rest of the world make carefree holiday. 'I work a ten-hour day. Have to what with the cost of running this place. The first I heard of any girl was when my wife told me last night she'd given information to the police.' He glared at Burden. 'I was working when you lot came.'

'Perhaps we shouldn't keep you from your work now?'

'Oh, please don't go, Edward, please don't. You said I was silly to say what I said last night and now . . .'

'I can do with a short break,' said Peveril lugubriously. 'I've been at it since eight, thanks to being made totally idle by a weekend of uproar. I'm worn out.'

Comforted but still jumpy, his wife rushed into the middle of things. 'It's a matter of chance I was here at all. I nearly went to the pictures – my husband had seen the film in London and told me to go – but it was such a lovely afternoon. I just looked out of the window there and I saw her. I saw the girl walking up towards the footpath.'

'Describe her to me. In as much detail as you can, please.'

'She was about my height and she had a lot of dyed blonde hair cut in the shaggy way they all go in for.' Mrs Peveril twitched at her own over-permed, frizzy dark hair with an unsteady hand. 'And she was very heavily made-up, tarty. She had on this trouser suit, bright mauve – it hurt your eyes – with a darker mauve edging to it, and mauve patent shoes with high heels. Her handbag was mauve, a great big showy handbag with a gilt buckle, and she was carrying a brown carrier bag. I watched her because I wanted to tell my husband what a sight she was – he's very particular in his tastes, being a sort of artist – and I save up little things to tell him when he's finished work.'

'But you didn't tell him, Mrs Peveril?'

'I must have forgotten.' She was suddenly flurried. 'I wonder why I didn't tell you, Edward?'

The 'sort of artist' turned down the corners of his mouth. 'I expect I was too tired to listen. If you've finished with her I'll get back to the grindstone.'

'I've almost finished. Where did she go?'

'Across the field,' said Mrs Peveril promptly. 'That is, down the footpath, you know. I stayed at the window a long time but she didn't come back.'

She came to the door with them and watched them nervously as they got back into their car. Wexford's driver, glancing up innocently, received from her such a sharp look that he went red and turned away.

'Well, Mike, I don't quite know what to make of the Peverils, but she certainly saw the girl. Her description was too accurate to admit of anything else. Our best bet is to conclude that Dawn went across that field to meet a man. Where would she have met him?'

'In the open, I suppose. If she was going to meet him in Stowerton she'd have gone to Stowerton – the buses go every ten minutes between four and seven. There's no shelter between here and Stowerton except trees and the old pumping station.'

Wexford nodded. He knew the place Burden spoke of, a shed containing disused pumping equipment and standing in thick woodland on the banks of the Kingsbrook.

'We'll have it searched,' he said. 'That's quite an idea. Meanwhile, I'd like to see how things are progressing in the High Street.'

Things had progressed considerably. When Wexford entered the hall of the Baptist church, Martin had two people waiting to see him, each with information that was to complicate rather than simplify the case.

The first of these, an assistant from the Snowdrop Laundry and Dry Cleaners in Kingsmarkham High Street, was a middle-aged cheerful woman who had known Dawn Stonor as a schoolgirl and since then had sometimes seen her on her rare visits to her mother.

'We sort of knew each other by sight really,' she said. 'She came in last Monday at about a quarter past four.'

'She was dressed in mauve?'

'That's right. A very smart trouser suit. I remember we cleaned it for her Easter time. When she came in on Monday I wasn't sure if she knew me, but I asked her how her mum was and her gran and she said all right. Well, she'd brought this blue frock in to be cleaned and she wanted to know if I could get it done express. She wanted to collect it the next morning. "We can just do it," I said, "seeing you've brought it before four-thirty." If they come in later than that, you see, they can't get their things back before the next afternoon.

' "I want to be on the ten-fifteen train tomorrow," she said, "so can I collect it at ten?" '

'She meant to collect it herself?' Wexford asked.

'Well, she said "I". She didn't say anything about her mum fetching it like she has in the past. No, she meant to get it herself. I said that'd be all right and I made out the slip for her. You can see our part of it if you like, I've got it here with me.'

Wexford thanked her and examined the slip, noting the name and the date.

'But she didn't collect it?'

'No. I had it all ready but she never came. I was going to pop up to her mum's with it this week and then I heard what had happened. Awful, isn't it? It made me go cold all over when I heard.'

Next Wexford saw the manager of the Luximart, a big new supermarket which stood between the Dragon and the Baptist church just beside the Forby bus stop. He was young, eager and helpful.

'The young lady came in here at half-past four. We don't get many customers late on a Monday on account of we don't sell meat on a Monday and the veg isn't fresh. Most people eat up the Sunday leftovers and shop on Tuesdays.

'She was almost my last customer and when she left she waited nearly half an hour for the Forby bus, the five-twelve. Stood outside here, she did. I cursed, I can tell you, because just after the bus had come and she'd got on it I was sweeping up in the shop and I found this slip from the cleaners.'

'May I see?'

'I was certain she'd dropped it. I was sure it hadn't been there before she came in and I was quite worried thinking maybe she'd have trouble collecting her cleaning. I reckoned she'd come back but she never did. Then when I saw your notices and heard the name . . .'

'You didn't know her?'

'Never saw her before,' said the manager, 'that I can recall.'

Wexford matched the two slips, the top and the carbon. *Miss Stonor*, he read, *15 Lower Road, Kingsmarkham. Blue dress, express, 46p.* 'Will you describe her, please?'

'Nice-looking blonde. Very smartly dressed in a sort of purple blouse slacks. I don't know, I can't describe girls' clothes. I reckon she had a purple bag. I remember thinking . . .' The manager looked up ruefully and bit his lip. 'I remember thinking she was a smashing piece, but it seems awful saying that now she's dead.'

'What did she buy?'

'I knew you'd ask me that. I've been trying to think. I was at the check-out and she called me over to the deep freeze and asked me what the strawberry sundaes were like. They're sort of mousse things in cartons. I said I'd recommend them and she put two in the trolley. Wait, I'm trying to see it, sort of get a picture . . .'

Wexford nodded, saying nothing. He knew that this method, a kind of free association, was the best way. Let the man close his eyes, transport himself mentally back into the shop, stand beside the girl, re-create the almost empty wire trolley . . .

'There was a can in the trolley.' He concentrated. 'I know what it was! Soup. Vichyssoise, the stuff you can have hot or cold. It's all coming back. She took a tin of chicken fillets off the shelf and tomatoes – yes, tomatoes in a pack. I think she bought bread, a cut loaf. She might have bought butter, I don't remember. I do remember she got a bottle of wine, though, because she had the cheapest line we do. Spanish beaujolais and some cigarettes. She hadn't a basket. I gave her a brown paper carrier.'

There was no one else to see. Wexford went back to the police station where he found Burden with the doctor. The wind rattled the windows and a thin rain spattered against the glass.

'She meant to spend the night here,' he said. 'She was going to call for the dress on Tuesday morning. And it was food she was carrying in that bag when Mrs Peveril saw her. Food for *two* people.'

'For her and her date,' said Burden.

'Then he wasn't a casual pick-up. A man she picked up would either not ask her to eat with him at all or else he'd invite her to some restaurant. You can't imagine a girl making a date with a stranger and that stranger saying, Bring a three-course meal with you and we'll have a picnic. She must have known him and known him well.' Wexford listed the items of food and said, 'What's the most interesting thing about that food, Mike?'

'It could have been eaten cold as it was or it could have been heated. In other words, it could have been bought especially to be eaten in the open air, or it could equally well have been heated – the soup and the chicken, that is – which means indoors, in a house.'

During this interchange the doctor, who had been sketching a duodenum on the back of Wexford's draft of the crime-prevention plans, looked up and said, 'It wasn't eaten at all. I've got a provisional medical report prepared for you – there'll be a more detailed one later from the experts, of course – but the girl's stomach was empty. She hadn't eaten anything for five or six hours. Maybe the boy friend ate the lot on his own.'

'Or else food and wine and carrier bag are hidden somewhere with the mauve trouser suit.'

'Not the wine,' said Croker. He stopped drawing and his face was suddenly grim. 'The wine was used. Remember the glass you found, Reg, the glass you cut your hand on? There was glass embedded in her face and neck. Her dress was stained with wine as well as blood. I don't think I'm being unduly melodramatic when I say that her attacker went completely mad. Perhaps you and Mike will be able to find out whatever it was she said or did to him. All I can say is that something she did tipped him over the edge. He beat her to death with that wine bottle. He beat her in such a frenzy that the glass broke against the bones of her face.'

It was dark inside the little shed, half-filled as it was by cumbersome, rusty machinery, and the men worked by the light of lamps they had brought with them. Outside the pumping station the river rattled noisily and the wind slapped the door monotonously against its rotted frame.

'If they came in here,' said Wexford at last, 'it was a very brief visit. No blood, no crumbs, no cigarette ends.' He touched his hair and brought away a handful of cobwebs. 'It's a filthy hole, not at all my idea of the sort of rendezvous likely to entice a girl like Dawn Stonor, who, I take it, was conscious of her appearance.' For a moment he watched the men lifting up old sacks and searching through coils of rotted rope. 'I wish to God I could understand why she put that red dress on,' he said. 'I've a feeling that if I could I'd have the key to the whole business.'

'Because she got dirty in here?' hazarded Burden.

'Doing what? Not eating, not smoking, not making love. Talking, maybe? Then where did the dress come from? She wasn't carrying it with her. Perhaps he was. I just don't think it's possible that in one day she got two garments soiled so as to be unwearable. The coincidence is too great, and it's beyond the bounds of credibility that he happened to have a dress with him ready for her to put on in case hers got dirty. And who was he?'

'We may get some help as far as that goes from the London end.'

'Let's hope so. Shall we go? All this dust is making me cough.'

What Burden termed help from the London end had come in while they were down by the river. It was not information, data, reported interviews, but help in actual human form. She was an attractive young woman, this girl who had shared a flat in Philimede Gardens, Earls Court, with Dawn Stonor. Wexford went into the interview room where they told him she was and found her drinking tea and chain-smoking, the ashtray on the table in front of her already choked with butts.

CHAPTER SEVEN

'My name's Joan Miall,' she said shaking hands in a very forthright manner. 'An inspector came this morning and asked me a lot of questions. He said you'd want to see me and I thought I'd save you the trouble by coming to see you.' She was dark with a very pretty intelligent face and deep blue eyes. She looked about twenty-four. 'I still can't believe Dawn's dead. It seems so fantastic.'

'It's good of you to come, Miss Miall. I shall have a great deal to ask you so I think we'll go upstairs to my office where we can be more comfortable.'

In the lift she didn't speak but she lit another cigarette. Wexford understood that this heavy smoking was an antidote to shock. He approved her plain knee-length skirt and scarlet shirt, the healthy fine-boned face which, scarcely touched with make-up, was framed in shining hair, long and parted in the centre. Her hands were ringless, the nails short and lacquered pale pink. The pleasant, semi-living room appointments of his office seemed to set her more at ease. She relaxed, smiled and stubbed out her cigarette. 'I smoke too much.'

'Maybe,' he said. 'You were very fond of Dawn?'

She hesitated. 'I don't know really. I shared a flat with her for four years. We saw each other every day. We worked together. It was a shock.'

'You both worked at the Townsman Club?'

'Yes, that was where we met. We'd both been through a bit of a bad time. Dawn had been living with a man who was almost pathologically jealous and I'd been sharing with my sister. My sister was terribly possessive. Dawn and I decided to take flat together and we made a pact not to fuss each other and not to worry if the other one didn't always come home. That's why I wasn't worried. Not until Saturday. Then I . . .'

'You're running on a bit, Miss Miall,' Wexford interrupted her. 'Tell me about last Monday first.'

The slight strain this called for demanded a fresh cigarette. She lit one, inhaled and leant back in her chair. 'Dawn had started a week's holiday the Saturday before, Saturday, June fourth. She couldn't make up her mind whether to go away or not. Her boy friend – he's called Paul Wickford and he keeps a garage near us – he wanted her to go touring in Devon with him, but she hadn't decided by that Monday morning.'

'You expected her back on Monday evening?'

'Yes, in a way. She went off in the morning to catch the train for Kingsmarkham and she wasn't very cheerful. She never was when she was going to see her mother, they didn't get on. Dawn got on better with her grandmother.' Joan Miall paused and seemed to consider. 'Paul came round at about six, but when she hadn't come by seven he drove me to the club and then he went back to our flat to wait for her. Well, when she wasn't there on the Tuesday or the Wednesday and I didn't see anything of Paul, I thought they'd gone off to Devon together. We never left notes for each other, you see. We had this non-interference pact.'

'She told her mother she was working that night.'

Joan smiled slightly. 'I expect she did. That would just be an excuse to get away. Four or five hours in her mother's company would be as much as she could stand.' She stubbed out her cigarette, flicked ash fastidiously from her fingers. 'On Saturday – last Saturday, I mean – Paul appeared again. He hadn't been in Devon. His mother died that very Monday night and he'd had to go up north to the funeral and to see about things. He didn't know where Dawn was any more than I did.

'Then yesterday when we were both getting really worried – Dawn was due back at work tonight – the police came and told me what had happened.'

'Miss Miall, when Dawn was found she was wearing a dark red dress.' He noted her quick glance of surprise but ignored it for the moment. 'Now we have that dress here,' he said. 'It's rather badly stained. I'm going to ask you if you will be very brave and look at that dress. I warn you that you could find it upsetting. Will you look at it?'

She nodded.

'Yes, if you think it'll help. I can't remember Dawn ever wearing red. It wasn't her colour. But I'll look at it.'

The dress was made of a dark red rayon fabric with cap sleeves, a shaped waist and self belt. Because of its colour, the stains didn't show up except as a great stiff patch on the bodice.

The girl whitened and compressed her lips. 'May I touch it?' she said faintly.

'Yes.'

Rather tremulously, she fingered the neck opening and looked at the label. 'This is only a size twelve,' she said. 'Dawn was quite a big girl. She took a fourteen.'

'But she was wearing this dress.'

'It wasn't hers and it must have been quite a tight fit on her.' Abruptly she turned away and shivered. 'Look, perhaps you don't know much about fashion, but that dress is old, seven or eight years out of date, maybe more. Dawn was very fashion-conscious,'

Wexford led her back to his office. She sat down and the colour returned to her cheeks. He waited a little, marvelling at the friend's distress, the mother's indifference, and then he said, 'Miss Miall, will you try and give me a sort of character sketch of Dawn? What sort of girl she was, whom she knew and how she reacted to other people?'

'I'll try.' said Joan Miall.

'I don't want to give you the impression,' the girl began, 'that she wasn't a nice person. She was. But there were some – well,

211

rather peculiar things about her.' She lifted her head and looked at him earnestly, almost aggressively.

'I'm not asking for a character *reference*, you know. And what you say will be between us. I shan't broadcast it about.'

'No, of course not. But she's dead and I have sort of old-fashioned ideas about not speaking ill of the dead. I expect you'll think that a doll who serves drinks in a club hasn't any right to get all upstage, sort of disapprove of other people's behaviour?'

Wexford didn't answer. He smiled gently and shook his head.

'Anyway,' she said, 'I didn't exactly disapprove of Dawn. It was just that – well, it's not always easy living with a compulsive liar. You don't know where you are with people like that. You don't know *them* and the relationship is sort of unreal. I know someone said that even a really bad liar tells more truth than lies, but you still can't tell what are lies and what truth, can you?'

It was on the tip of Wexford's tongue to ask what an intelligent girl like Joan Miall was doing at the Townsman Club, but he checked the impulse.

'So Dawn was a liar?' he said instead, reflecting that this wasn't going to make his task easier. He looked into the frank, clear eyes of the girl opposite him, a girl he was sure would be transparently truthful. 'What did she lie about?'

'Well, it was boasting and name-dropping really. She'd had an awful childhood. Her father used to knock her about, and her mother sort of knocked her about mentally. She'd tell her she was immoral and no good in one breath and then in the next she'd say how she missed her and beg her to come home and marry and settle down. Mrs Stonor was always telling her they were – what was the phrase? – Oh, yes, "Just ordinary folk", and Dawn had no business giving herself airs. Then she'd say the work she did was no better than being a tart.

'It made her want to prove herself. Sorry if I'm talking

like an amateur psychiatrist but I'm interested in that sort of thing. I tried to find out what made Dawn tick. When we first lived together I thought she really did know a lot of famous people. One day she brought a dog home and said she was going to look after it for a fortnight while its owner was away. She said the owner was a famous actor, a household word more or less. He's always on television.

'Then, after the dog had gone back, we were both in the club one night and this actor came in. Some member brought him as his guest. Of course I recognised him. He didn't even know Dawn. It wasn't that they'd quarrelled and weren't speaking. You could tell he just didn't know her.' Joan shrugged. She put her cigarettes into her bag and closed the bag decisively. 'She used to look through the evening paper and she'd spot a photograph of some well-known guy and say she'd worked with him or had an affair with him. I never said much. It embarrased me. The biggest name she ever dropped was a singer, terribly famous. She said she'd known him for years and very often they'd go out together. She *said*. A couple of weeks ago the phone rang and she answered it. She looked at me and covered up the mouthpiece and said it was him, but when she started talking to him she never said his name, just "Yes" and "No" and "That'd be lovely". She never actually called him Zeno. You can pretend a phone-caller is anyone, can't you? Your flatmate's not likely to go and listen on the extension.'

'Zeno?' said Wexford. 'D'you mean she claimed acquaintance with Zeno Vedast?'

'That's rather the word, "claimed". He never came to the flat. I never saw her with him. No, it was just the same as with the TV actor, name-dropping to impress, I'm afraid.'

'Miss Miall, was Dawn the sort of girl who might pick up a stranger and spend the night with him?'

She hesitated and then said impulsively, 'She might have. It sounds hateful but Dawn was very fond of money. She never

213

had any money when she was a child, just a shilling a week or something ridiculous, and she was supposed to save half of that in a piggy bank you couldn't open. And her parents can't have been that poor – they both worked. I'm telling you this to explain why she might have picked someone up if she thought there was anything in it for her. When she first came to the club she was told like we all are that dating a customer means instant dismissal. The members know that but some of them try it on. Well, Dawn accepted an invitation from a member, in spite of the rule. He said if she'd go away for the weekend with him he'd buy her a fur coat. She did go and he gave her ten pounds. She never got the coat and I think she felt awfully humiliated because she never did that again. She liked admiration too and if a man wanted to sleep with her she thought . . . Oh, well, that it means a lot more than it does. Sometimes when she wasn't working she'd be away for a night and I think she was with a man. She couldn't bring him home, you see, in case Paul came round. But, as I told you, we didn't ask each other questions.'

'This Mr Wickford was a steady boy friend?'

She nodded. 'They'd been going out together for two years. I think she'd have married Paul in the end. The trouble seemed to be that he wasn't rich enough for her or famous or anything. He's about thirty-five, divorced, very nice. He was frightfully upset when he heard what had happened to her and the doctor had to give him sedatives. I'm sure she would have married him if she could only have grown out of all those ideas about knowing famous people. She was a very nice girl really, generous, good fun, always ready to help anyone out. It was just that she couldn't help telling lies . . .'

'One last thing. Miss Miall. Dawn brought food in Kingsmarkham last Monday afternoon, a tin of soup, tinned chicken and two strawberry mousse things in cartons. Is it possible she bought it to take home for lunch for the two of you on Tuesday?'

'Definitely not.'

'Why are you so sure?'

'For one thing – please don't think I don't like this place, it's a very nice town – but no one who lives – er, lived – where Dawn did would buy food here to take home. We're surrounded by shops and big supermarkets. The other thing is, she wouldn't buy food for the two of us. I'm a bit of a faddist when it comes to food. Health-conscious. You wouldn't think so the way I smoke, would you?' She gave a slight laugh. 'I never eat food out of cans. Dawn knew that. We used to prepare our food quite separately unless one of us made a casserole or a salad. Dawn didn't care what she ate. She hated cooking and she used to say she ate to live.' Joan winced at the last word which had been used automatically, without thought. She lifted her eyes to Wexford and he saw that they shone with unshed tears. In a choking voice she said:

'She didn't live very long, did she?'

Michael Burden was a widower whose married life had been happy and who, as a result of this, tended to consider sexual relationships as ecstatically romantic or, when they were illicit, deeply sordid. But the solitary love affair he had had since his wife's death had slightly broadened his mind. He was now prepared to admit that unmarried people might love each other and consummate that love without degradation. Sometimes these newly enlightened views of his gave rise to romantic theories and it was one of these which he propounded to Wexford as they drank their coffee together on Tuesday morning.

'We've agreed,' he began, 'that her killer can't have been a casual pick-up because of the food-shopping angle. And we know the food wasn't bought for her and the Miall girl. Therefore, she knew the man and knew him well enough to arrange with him that she'd buy their meal and meet him after he'd finished work. The time of the meeting – surely between five-thirty and six? – indicates it was to be after he'd finished work. Right?'

'Imagine so, Mike.'

'Well, sir, I've been wondering if she and this bloke had one of those long close friendships extending over years.'

'What long close friendships? What are you on about?'

'You know my sister-in-law Grace?' Wexford nodded impatiently. Of course he knew Grace, the sister of Burden's dead wife who had looked after Burden's children when they had first lost their mother and who he had later hoped would be the second Mrs Burden. That had come to nothing. Grace had married someone else and now had a baby of her own. 'I mention her,' said Burden, 'because it was her experience that gave me the idea. She and Terry knew each other off and on for years before they got married. There was always a sort of bond between them, although they didn't meet much and each of them had other – well, friends. Terry even got engaged to someone else.'

'You're suggesting this was the case with Dawn?'

'She lived here till she was eighteen. Suppose she knew this bloke when they were both very young and they had an affair and then they both left Kingsmarkham to work elsewhere. Or he stayed here and she went to London. What I'm suggesting is that they kept in touch and whenever she came home or he went to London they had one of these dates, secret dates necessarily because he was married and she was more or less engaged to Wickford. Frankly, I think this covers every aspect of the case and deals with all the difficulties.'

Wexford stirred his coffee, looked longingly towards the sugar bowl and resisted the temptation to take another lump. 'It doesn't deal with that bloody red dress,' he said viciously.

'It does if they met in this chap's house. We'd have to admit the possibility of coincidence, that she stained the mauve outfit and then put on a dress belonging to this man's wife.'

'The wife being out presumably. She goes there, he lets

her in. What happens to the mauve garment? They had no drinks for her to spill, ate nothing for her to drop, made no love to – er, crush it. (I put it like that, Mike, to save your delicate sensibilities.) Maybe the violence of his welcoming embrace creased it up and she was so dainty about her appearance that she rushed upstairs and slipped into one of her rival's ancient cast-offs. He was so upset about her thinking more of her clothes than of him he upped and banged her with the bottle. Is that it?'

'It must have been something like that,' said Burden rather stiffly. Wexford was always pouring cold water on his flights of fancy and he never got used to it.

'Where was this house of assignation, then?'

'On the outskirts of Stowerton, the Forby side. She went by the fields because he was going to meet her there and take her back to his house. They arranged it that way just in case the wife changed her mind about going away.' He made a moue of distaste, sordidness temporarily conquering romance. 'Some people do go on like that, you know.'

'You seem to know, anyway. So all we have to do now is find a bloke living in a house on the north side of Stowerton who's known Dawn Stonor since they went to Sunday school together and whose wife was away Monday night. Oh, and find if the wife has missed a red dress.'

'You don't sound too enthusiastic, sir.'

'I'm not,' Wexford said frankly. 'The people you know may go on like that but the people I know don't. They act like *people*, not characters in a second feature film that's been thrown together for the sake of sensation rather than illustrating human nature. But since my mind is otherwise a blank, I reckon we'd better get asking Mrs Stonor who Dawn knew around Stowerton and who had a lifelong sentimental bond with her.'

CHAPTER EIGHT

'The folks round here,' said Mrs Stonor, 'weren't good enough for Dawn. She was a proper little snob, though what she'd got to be snobbish about I never will know.'

For all her frankly expressed unmaternal sentiments, Mrs Stonor was dressed in deepest black. She and the old woman who was with her, and who had been introduced as 'My mother, Mrs Peckham', had been sitting in semi-darkness, for the curtains were drawn. When the two policemen entered the room a light was switched on. Wexford noticed that a wall mirror had been covered by a black cloth.

'We think it possible,' he said, 'that Dawn went to meet an old friend on Monday night. I want you to try and remember the names of any old boy friends she had before she left home or any name she may have mentioned to you on her visit here.'

Instead of replying, Mrs Stonor addressed the old woman who was leaning forwardly avidly, clutching the two sticks that supported her when she walked. 'You can get off back to bed now, Mother. All this has got nothing to do with you. You've been up too long as it is.'

'I'm not tired,' said Mrs Peckham. She was very old, well over eighty. Her body was thin and tiny and her face simian, a maze of wrinkles. What sparse white hair she had was scragged on to the top of her head into a knot stuck full of pins. 'I don't want to go to bed, Phyllis. It's not often I have a bit of excitement.'

'Excitement! I like that. A nice way to talk when Dawn's had her head bashed in by a maniac. Come along now. I'll take your arm up the stairs.'

A small devil in Wexford's head spoke for him. 'Mrs

Peckham should stay. She may be able to help.' He said it more to irritate Mrs Stonor than because he thought her mother would be able to furnish them with information.

Mrs Peckham grinned with pleasure, showing a set of over-large false teeth. Reprieved, she helped herself to a sweet from the bag on the table beside her and began a ferocious crunching. Her daughter turned down the corners of her mouth and folded her hands.

'Can you think of anyone, Mrs Stonor?'

Still sulky from having her wishes baulked, Mrs Stonor said, 'Her dad never let her have boy friends. He wanted her to grow up respectable. We had a job with her as it was, always telling lies and staying out late. My husband tried every way we could think of to teach her the meaning of decency.'

'Tried his strap, mostly,' said Mrs Peckham. Protected by the presence of the policemen, she gave her daughter a triumphant and unpleasant grin. Wexford could see that she was one of those old pensioners who, dependent for all her needs on a hated child, was subservient, cringing, defiant or malicious as her fancy took her or circumstances demanded. When Mrs Stonor made no reply but only lifted her chin, her mother tried another dig. 'You and George ought never to have had no kids. Always smacking her and yelling at her. Knock one devil out and two in, that's what I say.'

Wexford cleared his throat. 'We don't seem to be getting very far. I can't believe Dawn never mentioned any man she was friendly with.'

'I never said she didn't. You'll get your stomach trouble again, Mother, if you don't leave them acid drops alone. The fact is, it was all lies with Dawn. I got so I let what she said go in one ear and out the other. I do know she had this man Wickford on account of her bringing him down here for the day last year. They didn't stop long. Dawn could see what I thought about *him*. A divorced man, running a garage! That was the best she could do for herself.'

219

'There was no one else?' Burden asked coldly.

'I said I *don't know*. You're not going to tell me she got herself done in by some boy she was at school with, are you? That's all the local boys she knew.'

Mrs Peckham, having incompletely unwrapped her latest sweet, was removing shreds of paper from her mouth. 'There was Harold Goodbody,' she said.

'Don't be so stupid, Mother. As if Harold'd have anything to do with a girl like Dawn. Harold climbed too high for the likes of her.'

'Who is this man?' asked Wexford.

The sweet lodged in a wizened cheek pouch, the noisy sucking abated, Mrs Peckham heaved a heavy but not unhappy sigh. 'He was a lovely boy, was Harold. Him and his mum and dad used to live round here in the next street. I wasn't here then, I had my own cottage, but I used to see Harold when I had my job serving dinners at the school. Oh, he was a lad! Always one for a joke was Harold, April Fools all the year round for him. Him and Dawnie was pals from their first day at school. Then I came here to live with Phyllis and George and Dawnie'd bring him back to tea.'

'I never knew that,' said Mrs Stonor, bristling. 'George wouldn't have had that.'

'George wasn't here, was he? And you was working at that shop. I didn't see no harm in Dawnie bringing her friend home.' Mrs Peckham turned her back on her daughter and faced Wexford. 'Harold was a real freak to look at, all bones and his hair nearly as white as mine. I'd have boiled eggs all ready for the three of us, but when Dawnie and me started cracking ours we'd find the empty shells. Harold'd brought a couple of empty shells to fool us. Ooh, he was funny! He had a joke ink blot and a rubber spider. Made us scream, that spider did. One day I caught him playing with the phone. He'd ring this number and when the woman answered it said he was the engineers. He said to her there was an emergency.

She was to pour boiling water down the receiver, leave it for ten minutes and then cut the lead with scissors. She was going to too, she believed him, but I put a a stop to that, though I was laughing fit to die. Harold was a real scream.'

'Yes, I'm sure,' said Wexford. 'How old was he when all this fun and games was going on?'

'About fifteen.'

'And he still lives round here?'

'No, of course he don't. That Mr Silk from Sundays took him up and he left home and went to London when he was seventeen and got famous, didn't he?'

Wexford blinked. 'Famous? Harold Goodbody?'

Mrs Peckham wagged her gnarled hands impatiently. 'He changed his name when he got to be a singer. What did he call himself? Now I'm getting on I seem to forget everything. John Lennon, that was it.'

'I hardly think . . .' Wexford began.

Mrs Stonor, who had remained silent and scornful, opened her mouth and snapped, 'Zeno Vedast. He calls himself Zeno Vedast.'

'Dawn was at school with Zeno Vedast?' Wexford said blankly. So it hadn't been all boasting, vain name-dropping? Or some of it hadn't. 'They were friends?'

'You don't want to listen to Mother,' said Mrs Stonor. I daresay Dawn saw a bit of him when they were at school. She never saw him in London.'

'Oh, yes, she did, Phyllis. She told me so last Monday when she was home. She'd tell me things she'd never tell you. She knew you'd pour cold water on everything she did.'

'What did she say, Mrs Peckham?'

'She came into my room when I was in bed. You remember Hal, don't you Gran? she says. We always called him Hal. Well, I went out to dinner with him on Friday night, she said.'

'And you believed her?' Mrs Stonor gave the brittle laugh

221

that is not a laugh at all. 'Harold Goodbody was in Manchester Friday night. I saw him myself on telly, I saw him live. She was making up tales like she always did.'

Mrs Peckham scrunched indignantly. 'She got the night wrong, that's all. Poor little Dawnie.'

'Don't you be so stupid. He's a *famous* singer. Though what's so wonderful about his voice I never shall know. Richard Tauber, now that was a man who *had* a voice.'

Burden asked, 'Do his parents still live here?'

Mrs Stonor looked for a moment as if she was going to tell him not to be so stupid. She restrained herself and said sourly, 'When he got rich he bought them a great big detached place up near London. All right for some, isn't it? I've always been decent and brought my daughter up right and what did she ever do for me? I well remember Freda Goodbody going round to her neighbours to borrow a quarter of tea on account of Goodbody spending all his wages on the dogs. Harold never had more than one pair of shoes at a time and they was cast-offs from his cousin. "My darling boy" and "my precious Hal" she used to say but she used to give him baked beans for his Sunday dinner.'

Suddenly Mrs Peckham waxed appropriately biblical. ' "Better a dish of herbs where love is", she said, "than a stalled ox and hatred therewith".' She took the last acid drop and sucked it noisily.

'There you are, sir,' said Burden when they were in the car. 'A lifelong friendship, like I said.'

'Well, not quite like you said, Mike. Zeno Vedast doesn't live in Stowerton, he has no wife, and I don't suppose he makes a habit of eating tinned food in fields with waitresses. The odd thing is that she *did* know him. It seems to bear out what Joan Miall said that, in the nature of things, even a chronic liar must tell more truth than lies. We all know the story of the boy who cried wolf. Dawn Stonor was a lion-hunter. She cried lion and this time the lion was real. But we haven't a shred of evidence to connect Vedast with her last Monday. Very likely he was still in Manchester. All I can say at the moment is that it's intriguing, it's odd.'

'Surely you think we ought to see him?'

'Of course we must see every man Dawn knew, unless he has a watertight alibi for that Monday night. We still don't know what Wickford was doing after seven.' The chief inspector tapped his driver's shoulder. 'Back to the station, please, Stephens.'

The man half-turned. He was young, rather shy, recently transferred from Brighton. He blushed when Wexford addressed him, rather as he had coloured under Mrs Peveril's stare.

'Did you want to say something to me?' Wexford asked gently.

'No, sir.'

'Back to the station, then. We can't sit here all day.'

By Wednesday Paul Wickford had been cleared of suspicion. After leaving Joan Miall at the Townsman Club in Hertford Street, he had gone into a pub in Shepherd Market where he had drunk one vodka and tonic before driving back to Earls Court. Waiting for him at his flat was his brother who brought the news of their mother's serious illness and asked Paul to drive with him immediately to Sheffield. Paul had then asked the tenant of the second floor flat to cancel his milk and papers and, if he happened to see Dawn Stonor, to tell her where he had gone. The two brothers had reached their mother's house in Sheffield soon after midnight, and by the following morning she was dead.

In spite of there being only thin evidence of Dawn's killer having lived on the outskirts of Stowerton, a house-to-house investigation had begun on Tuesday afternoon of the whole district. No one had seen Dawn; no one had seen a girl in mauve alone or with a man. Only two wives had been absent from home on the evening in question, one with her husband and one leaving him behind to mind their four children. No

wife had been away for the whole night and no wife had
missed a red dress. Wexford's men searched the fields for the
trouser suit and the food. It was dreary work, for the rain fell
heavily and there were fears that the river would flood.

Mrs Clarke and Mrs Peveril remained the only people who
had seen Dawn after five-twenty, Mrs Peveril the last person
– except her killer – to have seen her alive. Wexford concentrated on these women, questioning them exhaustively, and it
wasn't long before he found something odd in their evidence.
It had not previously occurred to him that they might know
each other, and it was only when, sitting in Mrs Clarke's living
room, listening to her answer the phone, that the thought
occurred to him.

'I can't talk now, Margaret. I'll ring you later. I hope
Edward soon feels better.'

She didn't say who had been at the other end of the line.
Why should she? She sat down with a bright, insincere smile.

'So sorry. You were saying?'

Wexford said sharply, 'Were you talking to Mrs Peveril?'

'How *could* you know? I was, as a matter of fact.'

Then I imagine you are the one person she claims acquaintance with in this district?'

'Poor Margaret. She's so neurotic and she had an awful
time with Edward. I suppose I am her only friend. She doesn't
make friends easily.'

'Mrs Clarke, you were first questioned about Dawn Stonor
last Sunday evening, I think? We questioned people on this
side of the estate first.'

'Well, you ought to know that better than me.'

She looked a little offended, bored, but not at all frightened. Wexford considered carefully. Burden and Martin and
Gates had begun their questions here at seven, not reaching
The Pathway till nine. 'Did you phone Mrs Peveril on Sunday
evening before nine?' Her glance became wary, defensive. 'I
see you did. You told her you'd been questioned and, more-

over, that you'd been able to help. It was only natural for you to talk to your friend about it. I expect you described the girl to her and told her which way you'd seen her go.'

'Is there anything wrong in that?'

'Discretion would have been wiser. Never mind. Describe Dawn Stonor to me again now, please.'

'But I've done it hundreds of times,' cried Mrs Clarke with exasperated exaggeration. 'I've told you over and over again.'

'Once more, for the last time.'

'I was coming along to get the bus into Kingsmarkham. I saw her get off the bus that went the other way. She crossed the road and went into The Pathway.' Mrs Clarke spoke slowly and deliberately as might a parent explaining for the dozenth time to a not very bright child the point of a simple story. 'She had fair hair, she was in her twenties, and she wore a lilac-coloured trouser suit and mauve shoes.'

'That's what you told Mrs Peveril?'

'Yes, and you and all your people. I couldn't say any more because I don't know any more.'

'You didn't, for instance, notice her large mauve bag with a gilt buckle or that there was a darker edging to the suit?'

'No, I didn't. I didn't notice that and you saying it doesn't bring it back to me or anything. I'm sorry but I've told you everything I know.'

He shook his head, not in denial of her statement, but at his own bewilderment. At first, briefly, when she put the phone down he had suddenly been certain that Mrs Peveril had never seen Dawn at all, that the news from her friend had sparked off an urge for sensationalism, giving her an opportunity to make herself important. He remembered how, although she said she had taken careful note of the girl's appearance in order to tell her husband about her, she had never told him. But now he knew she must have seen her. How else could she, and she alone, have known of the bag and the purple border to the tunic?

CHAPTER NINE

Three houses that backed on to Sundays, three garden gates opening on a narrow strip of land beyond which was the quarry . . . Each garden separated from its neighbours by high woven chestnut fencing, a strip of land overgrown with dense bushes and quite tall trees. Wexford thought how easy it would have been to carry a body out of one of those houses by night and drop it into the quarry. And yet, if Dawn had gone into one of those houses instead of across the fields, if Mrs Peveril had seen her do so and was a seeker after sensation, wouldn't these facts have made a far greater sensation?

'I thought you'd leave me alone after I'd told you the truth,' said Mrs Peveril fretfully. 'I shall be ill if you badger me. All right, Mrs Clarke did phone me. That doesn't mean I didn't see her too, does it? I saw her and I saw her walk across those fields.'

'She couldn't have gone into any of those houses, anyway, sir,' said Burden. 'Unless it was into Mrs Peveril's own house. In which case Mrs P. presumably wouldn't say she'd seen her at all. Dawn can't have gone into Dunsand's or Miss Mowler's. We've checked at Myringham, at the University, and Dunsand didn't leave there till six. He'd have been lucky to get home by six-thirty to seven. Miss Mowler was with her friend in Kingsmarkham till a quarter to eight.'

They went back to the police station and were about to enter the lift when a sharp draught of wind told Wexford that the double doors to the entrance foyer had been swept unceremoniously open. He turned and saw an extraordinary figure. The man was immensely tall – far taller than Wexford who topped six feet – with a bush of jet-black hair. He wore an ankle-length pony-skin coat and carried a canvas bag whose sopping wet contents had soaked the canvas and were dripping on to the floor. Once inside, he paused, looked about him confidently and was making for Sergeant Camb who sat drinking tea behind his counter when Wexford intercepted him.

'Mr Mbowele, I believe? We've met before.' Wexford put out his hand which was immediately gripped in a huge copper-coloured vice of bone-crushing fingers. 'What can I do for you?'

The young African was extremely handsome. He had all the glowing virile grace which led clothes designers and model agencies and photographers to take up the slogan – 'Black is beautiful'. Beaming at Wexford, his soft, dark eyes alight, he withdrew his hand, dropped the sodden bag on to the floor and undid his coat. Under it his chest was bare, hung with a chain of small green stones.

'I don't altogether dig this rain, man,' he said, shaking drops of water off his hair. 'You call this June?'

'I'm not responsible for the weather.' Wexford pointed to the bag. 'And rain wasn't responsible for that unless the floods have started.'

'I fished it out of the river,' said Louis Mbowele. 'Not here. At Myringham. That's quite a river now, your little Kings-brook, man. I go down the river every morning and walk. I can think down there.' He stretched out his arms. It was easy to imagine him striding by the full flowing river, his mind equally in spate, his body brimming with vibrant energy. 'I was thinking,' he said, 'about Wittgenstein's principle of atom-icity. . . .'

'About *what*?'

'For an essay. It's not important. I looked in the river and I saw this purple silk thing . . .'

'Is that what's in the bag?'

'Didn't you get that? I knew what it was, man, I'd read the papers. I waded in and fished it out and put it in this bag – it's my girl friend's bag – and brought it here.'

227

'You shouldn't have touched it, Mr Mbowele.'

'Louis, man, Louis. We're all friends, aren't we? I've no prejudice against the fuzz? The fuzz have their place in a well-organized state. I'm no anarchist.'

Wexford sighed. 'You'd better come upstairs and bring the bag with you.'

In the office Louis made himself immediately at home by taking off the pony-skin coat and drying his hair on its lining. He sat on a chair like one who is more accustomed to sit on the floor, one leg stuck out and the other hooked over the chair arm.

'Exactly where did you find this, Louis?'

'In the river between Mill Street and the college grounds. It'd been swept down from round here somewhere. Look, why freak out about it? If I'd left it there it'd be down by the sea somewhere now. Keep your cool, man.'

'I am not losing my cool,' said Wexford who couldn't help smiling. 'Was there anything else in the river?'

'Fish,' said Louis, grinning, 'and sticks and stones and a hell of a lot of water.'

It was pointless, anyway, to ask about the paper carrier of food. What carrier bag, what cardboard cartons, would survive ten days and fifteen miles of pounding in that swollen stream? The can and the jar would survive, of course. But only a miracle would have brought them to precisely the same spot in the river as the trouser suit when Louis Mbowele had found it. Maybe the Wittgenstein principle provided for that sort of coincidence, but Wexford decided not to pursue it. The bag and, to a lesser extent the coat, were soaking his carpet.

'Well, I'm very grateful to you. You've been most public-spirited.' Wexford risked his hand again and managed not to wince when the vice enclosed it. 'There's a bus goes to Myringham at ten past which you ought to be in time for.'

'I ought if I'm going to get to Len's tutorial.' He glanced at the window. It was pouring. 'Have you ever been to Marumi?'

'Marumi?'

'My country. Sometimes you get no rain there for three years. Man, is that country dry! You like the sun?'

'It makes a change,' said Wexford.

'You said I was to remember you when I came into my kingdom. It won't be a kingdom but I'll need fuzz and I could get along great with you if you got rid of your hangups. How does it grab you?'

'I'll be too old by that time, Louis.'

'Age,' said the philosopher, 'is just a state of mind.' He looked, Wexford thought, about twenty. 'It won't be that long, man, not long at all. Get yourself together. Think it over.'

From the window Wexford watched him cross the street, swinging the wet, empty bag. He chuckled. When Burden came into the room, he looked up from the mauve rags he was examining.

'Just been offered a job, Mike.'

'Doing what?'

'My own thing, man, my own thing. When the rain and boredom here freak me out I can go boss the fuzz in a sort of black Ruritania. Can you see me in epaulettes with a Mauser on each hip?'

'My God,' said Burden. He fingered the torn material fastidiously. 'Is that the missing suit?'

Wexford nodded. 'Down to the purple edging, as described by our accurate Mrs Peveril. Louis Mbowele found it in the river at Myringham. It had obviously been washed down there by the heavy rains.'

'From those fields?'

'From up there somewhere. She was killed up there. I'm as sure of that as I'm sure I'll never be the Maigret of Marumi.'

Wexford remembered Miss Mowler from when she had been a district nurse in Kingsmarkham. His wife had broken her ankle and Miss Mowler had called three times a week to bath her and keep an eye on the plaster cast. She greeted him like an old friend.

'Mrs Wexford not been climbing any more ladders, I hope? And how are your lovely girls? I saw Sheila on television last week. She's getting quite well known, isn't she? And amazingly good-looking.'

'You mean it's amazing with me for her dad?'

'Oh, Mr Wexford, you know I didn't mean that!' Miss Mowler blushed and looked very confused. She tried to cover her gaffe with a string of explanations, but Wexford laughed and cut her short.

'I've come to talk to you about this murder, Miss Mowler.'

'But I can't help you. I wasn't here.'

'No, but you were here later in the evening. If there was anything you noticed, any little oddity . . .'

'I really can't help you,' she said earnestly. 'I've only been here three months and I hardly even know my neighbours.'

'Tell me what you do know of them, of the Peverils especially.'

The hall in the bungalow was rather garishly decorated, black and gilt predominating. The black bitumastic flooring curved upwards at the edges to meet an astonishingly hideous wallpaper. Wexford was rather surprised that the sprays of lipstick-red flowers, each petal a pear-shaped scarlet blot, with spiralling black stems and glossy golden leaves, should be to Miss Mowler's taste. He did not tell her so as she led him into the living room, but he must have looked it, for she plunged into characteristic excuses.

'Awful, isn't it? The builder finished both these bungalows completely before he sold them. Dreadful taste. You see I've got blue birds and orange lilies on the walls in here. And Mr Dunsand's next door is exactly the same. I believe he's going to re-decorate completely in his holidays. But doing that is so expensive and arduous if you're a lone woman like I am. The trouble is it's very good-quality paper and completely washable. I don't know if the Peverils' is the same. I believe they were able to choose their own decorations, but I've never been in there.'

'Mrs Peveril is a strange woman.'

'A very neurotic one, I should think. I heard her quarrelling once in the garden with her husband. She was crying quite hysterically.'

'What were they quarrelling about, Miss Mowler?' Wexford asked.

'Well, she was accusing him of being unfaithful to her. I couldn't help overhearing.' Afraid of another digression in which a spate of excuses would be put forward, Wexford shook his head and smiled. 'Oh, well, it's different rather with a policeman, isn't it? It's not gossip. Mrs Peveril talked to me in the street. I hardly know her but that doesn't stop her saying the most – well, intimate things. I do think it's a mistake for a man to work at home, don't you?'

'Why, Miss Mowler?'

'He and his wife never get away from each other. And if the wife's possessive and jealous she'll resent it and begin suspecting things if ever he does go out without her. Mrs Peveril seems to depend on her husband for every sort of support, and of course the poor man isn't adequate. Who is? I don't think he wanted to come here. She was the moving spirit behind that . . . Oh, I didn't mean to make a pun. She's the sort of woman who's always running away if you know what I mean.'

'Does she ever go out without her husband?'

'Oh dear, women like that can never appreciate that what's sauce for the goose ought to be sauce for the gander. She certainly goes out to her dressmaking class every Monday evening and sometimes she has another evening out with Mrs Clarke.'

'I suppose you knew Dawn Stonor?'

Any allegation that she might have been acquainted with

a murder victim might have been expected to evoke fulsome excuses from a woman of Miss Mowler's temperament. Instead, she set her mouth and looked affronted. 'Very selfish, flighty sort of girl. I know the family very well. Naturally, I look in on the grandmother, Mrs Peckham, from time to time. It would have made a world of difference to that old lady's life if Dawn had bothered to go home more often. But there you are, that's the young people of today all over. While I was still working I used to tell Dawn about it but she fired right up at me, said she couldn't stand the place or her mother. There was some nonsense about having an unhappy childhood. They've all had unhappy childhoods, Mr Wexford, to account for every bit of bad behaviour.' She tossed her head. 'I haven't seen her in two or three years now and I can't say I'm sorry.'

It was such a change for Miss Mowler not to be able to say she was sorry that Wexford concluded Dawn's firing up must have riled her excessively. He thanked her and left. Dunsand's bungalow had the closed-up, discouraging look of a house that is seldom occupied by day, all the windows shut, a milk bottle with a note stuck in it on the doorstep. He caught sight of Mrs Peveril, neatly overalled, watering a window box. She saw him, pretending she hadn't, and rushed indoors, slamming the front door.

She was a biggish woman, the victim of premature middle-aged spread, several stones heavier than Miss Mowler who was twenty-five years her senior. He hadn't really noticed that before. She wouldn't be a size twelve, more a sixteen. But a woman can put on a lot of weight in seven years, and Joan Miall had said the dress was seven or eight years old . . .

He had himself driven to Lower Road and again he was aware of a fidgety unease on the part of young Stevens, his driver. These days the man seemed always on the point of saying something to him, of unburdening his soul perhaps. He would say 'Yes, sir' and 'No, sir', but there was no finality about these responses, rather a vague note of hesitation and often a preoccupied pause before the man turned away and started the car. Wexford tried asking him what was the matter but he was always answered by a respectful shake of the head, and he concluded that Stevens had some domestic trouble weighing on him that he longed to discuss but was too shy and too reticent to reveal.

Mrs Stonor was in her kitchen, ironing, her mother in a rocking chair beside her. It was a chair which squeaked each time it was moved and Mrs Peckham, who seemed in an even more maliciously cheerful frame of mind today, moved it constantly, taking delight in the noise it made – they say you cannot make a noise to annoy yourself – and munching Edinburgh rock.

'I never heard her mention no Peveril,' said Mrs Stonor, passing her iron across a pair of pink locknit knickers that could only have belonged to her mother yet were capacious enough to have contained the whole of that little, dried-up body. 'She was proud of *not* knowing anyone around here, called them provincials of some fine thing. There's ever such a nice woman as is manageress of the cleaners and she'd known Dawn all her life. Dawn had to pretend she'd never seen her before. What d'you think of that?'

Wexford had to keep his thoughts to himself. He was marvelling, not for the first time, at certain popular fallacies. That children naturally love their parents is a belief which has all but died away. The world still holds that parents love their children, love them automatically, through thick and thin, through disappointment and disillusion. He himself had until recently believed that the loss of a child is the one insupportable grief. When would people come to understand that the death of a son or daughter, removing the need of a parent to put a good face on things, to lie to neighbours, to sustain a false image, can be a relief?

'If she had fallen in love with a local man,' he said carefully, 'perhaps these prejudices of hers wouldn't have counted for much.' He knew as he spoke that he was talking a foreign language to Mrs Stonor.

She seized upon the one point that meant anything to her. 'She wasn't capable of loving anyone.'

Mrs Peckham snorted. With surprising psychological insight, she said, 'Maybe she didn't know how. Kids don't know how if they don't get none theirselves. Same thing with dogs.' She passed Wexford the bag and grinned when he took a piece. 'And monkeys,' she added. 'I read that in me *Reader's Digest.*'

'We're wondering, Mrs Stonor, if she went into a man's house.' With any other bereaved mother he would have softened his words; with this one any tact seemed superfluous sentimentality. 'We think she may have had an assignation with a local man while his wife was away.'

'I wouldn't put it past her. She hadn't got no morals. But she wouldn't go into a fellow's house – even I can see that. That's stupid. She'd got a flat of her own, hadn't she? Them girls was only too ready to make themselves scarce if the other one was up to any funny business.' It was atrociously put, but it was unanswerable. 'Dawn didn't even have the decency to hide any of that from me,' Mrs Stonor said fiercely. 'She told me she'd been with men in that way. She called it being honest and leading her own life. As if she knew the meaning of honesty! I'd have died before I'd have told such things to my mother.'

A shrieking cackle come from Mrs Peckham. 'You'd nothing to tell, Phyllis. You aren't 'uman.'

'Don't be so stupid, Mother. The sergeant don't want you poking your nose in all the time, and it's time you had your rest. You've been fancying yourself ever since that young man came to see you this morning, buttering you up like I don't know what.'

Amused at his sudden demotion two rungs down the ladder, Wexford, who had risen to go, gave the older woman a conspiratorial half-smile. 'A grandson, Mrs Peckham?'

'No, I never had no kids but Phyllis. More's the pity.' She said it not as if she pined for a replica of Mrs Stonor but perhaps for her antithesis. 'Mind you, he was like a grandson in a way, was Hal.'

'Will you do as I ask, Mother, and get off to bed?'

'I'm going, Phyllis. I'm on me way.' An awareness that, after all, she depended for her bed and board on her daughter's good graces briefly softened Mrs Peckham's asperity, but not for long. She heaved herself up, clutching her sweets. 'You've got it in for poor Hal just because he wasn't all over you like he was me. He kissed me,' she said proudly.

'Mrs Peckham, am I right in thinking that Zeno Vedast has been here to see you? Do you mean while the festival was on? You didn't tell me that before.'

She propped herself on her walking aid, hunching her thin shoulders. 'He come this morning,' she said. 'Looking out for a house for hisself round here, one of them big places as we used to call gentleman's houses. Ooh, he's very grand in his ideas, is Hal. He's got a whole suite to hisself at that big hotel in the Forest, but he wasn't too proud to come and see old Granny Peckham and say how cut up he was about poor Dawnie. He come in a big gold car and he kissed me and brought me a two-pound box of Black Magic.' Her eyes gleamed greedily at the thought of the chocolates, waiting for her perhaps in her bedroom. She sighed contentedly. 'I'll get off for me lay-down now.' she said.

CHAPTER TEN

The Burden children were old enough now to come home to an empty house and get their own tea, but more often they went straight from school to the house of their Aunt Grace, and in the holidays Pat Burden spent most of her time there, playing with the baby. Her brother led the marauding life of a teenage boy, wandering with a small gang of contemporaries in the fields, fishing in the Kingsbrook or playing the jukebox at the Carousel café. Burden knew very well that his son's life would have differed very little from this pattern even if there had been a mother at the bungalow in Tabard Road. He understood that a girl child needs an adult female on whom to model herself and he knew that she had that in Grace. But he worried incessantly about his children. Would John become a delinquent if he were out after nine in the evening? Would Pat carry a trauma through life because at the age of thirteen she was occasionally expected to open a tin or make tea? Did he give them too much pocket money or not enough? Ought he, for their sakes, to marry again? Innocent of any, he was loaded down with guilt.

He went to absurd lengths to ensure that neither of them had to do any work they would not have done had his wife lived. For this reason he was always taking them out to meals or rushing home with packages of expensive frozen food. Pat must never walk the half-mile from Grace's house to Tabard Road. He would have let her walk it without a thought if Jean had lived. But motherless children had to be fetched in father's car. He suffered agonies of frustration and recrimination if he was busy on a case and Pat had to wait an hour or even be abandoned to her aunt for an evening.

Wexford knew this. Whereas he would never excuse Burden

from essential work on these grounds, he regretfully gave up the practice of detaining the inspector after hours to sit with him in the Olive and Dove and thrash out some current problem. Burden was worse than useless as a participant in these discussions. His eyes were always on the clock. Every drink he had was 'one for the road', and from time to time he would start from his seat and express the worry uppermost in his mind. Had John come in yet?

But old habits die hard. Wexford preferred the atmosphere in the Olive to the adolescent-ruled, untidy living room of the bungalow. He felt guilty when Pat was prevented from doing her ballet exercises and John had to turn off the record player, but he had to talk to Burden sometimes, discuss things with him outside hours. As he came to the door that evening, he heard the pom-pom, the roar and the whine of pop music before he rang the bell.

Burden was in his shirt sleeves, a plastic apron round his waist. He took this off hurriedly when he saw who his caller was. 'Just finishing the dishes,' he said. 'I'll nip out for some beer, shall I?'

'No need. I've brought it. What did you think I'd got in the bag? More treasures from the river? Who's the vocalist, John?'

'Zeno Vedast,' said John reverently. He looked at his father. 'I suppose I'll have to turn it off now.'

'Not on my account,' said Wexford. 'I rather like his voice.'

Vedast wasn't singing any of the festival songs but an older hit which had for so long been number one in the charts that even Wexford had heard it. Once or twice he had heard himself humming the melody. It was a gentle folk song about a country wedding.

'Dad's going to buy me the Sundays album for my birthday.'

'That'll set you back a bit, Mike.'

'Six quid,' said Burden gloomily.

'I wonder if any of these songs will live? We tend to forget that some of the greatest songs were pop in their day. After *The Marriage of Figaro* was first performed in the seventeen-eighties, they say Mozart heard the errand boys whistling *Non piu andrai* in the streets of Vienna. And it's still popular.'

'Oh, yes?' said Burden politely and uncomprehendingly. 'You can turn it off now, John. Mr Wexford didn't come round here to talk about Zeno Vedast or Goodbody or whatever his name is.'

'That's just what I did come for.' Wexford went into the kitchen and picked up a tea towel. He began polishing glasses, resisting Burden's efforts to stop him. 'I've a feeling that before we go any further we ought to see Dawn's lion, the lion who roars like any sucking dove.'

'Wherever he may be at this moment.'

'That's no problem, Mike. He's here. Or, at any rate, he's at the Cheriton Forest Hotel.' Wexford drank the half-pint Burden had poured out for him and told the inspector about his talk with Mrs Peckham. 'I don't know that it means much. He may make a point of visiting old ladies rather on the lines of a parliamentary candidate nursing babies. Never neglect any opportunity of currying favour and influencing people. Or he may be an ordinary nice bloke who wanted to condole with the dead girl's grandma. It certainly doesn't mean he'd seen Dawn recently.'

John put his head round the door. 'I'm going out, Dad.'

Burden began to flap. 'Where? Why? What d'you want to go out now for?'

'Only down the Carousel.'

Wexford said smoothly, 'That's fine, John, because we're going out too. Your father won't be back till ten-thirty, so you'd better have the key. You're bound to be in before him, aren't you?'

Burden handed over the key in meek stupefaction and John took it as if it were something precious and wonderful. When

SOME LIE AND SOME DIE

the boy had gone – rapidly before there could be any changes of heart – Burden said suspiciously, 'You talked to him exactly as if he were grown-up.'

'Don't have any more beer, Mike. I want you to drive us.'

'To Cheriton Forest, I suppose?'

'Mm-hm. Vedast's dining in tonight. I checked.' Wexford looked at his watch. 'He ought to have just about finished his dinner.'

'Oh God. I don't know. Pat's at Grace's. John . . .'

'The boy's glad you're going out. It was a relief. Couldn't you see that? You won't go out for his sake. D'you want him to get so he can't go out for yours?'

'I sometimes think human relationships are impossible. Communication's impossible.'

'And you're a fool,' said Wexford, but he said it affectionately.

Cheriton Forest, a large fir plantation, lies some two miles to the south of Kingsmarkham. It is intersected by a number of sandy rides and one metalled road on which, in a big heathy clearing, is situated the Cheriton Forest Hotel.

This is a newer and far more fashionable hotel than the Olive and Dove in Kingsmarkham. The original building, put up in the thirties, is supposed to be a copy of a Tudor manor house. But there are too many beams and studs, the plaster is too white and the beams too black, the woodwork a decoration rather than an integral part of the structure. And the whole thing which might have mellowed with time has been vulgarized by a vast glass cocktail bar and by rows of motel bungalows added on in the late sixties.

When Wexford and Burden arrived at the hotel it was still broad daylight, a dull summer evening, windy and cool. The wind stirred the forest trees, ruffling them against a pale sky where grey clouds, rimmed in the west with pink, moved, gathered, lost their shapes, torn by the wind.

On a Saturday night the forecourt would by this time have been crammed with cars and the cocktail bar full of people. But this was mid-week. Through a mullioned window a few sedate diners could be seen at tables, waiters moving unhurriedly with trays. This dining-room window was closed as were all the others in the building except one on the floor above, a pair of french windows giving on to a balcony which was quite out of keeping with the design of the hotel. The wind sent these diamond-paned glass doors banging shut and bursting open again, and from time to time it caught the velvet curtains, beating them, making them toss like washing on a line.

There was plenty of room in the parking bays for the half-dozen vehicles which stood there. Only one was on the forecourt proper, a golden Rolls-Royce parked askew, the silver gable of its grid nosing into a flower-bed and crushing geranium blossoms.

Wexford stared at this car from the windows of his own which Burden was steering, with rule-abiding propriety, into a vacant bay. He had heard of the fashion of covering the bodywork of cars in a furry coating to seem like skin or coarse velvet, but he had never yet seen this done in use, except in glossy advertisements. The Rolls wore a skin of pale golden fur, the vibrant sand colour of a lion's pelt which gleamed softly and richly, and on its bonnet, just above the grid, was attached a statuette of a plunging lion that seemed to be made of solid gold.

'This beast-of-prey motif keeps cropping up,' he said. He approached the car to get a closer look and as he did so the driver's door opened and a girl got out. It was Nell Tate.

'Good evening,' he said. 'We've met before.'

'I don't think so. I don't remember.' It was the voice of a person accustomed to defending a celebrity from intrusive fans.

'At the festival.' Wexford introduced himself and Burden. 'I'd like a word with Mr Vedast.'

Nell Tate looked seriously alarmed. 'You can't see Zeno. He's resting. He's probably asleep. We're all trying to get a quiet evening. I only came down to get something out of the car.'

She looked as if she were in need of rest. Beautifully dressed in a long clinging gown of silver lace under which she obviously wore nothing at all, heavy platinum ornaments at neck and wrists, she had a look of hag-ridden exhaustion. Under the silver and purple paint, her left eye was very swollen, the white of it bloodshot between puffy, painful lids. Studying it covertly, Wexford thought that considerable courage must have been needed to stick false lashes on to that bruised membrane.

'There's no hurry,' he said smoothly. 'We'll wait. Are you in the motel?'

'Oh, no.' She had a false poise that was growing brittle. 'We've got what they call the Elizabethan suite. Can you give me some idea what it's about?'

'Dawn Stonor. Tell him we want to talk to him about Dawn Stonor.'

She didn't even go through the pretence of looking bewildered or asking who this was. 'I'll tell him. Couldn't you come back tomorrow?'

'I think we'll wait,' said Wexford. He and Burden followed her into the foyer of the hotel, a porter having sprung forward to open the door for her. Observing the way she swept past the man, her head going up and her shoulders wriggling, passing him without a word or a nod, Wexford hardened his heart. 'We'll give you a quarter of an hour and then we'll come up.'

She made for the lift. The spurned porter, not at all put out, watched her admiringly. Once in the lift, before the doors closed on her, she appeared multiplied three times by the mirrors which lined its walls. Four blonde girls in silver, four bruised eyes, glared at Wexford and then the doors closed and she was whisked upwards.

'Lovely,' said the porter feelingly.

'What are they doing here?'

'Mr Vedast's here to purchase a country property, sir.'

Anyone else, thought Wexford, would have just bought a house. He fished for a couple of coins and found only a fifty-pence piece. 'Any luck, yet?'

'Thank you very much, sir. They go out looking every day, sir, him and Mr and Mrs Tate. We've had a few fans outside but they didn't have no joy on account of Mr Vedast takes all his meals in his suite.'

'She was scared stiff when you said who we were,' said Burden when the porter had gone out of earshot.

'I know, but that may be only that she's afraid of having him disturbed. I wonder if it was he who gave her that black eye?'

'More likely her husband, poor devil. That's a *ménage à trois* if ever there was one. D'you think there are two bed-rooms or only one in that suite?'

'For a self-avowed puritan, Mike, you take a very lubricious interest in these things. Here you are, get your nose into *Nova* and you can pass me *The Field*.'

For fifteen minutes they leafed through the glossy periodicals provided in the Shakespeare Lounge. A very old couple came in and switched on the television. When they were satisfied that it was glowing with colour and braying forth cricket scores, they ignored it and began to read novels. A Dalmatian entered, wandered about and fell into a despairing heap in front of the cold electric heater.

'Right, time's up,' said Wexford. 'Now for the lion's den.'

CHAPTER ELEVEN

The suite was on the first floor. They were admitted not by Nell but by a small dark man of about thirty who introduced himself as Godfrey Tate and who favoured them with a narrow smile. There was something spare and economical about him from his longish thin black hair and dab of moustache to his tiny feet in lace-up boots. He wore tube-like black slacks, a very tight skimpy black shirt, and the air of one who rations his movements, his speech and his manners to the starkest barrenness social usage permits.

'Zeno can spare you ten minutes.'

They were in a small entrance hall filled with flowers, displays of roses, sweet peas and stephanotis, whose perfume hung cloyingly on the air. Burden knocked a rosebud out of a vase and cursed softly. The living room was large and not at all Elizabethan, being done up in the style of a provincial casino with panels of pink mirror on the walls, niches containing more flowers in gilt urns, and french windows, hung with velvet and opening on to a balcony. In here the atmosphere was not stuffy or soporific. All the doors were open, showing a bathroom whose floor was cluttered with wet towels, and the interiors of two bedrooms, one containing a huge double bed and the other two singles. All had been occupied until recently as the tumbled bedclothes showed, but as to who had occupied which and with whom it was impossible to tell. Both bedrooms, like the living room, were littered all over with discarded clothes, magazines, records, and suitcases spilling out their contents. A lusty gale blew through the open windows, shaking the flowers and making the curtains billow and thrash.

Nell Tate looked blue with cold, her arms spiky with gooseflesh. Not so her companion, who, bare-chested, sat at a table by the window eating roast duck with the enthusiasm of one who has been brought up on baked beans.

'Good evening, Mr Vedast. I'm sorry to disturb your dinner.'

Vedast didn't get up, but his hairless, polished-looking face, all bones and almost Slavonic planes, split into a wide grin. 'Hallo. Good evening. Have some coffee.' His voice had no affectations. It was still what it must have always been, the local mixture of Sussex burr and mild cockney. 'Make them send up more coffee, Nello, and take all this away.' He made a sweeping gesture with his arm, indicating the two other plates on which the food had only been picked at, the covered dishes, the basket of melba toast. 'Phone down now. Go on.' No one had touched the cream trifle. Vedast took the whole bowl and set in his lap.

'Maybe they'd rather have a drink,' said Godfrey Tate.

'You mean *you* would, Goffo. Didn't you know they're not allowed to drink on duty?' Spooning up trifle, Vedast grinned at Wexford. He had an ugly attractive face, *joli laid*, very white and oddly bare. His eyes were a light, clear brown that sometimes looked yellow. 'The trouble with Nello and Goffo,' he said, 'is that they never read. They're not informed. Get on with your phoning and drinking, dears.'

Like discontented slaves, the Tates did his bidding. Tate took an almost empty bottle of brandy from a pseudo Louis Quinze cabinet and tipped what remained of it into a glass. He stood drinking it and watching his wife darkly while she phoned down for more coffee. Vedast laughed.

'Why don't you sit down? Not too cold in here, is it?' He put out his hand to Nell and beckoned her, pursing his lips into a whistle shape. She came up to him eagerly, too eagerly. She was trembling with cold. It was all she could do to stop her teeth from chattering. 'Fresh air is good for Nello and Goffo. If I didn't look after their health they'd be like two little broiler chickens, shut up all day in hot hutches. I think we'll do our house-hunting on foot tomorrow, Nello.'

'Then you can count me out,' said Tate.

'Must we? You won't mind if Nello comes with me, will you?' Emaciated, starved-looking Vedast finished the dessert which had been intended for three people. 'Perhaps our visitors can tell us of all sorts of lovely houses going spare round here?'

'We aren't house agents, Mr Vedast,' said Burden, 'and we've come to ask you questions, not answer them.'

The coffee arrived before Vedast could reply to this. Tate took one look at it, swallowed his drink and searched in the cupboard for a fresh bottle of brandy. While his wife poured coffee, he found a bottle tucked away at the back and quite full though already opened. A liberal measure in his glass, he took a long deep draught.

Immediately he was convulsed, choking and clapping one hand over his mouth.

'Christ!' A dribble of liquid came out through his fingers. 'That's not brandy! What the hell is it?'

Vedast laughed, his head on one side. 'Meths and cold tea, Goffo. Just a little experiment to see if you could tell the difference.' Nell giggled, squeezed close against Vedast's side. 'I poured the brandy down the loo. Best place for it.'

Tate said nothing. He went into the bathroom and slammed the door.

'Poor little man! Never mind, we'll take him out to dinner tomorrow at that lovely place in Pomfret. Kiss, Nello? That's right. No hard feelings because I like playing tricks on your old man? How is your coffee, Chief Inspector?'

'Well, it *is* coffee, Mr Vedast. Apparently one runs a risk drinking in your establishment.'

'I wouldn't dare doctor your coffee. I've a great respect for the law.'

'Good,' said Wexford drily. 'I hope you've enough respect to tell me what was your relationship with Dawn Stonor.'

For a moment Vedast was silent but he didn't seem

disturbed. He was waiting while Nell poured cream into his cup and then added four lumps of sugar.

'Thank you, Nello darling. Now you run away and paint something. Your poor eye, for instance.'

'Do I have to?' said Nell like a child who has been told she must go to the dentist.

'Of course you do when Zeno says so. The quicker you go the sooner it will all be over. Run along.'

She ran along. She wasn't a child but a grown woman, shivering with cold and with a black eye. Vedast smiled indulgently. He walked to the bathroom door and paused, listening to Tate running taps and brushing his teeth. Then he came back, kicking shut the door of the drinks cabinet as he passed it, and stretched himself out full-length on the pink velvet sofa.

'You wanted to ask me about Dawnie,' he said. 'I suppose you've been talking to Mummy Stonor or even Granny Peckham?'

'They say you were at school with Dawn.'

'So I was. So were ever such a lot of other people. Why pick on me?'

'Mr Vedast,' said Wexford heavily, 'Dawn told her flatmate that you and she had remained friends since you left school, and she told her grandmother that you took her out to dinner on the Friday before she died. We know that can't have been true since you were in Manchester that day, but we'd like to know how well you knew Dawn and when you last saw her.'

Vedast took a lump of sugar and sucked it. He seemed completely relaxed, one leg casually crossed over the other. Still in their raincoats, Wexford and Burden were not even comfortably warm, but Vedast, almost naked, showed no sign of being affected by the cold damp wind. The golden hairs on his chest lay flat under the light gold chain which hung against them.

'When we both lived here,' he said, 'she was my girl friend.'

'You mean you were lovers?'

Vedast nodded, smiling pleasantly. 'I was her first lover. We were sixteen. Rather moving, don't you think? Martin Silk discovered me and all sorts of exciting things happened to me which wouldn't interest you at all. Dawnie and I lost touch. I didn't see her again till this year.'

'Where did you see her?'

'In the Townsman Club,' said Vedast promptly. 'Nello and Goffo and I went there as guests of a friend of mine, and there was Dawnie serving drinks. My poor little Dawnie in a yellow satin corset and tights! I nearly laughed but that would have been unkind. She came and sat down at our table and we had a long chat about old times. She even remembered what I like to drink, orange juice with sugar in it.'

'Did you communicate with her after that?'

'Just once.' Vedast spoke very lightly, very easily, his fingers playing with the gold chain. 'Nello and Goffo had gone away to see Goffo's mum and I was rather lonely, all on my own and sad, you know.' He smiled, the unspoilt star, the poor little rich boy. 'Dawnie had written down her phone number for me at the club. Nello didn't like that a bit, you can imagine. I thought, why not give Dawnie a ring?'

'And did you?'

'Of course I did.' Now Vedast's smile was apologetic, a little rueful, the smile of the unspoilt star who longs for the companions of his humbler days to treat him as the simple country boy he really is at heart. 'But it's very off-putting, isn't it, when people sort of swamp you? D'you know what I mean? When they're terribly enthusiastic, sort of fawning?'

'You mean you got bored?' said Burden bluntly.

'It sounds unkind, put that way. Let's say I thought it better not to revive something which was dead and gone. Sorry, that wasn't very tactful. What I mean is I choked Dawnie off. I said it would be lovely if we could meet again sometime, but I was so busy at present.'

'When did this telephone conversation take place, Mr Vedast?'

'Three or four weeks ago. It was just a little chat, leading to nothing. Fancy Dawnie telling Granny Peckham we'd met! Nello and Goffo could tell you when it was they went away.' He fixed his cat's eyes, yellowish, narrow, on Wexford, opening them very wide suddenly, and again they had a sharp sly glint. 'And they'll tell you where I was on June sixth. I know that'll be the next thing you'll ask.'

'Where were you, Mr Vedast?'

'At my house in Duvette Gardens, South Kensington. Nello and Goffo and I were all there. We came back from Manchester during the Sunday night and just lazed about and slept all that Monday. Here's Goffo, all clean and purified. He'll tell you.'

Godfrey Tate had emerged from the bathroom, blank-faced, contained, wary, but showing no grudge against Vedast for the humiliating trick to which the singer had subjected him.

'Who's taking my name in vain?' he said with an almost pathetically unsuccessful attempt at jocularity.

'Tell the officers where I was on June sixth, Goffo.'

'With me and Nell.' He responded so promptly, so glibly, that it was evident the stating of this alibi had been rehearsed. 'We were all together in Duvette Gardens all day and all night. Nell can tell you the same. Nell!'

Wexford was sure she had been listening behind the door, for she exclaimed when her husband opened it as if she had been knocked backwards.

'Of course we were all there,' she said. She had covered herself with a long coat but she was still cold and she moved towards the window as if to close it. When Vedast, still smiling, shook his head, she sat down obediently, huddled in the coat, and at a glance from him, said, 'We didn't go out all day. We were exhausted after Manchester.' One hand went up to the sore eye, hovered and fell again into her lap.

'And now,' said the singer, 'tell the officers when you went off on your trip to see Goffo's mum.'

If Tate had had a tail, Wexford thought, he would at this point have wagged it. Rather like a performing dog who loves yet fears his master and who is utterly hypnotized by him, he sat up, raised his head eagerly.

'About a month ago, wasn't it?' prompted Vedast.

'We went on May twenty-second,' said Nell, 'and . . .'

'Came back on Wednesday, the twenty-fifth,' her husband ended for her.

Vedast looked pleased. For a moment it looked as if he would pat his dogs on their heads, but instead he smiled at Tate and blew a kiss at Tate's wife. 'You see, Chief Inspector? We lead a very quiet life. I didn't kill Dawnie out of passion, Goffo didn't kill her because I told him to – though I'm sure he would have done if I had – and Nello didn't kill her out of jealousy. So we can't help you. We've got masses of stuff from agents to look through tonight, so may we get on with our house-hunting?'

'Yes, Mr Vedast, you may, but I can't promise I shan't want to see you again.'

Vedast sprang to his feet in one supple movement. 'No, don't promise. I should love to see you again. We've had such a nice talk. We don't see many people, we have to be so careful.' Wexford's hand was cordially shaken. 'See them out, Goffo, and lock up the car.'

'I wish you good hunting, Mr Vedast,' said Wexford.

John Burden was at home and already in bed, having left a note for his father to tell him that Pat would be staying the night with her aunt. The key had been left under a flower-pot, which shocked the policeman in Burden while the father showed a fatuous pride in his son's forethought. He removed the Vedast L.P. from the turntable and closed the record player.

'One of these songs,' he said, 'is called "Whistle and I'll come to you, my love".'

'Very appropriate,' Wexford glanced at the record sleeve. 'He must have written that for the Tates' theme song.'

'My God, yes. Why do they put up with it?'

'She for love, he for money. Both for the reflected glory. He hit the nail right on the head when he said "Goffo" would have killed Dawn if he'd told him to. They'd do anything for him. "Being your slave, what should I do but tend upon the hours and times of your desire?" It's not just love and money and glory, but the power of the man's personality. It's sinister, it's most unpleasant. In a set-up of this kind that alibi goes for nothing. An alibi supported by slaves is no alibi. The Romans in their heyday were very chary about admitting slaves' evidence.'

Burden chuckled. 'I daresay you're right, Caesar. How did he know he needed an alibi for the sixth of June, anyway? We didn't tell him.'

'Mrs Stonor or Mrs Peckham may have told him. There was something about it in the papers, about our thinking that the probable date of her death. I don't really suppose he's involved at all. He likes playing with us, that's all. He likes sailing near the wind. Above all, he enjoys frightening the others.' Wexford added in the words of the Duke of Wellington: ' "By God, he frightens me!" '

CHAPTER TWELVE

The interior decorations of Leonard Dunsand's bungalow were precisely the same as those of Miss Mowler's. Identical red spotted paper covered the hall walls, identical birds and lilies pained the eye in the living room. But Miss Mowler, for all her genteel shudders at the builder's bad taste, had shown little more judgment in her own and had filled the place with garish furniture and mass-produced pictures. Dunsand's drab pieces, brown leather smoking-room chairs, late Victorian tables and, above all, shelf upon shelf of scholarly books, looked absurdly incongruous here. Little shrivelled cacti, lifeless greenish-brown pin-cushions, stood in pots on the window-sills. There was nothing in the hall but a bare mahogany table and no carpet on the floor. It was the typical home of the celibate intellectual, uncharacteristic only in that it was as clean as Mrs Peveril's and that, on a table in the living room, lay a stack of holiday brochures, their covers even more vividly coloured than the wallpaper.

Dunsand, who had just come home from work, asked them to sit down in a colourless but cultivated voice. He seemed about forty with thinning mousey hair and rubbery face whose features were too puffy for that tight mouth. Thick glasses distorted his eyes, making them appear protuberant. He wore an immaculate, extremely conventional dark suit, white shirt and dark tie. Neither obstructive nor ingratiating, he repeated what he had already told Burden, that he had reached home at about six-forty on June sixth and had noticed no unusual happenings in The Pathway during that evening.

'I prepared myself a meal,' he said, 'and then I did some housework. This place is very ugly inside but I see no reason why it should also be dirty.'

251

'Did you see anything of your neighbours?'

'I saw Mrs Peveril go down the road at half past seven. I understand she attends an evening class in some sort of handicraft.'

'You didn't go out yourself? It was a fine evening.'

'Was it?' said Dunsand politely. 'No, I didn't go out.'

'Are you on friendly terms with your neighbours, Mr Dunsand?'

'Oh, yes, very.'

'You go into their houses, for instance? They visit you?'

'No. I think I misunderstood you. I simply mean we nod to each other and say a word if we meet in the street.'

Wexford sighed to himself. He found Dunsand depressing and he pitied his students. Philosophy, he knew – although he knew little about it – is not all ethics, witty syllogisms, anecdotes about Pythagoras, but logic, abstruse mathematics, points and instants, epistemological premisses. Imagine this one holding forth for a couple of hours on Wittgenstein!

'So you can tell us nothing of Mr and Mrs Peveril's way of life, their habits, who calls on them and so on?'

'No, nothing.' Dunsand spoke in the same drab level voice, but Wexford fancied that for a brief moment he had caught a certain animation in the man's eye, a sign of life, a flash perhaps of pain. It was gone, the magnified eyes were still and staring. 'I think I can say, Chief Inspector, that I know nothing of any private life but my own.'

'And that is . . .?' Wexford said hesitantly.

'What you see.' Dunsand cleared his throat. 'Beginning to rain again,' he said. 'If you don't want to ask me anything else I'll go and put my car away.'

'Do you ever go to London, Mr Peveril?'

'Of course I do in connection with my work.' Peveril put a gloomy and irritable emphasis on the last word. He had once more been fetched from his studio and his fingers were actually inky. Wexford couldn't help feeling that the ink had been put there deliberately just as the man's hair had been purposely shaken and made to stand up in awry spikes. 'I go up occasionally, once a fortnight, once a month.'

'And stay overnight?'

'I have done.'

'When did you last go?'

'Oh God, it would have been June first, I think. I didn't stay.' Peveril glanced towards the closed door which excluded his wife. 'Scenes,' he said stiffly, 'are made if I venture to spend a night away from the matrimonial nest.' Misanthropic, his whole manner showing how distasteful he found this probing, he nevertheless was unable to resist making frank disclosures. 'You'd imagine that a woman who has everything soft and easy for her, never earned a penny since she found someone to keep her, wouldn't deny the breadwinner a few hours of freedom. But there it is. If I go to London I have to phone her when I get there and leave a number for her to call me whenever she fancies, that means about three times in one evening.'

Wexford shrugged. It was not an uncommon type of marriage that Peveril had described; he was only one of many who had elected to make the dreariest and the longest journey with a jealous foe. But why talk about it? Because it would induce his interrogator to believe that such surveillance kept him from other women? Wexford almost smiled at such naivety. He knew that good-looking, dissatisfied men of Peveril's stamp, childless men long out of love with their wives, could be Houdini-like in the facility with which they escaped from domestic bonds. He left the subject.

'Your wife went to an evening class on that Monday evening,' he said. 'Would you mind telling me what your movements were?'

'I *moved* into my studio to work and I didn't *move* out of it until my wife got back at eleven.'

'There are no buses at that time of night. She didn't take your car?'

An edge of contempt to his voice, Peveril said, 'She can't drive. She walked into Kingsmarkham and some woman gave her a lift back.'

'You didn't think of driving her, then? It was a fine evening and it isn't far.'

'Damn it all!' said Peveril, his ready temper rising. 'Why the hell should I drive her to some daft hen party where they don't learn a bloody thing? It's not as if she was going to work, going to bring in some much-needed money.' He added sullenly, 'I usually do drive her, as a matter of fact.'

'Why didn't you that night?'

'The worm turned,' said Peveril. 'That's why not. Now I'd appreciate it if you'd let me get on with my work.'

It was on the red dress that Wexford concentrated that Friday. He called a semi-informal conference consisting of himself, Burden, Dr Crocker, Sergeant Martin and Detective Polly Davies. They sat in his office, their chairs in a circle, with the dress laid on his desk. Then Wexford decided that for them all to get a better view of it while they talked, the best thing would be to hang it from the ceiling. A hanger was produced by Polly, and dress and hanger suspended from the lead of Wexford's central light.

Laboratory experts had subjected it to a thorough examination. They had found that it was made of synthetic fibre and that it had been frequently worn probably by the same person, a brown-haired, fair-skinned Caucasian. There were no sweat stains in the armpits. In the fibre had been found traces of an unidentified perfume, talcum powder, anti-perspirant and carbon tetrachloride, a cleaning fluid. Other researches showed the dress to have been manufactured some eight or nine years previously at a North London factory for distribution by a small fashion house that dealt in medium-priced clothes. It might have been bought in London, Manchester, Birmingham or a host of other towns and cities in the British Isles. No Kingsmarkham store had ever stocked the garments from this fashion house, but they were, and had for a long time been, obtainable in Brighton.

The dress itself was a dark purplish red, darker than magenta and bluer than burgundy. It had a plain round neck, three-quarter-length sleeves, a fitted waist with self belt and a skirt designed just to show the wearer's knees. This indicated that it had been bought for a woman about five feet seven inches tall, a woman who was also, but not exceptionally, slim, for it was a size twelve. On Dawn Stonor it had been a tight fit and an unfashionable length for this or any other epoch.

'Comments, please,' said Wexford. 'You first, Polly. You look as if you've got something to say.'

'Well, sir, I was just thinking that she must have looked really grotty in it.' Polly was a lively, black-haired young woman who habitually dressed in the 'dolly' mode, mini-skirts, natty waistcoats and velvet baker-boy caps. Her way of painting her mouth strawberry red and blotching two red dabs on her cheeks made her look less intelligent than she was. Now she saw from Wexford's frown that her imprecise epithet had displeased him and she corrected herself hurriedly. 'I mean, it wouldn't have suited her and she'd have looked dowdy and awful. A real freak. I know that sounds unkind – of course she looked dreadful when she was found – but what I'm trying to say is that she must have looked dreadful from the moment she put it on.'

'You'd say, would you, that the dress itself is unattractive as a garment? I'm asking you particularly, Polly, because you're a woman and more likely to see these things than we are.'

'It's hard to say, sir, when something's gone out of date. I suppose with jewellery and so forth it might have looked all right on a dark person it fitted well. It wouldn't have looked good on Dawn because she had sort of reddish-blonde hair and she must have absolutely bulged out of it. I can't think she'd ever have put it on from *choice*. And another thing, sir, you said I'm more likely to notice these things than you are, but – well, just for an experiment, could you all say what you think of it as, say, a dress you'd like your wives to wear?'

'Anything you say. Doctor?'

Crocker uncrossed his elegant legs and put his head on one side. 'It's a bit difficult,' he began, 'to separate it from the unpleasant associations it has, but I'll try. It's rather *dull*. Let me say that if my wife wore it I'd feel she wasn't letting me down in any way. I wouldn't mind who saw her in it. It's got what I believe they call an "uncluttered line" and it would show off a woman's figure in a discreet kind of way. On the other hand, supposing I was the sort of man who took other women out, I don't think I'd feel any too thrilled if my girl friend turned up to a date wearing it because it wouldn't be – well, adventurous enough.'

'Mike?'

Burden had no wife, but he had come to terms with his condition. He was able to talk of wives now without inner pain or outward embarrassment. 'I agree with the doctor that it's rather distasteful to imagine anyone close to you wearing it because of the circumstances and so on associated with it. When I make myself look at it as I might look at a dress in shop window I'd say I rather like it. No doubt, I've no idea of fashion, but I'd call it smart. If I were – er, a married man I'd like to see my wife in it.'

'Sergeant?'

'It's a smart dress, sir,' said Martin eagerly. 'My wife's got a dress rather like it and that sort of shade. I bought it for her last Christmas, chose it myself, come to that. My daughter – she's twenty-two – she says she wouldn't be seen dead in it, but you know these young girls – beg your pardon, Polly. That's a nice, smart dress, sir, or was.'

'Now for me,' said Wexford. 'I like it. It looks comfortable and practical for everyday wear. One would feel pleasantly uxorious and somehow secure sitting down in the evening with a woman in that dress. And I think it would be becoming on the right person. As the doctor says, it follows the natural lines of a woman's figure. It's not daring or dramatic or embarrassing. It's conservative. There you are, Polly. What do you make of all that?'

Polly laughed. 'It tells me more about all you than the dress,' she said pertly. 'But what it does tell me is that it's a *man's* dress, sir. I mean, it's the sort of thing a man would choose because it's figure-flattering and plain and somehow as you said, secure. Dr Crocker said he wouldn't want to see his girl friend in it. Doesn't all this mean it's a *wife's* dress chosen by a *husband* partly because he subconsciously realizes it shows she's a good little married lady and any other man seeing her in it will know she's not made of girl-friend stuff?'

'Perhaps it does,' said Wexford thoughtfully. The window was open and the dress swayed and swivelled in the breeze. Find the owner, he thought, and then I have all I need to know. 'That's intelligent of you, Polly, but where does it get us? You've convinced me it was owned at one time by a married woman who bought it to please her husband. We already know Dawn didn't own it. Its owner might have sent it to a jumble sale, given it to her cleaner or taken it to the Oxfam shop.'

'We could check with the Oxfam people here, sir.'

'Yes, Sergeant, that must be done. I believe you said, Mike, that Mrs Peveril denies ownership?'

'She may be lying. When it was shown to her I thought she was going to faint. With that stain on it it isn't a particularly attractive object and there are, as we've said, the associations. But she reacted to it very strongly. On the other hand, we know she's a nervy and hysterical woman. It could be a natural reaction.'

'Have you talked to Mrs Clarke again?'

'She says her friend had some sort of mental breakdown last year and lost a lot of weight, so it hardly looks as if she was ever slim enough to wear the dress. But Mrs Clarke has only known her four years.'

'Eight years ago,' Wexford said thoughtfully, 'the Peverils might still have been on romantic terms. He might have been choosing clothes for her that were particularly to his taste. But I agree with you that the question of size makes that unlikely. Well, I won't detain you any longer. It's a massive plan I've got in mind, but I think it's the only course to take. Somehow or other we're going to have to question every woman in Kingsmarkham and Stowerton between the ages of thirty and sixty, show them the dress and get reactions. Ask each one if it's hers or, if not, whether she's ever seen anyone else wearing it.'

His announcement was received with groans by all but the doctor, who left quickly, declaring that his presence was needed at the infirmary.

CHAPTER THIRTEEN

The response to Wexford's appeal was enormous and immediate. Women queued up outside the Baptist church hall to view the dress as they might have queued on the first day of a significant sale. Public-spirited? Wexford thought their enthusiasm sprang more from a need to seem for a little while important. People like to be caught up in the whirlwind of something sensational and they like it even more if, instead of being part of a crowd, each can for a brief moment be an individual, noticed, attended to, taken seriously. They like to leave their names and addresses, see themselves recorded. He supposed they also liked to feast their eyes on the relic of a violent act. Was it so bad if they did? Was it what the young festival visitors would have called sick? Or was it rather evidence of a strong human vitality, the curiosity that wants to see everything, know everything, be in the swim, that when refined and made scholarly, is the prerogative of the historian and the archaeologist?

He had long ago ceased to allow hope to triumph over experience. He didn't suppose that some woman would come forward and say her husband had unexpectedly and inexplicably borrowed the dress from her that Monday evening. Nor did he anticipate any dramatic scene in the hall, a wife screaming or falling into a faint because she recognized the dress and realized simultaneously what recognition implied. No woman harbouring a guilty secret would come there voluntarily. But he did hope for something. Someone would say she had seen the garment on a friend or an acquaintance; someone would admit to having possessed it and then to have given it away or sold it.

No one did. All Friday afternoon they filed along the

wooden passage that smelt of hymn books and Boy Scouts, passed into the grim brown hall to sit on the Women's Fellowship chairs and stare at the posters for coffee mornings and social evenings. Then, one by one, they went behind the screens where Martin and Polly had the dress laid out on a trestle table. One by one they came out with the baulked, rather irritable, look on their faces of do-gooders whom ill-luck had robbed of the chance to be more than negatively helpful.

'I suppose,' said Burden, 'that she could have been picked up by a man in a car. A prearranged pick-up, of course. He might have come from anywhere.'

'In that case, why take a bus to Sundays and walk across the fields? Mrs Peveril says she saw her go into those fields and her description is so accurate that I think we must believe her. Dawn may have been early for her date – that was the only bus as we've said before – gone into the fields to sit down and wait, and then doubled back. But if she did that, she didn't go far back.'

'What makes you say that?'

'Four people saw her between the time she left her mother's house and the time she went into those fields, five-thirty. We've not been able to find anyone who saw her *after* five-thirty, though God knows, we've made enough appeals and questioned enough people. Therefore it's almost certain she went into some house somewhere just after five-thirty.'

Burden frowned. 'On the Sundays estate, you mean?'

'To put it more narrowly than that, in The Pathway. The body was in the quarry, Mike. It was carried or dragged to the quarry, not transported in a car. You know what a job it was to get our own cars down there. When the gates to the drive are locked no car could get in.' Wexford glanced at his watch. 'It's five-thirty and the Olive's open. Can't we leave Martin to carry on with this and adjourn for a drink? I'd rather talk all this out sitting down over a pint.'

Burden's brow creased further and he bit his lip. 'What about Pat? She'll have to get her own tea. She'll have to walk to her dancing lesson. John'll be alone.'

In a tone that is usually described as patient but which, in fact indicates an extreme degree of controlled exasperation, Wexford said, 'He is six feet tall. He is fifteen. By the time he was that age my old dad had been out at work eighteen months. Why can't he escort his sister to her dancing class? Taking it for granted, of course, that if she walks three hundred yards alone on a bright summer evening, she's bound to be set on by kidnappers.'

'I'll phone them,' said Burden with a shamefaced grin.

The saloon bar of the Olive and Dove was almost empty, a little gloomy and uninviting as deserted low-ceilinged places always are when the sun shines brightly outside. Wexford carried their drinks into the garden where wooden tables and chairs were arranged under an arbour. Vines and clematises made a leafy roof over their heads. It was the home-going hour, the time when the peace and the quiet of this spot was usually shattered by the sound of brakes and shifting gears as traffic poured over the Kingsbrook bridge.

Today all man-made noise was drowned by the chatter of the swollen river running beside the terraced garden. It was a steady low roar, constant and unchanging, but like all natural sound it was neither tedious to the ear nor a hindrance to conversation. It was soothing. It spoke of timeless forces, pure and untameable, which in a world of ugliness and violence resisted man's indifferent toiling of the earth. Listening to it, sitting in silence, Wexford thought of that ugliness, the scheme of things in which a girl could be beaten to death, thrown into a bower which had been made and used for love, thrown like garbage.

He shivered. He could never quite get used to it, the appalling things that happened, the waste, the pointlessness. But now he had to think of practical matters, of why and how this particular ugliness had taken place, and when Burden came to the table he said:

'You've talked to the occupants of the other two houses in The Pathway and I haven't. Would you say we could exclude them?'

'The Streets are a married couple with four children, all of whom were at home with their parents the whole evening. None of them saw Dawn. Mrs Street saw Miss Mowler come home at eight o'clock. Apart from that, none of them saw any of their neighbours that evening. They heard nothing and they remained in the front of the house from about six till about ten. Mrs Street's kitchen is in the front.

'The Robinsons are elderly. He's bedridden and they have a fiercely respectable old housekeeper. Mr Robinson's bedroom overlooks Sundays but not the quarry. His wife spent the evening with him in his bedroom as she always does and went to her own room at nine-thirty. She saw and heard nothing. The housekeeper saw Dunsand come home at twenty to seven and Miss Mowler at eight. She didn't see the Peverils and she herself went to bed at ten.'

Wexford nodded. 'How about Silk?'

'Up in London from June sixth to June eighth, making last-minute festival arrangements. Says he left Sundays at about seven on the evening of the sixth.'

'Can anyone corroborate that?'

'His wife and his two grown-up children are in Italy. They've been there since the end of May and they aren't back yet. Silk says they always go abroad for two months in the summer, but it looks to me as if they aren't as keen as he on the pop scene.'

'And it's his quarry,' said Wexford thoughtfully. 'If anybody had easy access to it, he did. I imagine he's often in London, too. I don't suppose he was at school with Dawn, was he?'

'Hardly, sir,' said Burden. 'He's as old as you.' He added generously: 'And looks a good deal more.'

Wexford laughed. 'I won't bother to grow my hair, then. It doesn't seem likely that Dawn would have played around with him, and if she had done she'd have gone straight up to the house, surely, not tried to sneak round by a back way. There was no wife at Sundays for her to hide from.'

'And no possible reason for her to bring a picnic.'

'No, I think we can exclude Silk on the grounds of age and general ineligibility. That leaves us with the Peverils, Dunsand and Miss Mowler. But Peveril wasn't alone in his house at five-thirty and Miss Mowler and Dunsand weren't even at home. And yet who but the occupants of one of those three houses could have put Dawn's body in the quarry without being seen?'

Burden glanced surreptitiously at his watch, shifting uneasily. 'Then we're saying she doubled back, sir, and was admitted to one of those houses. Somebody let her in. Not Dunsand or Miss Mowler. Peveril or Mrs Peveril, then? That must mean the Peverils are in it up to their necks. In that case, why does Mrs Peveril say she saw the girl at all? Why say anything?'

'Possibly because she isn't up to her neck in it at all. Because she *did* see Dawn go into those fields and didn't know of any connection between the girl she saw and her husband. Dawn caught that bus because it was the only bus she could catch. She loitered in the fields for two hours – remember how warm and sunny it was – and returned to Peveril's house *after* Mrs Peveril had left for her class. D'you want another drink?'

'Oh, no,' said Burden quickly. 'Good heavens, no.'

'Then we may as well get back to your place. I can't stand this watch-watching.'

Outside the Baptist church the queues had lengthened. Housewives departing to prepare evening meals had been replaced by working women released from shops and offices.

'Better get something special for the children's dinner,' said conscientious Burden. 'The Luximart stays open late on Fridays. You eating with us?'

'No, thanks. My wife'll have something for me at eight.'

They went into the shop where they were immediately recognized by the manager. He insisted on pointing out to them personally items precisely similar to those Dawn had bought from the six tomatoes in a plastic-covered tray to the bottle of cheap wine. The shop was full and the manager spoke loudly as if anxious to cash in on and reap the benefits of a particularly ghoulish form of advertising.

'Tomatoes as purchased by our very own murder victim,' said Wexford disgustedly.

Burden avoided them studiously and averted his eyes from the row of strawberry mousses. 'You forgot the food in your theory,' he whispered. 'Peveril would have already eaten. His wife would have given him his dinner before she went out.' Regardless of expense, he selected three packages of *bœuf bourguignon* from the frozen-food trough. 'She meant to stay overnight too. You forgot that. Or was Peveril going to hide her in his studio when his wife got home at eleven?'

'Everything all right, sir?' said the manager. 'How about a bottle of wine to go with that?'

'No, thanks.' Burden paid and they left, their progress watched by a dozen pairs of curious eyes. The sun was still bright, the wind brisk. Martin was fixing a fresh, larger, poster of Dawn's picture to the church-hall door.

'Anything yet?' asked Wexford.

'We've had five hundred women pass through here, sir, and not one of them able to give us a bit of help.'

'Keep on at it tomorrow.'

They walked the length of the High Street and turned left into Tabard Road. Burden's step always quickened at this point. Once he had made himself aware that no fire engines or ambulances thronged the street outside his bungalow he relaxed and his breathing became more even.

'Was Peveril going to keep her hidden all night?' he said. 'Or, failing that, maybe she got into Dunsand's place through the larder window. There's an idea for you. Poor old Dunsand who has to fend for himself like me, living on frozen food he buys on his way home, no doubt. Miss Mowler must have actually known her – district nurses know everybody. Perhaps Dawn hid in her garden until eight o'clock, keeping herself from boredom by trying on a dress she found hanging in the shed?'

'I'm the one who asks the derisive questions, not you, remember? All this reversing our roles throws me off balance.' Wexford raised his eyebrows at the three bicycles leaning against Burdens' gate and the moped parked at the kerb. 'Doesn't look as if your boy's moping in solitude,' he said. 'Good thing he's been prudent and shut the windows.'

The six teenagers who were gyrating energetically in Burden's living room stopped abashed when the policemen came in, and Pat, standing by the record player, pressed the 'reject' lever. Vedast's line, 'Come once more and be my wife', groaned away on a dying fall, the last word a melancholy moan.

'Having your dancing lesson at home tonight, my dear?' said Wexford, smiling.

The two Burden children began to make hasty excuses while their friends made for the door with the silent speed that looks like treachery but is in fact the loyalty of those accustomed to parental censure and who know it is better faced without an audience. Wexford didn't think they ought to have to apologize for innocently enjoying themselves and he interrupted Burden's half-hearted reproaches.

'Play it again, will you, Pat?'

Expertly she found the right track on the L.P. without having to check with the sleeve and lowered the pick-up arm delicately.

'I don't like you doing that,' said John. 'You'll scratch it.'

'I won't. I'm more careful with records than you are. So there!' The Burden children were usually at loggerheads and seldom missed an opportunity to rile each other. 'It's a horrible song, anyway. All sloppy love stuff. Folk music ought to have some point to it and Zeno Vedast's hasn't any point at all.'

'What d'you mean by "point", Pat?'

'Well, be anti-war, Mr Wexford, or for everybody loving each other not just one stupid girl. Or anti-ugliness and mess like Betti Ho. Zeno Vedast's songs are all for him, all for self.'

Wexford listened interestedly to this but Burden said sourly, 'Everybody loving each other! You can talk.' He sniffed. 'I don't hold with all this putting the world right.'

'Then you shouldn't be a policeman,' said Wexford. 'Play it, Pat.'

The song started with a little grinding scratch which made John frown and purse his lips. Then Vedast's strings twanged and the clear, unaffected voice began to sing:

> 'I don't miss her smile or the flowers,
> I don't eclipse distance or hours . . .'

'He writes his own songs?' Wexford whispered.

'Oh, yes, always,' said John reverently. 'This one's two years old but it's his best.'

'Boring!' Pat ducked behind the player to avoid her brother's wrath.

It wasn't boring. Listening to the slight, delicate story which the verses and the chorus told, Wexford had a strong sense that the singer was relating a true experience. Suddenly the backing grew loud and Vedast's voice bitter, keening:

> 'Now she's gone in the harsh light of day,
> When she'll return the night would not say,
> And I am left to vision the time
> When once more she'll come and be mine.

So come by, come nigh,
come try and tell why
some sigh, some cry,
some lie and some di-i-ie.'

Burden broke the silence which followed. 'I'm going to get this food heated up.' He went into the kitchen but Wexford lingered.

'Does he ever write joke songs, John?'

'*Joke* songs?'

'Yes – I mean, well, they're hardly in the same class, but Haydn and Mozart sometimes wrote jokes into their music. If you're a joker in private life, joking often comes into your work as well. D'you know the Surprise Symphony?'

Pat said, 'We did it at school. There's a sort of soft gentle bit and then a big boom that makes us jump.'

Wexford nodded. 'I wondered if Vedast . . .'

'Some of them are a bit like that,' said John. 'Sudden loud bits or a funny change of key. And all his songs are supposed to be somebody's story or to have a special meaning for a friend.' He added eagerly: 'I'll play you some more, shall I?'

'Not now.' Burden came back to lay the table. Pat tried to take the knives and forks out of his hand, but the daughter who had been admonished for showing insufficient love must not be allowed to show it now by helping her father. He kept his hold on the cutlery and shook his head with rather a martyred air. 'Ready in five minutes. You'd better wash your hands and sit up at the table.'

Wexford followed him into the kitchen.

'I've learnt some interesting facts about our slave-driver. I wonder how long he's staying in this neck of the woods?'

'John says indefinitely. You don't really think he had anything to do with all this?'

Wexford shrugged. 'He intrigues me. I can't do what Scott advises and stop mine ear against the singer. His song

267

is beginning to haunt me. I think I'll buy a single of it tomorrow.'

Burden switched off the oven. 'We might play it over and over in your office,' he said sarcastically. 'Get a couple of the W.P.C.s in and dance. Have ourselves a rave-up. There won't be anything else to do if no one's identified that dress.'

'There will be for me,' said Wexford, taking his leave. 'I'm going to London to have another talk with Joan Miall.'

CHAPTER FOURTEEN

Wexford bought a local paper to read in the train. The *Kingsmarkham Courier* came out on a Friday and Dawn's body had been found on the previous Monday, so that news was stale even by local standards. Harry Wild, the chief reporter, had made what he could of it by giving headline publicity to Wexford's appeals in connection with the red dress, but by far the greater part of the front page was devoted to Zeno Vedast. A large photograph, taken by a not very expert *Courier* staff man, showed the singer and the Tates leaning against the bonnet of the golden Rolls. Nell was smiling serenely, one hand caressing the lion ornament. Wild had married his two lead stories by including his caption to the picture a frank confession from Vedast that he had been at school with Dawn Stonor. Reading it, Wexford felt even more convinced that Vedast could not be involved in Dawn's death, that he had nothing to hide. But why then was he staying on in Cheriton Forest, staying even though, as the caption stated, he had found and started negotiations for the house he intended to buy? Could it be that he was staying to see the case through, to await the outcome?

Joan Miall's flat was on the second floor of a tall shabby house between the Earls Court Road and Warwick Road. It wasn't a shabby flat, but smartly and even adventurously decorated, the ceilings painted in bold dark colours to reduce their height. A close observer could tell that the furniture was mostly secondhand, but the girls had re-covered the armchairs, put new pictures in old frames and filled the shelves with brightly jacketed paperbacks. There were a great many plants, fresh and green from recent watering.

She received him without pomp, without preparation. She

wore red trousers, a red spotted smock and no make-up. A big old vacuum cleaner, cast off perhaps by some more affluent relative, was plugged in just inside the front door. He had heard its whine die away when he rang the bell.

She was expecting him and she put on a kettle to make coffee. 'I miss Dawn,' she said. 'Especially round about lunch-time. We were almost always together then. I keep expecting to hear her call out from her bedroom that she's dying for a cup of coffee. Oh, "dying" – the expressions one uses! But she often said she was dying. Dying of boredom, dying for a drink.'

'I know so little about her. If I knew more, I might know how and why. You see, Miss Miall, there are two kinds of murder victim, those who are killed by a stranger for gain or for some obscure pathological reason, and those who are killed by someone who is not a stranger, someone who might be or have been a friend. It is in those cases that it's invaluable to know as much as may be known about the character and the tastes and the peculiarities of the victim.'

'Yes, I do see. Of course I do.' She paused, frowning. 'But people are little worlds, aren't they? There's so much in everyone, depths, and layers, strange countries if we're talking about worlds. I might just be showing you the wrong country.'

It took her a little while to get the coffee. She was a faddist, he remembered. He heard and smelt her grinding coffee beans – nothing pre-ground out of a packet for her – and when she came in with the tray he saw that the coffee was in an earthenware jug. But as soon as she sat down she lit a cigarette and she sighed with a kind of relief as she exhaled. It recalled to him her words about the strange countries in each person's make-up. She hadn't mentioned the inconsistencies which those who delve into character must encounter as bafflingly as the unknown.

'Did you both work every night at the Townsman?' he began.

'It's more complicated than that. We do lunches as well.

Members can lunch between twelve and three, so we either work an eleven till five shift or one from seven at night to two in the morning. If you do the night shift, you can be sure you won't have to do the lunchtime one next day, but otherwise it's rather haphazard. We get two full days off a week, not necessarily Saturday and Sunday, of course. Dawn and I often worked the same shift, but just as often we didn't. There were lots and lots of times when she was alone here seeing people and getting calls I knew nothing about.'

'You knew about the one particular call you told me of.'

'Yes,' she said, 'I've thought a lot about that since then, trying to sort it all out, and I've remembered all sorts of things I didn't tell you. But the things I've remembered aren't helpful. They really only prove it *wasn't* Zeno Vedast who phoned her.'

'I'd like to hear them just the same.'

'I forgot to tell you that his name came up long before the phone call. It must have been in March or April. Of course, we'd see him on TV or read about him in the papers and she'd say she'd known him for years, but she never actually spoke of him as a friend she *saw*. Then one morning – I think it was the end of March – she said he'd been in the club the night before. I hadn't been working that night and, frankly, I didn't believe her. I knew he wasn't a member. I asked one of the other girls and she said Zeno Vedast had been in and had sort of chatted Dawn up a bit. I still wasn't convinced and I'm not now – about the friendship. I mean. We get a lot of celebrities in the club and they do chat us up. That's what we're there for.'

'When did the phone call come, Miss Miall?'

'It was a Monday.' She frowned, concentrating. 'Dawn had had the day off, I'd been working the lunchtime shift. Let me see – it wasn't the last Monday in May. I think it must have been May twenty-third, about half past eight in the evening. We were sitting in here by ourselves, watching television. The phone rang and Dawn answered it. She said hallo and then

271

something like, 'How super of you to phone me.' She covered up the mouthpiece and whispered to me to turn down the TV. Then she said, "It's Zeno Vedast." I was embarrassed. I thought she must be in a really neurotic state if she was prepared to fantasize that far.'

Wexford accepted a second cup of coffee. 'Miss Miall, suppose I told you that Vedast did recognize her in the club, that it was he who phoned that night, what would you say to that?'

'That I knew her and you didn't,' the girl said obstinately. 'He was in the club all right. I know that. He talked to her. A maharajah talked to me for half an hour one night but that doesn't make us lifelong friends. I'll tell you why I'm sure it wasn't Zeno Vedast who phoned. When some celebrity really took notice of Dawn – a film star paying her attention at the club, say – she'd be full of it for days. When it was just make-believe – or let-me-believe like in his song – when she saw someone she said she knew in a photograph or on the TV, she'd comment on it, sort of reminisce a bit, and then forget all about it. After that phone call she wasn't a bit elated. She just said, "I told you I knew him," and then she was quite gloomy, the way she was after she'd had a nasty letter from her mother or some man had stood her up.'

'Who did you think had phoned her then?'

'Some new man she'd met,' Joan Miall said firmly. 'Someone who was attracted to her but who wasn't rich enough or well known enough to be worth bragging about.' A shade of sadness crossed her pretty face. 'Dawn was getting a bit old for our kind of work and she didn't wear well. I know that sounds ridiculous. She was only twenty-eight. But it bothered her a lot, knowing she'd be past it in a couple of years. She'd have had to get a different job or – marry Paul. She was desperate to make everyone believe she was as attractive as ever and to her way of thinking you measure attractiveness by the number of successful men who want to take you out.'

Wexford sighed. When you are twenty-five, thirty seems old. That was all right, that was natural. But surely when you are forty, thirty ought to seem young? It sickened him that this girl and her dead friend had moved in a world where to a man of fifty a girl of twenty-eight was getting 'past it'.

'This new man,' he said, 'you've no foundation for believing in his existence? Nothing to make you think he existed but a phone call which I tell you Vedast himself made?'

'Yes, I have. She went out with him the following week.'

'Miss Miall,' Wexford said rather severely, 'you should have told me of this before. Is this one of the "unhelpful" things you've remembered?'

'One of the things that prove it wasn't Vedast, yes. But I don't know his name. I don't even know if he wasn't another of Dawn's dreams.'

There was a framed photograph on the mantelpiece, an enlarged snapshot of a dark young man and a girl on a beach somewhere. Wexford picked up the picture and scrutinized it.

'That's Paul,' said Joan Miall.

It took him a few moments to realize that the girl was Dawn. In shorts and a shirt, her hair wind-blown, she looked quite different from the painted, overdressed creature whose portrait on posters was stuck up all over Kingsmarkham like a cabaret star's publicity. At last, he thought, she had achieved a kind of fame. Though posthumously, she had got herself into the public eye. But she looked happier in the snapshot. No, happy wasn't the right word – content, rather, tranquil, and perhaps just a tiny bit bored?

There had been no ecstasy, no excitement, in being on a beach with her ordinary fiancé. Mrs Stonor had seen to that. By belittling her daughter, by comparing her unfavourably to others, by denying her love, she had so warped her personality that everyday affection meant nothing to her. Dawn understood love only when it came from and was directed to money

273

and success, the love of a man who would make her rich and get her name in the papers. Well, some man had got her name in the papers . . .

'Go on, Miss Miall,' said Wexford, laying the photograph down.

'The day I'm going to tell you about was June first. It was a Wednesday and it was Paul's birthday.'

The date meant something to Wexford. He nodded, listening alertly.

'On the Tuesday, the day before, Dawn and I had both had our day off. She went out in the afternoon and bought the blue dress, the one she wore to go and see her mother. I remember I asked her if she'd bought it to take away on holiday with Paul. Well, she said she couldn't make up her mind whether she was going away with Paul or not but she wouldn't say why not, only that it might be boring. They hadn't quarrelled. Paul spent the evening with us and stayed the night with Dawn. They seemed very happy.'

'Let's come to June first.'

'Paul went off to work before we were up. He was going to come back for a birthday lunch Dawn was giving him and then take the afternoon off. Dawn and I were both due to work the evening shift. She went out to buy food for lunch, steak and salad – I insisted on fresh stuff – and after she came back, while she was laying the table, the phone rang. I answered it and a man's voice asked to speak to Dawn. I didn't ask who it was and he didn't say. I gave the phone to Dawn and I didn't stay to hear what she said. I went on with preparing the lunch. She came back into the kitchen and she was very flushed and excited-looking but a bit – well, narked too. I'm explaining this badly but I do remember just what she was like. She was excited and yet she was upset. I could see she didn't want to say who had rung her so I didn't ask.'

'Did you ever find out?'

'No, I didn't. But there's more to come. Paul was expected at half past one. By about a quarter to twelve everything was ready for lunch. We just had to grill the steaks when Paul came. Dawn was already dressed and made-up, but at twelve she went away and changed and when she came out of her bedroom she was wearing her new dress and she'd done her hair on top of her head and put on a lot more eye make-up. In fact, she'd overdone the whole thing and she was wearing far too much perfume. I was sitting in here reading a magazine. She came in and said, "I've got to go out for an hour or so. If Paul gets here before I'm back you can tell him some tale. Say I forgot the wine or something." Well, as I said, we didn't ask each other questions. I wasn't too thrilled about lying to Paul. The wine was already on the table so I couldn't say that. I just hoped she wouldn't be long.'

'Was she?' Wexford asked.

'She went out at sometime between twelve and half past. Paul was a bit late. He got here at twenty to two and still she wasn't back. I told him she had some last-minute shopping, but I could see he was hurt. After all, it was his birthday and they were more or less engaged.'

'When did she come back?'

'Ten past three. I remember the time exactly because when she came in I realized she must have been in a pub and they close at three. She'd had too much to drink, anyway. Her face was all puffy and her speech wasn't quite clear. Paul's a very good-tempered bloke but he was nearly doing his nut by this time.'

'Where did she say she'd been?'

'She said she'd met a girl who used to work in the club and was now a model – poor Dawn could never resist the fame and glamour bit – and they'd gone into a pub and forgotten the time talking.'

'You didn't believe her?'

'Of course I didn't. Later on, after Paul had gone Dawn

wrote to her mother to say she'd go and see her on the following Monday.'

'You didn't connect the pub visit with the letter?'

'I didn't at the time,' the girl said thoughtfully, 'but I do now. You see, it was very unlike Dawn to make up her mind about anything to do with her mother on the spur of the moment. She knew she had to go to Kingsmarkham sometimes but usually she'd start sort of arguing with herself about it weeks beforehand. You know, saying she'd have to go but she didn't want to and maybe she could let it ride for a few more weeks. Then she'd write a letter and tear it up and sort of swear about it. It'd take her weeks to get a letter actually written and posted. But it didn't this time. She sat down and dashed it off.'

Wexford said, 'Did she ever mention what happened on June first again?'

She nodded, looking unhappy. 'On the Saturday, the first day of her holiday. She said, "What would you think of a bloke who said he was dying to see you and the best date he could fix up was a few drinks in a pub at lunchtime?" She went to that mirror over there and put her face right close up to it, staring at herself and pulling the skin under her eyes. "If you were really crazy about a man," she said, "you wouldn't care, would you? You'd just want his company. You wouldn't worry if he was too scared or too mean to take you to a hotel for the night." I didn't really know whether she was referring to me or herself. I thought she might be talking about me because my boy friend is poor. Then Paul came and took her out and I gathered she meant to go away on holiday with him.'

Joan Miall sighed. She reached for a fresh cigarette but the packet was empty. The air in the room was blue with hanging smoke. Wexford thanked her and went away. In the Earls Court Road he went into a record shop and bought a single of 'Let-me-believe'.

CHAPTER FIFTEEN

The red dress was back in Wexford's office. Several thousand women had looked at it, handled it, backed away from the dark stain; not one had recognized it. It lay on the rosewood surface, on the wood whose colour matched it, an old shabby dress, folded, soiled, keeping its secret as implacably as ever.

Wexford touched it, glanced again at the label and at the whitish talc marks around the neckline. Dawn had worn it but she had never owned it. She had found it in Kingsmarkham and for some unfathomable reason had put it on, she who had been fashion-conscious and who was already dressed in garments which matched her shoes and her bag. She had found it in Kingsmarkham, but, unless deception had been practised, no Kingsmarkham or Stowerton woman had ever owned it. A woman never forgets any dress she has owned, not even if fifty years have elapsed between her discarding of it and her being confronted with it again, much less if only seven or eight years have passed.

Burden came into the office, glanced at Wexford, glared at the dress as if to say, Why bother with it? Why let it keep confusing us, holding us up? Aloud he said, 'How did you get on with the Miall girl?'

'It looks as if Dawn had another man friend. Mike, I'm wondering if it could have been Peveril. He was in London on June first, and on that day Dawn met a man for a drink. She went out to meet someone in an underhand way when she had a pretty pressing engagement at home. Now that date took place only five days before the day she died.'

'Go on,' said Burden, interested.

'Dawn was in Kingsmarkham at Easter. The Peverils were already living in The Pathway at Easter. Suppose Peveril

RUTH RENDELL

picked her up somewhere in Kingsmarkham, had a drink with
her, got her to give him her phone number?'

'Didn't he ever phone her?'

'According to Joan Miall, Dawn had a rather mysterious
phone call from a man on Monday, May twenty-third. That
could have been Peveril. His wife goes out on Monday evenings and that would have given him his opportunity.'

'Sounds promising.'

'Unfortunately, it isn't. We know Zeno Vedast phoned
Dawn about that time. He says he did, and Dawn told Joan
Miall it was he as soon as she answered the phone. Joan didn't
believe her because afterwards she wasn't elated or excited.
But, on his own admission, Vedast put her off with vague
promises. Dawn wasn't a fool. She could tell he was bored
and that rocked her so much that she couldn't even bring
herself to brag about knowing him any more or weave any of
her usual fantasies. Therefore, I think we must conclude that
it was Vedast who phoned her that night and that Vedast had
no further communication with her. He's out of it. But that
doesn't mean Peveril didn't phone her. He could easily have
done so on some occasion when Joan wasn't there.

'During the weekend following her pub date, the weekend
preceding her death, she gave Joan to understand that she was
embarking on an affair with a man too mean or too scared
to take her to an hotel. That description would fit Edward
Peveril, a man who owned a house from which his wife would
be absent for several hours on a Monday evening; Edward
Peveril who came out to us while we were at the festival and
tried to distract our attention from the quarry as soon as he
knew who we were; Edward Peveril who no longer cares for
his wife and who, on Miss Mowler's evidence, is occasionally
unfaithful to her.'

Burden pondered. 'What do you think happened that
night, then?'

'Whatever happened, Mrs Peveril must know of it.'

278

'You don't mean connived at it, sir?'

'Not beforehand, certainly. She may have been suspicious beforehand. Don't forget that she told us it was a matter of chance that she was in the house at all at five-thirty. Her *husband* had tried to persuade her to go to a film in Kingsmarkham that afternoon and stay on for her evening class. Why didn't she do that? Because she was suspicious of his motives? Confident that he could persuade her, he asked Dawn to bring with her a meal for the two of them. But Mrs Peveril didn't go out. She saw Dawn at five-thirty, the actual time of the appointment, *and Dawn saw her.* Therefore, carrying her bag of food, she waited in those fields until she saw Margaret Peveril go out.

'Dawn was then admitted by Peveril. She began to prepare the food, changing into an old dress Peveril gave her so as not to spoil the mauve thing. Before the meal was ready, she asked Peveril if it would be all right for her to stay the night as he, knowing this couldn't be but using any inducements to get Dawn to come, had previously promised. When he told her that idea was off, they quarrelled, she threatening to stay and confront his wife. He killed her in a panic.'

Burden said, 'But when Mrs Peveril came home he threw himself on her mercy. She was needed to help him clean up and dispose of the body.'

'I don't know, Mike. I haven't great confidence in this theory. Why did Mrs Peveril mention having seen the girl at all if it's true? I can't get a warrant on this evidence but tomorrow I'm going to ask Peveril's permission to search. Tomorrow's Sunday and it's your day off.'

'Oh, I'll come,' said Burden.

'No. Have your Sunday with the kids. If we find anything I'll let you know at once.'

Wexford allowed his glance to fall once more on the dress, caught now in a ray of evening sunshine which touched it like a stage spotlight. He tried to imagine Margaret Peveril slender, rejuvenated, but he could only see her as she was, bigger and fleshier than Dawn, a woman whose whole build showed that she could never, since her teens, have worn that dress. He shrugged.

He didn't attempt to get a search warrant. With Martin and three constables, he went to The Pathway in the morning, a misty, cool morning such as heralds a fine day. The sunshine hung like a sheet of gold satin under a fine tulle veil.

Muttering and pleading that his work would be disturbed, Peveril agreed without much protest to his house being searched. Wexford was disappointed. He had expected the man to put up a front of aggressive opposition. They lifted the fitted carpets, scrutinized skirting boards, examined the hems of curtains. Mrs Peveril watched them, biting her nails. This ultimate desecration of her home had driven her into a kind of fugue, a total withdrawal into apathy and silence. Her husband sat in his studio, surrounded by men crawling on the floor and peering under cabinets; he doodled on his drawing board, making meaningless sketches which could not, under any circumstances, have been saleable.

Miss Mowler, returning home from church, came up to Wexford at the gate and asked if the men would like tea. Wexford refused. He noticed, not for the first time, how the churchgoing woman who might conveniently carry a prayer book in her handbag, always holds it ostentatiously in her hands, an outward and visible sign of spiritual superiority. Dunsand was mowing his lawn, emptying the cuttings into a spruce little green wheelbarrow. Wexford went back into the house. Presently he looked out of the window and, to his astonishment, saw Louis Mbowele approaching, his coat swinging open to allow the soft summer air to fan his brown, bead-hung chest. Louis went into Dunsand's garden, the mowing was abandoned and the two men entered the bungalow. Not so very astonishing, after all. Wexford remembered that

Louis was a philosophy student at Myringham where Dunsand taught philosophy.

'How are you doing?' he said to Martin.

'She wasn't killed here, sir. Unless it was in the bathroom. I reckon you could stick a pig in that bathroom and not leave a trace.'

'We may as well get out then. This is supposed to be a day of rest and I'm going home.'

'Just one thing, sir. Young Stevens asked me if you'd see him before he goes off duty. He's at the station. He mentioned it last night but what with all this it went out of my head. He's got something on his mind but he won't tell me what.'

The house was restored to order. Wexford apologized sparingly to Mrs Peveril.

'I told you she didn't come here,' she said with a cowed resentful look. 'I told you she went right away from here. She went across the fields.'

Wexford got into the car beside Martin. 'I wish she wouldn't keep saying that, you know, gratuitously, as it were.' He slammed the door. Martin listened politely as he was obliged to do, his mind on his Sunday dinner which would probably be spoilt by now, anyway. 'Why does she say it if it isn't true?' said Wexford.

'Maybe it is true, sir.'

'Then why didn't anyone else see her after five-thirty? Think of all those blokes coming home for their dinners at Sundays and in Stowerton around six. They'd have seen her. She was the kind of girl men notice.'

The mention of dinner made Sergeant Martin even more obtuse than usual. 'Maybe she sat in the fields for hours, sir, sat there till it was dark.'

'Oh God!' Wexford roared. 'If she was going to have to hang about for hours she'd have stayed at her mother's or if that was unbearable, gone to the pictures in Kingsmarkham.'

'But the last bus, sir?'

RUTH RENDELL

'It's less than a mile, man. She was a strong healthy girl. Wouldn't she have walked it later rather than sit about in a field?'

'Then Mrs Peveril never saw her.'

'Oh, yes, she did. She observed her closely, every detail of her appearance.'

The car drew up and the two men got out, Martin to depart for a long and well-deserved dinner, Wexford to see Stevens who was already waiting for him in his office. The shy and inarticulate young policeman stood to attention rigidly which made Wexford even crosser and also made him want to laugh. He told the man to sit down and Stevens did so, less at ease in a chair than stiffly on his feet.

Wexford didn't laugh. He said quite gently, 'We do have a welfare officer, Stevens, if the men have some domestic or private problem that's interfering with their work.'

'But it's work that's interfering with my work, sir,' Stevens stuttered.

'I don't know what you mean.'

The man swallowed. 'Sir.' He stopped. He said it again. 'Sir,' and then, rushing, the words tumbling out, 'Mrs Peveril, sir, I've wanted to tell you for days. I didn't think it was for me to put myself forward. I didn't know what to do.'

'If you know something about Mrs Peveril that I ought to know, you must tell me at once. You know that, Stevens. Now come on, pull yourself together.'

'Sir, I was transferred here from Brighton last year.' He waited for Wexford's nod of encouragement which came with brisk impatience. 'There was a bank robbery, sir, last summer. Mrs Peveril saw the raid and she – she came to the police voluntarily to give evidence. The superintendent interviewed her a lot, sir, and she had to try to identify the villains. We never caught them.'

'You recognized her? Her name? Her face?'

'Her face, sir, and then when I heard her name I remembered. She knew me too. She was very hysterical, sir, a bad witness, kept saying it was all making her ill. I've had it on my conscience all week and then I kept thinking, well, so what? She didn't hold up the bank clerk. And then it got so I thought – well, I had to tell you, sir.'

'Stevens,' sighed Wexford, 'you've got a lot to learn. Never mind, you've told me at last. Go away and have your dinner. I'll check all this with Brighton.'

He began to have an inkling of what had happened. But he must check before going back to The Pathway. There wasn't going to be any Sunday dinner for him.

The Peverils were just finishing theirs. It struck Wexford that this was the first time he had encountered Peveril not working or coming straight from his work or fidgeting to get back to it.

'What is it this time?' he said, looking up from roast beef and Yorkshire pudding.

'I'm sorry to disturb your lunch, Mr Peveril. I want to talk to your wife.'

Peveril promptly picked up his plate, tucked his napkin into the neck of his sweater and, having paused to grab the mustard pot, was making for the door to his studio.

'Don't leave me, Edward!' said his wife in the thin, high-pitched voice which, if it were louder, would be a scream. 'You never give me any support, you never have done. I shall be ill again. I can't bear being questioned. I'm frightened.'

'You're always bloody frightened. Don't hang on me.' He pushed her away. 'Can't you see I've got a plate in my hand?'

'Edward, can't you see, he's going to make me say who did it! He's going to make me pick someone out!'

'Mrs Peveril, sit down. Please sit down. I'd be glad if you wouldn't go away, sir. I don't think it's for me to interfere between husband and wife but, if I may say so, Mrs Peveril might not be quite so frightened if you'd try to give her the support she wants. Please, sir, do as I ask.'

Wexford's tone had been very stern and commanding. It was effective. Bullies crumple fast when sharply admonished, and Peveril, though he moved no closer to his wife and did not look at her, sat down, put his plate on the edge of the table and folded his arms sullenly. Mrs Peveril crept towards him and hesitated, biting her thumbnail. She gave Wexford the half-sly, half-desperate look of the hysteric who is trying to preserve intact the thickly packed layers of neurosis.

'Now will you both listen quietly to what I have to say?' He waited. Neither spoke. 'Mrs Peveril, let me tell you what I think happened. In Brighton you witnessed a bank robbery.' Her eyes opened wide. She gave a little chattering murmur. 'That was a most upsetting experience for you, but you very properly came forward to give information to the police. You were a key witness. Naturally, the police questioned you exhaustively. You fancied yourself badgered and you became frightened, ill perhaps with fright, both from the constant visits of the police and from a notion that some revenge might be taken against you for the information you had given. You moved here to get away from that. Am I right?'

Mrs Peveril said nothing. Her husband, who never missed a cue, said, 'Sure, you're right. Never mind where I had my roots, my contacts, my ideal studio. Madam wanted to run away so we ran away.'

'Please, Mr Peveril.' Wexford turned to the woman, sensing that he must be very careful, very gentle. Her stillness, the compulsive nail biting, the hard set furrows in her face, were ominous. 'You had only been here a few months when you realized, because of what you had seen, that you might soon be involved in another and perhaps more disturbing criminal case. Mrs Peveril, we know you saw Dawn Stonor on Monday, June sixth. You gave an accurate description of her, more precise than any other we have. I suggest to you – please don't be alarmed – that you either admitted her to this house or saw her enter another house. You told us you saw her cross

the fields because you believed that would be the surest way
to draw our attention, the attention you find so frightening,
away from you and your own neighbourhood.'

It might have been all right. She took her hand from her
mouth and bit her lip. She made a little preparatory murmur.
It would have been all right if Peveril hadn't started to his
feet and shouted at her, 'Christ, is that true? You bloody fool!
I thought there was something fishy, I knew it. You told lies
to the police and nearly landed me right in it. My God!'

She began to scream. 'I never saw her at all! I never saw
her!' A slap on the face would have been effective. Instead,
her husband began shaking her so that the screams came out
in stifled strangled gasps. She crumpled and fell on the floor.
Peveril took a step backwards, white-faced.

'Get Miss Mowler,' snapped Wexford.

By the time he returned with the nurse, Mrs Peveril was
lying back in a chair, moaning softly. Miss Mowler gave her
a bracing, toothy smile.

'We'll get you to bed, dear, and then I'll make you a nice
strong cup of tea.'

Mrs Peveril cringed away from her. 'Go away. I don't want
you. I want Edward.'

'All right, dear. Just as you like. Edward can get you to
bed while I make the tea.'

At the use of his Christian name Peveril frowned ferocious-
ly, but he gave an arm to his wife and helped her up the
stairs. Miss Mowler bustled about, removing plates of congeal-
ing food, boiling a kettle, hunting for aspirins. A little thin
woman, she was quick in her movements and efficient. She
talked all the time she worked, apologizing for non-existent
faults. What a pity she hadn't been on the spot when 'it'
happened. If only she had been in her garden, for instance.
How unfortunate that, what with one thing and another, she
had had to wash her hands and take off her overall before
accompanying Mr Peveril to the house. Wexford said very

little. He was thinking that he would be lucky to get any more out of Mrs Peveril that day.

The tea was taken up. Peveril didn't reappear. Wexford followed Miss Mowler back into her own bungalow where newspapers were spread over the hall carpet and a kind of late spring cleaning seemed to be in progress.

'I spilt a cup of cocoa down the wall. It's a blessing this paper's washable. I don't know what you must think of me, washing walls on a Sunday afternoon.'

'The better the day, the better the deed,' said Wexford politely. 'I want to have another look at the quarry, Miss Mowler. May I make my way there through your garden?'

He was permitted to do so but only after he had refused pressing offers of tea and coffee, sherry, a sandwich. Miss Mowler, having been assured that he didn't need her to accompany him down the path and open the gate for him, returned to her work. He let himself out of the garden and into the narrow no man's land that separated the estate from Sundays.

CHAPTER SIXTEEN

Heavy rains had fallen and now the sun had returned as bright and hot as ever. But it was too soon yet for new grass to show, too soon for even the beginnings of the green carpet which by autumn would once more cover the desert plain which Sundays park had become. Wexford sat down on the edge of the quarry. Here nature was winning, for the flowers and shrubs, the delicate yet lush herbage of June, had been assailed by only half a dozen trampling feet. New roses, new harebells, were opening to replace the crushed blossoms. He looked at the broken wire, the wall, the three gates, but they told him nothing more, and gradually the scented air, sunwarmed and soft, drove thoughts of the case from his mind. A butterfly, a Clouded Yellow, drifted languidly past him and alighted on a rose, its petals paler and creamier than the buttercup-coloured wings. Not so many butterflies these days as when he was a child, not so many as when even his daughters were children. Under his breath he caught himself humming a tune. At first he thought it was that song of Vedast's which stuck in his mind and irritated him. Then he realized it wasn't that one but a ballad of Betti Ho's in which she prophesied that her children would never see a butterfly except in a museum. The Clouded Yellow took to the air again, hovering, floating ...

'You're trespassing!'

Wexford started to his feet, shaking himself out of his dream.

'You're trespassing,' said Silk again, half-serious, half-peevishly ironic. 'I don't see why I should always have the fuzz trampling over my land.'

Looking up into the irritable white face and the smiling black one, Wexford said, 'I'm not trampling. I was sitting and thinking. What are you two up to? Planning another festival?'

'No, we're going to try and get a commune going here during the university vacation. Louis and I and his girl friend and about half a dozen others. Louis wants to see how it works out with a view to operating a kibbutz system in Marumi.'

'Really?' said Wexford blankly. He didn't see how gathering together a house party in a fully-equipped and furnished mansion could be a rehearsal for kibbutzim in an equatorial state, but he didn't say so. 'Well, I think I'll trample off now.'

'So will I,' said Louis unexpectedly. He gave his radiant grin and patted Silk on the grey head which reached just to his shoulder. 'Peace be with you.'

They skirted the Peverils' fence and emerged at the head of The Pathway. Mrs Peveril's bedroom curtains were drawn. Dunsand was pulling puny little weeds out of his flowerless borders. Beside Miss Mowler's car a bucket of soapy water stood unattended. It was hot, sunny, a radiant day. The English do not relax in deck-chairs in their front gardens and, apart from the crouching figure of the philosophy lecturer, the place was deserted. Louis waved graciously to him.

'Want a lift into Kingsmarkham?'

'Thanks,' Louis said. 'That way I might get the three-thirty bus to Myringham.'

Wexford's car was a fair-sized one, but no car except perhaps Vedast's Rolls would have been roomy enough to accommodate Louis Mbowele comfortably. Laughing, he hunched himself inside the folds of his pony-skin and slid the passenger seat back to its fullest extent.

Wexford said, 'When you get to the top of wherever it is you're going, are you going to *make* them live in communes?'

'It's the only way of life, man.'

'And force them to be equal and dictate the pattern of their houses and the subjects of their study and operate a censorship and forbid other political parties?'

'For a time, for a time. It's necessary. They have to learn. When they see it all works and the new generation's grown

up and we have peace and full bellies, then we can start to
relax. It's necessary to make them do what they aren't just too
crazy to do right now. So you have to make them for their
own good.'

'Do you know a saying of James Boswell? "We have no
right to make people happy against their will"?'

Louis nodded, smiling no longer.

'I know it, man, and I know the connection in which it
was said. The slave trade. The traders excused themselves on
the ground that my people would be happier on plantations
than in jungles. This is different. This is for real. And it's only
for a time.'

'Oh, Louis,' said Wexford, turning into the Forby road,
'that's what they all say.'

They drove into Kingsmarkham in silence. The heat of the
day, his failure to get anywhere, enervated Wexford. There
seemed nothing else to do with his afternoon but go home,
eat his stale lunch, maybe sleep. Then, as they approached
the place where the Myringham bus stopped, he became aware
of the long silence and wondered if he had offended the young
African. Louis looked as if he would have a hearty appetite,
and the Olive and Dove did a good Sunday lunch. . . .

'Have you eaten?' he said.

'Sure. I cadged some bread and cheese off Len.'

'Mr Dunsand? Why did you have to cadge? Isn't he very
hospitable?'

Louis grinned. Evidently, he hadn't been offended, only
sleepy from the sun. 'He's a recluse,' he said. 'He finds it hard
to communicate. Still, I took him out to lunch a while back
in Myringham – last Wednesday fortnight it was – so I guess
he owed me a meal. I asked him to join our commune but
he's not together enough for that.'

'Strange. You'd think a lecturer in philosophy would . . .'

'Have found the way? Found himself?' Louis leapt out of
the car and strode round to open Wexford's door. 'That's a

289

popular misconception, man. It's living – a broad spectrum of living – that teaches you how to live, not philosophy. Philosophy teaches you how to *think*.'

The bus was late. Louis, scorning to join the queue, sat down on the steps of the Snowdrop Cleaners, and Wexford, leaving the car at the kerb, followed him.

'How do you get on with him?'

Louis considered. The dozen or so people in the queue bestowed upon him glances of intense, if repressed, curiosity. Few black-skinned men and women had penetrated to this country town, and to them his coat, his beads and the green silk scarf he wore round his head – although no more than fashionable 'gear' for black and white alike – perhaps appeared as tribal paraphernalia. He returned their looks with the gracious smile of a prince, a tawny Rasselas, and said to Wexford:

'He's all right as a teacher, he knows his subject. But he doesn't seem to like people. You see, he's afraid of them.'

'What else is there to be afraid of?' asked Wexford to whom this idea, in all its truth, had come suddenly as if out of the air. 'Except, maybe, thunderstorms, floods, what insurance companies call Acts of God. If you say you're afraid of bombs or war, it's people who make the bombs and the war.'

'You're right. But, oh, man, there are a lot of people and they are frightening. And it's worse when one of the people you're frightened of is yourself.' Louis gazed into the heart of the afternoon sun. 'Someone told me he was better when his wife lived with him. He used to go away on holidays then, the Majorca bit, the Costa Brava scramble. He doesn't do anything now but read and paint the house. and mow the lawn. But you can't picture him married to *her*, can you?' Louis got up, thrust out his hand. 'Here's the bus.'

'Picture her? I don't know her. Do you?'

Extending one huge furry arm to support her, Louis helped a fragile-looking old lady on to the bus platform. In the manner of one whose girlhood dreams have at last been realized and who has fallen into the hands of a sheikh, she blushed, giggled and almost panicked. The other passengers stared and whispered.

'Come along now,' said the driver. 'We haven't got all day.'

Louis grinned. Head and shoulders above the rest, he gave his fare, looking over a diminutive woman's hat at Wexford.

'I don't know her. Old Silk told me who she was at the festival, pointed her out while Zeno Vedast was singing. Man, you stood next to her.'

'I did?'

The bus started.

'Peace be with you,' Louis shouted.

'And with you,' said Wexford.

The golden car wasn't there. Perhaps it had been silly of him to think it would be. On such a fine afternoon they would all have gone out to see the house Vedast was buying. On the almost bare forecourt, blanched ashen pale by hard sunlight, his own car looked forlorn. The Cheriton Forest Hotel seemed asleep. But the porter who had admired Nell Tate was awake. He sat in the deserted hall, reading the *Sunday Express* and smoking a cigarette which he stubbed out quickly when Wexford appeared.

'I'm afraid not, sir,' he said in answer to the chief inspector's enquiry. 'Mr Vedast and Mrs Tate went out in Mr Vedast's car after lunch.'

'You don't know when they'll be back?'

Memories of fifty-pence pieces easily earned stirred in the porter's mind. He was obviously reluctant to deny Wexford anything. 'Mr Tate took his coffee out into the garden, sir. Would you care for me to . . .?'

'No, I'll find him myself.'

'As you like sir,' said the man, philosophically contemplating the smaller coin his efforts had won him.

Wexford strolled round the gabled, studded, mullioned and heavily rose-hung building. There was nobody about. Birds sang sleepily in the deciduous trees which bordered the fir plantations. He reached the back and saw the elderly couple with whom he had shared the Shakespeare Lounge snoring in long chairs on the terrace. A gravel path wound between rosebeds to a small round lawn in the middle of which was an umbrella with a table and chair under it. A man sat in the chair, his back to the terrace. The porter, a tactful servant, had described Tate as taking his coffee in the garden and there was certainly a diminutive cup on the table beside him. But what Tate was taking was brandy. An eager hand had just grasped the bottle of Courvoisier and was about to tip a further measure into the already half-full glass.

'Good afternoon, Mr Tate.'

If Wexford had hoped to make Tate jump he was disappointed. The man didn't get up. He filled his glass, replaced the bottle top and said, 'Hallo. Have a drink.'

Wexford remembered that he was driving, that he had had no lunch, and he refused. 'I'd like to talk to you. D'you mind if I fetch myself a chair?'

'No,' said Tate economically.

Wexford fetched himself a deck-chair and drew it under the umbrella's shade. Tate didn't say anything. His face quite blank, he contemplated the view of the hilly forest, lying black and furry-looking, and a smooth blue sky. He wasn't in the least drunk. Alcoholics never get drunk. Wexford thought that this was probably Tate's misfortune, that he had drunk so much and drunk so chronically that, perpetually intoxicated, he could never now enjoy the felicity of what most people call intoxication. His skin was a rough greyish red, his eyeballs veined with red, their rims vermilion and moist. And yet he was a young man still, unlined, thin, not bad-looking, his hair untouched by grey.

'Mr Tate, I really wanted to talk to your wife.'

'She's gone out with Zeno to see the new house.'

As he had thought. 'So Mr Vedast found one to his liking?'

Tate agreed that this was so. He sipped his brandy. 'It's called Cheriton Hall.'

'Ah, yes. I think I know it. On the Pomfret side of the forest. Will you all live there?'

'We go where Zeno goes.'

Guessing, hoping, very much in the dark, Wexford essayed, 'Your wife won't find it awkward living so comparatively close to her ex-husband?'

The unhealthy colour in Tate's face deepened, the grey overpowering the red. He made no answer but he fixed on Wexford a truculent and rather puzzled stare.

'I'm right in thinking your wife was once married to Mr Dunsand?' Tate shrugged. The shrug implied an indifference to Wexford's opinions rather than a doubt as to their veracity. 'For the past week,' Wexford went on, 'I've been trying to discover a connection between Dawn Stonor and some resident of the Sundays estate, especially of The Pathway. Until now I've been unable to succeed.'

'Small world,' said Tate uneasily.

'Is it? I think it's an enormous world. I think it's extraordinary that Dawn should have last been seen alive in The Pathway where Mrs Tate's ex-husband lives. I think particularly odd now that I know Dawn was once a close friend of Zeno Vedast who is now a – er, close friend of your wife's. And yet I'm to dismiss it as being due to the smallness-of the world.'

Tate shrugged again. 'Zeno and Nell and me were all in Duvette Gardens that night you're talking about.' He put Vedast's name before his wife's, Wexford noticed. 'We were all together and that guy Silk looked in about ten to talk about the festival.' Morosely, he said, 'We've never been near that place.'

'Surely you were when you were at the festival, very near? Didn't your wife point Mr Dunsand's house out to you?'

It was a trap and the slow-witted Tate fell into it. 'She said, that's Len's house, yes.'

Wexford pounced. 'So she knew it? He'd only lived there a matter of weeks but she knew it. Not by the street name and the number. She knew it by the look of it!'

'I shouldn't like to have your job, meddling in people's private affairs.'

'And I shouldn't like to have yours, Mr Tate,' said Wexford crisply. He leant across the table, forcing the other man to look at him. 'Whose wife is she, yours or that singer you fawn on? Yours or the man who divorced her? What sort of a set-up are you running here? Or do you do just what you're told, lie, pimp, connive at obstructing the police, anything he and she tell you?'

There was too little of one kind of spirit in Tate and too much of the other for him to react violently to these insults. He passed a hand across bleary eyes as if his head ached and said in a sour cowed voice, 'Christ, how you do go on! Never you mind my wife. I can deal with her.'

'By blacking her eye?'

'She told you? I bet she didn't tell you why.'

'I think it was because you found out she'd been seeing Dunsand. At the festival when she pointed out his house you put two and two together. You didn't mind about Vedast, that was different. Maybe you found she'd got a key to his house so you had it out with her and blacked her eye.'

Tate half-smiled. It was the smile of one who is accustomed to subservience to a superior intellect, a smile of grudging admiration. He took something out of his trouser pocket and laid it on the table. A key.

'I found it in her handbag. It'll be safer with you. She might get it away from me and use it again.' He got up abruptly, took his bottle and walked very carefully and steadily up the terrace steps and into the hotel.

Wexford pocketed the key. He tiptoed past the old couple, made his way through a cool and shadowy corridor to the front entrance. Then, seeing the golden car had arrived, he slipped back into the porch and waited.

Nell and Zeno Vedast got out. The swelling had gone down from the girl's eye and her painted face was almost serene. Her hair, freshly washed, was a yellow cloud but the bright light showed darker roots. Vedast, wearing jeans and a thin embroidered waistcoat, took a springy stride towards Wexford's car and stood contemplating it, smiling, his head on one side. His face wore very much the expression Wexford had seen there just before Tate drank the doctored liquor, and he heard him say:

'That parking ticket we got, shall we put it on his windscreen?'

'What's the point?' said Nell.

'Fun is the point, Nello darling. A joke. He'll twig it in two seconds but think how mad he'll be first. Go and get it, Nello. It's on the back seat.'

She opened the rear door of the Rolls. Hypnotized by him, obedient as ever, she gave him the ticket. But as he was lifting one of the wipers she broke out:

'I'm sick of jokes. Why can't we grow up, do things for real? I hate always playing games.'

'Do you really, Nello? You are a funny girl.' Vedast clipped the ticket under the wiper and laughed. He shook back his hair and his yellow eyes glowed. 'I don't believe you. I think you liked all that funny dressing up and pretending to be good and making cosy little plans.' He took her hand, kissed her cheek lightly. 'That's why we get on so well, dear, you and me with our little fantasies. Shall we go and rouse Goffo from his Sunday stupor?'

She nodded, clutching his arm. They went off towards the rose garden. When they had disappeared around the side of the hotel Wexford emerged thoughtfully. Having a strong objection to the scattering of litter, he placed the parking ticket under the paws of the golden lion and then he drove away.

CHAPTER SEVENTEEN

Some little good had come out of Mrs Peveril's hysterical breakdown. The information she was now willing to give was imparted too late to be of much use – Wexford knew it already, or most of it – but her despair had shocked her husband into anxiety for her.

He said soberly, 'You were pretty decent, very patient actually. I never realized what a bad state she'd got herself into. Will she have to appear in court?'

'I don't know, Mr Peveril. I still don't quite know what she did see. I must have a final word with her.'

'If she does have to I'll be there. She won't mind so much if I'm with her. The fact is I've been too wrapped up in my work. I let her face all that business in Brighton alone and it was too much for her. When this is over I'm going to scrape up the cash and take her away for a good holiday.'

The uxoriousness wouldn't last, Wexford knew that. Such a *volte-face* often takes place at crises in a marriage but it is only in romances that it becomes a permanency.

And Peveril revealed just how ephemeral it was when, as they went upstairs to see his wife, he muttered, 'You have to bloody wet-nurse some women all their lives, don't you? If I'm not wanted for the next half-hour I may as well catch up on a spot of work.'

Mrs Peveril, wan-looking but calm, sat up in bed wrapped in a jaded broderie anglais dressing gown.

'It was like you said,' she admitted. 'I wanted to make you all think she'd gone a long, long way from here. I wanted to be left in peace. When I first saw her I meant to tell Edward what I'd seen but I didn't because he gets cross with me if I gossip. He says he works for me all day and all I've got to do with myself is look out of the window and tell stories about the neighbours.' She sighed heavily. 'Then when Mrs Clarke phoned me on that Sunday night and said you were coming round asking, I thought I'd say she'd gone into the fields. If I'd said she'd gone next door you'd never have left me alone. I thought saying I hadn't seen her at all would be perjury.'

Wexford shook his head. It was quite useless to point out to her that what she had said was equally perjury.

'You saw her go next door to Mr Dunsand's? At what time?'

'At half past five. I did say,' said Mrs Peveril, eagerly attempting to retrieve her integrity, 'I saw her at five-thirty. I watched her. I saw her go into the porch and someone must have let her in because she never came out again.' Prevarication at an end now, Mrs Peveril was cheerfully burning her boats, gabbling out belated information. Wexford knew she was speaking the truth. 'I was very interested. You see, I couldn't think who she could be. Mr Dunsand never has any visitors except sometimes his students.'

'Never?' Wexford asked quickly.

She said ingenuously, 'Oh, no, I should have noticed. I spend a lot of time at my window when Edward's in his studio and you can see everything these light evenings, can't you? That's why I was so *intrigued* by this girl.' Fear touched her afresh and the wan look returned. 'You'll protect me, won't you? I mean, when I've been to the court and said how Mr Dunsand did it you won't let me come to any harm?'

'When you have been to the court and told the truth, Mrs Peveril,' Wexford corrected her, 'we'll see that you're quite safe.'

With a passing, thoughtful glance at Dunsand's bungalow, its windows closed against the midsummer evening, Wexford drove to Tabard Road. He found Burden and the children in the garden and for once there was no music playing. Burden was too respectable and had far too much social conscience

297

to allow record players or transistors out of doors. The boy and girl sat at a wicker table, arguing and making some pretence of doing their homework. John, who was always pleased to see the chief inspector whom he regarded as an ally and friend of oppressed youth, fetched him a chair and said:

'Could you give me a bit of help, Mr Wexford? I've got to do an essay on the French Revolution, and Dad's no use. He's not educated.'

'Really!' spluttered Burden. 'Don't be so rude.'

His son ignored him. 'I've left my book at school and I can't remember the new names the Convention gave to the months. I'll have to know them and I thought . . .'

'I'll try.' Wexford hesitated. 'We're in *Messidor* now, that's June. You're supposed to start with September. Let's see . . . *Vendemiaire, Brumaire, Frimaire; Nivose, Pluviose, Ventose;* then *Germinal* like Zola's book, *Floreal* and *Prairial; Messidor, Thermidor* and – wait . . .'

'*Fructidor!*' exclaimed John.

Wexford chuckled. 'You might care to know the contemporary and rather scathing English translation: Wheezy, Sneezy, Freezy; Slippy, Drippy, Nippy; Showery, Flowery, Bowery; Wheaty, Heaty, Sweety. There, you can put that in your essay and maybe you'll get an A.' He cut short the boy's thanks and said, 'One good turn deserves another. Now I want a bit of help from you.'

'*Me?*'

'Mm-hm. About Zeno Vedast. Or, more precisely, about Godfrey Tate. You must know something about him. You told your father who his wife was.'

'I read about it,' John said, 'in the *Musical Express*. Anything about Zeno's news, you see.' He put down his pen and flashed a look of triumph at his father. 'What d'you want to know, Mr Wexford?'

'Anything about Zeno. What you read.'

'Zeno ran her over in his car . . .'

'He *what* . . . ?'

'It was like this. He went to Myringham to give a concert – it was sponsored by that Mr Silk, Silk Enterprises – and there was a big crowd outside the theatre afterwards and she got in front of his car and got hurt. It said in the paper that Silk Enterprises paid for a private room in the hospital for her and sent her flowers and fruit and things. I expect Zeno thought that would be good publicity, don't you? It was about two years ago, maybe three. Dad,' said John resentfully, 'won't let me save copies of old magazines. He says it's hoarding. She was married to someone else, then. I think he was called Dunn, something like Dunn.'

'Go on.'

'When she got married again it was in the papers because Zeno was at the wedding and Mr Silk. I expect she'd rather have married Zeno.'

'I daresay she would, John, but he wouldn't have her so she took the next best thing. Catch as catch can.'

'Good heavens,' said Burden crossly, 'must you fill him up with these cynical views of life?'

Wexford winked indiscreetly at the boy and for the time being said no more. He was thinking of the bald story he had been told and, more particularly, of the gaps in it which only an older person with experience of life could fill. Nell was still young. She must have been very young when she first married Dunsand. He wondered what had led to that illassorted marriage, what had made her choose the reserved, repressed lecturer for a husband. An unhappy home life like Dawn Stonor's? The need to escape from some dreary backwater? If this were so, it must have been a case of out of the frying pan into the fire. He pictured her among the faculty wives, decades her senior, the long evenings at home with Dunsand, the leather chairs, Wittgenstein, the lawnmowing . . . Still a teenager at heart, she must have longed for younger people, for music, for excitement. And yet there was in her the stuff that makes a slave. Had she also been Dunsand's slave? Perhaps. But she had escaped – into a glamorous, eventful, luxurious life that was nonetheless slavery. About two years ago, at the time the song was written.

> 'So come by, come nigh,
>   come try and tell why
>   some sigh, some cry,
>   some lie and some die.'

He had sung it aloud and the others were staring at him. Pat giggled.

John said, 'Very groovey, Mr Wexford.'

In the same parlance Wexford said, 'I shouldn't make much bread that way, John. Apart from not being able to sing, I don't have the figure for it.' He raised his heavy body out of the chair and said rather sharply to the inspector, 'Come into the house.'

'First thing tomorrow,' Wexford said, 'I want you to swear out a warrant to search Dunsand's house.'

'What, another fruitless search?'

'Maybe it won't be fruitless.'

Burden took Pat's ballet shoes off the seat of one chair and John's tennis racket off another. 'On what evidence, for God's sake?'

'If Mrs Peveril has any value as a witness at all, Dawn Stonor went to Dunsand's house. She was last seen going to his house and she was never seen coming out of it, never seen again. I would calculate that it's a shorter distance from his back fence to the quarry than from any other back fence. She was killed in that house, Mike.'

'Will you ask Dunsand's consent first?'

'Yes, but he'll refuse. At least, I think so. I shall also ask him not to go to work tomorrow. They come down this week, so he can't have anything very pressing to do.'

Burden looked bewildered. 'You were just as sure it happened in Peveril's house, sir. Are you saying she knew Dunsand, that it was Dunsand she met in that pub on June first?'

'No. I know it wasn't. Dunsand was in Myringham on June first. Louis Mbowele told me that.'

'And Dunsand can't have let her in on that Monday. He wasn't there at five-thirty. We're as certain as can be she didn't know Dunsand. Can you imagine him picking a girl up, asking her to come to his house?'

'You must remember that Dunsand isn't the only person who could have let her in. Nell Tate had a key.'

'She used to go and see her ex-husband?' Burden asked doubtfully.

'I should think not,' Wexford rejoined slowly. 'Mrs Peveril would have seen her if she had been and Mrs Peveril never saw her. Perhaps he sent her the key in the hope that she would visit him. The fact remains that she had a key and she could have been in Dunsand's house by five-thirty. Did you ever check on that Duvette Gardens alibi?'

Burden looked a little offended. He was conscientious, proud of his thoroughness. 'Of course I did. Although, there didn't seem much point when you got so interested in Peveril. I got the Met. on it.'

'And?'

'Vedast's car was stuck outside all day and all night, gathering his usual parking tickets. Nobody seems to have a clue whether they were inside the house. One of them may not have been. We just can't tell.'

Wexford nodded. 'The Tates would lie themselves black in the face to protect their master and he'd lie to protect his little ones. I think he cares a good deal more for "Goffo" than for "Nello", though, don't you? I wish I could see a motive. One might suggest that Nell was jealous of Dawn's relationship with Zeno Vedast, only there wasn't a relationship any more. Vedast might have had a date to meet Dawn somewhere in the neighbourhood and Nell found out about it and lured her into the house to kill her. D'you fancy that idea?'

'Of course I don't.'

'Tate might have fallen in love with Dawn when they met at the Townsman Club and got the key from his wife to use Dunsand's house for a love nest. Then Vedast killed her to prevent her spoiling their jolly little *tria juncta in uno*. Does that suit you better?'

'Well, I suppose anything's possible with people of their sort.'

'Sure it is. Nell arranged to meet Dawn there because she had Dunsand's loneliness on her conscience. She thought Dawn might make him a suitable second wife – no less suitable than his first, at any rate – but when Dawn had confessed that Vedast had phoned her, shown interest in her, Nell got into a rage. She would, of course, have instructed Dawn to bring with her a second-hand red dress because Dunsand likes second-hand clothes, red is his favourite colour, and he prefers dresses to be a tight fit.'

Burden said distantly, 'I don't see the point of all this, sir. Aren't you rather arguing with yourself? It's you who want to search the place, not I.'

'I expect I am, Mike,' said Wexford. 'I haven't an idea how it happened, but two things I'm certain of. We shall find traces of blood in Dunsand's house tomorrow, and Dunsand will confess to having killed Dawn Stonor from the chivalrous motive of protecting his former and still much-loved wife. It's going to be a heavy day so I think I'll be off home now.'

CHAPTER EIGHTEEN

While they ransacked the bungalow, Wexford sat with Dunsand in the sombre living room. The search warrant had been shown to him and he had read it carefully, scrupulously, in total silence. He lifted his shoulders, nodded and followed Wexford into the living room, pausing at the window to pick a dead flower off one of the dehydrated cacti. Then he sat down and began to leaf through one of the travel brochures in the manner of a patient in a doctor's waiting room. The light fell on his glasses, turning them into gleaming opaque ovals. His eyes were invisible, his thick mouth closed and set, so that his whole face was expressionless. But as he turned the pages and came to one on which some words had been pencilled in the margin, there came suddenly a tightening of those rubbery cheek muscles that was like a wince.

'Your wife had a key to this house, Mr Dunsand.'

He looked up. 'Yes. I sent it to her. But she's my wife no longer.'

'I beg your pardon. We believe she or a friend of hers was here on June sixth.'

'No,' he said. 'Oh no.'

Wexford thought he had closed his eyes, although he could not be sure. He was aware of a terrible stillness in the room, a profound silence, which the movements in the hall and overhead accentuated rather than disturbed. Dunsand was not in the least like Godfrey Tate to look at or in manner, yet they shared this strange reticence. Both Nell Tate's husbands possessed the rare quality of being able to answer a searching question with a straight yes or no. Had she chosen them for this or had she made them so? Had she chosen them at all?

The man Wexford could be sure she had chosen was chatty, verbose, an extrovert whom some would call charming.

He tried again. 'Do you ever see your former wife?'

'No.'

'Never, Mr Dunsand?'

'Not now. I shall never see her again now.'

'You're aware that she's staying at the Cheriton Forest Hotel?'

'Yes. I saw it in the paper, a picture of her with a lot of flowers. She used to fill the house with flowers.' He glanced at the moribund cacti and then he picked up his brochure again. Underneath it on the pile was a pamphlet advertising dishwashers and another for garden equipment. 'I'd rather not talk any more now, if you don't mind.' He added curiously, 'I'm not obliged to say anything, am I?'

Wexford left him and went into one of the bedrooms. Bryant, Gates and Loring were crawling about, examining the carpet.

'Are there any women's clothes in the wardrobes?'

'No, sir, and there's no blood. We've done the whole place. This is the last room. We've even been up in the loft.'

'I heard you. Contents of the refrigerator?'

'It's empty. He's been defrosting it. He's very houseproud, sir. If you're thinking of that food she bought, the dustbins have been emptied twice since June sixth.'

Aghast, suddenly weary, Wexford said, 'I *know* she was killed here!'

'The hall floor's bitumastic, sir, the kind of stuff that's poured on as liquid and then left to set. There are no joins. I suppose we could get it taken up. We could have the tiles off the bathroom walls.'

Wexford went back into the room where Dunsand was. He cleared his throat and then found he was at a loss for words. His eyes met not Dunsand's own but the thick baffling glass which shielded them. Dunsand got up and handed him two identical keys.

'One of these,' he said in a calm, neutral voice, 'is mine. The other I sent to my former wife and she returned it to me by post.' Wexford looked at the keys, the first of which was scraped and scarred from daily use, the second scarcely marked. 'Mrs Tate,' said Dunsand with awful precision, 'was never here. I should like to make a point of that.' Things were happening, Wexford thought, at least to some extent according to the pattern he had forecast. Dunsand swallowed, looked down at the floor. 'I found the girl here when I got home on June sixth. She must have got in by the window. The kitchen fanlight had been left unfastened. I encountered her as soon as I let myself in. She was giving the place what I think thieves call a "going over". We struggled and I – killed her. I hit her with a bottle of wine she had left on the hall table.'

'Mr Dunsand . . .' Wexford began almost despairingly.

'No, wait. Let me finish. She had brought some things with her, apart from the wine, some shopping in a bag and some clothes. Perhaps she thought my house was empty and she meant to camp there – "squat" is the word, isn't it? After it got dark I put her body in the quarry and the other things into the river under the bridge. Then I washed the floor and the walls.' Staring at Wexford, he said abruptly, 'Aren't you going to caution me? Shouldn't there be witnesses to take all this down?'

'This confession – you insist on making it?'

'Of course. It's true. I killed her. I knew it was only a matter of time before you arrested me.' He took off his glasses and rubbed them against his sleeve. His naked eyes were frightening. There was something terrible yet indefinable in their depths, a light that told perhaps of passion, of single-minded fanaticism under that flaccid exterior. He was used to teaching, to instructing. Now, in a teacher's voice, he proceeded to direct Wexford.

'The proper thing, I think, will be for me to go to the police station and make a statement.' He put on his glasses, wiped a beading of sweat from above his left eyebrow. 'I could go in my own car or accompany you if you think that wiser. I'm quite ready.'

'Well, you were right,' said Burden in grudging admiration.

'Only up to a point. We didn't find a trace of blood.'

'He must be a nut or a saint, taking that on himself to shield a woman like Nell Tate.' Burden began to pace the office, growing vehement. 'That statement he made, it doesn't even remotely fit the facts. For one thing, Dawn was let into the house. She didn't go round the back. And for another, why should she suppose Dunsand's house to have been empty – I mean, unoccupied? If she had, she wouldn't have camped there on her own. She had a home to go to. Can you see Dunsand beating a woman to death because he suspected her of breaking into his house? Crocker said her killer was mad with rage, in a frenzy. That phlegmatic character in a frenzy?'

'He and Tate,' said Wexford, 'are apparently both phlegmatic characters. They are still waters which not only run deep but which may have turbulent undercurrents. Strange, isn't it? Dunsand hasn't asked for a lawyer, hasn't put up the least resistance. He's behaved almost fatalistically. That woman breaks the men she doesn't want but can't scratch the surface of the man she does want.'

Burden shook his head impatiently. 'What do we do now? What next?'

'Go back to Dunsand's place, I suppose. Have another look round and experiment with those keys a bit.'

Bright noon in The Pathway, the hottest day yet of a summer that promised to be all halcyon. The sun had brought into blossom tiny pink flowers on the plants in Miss Mowler's garden. In the meadows in the crook of the armshaped road they were cutting hay, cropping flowers far more lush and vigorous than those man had planted. The crude pink of Dunsand's bungalow was blanched to a rosy pallor by the hard hot light.

Wexford went up to the front door and tried Dunsand's keys. Both worked. The third key, the one Tate had given him, looked different, and by now he was sure it wouldn't move the lock. It didn't.

'It's a much older key than the others,' said Burden. 'What's Tate playing at?'

'Let's go inside.'

The whole house had been searched, but for evidence of a crime, not for clues to a life. Wexford remembered how Dunsand had planned to redecorate the place. He held on to that, certain it must have some significance. In a week's time perhaps that ugly wallpaper, those wriggling black stems, those golden flowers, would have been removed. Dunsand would have stripped it down, replaced it. But Dunsand had confessed . . .

Reticently, disliking the job, he went into the living room where the cacti were, where Dunsand had sat, blindly studying his brochures, and opened the desk. He found no letters, only bills; no marriage certificates, no album of photographs. But in a small drawer under the roll-top he discovered Dunsand's address book, a brown leather-covered book very sparing of entries. A London phone number was recorded under the letter T, just a number followed by a dash and the name Helen. Wexford noted the code and thought it might probably be Vedast's. He looked under S and under D but found no reference to Dawn Stonor.

It was at this point that it occurred to him how she, the dead, she whose death was the cause of this enquiry, had for some days past seemed to fade from its screen. It was as if she, as a real person, a personality, had lost her importance, and that he was searching for the answer to some other puzzle in the ramifications of which her death had been almost incidental. And he saw her – vividly but briefly – as a pawn, a used creature, her life blundering across other, brighter lives, falling through folly and vanity into death.

But the vision went, leaving him no wiser, and he thrust his hands once more into the pigeon-holes of the desk. A bunch of photographs came to light at last. They were in an envelope stuffed into a slot at the side of the roll-top interior, and they were mostly snapshots of Dunsand, much younger, with people who were evidently his parents, but underneath them were two much larger shots which Wexford took to the window. The strong light showed him first a wedding photograph, Dunsand still young, Dunsand smiling down without reserve at his bride in her badly fitting wedding dress, her veil wind-blown, young bony hands clutching a tight posy of rosebuds. Unless he had been twice married, the bride must be Nell. Time and art had changed her so much in the intervening years – eight? ten? – since the picture was taken as to make her scarcely recognisable as its subject. Her hair was dark, cropped short, her face fresh and childlike. But it was she. The big yearning eyes were unchanged and the short upper lip, showing even in those days its petulant curl.

He brought out the other photograph, the last one, from under it. Nell again, Nell fractionally older, her hair still short and feathery, her skin apparently innocent of make-up. The portrait was coloured, tinted in the shades of old china, rose and sepia and ice-blue and plum red. Nell's new wedding ring gleamed brassily against the dull red stuff of her dress, and on the simple bodice, just below the round neckline, hung a pearl drop on a gold chain.

Wexford went ponderously out into the hall.

CHAPTER NINETEEN

On all-fours Burden was examining the floor and the hideous shiny wallpaper with its pattern of little gold flowers and tiny, regularly recurring crimson leaves, wallpaper which met a floor that curved up to join it without any intervening skirting board.

'Get up, Mike. It's useless. We've done all that already.'

'One must do something,' said Burden irritably. He got up and brushed his hands against each other. 'What's the matter? You've found something!'

'This.'

'It's the dress! But who's the girl?'

'Nell Tate.'

Burden stared incredulously at the portrait. Then he put it beside the wedding picture, nodded, looked up at the chief inspector. 'I like her better how she was,' he said quietly.

'So would most men, but maybe she doesn't know that.' Wexford slipped the two photographs back into the envelope. 'Mike, I've a curious feeling I'm losing touch with Dawn Stonor, that she's fading away from me and I'm coming to grips with something stranger, something almost more terrible than her actual death. There must be many murder victims,' he said slowly, 'who meet their deaths without knowing in the least why they are to die.'

'Most of them, I should think. Victims of poisoners, old shopkeepers who know the till's empty, all children.'

'She wasn't a child,' said Wexford. 'Perhaps your list isn't completely comprehensive. I don't know, Mike. I'm only dreaming, not really getting anywhere. This is a gloomy place, isn't it? The windows are huge and yet the light doesn't seem to get in. Of course, it's an illusion, it's something to do with the dulling, deadening influence of the man's personality.'

They moved back into the living room where the books frowned on the blue birds and the orange lilies that covered the walls.

Burden said, 'We're getting too dreamlike for me. I'd be happier if I could understand about the keys, if I could see how Dawn got in here.'

'Someone let her in. Someone asked her to come and that someone was here to let her in when she arrived at five-thirty. Not Dunsand.'

'But he cleared up the mess. He was left to dispose of the body he found when he got home.'

'I suppose so. You talk about mess, Mike. What mess? Where is it? Where are the traces of it? Is the killer the one killer we've ever come across who can commit a crime as bloody as this one and leave no blood? I don't believe it.'

'This place will have to be taken apart,' Burden said, crossing the passage and entering the bathroom. 'If it was done without leaving any apparent trace it must have been done in here.' He looked at the gleaming taps, the spotless bath and basin. The sunlight showed no film of dust on glass, no fingermarks on mirrors.

Wexford nodded. 'Yes,' he said, 'the tiles off, the pipes out. And if that yields nothing, the same with the kitchen.'

'Dunsand may crack. He may tell us what at the moment he's doing his utmost to conceal.'

'If he has anything to conceal.'

'Come on, sir. He must know more than he's told us. He must know why his wife would kill an unknown girl in his house, how it happened, the circumstances. He must know that.'

'I wonder?' said Wexford. 'Does he know any more than that his wife – the woman he still thinks of as his wife – may be in danger? I believe he knows very little, Mike, as little of the whole of it as the girl who died.'

Wexford stared up at the ceiling, scanned the smooth glossy walls. The whole place smelt soapy, too clean.

'Mind you don't trip,' said Burden. 'Your shoelace is undone. It's no good looking up there. It's no use looking at all. If she was killed here, someone worked a miracle of butchery.'

Wexford stooped down to re-tie the lace. A bright circle of gold, a little sunbeam refracted through a pane, had lighted on the wall beside his left leg. He stared at the trembling illumination. The gold flowers occurred on the paper in vertical lines about two inches apart, a thin black stripe dividing each line from the next, and the red leaves, pear-shaped, were printed in clusters of three between each flower. Flower, cluster, flower, followed each other immaculately and evenly to meet the bitumastic ridge. There were signs of faint blurring on the pattern, the result perhaps of washing the paper, but nothing had been obliterated. Three leaves, flower, three leaves . . .

'Mike,' he said in a strange voice, 'your sight's better than mine. Have a look at this.'

'I looked before and you stopped me. It's been washed. So what?'

'You were looking for signs of washing, maybe for a missing bit of the pattern. Look again.'

Impatiently Burden got to his knees. He concentrated on the puddle of light.

'Not a missing leaf,' said Wexford. 'In the lowest cluster there aren't three leaves but four.'

They squatted down side by side and examined the hall paper.

'You see,' Wexford said excitedly, 'in this one and this one, in all of them, there are three little pear-shaped leaves like the leaves in a fleur-de-lis. But in the one we're looking at there's a fourth leaf under the centre one.'

'And it's not quite the same colour. It's darker, it's browner.'

'It's blood,' said Wexford, and he added wonderingly, 'One little spot of blood.'

'Shall I . . . ?'

'No, don't touch it. The experts can come here, get their sample themselves. It's too precious for us to mess about with. Mike, d'you realize that's the one real piece of evidence we've got?'

'If it's blood, if it's hers.'

'I know it's hers. It has to be.'

They went outside where the sun blazed on the road, melting tar and creating, where concrete ended and fields began, a mirage like a veil of shimmering water. The car was oven-hot inside, its seats burning to the touch. Burden rolled down his window and drove in his shirt sleeves.

'Now to check the key,' said Wexford.

'Which one, sir? The one that didn't fit?'

'Yes. I think we'll find a door that it will open.' Sweating profusely, Wexford pulled down the eyeshade across the windscreen. 'But that's a simple job, a job for Martin.'

'I'm not with you,' said Burden, falling into line behind the bus that, with its load of Sundays estate passengers, made its way along the sunny road to Kingsmarkham. 'I haven't a clue what particular door you expect it to unlock.'

Wexford smiled. 'A lot of doors are beginning to unlock inside my head, Mike, but this one, this actual door, is in Myringham. It's the door to the house Dunsand lived in before he moved here.'

The afternoon wore on and the heat seemed to mount, reaching the eighties by four o'clock. Wexford shut himself up in his office, the windows open, the blinds down. He sat alone, waiting, thinking, and then, on the principle that it is better to shut away a problem whose answer continually eludes one, to exclude it and return to it later, he resumed work on that crime-prevention directive which had laid unattended since before the festival.

The reports began to come in. The blood was human and of Dawn Stonor's group. The key which Tate had given him in the hotel garden opened the door of Leonard Dunsand's former home in Myringham. But at Sundays, where questioning of housewives had continued all the afternoon, no one had been found to say that she had ever seen Nell Tate, much less observed her call at Dunsand's house.

The five-twelve bus stopped outside the Baptist church. Wexford watched the passengers get on it. A girl came out of the Luximart, carrying a brown paper bag. She wasn't wearing mauve, she wasn't in the least like Dawn, and she was going to her new house at Sundays, not to her death. Wexford phoned the Cheriton Forest Hotel. Yes, Mr Vedast was still there. Mr Vedast planned to leave that evening. The receptionist couldn't say any more, perhaps, if Wexford was the press, she had said too much already . . .

He turned the sheets of the crime-prevention directive face downwards. He returned to his problem as the day began to cool and the sun's rays slanted. At seven he went across the road to the Carousel café where he found Burden and his children eating steak and salad while Emmanuel Ellerman's hit song 'High Tide' brayed at them from wall speakers.

'Pity you've eaten,' said Wexford. 'I was going to take you out to dinner at the Cheriton Forest.' He ordered a sandwich. 'We shall have to be content to take our coffee with Zeno Vedast instead.'

'I don't suppose . . .' began John wistfully.

'I'm afraid you can't come, John. This is a serious visit, an official visit.'

'Pat and I were going to hang about in the High Street to see him pass though. He's going back to London tonight.'

'I don't think he'll be going just yet,' said Wexford.

CHAPTER TWENTY

The receptionist put a call through to the Elizabethan Suite. 'Mr Vedast says will you wait, please? Mr Vedast is engaged at present.' She was young, the right age to be among Vedast's adorers. 'If you'd care to go into the Shakespeare Lounge, it's over there on the . . .'

'We know the way,' said Wexford.

There was no one in the lounge but the dog. It got up when they came in, stared at them morosely, then collapsed again some two yards from where it had previously been lying.

'I'm in the dark,' said Burden, impatiently rejecting the magazines Wexford passed to him. 'I think you ought to tell me why we're here.'

'Why are we ever anywhere?' Wexford sighed. 'To ask, to deduce, to conclude and to catch. Only it's a little different this time.'

'Oh, riddles, philosophy. What I want to know is . . .'

'Wait.'

Godfrey Tate had come very quietly into the room, Godfrey Tate in his usual dapper black that made his torso look as thin as a teenager's and his limbs spidery.

'Zeno's got that guy Silk with him,' he said, without greeting, without preamble. 'He says to ask you what you want.'

Wexford said quietly, 'I want to tell him what I think of him.'

Tate was bemused with drink, not 'high' on alcohol, but low, dulled, cut off, almost somnambulistic. 'Do I tell him that?'

'Mr Tate, it's a matter of indifference to me what you tell him. Why is Silk here?'

314

'He'd heard Dunsand's been arrested. He came to tell Nell.'

'And now you're celebrating?'

Tate blinked at him. He turned, shuffled towards the door.

'See you,' said Wexford, looking at his watch, 'in ten minutes.'

But before the ten minutes were up – minutes in which Burden had picked up magazine after magazine, discarding them all, and Wexford had sat still, watching the hall – Martin Silk emerged from the lift. Long hair on the elderly makes its wearer look like a nineteenth-century statesman, but in Silk's case the resemblance ended at his neck. He wore a white tee-shirt with a bunch of grapes appliquéd on the chest. As he passed the reception desk he swaggered like a proud adolescent, thrusting his hips forward, but as he neared the lounge door he began to scuttle, an old man getting away from trouble.

'Mr Silk!'

Silk stopped and forced a broad smile, creasing his face into a thousand wrinkles, enclosing his eyes in cracked parchment skin.

'I hope we haven't driven you away,' said Wexford. 'You're welcome to stay as far as we're concerned.'

Sidling into the lounge, Silk perched himself on the arm of a chair. His knee joint cracked as he swung one leg.

'Merely a social call,' he said. 'I dropped by to tell Zeno there's quite a crowd waiting in Kingsmarkham to give him a send-off. Of course,' he added spuriously, 'I shall be seeing a lot of him now he's bought this lush pad.'

'But you've always seen a lot of him, haven't you, Mr Silk? One might say that you've been a sort of . . .' Wexford glanced meaningly at the shaggy grey hair, ' . . . a sort of *éminence grise* in his life. Or are you another slave?'

'I don't know what you mean.'

'But for you he'd still be Harold Goodbody and he never would have met Nell Dunsand.'

Silk stared at him. 'I acted for the best. We can't know
what tragedies may hang on our small actions. I gave to youth
a musical genius. If Dunsand freaked out, if certain people
were – well, expendable . . .'

'Is that how you see it? Mr Silk, you interfere too much.
You organize too much. Be warned, and don't interfere with
Louis Mbowele. You might cause a war this time.'

'Really, I think you're twisted, sick. You're not together.
Who is, at your age?' He sneered. 'The hung-up generation.'

'If I belong to it,' Wexford retorted, 'so do you. We're the
same age. Only I know it, I accept it. You don't. I accept that
all the sport is stale and all the wheels run down. And when
I consider what some people call sport, I'm not all that sorry.'

At Wexford's words, particularly the reminder of his true
age, a look of real pain crossed Silk's face. Mirrors show us
what we want to see, but sometimes we look into living, human
mirrors and then, briefly, the fantasizing has to stop. Wexford
was fat, Silk skinny, the one in a crumpled old suit, the other
in tee-shirt and jeans, but they were both sixty. The mirror
comparison lay in their shared age, the shared weariness of
muscle and bone, and painfully Silk saw it.

He said shrilly, 'What are you doing here?'

'Talking to you at the moment. Now we're going upstairs
to talk to your genius.'

'But you've got Dunsand. Zeno wasn't even there. I was
with Zeno and the Tates in Kensington. You've got Dunsand
under lock and key!'

'What an old-fashioned expression!' Wexford mocked. 'Can't
you find a more trendy way of putting it? Come on, Mike,
we've wasted enough time.'

They walked up. Silk stood at the foot of the staircase
watching them, hesitating, torn perhaps between a fear of his
protégé coming to harm and an even greater fear of more
cruel jibes levelled at him concerning his age.

Wexford said, 'He knows nothing about it. He knows less

even than Wexford.' He smiled obscurely, tapped on the door of the Elizabethan Suite.

They were packing. At last they were going home. His face an even duskier red than usual, Tate was on his knees, trying to fasten an overfull suitcase, while Vedast sat cross-legged on top of a lacquer cabinet watching him. Wordlessly, Nell led them through the labyrinth of piled luggage and mountains of frippery, magazines and records.

Dead flowers, smelling foetid, were heaped on the balcony. Fresh flowers had arrived that day, perhaps that afternoon, roses, lilies, carnations, and they were dying too. No one had bothered to put them in water.

Nell was as carefully dressed and made-up as usual, but her exertions in the heat had given her an air of dishevelment, for it was still hot, the evening air windless, the sun a smouldering crimson knot over the forest. She scowled at the policemen, met Vedast's cool gaze, and turned immediately to look at herself in one of the mirrors. Vedast gave a light laugh.

'Fasten that case, Goffo. Get a move on, dears. Why don't you go and order some coffee, Nello?' He swayed his body towards Wexford. 'That will give her a chance to repair her poor face,' he said as if she wasn't there.

Burden, who had followed the chief inspector's example and cleared a seat for himself, said gruffly, 'No coffee for us.'

'Just as you like.' Vedast flicked his fingers at Nell, who, still in front of the mirror, was apathetically fidgeting with her hair while watching the policemen in the glass. She sprang round as if those snapping fingers had actually touched her, fetched his orange juice and handed it to him with a pleading look. He removed a lump of ice and licked it. 'How glum you all look!' he said, surveying the four faces. 'You're frightening my little ones, Chief Inspector. Why don't we take it as read. I know what happened and so, presumably, do you – now. It *did* take you a long time. But you can't prove it. So why don't we just congratulate each other like clever cats and mice and you pop off home?'

Wexford quoted softly, ' "What need we fear who knows it when none can call our power to account?" '

The Tates looked at him uncomprehendingly, Nell edging closer to Vedast, who said, 'Macbeth. I sometimes think of changing over to the legitimate theatre. I've had no end of offers.' He swallowed what remained of his ice cube. 'But I don't want to start now, thank you so much. We're none of us feeling quite strong enough for drama.'

'You mean you've had enough of it? You've made your tragedy and now you're exhausted? The function of tragedy, as I'm sure you know, Mr Vedast, is to purge with pity and terror, and that's what I'm going to try to do to you – or some of you. So sit down, Mr Tate, and you too, Mrs Tate, and listen to me.'

Both Nell and her husband looked doubtfully at Vedast for instructions. He nodded lightly.

'Do what the man says, dears.'

Nell flounced on to the sofa, tipping off a heap of dirty clothes and what seemed to be a stack of fan letters. A full glass in his hand, a hand which trembled, Tate crept towards her.

She made a slight movement of rejection, turning her shoulder and at the same time spreading out her thick, stiffly embroidered skirts so that there was no room for her husband to sit beside her. He gave her a bitter look, a look of dark reproach, from under swollen veined eyelids. Clasping his drink as if it were a protective talisman, he perched himself on the sofa arm.

The singer watched them, amused that they had obeyed so easily. A law unto himself, he got down from the cabinet and lounged against the open french window. With the setting of the sun, a light breeze had begun to blow. It fanned his hair, lifting it into a golden aureole. Outside the blue of the sky was deepening to violet, feathered with flamingo red. The frosty orange glass glowed in his hand like a lamp. He stood as if he were about to sing, his chin lifted, his hips thrust forward, quite still, utterly relaxed.

'A tragedy,' said Wexford, 'in two parts.'

'It concerns,' he began, 'two people who by their looks and the power of their personalities were able to command obsessive love. You, Mr Vedast, and you, Mrs Tate. I'm not flattering you. Anyone may become the object of such love and, in my experience, those who do are usually shallow, narcissistic and self-centred.'

Nell said shrilly, 'Are you going to let him talk to me like that, Godfrey?'

Hunched up, nursing his glass, Tate gave her a black look. He said nothing. The breeze chilled him, making the dark hairs on his wrists stand erect.

'The need to love like this lies in the characters of the lovers who fasten generally on the first desirable person who comes in their way, fasten and, if they can, hold on. Unfortunately, the beloved objects trade on this and use it for their own ends, for cruelty and victimisation. Just in case Mrs Tate is under any misapprehension as to whom I mean when I speak of the man who loves her obsessively, in case she should be so obtuse as to suppose I mean Mr Vedast, I'll tell her now that I refer to her first husband, Leonard Dunsand. A foolish, clever, learned, dull and conventional little man who has loved her since she was eighteen when he married her.'

One of those people who will bear any insult provided it carries with it a hint of flattery, Nell apparently couldn't resist preening herself at this. She crossed her long and very shapely legs and gave a sidelong glance in Vedast's direction. Vedast stroked the string of beads he wore, running them through his fingers.

Wexford went on: 'Who is probably the only man sufficiently

319

capable of self-delusion to love her sincerely, the only man who ever will.' He waited for some reaction from Nell's present husband. Tate reacted characteristically, behaving as he always did in crises or threatened crises. Without getting up, he reached for the brandy bottle. 'If you are in a position to be thankful for anything, Mr Tate, be thankful that you are more sophisticated and have eyes to see. Pity you've clouded them so much with that stuff.'

'I can look after myself,' said Tate in a low voice.

'I never saw a man less capable of doing so, unless it is Mr Dunsand.'

'I'll look after Goffo.' Vedast turned idly, smiling, cooling his hands on the glass, caressing it. 'Do tell us who's in love with me. I'm dying to know.'

'Thousands, I imagine. The one in particular I speak of is dead. She was dying for you too often and at last she really died. You were her first lover. That's supposed to have some profound effect on a woman and, whether it's true or not, it had a profound effect on Dawn Stonor. I wonder how much of that story Mr and Mrs Tate know?' While Vedast resumed his scanning of the sky in which a few pale stars had appeared, Wexford leant towards the Tates. 'They were at school together, Dawn and a boy called Harold Goodbody, a boy who went to tea with his girl friend's grandmother because he only had baked beans at home; Harold Goodbody who wore his cousin's cast-off shoes and whose father spent the housekeeping on dog racing; Harold Goodbody who played April Fool tricks to amuse his friends, who doubtless carried young Dawn's satchel for her. A rustic idyll, wasn't it? Dawn Stonor and her first love, Harold Goodbody.'

'I would prefer you not to call me that,' said Vedast, and for the first time Wexford heard an edge of temper to his voice.

'You'd prefer me to go away, but I shan't do that,' Wexford flashed back. 'You said you were dying to hear and you shall hear.' He leaned back, pleased at the unease his words had provoked in Nell, pleased by Tate's cringing. 'You left your friend,' he said to Vedast, 'and went to London. For you the idyll was over. Soon afterwards she went to London too, but by then you were beyond her reach. And yet she never forgot you. She told her friends and she pretended, perhaps to herself as well as to her friends, that you had always remained lovers and between you was some enduring bond.' Wexford glanced at Burden and inclined his head, giving the inspector honour for this idea which at first he had ridiculed. 'In fact,' he went on, 'nearly a decade passed by before you saw each other again. In that time you had become very famous, many exciting things had happened to you. Very little had happened to her. She was a waitress in a club and she remained a waitress.

'It was a pity you ever went into that club. If you hadn't, Dawn might at this moment be making wedding plans with her fiancé. Why did you go?'

Vedast shrugged. 'This bloke asked us. We hadn't anything better to do.'

'You could hardly have done worse.'

'I didn't kill her. I never touched her.'

Wexford turned towards the Tates, to Godfrey Tate whose bloodshot eyes were wide open and staring.

CHAPTER TWENTY-ONE

'I shall now go back,' said the chief inspector, 'to one of your exciting happenings, although I don't believe you'll regard it as a highspot when you come to write your memoirs. I refer to your meeting with Mrs Tate, and to describe that I must return to the other love story.'

A glance from Vedast was enough to make Nell get up and switch on the rose-shaded lamps. She moved stiffly, tripping over the red grip and cursing. Vedast gave her his empty glass and she refilled it. He took it without thanks like a duke receiving the drink he has ordered from a parlourmaid.

'Ice, Nello,' he said.

She spooned two cubes out of a pool of water in a bowl on the cabinet. Tate was crouched over his brandy, gazing into the golden liquid. The rosy light played on him, muting the harsh blackness of his hair. Nell gave Vedast his glass again, keeping her hands clasped round it so that his fingers would brush hers as he took it. They brushed them as a stranger's might without lingering. She seemed desperate to stay beside him, to remain with him on the cool, darkening balcony whose rail, reddened by the setting sun, was now a black filagree trellis behind the mound of dead blossoms.

'Go away, Nello. You fidget me.'

She hung her head, crept just inside the window and dropped on to an upright chair, her arms hanging limply by her sides.

'That's right, Mrs Tate, sit where I can see you. You're a very good-looking woman, but you've changed a good deal since you were a bride for the first time. For one thing, you've tinted your hair. I don't suppose you ever wear dark red these days, do you?

'Mr Dunsand liked your short dark hair. He liked you in simple, wifely dresses. I understand from what information was gathered today in Myringham that you were known as a quiet little thing, a good cook, fond of flowers, of homemaking, but inclined to be bored with the society you moved in. They were all so much older than you, those faculty wives, weren't they? You would have preferred the company of your husband's students. Those coffee mornings, those empty afternoons, were very dull for you. But they were nothing to the evenings when, after you had prepared the kind of meal Mr Dunsand liked, you had to sit for hours alone with him, the record player switched off, and plan together your annual holiday, plan your budget, decide what new equipment or furniture you could afford that year.

'To Mr Dunsand it was the very essence of contentment. I expect you played your part well. Women like you, born sycophants, usually do, and all the time they wait quietly for the means of escape. Your chance came when Zeno Vedast, your idol, gave a concert in Myringham. I don't suppose Mr Dunsand wanted you to go to that concert. The idea of his wife, the wife who depended on him utterly for her support, disporting herself among a bunch of teenagers at a pop concert, can hardly have appealed to him. No, he couldn't have liked to think of you raving among his own students, but you went. If you hadn't gone, Dawn Stonor would be alive today, making wedding plans with her fiancé.

'I don't think you threw yourself under Mr Vedast's car deliberately – you wouldn't have the courage – let's say it was an unconscious urge you couldn't control or resist.

'Mr Vedast had put you in a private room at the hospital. How you must have prayed for Mr Vedast himself to appear with the grapes and the chocolates! You didn't know him. You don't know him now. He sent his minion, and it was any port in a storm for you, Mrs Tate. But you're not unique, don't think it. Many a master in the past has married a likely wench off to his servant so that he can have the enjoying of her without any of the trouble.'

'You've no right to insult me!' Nell flared. She waited for her husband to defend her. When he said nothing, while Vedast smiled and sipped his orange juice, she said, 'Why shouldn't I have left my husband? Why shouldn't I have got married again? I'm not the only one. I was sick to death of living with Len.'

Vedast turned. He said smoothly, 'Like the judges say, this isn't a court of morals, Mr Wexford.'

'Oh, but it is. It must be because it can't be a court of justice.'

'In that case . . .' Nell got up. 'In that case, I'm going. Let's go, Zeno. He can't keep us here.'

'Do as you like, Nello.' Vedast gave her a sly sidelong glance. She couldn't do as she liked. She never had been able to. 'You go if you want,' he said in the voice, usual with him, that was both gentle and unkind. 'I'm staying. I'm fascinated. How about you, Goffo, are you going to take your wife away or stay and support your old mate?'

'Mr Tate stays,' said Burden sharply.

Wexford just glanced at him, raising his eyebrows. 'Let us have an intermission,' he said. 'An interval to relax in. If my voice were better, I'd offer to sing you a song, but in this company . . .' He hesitated, then said, 'You all know the song. It was written at the time of Mrs Tate's second marriage. It would be ingenuous of me to suppose it doesn't illustrate a true story, render someone's real suffering. That's why it was written. Poets,' he said, 'are said to make little songs out of their great sorrows. You . . .' His eyes went to the window, ' . . . amused yourself and feathered your luxurious nest by making a song out of someone else's.'

Vedast jerked round. He came into the room, his yellow eyes sharp and narrow.

'I'll sing it,' he said. 'There's nothing wrong with my voice.'

Wexford nodded. He could tell what Burden was thinking, that his son, that any fan at the festival, would have given a week's wages, a month's grant, a term's pocket money, to have been in their shoes. Vedast, who could command thousands for one concert, was going to sing in private for them. He felt a little sick.

In the pale rosy light, the soft kind light, Vedast looked very young, a teenager himself. He stood in a corner of the room, resting his bare elbows on a shelf from which rose-buds hung, young, fresh rose-buds dead before they opened from dehydration. He waited in the silence of the evening, the silence of the forest which surrounded them. The first word came loud like a note vibrating from a string, then the clear, light voice dropped a little, filling the room with sweet bitterness.

Nell watched the singer adoringly, tapping in time to the tune throughout the first verse, the first chorus. Wexford frowned at her and she tossed her head, flinging herself back petulantly against a cushion. His sickness was passing. He listened to the words as if he had never heard them before, as if he had never fully understood the depth of their meaning.

> 'Remember me and my life-without-life.
> Come once more to be my wife,
> Come today before I grieve,
> Enter the web of let-me-believe.
>
> So come by, come nigh,
>   come try and tell why
>   some sigh, some cry,
>   some lie and some die . . .'

There was no applause. Vedast dropped his head. Then he flung it back, shaking his hair.

'Thank you,' said Wexford crisply. 'It's all in that song, isn't it? All Mr Dunsand's sorrow is there. He pleaded with

325

you, I imagine, not to break with him entirely, not to leave him utterly without life, to let him believe sometimes, very occasionally, that you were still his wife. And you repeated those conversations to Mr Vedast, giving him such a good idea for a song.'

Tate looked up, frowning, a trickle of brandy coursing down his chin. He wiped his mouth on his sleeve.

'Why did you agree to what Mr Dunsand asked?'

'I didn't want to hurt him too much,' Nell muttered.

A dull, humourless laugh escaped from Burden and it was echoed, surprisingly, by Tate. Wexford didn't laugh. 'Mrs Tate, is that you talking? *You?* When have you ever minded whom you hurt, you who are an expert treader on other people's dreams? If you won't tell me why, I shall have to guess.'

'It was to nark me,' Tate interrupted.

'But you didn't know until after the festival,' Wexford said quickly.

Bewildered, Tate said, 'That's true. She'd been seeing him two or three times a year, going to his house and bloody well sleeping with him. I blacked her eye for her.'

'So you told me. And you gave me a key. Only it wasn't the key to Mr Dunsand's house in The Pathway. It opens the front door of his former home in Myringham. Mrs Tate had never been to The Pathway house. She knew it only because Mr Dunsand described it to her over the phone as the middle house of the three. But he sent her a key, intending that she should keep up the custom of the Myringham days.'

Tate said slowly:

'What custom? What are you on about.'

'I believe you, Mr Tate, when you say you knew nothing of these visits of your wife's until after the festival when, frightened of what she had done but not frightened enough to confess everything, she told you she had been seeing her first husband. I believe you are entirely innocent of this crime, in no way an accessory. You had been kept in the dark as you are, I daresay, about many things.' Tate shrugged awkwardly. The level of golden liquor in the bottle was going steadily down. He poured himself some more in silence. 'Nor do I think you would have been a party to any of this had you known about it,' said Wexford.

'Mr Vedast wasn't in the dark. He knew. Mrs Tate told him she had promised these – shall I say loans? – loans of herself to Mr Dunsand. And so I come back to why. Why did she do it? You're not a very happy woman, are you, Mrs Tate? Apparently you have everything you wanted, but only apparently. I think that very soon after your second marriage you saw what you had got, luxury and excitement, yes, but at what a price. Another not very inspiring husband – forgive me, Mr Tate – though a complaisant one, a condescending master, kind when you were obedient. So you agreed to Mr Dunsand's requests for the sake of the contrast. Those few evenings, those nights, you spent with him, showed you that what you had was at least preferable to your former married life. After a night in Myringham you could go back to London, to Europe, to Bermuda, your loins girded, as it were, with the memory of the alternative.'

'Is that true, Nello? I never knew that.'

'I'm glad to be able to tell you something you don't know, Mr Vedast. But you knew of the part she played while she was there, didn't you? I'm sure Mrs Tate told you all the details, the props, the costume required, shall I say? I'm sure she told you of the setting of the little play they enacted two or three times a year, the activities, following always the same pattern, in which the actors indulged, marriage *à la mode* Dunsand. Indeed, I know she did. Had she not, you wouldn't have been able to play your – your practical joke.'

Nell said, 'I want a drink, Godfrey.'

'Get it yourself.'

She did so, clattering the bottle neck against the glass,

spilling vermouth on to the pale embroidery on her white linen skirt. It made a red stain like blood.

Wexford said, 'I expect you thought all this very amusing, Mr Vedast, until there was a threat of the performance of this play interfering with your own plans. About a month ago Mrs Tate told you that she would be paying her first visit to Mr Dunsand's new home on the afternoon of Monday, June sixth. But that didn't suit you, for you and Mr and Mrs Tate would only just have returned from Manchester where you had a concert engagement.'

Tate shook his head. 'No, that's not right,' he said. 'He meant to stay over till the Monday. It was me said at the last moment it'd be too tiring for him.'

'Ah.' Wexford sighed. 'Even better – or worse. When Mrs Tate first confided in you, you intended that she and you and Mr Tate would all be away from the South on June sixth.' He looked at Nell, at the red stain on her dress which she had not attempted to remove, at the red colour that burned on her face. 'Why didn't you just change the date of your appointment with your first husband, Mrs Tate? Surely you could have put it off for a few days?'

For a moment she looked as if she were searching in her mind for an excuse. She put out a trembling hand to Vedast who ignored her, who smiled, his head on one side.

'Because that would have "hurt" Mr Dunsand?' Wexford went on relentlessly. 'Or did you do what you always do, obeyed Mr Vedast?'

In a small, thin voice, she said, 'I left it to Zeno.'

'You left it to Zeno. He was to get in touch with Mr Dunsand, was he? He, a world-famous singer, a pop idol, was to phone Mr Dunsand and tell him you couldn't make it but would, say, Wednesday do instead?'

She was near to tears. She held her hands crushed together so that the peeling nails dug into the flesh. 'You know it wasn't like that. You know you're just tormenting me.'

'Not everyone is as zealous as you, Mrs Tate, about the feelings of others. Not everyone is as anxious as you to go through life without doing hurt. But it's true that I know what happened.' Wexford got up and walked over to Vedast who had taken up a Yoga position, a half-Lotus, on the floor by the open window. He stood over the singer, looking down, his own grey eyes meeting the amber ones.

'No, Mr Vedast,' he said. 'To a person of your temperament it was far more amusing to keep the date, changing not the day but the female protagonist.'

Tate broke the silence.

'What d'you mean? I don't follow you. Female whatsit, what does it mean?'

Wexford came over to him. He spoke gently. 'It means, Mr Tate, that your employer saw a way of getting Mrs Tate out of her appointment, and perhaps all further similar appointments, and at the same time of playing one of his favourite jokes.

'He decided to send a substitute for your wife to The Pathway. First, I suspect, he thought of sending a call girl. But why go to all that trouble when he could send Dawn Stonor whose acquaintance he had renewed some weeks before and whom he had telephoned on May twenty-third?'

CHAPTER TWENTY-TWO

Wexford sat down in the centre of the room. 'I don't know why you phoned Dawn that last night,' he went on, addressing himself directly to Vedast. 'I think your motive was akin to Mrs Tate's motive for visiting her former husband. Probably at the Townsman Club you contrasted Dawn's humble situation with your successful one, remembering how you came from similar beginnings, how you had had even chances of money, fame, glory – but you had achieved them and she had not.

'On May twenty-third Mr and Mrs Tate were away. You were bored. Perhaps you even felt insecure. Why not phone Dawn, do a little slumming, so that afterwards you might have the pleasure of appreciating what you are and what you might have been? I daresay that phone conversation had the desired effect on you. You were quickly tired of her eagerness and you rang off, having vaguely suggested you see each other "sometime" but not, in fact, ever intending to see her again.

'During that week, I believe, Mrs Tate told you of the visit she planned to make to Mr Dunsand's new house. On the phone you had already, I think, boasted to Dawn of the house you were yourself thinking of buying near Kingsmarkham. Why not play a joke, the biggest joke of your career?'

'My thought processes,' said Vedast, 'don't work quite like that. Stop hovering, Nello. Go and sit down somewhere.'

The only spot in the room where she wanted to be was at his side. She looked at the sofa where her husband sat hunched, at the two occupied chairs, at the empty chairs which were either near her husband or near the policemen. And like an insect with bright antennae, bright wings, she fluttered desperately, hovered, as Vedast had put it, finally alighting –

her heels were high, her shoes platformed – on another spot of carpet as near to him as she had been when he had shooed her away. The insect had come back to the flame.

Wexford had paused when the interruption came but, apart from hesitating briefly, he took no notice of her.

'The first of June,' he said to Vedast, 'was the birthday of the man Dawn was very probably going to marry, the man she would have married if you had left her alone. She was at home, waiting for him to come to lunch. You didn't know that. Would you have cared if you had? You phoned her in the morning and asked her to meet you for a drink.' Burden stirred in his chair, his eyebrows lifting. 'She wasn't very elated about it. Perhaps she realized that a man like you, a man so rich as you are, who could afford without noticing it the most expensive restaurant in London, only takes a girl for drinks in a pub if he despises her, if he thinks she isn't worth any more. But she dressed carefully for you just the same; changing out of the clothes that were good enough for an ordinary fiancé.

'And later, when the excitement of that lunchtime date had begun to recede, she asked herself – and her flatmate – if she *was* despised, if that was the reason why you were only prepared to have a hole-in-corner, *sub rosa* affair with her, hiding her in a house no one knew you had bought instead of taking her to an hotel.

'In that pub, between one o'clock and three, you asked her, after some preliminary flattery and flirtation, no doubt, to spend the night of the following Monday with you in your new house. Of course, she agreed. She would be on holiday. She could go and see her mother and then go on to The Pathway. That she and Dunsand were *people* with feelings never entered your head, did it? You were as careless of his as of hers. That Mrs Tate was in the habit of preparing for him on these occasions a special meal of his favourite food, of bringing good wine and beautiful flowers – to fill the void? – didn't trouble you at all. You told Dawn anything would do, just

331

some quick picnic food for you and her to share. Any old wine, the cheapest she could get.

'She must go there first, you told her, and you gave her the key Mr Dunsand had sent to Mrs Tate and which Mrs Tate had given you. No responsibility, Mrs Tate? You left it all to Zeno?' Wexford turned back to Vedast. 'You'd be along around half past six. As soon as she was in the house she was to go upstairs where she would find a red dress.

'Now this dress had been laid out on the bed by Mr Dunsand. During his married life this dress of Mrs Tate's had been his favourite. When she wore it, sat down to dinner with him, listened to his account of his day and gave him account of hers, he could fancy himself protected from the "harsh light of day" and back safe and happy with his wife.

'Dawn knew nothing of this. She was told nothing of this. You asked her to wear this dress because it belonged to a fashion current when you were still together, still lovers, and you told her it would recall to you that past time.'

Looking ill, the colour all gone from his face, leaving a swarthy pallor, Tate lurched to his feet. He edged round the sofa and said to Vedast, 'Is that true?'

'We didn't mean any harm.'

'No harm? Christ . . . You did that and *she* knew it. God, I feel like I've never known either of you, never seen you before . . .'

'Godfrey . . .' Nell put out a feeble hand. 'I didn't do anything. I only told him – well, you know.'

'Have another drink, Goffo,' Vedast drawled.

'I don't want any more.' Tate made this remark in a thick but wondering voice. He swung on Wexford. 'Go on, then. What happened? Tell me the rest. Him . . .' He pointed at Vedast as if reluctant to use his name. 'Him and her, they were with me that evening. Honest, they were. They can't have killed her.'

'Who kills, Mr Tate, the one who holds the knife, the one who says "stab!" or the one who sends the victim to the appointed place? Which of the three Fates is responsible for our destinies, she who spins the thread, she who cuts it or she who merely holds the scissors?' Wexford could tell from Tate's puzzled, vacant expression that all this was going over his head. 'Maybe Mr Dunsand could tell us. He's the philosopher.' Glancing at Burden, hoping there would be no actual exclamation of shock, he said. 'He killed her, of course. He's admitted it. He isn't the kind of man to prevaricate for long. Only chivalry made him tell a few lies to avoid any involvement of . . .' Scornful eyes came to rest on Nell, '. . . of his beloved former wife.'

Wexford went on carefully, 'As to what he did, I'll tell you. He came home, longing, of course, for the evening and the night ahead. He let himself in with his own key at twenty to seven. By that time Dawn must have been feeling uneasy. There were many things to make her uneasy, the modest size of the place, the austere furnishings, the superabundance of learned books. And the dress – a dress that was too small for her, unbecoming, too tight. Of course she felt uneasy. Of course, when she heard a key in the lock, she came out of the living room shyly, not speaking, just standing there.

'Instead of Vedast, she saw a little middle-aged stranger. Instead of his wife, Dunsand saw – what? What, Mrs Tate?'

'Dawn Stonor,' she said in a small, sullen voice.

'Oh, no. She didn't exist for him. He never even knew her name. He saw his wife, yet not his wife, a girl of his wife's age but bigger, coarser, with even more make-up, with brassier hair, yet wearing his wife's dress, his favourite dress.

'Perhaps he didn't believe in the reality of this sight. Even to a better-balanced man than Dunsand, what he saw looming in the little hall would have seemed a hallucination. To him it wasn't just a travesty of his wife but a kind of succubus sent by something which existed in his clever sick mind to torment

333

him. He wanted to destroy what he saw and he simply did so, attacking the hallucinatory shape with the first weapon that came to hand, the wine bottle his visitant had left on the hall table.'

Vedast got up, lifted his head sharply as he had lifted it at the festival, shook back his lion's mane. 'How was I to know things would go that way?' He held out his glass. 'Get me some more of that stuff, will you, Goffo.'

Tate said, 'Not me. Get your own bloody drink.'

'Temper, temper.' The golden eyebrows went up, the teeth showed in what was perhaps a smile.

'Can't you do anything to him?' Tate said to Wexford. 'He killed her. He's the real killer.'

'I know it, Mr Tate, but no, I can't do anything to him. What should be done to him? He is as sick as Mr Dunsand, a megalomaniac who lives on fantasies.'

'Don't give me that balls. He ought to be shot. Hanging'd be too good for him.'

' "Heaven hath no rage like love to hatred turned" . . . You are not obliged to associate with them, Mr Tate. You need not, just because you also married her, copy her first husband and be chivalrous.'

'Too bloody right, I needn't.' Shock had brought Tate complete cold sobriety. On his knees, he flung armfuls of garments into the red grip, seized it and a smaller suitcase. 'I'm going. I'm quitting.' He got up, said to Vedast, 'You owe me a hundred quid. You can sent it care of my mum's. *She* knows the address.'

'You can't go,' said Vedast and at last he wasn't playing. His voice had lost its lightness. 'We've been together for eight years. What'll I do without you?'

'Cut your bloody throat, but cut hers first.' Tate held out his hand to Wexford. 'I used to call you lot pigs,' he said, 'and maybe I will again. But, thanks, you've done me a good turn. If you've done nothing else you've got me away from them. I might even stop drinking now.' Then he used the first cultivated, literate phrase Wexford had ever heard from his lips but, even as he said it, the chief inspector knew he had learnt it parrot fashion from the 'scene' with which he had been associated. 'They'd have destroyed me utterly.'

'I really think they would, Mr Tate.'

When he had gone, slamming the suite door, the slave who remained seized Vedast's arm and said, 'Good riddance. I just feel relief, don't you?'

Vedast made no reply. He picked up the phone sullenly, asked for a porter. Immediately Nell, taking her cue, bundled heaps of clothes into cases, bags, carriers. Wexford and Burden, ready to leave, helpless, impotent, watched her. The cases were all packed in five minutes. Vedast stood at the window, his expression inscrutable. He looked over the balcony rail once, perhaps at the departing Tate. The porter came in, took two cases in his hands, one under his arm. Nell flung a white coat round her shoulders.

'I take it we shan't be wanted any more?'

'You will be wanted at Mr Dunsand's trial. Before that, statements will have to be taken from you.'

'Me?' said Vedast. 'I can't appear in court. It will be ghastly bad publicity. Why did Goffo have to go like that? Goffo could have coped.'

'I'll cope,' said Nell fondly. 'Let's go now, shall we? It's nearly midnight. Let's get going.'

He pushed her away. 'I'm going,' he said. 'I'm going by myself. You can get a taxi to whatever station there is in this hole.'

'But we've got the car!'

Petulantly, like a little boy, he said, 'It's my car. *I'm* going in it. You'd better face it, Nello, you're no use to me without Godfrey. He looked after me and then – then you came along.' His face cleared a little. 'You were a nice bit of decoration,' he said.

The flesh of her face seemed to sag. Her lip curled up, her eyes widened, stretching the skin, wrinkling it. 'You can't mean it, Zeno. Zeno, don't leave me! I've worshipped you since I was twenty. I've never thought of any man but you.'

'No, dear, I know. You just married them.'

As the porter returned to fetch the remaining luggage, Vedast tried to unhook her hands from his shoulders. 'Nello, do as I say. Let go of me. I'm going to pay the bill and then I'm going.' He went up to Wexford, the bantering tone quelled by what he had to say and by the presence of the inquisitive porter. 'I suppose we can keep all this quiet?' One of the long, lean hands sketched a gesture towards a jeans pocket. 'I imagine . . .'

'Mr Vedast, we are leaving.'

'I'll come down with you.'

'Zeno!' Nell screamed. 'Zeno, I love you!'

The two policemen had moved a pace or two away from the singer, moved distastefully. Nell flung herself upon Vedast. Her coat fell from her shoulders. She clung to his neck, pushing her fingers through the golden hair, pressing her body against him.

'Where am I to go? What am I to do?'

Struggling, pushing her, he said, 'You can go to Godfrey's mum. Go where you like, only get off me. Get off! Christ, Dawn Stonor'd have been a better bet than you. Get off!'

They grappled together like wrestlers, Nell screaming and clinging. Vedast was strong and muscular but not quite strong enough. He kicked and punched, grabbing at her hair, tearing it. They toppled and rolled on the floor among the dead flowers, the empty bottles, knocking over and breaking into fragments the orange-juice glass.

'Let's go,' said Wexford laconically.

In the corridor bedroom doors had been cautiously opened and sleepy people stared out. On the stairs the policemen passed four or five of the hotel night staff running up, alarmed by the screams, the thumps on the floorboards. Lights began to come on as the somnolent hotel woke to life.

The night was as clear, as softly violet-blue as the night of the festival, but now the moon was waning. And there were no ballads to be heard here, no plangent note from a string plucked with controlled power. Wexford could still hear Vedast's voice, though, raised now in a high-pitched lunatic scream, a sound none of his fans would have recognized. Instead of that vibrant twang came the crash of flying furniture; instead of melody, Nell's hysterical sobbing, and instead of applause, the manager gravely and quite ineffectively begging his guests to stop.

'Perhaps they'll kill each other,' said Burden as they passed the furred golden car.

'Perhaps they will. Who cares?' Wexford sighed. 'Vedast won't like it in court. Will it have any effect on his career?'

Once again Burden was being appealed to as the expert on such matters. 'I doubt it,' he said, starting the car. 'These singers, they're always appearing in court on drug offences. Did you ever hear of their records selling less well afterwards?'

'Drugs are one thing. Provided you don't deal in them, drugs harm no one but yourself. But there's a big thing among young people at the moment for loving your neighbour, for not hurting – above all, for keeping in mind that people are people. I don't think they'll be too pleased when they know their idol forgot or, rather, neglected to care for that fact.'

'Poor old Dunsand. What of him?'

'His career will be ruined, but it won't be prison for him. Mental hospital for years? Is that much better? It was a succubus he killed. Unfortunately for him, we know succubi don't exist – they're flesh and blood.'

A single light showed in Burden's bungalow. In an armchair in the living room John lay asleep, his hair tousled, a half-empty glass of milk beside him. The indicator light on the record player still glowed red.

'God, I forgot the kids! I was so carried away I forgot them.' Burden stooped tenderly over his son, but the boy didn't stir. 'He waited up for me,' he said wonderingly.

Wexford smiled rather sadly. 'Poor John. Somehow I don't think he'll get the Sundays album for his birthday now.'

'He certainly won't.' Burden took a stride to the record player, his face flushing with anger when he saw what lay on the turntable. Savagely, he seized 'Let-me-believe' in both hands and seemed about to twist it, to bend it double, when Wexford laid a gentle, warning hand on his arm.

'No, Mike,' he said. 'Don't do that. Leave it to John and – and all of them. Let them be his judges.'

Shake Hands
For Ever

For my aunts, Jenny Waldorff,
Laura Winfield, Margot Richards and
Phyllis Ridgway, with my love

CHAPTER ONE

The woman standing under the departures board at Victoria station had a flat rectangular body and an iron-hard rectangular face. A hat of fawn-coloured corrugated felt rather like a walnut shell encased her head, her hands were gloved in fawn-coloured cotton, and at her feet was the durable but scarcely used brown leather suitcase she had taken on her honeymoon forty-five years before. Her eyes scanned the scurrying commuters while her mouth grew more and more set, the lips thinning to a hairline crack.

She was waiting for her son. He was one minute late and his unpunctuality had begun to afford her a glowing satisfaction. She was hardly aware of this pleasure and, had she been accused of it, would have denied it, just as she would have denied the delight all failure and backsliding in other people brought her. But it was present as an undefined sense of well-being that was to vanish almost as soon as it had been born and be succeeded on Robert's sudden hasty arrival by her usual ill-temper. He was so nearly on time as to make any remarks about his lateness absurd, so she contented herself with offering her leathery cheek to his lips and saying:

'There you are then.'

'Have you got your ticket?' said Robert Hathall.

She hadn't. She knew that money had been tight with him for the three years of his second marriage, but that was his fault. Paying her share would only encourage him.

'You'd better go and get them,' she said, 'unless you want us to miss the train,' and she held even more tightly to her zipped-up handbag.

He was a long time about it. She noted that the Eastbourne train, stopping at Toxborough, Myringham and Kingsmarkham, was due to depart at six twelve, and it was five past now. No fully formed uncompromising thought that it would be nice to miss the train entered her mind, any more than she had consciously told herself it would be nice to find her daughter-in-law in tears, the house filthy and no meal cooked, but once more the seeds of pleasurable resentment began germinating. She had looked forward to this weekend with a deep content-ment, certain it would go wrong. Nothing would suit her better than that it should begin to go wrong by their arriving late through no fault of hers, and that their lateness should result in a quarrel between Robert and Angela. But all this smoul-dered silent and unanalyzed under her immediate awareness that Robert was making a mess of things again.

Nevertheless, they caught the train. It was crowded and they both had to stand. Mrs Hathall never complained. She would have fainted before citing her age and her varicose veins as reasons why this or that man should give up his seat to her. Stoicism governed her. Instead, she planted her thick body which, buttoned up in a stiff fawn coat, had the appearance of a wardrobe, in such a way as to prevent the passenger in the window seat from moving his legs or reading his news-paper. She had only one thing to say to Robert and that could keep till there were fewer listeners, and she found it hard to suppose he could have anything to say to her. Hadn't they, after all, spent every weekday evening together for the past two months? But people she had noticed with some puzzle-ment, were prone to chatter when they had nothing to say. Even her own son was guilty of this. She listened grimly while he went on about the beautiful scenery through which they would soon pass, the amenities of Bury Cottage, and how much Angela was looking forward to seeing her. Mrs Hathall per-mitted herself a kind of snort at this last. A two-syllabled grunt made somewhere in her glottis that could be roughly inter-preted as a laugh. Her lips didn't move. She was reflecting on the one and only time she had met her daughter-in-law, in that room in Earls Court, when Angela had committed the outrage of referring to Eileen as a greedy bitch. Much would have to be done, many amends be made, before that indiscretion could be forgotten. Mrs Hathall remembered how she had marched straight out of that room and down the stairs, resolving never – never under any circumstances – to see Angela again. It only proved how forbearing she was that she was going to Kingsmarkham now.

At Myringham the passenger by the window, his legs numb, staggered out of the train and Mrs Hathall got his seat. Robert, she could tell, was getting nervous. There was nothing surprising in that. He knew very well this Angela couldn't compete with Eileen as cook and housekeeper and he was wondering just how far below his first wife's standards his second would fall. His next words confirmed her conviction that this was troubling his mind.

'Angela's spent the week spring-cleaning the place to make it nice for you.'

Mrs Hathall was shocked that anyone could make such a statement aloud and in front of a carriage full of people. What she would have liked to say was, firstly, that he should keep his voice down and, secondly, that any decent women kept her house clean at all times. But she contented herself with a 'I'm sure she needn't put herself out for me' and added repressively that it was time he got her suitcase down.

'It's five minutes yet,' said Robert.

She replied by getting heavily to her feet and struggling with the case herself. Robert and another man intervened to help her, the case nearly fell on to the head of a girl with a baby in her arms, and by the time the train drew to a halt at Kingsmarkham, sending them all staggering and clutching each other, the carriage was in a small uproar.

Out on the platform, Mrs Hathall said, 'That could have been avoided if you'd done as you were asked. You always were obstinate.'

She couldn't understand why he didn't retaliate and fight back. He must be more strung-up than she had thought. To goad him further, she said, 'I suppose we're going to have a taxi?'

'Angela's meeting us in the car.'

Then there wasn't much time for her to say what she had to. She pushed her suitcase at him and took hold of his arm in a proprietory manner. It wasn't that she needed his support or his reassurance, but she felt it essential that this daughter-in-law – how galling and disreputable to have two daughters-in-law! – should, in her first glimpse of them, see them consolidated and arm-in-arm.

'Eileen came in this morning,' she said as they gave up their tickets.

He shrugged absently. 'I wonder you two don't live together.'

'That'd make things easy for you. You wouldn't have to keep a roof over her head.' Mrs Hathall tightened her grip on the arm which he had attempted to jerk away. 'She said to give you her love and say why don't you go round one evening while you're in London.'

'You must be joking,' said Robert Hathall, but he said it vaguely and without much rancour. He was scanning the car park.

Pursuing her theme, Mrs Hathall began 'It's a wicked shame . . .' and then stopped in mid-sentence. A marvellous realization was dawning on her. She knew that car of Robert's, would know it anywhere, he'd had it long enough thanks to the straits that women had brought him to. She too let her sharp eyes rove round the tarmac square, and then she said in a satisfied tone, 'Doesn't look as if she'd put herself out to meet us.'

Robert seemed discomfited. 'The train was a couple of minutes early.'

'It was three minutes late,' said his mother. She sighed happily. Eileen would have been there to meet them all right.

Eileen would have been on the platform with a kiss for her mother-in-law and a cheerful promise of the nice tea that awaited them. And her granddaughter too . . . Mrs Hathall remarked as if to herself but loud enough to be heard, 'Poor little Rosemary.'

It was very unlike Robert, who was his mother's son, to take this sort of aggravation without comment, but again he made none. 'It doesn't matter,' he said. 'It's not that far.'

'I can walk,' said Mrs Hathall in the stoical tone of one who realizes that there will be worse trials to come and that the first and lightest must be bravely borne. 'I'm quite used to walking.'

Their journey took them up the station approach and Station Road, across Kingsmarkham High Street and along the Stowerton Road. It was a fine September evening, the air aglow with sunset light, the trees heavily foliaged, the gardens bright with the last and finest flowers of summer. But Mrs Hathall, who might have said like the lover in the ballad, 'What are the beauties of nature to me?', disregarded it all. Her wistfulness had given way to certainty. Robert's depression could mean only one thing. This wife of his, this thief, this breaker of a happy marriage, was going to let him down and he knew it.

They turned into Wool Lane, a narrow tree-shaded byway without a pavement. 'That's what I call a nice house,' said Mrs Hathall.

Robert glanced at the detached, between-the-wars villa. 'It's the only one down here apart from ours. A woman called Lake lives there. She's a widow.'

'Pity it's not yours,' said his mother with a wealth of implication. 'Is it much further?'

'Round the next bend. I can't think what's happened to Angela.' He looked at her uneasily. 'I'm sorry about this, Mother. I really am sorry.'

She was so amazed that he should depart from family

tradition as actually to apologize for anything, that she could make no answer to this and remained silent until the cottage came into view. A slight disappointment marred her satisfaction, for this was a house, a decent though old house of brown brick with a neat slate roof. 'Is this it?'

He nodded and opened the gate for her. Mrs Hathall observed that the garden was untended, the flower-beds full of weeds and the grass inches high. Under a neglected-looking tree lay a scattering of rotten plums. She said, 'Hmm,' a noncommittal noise characteristic of her and signifying that things were turning out the way she expected. He put the key in the front-door lock and the door swung open. 'Come along in, Mother.'

He was certainly upset now. There was no mistaking it. She knew that way he had of compressing his lips while a little muscle worked in his left cheek. And there was a harsh nervous note in his voice as he called out, 'Angela, we're here!'

Mrs Hathall followed him into the living room. She could hardly believe her eyes. Where were the dirty teacups, finger-marked gin glasses, scattered clothes, crumbs and dust? She planted herself rectangularly on the spotless carpet and turned slowly round, scrutinizing the ceiling for cobwebs, the windows for smears, the ashtrays for that forgotten cigarette end. A strange uncomfortable chill took hold of her. She felt like a champion who, confident of victory, certain of her own superiority, loses the first set to a tyro.

Robert came back and said, 'I can't think where Angela's got to. She's not in the garden. I'll just go into the garage and see if the car's there. Would you like to go on upstairs, Mother? Your bedroom's the big one at the back.'

Having ascertained that the dining-room table wasn't laid and that there was no sign of preparations for a meal in the immaculate kitchen where the rubber gloves and dusting gloves of household labour lay beside the sink, Mrs Hathall mounted the stairs. She ran one finger along the picture rail on the landing. Not a mark, the woodwork might have been newly painted. The bedroom which was to be hers was as exquisitely clean as the rest of the house, the bed turned down to show candy-striped sheets, one dressing-table drawer open and lined with tissue paper. She noted it all but never once, as one revelation followed another, did she allow this evidence of Angela's excellence to mitigate her hatred. It was a pity that her daughter-in-law should have armed herself with this wea-pon, a pity and that was all. No doubt her other faults, such as this one of not being here to greet her, would more than compensate for this small virtue.

Mrs Hathall went into the bathroom. Polished enamel, clean fluffy towels, guest soap . . . She set her mouth grimly. Money couldn't have been as tight as Robert made out. She told herself only that she resented his deception, not putting even into thought-words that she was confronting a second deprivation, that of not being able to throw their poverty and the reason for it in their faces. She washed her hands and came out on to the landing. The door to the main bedroom was slightly ajar. Mrs Hathall hesitated. But the temptation to take a look inside and perhaps find a tumbled bed, a mess of squalid cosmetics, was too great to resist. She entered the room carefully.

The bed wasn't tumbled but neatly made. On top of the covers lay a girl face-downwards, apparently deeply asleep. Her dark, rather shaggy, hair lay spread over her shoulders and her left arm was flung out. Mrs Hathall said, 'Hmm,' all her warm pleasure welling back unalloyed. Robert's wife was lying asleep, perhaps even drunk. She hadn't bothered to take off her canvas shoes before collapsing there and she was dressed exactly as she had been that day in Earls Court, probably as she always dressed, in shabby faded blue jeans and a red check shirt. Mrs Hathall thought of Eileen's pretty afternoon dresses and short permed hair, of Eileen who would only have slept in the daytime if she had been at death's door, and then she went over to the bed and stared down, frowning. 'Hmm,' she said again, but this time it was a 'Hmm' of admonition, designed to announce her presence and get an immediate shamed response.

There was none. The genuine anger of the person who feels herself unbearably slighted seized Mrs Hathall. She put her hand on her daughter-in-law's shoulder to shake it. But she didn't shake it. The flesh of that neck was icy cold, and as she lifted the veil of hair, she saw a pallid cheek, swollen and bluish.

Most women would have screamed. Mrs Hathall made no sound. Her body became a little more set and cupboard-like as she drew herself upright and placed her thick large hand to her palpitating heart. Many times in her long life she had seen death, her parents', her husband's, uncles', aunts', but she had never before seen what the purplish mark on that neck showed – death by violence. No thought of triumph came to her and no fear. She felt nothing but shock. Heavily, she plodded across the room and began to descend the stairs.

Robert was waiting at the foot of them. In so far as she was capable of love, she loved him, and in going up to him and placing her hand on his arm, she addressed him in a muted reluctant voice, the nearest she could get to tenderness. And she used the only words she knew for breaking this kind of bad news.

'There's been an accident. You'd best go up and see for yourself. It's – it's too late to do anything. Try and take it like a man.'

He stood quite still. He didn't speak.

'She's gone, Robert, your wife's dead.' She repeated the words because he didn't seem to take them in. 'Angela's dead, son.'

A vague uncomfortable feeling came over her that she ought to embrace him, speak some tender word, but she had long ago forgotten how. Besides, she was shaking now and her heart was pumping irregularly. He had neither paled nor flushed. Steadily he walked past her and mounted the stairs. She waited there, impotent, awe-stricken, rubbing her hands together and hunching her shoulders. Then he called out from above in a harsh but calm voice:

'Phone the police, Mother, and tell them what's happened.'

She was glad of something to do, and finding the phone on a low table under a bookshelf, she set her finger to the nine slot in the dial.

CHAPTER TWO

He was a tall man, carrying insufficient weight for his wide frame. And he had an unhealthy look, his belly sagging a little, his skin a mottled red. Though still black, his hair was thinning and dry, and his features were bold and harsh. He sat in an armchair, slumped as if he had been injured and then flung there. By contrast, his mother sat upright, her solid legs pressed close together, her hands palm-downwards on her lap, her hard eyes fixed on her son with more of sternness than sympathy.

Chief Inspector Wexford thought of those Spartan mothers who preferred seeing their sons brought home on their shields to knowing they were taken captive. He wouldn't have been surprised if she had told this man to pull himself together, but she hadn't yet uttered a word or made any sign to himself and Inspector Burden beyond giving them a curt nod when admitting them to the house. She looked, he thought, like an old-style prison wardress or mistress of a workhouse.

From upstairs the footfalls of other policemen could be heard, passing to and fro. The woman's body had been photographed where it lay, had been identified by the widower and removed to the mortuary. But the men still had much to do. The house was being examined for fingerprints, for the weapon, for some clue as to how this girl had met her death. And it was a big house for a cottage, with five good-sized rooms apart from the kitchen and the bathroom. They had been there since eight and now it was nearly midnight.

Wexford, who stood by the table on which lay the dead woman's driving licence, purse and the other contents of her handbag, was examining her passport. It identified her as a British subject, born in Melbourne, Australia, thirty-two years old, occupation housewife, hair dark brown, eyes grey, height five feet five inches, no distinguishing marks. Angela Margaret Hathall. The passport was three years old and had never been used to pass any port. The photograph in it bore about as much resemblance to the dead woman as such photographs usually bear to their subjects.

'Your wife lived alone here during the week, Mr Hathall?' he said, moving away from the table and sitting down.

Hathall nodded. He answered in a low voice not much above a whisper. 'I used to work in Toxborough. When I got a new job in London I couldn't travel up and down. That was in July. I've been living with my mother during the week, coming home for weekends.'

'You and your mother arrived here at seven-thirty, I think?'

'Twenty past,' said Mrs Hathall, speaking for the first time. She had a harsh metallic voice. Under the South London accent lay a hint of North Country origins.

'So you hadn't seen your wife since – when? Last Sunday? Monday?'

'Sunday night,' said Hathall. 'I went to my mother's by train on Sunday night. My – Angela drove me to the station. I – I phoned her every day. I phoned her today. At lunchtime. She was all right.' He made a breath-catching sound like a sob, and his body swayed forward. 'Who – who would have done this? Who would have wanted to kill – *Angela*?'

The words had a stagy ring, a false sound, as if they had been learned from some television play or cliché-ridden thriller. But Wexford knew that grief can sometimes only be expressed in platitudes. We are original in our happy moments. Sorrow has only one voice, one cry.

He answered the question in similarly hackneyed words. 'That's what we have to find out, Mr Hathall. You were at work all day?'

'Marcus Flower, Public Relations Consultants. Half Moon Street. I'm an accountant.' Hathall cleared his throat. 'You can check with them that I was there all day.'

Wexford didn't quite raise his eyebrows. He stroked his chin and looked at the man in silence. Burden's face gave nothing away, but he could tell the inspector was thinking the same thought as his own. And during this silence Hathall, who had uttered this last sentence almost with eagerness, gave a louder sob and buried his face in his hands.

Rigid as stone, Mrs Hathall said, 'Don't give way, son. Bear it like a man.'

But I must feel it like a man . . . As the bit from *Macbeth* came into Wexford's mind, he wondered fleetingly why he felt so little sympathy for Hathall, why he wasn't moved. Was he getting the way he'd always sworn he wouldn't get? Was he getting hard and indifferent at last? Or was there really something false in the man's behaviour that gave the lie to these sobs and this abandonment to grief? Probably he was just tired, reading meanings where there were none; probably the woman had picked up a stranger and that stranger had killed her. He waited till Hathall had taken his hands away and raised his face.

'Your car is missing?'

'It was gone from the garage when I got home.' There were no tears on the hard thin cheeks. Would a son of that flint-faced woman be capable of squeezing out tears?

'I'll want a description of your car and its number. Sergeant Martin will get the details from you in a minute.' Wexford got up. 'The doctor has given you a sedative, I believe. I suggest you take it and try to get some sleep. In the morning I should like to talk to you again, but there's very little more we can do tonight.'

Mrs Hathall shut the door on them in the manner of one snapping 'Not today, thanks' at a couple of hawkers. For a moment or two Wexford stood on the path, surveying the place. Light from the bedroom windows showed him a couple of lawns that hadn't been mown for months and a bare plum tree. The path was paved but the drive which ran

between the house wall and the right-hand fence was a strip
of concrete.

'Where's this garage he was talking about?'

'Must be round the back,' said Burden. 'There wasn't room
to build a garage on the side.'

They followed the drive round the back of the cottage. It
led them to an asbestos hut with a felt roof, a building which
couldn't be seen from the lane.

'If she went for a drive,' said Wexford, 'and brought
someone back with her, the chances are they got the car into
this garage without a soul seeing them. They'd have gone into
the house by the kitchen door. We'll be lucky if we find anyone
who saw them.'

In silence they regarded the moonlit empty fields that
mounted towards wooded hills. Here and there, in the distance,
an occasional light twinkled. And as they walked back towards
the road, they were aware of how isolated the house was, how
secluded the lane. Its high banks, crowned by massive overhanging trees, made it a black tunnel by night, a sylvan
unfrequented corridor by day.

'The nearest house,' said Wexford, 'is that place up by the
Stowerton Road, and the only other one is Wool Farm. That's
a good half-mile down there.' He pointed through the tree
tunnel and then he went off to his car. 'We can say good-bye
to our weekend,' he said. 'See you first thing in the morning.'

The chief inspector's own home was to the north of
Kingsmarkham on the other side of the Kingsbrook. His
bedroom light was on and his wife still awake when he let
himself in. Dora Wexford was too placid and too sensible to
wait up for her husband, but she had been baby-sitting for her
elder daughter and had only just got back. He found her sitting
up in bed reading, a glass of hot milk beside her, and although
he had only parted from her four hours before, he went up
to her and kissed her warmly. The kiss was warmer than usual
because, happy as his marriage was, contented with his lot as

he was, it sometimes took external disaster to bring home to him his good fortune and how much he valued his wife. Another man's wife was dead, had died foully . . . He pushed aside squeamishness, his small-hours sensitivity and, starting to undress, asked Dora what she knew of the occupants of Bury Cottage.

'Where's Bury Cottage?'

'In Wool Lane. A man called Hathall lives there. His wife was strangled this afternoon.'

Thirty years of marriage to a policeman hadn't blunted Dora Wexford's sensibilities or coarsened her speech or made her untender, but it was only natural that she could no longer react to such a statement with the average woman's horror.

'Oh, dear,' she said, and conventionally, 'How dreadful! Is it going to be straightforward?'

'Don't know yet.' Her soft calm voice steadied him as it always did. 'Have you ever come across these people?'

'The only person I've ever come across in Wool Lane is that Mrs Lake. She came to the Women's Institute a couple of times, but I think she was too busy in other directions to bother much with that. Very much a one for the men, you know.'

'You don't mean the Women's Institute blackballed her?' said Wexford in mock-horror.

'Don't so so silly, darling. We're not narrow-minded. She's a widow, after all. I can't think why she hasn't married again.'

'Maybe she's like George the Second.'

'Not a bit. She's very pretty. What *do* you mean?'

'He promised his wife on her death-bed that he wouldn't marry again but only take mistresses.' While Dora giggled, Wexford studied his figure in the glass, drawing in the muscles of his belly. In the past year he had lost three stone in weight, thanks to diet, exercise and the terror inspired in him by his doctor, and for the first time in a decade he could regard his own reflection with contentment if not with actual delight. Now he could feel that it had been worth it. The agony of going without everything he liked to eat and drink had been worth while. *Il faut souffrir pour être beau.* If only there was something one could go without, some strenuous game one could play, that would result in remedying hair loss . . .

'Come to bed,' said Dora. 'If you don't stop preening yourself, I'll think you're going to take mistresses, and I'm not dead yet.'

Wexford grinned and got into bed. Quite early in his career he had taught himself not to dwell on work during the night, and work had seldom kept him awake or troubled his dreams. But as he switched off the bed lamp and cuddled up to Dora – so much easier and pleasanter now he was thin – he allowed himself a few minutes' reflection on the events of the evening. It could be a straightforward case, it very well could be. Angela Hathall had been young and probably nice to look at. She was childless, and though house-proud, must have found time hanging heavily on her hands during those lonely weekdays and lonely nights. What more likely than that she had picked up some man and brought him back to Bury Cottage? Wexford knew that a woman need not be desperate or a nymphomaniac or on the road to prostitution to do this. She need not even intend infidelity. For women's attitudes to sex, whatever the new thought may hold, are not the same as men's. And though it is broadly true that a man who will pick up an unknown woman is only 'after one thing' and broadly speaking she knows it, she will cling to the generous belief that he wants nothing but conversation and perhaps a kiss. Had this been Angela Hathall's belief? Had she picked up a man in her car, a man who wanted more than that and had strangled her because he couldn't get it? Had he killed her and left her on the bed and then made a getaway in her car?

It could be. Wexford decided he would work along these lines. Turning his thoughts to more pleasant topics, his grand-children, his recent holiday, he was soon asleep.

CHAPTER THREE

'Mr Hathall,' Wexford said, 'you no doubt have your own ideas as to how this sort of enquiry should be conducted. You will perhaps think my methods unorthodox, but they are my methods and I can assure you they get results. I can't conduct my investigation on circumstantial evidence alone. It's necessary for me to know as much as I can about the persons involved, so if you can answer my questions simply and realistically we shall get on a lot faster. I can assure you I shall ask them from the pure and direct motive of wanting to discover who killed your wife. If you take offence we shall be delayed. If you insist that certain matters concern only your private life and refuse to disclose them, a good deal of precious time may be lost. Do you understand that and will you be cooperative?'

This speech had been occasioned by Hathall's reaction to the first query that Wexford had put to him at nine on the Saturday morning. It had been a simple request for information as to whether Angela had been in the habit of giving lifts to strangers, but Hathall who seemed refreshed by his night of drugged sleep, had flared at it in a burst of ill-temper.

'What right have you got to impugn my wife's moral character?'

Wexford had said quietly, 'The great majority of people who give lifts to hitchhikers have no thought in their minds beyond that of being helpful,' and then, when Hathall continued to stare at him with bitter angry eyes, he had delivered his lecture.

The widower made an impatient gesture, shrugging and throwing out his hands. 'In a case like this I should have thought you'd go on fingerprints and – well, that sort of thing.

I mean, it's obvious some man got in here and . . . He must have left traces. I've read about how these things are conducted. It's a question of deduction from hairs and footmarks and – well, fingerprints.'

'I've already said I'm sure you have your own ideas as to how an enquiry should be conducted. My methods include those you have put forward. You saw for yourself how thoroughly this house was gone over last night, but we're not magicians, Mr Hathall. We can't find a fingerprint or a hair at midnight and tell you whose it is nine hours later.'

'When will you be able to?'

'That I can't say. Certainly by later today I should have some idea as to whether a stranger entered Bury Cottage yesterday afternoon.'

'A *stranger*? Of course it was a stranger. I could have told you that myself at eight o'clock last night. A pathological killer who got in here, broke in, I daresay, and – and afterwards stole my car. Have you found my car yet?'

Very smoothly and coldly, Wexford said, 'I don't know, Mr Hathall. I am not God, nor have I second sight. I haven't yet even had time to contact my officers. If you'll answer the one question I've put to you, I'll leave you for a while and go and talk to your mother.'

'My mother knows nothing whatever about it. My mother never set foot in his house till last night.'

'My question, Mr Hathall.'

'No, she wasn't in the habit of giving lifts,' Hathall shouted, his face crimson and distorted. 'She was too shy and nervous even to make friends down here. I was the only person she could trust, and no wonder after what she'd been through. The man who got in here knew that, he knew she was always alone. You want to work on that, get to work on that one. That's my private life, as you call it. I'd only been married three years and I worshipped my wife. But I left her alone all week because I couldn't face the journey up and down and this is what it's come to. She was scared stiff of being alone here. I said it wouldn't be for much longer and to stick it for my sake. Well, it wasn't for much longer, was it?'

He threw his arm over the back of the chair and buried his face in the crook of his elbow, his body shaking. Wexford watched him thoughtfully but said no more. He made his way towards the kitchen where he found Mrs Hathall at the sink, washing breakfast dishes. There was a pair of rubber gloves on the counter but they were dry and Mrs Hathall's bare hands were immersed in the suds. She was the sort of woman, he decided, who would be masochistic about housework, would probably use a brush rather than a vacuum cleaner and aver that washing machines didn't get your clothes clean. He saw that instead of an apron she wore a checked tea towel tied round her waist, and this struck him as strange. Obviously she wouldn't have brought an apron with her for a weekend visit, but surely anyone as house-proud as Angela would have possessed several? However, he made no comment on it, but said good morning and asked Mrs Hathall if she would mind answering a few questions while she worked.

'Hmm,' said Mrs Hathall. She rinsed her hands and turned round slowly to dry them on a towel which hung from a rack. 'It's no good asking me. I don't know what she got up to while he was away.'

'I understand your daughter-in-law was shy and lonely, kept herself to herself, as you might say.' The noise she made fascinated him. It was part choke, part grunt, with a hint of the death rattle. He assumed it was, in fact, a laugh. 'She didn't impress you in that way?'

'Erotic,' said Mrs Hathall.

'*I beg your pardon?*'

She looked at him with scorn. 'Nervy. More like hysterical.'

'Ah,' said Wexford. This particular malapropism was new to him and he savoured it. 'Why was that, I wonder? Why was she – er, neurotic?'

'I couldn't say. I only saw her once.'

But they had been married for three years . . . 'I'm not sure I understand, Mrs Hathall.'

She shifted her gaze from his face to the window, from the window to the sink, and then she picked up another cloth and began drying the dishes. Her solid board of a body, its back turned to him, was as expressive of discouragement and exclusion as a closed door. She dried every cup and glass and plate and piece of cutlery in silence, scoured the draining board, dried it, hung the cloth up with the concentration of one practising an intricate and hard-learned skill. But at last she was obliged to turn again and confront his seated patient figure.

'I've got the beds to make,' she said.

'Your daughter-in-law has been murdered, Mrs Hathall.'

'I ought to know that. I found her.'

'Yes. How was that exactly?'

'I've already said. I've told it all already.' She opened the broom cupboard, took a brush, a duster, superfluous tools unneeded in that speckless house. 'I've got work to do, if you haven't.'

'Mrs Hathall,' he said softly, 'do you realize that you will have to appear at the inquest? You're a most important witness. You will be very closely questioned and you will *not be able* to refuse to answer then. I can understand that you have never before come into contact with the law, but I must tell you that there are serious penalties attached to obstructing the police.'

She stared at him sullenly, only a little awed. 'I should never have come here,' she muttered. 'I said I'd never set foot here and I should have stuck to it.'

'Why did you come?'

'Because my son insisted. He wanted things patched up.' She plodded to within a yard of him and stopped. Wexford was reminded of an illustration in a storybook belonging to one of his grandsons, a picture of a cabinet with arms and legs and a surly face. 'I'll tell you one thing,' she said, 'if that Angela was nervy, it was shame that did it. She was ashamed of breaking up his marriage and making him a poor man. And so she should have been, she ruined three people's lives. I'll say that at your inquest. I don't mind telling anyone that.'

'I doubt,' said Wexford, 'if you will be asked. I'm asking you about last night.'

She jerked up her head. Petulantly, she said, 'I'm sure I've nothing to hide. I'm thinking of him, having everything dragged out in the open. She was supposed to meet us at the station last night.' A dry 'Hmm' snapped off the last word.

'But she was dead, Mrs Hathall.'

Ignoring him, she went on shortly and rapidly, 'We got here and he went to look for her. He called out to her. He looked everywhere downstairs and in the garden and in the garage.'

'And upstairs?'

'He didn't go upstairs. He told me to go upstairs and take my things off. I went in their bedroom and there she was. Satisfied? Ask him and see if he can tell you different.' The walking cupboard stumped out of the room and the stairs creaked as it mounted them.

Wexford went back into the room where Hathall was, not moving stealthily but not making much noise either. He had been in the kitchen for about half an hour, and perhaps Hathall believed he had already left the house, for he had made a very rapid recovery from his abandonment to grief, and was standing by the window peering closely at something on the front page of the morning paper. The expression on his lean ruddy face was one of extreme concentration, intense, even calculating, and his hands were quite steady. Wexford gave a slight cough. Hathall didn't jump. He turned round and the anguish which Wexford could have sworn was real again convulsed his face.

'I won't bother you again, now Mr Hathall. I've been

thinking about this and I believe it would be much better for you to talk to me in different surroundings. Under the circumstances, these aren't perhaps the best for the sort of talk we must have. Will you come down to the police station at about three, please, and ask for me?'

Hathall nodded. He seemed relieved. 'I'm sorry I lost my temper just now.'

'That's all right. It was natural. Before you come this afternoon, would you have a look through your wife's things and tell me if you think anything is missing?'

'Yes, I'll do that. Your men won't want to go over the place any more?'

'No, all that's over.'

As soon as Wexford reached his own office in Kingsmark-ham police station, he looked through the morning papers and found the one Hathall had been scrutinizing, the *Daily Tele-graph*. At the foot of the front page, in the stop press, was a paragraph about an inch deep which read: 'Mrs Angela Hathall, 32, was last night found dead at her home in Wool Lane, Kingsmarkham, Sussex. She had been strangled. Police are treating the case as murder.' It was this on which Hathall's eyes had been fixed with such intensity. Wexford pondered for a moment. If his wife had been found murdered, the last thing he would have wanted would be to read about it in the paper. He spoke this thought aloud as Burden came into the room, adding that it didn't do to project one's own feelings on to others, for we can't all be the same.

'Sometimes,' said Burden rather gloomily, 'I think that if everyone was like you and me the world would be a better place.'

'Arrogant devil, you are. Have we got anything from the fingerprint boys yet? Hathall's dead keen on prints. He's one of those people who labour under the misapprehension that we're like foxhounds. Show us a print or a footmark and we put our noses to the ground and follow spoor until we run down our quarry about two hours later.'

RUTH RENDELL

Burden snorted. He thrust a sheaf of papers under the chief inspector's nose. 'It's all here,' he said. 'I've had a look and there are points of interest, but the fox isn't going to turn up in two hours or anything like it. Whoever he is, he's far, far away, and you can tell John Peel that one.'

Grinning, Wexford said, 'No sign of that car, I suppose?'

'It'll probably turn up in Glasgow or somewhere in the middle of next week. Martin checked with that company of Hathall's, Marcus Flower. He had a word with his secretary. She's called Linda Kipling and she says Hathall was there all day yesterday. They both came in at about ten – my God, I should be so lucky! – and apart from an hour and a half off for lunch, Hathall was there till he left at five-thirty.'

'Just because I said he'd been reading about his wife's murder in the paper, I didn't mean I thought he'd done it, you know.' Wexford patted the seat of the chair next to his own and said, 'Sit down, Mike, and tell me what's in that – that ream you've brought me. Condense it. I'll have a look at it myself later.'

The inspector sat down and put on his newly acquired glasses. They were elegant glasses with narrow black frames and they gave Burden the look of a successful barrister. With his large collection of well-tailored suits, his expertly cut fair hair and a figure that needed no dieting to keep it trim, he had never had the air of a detective – a fact which had been to his advantage. His voice was prim and precise, a little more selfconscious than usual, because he wasn't yet accustomed to the glasses which he seemed to regard as changing his whole appearance and indeed his personality.

'The first thing to note, I'd say,' he began, 'is that there weren't nearly as many prints about the house as one would expect. It was exceptionally well-kept house, everything very clean and well polished. She must have cleaned it very thoroughly indeed because there were hardly any of Hathall's own prints. There was a clear whole handprint on the front door and prints on other doors and the banisters, but those were obviously made after he got home last night. Mrs Hathall senior's prints were on the kitchen counter, the banisters, in the back bedroom, on the bathroom taps and lavatory cistern, on the telephone and, oddly enough, on the picture rail on the landing.'

'Not oddly enough at all,' said Wexford. 'She's the sort of old battleaxe who'd feel along a picture rail to see if her daughter-in-law had dusted it. And if she hadn't, she'd probably write "slut" or something equally provocative in the dust.'

Burden adjusted his glasses, smudged them with his fingertip and rubbed impatiently at them with his short cuff. 'Angela's prints were on the back door, the door from the kitchen into the hall, her bedroom door and on various bottles and jars on her dressing table. But they weren't anywhere else. Apparently she wore gloves for doing her housework, and if she took off her gloves to go to the bathroom, she wiped everything afterwards.'

'Sounds bloody obsessional to me. But I suppose some women do go on like that.'

Burden, whose expression conveyed that he rather approved of women who went on like that, said, 'The only other prints in the house were those of one unknown man and one unknown woman. The man's were found only on books and on the inside of a bedroom cupboard door, not Angela's bedroom. There's one single print of this other woman. It too was a whole handprint, the right hand, very clear, showing a small L-shaped scar on the forefinger, and it was found on the edge of the bath.'

'Hmm,' said Wexford, and because the sound reminded him of Mrs Hathall, he changed it to 'Huh.' He paused thoughtfully. 'I don't suppose these prints are on record?'

'Don't know yet. Give them time.'

'No, I mustn't be like Hathall. Is there anything else?'

'Some coarse long dark hair, three of them, on the bathroom

floor. They're not Angela's. Hers were finer. Hers alone were in her hairbrush on the dressing table.'

'Man's or woman's?'

'Impossible to tell. You know how long some blokes wear their hair these days.' Burden touched his own sleek crop and took off his glasses. 'We shan't get anything from the post-mortem till tonight.'

'OK. We have to find that car and we have to find someone who saw her go out in it and, let's hope, someone who saw her and her pick-up come back in it – if that's the way it was. We have to find her friends. She must have had *some* friends.'

They went down in the lift and crossed the black and white checkerboard foyer. While Burden paused for a word with the station sergeant, Wexford went up to the swing doors that gave on to the steps and the courtyard. A woman was coming up those steps, walking confidently in the manner of one who had never known rejection. Wexford held the right-hand door open for her, and as she came face to face with him she stopped and looked him full in the eyes.

She wasn't young. Her age couldn't have been far short of fifty, but it was at once apparent that she was one of those rare creatures whom time cannot wither or stale or devitalize. Every fine line on her face seemed the mark of laughter and mischievous wit, but there were few of these around her large bright blue and surprisingly young eyes. She smiled at him, a smile to make a man's heart turn over, and said:

'Good morning. My name is Nancy Lake. I want to see a policeman, the top one, someone very important. Are you important?'

'I daresay I will do,' said Wexford.

She looked him over as no woman had looked him over for twenty years. The smile became musing, delicate eyebrows went up. 'I really think you might,' she said, and stepping inside, 'However, we must be serious. I've come to tell you I think I was the last person to see Angela Hathall alive.'

CHAPTER FOUR

When a pretty woman ages, a man's reaction is usually to reflect on how lovely she must once have been. This was not Nancy Lake's effect. There was something very much of the here and now about her. When with her you thought no more of her youth and her coming old age than you think of spring or Christmas when you are enjoying late summer. She was of the season in which they were, a harvest-time woman, who brought to mind grape festivals and ripened fruit and long warm nights. These thoughts came to Wexford much later. As he led her into his office, he was aware only of how extremely pleasing this diversion was in the midst of murder and recalcitrant witnesses and fingerprints and missing cars. Besides, it wasn't exactly a diversion. Happy is the man who can combine pleasure and business ...

'What a nice room,' she said. Her voice was low and sweet and lively. 'I thought police stations were brown and murky with photographs on the walls of great brutes all wanted for robbing banks.' She glanced with warm approval at his carpet, his yellow chairs, his rosewood desk. 'This is lovely. And what a nice view over all those delicious little roofs. May I sit down?'

Wexford was already holding the chair for her. He was recalling what Dora had said about this woman being 'very much for the men' and added to this statement one of his own: that the men would be very much for her. She was dark. Her hair was abundant and of a rich chestnut brown, probably dyed. But her skin had kept a rose and amber glow, the extreme of a peach, and a delicate light seemed to shine from beneath its surface as is sometimes seen in the faces of young girls or children, but which is rarely retained into middle age.

The red lips seemed always on the edge of a smile. It was as if she knew some delightful secret which she would almost, but never wholly, divulge. Her dress was just what, in Wexford's opinion, a woman's dress should be, full in the skirt, tight in the waist, of mauve and blue printed cotton, its low neck showing an inch or two of the upper slopes of a full golden bosom. She saw that he was studying her and she seemed to enjoy his scrutiny, basking in it, understanding more thoroughly than he himself what it meant.

He shifted his gaze abruptly. 'You live in the house at the Kingsmarkham end of Wool Lane, I believe?'

'It's called Sunnybank. I always think that sounds like a mental hospital. But my late husband chose the name and I expect he had his reasons.'

Wexford made a determined and eventually successful attempt to look grave. 'Were you a friend of Mrs Hathall's?'

'Oh, *no*.' He thought she was capable of saying she had no women friends, which would have displeased him, but she didn't. 'I only went there for the miracles.'

'The *what*?'

'An in-joke. I'm sorry. I meant the yellow egg plums.'

'Ah, mira*belles*.' This was the second malapropism of his day, but he decided this particular instance was a deliberate mistake. 'You went there yesterday to pick plums?'

'I always do. Every year. I used to when old Mr Somerset lived there, and when the Hathalls came they said I could have them. I make them into jam.'

He had a sudden vision of Nancy Lake standing in a sunfilled kitchen, stirring a pot full of the golden fruit. He smelled the scent of it, saw her face as she dipped in a finger and brought it to those full red lips. The vision threatened to develop into a fantasy. He shook it off. 'When did you go there?'

The roughness in his voice made her eyebrows go up. 'I phoned Angela at nine in the morning and asked if I could go up there and pick them. I'd noticed they were falling. She seemed quite pleased – for her. She wasn't a very gracious person, you know.'

'I don't know. I hope you'll tell me.'

She moved her hands a little, deprecatingly, casually. 'She said to come about half past twelve. I picked the plums and she gave me a cup of coffee. I think she only asked me in to show me how nice the house looked.'

'Why? Didn't it always look nice?'

'Goodness, no. Not that I care, that was her business. I'm not much for housework myself, but Angela's house was usually a bit of pigsty. Anyway, it was a mess last March which was when I was last in it. She told me she'd cleaned it up to impress Robert's mother.'

Wexford nodded. He had to make an effort of will to continue questioning her in the impersonal way, for she exercised a spell, the magical combination of feminine niceness and strong sexuality. But the effort had to be made. 'Did she tell you she was expecting another caller, Mrs Lake?'

'No, she said she was going out in the car, but she didn't say where.' Nancy Lake leaned across the desk rather earnestly, bringing her face to within a foot of his. Her perfume was fruity and warm. 'She asked me in and gave me coffee, but as soon as I'd had one cup she seemed to want to get rid of me. That's what I meant by saying she only wanted to show me how nice the house looked.'

'What time did you leave?'

'Let me see. It would have been just before half past one. But I was only in the house ten minutes. The rest of the time I was picking the miracles.'

The temptation to remain close to that vital, mobile and somehow mischievous face was great, but it had to be resisted. Wexford swivelled his chair round with deliberate casualness, turning to Nancy Lake a stern and businesslike profile. 'You didn't see her leave Bury Cottage or return to it later?'

'No, I went to Myringham. I was in Myringham the whole afternoon and part of the evening.'

For the first time there was something guarded and secretive in her reply, but he made no comment. 'Tell me about Angela Hathall. What sort of person was she?'

'Brusque, tough, ungracious.' She shrugged, as if such failings in a woman were beyond her comprehension. 'Perhaps that's why she and Robert got on so well together.'

'Did they? They were a happy couple?'

'Oh, very. They had no eyes for anyone else, as the saying is.' Nancy Lake gave a light laugh. 'All in all to each other, you know. They had no friends, as far as I could tell.'

'I've been given the impression she was shy and nervous.'

'Have you now? I wouldn't say that. I got the idea she was on her own so much because she liked it that way. Of course, they'd been very badly off till he got this new job. She told me they only had fifteen pounds a week to live on after all his outgoings. He was paying alimony or whatever it's called to his first wife.' She paused and smiled. 'People make such messes of their lives, don't they?'

There was a hint of ruthfulness in her voice as if she had experience of such messes. He turned round again, for a thought had struck him. 'May I see your right hand, Mrs Lake?'

She gave it to him without question, not laying it on the table but placing it palm-downwards in his. It was almost a lover-like gesture and one that has become typical of the beginning of a relationship between a man and a woman, this covering of hand by hand, a first approach, a show of comfort and trust. Wexford felt its warmth, observed how smooth and tended it was, noted the soft sheen of the nails and the diamond ring which encircled the middle finger. Bemused, he let it rest there a fraction too long.

'If anyone had told me,' she said, her eyes dancing, 'that I should be holding hands with a policeman this morning, I shouldn't have believed them.'

Wexford said stiffly, 'I beg your pardon,' and turned her hand over. No L-shaped scar marred the smooth surface of the tip of her forefinger, and he let the hand drop.

'Is that how you check fingerprints? Goodness, I always thought it was a much more complicated process.'

'It is.' He didn't explain. 'Did Angela Hathall have a woman in to help with the cleaning?'

'Not as far as I know. They couldn't have afforded it.' She was doing her best to conceal her delight at his discomfiture, but he saw her lips twitch and delight won. 'Can I be of any further service to you, Mr Wexford? You wouldn't care to make casts of my footprints, for instance, or take a blood sample?'

'No, thank you. That won't be necessary. But I may want to talk to you again, Mrs Lake.'

'I do hope you will.' She got up gracefully and took a few steps towards the window. Wexford, who was obliged to rise when she did, found himself standing close beside her. She had manoeuvred this, he knew she had, but he could only feel flattered. How many years was it since a woman had flirted with him, had wanted to be with him and enjoyed the touch of his hand? Dora had done so, of course, his wife had done so . . . As he was drawing himself up, conscious of his new firm figure, he remembered his wife. He remembered that he was not only a policeman but a husband who must be mindful of his marriage vows. But Nancy Lake had laid her hand lightly on his arm, was drawing his attention to the sunshine outside, the cars in the High Street that had begun their long progress to the coast.

'Just the weather for a day by the sea, isn't it?' she said. The remark sounded wistful, like an invitation. 'What a shame you have to work on a Saturday.' What a shame work and convention and prudence prevented him from leading this woman to his car, driving her to some quiet hotel. Champagne and roses, he thought, and that hand once more reaching

371

across a table to lie warmly in his . . . 'And the winter will soon be here,' she said.

Surely she couldn't have meant it, couldn't have intended that double meaning? That the winter would soon be there for both of them, the flesh falling, the blood growing cold . . . 'I mustn't keep you,' he said, his voice as icy as that coming winter.

She laughed, not at all offended, but she took her hand from his arm and walked towards the door. 'You might at least say it was good of me to come.'

'It was. Very public-spirited. Good morning, Mrs Lake.'

'Good morning, Mr Wexford. You must come to tea quite soon and I'll give you some miracle jam.'

He sent for someone to see her out. Instead of sitting down once more behind his desk, he returned to the window and looked down, and there she was, crossing the courtyard with the assurance of youth, as if the world belonged to her. It didn't occur to him that she would look back and up but she did, suddenly, as if his thoughts had communicated themselves to her and called that swift glance. She waved. Her arm went up straight and she waved her hand. They might have known each other all their lives, so warm and free and intimate was that gesture, having separated after a delightful assignation that was no less sweet because it was customary. He raised his own arm in something like a salute, and then, when she had disappeared among the crowd of Saturday shoppers, he too went down to find Burden and take him off for lunch.

The Carousel Café, opposite the police station, was always crowded at Saturday lunchtime, but at least the juke box was silent. The real noise would start when the kids came in at six. Burden was sitting at the corner table they kept permanently reserved, and when Wexford approached, the proprietor, a meek Italian, came up to him deferentially and with considerable respect.

'My special today for you, Chief Inspector. The liver and bacon I can recommend.'

'All right, Antonio, but none of your reconstituted potato, eh? And no monosodium glutamate.'

Antonio looked puzzled. 'This is not on my menu, Mr Wexford.'

'No, but it's there all right, the secret agent, the alimentary fifth column. I trust you've had no more speedy goings-on of late?'

'Thanks to you, sir, we have not.'

The reference was to an act of mischief performed a couple of weeks before by one of Antonio's youthful part-time employees. Bored by the sobriety of the clientele, this boy had introduced into the glass tank of orange juice with its floating plastic oranges, one hundred amphetamine tablets, and the result had been a merry near-riot, a hitherto decorous businessman actually dancing on a table top. Wexford, chancing to call in and, on account of his diet, sampling the orange juice himself, had located the source of this almost Saturnalian jollity and, simultaneously, the joker. Recalling all this now, he laughed heartily.

'What's so funny?' said Burden sourly. 'Or has that Mrs Lake been cheering you up?' When Wexford stopped laughing but didn't answer, he said, 'Martin's taken a room in the church hall, a sort of enquiry post and general information pool. The public are being notified in the hope that anyone who may have seen Angela on Friday afternoon will come in and tell us about it. And if she didn't go out, there's a possibility her visitor was seen.'

'She went out,' said Wexford. 'She told Mrs Lake she was going out in the car. I wonder who the lady with the L-shaped scar is, Mike. Not Mrs Lake, and Mrs Lake says Angela didn't have a cleaner, or, come to that, any friends.'

'And who's the man who fingers the inside of cupboard doors?'

The arrival of the liver and bacon and Burden's spaghetti Bolognese silenced them for a few minutes. Wexford drank his orange juice, wistfully thinking how much he would enjoy it if this tankful had been 'speeded' up and Burden were suddenly to become merry and uninhibited. But the inspector, eating fastidiously, wore the resigned look of one who has sacrificed his weekend to duty. Deep lines, stretching from nostrils to the corners of his mouth, intensified as he said:

'I was going to take my kids to the seaside.'

Wexford thought of Nancy Lake who would look well in a swimsuit, but he switched off the picture before it developed into a full-colour three-dimensional image. 'Mike, at this stage of a case we usually ask each other if we've noticed anything odd, any discrepancies or downright untruths. Have you noticed anything?'

'Can't say I have, except the lack of prints.'

'She'd spring-cleaned the place to impress the old woman, though I agree it was strange she seems to have wiped everything again before going off on her car jaunt. Mrs Lake had coffee with her at about one, but Mrs Lake's prints aren't anywhere. But there's something else that strikes me as even odder than that, the way Hathall behaved when he got into the house last night.'

Burden pushed away his empty plate, contemplated the menu, and rejecting the idea of a sweet, signalled to Antonio for coffee. 'Was it odd?' he said.

'Hathall and his wife had been married for three years. During that time the old woman had only met her daughter-in-law once, and there had evidently been considerable antagonism between them. This appears to have something to do with Angela's having broken up Hathall's first marriage. Be that as it may – and I mean to learn more about it – Angela and her mother-in-law seem to have been at loggerheads. Yet there was a kind of *rapprochement*, the old woman had been persuaded to come for the weekend and Angela was preparing to receive her to the extent of titivating the place far beyond her normal standard. Now Angela was supposed to be meeting them at the station, but she didn't turn up. Hathall says she was shy and nervous, Mrs Lake that she was brusque and ungracious. Bearing this in mind, what conclusions would you expect Hathall to have drawn when his wife wasn't at the station?'

'That she'd got cold feet. That she was too frightened to face her mother-in-law.'

'Exactly. But what happened when he got to Bury Cottage? He couldn't find Angela. He looked for her *downstairs* and in the garden. He never went upstairs at all. And yet by then he must have suspected Angela's nervousness and concluded surely that a nervous woman takes refuge not in the garden but in her own bedroom. But instead of looking upstairs for her, *he sent his mother*, the very person he must have believed Angela to be frightened of. This shy and nervous girl to whom he is alleged to be devoted was cowering – he must have thought – in her bedroom, but instead of going up to reassure her and then bring her to confront his mother with him there to support her, he goes off to the garage. That, Mike, is very odd indeed.'

Burden nodded. 'Drink your coffee,' he said. 'You said Hathall was coming in at three. Maybe he'll give you an answer.'

CHAPTER FIVE

Although Wexford pretended to study the list of missing articles
– a bracelet, a couple of rings and a gilt neck chain – Hathall
had brought him, he was really observing the man himself.
He had come into the office with head bowed, and now he
sat silent, his hands folded in his lap. But the combination of
ruddy skin and black hair gives a man an angry look. Hathall,
in spite of his grief, looked angry and resentful. His hard
craggy features had the appearance of being carved out of
roseate granite, his hands were large and red, and even his
eyes, though not bloodshot, held a red gleam. Wexford wouldn't
have judged him attractive to women, yet he had had two
wives. Was it perhaps that certain women, very feminine or
nervous or maladjusted women, saw him as a rock to which
they might cling, a stronghold where they might find shelter?
Possibly that colouring of his indicated passion and tenacity
and strength as well as ill-temper.

Wexford placed the list on his desk and, looking up, said,
'What do you think happened yesterday afternoon, Mr Hathall?'

'Are you asking *me* that?'

'Presumably you knew your wife better than anyone else
knew her. You'd know who would be likely to call on her or
be fetched home by her.'

Hathall frowned, and the frown darkened his whole face.
'I've already said, some man got into the house for the purpose
of robbery. He took those things on that list and when my
wife interrupted him, he – he killed her. What else could it
have been? It's obvious.'

'I don't think so. I believe that whoever came to your
house wiped the place clean of a considerable number of

376

fingerprints. A thief wouldn't have needed to do that. He'd have worn gloves. And although he might have struck your wife, he wouldn't have strangled her. Besides, I see here that you value the missing property at less than fifty pounds all told. True, people have been killed for less, but I doubt if any woman has ever been strangled for such a reason.'

When Wexford repeated the word 'strangled,' Hathall again bowed his head. 'What alternative is there?' he muttered.

'Tell me who came to your house. What friends or acquaintances called on your wife?'

'We had no friends,' said Hathall. 'When we came here we were more or less on the breadline. You need money to make friends in a place like this. We hadn't got the money to join clubs or give dinner parties or even have people in for drinks. Angela often didn't see a soul from Sunday night till Friday night. And the friends I'd had before I married her – well, my first wife saw to it I'd lost them.' He coughed impatiently and tossed his head in the way his mother had. 'Look, I think I'd better tell you a bit about what Angela and I had been through, and then perhaps you'll see that all this talk of friends calling is arrant nonsense.'

'Perhaps you had, Mr Hathall.'

'It'll be my life history.' Hathall gave a humourless bark of laughter. It was the bitter laugh of the paranoiac. 'I started off as an office boy with a firm of accountants, Craig and Butler, of Gray's Inn Road. Later on, when I was a clerk there, the senior partner wanted me to be articled and persuaded me to study for the Institute's exams. In the meantime I'd got married and I was buying a house in Croydon on a mortgage, so the extra money was handy.' He looked up with another aggrieved frown. 'I don't think there's ever been a time till now when I've had a reasonable amount of money to live on, and now I've got it it's no good to me.

'My first marriage wasn't happy. My mother may think it was but outsiders don't know. I got married seventeen years ago and two years later I knew I'd made a mistake. But we'd got a daughter by that time, so there wasn't anything I could do about it. I expect I'd have jogged along and made the best of it if I hadn't met Angela at an office party. When I fell in love with her and knew that – well, what I felt for her was returned, I asked my wife for a divorce. Eileen – that's my first wife's name – made hideous scenes. She brought my mother into it and she even brought Rosemary in – a kid of eleven. I can't describe what my life was like and I won't try to.'

'This was five years ago?'

'About five years ago, yes. Eventually I left home and went to live with Angela. She had a room in Earls Court and she was working at the library of the National Archaeolgists' League.' Hathall, who had said he couldn't describe what his life had been like, immediately proceeded to do so. 'Eileen set about a – a campaign of persecution. She made scenes at my office and at Angela's place of work. She even came to Earls Court. I begged her for a divorce. Angela had a good job and I was doing all right. I thought I could have afforded it, whatever demands Eileen made. In the end she agreed, but by that time Butler had sacked me on account of Eileen's scenes, sacked me out of hand. It was a piece of outrageous injustice. And, to crown it all, Angela had to leave the library. She was on the verge of a nervous breakdown.

'I got a part-time job as accountant with a firm of toy manufacturers, Kidd and Co., of Toxborough, and Angela and I got a room nearby. We were on our beam ends. Angela couldn't work. The divorce judge awarded Eileen my house and custody of my daughter and a very unfairly large slice out of my very inadequate income. Then we had what looked like a piece of luck at last. Angela has a cousin down here, a man called Mark Somerset, who let us have Bury Cottage. It had been his father's, but of course there wasn't any question of its being rent-free – he didn't take his generosity that far, in spite of being a blood relation. And I can't say he ever did anything else for us. He didn't even befriend Angela, though he must have known how lonely she was.

'Things went on like this for nearly three years. We were literally living on about fifteen pounds a week. I was still paying off the mortgage on a house I haven't set foot in for four years. My mother and my first wife had poisoned my daughter's mind against me. What's the use of a judge giving you reasonable access to a child if the child refuses to come near you? I remember you said you'd want to know about my private life. Well, that was it. Nothing but harassment and persecution. Angela was the one bright spot in it and now — and now she's dead.'

Wexford, who believed that, with certain exceptions, a man only suffers chronic and acute persecution if something masochistic in his psychological makeup seeks persecution, pursed his lips. 'This man Somerset, did he ever come to Bury Cottage?'

'Never. He showed us over the place when he first offered it to us, and after that, apart from a chance meeting in the street in Myringham, we never saw him again. It was as if he'd taken an unreasonable dislike to Angela.'

So many people had disliked or resented her. She sounded, Wexford thought, as inclined to paranoia as her husband. Generally speaking, nice people are not much disliked. And a kind of widespread conspiracy of hatred against them, which Hathall seemed to infer, is never feasible.

'You say this was an unreasonable dislike. Mr Hathall. Was your mother's dislike equally unreasonable?'

'My mother is devoted to Eileen. She's old-fashioned and rigid and she was prejudiced against Angela for what she calls her taking me away from Eileen. It's complete nonsense to say that a woman can steal another woman's husband if he doesn't want to be — well, stolen.'

'They only met once, I believe. Was that meeting not a success?'

'I persuaded my mother to come to Earls Court and meet Angela. I should have known better, but I thought that when she actually got to know her she might get over the feeling she was a kind of scarlet woman. My mother took exception to Angela's clothes – she was wearing those jeans and that red shirt – and when she said something uncomplimentary about Eileen my mother walked straight out of the house.'

Hathall's face had grown even redder at the memory. Wexford said, 'So they weren't on speaking terms for the whole of your second marriage?'

'My mother refused to visit us or have us come to her. She saw me, of course. I tell you frankly, I'd have liked to cut myself off from her entirely but I felt I had a duty towards her.'

Wexford always took such assertions of virtue with a grain of salt. He couldn't help wondering if old Mrs Hathall, who must have been nearly seventy, had some savings to leave.

'What brought about the idea of the reunion you planned for this weekend?'

'When I landed this job with Marcus Flower – at, incidentally, double the salary I'd been getting from Kidd's – I decided to spend my week nights at my mother's place. She lives in Balham, so it wasn't too far for me to go into Victoria. Angela and I were looking for a flat to buy in London, so it wouldn't have gone on for too long. But, as usual with me, disaster hit me. However, as I was saying, I'd spent every week night at my mother's since July and I'd had a chance to talk to her about Angela and how much I'd like them to be on good terms. It took eight weeks of persuasion, but she did at last agree to come here for a weekend. Angela was very nervous at the whole idea. Of course she was as anxious for my mother to like her as I was, but she was very apprehensive. She scrubbed the whole place from top to bottom so that my mother couldn't find any fault there. I shall never know now whether it would have worked out.'

'Now, Mr Hathall, when you got to the station last night and your wife wasn't there to meet you as had been arranged, what was your reaction?'

'I don't follow you,' said Hathall shortly.

'What did you feel? Alarmed? Annoyed? Or just disappointed?'

Hathall hesitated. 'I certainly wasn't annoyed,' he said. 'I suppose I thought it was an unfortunate start to the weekend. I assumed Angela had been too nervous to come after all.'

'I see. And when you reached the house, what did you do?'

'I don't know what all this is leading up to, but I suppose there's some purpose behind it.' Again Hathall gave the impatient toss of the head. 'I called out to Angela. When she didn't answer, I looked for her in the dining room and in the kitchen. She wasn't there, so I went out into the garden. Then I told my mother to go upstairs while I looked to see if the car was in the garage.'

'You thought perhaps that you on foot and your wife in the car might have missed each other?'

'I don't know what I thought. I just naturally looked everywhere for her.'

'But not upstairs, Mr Hathall?' said Wexford quietly.

'Not at first. I would have done.'

'Wasn't it likely that of all places in the house a nervous woman, afraid to meet her mother-in-law, would have been, was her own bedroom? But you didn't go there first, as might have been expected. You went to the garage and sent your mother upstairs.'

Hathall, who might have blustered, who might have told Wexford to state plainly what he was getting at, said instead in a rather stiff and awkward tone, 'We can't always account for our actions.'

'I disagree. I think we can if we look honestly into our motives.'

'Well, I suppose I thought if she hadn't answered my call, she couldn't be in the house. Yes, I did think that. I thought she must have set off in the car and we'd missed each other because she'd gone some other way round.'

But some other way round would have meant driving a mile down Wool Lane to its junction with the Pomfret to Myringham road, then following this road to Pomfret or Stowerton before doubling back to Kingsmarkham station, a journey of five miles at least instead of a half-mile trip. But Wexford said no more about it. Another factor in the man's behaviour had suddenly struck him, and he wanted to be alone to think about it, to work out whether it was significant or merely the result of a quirk in his character.

As Hathall rose to go, he said, 'May I ask you something now?'

'By all means.'

But Hathall seemed to hesitate, as if still to postpone some burning question or to conceal it under another of less moment. 'Have you had anything from the – well, the pathologist yet?'

'Not yet, Mr Hathall.'

The red rock face tightened. 'These fingerprints. Have you got something from them yet? Isn't there some clue there?'

'Very little, as far as we can tell.'

'It seems a slow process to me. But I know nothing about it. You'll keep me informed, will you?'

He had spoken hectoringly, like a company chairman addressing a junior executive. 'Once an arrest has been made,' said Wexford, 'you may be sure you won't be left in the dark.'

'That's all very well, but neither will any newspaper reader. I should like to know about this . . .' He bit off the sentence as if he had been tending towards an end it might have been unwise to approach. 'I should like to know about this pathologist's report.'

'I will call on you tomorrow, Mr Hathall,' said Wexford.

'In the meantime, try to keep calm and rest as much as you can.'

Hathall left the office, bowing his head as he went. Wexford couldn't escape the notion that he had bowed it to impress the young detective constable who had shown him out. Yet the man's grief seemed real. But grief, as Wexford knew, is much easier to simulate than happiness. It demands little more than a subdued voice, the occasional outburst of righteous anger, the reiteration of one's pain. A man like Hathall, who believed the world owed him a living and who suffered from a persecution complex, would have no difficulty in intensifying his normal attitude.

But why had he shown no sign of shock? Why, above all, had he never shown that stunned disbelief which is the first characteristic reaction of one whose wife or husband or child has met with a violent death? Wexford thought back over the three conversations he had had with Hathall, but he wasn't able to recall a single instance of disbelief in awful reality. And he recalled similar situations, bereaved husbands who had interrupted his questions with cries that it couldn't be true, widows who had exclaimed that it couldn't be happening to them, that it was a dream from which they must soon awaken. Disbelief temporarily crowds out grief. Sometimes whole days pass before the fact can be realized, let alone accepted. Hathall had realized and accepted at once. It seemed to Wexford, as he sat musing and awaiting the post-mortem results, that he had accepted even before he let himself in at his own front door.

'So she was strangled with a gilt necklace,' said Burden. 'It must have been a pretty tough one.'

Looking up from the report, Wexford said, 'It could be the one on Hathall's list. It says here a gilt ligature. Some shreds of gilding were found embedded in her skin. No tissue from her killer found under her fingernails, so there was presumably no struggle. Time of death, between one-thirty and three-thirty. Well, we know it wasn't one-thirty because that was when Mrs Lake left her. She seems to have been a healthy woman, she wasn't pregnant, and there was no sexual assault.' He gave Burden a condensed version of what Robert Hathall had told him. 'The whole thing's beginning to look peculiar now, isn't it?'

'You mean you've got it into your head that Hathall had some sort of guilty knowledge?'

'I know he didn't kill her. He couldn't have done. When she died he was at this Marcus Flower place with Linda Whatsit and God knows how many other people. And I don't see any motive there. He seems to have been fond of her, if no one else was. But why didn't he go upstairs last night, why isn't he stunned with shock, and why does he get so worked-up about fingerprints?'

'The killer must have hung around after the deed was done to wipe off prints, you know. He must have touched things in the bedroom and the other rooms, and then forgotten what he *had* touched, so that he had to do a big clean-up job to be on the safe side. Otherwise Angela's and Mrs Lake's prints would have been in the living room. Doesn't that argue a lack of premeditation?'

'Probably. And I think you're right. I don't for a moment believe Angela was so fanatical or so frightened of her mother-in-law that she polished the living room after Mrs Lake had gone as well as before she came.'

'It's a funny thing, that he went to all that trouble, yet still left prints on the inside of a door to a cupboard in a spare room, a cupboard that was apparently never used.'

'If he did, Mike,' said Wexford, 'if he did. I think we're going to find that those prints belong to a Mr Mark Somerset, the owner of Bury Cottage. We'll find out just where in Myringham he lives and then we'd better get over to see him.'

CHAPTER SIX

Myringham, where the University of the South is situated, lies about fifteen miles from Kingsmarkham. It boasts a museum, a motte and bailey castle and one of the best-preserved remains of a Roman villa in Britain. And although a new centre has grown up between the university buildings and the railway station, a place of tower blocks and shopping precincts and multi-storey car parks, all this red brick and concrete has been kept well away from the old town which stands, unspoiled, on the banks of the Kingsbrook.

Here there are narrow lanes and winding by-streets that call to the mind of the visitor the paintings of Jacob Vrel. The houses are very old, some – of brown brick and worm-eaten grey-brown timber – built before the Wars of the Roses, or even, it is said, before Agincourt. Not all of them have owner-occupiers or steady tenants, for some have fallen into such disrepair, such dismal decay, that their owners cannot afford to put them in order. Squatters have taken possession of them, secure in their ancient right from police interference, safe from eviction because their 'landlords' are prevented by law from demolishing their property and by lack of money from repairing it.

But these form only a small colony of the Old Town. Mark Somerset lived in the smarter part, in one of the old houses by the river. In the days when England was Catholic it had been a priest's house and in one of the walls of its garden was a narrow and beautiful stained-glass window, for this was also a wall of St. Luke's Church. The Myringham Catholics had a new church now in the new town, and the presbytery was a modern house. But here where the brown walls clustered about the church and the mill, the fifteenth century still lingered.

There was nothing fifteenth century about Mark Somerset.

385

An athletic-looking man in his fifties, he wore neat black jeans and a tee-shirt, and Wexford detected his age only by the lines about his bright blue eyes and the veining of his strong hands. The man's belly was flat, his chest well muscled, and he had the good fortune to keep his hair which, having once been golden, was now silver-gilt.

'Ah, the fuzz,' he said, his smile and pleasant tone robbing the greeting of rudeness. 'I thought you'd turn up.'

'Shouldn't we have turned up, Mr Somerset?'

'Don't know. That's for you to decide. Come in, but be as quiet as you can in the hall, will you? My wife only came out of hospital this morning and she's just managed to get off to sleep.'

'Nothing serious, I hope?' said Burden fatuously – and unnecessarily, in Wexford's view.

Somerset smiled. It was a smile of sad experience, of endurance, tinged very slightly with contempt. He spoke in a near-whisper. 'She's been an invalid for years. But you haven't come to talk about that. Shall we go in here?'

The room had a beamed ceiling and panelled walls. A pair of glass doors, a later but pleasing addition, were open to a small paved garden backed by the riverside trees, and the foliage of these trees looked like black lace against the amber flare of the setting sun. Beside these doors was a low table on which was a bottle of hock in an ice-bucket.

'I'm a sports coach at the university,' said Somerset. 'Saturday night's the only time I allow myself a drink. Will you have some wine?'

The two policemen accepted and Somerset fetched three glasses from a cabinet. The Liebfraumilch had the delicate quality peculiar to some kinds of hock, that of tasting like liquid flowers. It was ice-cold, scented, dry.

'This is very kind of you, Mr Somerset,' said Wexford. 'You're disarming me. I hardly like to ask you now if we may take your fingerprints.'

386

Somerset laughed. 'You can take my fingerprints with pleasure. I suppose you've found the prints of some unknown mystery man at Bury Cottage, have you? They're probably mine, thought I haven't been in the place for three years. They can't be my father's. I had the whole place redecorated after he died.' He spread out his strong work-broadened hands with a kind of bold innocence.

'I understand you didn't get on with your cousin?'

'Well, now,' said Somerset, 'rather than let you interrogate me and probably put to me a lot of time wasting questions, wouldn't it be better if I told you what I know about my cousin and gave you a sort of history of our relationship? Then you can ask me what you like afterwards.'

Wexford said, 'That's exactly what we want.'

'Good.' Somerset had the good teacher's succinct crisp manner. 'You wouldn't want me to have any squeamishness about not speaking ill of the dead, would you? Not that I have much ill to speak of Angela. I was sorry for her. I thought she was feeble, and I don't much care for feeble people. I first met her about five years ago. She'd come to this country from Australia and I'd never seen her before. But she was my cousin all right, the daughter of my father's dead brother, so you needn't get any ideas she might have been an impostor.'

'You have been reading too many detective stories, Mr Somerset.'

'Maybe.' Somerset grinned and went on, 'She looked me up because I and my father were the only relatives she had in this country, and she was lonely in London. Or so she said. I think she was on the look-out for any pickings there might be for her. She was a greedy girl, poor Angela. She hadn't met Robert at that time. When she did she stopped coming out here and I didn't hear from her again until they were about to get married and hadn't anywhere to live. I'd written to her to tell her of my father's death – to which, by the way, she didn't reply – and she wanted to know if I'd let her and Robert have Bury Cottage.

'Well, I'd been meaning to sell it, but I couldn't get the price I wanted, so I agreed and let it to Angela and Robert for five pounds a week.'

'A very low rent, Mr Somerset,' said Wexford, interrupting him. 'You could have got at least twice that.'

Somerset shrugged. Without asking them he refilled their glasses. 'Apparently, they were very badly off, and she was my cousin. I have some silly old-fashioned ideas about blood being thicker than water, Mr Wexford, and I can't shake them off. I didn't in the least mind letting them have the place furnished at what was little more than a nominal rent. What I did mind was when Angela sent me her electricity bill for me to pay.'

'You'd made no agreement about that, of course?'

'Of course not. I asked her to come over here and we'd talk about it. Well, she came and spun me the old sob story I'd heard from her before about their poverty, her nerves and her unhappy adolescence with her mother who wouldn't let her go to university. I suggested that if money was so tight with them she should get a job. She was a qualified librarian and she could easily have got a library job at Kingsmarkham or Stowerton. She pleaded her mental breakdown, but she seemed perfectly healthy to me. I think she was just lazy. Anyway, she flounced out of the house, telling me I was mean, and I didn't see either her or Robert again until about eighteen months ago. On that occasion they didn't see me. I was out with a friend in Pomfret and I saw Robert and Angela through the windows of a restaurant. It was a very expensive restaurant and they seemed to be doing themselves proud, so I came to the conclusion they were doing a good deal better financially.

'We actually *met* again only once more. That was last April. We ran into each other in Myringham in that monstrosity the planners are pleased to call a shopping precinct. They were loaded down with stuff they'd bought, but they seemed depressed in spite of the fact that Robert had got himself this new job. Perhaps they were only embarrassed at coming face to face with me. I never saw Angela again. She wrote to me about a month ago to say that they'd want to leave the cottage as soon as they'd got a place in London, and that that would probably be in the New Year.'

'Were they a happy couple?' Burden asked when Somerset had finished.

'Very, as far as I could tell.' Somerset got up to close the glass doors as the sunset light faded and a little wind rose. 'They had so much in common. Should I be very mean-spirited if I said that what they had in common were paranoia, greed and a general idea that the world owed them a living? I'm sorry she's dead, I'm sorry to hear of anyone dying like that, but I can't say I liked her. Men can be as gauche and tough as they please, but I like a little grace in a woman, don't you? I don't want to be fanciful, but I sometimes thought Robert and Angela got on so well because they were united in gracelessness against the world.'

'You've been very helpful, Mr Somerset,' said Wexford more as a matter of form than with sincerity. Somerset had told him much he didn't know, but had he told him anything that mattered? 'You won't take it amiss, I'm sure, if I ask you what you were doing yesterday afternoon.'

He could have sworn the man hesitated. It was as if he had already thought up how he must answer, but still had to brace himself to give that answer. 'I was here alone. I took the afternoon off to get things ready for my wife's coming home. I'm afraid I was quite alone, and I didn't see anyone, so I can't give you confirmation.'

'Very well,' said Wexford. 'That can't be helped. I don't suppose you have any idea as to what friends your cousin had?'

'None at all. According to her, she had no friends. Everyone she'd ever known but Robert had been cruel to her, she said,

RUTH RENDELL

so making friends was just to invite more cruelty.' Somerset drained his glass. 'Have some more wine?'

'No, thank you. We've taken enough of your Saturday-night ration as it is.'

Somerset gave them his pleasant frank smile. 'I'll see you to the door.'

As they came out into the hall, a querulous voice sounded from upstairs: 'Marky, Marky, where are you?'

Somerset winced, perhaps only at the ugly diminutive. But blood is thicker than water, and a man and his wife are one. He went to the foot of the stairs, called out that he was just coming, and opened the front door. Wexford and Burden said good night quickly for the voice from above had risen to a thin petulant wail.

In the morning Wexford returned as he had promised to Bury Cottage. He had news, some of which had only just reached him, for Robert Hathall, but he had no intention of telling the widower what he most wanted to know.

Mrs Hathall let him in and said her son was still asleep. She showed him into the living room and told him to wait there, but she offered him neither tea nor coffee. She was the kind of woman, he decided, who had probably seldom if ever in her life dispensed refreshment to anyone but members of her own family. They were a strange guarded lot, the Hathalls, whose isolationism apparently infected the people they married, for when he asked Mrs Hathall if Angela's predecessor had ever been to the cottage, she said:

'Eileen wouldn't have lowered herself. She keeps herself to herself.'

'And Rosemary, your granddaughter?'

'Rosemary came once, and once was enough. Anyway, she's too busy with her schoolwork to go out and about.'

'Will you give me Mrs Eileen Hathall's address, please?'

Mrs Hathall's face grew as red as her son's, as red as the

390

wrinkled skin on a turkey's neck. 'No, I won't! You've no business with Eileen. Find it out for yourself.' She banged the door on him and he was left, alone.

It was the first time he had ever been alone there, so he used the waiting time to survey the room. The furniture, which he had supposed to be Angela's and had therefore credited her with taste, was in fact Somerset's, the lifelong collection perhaps of Somerset's father. It was the prettiest kind of late-Victorian with some earlier pieces, spindle-legged chairs, an elegant small oval table. By the window was a red and white Venetian glass oil-lamp that had never been converted to electricity. A glass-fronted bookcase contained, for the most part, the kind of works an old man would have collected and loved: a complete set of Kipling bound in red leather, some H.G. Wells, Gosse's *Father and Son*, a little of Ruskin and a lot of Trollope. But on the top shelf, where previously perhaps had stood an ornament, were the Hathall's own books. There were half a dozen thrillers in paperback, two or three works of 'pop' archaeology, a couple of novels which had aroused controversy over their sexual content when they had been published, and two handsomely jacketed imposing tomes.

Wexford took down the first of these. It was a volume of colour prints of ancient Egyptian jewellery, contained scarcely any text apart from the captions beneath the pictures, and bore inside its front cover a plate which proclaimed it as the property of the library of the National Archaeologists' League. Stolen, of course, by Angela. But books, like umbrellas, pens and boxes of matches, belong in a category of objects the stealing of which is a very venial offence, and Wexford thought little of it. He replaced the book and took out the last one on the shelf. Its title was *Of Men and Angels, A Study of Ancient British Tongues*, and when he opened it he saw that it was a very learned work with chapters on the origins of Welsh, Erse, Scottish Gaelic and Cornish and their common Celtic source. Its price was nearly six pounds, and he wondered that anyone as poor as the Hathalls had claimed to have been should have spent so much on something which was surely as far above their heads as it was above his own.

He was still holding the book when Hathall came into the room. He saw the man's eyes go warily to it, then look sharply away.

'I didn't know you were a student of Celtic languages, Mr Hathall,' he said pleasantly.

'It was Angela's. I don't know where it came from, but she'd had it for ages.'

'Strange, since it was only published this year. But no matter. I thought you'd like to know that your car has been found. It had been abandoned in London, in a side street near Wood Green station. Are you familiar with the district?'

'I've never been there.' Hathall's gaze kept returning, with a kind of reluctant fascination or perhaps apprehensively, to the book Wexford still kept hold of. And for this very reason Wexford determined to keep hold of it and not to remove the finger which he had slipped at random between its pages as if to keep a place. 'When can I have it back?'

'In two or three days. When we've had a good look at it.'

'Examined it for those famous fingerprints you're always on about, I suppose?'

'Am I, Mr Hathall? I? Aren't you rather projecting on to me what you think I ought to feel?' Wexford looked blandly at him. No, he wouldn't gratify the man's curiosity, though it was hard to tell now what Hathall most longed for. A revelation of what the fingerprints had disclosed? Or for that book to be laid down casually as of no account? 'My present feeling is that you should stop worrying about investigations which only we can make. Your mind may be eased a little when I tell your wife hadn't been sexually assaulted.' He waited for some sign of relief, but only saw those eyes with their red glint dart once more to the book. And there was no response when he said as he prepared to leave. 'Your wife died very quickly, in perhaps no more than fifteen seconds. It's possible that she scarcely knew what was happening to her.'

Getting up, he eased his finger from the pages of the book and slipped the jacket flap in where it had been. 'You won't mind if I borrow this for a few days, will you?' he said, and Hathall shrugged but still said nothing at all.

CHAPTER SEVEN

The inquest took place on Tuesday morning, and a verdict was returned of murder by person or persons unknown. Afterwards, as Wexford was crossing the courtyard between the coroner's court and the police station, he saw Nancy Lake go up to Robert Hathall and his mother. She began to speak to Hathall, to condole with him perhaps or offer him a lift home to Wool Lane in her car. Hathall snapped something short and sharp at her, took his mother's arm and walked off rapidly, leaving Nancy standing there, one hand up to her lips. Wexford watched this little pantomime, which had taken place out of earshot, and was nearing the car-park exit when a car drew up alongside him and a sweet vibrant voice said:

'Are you very busy, Chief Inspector?'

'Why do you ask, Mrs Lake?'

'Not because I have any fascinating clues to give you.' She put her hand out of the window and beckoned to him. It was a mischievous and seductive gesture. He found it irresistable and he went up to her and bent down. 'The fact is,' she said, 'that I have a table for two booked at the Peacock in Pomfret and my escort has most churlishly stood me up. Would you think it very forward of me if I asked you to lunch with me instead?'

He was staggered. There was no doubt now that this rich, pretty and entirely charming woman was making advances to him – *him*! It was forward all right, it was almost unprecedented. She looked at him calmly, the corners of her mouth tilted, her eyes shining.

But it wouldn't do. Along whatever paths of fantasy his imagination might lead him, into whatever picture galleries of erotica, it wouldn't do. Once though, when he was young and

without ties or prestige or pressures, it could have been a
different story. And in those days he had taken such offers or
made them without much appreciation and with little awareness of their delight. Ah, to be a little bit younger and know
what one knows now . . .!

'But I also have a table booked for lunch,' he said, 'at the
Carousel café.'

'You won't cancel that and be my guest?'

'Mrs Lake, I am, as you said, very very busy. Would you
think *me* forward if I said you would distract me from my
business?'

She laughed, but it wasn't a laugh of merriment, and her
eyes had ceased to dance. 'It's something, I suppose, to be a
distraction,' she said. 'You make me wonder if I've ever been
anything but a – distraction. Good-bye.'

He went quickly away and up in the lift to his office,
wondering if he had been a fool, if such a chance would ever
come to him again. He attached no special significance to her
words, neither to ponder on them nor to try and interpret
them, for he couldn't think of her intellectually. In his mind,
her face went with him, so seductive, so hopeful, then so
downcast because he had refused her invitation. He tried to
thrust this image away and concentrate on what was before
him, the dry and technical report on the examination of
Robert Hathall's car, but it kept returning, and with it her
entrancing voice, reduced now to a cajoling whisper.

Not that there was much in the report to get excited about.
The car had been found parked in a street near Alexandra
Park, and the discovery had been made by a constable on the
beat. It was empty but for a couple of maps and a ballpoint
pen on the dashboard shelf, and inside and out it had been
wiped clean. The only prints were those of Robert Hathall,
found on the outside of the boot and bonnet lids, and the only
hairs two of Angela's on the driving seat.

He sent for Sergeant Martin, but got nothing encouraging

from him. No one claiming to be a friend of Angela's had come forward, and nobody, apparently, had seen her go out or return home on Friday afternoon. Burden was out, making enquiries – for the second or third time – among the workers at Wool Farm, so Wexford went alone to the Carousel Café for a solitary lunch.

It was early, not much past midday, and the café was still half-empty. He had been sitting at his corner table for perhaps five minutes and had ordered Antonio's speciality of the day, roast lamb, when he felt a light touch that was almost a caress on his shoulder. Wexford had had too many shocks in his life to jump. He turned round slowly and said with a cool note in his voice that he didn't feel, 'This is an unexpected pleasure.'

Nancy Lake sat down opposite him. She made the place look squalid. Her cream silk suit, her chestnut silk hair, her diamonds and her smile threw into sordid relief Antonio's Woolworth cutlery and the tomato-shaped plastic sauce container.

'The mountain,' she said, 'wouldn't come to Mahomet.'

He grinned. It was pointless to pretend he wasn't delighted to see her. 'Ah, you should have seen me a year ago,' he said. 'Then I *was* a mountain. What will you eat? The roast lamb will be bad, but better than the pie.'

'I don't want to eat anything. I'll just have coffee. Aren't you flattered that I didn't come for the food?'

He was. Eyeing the heaped plate which Antonio set before him, he said, 'It's not much of a compliment, though. Coffee only for the lady, please.' Were her attractions enhanced, he asked himself, by Antonio's obvious admiration of them? She was aware of it all, he could see that, and in her awareness, her experienced acceptance of her powers, lay one of the few signs of her age.

She was silent for a few moments while he ate, and he

noticed that her expression was one of rueful repose. But suddenly, as he was preparing to ask her why Robert Hathall had repulsed her so violently that morning, she looked up and said:

'I'm sad, Mr Wexford. Things aren't going well for me.'

He was very surprised. 'Do you want to tell me about it?' How strange that their intimacy had advanced so far that he could ask her that . . .

'I don't know,' she said. 'No, I don't think so. One gets conditioned into habits of secrecy and discretion, even if one doesn't personally see much point in them.'

'That's true. Or can be true in certain circumstances.' The circumstances Dora had referred to?

Yet she was on the brink of telling him. Perhaps it was only the arrival of her coffee and Antonio's admiring flutterings that deterred her. She gave a little shrug, but instead of the small-talk he expected, she said something that astonished him. It was so surprising and so intensely spoken that he pushed away his plate and stared at her.

'Is it very wrong, d'you think, to want someone to die?'

'Not,' he said, puzzled, 'if that wish remains just a wish. Most of us wish that sometimes, and most of us, fortunately, let I dare not wait upon I would.'

'Like the poor cat in the adage?'

He was delighted that she had capped his quotation. 'Is this – er, enemy of yours connected with these habits of secrecy and discretion?'

She nodded. 'But I shouldn't have brought it up. It was silly of me. I'm very lucky really, only it gets hard sometimes, alternating between being a queen and a – distraction. I shall get my crown back, this year, next year, sometime. I shall never abdicate. Goodness, all this mystery! And you're much too clever not to have guessed what I'm on about, aren't you?' He didn't reply to that one. 'Let's change the subject,' she said.

So they changed the subject. Afterwards, when she had left him and he found himself standing, bemused, in the High Street, he could hardly have said what they had talked about, only that it had been pleasant, too pleasant, and had left him with most unpleasant feelings of guilt. But he would see her no more. If necessary, he would eat his lunch in the police canteen, he would avoid her, he would never again be alone with her, even in a restaurant. It was as if he had committed adultery, had confessed it, and been told to 'avoid the occasion.' But he had committed nothing, not even himself. He had only talked and listened.

Had what he had listened to helped him? Perhaps. All that circumlocution, those hints at an enemy, at secrecy and discretion, that had been a pointer. Hathall, he knew, would admit nothing, would have had his ego boosted by the coroner's sympathy. Yet, knowing all this, he nevertheless set off along the High Street towards Wool Lane. He had no idea that it was to be his last visit to Bury Cottage, and that, although he would see Hathall again, it was to be more than a year before they exchanged another word.

Wexford had forgotten all about the book of Celtic languages, hadn't, in fact, bothered to glance at it again, but it was with a request for its immediate return that Hathall greeted him.

'I'll have it sent over to you tomorrow,' he said.

Hathall looked relieved. 'There's also the matter of my car. I need my car.'

'You can have that tomorrow as well.'

The sour old woman was evidently in the kitchen, closeted behind a shut door. She had maintained the house in the immaculate condition in which her dead daughter-in-law had left it, but the touch of an alien and tasteless hand was already apparent. On old Mr Somerset's oval table stood a vase of plastic flowers. What impulse, festive or funeral, had prompted Mrs Hathall to buy them and place them there? *Plastic* flowers, thought Wexford, in the season of mellow fruitfulness when real flowers filled the gardens and the hedgerows and the florist's shops.

Hathall didn't ask him to sit down and he didn't sit down himself. He stood with one elbow resting on the mantelpiece, his fist pressed into his hard red cheek.

'So you didn't find anything incriminating in my car?'

'I didn't say that, Mr Hathall.'

'Well, did you?'

'As a matter of fact, no. Whoever killed your wife was very clever. I don't know that I've ever come across anyone in this sort of situation who covered his tracks so expertly.' Wexford piled it on, letting a note of grudging admiration creep into his voice. Hathall listened impassively. And if gratified was too strong a word to use to describe his expression, satisfied wasn't. The fist uncurled and relaxed, and he leaned back against the fireplace with something like arrogance. 'He seems to have worn gloves to drive your car,' Wexford said, 'and to have given it a wash as well, for good measure. Apparently, he wasn't seen to park the car, and no one was seen driving it on Friday. At the moment, we really have very few leads to go on.'

'Will – will you find any more?' He was eager to know, but as anxious to disguise his eagerness.

'It's early days yet, Mr Hathall. Who knows?' Perhaps it was cruel to play with the man. Does the end ever justify the means? And Wexford didn't know what end he was aiming for, or where next to grab in this game of hide-and-seek in a dark room. 'I can tell you that we found the fingerprints of a man, other than your own, in this house.'

'Are they on – what d'you call it? – record?'

'They proved to be those of Mr Mark Somerset.'

'Ah, well . . .' Suddenly Hathall looked more genial than Wexford had ever seen him. Perhaps only an inhibition as to touching prevented him from stepping forward to pat the chief inspector on the back. 'I'm sorry,' he said. 'I'm not myself at the moment. I should have asked you to sit down. So the only prints you found were those of Mr Somerset, were they? Dear Cousin Mark, our tight-fisted landlord.'

'I didn't say that, Mr Hathall.'

'Well, and mine and – and Angela's, of course.'

'Of course. But apart from those, we found a whole handprint of a woman in your bathroom. It's the print of her right hand, and in the tip of the forefinger is an L-shaped scar.'

Wexford had expected a reaction. But he believed Hathall to be so well under control that he had thought that reaction would show itself only as fresh indignation. He would expostulate perhaps, ask why the police hadn't followed this evidence up, or with a shrug of impatience suggest that this was the handprint of some friend of his wife's whose existence, in his grief, he had forgotten to mention. Never had he supposed, feeling his way in the dark as he was, that his words would have had a cataclysmic effect.

For Hathall froze where he stood. Life seemed driven out of him. It was as if he had suddenly been stricken with a pain so great that it had paralyzed him or forced him to hold himself still for the protection of his heart and his whole nervous system. And yet he said nothing, he made no sound. His self-control *was* magnificent. But his body, his physical self, was triumphing over his mental processes. It was as strong an example of matter over mind as Wexford had ever seen. The shock had come to Hathall at last. The stunning, with its attendant disbelief and terror and realization of what the future must now be, which should have bludgeoned him when he first saw his wife's body, was taking effect five days later. He was poleaxed by it.

Wexford was excited but he behaved very casually. 'Perhaps you can throw some light on whose this handprint may be?'

Hathall drew in his breath. He seemed to have a very real need of oxygen. Slowly he shook his head.

'No idea at all, Mr Hathall?'

The head-shaking went on. It was robot-like, automatic, as if running on some dreadful cerebral clockwork, and Wexford had the notion that Hathall would have to take his head in both hands and grasp it to stop that slow mechanical movement.

'A clear handprint on the side of your bath. An L-shaped scar on the right forefinger. We shall, of course, take it as a lead for our main line of enquiry.'

Hathall jerked up his chin. A spasm ran through his body. He forced a thin constricted voice through stiff lips. 'On the bath, you said?'

'On the bath. I'm right, aren't I, in thinking you can guess whose it may be?'

'I haven't,' Hathall said tremulously and weakly, 'the faintest idea.' His skin had taken on a mottled pallor, but now the blood returned to it and pulsed in the veins on his forehead. The worst of the shock was over. It had been replaced by – what? Not anger, not indignation. Sorrow, Wexford thought, surprised. He was overcome at this late stage by real sorrow . . .

Wexford felt no impulse to be merciful. He said relentlessly, 'I've noticed how anxious you've been right through my enquiries to know what we've deduced from fingerprints. In fact, I've never known a bereaved husband to take quite such a keen interest in forensics. Therefore, I can't help feeling you expected a certain print to be found. If that's so and we've found it, I must tell you that you'll be obstructing this enquiry if you keep what may be vital information to yourself.'

'Don't threaten me!' Though the words were sharp, the voice that spoke them was feeble and the huffiness in the tone pathetically assumed. 'Don't think you can persecute me.'

'I should rather advise *you* to think over what I've said,

and then, if you are wise, you'll make a frank disclosure to us of what I'm sure you know.'

But even as he spoke, looking into the man's miserable, shocked eyes, he knew that any such disclosure would be far from wise. For whatever alibi the man might have, whatever love for her and devotion to her he might profess, he had killed his wife. And as he left the room, making his own way out of the house, he imagined Robert Hathall collapsing into a chair, breathing shallowly, feeling his racing heart, gathering his resources for very survival.

The revelation that they had found a woman's handprint had done this to him. Therefore, he knew who that woman was. He had been anxious about fingerprints because all the time he had dreaded she might have left this evidence behind. But his reaction hadn't been that of a man who merely suspects something or fears the confirmation of a fact he has guessed at. It had been the reaction of someone who fears for his own liberty and peace, the liberty and peace too of another, and, above all, that he and that other might not now have that liberty and peace together.

CHAPTER EIGHT

His discovery had driven from Wexford's mind memories of that lunchtime interlude. But when he walked into his own house soon after four they returned to him, discoloured by guilt. And if he hadn't spent that hour in Nancy Lake's company, or if it had been less enjoyable, he might not now have given Dora such a hearty kiss or asked her what he did ask her.

'How would you like to go up to London for a couple of days?'

'You mean you have to go?'

Wexford nodded.

'And you can't bear to be parted from me?' Wexford felt himself blushing. Why did she have to be so perceptive? It was almost as if she read his thoughts. But if she had been less perceptive, would he have married her? 'I'd love to darling,' she said blandly. 'When?'

'If Howard and Denise will have us, as soon as you can pack a bag.' He grinned, knowing the quantity of clothes she would want to take with her for even two days with her fashionable niece. 'Like – ten minutes?'

'Give me an hour,' said Dora.

'OK. I'll phone Denise.'

Chief Superintendent Howard Fortune, the head of Kenbourne Vale CID, was the son of Wexford's dead sister. For years Wexford had been in awe of him, his awe mixed with envy of this nephew, so aptly named, into whose lap so many good things had fallen, apparently without effort on his part, a first-class honours degree, a house in Chelsea, marriage to a beautiful fashion model, rapid promotion until his rank far surpassed his uncle's. And these two had taken on in his eyes the hard gloss of jet-set people, entering, although he hardly knew them, into that category of rich relations who will despise us from a distance and snub us if we make overtures to them. With misgivings he had gone to stay with them to convalesce after an illness, and his misgivings had turned out to be groundless, the silly suspicions that are borne only of a grudge. For Howard and Denise had been kind and hospitable and un-assuming, and when he had helped Howard solve a Kenbourne Vale murder case – solved it himself, Howard said – he had felt he was vindicated and a friendship established.

Just how firm that friendship was to be had been shown by the Fortunes' enjoyment of family Christmases at Wexford's house, by the new *rapport* between uncle and nephew, and revealed itself again in the greeting the chief inspector and his wife got as their taxi brought them to the house in Teresa Street. It was just after seven and one of Denise's elaborate dinners was almost ready.

'But you've got so thin, Uncle Reg,' she said as she kissed him. 'Here was I, counting calories for you, and now it looks as if it was all labour in vain. You look quite handsome.'

'Thank you, my dear. I must confess my weight loss has removed one of my principal fears of London.'

'And what would that be?'

'That *was* that I'd get myself inside one of those automatic ticket things on the Underground – you know, the kind with the snapping jaws – and be unable to get out.'

Denise laughed and took them into the living room. Since that first visit, Wexford had got over his fear of knocking over Denise's flower arrangements and conquered his awe of her fragile china ornaments and the pastel satin upholstery he was sure he would ruin with coffee stains. The abundance of everything, the smooth-running splendours and the air of gracious living, no longer intimidated him. He could sit with ease on a chair in one of those little circles of chairs and a silk sofa that reminded him of photographs of royal palace interiors. He could laugh about the tropical central heating, or as now when it wasn't on, comment on its summer counter-part, the newly installed air conditioning.

'It reminds me,' he said, 'of that description of Scott's of the Lady Rowena's apartments. "The rich hangings shook to the night blast . . . the flame of the torches streamed sideways into the air like the unfurled pennon of a chieftain." Only, in our case, it's house plants that stream and not flames.'

They had an in-joke about their exchange of quotations, for at one time Wexford had used them to assert his intellectual equality, and Howard had replied, or so his uncle believed, to keep discreetly off the subject of their shared occupation.

'Literary chit-chat, Reg?' said Howard, smiling.

'To break the ice only – and you'll get real ice on your flower vases if you keep that going, Denise. No, I want to talk to you about why I've come up here, but that'll keep till after dinner.'

'And I thought you'd come up here to see me!' said Denise.

'So I have, my dear, but another young woman is inter-esting me a good deal more at present.'

'What's she got that I haven't got?'

Wexford took her hand and, pretending to scrutinize it, said, 'An L-shaped scar on her forefinger.'

When Wexford was in London he always hoped people would take him for a Londoner. To sustain this illusion, he took certain measures such as remaining in his seat until the tube train had actually come to a halt at his destination instead of leaping up nervously thirty seconds beforehand as is the habit of non-Londoners. And he refrained from enquiring of other passengers if the train he was in was actually going to the place announced by the confusing indicator. As a result, he had once found himself in Uxbridge instead of Harrow-on-the-Hill. But there is no easy way of getting from the western reaches of Chelsea to the West End by Tube, so Wexford boarded the number 14 bus, an old friend.

Instead of one person, Marcus Flower turned out to be two, Jason Marcus and Stephen Flower, the former looking like a long-haired and youthful Ronald Colman and the latter a short-haired and superannuated Mick Jagger. Wexford refused a cup of the black coffee they were drinking – apparently as a hangover remedy – and said he had really come to talk to Linda Kipling. Marcus and Flower went off into a double act of innuendo at this, declaring that Miss Kipling was far better worth seeing than they, that no one ever came there except to look at the girls, and then, falling simultaneously grave, said almost in unison how frightfully sorry they had been to hear of 'poor old Bob's loss' about which they had been 'absolutely cut up.'

Wexford was then conducted by Marcus through a series of offices that were strangely lush and stark at the same time, rooms where the furniture was made of steel and leather and set against extravagant velvet drapes and high-pile carpets. On the walls were abstract paintings of the splashed ketchup and copulating spiders *genre*, and on low tables magazine pornography so soft as to be gently blancmange-like in texture and kind. The secretaries, three of them, were all together in a blue velvet room, the one who had received him, a red-headed one, and Linda Kipling. Two others, said Linda, were in one case at the hairdresser's and in the other at a wedding. It was that sort of place.

She led him into an empty office where she sat down on the kind of black leather and metal bench you find in airport lounges. She had the look of a dummy in the window of a very expensive dress shop, realistic but not real, as if made of high-quality plastic. Contemplating her fingernails, which were green, she told him that Robert Hathall had phoned his wife every day at lunchtime since he had been with them, either calling her himself or asking her to put the call through for him. This she had thought 'terribly sweet,' though now, of course, it was 'terribly tragic.'

'You'd say he was very happily married, would you, Miss Kipling? Talked about his wife a lot, kept her photograph on his desk, that sort of thing?'

'He did have her photograph, but Liz said it was frightfully bourgeois, doing things like that, so he put it away. I wouldn't know if he was happy. He was never very *lively*, not like Jason and Steve and some of the other blokes.'

'What was he like last Friday?'

'The same as usual. *Just* the same. I've told that to a policeman already. I don't know what's the good of saying the same thing over and over again. He was just the same as usual. He got in a bit before ten and he was in here all the morning working out the details of a sort of scheme for private hospital treatment for those of the staff who wanted it. Insurance, you know.' Linda looked her contempt for those executives who couldn't afford to pay for their own private treatment. 'He phoned his wife a bit before one and then he went out to lunch in a pub with Jason. They weren't gone long. I know he was back here by half past two. He dictated three letters to me.' She seemed aggrieved at the memory, as if this had been an unfairly demanding task. 'And he went off at five-thirty to meet his mother and take her off to wherever she lives, somewhere in Sussex.'

'Did he ever get phone calls here from women or a woman?'

'His wife never phoned *him*.' His meaning sank in and she stared at him. She was one of those people who are so narrow and who have imaginations so limited that hints at anything unexpected in the field of sex or social conduct or the emotions throw them into fits of nervous giggles. She giggled now. 'A girl-friend, d'you mean? Nobody like that phoned him. No one ever phoned him.'

'Was he attracted by any of the girls here?'

She looked astonished and edged slightly away. 'The girls *here?*'

'Well, there are five girls here, Miss Kipling, and if the three of you I've seen are anything to go by, you're not exactly repulsive. Did Mr Hathall have a special friendship with any girl here?'

The green fingernails fluttered. 'Do you mean a relationship? D'you mean, was he *sleeping* with anyone?'

'If you like to put it that way. After all, he was a lonely man, temporarily separated from his wife. I suppose you were all here on Friday afternoon, none of you out having her hair done or at a wedding?'

'Of course we were all here! And as to Bob Hathall having a relationship with any of us, you might care to know that June and Liz are married, Clare's engaged to Jason and Suzanne is Lord Carthew's daughter.'

'Does that exempt her from sleeping with a man?'

'It exempts her from sleeping with someone of Bob Hathall's – er, kind. And that goes for all of us. We mayn't be "exactly repulsive," as you put it, but we haven't come down to that!'

Wexford said good morning to her and walked out, feeling rather sorry he had paid her even that one grudging compliment. In Piccadilly, he went into a call-box and dialled the number of Craig and Butler, Accountants, of Gray's Inn Road. Mr Butler, he was told, was at present engaged, but would be happy to see him at three o'clock that afternoon. How should he spend the intervening time? Although he had discovered Mrs Eileen Hathall's address, Croydon was too far distant to sandwich in a visit there between now and three. Why not find out a little more about Angela herself and get some background to this marriage that everyone said was happy but which had ended in murder? He leafed through the directory and found it: The National Archaeologists' League Library, 17 Trident Place, Knightsbridge SW7. Briskly, he walked up to the Tube station in Piccadilly Circus.

Trident Place wasn't easy to find. Although he had consulted his *A to Z Guide* in the privacy of the call-box, he found he had to look at it again in full view of sophisticated Londoners. As he was telling himself he was an old fool to be so self-conscious, he was rewarded by the sight of Sloane Street from which, according to the guide, Trident Place debouched.

It was a wide street of four-storey mid-Victorian houses, all smart and well kept. Number seven had a pair of heavy glass doors, framed in mahogany, through which Wexford went into a hall hung with monochrome photographs of amphorae and with portraits of gloomy-looking unearthers of the past, and thence through another door into the library itself. The atmosphere was that of all such places, utterly quiet, scholarly, redolent of books, ancient and modern. There were very few people about. A member was busy with one of the huge leather-bound catalogues, another was signing for the books he had taken out. Two girls and a young man were occupied in a quiet and studious way behind the polished oak counter, and it was one of these girls who came out and took Wexford upstairs, past more portraits, more photographs, past the sepulchrally silent reading room, to the office of the chief librarian, Miss Marie Marcovitch.

Miss Marcovitch was a little elderly woman, presumably of Central European Jewish origin. She spoke fluent academic English with a slight accent. As unlike Linda Kipling as one woman can be unlike another, she asked him to sit down and showed no surprise that he had come to question her about a murder case, although she had not at first connected the girl who used to work for her with the dead woman.

'She left here, of course, before her marriage,' said Wexford. 'How would you describe her, as tough and ungracious, or nervous and shy?'

'Well, she was quiet. I could put it like this – but, no, the poor girl is dead.' After her small hesitation, Miss Marcovitch went on hastily, 'I really don't know what I can tell you about her. She was quite ordinary.'

'I should like you to tell me everything you know.'

'A tall order, even though she *was* ordinary. She came to work here about five years ago. It's not the usual practice of the library to employ people without university degrees, but Angela was a qualified librarian and she had some knowledge of archaeology. She'd no practical experience, but neither, for that matter, have I.'

The bookish atmosphere had reminded Wexford of a book he still had in his possession. 'Was she interested in Celtic languages?'

Miss Marcovitch looked surprised. 'Not that I know of.'

'Never mind. Please go on.'

'I hardly know how to go on, Chief Inspector. Angela did her work quite satisfactorily, though she was absent rather a lot on vague medical grounds. She was bad about money . . .' Again Wexford noticed the hesitation. 'I mean, she couldn't manage on her salary and she used to complain that it was inadequate. I gathered she borrowed small sums from other members of the staff, but that was no business of mine.'

'I believe she worked here for some months before she met Mr Hathall?'

'I'm not at all sure when she did meet Mr Hathall. First of all she was friendly with a Mr Craig who used to be on our staff but who has since left. Indeed, all the members of our staff from that time have left except myself. I'm afraid I never met Mr Hathall.'

'But you did meet the first Mrs Hathall?'

The librarian pursed her lips and folded her small shrivelled hands in her lap. 'This seems very much like scandal-mongering,' she said primly.

'So much of my work is, Miss Marcovitch.'

'Well . . .' She gave a sudden unexpected smile, bright and almost naughty. 'In for a penny, in for a pound, eh? I did meet the first Mrs Hathall. I happened to be in the library itself when she came in. You'll have noticed that this is a very quiet place. Voices aren't raised and movements aren't swift, an atmosphere which suits members and staff alike. I must confess to having been very angry indeed when this woman burst into the library, rushed up to where Angela was behind the counter and began to rant and rave at her. It was impossible for members not to realize that she was reproaching Angela for what she called stealing her husband. I asked Mr Craig to get rid of the woman as quietly as he could, and then I took Angela upstairs with me. When she calmed down I told her that, although her private affairs were no business of mine, such a thing mustn't be allowed to occur again.'

'It didn't occur again?'

'No, but Angela's work began to suffer. She was the kind that goes to pieces easily under strain. I was sorry for her, but not otherwise sorry, when she said she'd have to give up her job on her doctor's advice.'

The librarian finished speaking, seemed to have said everything she had to say and was on her feet. But Wexford, instead of getting up, said in a dry voice, 'In for a pound, Miss Marcovitch?'

She coloured and gave a little embarrassed laugh. 'How perspicacious of you, Chief Inspector! Yes, there is one more thing. I suppose you noticed my hesitations. I've never told anyone about this, but – well, I will tell you.' She sat down again, and her manner became more pedantic. 'In view of the fact that the library members pay a large subscription – twenty-five pounds annually – and are by their nature careful of books, we charge no fines should they keep books beyond the allotted period of one month. Naturally, however, we don't publicize this, and many new members have been pleasantly surprised to find that, on returning books they have kept for perhaps two or three months, no charge is made.

'About three and a half years ago, a little while after Angela had left us, I happened to be helping out at the returns counter when a member handed to me three books that I saw were six weeks overdue. I should have made no comment on this had the member not produced one pound eighty, which he assured me was the proper fine for overdue books, ten pence per week per book. When I told him no fines were ever exacted in this library, he said he'd only been a member for a year and had only once before kept books longer than a month. On that occasion the "young lady" had asked him for one pound twenty, and he hadn't protested, thinking it to be reasonable.

'Of course I made enquiries among the staff who all appeared perfectly innocent, but the two girls told me that other members had recently also tried to get them to accept fines for overdue books, which they had refused and had given an explanation of our rules.'

'You think Angela Hathall was responsible?' Wexford asked.

'Who else could have been? But she had gone, no very great harm was done, and I didn't relish raising this matter at a meeting of the trustees which might have led to trouble and perhaps to a prosecution with members called as witnesses and so on. Besides, the girl had been under a strain and it was a very small fraud. I doubt if she made more than ten pounds out of it at the most.'

CHAPTER NINE

A very small fraud . . . Wexford hadn't expected to encounter fraud at all, and it was probably irrelevant. But the shadowy figure of Angela Hathall had now, like a shape looming out of fog, begun to take more definite outlines. A paranoid personality with a tendency to hypochondria; intelligent but unable to persevere at a steady job; her mental state easily overthrown by adversity; financially unstable and not above making extra money by fraudulent means. How, then, had she managed on the fifteen pounds a week which was all she and her husband had had to live on for a period of nearly three years?

He left the library and took the Tube to Chancery Lane. Craig and Butler, Accountants, had their offices on the third floor of an old building near the Royal Free Hospital. He noted the place, had a salad and orange juice lunch in a café, and at one minute to three was shown up into the office of the senior partner, William Butler. The room was as old-fashioned and nearly as quiet as the library, and Mr Butler as wizened as Miss Marcovitch. But he wore a jolly smile, the atmosphere was of business rather than scholarship, and the only portrait a highly coloured oil of an elderly man in evening dress.

'My former partner, Mr Craig,' said William Butler.

'It would be his son, I imagine, who introduced Robert and Angela Hathall?'

'His nephew. Paul Craig, the son, has been my partner since his father's retirement. It's Jonathan Craig who used to work at the archaeologists' place.'

'I believe the introduction took place at an office party here?'

The old man gave a sharp scratchy little chuckle. 'A party *here?* Where would we put the food and drink, not to mention the guests? They'd be reminded of their income tax and get gloomy and depressed. No, that party was at Mr Craig's own home in Hampstead on his retirement from the firm after forty-five years.'

'You met Angela Hathall there?'

'It was the only time I did meet her. Nice-looking creature, though with a bit of that Shetland pony look so many of them have nowadays. Wearing trousers too. Personally, I think a woman should put on a skirt to go to a party. Bob Hathall was very smitten with her from the first, you could see that.'

'That can't have pleased Mr Jonathan Craig.'

Again Mr Butler gave his fiddle-string squawk. 'He wasn't serious about *her*. Got married since, as a matter of fact. His wife's nothing to look at but loaded, my dear fellow, pots of it. This Angela wouldn't have gone down at all well with the family, they're not easygoing like me. Mind you, even I took a bit of a dim view when she went up to Paul and said what a lovely job he'd got, just the thing for knowing how to fiddle one's tax. Saying that to an accountant's like telling a doctor he's lucky to be able to get hold of heroin.' And Mr Butler chortled merrily. 'I met the first Mrs Hathall too, you know,' he said. 'She was a lively one. We had quite a scene, what with her banging about trying to get to Bob, and Bob locking himself up in his office. What a voice she's got when she's roused! Another time she sat on the stairs all day waiting for Bob to come out. He locked himself up again and never went out all night. God knows when she went home. The next day she turned up again and screamed at me to make him go back to her and their daughter. Fine set-out that was. I'll never forget it.'

'As a result,' said Wexford, 'you gave him the sack.'

'I never did! Is that what he says?'

Wexford nodded.

'God damn it! Bob Hathall always was a liar. I'll tell you what happened, and you can believe it or not, as you like. I had him in here after all that set-out and told him he'd better manage his private affairs a bit better. We had a bit of an argument and the upshot was he flew into a rage and said he was leaving. I tried to dissuade him. He'd come to us as an office boy and done all his training here. I told him that if he was getting a divorce he'd need all the money he could lay his hands on and there'd be a rise for him in the New Year. But he wouldn't listen, kept saying everyone was against him and this Angela. So he left and got himself some tin-pot part-time job, and serve him right.'

Recalling Angela's fraud and her remark to Paul Craig, and telling himself that birds of a feather flock together, Wexford asked Mr Butler if Robert Hathall had ever done anything which could be construed even mildly as on the shady side of the law. Mr Butler looked shocked.

'Certainly not. I've said he wasn't always strictly truthful, but otherwise he was honest.'

'Susceptible to women, would you say?'

William Butler gave another squawk and shook his head vehemently. 'He was fifteen when he first came here, and even in those days he was walking out with that first wife of his. They were engaged for God knows how many years. I tell you, Bob was so narrow and downright repressed, he didn't know there were other women on the face of the earth. We'd got a pretty typist in here, and for all the notice he took, she might have been a type*writer*. No, that was why he went overboard for that Angela, went daft about her like some silly romantic schoolboy. He woke up, the scales fell from his eyes. It's often the way. Those late developers are always the worst.'

'So perhaps, having awakened, he began looking around some more?'

'Perhaps he did, but I can't help you there. You thinking he might have done away with that Angela?'

415

'I shouldn't care to commit myself on that, Mr Butler,' said Wexford as he took his leave.

'No. Silly question, eh? I thought he was going to murder that other one, I can tell you. That's just where she had her sit-in, the step you're on now. I'll never forget it, never as long as I live.'

Howard Fortune was a tall thin man, skeletally thin in spite of his enormous appetite. He had the Wexford family's pale hair, the colour of faded brown paper, and the light grey-blue eyes, small and sharp. In spite of the difference in their figures, he had always resembled his uncle, and now that Wexford had lost so much weight, that resemblance was heightened. Sitting opposite each other in Howard's study, they might have been father and son, for likeness apart, Wexford was now able to talk to his nephew as familiarly as he talked to Burden, and Howard to respond without the delicacy and self-conscious tact of former days.

Their wives were out. Having spent the day shopping, they had adjourned to a theatre, and uncle and nephew had eaten their dinner alone. Now, while Howard drank brandy and he contented himself with a glass of white wine, Wexford enlarged on the theory he had put forward the night before.

'As far as I see it,' he said, 'the only way to account for Hathall's horror – and it was horror, Howard – when I told him about the handprint, is that he arranged the killing of Angela with the help of a woman accomplice.'

'With whom he was having a love affair?'

'Presumably. That would be the motive.'

'A thin motive these days, isn't it? Divorce is fairly easy and there were no children to consider.'

'You've missed the point.' Wexford spoke with a sharpness that would once have been impossible. 'Even with this new job of his, he couldn't have afforded two discarded wives. He's just the sort of man who'd think himself almost justified in killing if killing was going to rid him of further persecution.'

'So this girl-friend of his came to the cottage in the afternoon . . .'

'Or was fetched by Angela.'

'I can't see that part, Reg.'

'A neighbour, a woman called Lake, says Angela told her she was going out.' Wexford sipped his drink to cover the slight confusion even the mention of Nancy Lake's name caused in him. 'I have to bear that in mind.'

'Well, maybe. The girl killed Angela by strangling her with a gilt necklace which hasn't been found, then wiped the place clean of her own prints but left one on the side of the bath. Is that the idea?'

'That's the idea. Then she drove Robert Hathall's car to London, where she abandoned it in Wood Green. I may go there tomorrow, but I haven't much hope. The chances are she lives as far from Wood Green as possible.'

'And then you'll go to this toy factory place in – what's it called? – Toxborough? I can't understand why you're leaving it till last. He worked there, after all, from the time of his marriage till last July.'

'And that's the very reason why,' said Wexford. 'It's just possible he knew this woman *before* he met Angela, or met her when his marriage was three years old. But there's no doubt he was deeply in love with Angela – everyone admits that – so is it likely he'd have begun a new relationship during the earliest part of his marriage?'

'No, I see that. Does it have to be someone he'd met at work? Why not a friend he'd met socially or the wife of a friend?'

'Because he doesn't seem to have had any friends, and that's not so difficult to understand. In his first marriage, the way I picture it, he and his wife would have been friendly with other married couples. But you know how it goes, Howard.

In these cases, a married couple's friends are their neighbours or her woman friends and their husbands. Isn't it probable that at the time of the divorce all these people would have rallied round Eileen Hathall? In other words, they'd remain her friends and desert him.'

'This unknown woman could be someone he'd picked up in the street or got talking to by chance in a pub. Have you thought of that?'

'Of course. If it's so, my chances of finding her are thin.'

'Well, Wood Green for you tomorrow. I'm taking the day off myself. I have to speak at a dinner at Brighton in the evening and I thought of taking a leisurely drive down, but maybe I'll come up to darkest Ally Pally with you first.'

The phone ringing cut short Wexford's thanks at this offer. Howard picked up the receiver and his first words, spoken cordially but without much familiarity, told his uncle that the caller was someone he knew socially but not very well. Then the phone was passed to him and he heard Burden's voice.

'Good news first,' said the inspector, 'if you can call it good,' and he told Wexford that at last someone had come forward to say he had seen Hathall's car driven into the drive of Bury Cottage at five past three on the previous Friday afternoon. But he had seen only the driver whom he described as a dark-haired young woman wearing some sort of red checked shirt or blouse. That she had had a passenger he was sure, and almost sure it had been a woman, but he was able to fill in no more details. He had been cycling along Wool Lane in the direction of Wool Farm and had therefore been on the left-hand side of the road, the side which would naturally give him a view of the car's driver but not necessarily of the other occupant. The car had stopped since he had the right of way, and he had assumed, because its right-hand indicator was flashing, that it was about to turn into the cottage drive.

'Why didn't this cyclist guy come forward before?'

'He was on holiday down here, he and his bicycle,' said Burden, 'and he says he never saw a paper till today.'

'Some people,' Wexford growled, 'live like bloody chrysalises. If that's the good news, what's the bad?'

'It may not be bad, I wouldn't know. But the Chief Constable's been in here after you, and he wants to see you at three sharp tomorrow afternoon.'

'That puts paid to our Wood Green visit,' said Wexford thoughtfully to his nephew, and he told him what Burden had said. 'I'll have to go back and try and take in Croydon or Toxborough on my way. I shan't have time for both.'

'Look, Reg, why don't I drive you to Croydon and then to Kingsmarkham via Toxborough? I'd still have three or four hours before I need to be in Brighton.'

'Be a bit of a drag for you, won't it?'

'On the contrary. I don't mind telling you I'm very keen to take a look at this virago, the first Mrs Hathall. You come back with me and Dora can stay on. I know Denise wants her to be here on Friday for some party or other she's going to.'

And Dora, who came in ten minutes later, needed no encouragement to remain in London till the Sunday.

'But will you be all right on your own?'

'I'll be all right. I hope you will. Personally, I should think you'll perish with the cold in this bloody awful air-conditioning.'

'I have my subcutaneous fat, darling, to keep me warm.'

'Unlike you, Uncle Reg,' said Denise who, coming in, had heard the last sentence. 'All yours has melted away quite beautifully. I suppose it really *is* all diet? I was reading in a book the other day that men who have a succession of love affairs keep their figures because a man unconsciously draws in his stomach muscles every time he pays court to a new woman.'

'So now we know what to think,' said Dora.

But Wexford, who had at that moment drawn his in

consciously, wasn't brought to the blush which would have been his reaction the day before. He was wondering what he was to think of his summons by the Chief Constable, and making a disagreeable guess at the answer.

CHAPTER TEN

The house which Robert Hathall had bought at the time of his first marriage was one of those semi-detached villas which sprang up during the thirties in their thousands, in their tens of thousands. It had a bay window in the front living room, a gable over the front bedroom window, and a decorative wooden canopy, of the kind sometimes seen sheltering the platforms of provincial railway stations, over the front door. There were about four hundred others exactly like it in the street, a wide thoroughfare along which traffic streamed to the south.

'This house,' said Howard, 'was built for about six hundred pounds. Hathall would have paid around four thousand for it, I should think. When did he get married?'

'Seventeen years ago.'

'Four thousand would be right. And now it would fetch eighteen.'

'Only he can't sell it,' said Wexford. 'I daresay he could have done with eighteen thousand pounds.' They got out of the car and went up to the front door.

She had none of the outward signs of a virago. She was about forty, short, high-coloured, her stout stocky figure crammed into a tight green dress, and she was one of those women who have been roses and are now cabbages. Ghostly shades of the rose showed in the pretty fat-obscured features, the skin which was still good, and the gingery hair that had once been blonde. She took them into the room with the bay window. Its furnishings lacked the charm of those at Bury Cottage, but it was just as clean. There was something oppressive about its neatness and the absence of any single object not totally conventional. Wexford looked in vain for some

article, a hand-embroidered cushion maybe, an original drawing or a growing plant, that might express the personalities of
the woman and the girl who lived here. But there was nothing,
not a book, not a magazine even, no paraphernalia of a hobby.
It was like a Times Furnishing window display before the shop
assistant has added those touches that will give it an air of
home. Apart from a framed photograph, the only picture was
that reproduction of a Spanish gypsy with a black hat on her
curls and a rose between her teeth, which Wexford had seen
on a hundred lounge-bar walls. And even this stereotyped
picture had more life about it than the rest of the room, the
gypsy's mouth seeming to curl a little more disdainfully as she
surveyed the sterile surroundings in which she was doomed to
spend her time.

Although it was mid-morning and Eileen Hathall had been
forewarned of their coming, she offered them nothing to drink.
Her mother-in-law's ways had either rubbed off on her or else
her own lack of hospitality had been one of the traits which
so endeared the old woman to her. But that Mrs Hathall senior
had been deluded in other respects soon showed. Far from
keeping 'herself to herself,' Eileen was ready to be bitterly
expansive about her private life.

At first, however, she was subdued. Wexford began by
asking her how she had spent the previous Friday, and she
replied in a quiet reasonable voice that she had been at her
father's in Balham, remaining there till the evening because
her daughter had been on a day trip to France, sponsored by
her school, from which she hadn't returned until nearly midnight. She gave Wexford her widowed father's address which
Howard, who knew London well, remarked was in the next
street to where Mrs Hathall senior lived. That did it. Eileen's
colour rose and her eyes smouldered with the resentment
which was now perhaps the mainspring of her life.

'We grew up together, Bob and me. We went to the same
school and there wasn't a day went by we didn't see each

other. After we got married we were never apart for a single night till that woman came and stole him from me.'

Wexford, who held to the belief that it is impossible for an outsider to break up a secure and happy marriage, made no comment. He had often wondered too at the attitude of mind that regards people as things and marriage partners as objects which can be stolen like television sets or pearl necklaces.

'When did you last see your former husband, Mrs Hathall?'

'I haven't seen him for three and a half years.'

'But I suppose, although you have custody, he has reasonable access to Rosemary?'

Her face had grown bitter, a canker eating the blown rose. 'He was allowed to see her every other Sunday. I used to send her round to his mum and he'd fetch her from there and take her out for the day.'

'But you didn't see him yourself on these occasions?'

She looked down, perhaps to hide her humiliation. 'He said he wouldn't come if I was going to be there.'

'You said "used," Mrs Hathall. D'you mean this meeting between father and daughter has ceased?'

'Well, she's nearly grown-up, isn't she? She's old enough to have a mind of her own. Me and Bob's mum, we've always got on well, she's been like another mother to me. Rosemary could see the way we thought about it – I mean, she was old enough to understand what I'd suffered from her dad, and it's only natural she was resentful.' The virago was appearing and the tone of voice which Mr Butler had said would always remain in his memory. 'She took against him. She thought it was wicked what he'd done.'

'So she stopped seeing him?'

'She didn't *want* to see him. She said she'd got better things to do with her Sundays, and her gran and me, we thought she was quite right. Only once she went to that cottage place and when she came back she was in an awful state, tears and sobbing and I don't know what. And I don't wonder. Can you imagine a father actually letting his little girl see him kiss another woman? That's what happened. When the time came for him to bring Rosemary back, she saw him put his arms round that woman and kiss her. And it wasn't one of your ordinary kisses. Like what you'd see on the TV, Rosemary said, but I won't go into details, though I was disgusted, I can tell you. The upshot of it was that Rosemary can't stand her dad, and I don't blame her. I just hope it won't do something to her mentality the way these psychological people say it does.'

The red flush on her skin was high now and her eyes flashed. And now, as her bosom rose and she tossed her head, she had something in common with the gypsy on the wall.

'*He* didn't like it. He begged her to see him, wrote her letters and God knows what. Sent her presents and wanted to take her away on holiday. Him as said he hadn't got a penny to bless himself with. Fought tooth and nail he did to try and stop me getting this house and a bit of his money to live on. Oh, he's got money enough when he likes to spend it, money to spend on anyone but me.'

Howard had been looking at that single framed photograph and now he asked if it was of Rosemary.

'Yes, that's my Rosemary.' Still breathless from her outpouring of invective, Eileen spoke in gasps. 'That was taken six months ago.'

The two policemen looked at the portrait of a rather heavy-faced girl who wore a small gold cross hanging against her blouse, whose lank dark hair fell to her shoulders, and who bore a marked resemblance to her paternal grandmother. Wexford, who felt unable to tell an outright lie and say the girl was pretty, asked what she was going to do when she left school. This was a good move, for it had a calming effect on Eileen whose bitterness gave way, though only briefly, to pride.

'Go on to college. All her teachers say she's got it in her and I wouldn't stand in her way. It's not as if she's got to go out and earn money. Bob'll have plenty to spare *now*. I've told her I don't care if she goes on training till she's twenty-five. I'm going to get Bob's mum to ask him to give Rosemary a car for her eighteenth birthday. After all, that's like being twenty-one nowadays, isn't it? My brother's been teaching her to drive and she'll take her test the minute she's seventeen. It's his duty to give her a car. Just because he's ruined my life, that's no reason why he should ruin hers, is it?'

Wexford put out his hand to her as they left. She gave him hers rather reluctantly, but her reluctance was perhaps only part and parcel of that ungraciousness which seemed to be a feature of all the Hathalls and all their connections. Staring down, he held it just long enough to make sure there was no scar on the relevant finger.

'Let us be thankful for our wives,' said Howard devoutly when they were back in the car and driving southwards. 'He didn't kill Angela to go back to that one, at any rate.'

'Did you notice she didn't once mention Angela's death? Not even to say she wasn't sorry she was dead? I've never come across a family so nourished on hatred.' Wexford thought suddenly of his own two daughters who loved him, and on whose education he had spent money freely and happily because they loved him and he loved them. 'It must be bloody awful to have to support someone you hate and buy presents for someone who's been taught to hate you,' he said.

'Indeed it must. And where did the money come from for those presents and that projected holiday, Reg? Not out of fifteen pounds a week.'

By a quarter to twelve they were in Toxborough. Wexford's appointment at Kidd's factory was for half past, so they had a quick lunch in a pub on the outskirts before finding the industrial site. The factory, a large white concrete box, was the source of those children's toys which he had often seen on television commercials and which were marketed under the name of Kidd's Kits for Kids. The manager, a Mr Aveney, told him they had three hundred workers on the payroll, most of them women with part-time jobs. Their white-collar staff was small, consisting of himself, the personnel manager, the part-time accountant, Hathall's successor, his own secretary, two typists and a switchboard girl.

'You want to know what female office staff we had here when Mr Hathall was with us. I gathered that from what you said on the phone and I've done my best to make you a list of names and addresses. But the way they change and change about is ridiculous, Chief Inspector. Girls are crazy to change their jobs every few months these days. There isn't anyone in the office now who was here when Mr Hathall was here, and he's only been gone ten weeks. Not girls, that is. The personnel manager's been with us for five years, but his office is down in the works and I don't think they ever met.'

'Can you remember if he was particularly friendly with any girl?'

'I can remember he wasn't,' said Mr Aveney. 'He was crazy about that wife of his, the one who got herself killed. I never heard a man go on about a woman the way he went on about her. She was Marilyn Monroe and the Shah-ess of Persia and the Virgin Mary all rolled in one as far as he was concerned.'

But Wexford was tired of hearing about Robert Hathall's uxoriousness. He glanced at the list, formidably long, and there were the names, the sort of names they all seemed to have these days, Junes and Janes and Susans and Lindas and Julies. They had all lived in and around Toxborough and not one of them had stayed at Kidd's more than six months. He had a horrible prevision of weeks of work while half a dozen men scoured the Home Counties for this Jane, this Julie, this Susan, and then he put the list in his briefcase.

'Your friend said he'd like to have a look round the works, so if you'd care to, we'll go down and find him.'

They found Howard in the custody of a Julie who was

leading him between benches where women in overalls and with turbans round their heads were peeling the casts from plastic dolls. The factory was airy and pleasant, apart from the smell of cellulose, and from a couple of speakers came the seductive voice of Engelbert Humperdinck imploring his listeners to release him and let him love again.

'A bit of a dead loss that,' said Wexford when they had said good-bye to Mr Aveney. 'I thought it would be. Still, you'll be in plenty of time for your dinner date. It's no more than half an hour from here to Kingsmarkham. And I shall be in time to get myself promptly hauled over the coals. Would you like me to direct you round the back doubles so that we can miss the traffic and I can show you one or two points of interest?'

Howard said he would, so his uncle instructed him how to find the Myringham Road. They went through the centre of the town and past that shopping precinct whose ugliness had so offended Mark Somerset and where he had met the Hathalls on their shopping spree.

'Follow the signs for Pomfret rather than Kingsmarkham, and then I'll direct you into Kingsmarkham via Wool Lane.'

Obediently, Howard followed the signs and within ten minutes they were in country lanes. Here was unspoiled country, the soft Sussex of undulating hills topped with tree rings, of acres of fir forest and little brown-roofed farms nestling in woody hollows. The harvest was in, and where the wheat had been cut the fields were a pale blond, shining like sheets of silver gilt in the sun.

'When I'm out here,' said Howard, 'I feel the truth of what Orwell said about every man knowing in his heart that the loveliest thing to do in the world is to spend a fine day in the country. And when I'm in London I agree with Charles Lamb.'

'D'you mean preferring to see a theatre queue than all the flocks of silly sheep on Epsom Downs?'

Howard laughed and nodded. 'I take it I'm to avoid that turn that says Sewingbury?'

'You want the right turn for Kingsmarkham, coming up in about a mile. It's a little side road and eventually it becomes Wool Lane. I think Angela must have come along here in the car with her passenger last Friday. But where did she come *from?*'

Howard took the turn. They passed Wool Farm and saw the sign Wool Lane, at which the road became a narrow tunnel. If they had met another car, its driver or Howard would have had to pull right up on to the bank to allow the other's passage, but they met no cars. Motorists avoided the narrow perilous lane and few strangers took it for a through road at all.

'Bury Cottage,' Wexford said.

Howard slowed slightly. As he did so, Robert Hathall came round from the side of the house with a pair of garden shears in his hands. He didn't look up, but began chopping the heads off Michaelmas daisies. Wexford wondered if his mother had nagged him into this unaccustomed task.

'That's him,' he said. 'Did you get a look?'

'Enough to identify him again,' said Howard, 'though I don't suppose I shall have to.'

They parted at the police station. The Chief Constable's Rover was already parked on the forecourt. He was early for his appointment but so was Wexford. There was no need to rush up breathless and penitent, so he took his time about it, walking in almost casually to where the carpet and the coals awaited him.

'I can guess what it's about, sir. Hathall's been complaining.'

'That you can guess,' said Charles Griswold, 'only makes it worse.' He frowned and drew himself up to his full height which was a good deal more than Wexford's own six feet. The Chief Constable bore an uncanny likeness to the late General de Gaulle, whose initials he shared, and he must have been aware of it. A chance of nature may account for a physical resemblance to a famous man. Only knowledge of that resemblance, the continual reminders of it from friends and enemies, can account for similarities of the one personality to the other. Griswold was in the habit of speaking of Mid-Sussex, his area, in much the same tones as the dead statesman had spoken of *La France*. 'He's sent me a very strongly worded letter of complaint. Says you've been trying to trap him, using unorthodox methods. Sprang something about a fingerprint on him and then walked out of the house without waiting for his answer. Have you got any grounds for thinking he killed his wife?'

'Not with his own hands, sir. He was in his London office at the time.'

'Then what the hell are you playing at? I am proud of Mid-Sussex. My life's work has been devoted to Mid-Sussex. I was proud of the rectitude of my officers in Mid-Sussex, confident that their conduct might not only be beyond reproach but seen to be beyond reproach.' Griswold sighed heavily. In a moment, Wexford thought, he would be saying, '*L'état, c'est moi.*' 'Why are you harassing this man? Persecuting is what he calls it.'

'Persecuting,' said Wexford, 'is what he always calls it.'

'And that means?'

'He's paranoid, sir.'

'Don't give me that headshrinkers' jargon, Reg. Have you got one single piece of concrete evidence against this chap?'

'No. Only my personal and very strong feeling that he killed his wife.'

'Feeling? Feeling? We hear a damn sight too much about feelings these days and at your age you ought to bloody know better. What d'you mean then, that he had an accomplice? Have you got a *feeling* who this accomplice might be? Have you got any evidence about *him*?'

What could he say but 'No, sir, I haven't'? He added more firmly, 'May I see his letter?'

'No, you mayn't,' Griswold snapped. 'I've told you what's in it. Be thankful I'm sparing you his uncomplimentary remarks about your manners and your tactics. He says you've stolen a book of his.'

'For Christ's sake . . . You don't believe that?'

'Well, no, Reg, I don't. But have it sent back to him and fast. And lay off him pronto, d'you get that?'

'Lay off him?' said Wexford aghast. 'I have to talk to him. There's no other line of investigation I can pursue.'

'I said lay off him. That's an order. I won't have any more of it. I will not have the reputation of Mid-Sussex sacrificed to your *feelings*.'

CHAPTER ELEVEN

It was this which marked the end of Wexford's official investigation into the death of Angela Hathall.

Later, when he looked back, he was aware that three twenty-one on the afternoon of Thursday, October second, was the moment when all hope of solving her murder in a straightforward aboveboard way died. But at the time he didn't know that. He felt only grievance and anger, and he resigned himself to the delays and irritations which must ensue if Hathall couldn't be directly pursued. He still thought ways were open to him of discovering the identity of the woman without arousing fresh annoyance in Hathall. He could delegate. Burden and Martin could make approaches of a more tactful nature. Men could be put on the trail of those girls on Aveney's list. In a roundabout way it could be done. Hathall had betrayed himself, Hathall was guilty – therefore, the crime could ultimately be brought home to Hathall.

But he was disheartened. On his way back to Kingsmarkham he had considered phoning Nancy Lake, taking advantage – to put it into plain words – of Dora's absence, but even an innocent dinner with her, envisaged now, lost the savour the prospect of it had had. He didn't get in touch with her. He didn't phone Howard. He spent the lonely weekend of a grass widower, fulminating to himself about Hathall's good luck and about his own folly in being careless in his handling of an irritable and prickly personality.

Of Men and Angels was sent back, accompanied by a printed card on which Wexford had written a polite note regretting having kept it so long. No response came from Hathall, who must, the chief inspector thought, have been rubbing his hands with glee.

On Monday morning he went back to Kidd's factory at Toxborough.

Mr Aveney seemed pleased to see him – those who cannot be incriminated usually take a virtuous pleasure in their involvement in police enquiries – but he couldn't offer much help. 'Other women Mr Hathall might have met here?' he asked.

'I was thinking about sales reps. After all, it's children's toys you make.'

'The sales reps all work from our London office. There's only one woman among them and he never met her. What about those girls' names I gave you? No luck?'

Wexford shook his head. 'Not so far.'

'You won't. There's nothing there. That only leaves the cleaners. We've got one cleaning woman who's been here since we started up, but she's sixty-two. Of course she has a couple of girls working with her, but they're always changing like the rest of our staff. I suppose I *could* give you another list of names. I never see them and Mr Hathall wouldn't have. They've finished before we come in. The only one I can recall offhand I remember because she was so honest. She stayed behind one morning to hand me a pound note she'd found under someone's desk.'

'Don't bother with the list, Mr Aveney,' said Wexford. 'There's obviously nothing there.'

'You've got Hathall-itis,' said Burden as the second week after Angela's death came to an end.

'Sounds like bad breath.'

'I've never known you so – well, I was going to say pig-headed. You haven't got a scrap of evidence that Hathall so much as took another woman out, let alone conspired with her to do murder.'

'That handprint,' said Wexford obstinately, 'and those long dark hairs and that woman seen with Angela in the car.'

'He *thought* it was a woman. How many times have you and I seen someone across the street and not been able to

make up our minds whether it was a boy or a girl. You always
say the Adam's apple is the one sure distinguishing mark. Does
a cyclist glancing into a car notice if the passenger's got an
Adam's apple? We've followed up all the girls on that list, bar
the one that's in the United States and the one who was in
hospital on the nineteenth. Most of them could hardly remember who Hathall is.'

'What's your idea then? How do you account for that print
on the bath?'

'I'll tell you. It was a bloke killed Angela. She was lonely
and she picked him up like you said at first. He strangled her
– by accident maybe – while he was trying to get the necklace
off her. Why should he leave prints? Why should he touch
anything in the house – except Angela? If he did, there
wouldn't have been many and he could have wiped them off.
The woman who left the print, she's not even involved. She
was a passerby, a motorist, who called and asked to use the
phone . . .'

'And the loo?'

'Why not? These things happen. A similar thing happened
in my own home yesterday. My daughter was in on her own
and a young fellow who'd walked from Stowerton because he
couldn't hitch a lift, came and asked for a drink of water. She
let him in – I had something to say about that, as you can
imagine – and she let him use the bathroom too. Luckily, he
was OK and no harm was done. But why shouldn't something
like that have happened at Bury Cottage? The woman hasn't
come forward because she doesn't even know the name of the
house she called at or the name of the woman who let her in.
Her prints aren't on the phone or anywhere else because
Angela was still cleaning the place when she called. Isn't that
more reasonable than this conspiracy idea that hasn't the
slightest foundation?'

Griswold liked the theory. And Wexford found himself in
charge of an enquiry based on a postulation he couldn't for a

moment believe in. He was obliged to give his support to a nationwide hue and cry aimed at locating an amnesiac female motorist and a thief who killed by chance for a valueless necklace. Neither were found, neither took more definite shape than the vague outlines Burden had invented for them, but Griswold and Burden and the newspapers talked about them as if they existed. And Robert Hathall, Wexford learned at second-hand, had made a series of helpful suggestions as to one fresh lead after another. The Chief Constable couldn't understand – so the grass roots had it – what had given rise to the idea that the man suffered from a persecution complex or was bad-tempered. Nothing could have been more cooperative than his attitude once Wexford was removed from direct contact with him.

Wexford thought he would soon grow sick of the whole thing. The weeks dragged on and there were no new developments. At first it is maddening to have one's certain knowledge discounted and derided. Then, as fresh interests and fresh work enter, it becomes merely annoying; lastly, a bore. Wexford would have been very happy to have regarded Robert Hathall as a bore. After all, no one solves every murder case. Dozens have always, and always will have, eluded solution. Right should, of course, be done and justice hold sway, but the human element makes this impossible. Some must get away and Hathall was evidently going to be one of them. He ought by now to have been relegated to the ranks of the bores, for he wasn't an interesting man but essentially an irritating humourless bore. Yet Wexford couldn't think of him as such. In himself, he might be tedious but what he had done was not. Wexford wanted to know why he had done it and how and with what help and by what means. And above all he felt a righteous indignation that a man might kill his wife and bring his mother to find her body and yet be regarded by the powers-that-be as *cooperative*.

He mustn't let this thing develop into an obsession. He

reminded himself that he was a reasonable, level-headed man, a policeman with a job to do, not an executioner impelled to the hunt by some political mission or holy cause. Perhaps it was those months of starving himself that had robbed him of his steadiness, his equanimity. But only a fool would gain a good figure at the price of an unbalanced mind. Reminding himself of this excellent maxim, he kept cool when Burden told him Hathall was about to give up his tenancy of Bury Cottage, and replied with sarcasm rather than explosively.

'I suppose I'm to be allowed to know where he's going?'

Burden had been considered by Griswold as having a nice line in tact and had therefore, throughout the autumn, been the link with Hathall. The Mid-Sussex envoy was what Wexford called him, adding that he imagined 'our man' in Wool Lane would be in possession of such top-level secrets.

'He's staying with his mother in Balham for the time being and he talks of getting a flat in Hampstead.'

'The vendor will cheat him,' said Wexford bitterly, 'the train service will be appalling. He'll be made to pay an extortionate rent for his garage and someone's going to put up a tower block that'll spoil his view of the Heath. All in all, he'll be very happy.'

'I don't know why you make him out such a masochist.'

'I make him out a murderer.'

'Hathall didn't murder his wife,' said Burden. 'He's just got an unfortunate manner that got in your hair.'

'An unfortunate manner! Why not be blunt about it and say he has fits? He's allergic to fingerprints. Mention you've found one on his bath and he has an epileptic seizure.'

'You'd hardly call that evidence, would you?' said Burden rather coldly, and he put on his glasses for no better reason, Wexford thought than to peer censoriously through them at his superior officer.

But the idea of Hathall's departing and beginning the new life he had planned for himself and done murder to achieve was a disturbing one. That it had been allowed to happen was almost entirely due to his own mishandling of the investigation. He had spoiled things by being tough with and rude to the kind of man who would never respond to such treatment. And now there was nothing more he could do because Hathall's person was sacrosanct and every clue to the unknown woman's identity locked up in his sacrosanct mind. Was there any point in learning Hathall's new address? If he wasn't permitted to talk to him in Kingsmarkham, what hope had he of breaching his London privacy? For a long time personal pride stopped him asking Burden for news of Hathall, and Burden offered none until one day in spring, when they were lunching together at the Carousel. The inspector dropped Hathall's new address casually into their conversation, prefacing his remark with a 'by the by,' as if he were speaking of some slight acquaintance of theirs, a man in whom neither could have more than a passing interest.

'So now he tells me,' said Wexford to the tomato-shaped sauce bottle.

'There doesn't seem to be any reason why you shouldn't know.'

'Got it okayed by the Home Secretary first, did you?'

Having the address didn't really help matters and its location meant very little to Wexford. He was prepared to drop the subject there and then, knowing as he did that discussing Hathall with Burden only made them both feel awkward. Strangely enough, it was Burden who pursued it. Perhaps he hadn't cared for that crack about the Home Secretary or, more likely, disliked the idea of the significance that might attach to his announcement if he left it islanded.

'I've always thought,' he said, 'though I haven't said so before, that there was one major drawback to your theory. If Hathall had had an accomplice with that scar on her finger, he'd have insisted she wear gloves. Because if she left only one print, he'd never be able to live with her or marry

436

her or even seen her again. And you say he killed Angela in order to do that. So he can't have. It's simple when you think about it.'

Wexford didn't say anything. He betrayed no excitement. But that night when he got home he studied his map of London, made a phone call and spent some time poring over his latest bank statement.

The Fortunes had come to stay for the weekend. Uncle and nephew walked down Wool Lane and paused outside the cottage which hadn't yet been re-let. The 'miracle' tree was laden with white blossom, and behind the house young lambs were pastured on the hillside whose peak was crowned by a ring of trees.

'Hathall doesn't prefer the flocks of silly sheep either,' said Wexford, recalling a conversation they had had near this spot. 'He's taken himself as far from Epsom Downs as can be, yet he's a South Londoner. West Hampstead is where he's living. Dartmeet Avenue. D'you know it?'

'I know where it is. Between the Finchley Road and West End Lane. Why did he pick Hampstead?'

'Just because it's as far as possible from South London where his mother and his ex-wife and his daughter are.' Wexford pulled down a branch of plum blossom to his face and smelled its faint honey scent. 'Or that's what I *think*.' The branch sprang back, scattering petals on the grass. Musingly, he said, 'He appears to lead a celibate life. The only woman he's been seen with is his mother.'

Howard seemed intrigued. 'You mean you have a – a watcher?'

'He's not much of a spy,' Wexford admitted, 'but he was the best and safest I could find. As a matter of fact, he's the brother of an old customer of mine, a chap called Monkey Matthews. The brother's name is Ginge, so-called on account of his hair. He lives in Kilburn.'

Howard laughed, but sympathetically. 'What does this Ginge do? Tail him?'

'Not exactly. But he keeps an eye. I give him a remuneration. Out of my own pocket, naturally.'

'I didn't realize you were that serious.'

'I don't know when I was ever so serious about a thing like this in my whole career.'

They turned away. A little wind had sprung up and it was growing chilly. Howard gave a backward glance at the hedge tunnel which was already greening and thickening, and said quietly, 'What is it you hope for, Reg?'

His uncle didn't reply at once. They had passed the isolated villa where Nancy Lake's car stood on the garage drive, before he spoke. He had been deep in thought, so silent and preoccupied that Howard had perhaps thought he had forgotten the question or had no answer to it. But now as they came to the Stowerton Road, he said, 'For a long time I wondered why Hathall was so horrified – and that's an understatement – when I told him about the print. Because he didn't want the woman discovered, of course. But it wasn't just fear he showed. It was something more like a terrible sorrow he showed – when he'd recovered a bit, that is. And I came to the conclusion that his reaction was what it was because he'd had Angela killed expressly so that he could be with that woman. And now he knew he'd never dare see her again.

'And then he reflected. He wrote that letter of protest to Griswold to clear the field of me because he knew I knew. But it might still be possible for him to get away with it and have what he wanted, a life with that woman. Not as he'd planned it. Not a flit to London, then after a few weeks a friendship with a girl, the lonely widower seeking consolation with a new woman friend whom, as time went by, he could marry. Not that – now. Even though he'd pulled the wool over Griswold's eyes, he wouldn't dare try that one on. The

handprint had been found and however much we might seem
to be ignoring him, he couldn't hope to go in for a public
courtship and then marriage with a woman whose hand would
betray her. Betray her to anyone, Howard, not just to an
expert.'

'So what can he do?'

'He has two alternatives,' said Wexford crisply. 'He and
the woman may have agreed to part. Presumably, even if one
is madly in love, liberty is preferable to the indulgence of love.
Yes, they could have parted.'

' "Shake hands forever, cancel all our vows?" '

'The next bit is even more appropriate.

> "And if we meet at any time again,
> Be it not seen in either of our brows
> That we one jot of former love retain."

'Or,' Wexford went on, 'they could have decided – let's say
grandiloquently that their passion decided for them, love was
bigger than both of them – to have gone on meeting clandes-
tinely. Not to live together, never to meet in public, but to
carry on as if each of them had a jealous suspicious spouse.'

'What, go on like that indefinitely?'

'Maybe. Until it wears itself out or until they find some
other solution. But I think that's what they're doing, Howard.
If it isn't so, why has he picked Northwest London where no
one knows him as a place to live? Why not south of the river
where his mother is and his daughter? Or somewhere near his
work. He's earning a good salary now. He could just as well
have got himself a place in Central London. He's hidden
himself away so that he can sneak out in the evenings to be
with *her*.

'I'm going to try and find her,' Wexford said thoughtfully.
'It'll cost me some money and take up my spare time, but I
mean to have a go.'

CHAPTER TWELVE

In describing Ginge Matthews as not much of a spy, Wexford had rather underrated him. The miserable resources at his disposal made him bitter. He was perpetually irritated by Ginge's unwillingness to use the phone. Ginge was proud of his literary style which was culled from the witness-box manner of thick-headed and very junior police constables whose periphrasis he had overheard from the dock. In Ginge's reports his quarry never went anywhere, but always proceeded; his home was his domicile and, rather than going home, he withdrew or retired there. But in honesty and in fairness to Ginge, Wexford had to admit that, although he had learned nothing of the elusive woman during these past months, he had learned a good deal about Hathall's manner of life.

According to Ginge, the house where he had his flat was a big three-storeyed place and – reading between the lines – of Edwardian vintage. Hathall had no garage but left his car parked in the street. From meanness or the impossibility of finding a garage to rent? Wexford didn't know and Ginge couldn't tell him. Hathall left for work at nine in the morning and either walked or caught a bus from West End Green to West Hampstead Tube station where he took the Bakerloo Line train to (presumably) Piccadilly. He reached home again soon after six, and on several occasions Ginge, lurking in a phone box opposite number 62 Dartmeet Avenue, had seen him go out again in his car. Ginge always knew when he was at home in the evenings because then a light showed in the second floor bay window. He had never seen him accompanied by anyone except his mother – from his description it could only be old Mrs Hathall – whom he had brought to his flat by car one Saturday afternoon. Mother and son had had words, a harsh low-voiced quarrel on the pavement before they even got to the front door.

Ginge had no car. He had no job either, but the small amount of money Wexford could afford to give him didn't make it worth his while to spend more than one evening and perhaps one Saturday or Sunday afternoon a week watching Robert Hathall. It could easily have happened that Hathall brought his girl home on one or two of the other six evenings. And yet Wexford clung to hope. One day, sometime . . . He dreamed at night of Hathall, not very often, possibly once a fortnight, and in these dreams he saw him with the dark-haired girl with the scarred finger, or else alone as he had been when he had stood by the fireplace in Bury Cottage, paralyzed with fear and realization and – yes, with grief.

'On the afternoon of Saturday, June 15th inst., at 3.5 p.m., the party was seen to proceed from his domicile at 62 Dartmeet Avenue to West End Lane where he made purchases at a supermarket . . .' Wexford cursed. They were nearly all like that. And what proof had he that Ginge had even been there 'on the afternoon of Saturday, June 15th inst.'? Naturally, Ginge would say he had been there when there was a quid in it for every tailing session. July came and August, and Hathall, if Ginge was to be trusted, led a simple regular life, going to work, coming home, shopping on Saturdays, sometimes taking an evening drive. If Ginge could be trusted . . .

That he could be, up to a point, was proved in September just before the anniversary of Angela's death. 'There is reason to believe,' wrote Ginge, 'that the party had disposed of his motor vehicle, it having disappeared from its customary parking places. On the evening of Thursday, September 10th inst., having arrived home from his place of business at 6.10 p.m., he proceeded at 6.50 from his domicile and boarded the number 28 bus at West End Green NW6.'

Was there anything in it? Wexford didn't think so. On his salary Hathall could easily afford to run a car, but he might have got rid of it only because of the increasing difficulty of on-street parking. Still, it was a good thing from his point of view. Hathall could now be followed.

Wexford never wrote to Ginge. It was too risky. The little red-headed spy might not be above blackmail, and if any letters should fall into the hands of Griswold. . . . He sent his wages in notes in a plain envelope, and when he had to talk to him, which, on account of the paucity of news, happened rarely, he could always get him between twelve and one at a Kilburn public house called the Countess of Castlemaine.

'Follow him?' said Ginge nervously. 'What, on that bleeding 28?'

'I don't see why not. He's never seen you, has he?'

'Maybe he has. How should I know? It's not easy following a bloke on a bleeding bus.' Ginge's conversational manner was markedly different from his literary style, particularly as to his use of adjectives. 'If he goes up top, say, and I go inside, or vicey-versy . . .'

'Why does there have to be any vicey-versy?' said Wexford. 'You sit in the seat behind him and stick close. Right?'

Ginge didn't seem to think it was right at all, but he agreed rather dubiously to try it. Whether or not he had tried it, Wexford wasn't told, for Ginge's next report made no reference to buses. Yet the more he studied it with its magistrates' court circumlocutions, the more interested he was by it. 'Being in the neighborhood of Dartmeet Avenue NW6, at 3 p.m. on the 26th inst., I took it upon myself to investigate the party's place of domicile. During a conversation with the landlord, during which I represented myself as an official of the local rating authority, I enquired as to the number of apartments and was informed that only single rooms were to let in the establishment . . .'

Rather enterprising of Ginge, was Wexford's first thought, though he had probably only assumed this role to impress his employer and hope he would forget all about the more dangerous exercise of tailing Hathall on a bus. But that wasn't important. What astonished the chief inspector was that Hathall was a tenant rather than an owner-occupier and, moreover, the tenant of a room rather than a flat. Strange, very strange. He could have afforded to buy a flat on a mortgage. Why hadn't he? Because he didn't intend to be permanently domiciled (as Ginge would put it) in London? Or because he had other uses for his income? Both maybe. But Wexford seized upon this as the most peculiar circumstance he had yet discovered in Hathall's present life. Even with rents in London as extortionate as they were, he could hardly be paying more than fifteen pounds a week at the most for a room, yet, after deductions, he must be drawing sixty. Wexford had no confidant but Howard, and it was to Howard, on the phone, that he talked about it.

'You're thinking he could be supporting someone else?'

'I am,' said Wexford.

'Say fifteen a week for himself and fifteen for her on accommodation . . .? And if she's not working he has to keep her as well.'

'Christ, you don't know how good it is for me to hear someone talk about her as a real person, as "she." You believe she exists, don't you?'

'It wasn't a ghost made that print, Reg. It wasn't ectoplasm. She exists.'

In Kingsmarkham they had given up. They had stopped searching. Griswold had told the newspapers some rubbish – in Wexford's phrase – about the case not being closed, but it *was* closed. His statement was only face-saving. Mark Somerset had let Bury Cottage to a couple of young Americans, teachers of political economy at the University of the South. The front garden was tidied up and they talked of having the back garden landscaped at their own expense. One day the plums hung heavily on the tree, the next it was stripped. Wexford never found out if Nancy Lake had had them and made them into 'miracle' jam, for he had never seen Nancy since the day he was told to lay off Hathall.

Nothing came from Ginge for a fortnight. At last Wexford phoned him at the Countess of Castlemaine to be told that on his watching evenings Hathall had remained at home. He would, however, watch again that night and on the Saturday afternoon. On Monday his report came. Hathall had done his usual shopping on Saturday, but on the previous evening had walked down to the bus stop at West End Green at seven o'clock. Ginge had followed him, but being intimidated ('made cautious' was his expression) by Hathall's suspicious backward glances, hadn't pursued him on to the 28 bus which his quarry had caught at ten past seven. Wexford hurled the sheet of paper into the wastepaper basket. That was all he needed, for Hathall to get wise to Ginge.

Another week went by. Wexford was on the point of throwing Ginge's next communication away unopened. He felt he couldn't face another account of Hathall's Saturday shopping activities. But he did open the letter. And there, of course, was the usual nonsense about the supermarket visit. There too, appended casually as if it were of no importance, a throwaway line to fill up, was a note that after his shopping Hathall had called at a travel agency.

'The place he went to is called Sudamerica Tours, Howard. Ginge didn't dare follow him in, lily-livered idiot that he is.'

Howard's voice sounded thin and dry. 'You're thinking what I'm thinking.'

'Of course. Some place where we've no extradition treaty. He's been reading about train robbers and that gave him the idea. Bloody newspapers do more harm than good.'

'But, my God, Reg, he must be dead scared if he's prepared to throw up his job and flit to Brazil or somewhere. What's he going to do there? How will he live?'

'As birds do, nephew. God knows. Look, Howard, could

you do something for me? Could you get on to Marcus Flower and try and find out if they're sending him abroad? I daren't.'

'Well, I dare,' said Howard. 'But if they were, wouldn't they be arranging the whole thing and paying for it?'

'They wouldn't pay and arrange for his girl, would they?'

'I'll do my best and call you back this evening.'

Was that why Hathall had been living so economically? In order to save up his accomplice's fare? He would have to have a job there waiting for him, Wexford thought, or else be very desperate to get to safety. In that case, the money for two air fares would have to be found. In the *Kingsmarkham Courier*, which had been placed on his desk that morning, he remembered seeing an advertisement for trips to Rio de Janeiro. He fished it out from under a pile of papers and looked at the back page. There it was, the return fare priced at just under two hundred and fifty pounds. Add a bit more for two single fares, and Hathall's saving could be accounted for . . .

He was about to discard the newspaper when a name in the deaths column caught his eye. Somerset. 'On October 15th, at Church House, Old Myringham, Gwendolen Mary Somerset, beloved wife of Mark Somerset. Funeral St. Luke's Church October 22nd. No flowers, please, but donations to Stowerton Home for Incurables.' So the demanding and querulous wife had died at last. The *beloved* wife? Perhaps she had been, or perhaps this was the usual hypocrisy, so stale, hackneyed and automatic a formula as to be hardly hypocrisy any more. Wexford smiled drily and then forgot about it. He went home early – the town was quiet and crimeless – and waited for Howard's telephone call.

The phone rang at seven, but it was his younger daughter, Sheila. She and her mother chatted for about twenty minutes, and after that the phone didn't ring again. Wexford waited till about half past ten and then he dialled Howard's number.

'He's bloody well out,' he said crossly to his wife. 'I call that the limit.'

'Why shouldn't he go out in the evening? I'm sure he works hard enough.'

'Don't I work? I don't go gallivanting about in the evenings when I've promised to phone people.'

'No, and if you did perhaps your blood pressure wouldn't rage the way it's doing at this moment,' said Dora.

At eleven he tried to get Howard again, but again there was no reply and he went off to bed in a peevish frame of mind. It wasn't surprising that he had another of those obsessive Hathall dreams. He was at an airport. The great jet aircraft was ready to take off and the doors had been closed, but they opened again as he watched and there appeared at the head of the steps, like a royal couple waving graciously to the well-wishing crowd, Hathall and a woman. The woman raised her right hand in a gesture of farewell and he saw the L-shaped scar burning red, an angry cicatrice – L for love, for loss, for leave-taking. But before he could rush up the steps as he had begun to do, the stairs themselves melted away, the couple retreated, and the aircraft sailed up, up into the ice-blue winter sky.

Why is it that as you get older you tend to wake up at five and are unable to get off to sleep again? Something to do with the blood sugar level being low? Or the coming of dawn exerting an atavistic pull? Wexford knew further sleep would elude him, so he got up at half past six and made his own breakfast. He didn't like the idea of phoning Howard before eight, and by a quarter to he was so fidgety and restless that he took a cup of tea in to Dora and went off to work. By now, of course, Howard would have left for Kenbourne Vale. He began to feel bitterly injured, and those old feelings he used to have about Howard reasserted themselves. True, he had listened sympathetically to all his uncle's ramblings about this case, but what was he really thinking? That this was an elderly man's fantasy? Country bumpkin rubbish? It seemed likely that he had only played along to humour him and had deferred that call to Marcus Flower until he could spare the time from his more important metropolitan business. He probably hadn't made it yet. Still, it was no use getting paranoid in Hathall style. He must humble himself, phone Kenbourne Vale and ask again.

This he did at nine-thirty. Howard hadn't yet come in, and he found himself involved in a gossipy chat with Sergeant Clements, an old friend from days when they had worked together on the Kenbourne Vale cemetery murder. Wexford was too kind a man to cut the sergeant short after he had discovered that Howard was delayed at some top-level conference, and resigned himself to hearing all about Clements' adopted son, prospective adopted daughter, and new maisonette. A message would be left for the chief superintendent, Clements said at last, but he wasn't expected in till twelve.

The call finally came at ten past.

'I tried to get you at home before I left,' said Howard, 'but Dora said you'd gone. I haven't had a moment since, Reg.'

There was a note of barely suppressed excitement in his nephew's voice. Maybe he'd been promoted again, Wexford thought, and he said not very warmly, 'You did say you'd phone last night.'

'So I did. At seven. But your line was engaged. I couldn't after that. Denise and I went to the pictures.'

It was the tone of amusement – no, of glee – that did it. Forgetting all about rank, Wexford exploded. 'Charming,' he snapped. 'I hope the people in the row behind you chattered the whole way through and the people in front had it off on the seats and the people in the circle dropped orange peel on you. What about my chap? What about my South America thing?'

'Oh, that,' said Howard, and Wexford could have sworn he heard a yawn. 'He's leaving Marcus Flower, he's resigned. I couldn't get any more.'

'Thanks a lot. And that's all?'

Howard was laughing now. 'Oh, Reg,' he said, 'it's wicked to keep you in suspense, but you were so ripe for it. You're such an irascible old devil, I couldn't resist.' He controlled his laughter and suddenly his voice became solemn, measured. 'That is by no means all,' he said. 'I've seen him.'

'You *what?* D'you mean you've talked to Hathall?'

'No, I've *seen* him. Not alone. With a woman. I've seen him with a woman, Reg.'

'Oh, my God,' said Wexford softly. 'The Lord hath delivered him into mine hands.'

CHAPTER THIRTEEN

'I wouldn't be so sure of that,' said Howard. 'Not yet. But I'll tell you about it, shall I? Funny, isn't it, the way I said I didn't suppose I'd ever have to identify him? But I did identify him last night. Listen, and I'll tell you how it was.'

On the previous evening, Howard had attempted to call his uncle at seven but the line had been engaged. Since he had nothing but negative news for him, he decided to try again in the morning as he was pressed for time. He and Denise were to dine in the West End before going on to the nine o'clock showing of a film at the Curzon Cinema, and Howard had parked his car near the junction of Curzon Street and Half Moon Street. Having a few minutes to spare, he had been drawn by curiosity to have a look at the exterior of the offices he had phoned during the day, and he and Denise were approaching the Marcus Flower building when he saw a man and a woman coming towards it from the opposite direction. The man was Robert Hathall.

At the plate-glass window they paused and looked inside, surveying velvet drapery and wall-to-wall Wilton and marble staircase. Hathall seemed to be pointing out to his companion the glossy splendours of the place where he worked. The woman was of medium height, good-looking but not startlingly so, with very short blonde hair. Howard thought she was in her late twenties or early thirties.

'Could the hair have been a wig?' Wexford asked.

'No, but it could have been dyed. Naturally, I didn't see her hand. They were talking to each other in what I thought was an affectionate way and after a bit they walked off down towards Piccadilly. And, incidentally, I didn't enjoy the picture. Under the circumstances, I couldn't concentrate.'

'They haven't shaken hands forever, Howard. They haven't cancelled all their vows. It's as I thought, and now it can only be a matter of time before we find her.'

The following day was his day of rest, his day off. The ten-thirty train from Kingsmarkham got him to Victoria just before half past eleven and by noon he was in Kilburn. What quirk of romantic imagination had prompted the naming of this squalid Victorian public house after Charles the Second's principal mistress, Wexford couldn't fathom. It stood in a turning off the Edgware Road and it had the air of a gone-to-seed nineteenth-century gin palace. Ginge Matthews was sitting on a stool at the bar in earnest and apparently aggrieved conversation with the Irish barman. When he saw Wexford his eyes widened – or, rather, one eye widened. The other was half-closed and sunk in purple swelling.

'Take your drink over to the corner,' said Wexford. 'I'll join you in a minute. May I have a glass of dry wine, please?'

Ginge didn't look like his brother or talk like him and he certainly didn't smoke like him, but nevertheless they had something in common apart from their partiality for petty crime. Perhaps one of their parents had been possessed of a dynamic personality, or there might even have been something exceptionally vital in their genes. Whatever it was, it made Wexford say that the Matthews brothers were just like other people only more so. Both were inclined to do things to excess. Monkey smoked sixty king-sized cigarettes a day. Ginge didn't smoke at all but drank, when he could afford it, a concoction of pernod and Guinness.

Ginge hadn't spoken to Monkey for fifteen years and Monkey hadn't spoken to him. They had fallen out as the result of the bungling mess they had made of an attempt to break into a Kingsmarkham furrier's. Ginge had gone to prison and Monkey had not – most unfairly, as Ginge had reasonably thought – and when he came out, the younger brother had taken himself off to London where he had married a widow who owned her own house and a bit of money. Ginge had soon spent the money and she, perhaps in revenge, had presented him with five children. He didn't, therefore, enquire after his brother whom he blamed for many of his misfortunes, but remarked bitterly to Wexford when he joined him at a corner table:

'See my eye?'

'Of course I see it. What the hell have you done to yourself? Walked into your wife's fist?'

'Very funny. I'll tell you who done it. That bleeding Hathall. Last night when I was following him down to the 28 stop.'

'For Christ's sake!' said Wexford, aghast. 'You mean he's on to you?'

'Thanks for the sympathy.' Ginge's small round face flushed nearly as red as his hair. 'Course he was bound to spot me sooner or later on account of my bleeding hair. He hadn't got no cause to turn round and poke me in the bleeding eye, though, had he?'

'Is that what he did?'

'I'm telling you. Cut me, he did. The wife said I looked like Henry Cooper. It wasn't so bleeding funny, I can tell you.'

Wearily, Wexford said, 'Could you stop the bleeding?'

'It stopped in time, naturally, it did. But it isn't healed up yet and you can see the bleeding . . .'

'Oh, *God*. I mean stop saying "bleeding" every other word. It's putting me off my drink. Look, Ginge, I'm sorry about your eye, but there's no great harm done. Obviously, you'll have to be a damn sight more careful. For instance, you could try wearing a hat . . .'

'I'm not going back there again, Mr Wexford.'

'Never mind that now. Let me buy you another of those what-d'you-call-'ems. What *do* you call them?'

'You ask for a half of draught Guinness with a double pernod in.' Ginge added proudly and more cheerfully, 'I don't know what *they* call 'em but I call 'em Demon Kings.'

The stuff smelled dreadful. Wexford fetched himself another glass of white wine and Ginge said, 'You won't get very fat on that.'

'That's the idea. Now tell me where this 28 bus goes.'

Ginge took a swig of his Demon King and said with extreme rapidity, 'Golders Green, Child's Hill, Fortune Green, West End Lane, West Hampshire Station, Quex Road, Kilburn High Road...'

'For God's sake! I don't know any of these places, they don't mean a thing to me. Where does it end up?'

'Wandsworth Bridge.'

Disappointed at this disclosure yet pleased for once to be at an advantage in the face of so much sophisticated knowledge, Wexford said, 'He's only going to see his mother in Balham. That's near Balham.'

'Not where that bus goes isn't. Look, Mr Wexford,' said Ginge with patient indulgence, 'you don't know London, you've said so yourself. I've lived here fifteen years and I can tell you nobody as wasn't out of his bleeding twist would go to Balham that way. He'd go to West Hampstead Tube and change on to the Northern at Waterloo or the Elephant. Stands to reason he would.'

'Then he's dropping off somewhere along the route. Ginge, will you do one more thing for me? Is there a pub near this bus stop where you've seen him catch the 28?'

'Oppo-sight,' said Ginge warily.

'We'll give him a week. If he doesn't complain about you during the next week – Oh, all right, I know you think you're the one with grounds for complaint – but if he doesn't we'll know he either thinks you're a potential mugger...'

'Thanks very much.'

'... and doesn't connect you with me,' Wexford went on, ignoring the interruption, 'or else he's too scared at this stage to draw attention to himself. But, beginning next Monday, I want you to station yourself in that pub by six-thirty every night for a week. Just note how often he catches that bus. Will you do that? I don't want you to follow him and you won't be running any risk.'

'That's what you lot always say,' said Ginge. 'You want to remember he's already done some poor bleeder in. Who's going to see after my bleeding wife and kids if he gets throttling me with his bleeding gold chains?'

'The same as look after them now,' said Wexford silkily. 'The Social Security.'

'What a nasty tongue you've got.' For once Ginge sounded exactly like his brother, and briefly he looked like him as a greedy gleam appeared in his good eye. 'What's in it for me if I do?'

'A pound a day,' said Wexford, 'and as many of those – er, bleeding Demon Kings as you can get down you.'

Wexford waited anxiously for another summons from the Chief Constable, but none came, and by the end of the week he knew that Hathall wasn't going to complain. That, as he had told Ginge, didn't necessarily mean any more than that Hathall thought the man who was following him intended to attack him and had taken the law into his own hands. What was certain, though, was that whatever came out of Ginge's pub observations, he couldn't use the little red-headed man again. And it wasn't going to be much use finding out how often Hathall caught that bus if he could set no one to catch it with him.

Things were very quiet in Kingsmarkham. Nobody would object if he were to take the fortnight's holiday that was owing to him. People who take their summer holidays in November are always popular with colleagues. It all depended on Ginge. If it turned out that Hathall caught that bus regularly, why shouldn't he take his holiday and try to follow that bus by car? It would be difficult in the London traffic, which always intimidated him, but not all that difficult out of the rush hours. And ten to one, a hundred to one, Hathall wouldn't spot him.

Nobody on a bus looks at people in cars. Nobody on a bus can *see* the driver of a pursuing car. If only he knew when Hathall was leaving Marcus Flower and when he meant to leave the country . . .

But all this was driven out of his head by an event he couldn't have anticipated. He had been certain the weapon would never be found, that it was at the bottom of the Thames or tossed on to some local authority rubbish dump. When a young teacher of political science phoned him to say that a necklace had been found by the men excavating the garden of Bury Cottage and that her landlord, Mr Somerset, had advised her to inform the police, his first thought was that now he could overcome Griswold's scruples, now he could confront Hathall. He had himself driven down Wool Lane – observing on the way the For Sale board outside Nancy Lake's house – and then he walked into the wasteland, the area of open-cast mining, which had been Hathall's back garden. A load of Westmorland stone made a mountain range in one corner and a mechanical digger stood by the garage. Would Griswold say he should have had this garden dug over? When you're searching for a weapon, you don't dig up a garden that looks just like a bit of field without an exposed, freshly dug bit of earth in the whole of it. There hadn't been even a miniscule break in the long rank grass last September twelve-month. They had raked over every inch of it. How then had Hathall or his accomplice managed to bury the necklace and restore earth and grass without its being detected?

The teacher, Mrs Snyder, told him.

'There was a kind of cavity under here. A septic pit, would you call it? I guess Mr Somerset said something about a pit.'

'A cesspit or septic tank,' said Wexford. 'The main drainage came through to this part of Kingsmarkham about twenty years ago, but before that there'd have been a cesspit.'

'For heaven's sake! Why didn't they have it taken out?' said Mrs Snyder with the wonderment of a native of a richer and more hygiene-conscious country. 'Well, this necklace was in it, whatever it's called. That thing . . .' She pointed to the digger, '. . . smashed it open. Or so the workmen said. I didn't look personally. I don't want to seem to criticize your country, Captain, but a thing like that! A cess tank!'

Extremely amused by his new title which made him feel like a naval officer, Wexford said he quite understood that primitive methods of sewage disposal weren't pleasant to contemplate, and where was the necklace?

'I washed it and put it in the kitchen closet. I washed it in antiseptic.'

That hardly mattered now. It wouldn't, after its long immersion, bear prints, if it had ever done so. But the appearance of the necklace surprised him. It wasn't, as had been believed, composed of links, but was a solid collar of grey metal from which almost all the gilding had disappeared, and it was in the shape of a snake twisted into a circle, the snake's head passing, when the necklace was fastened, through a slot above its tail. Now he could see the answer to something that had long puzzled him. This was no chain that might snap when strained but a perfect strangler's weapon. All Hathall's accomplice had had to do was stand behind her victim, grasp the snake's head and pull . . .

But how could it have got into the disused cesspit? The metal cover, for use when the pit was emptied, had been buried under a layer of earth and so overgrown with grass that Wexford's men hadn't even guessed it might be there. He phoned Mark Somerset.

'I think I can tell you how it got there,' said Somerset. 'When the main drainage came through, my father, for the sake of economy, only had what's called the "black water" linked on to it. The "grey water" — that is, the waste from the bath, the hand basin and the kitchen sink — went on passing into the cesspit. Bury Cottage is on a bit of a slope, so he knew it wouldn't flood but would just soak away.'

'D'you mean someone could have simply dropped the thing down the sink plughole?'

'I don't see why not. If "someone" ran the taps hard, it'd get washed down.'

'Thank you, Mr Somerset. That's very helpful. By the way, I'd like to – er, express my sympathy for you in the loss of your wife.'

Was it his imagination, or did Somerset sound for the first time ill-at-ease? 'Well, yes, thanks,' he muttered and he rang off abruptly.

When he had had the necklace examined by laboratory experts, he asked for an appointment with the Chief Constable. This was granted for the following Friday afternoon and by two o'clock on that day he was in Griswold's own house, a tarted-up, unfarm-like farmhouse in a village called Millerton between Myringham and Sewingbury. It was known as High-trees Farm but Wexford privately called it Millerton-*Les-Deux-Églises*.

'What makes you think this is the weapon?' were Griswold's opening words.

'I feel it's the only type of necklace which could have been used, sir. A chain would have snapped. The lab boys say the gilt which remains on it is similar to the specimens of gilding taken from Angela Hathall's neck. Of course they can't be sure.'

'But I suppose they've got a "feeling"? Have you got any reason to believe that necklace hadn't been there for twenty years?'

Wexford knew better than to mention his feelings again. 'No, but I might have if I could talk to Hathall.'

'He wasn't there when she was killed,' said Griswold, his mouth turning down and his eyes growing hard.

'His girl-friend was.'

'Where? When? I am supposed to be the Chief Constable of Mid-Sussex where this murder was committed. Why am I not told if the identity of some female accomplice has been discovered?'

'I haven't exactly . . .'

'Reg,' said Griswold in a voice that had begun to tremble with anger, 'have you got any more evidence of Robert Hathall's complicity in this than you had fourteen months ago? Have you got one concrete piece of evidence? I asked you that before and I'm asking you again. *Have you?*'

Wexford hesitated. He couldn't reveal that he had had Hathall followed, still less that Chief Superintendent Howard Fortune, his own nephew, had seen him with a woman. What evidence of homicide lay in Hathall's economy or the sale of his car? What guilt was evinced by the man's living in North-west London or his having been seen to catch a London bus? There was the South American thing, of course . . . Grimly, Wexford faced just what that amounted to. Nothing. As far as he could prove, Hathall had been offered no job in South America, hadn't even bought a brochure about South America, let alone an air ticket. He had merely been seen to go into a travel agency, and seen by a man with a criminal record.

'No, sir.'

'Then the situation is unchanged. Totally unchanged. Remember that.'

CHAPTER FOURTEEN

Ginge had done as he was told, and on Friday, 8 November, a report arrived from him stating that he had been at his observation post in the pub each evening and on two of those evenings, the Monday and the Wednesday, Hathall had appeared at West End Green just before seven and had caught the 28 bus. That, at any rate, was something. There should have been another report on the Monday. Instead, the unheard-of happened and Ginge phoned. He was phoning from a call-box and he had, he told Wexford, plenty of two and ten pence pieces, and he knew a gentleman like the chief inspector would reimburse him.

'Give me the number and I'll call you myself.' For God's sake, how much of this was he supposed to stand out of his own pocket? Let the ratepayers fork out. Ginge picked up the receiver before the bell had rung twice. 'It has to be good, Ginge, to get you to the phone.'

'I reckon it's bleeding good,' said Ginge cockily. 'I seen him with a bird, that's what.'

The same climactic exultation is never reached twice. Wexford had heard those words – or words having the same meaning – before, and this time he didn't go off into flights about the Lord delivering Hathall into his hands. Instead he asked when and where.

'You know all that about me stationing myself in that pub and watching the bleeding bus stop? Well, I thought to myself there was no harm doing it again Sunday.' Make sure he got seven days' worth of cash and Demon Kings, thought Wexford. 'So I was in there Sunday dinnertime – that is, yesterday like – when I seen him. About one it was and pissing down with rain. He'd got a mac on and his umbrella up. He didn't stop to catch no bus but went right on walking down West End Lane. Well, I never give a bleeding thought to following him. I seen him go by and that was all. But I'd got to thinking I'd better be off to my own dinner – on account of the wife likes it on the table one-thirty sharp – so down I goes to the station.'

'Which station?'

'Wes' Haamsted Stesh'n,' said Ginge with a very lifelike imitation of a West Indian bus conductor. He chortled at his own wit. 'When I get there I'm putting a five-pee bit in the machine, on account of its being only one stop to Kilburn, when I see the party standing by the bleeding barrier. He'd got his back to me, thank Gawd, so I nips over to the bookstall and has a look at the girlie mags of what they've got a very choice selection. Well, bearing in mind my duty to you, Mr Wexford, I see my train come in but I don't run down the bleeding steps to catch it. I wait. And up the steps comes about twenty people. I never dared turn around, not wanting my other eye poked, but when I think the coast's clear, I has a bit of a shufty and he'd gone.

'I nips back into West End Lane like a shot and the rain's coming down like stair rods. But up ahead, on his way home, is bleeding Hathall with this bird. Walking very close, they was, under his bleeding umbrella, and the bird's wearing one of them see-through plastic macs with the hood up. I couldn't see no more of her, barring she was wearing a long skirt all trailing in the bleeding wet. So I went off home then and got a bleeding mouthful from the wife for being late for my dinner.'

'Virtue is its own reward, Ginge.'

'I don't know about that,' said Ginge, 'but you'll be wanting to know what my wages and the Demon Kings came to, and the bill's fifteen pound sixty-three. Terrible, the cost of bleeding living, isn't it?'

It wouldn't be necessary, Wexford decided as he put the phone down, to think any longer of ways and means of following a man on a bus. For this man had taken this bus only as far as West Hampstead station, had walked instead this Sunday because he had an umbrella and umbrellas are always a problem on buses. It must be possible now to catch Hathall and his woman together and follow them to Dartmeet Avenue.

'I've got a fortnight's holiday owing to me,' he said to his wife.

'You've got about three months' holiday owing to you with what's mounted up over the years.'

'I'm going to take a bit of it now. Next week, say.'

'What in November? Then we'll have to go somewhere warm. They say Malta's very nice in November.'

'Chelsea's very nice in November too, and that's where we're going.'

The first thing to do on the first day of his 'holiday' was to familiarize himself with a so far unknown bit of London's geography. Friday, 22 November, was a fine sunny day, June in appearance if January in temperature. How better to get to West Hampstead than on the 28 bus? Howard had told him that its route passed across the King's Road on its way to Wandsworth Bridge, so it wasn't a long walk from Teresa Street to the nearest stop. The bus went up through Fulham into West Kensington, an area he remembered from the time he had helped Howard on that former case, and he noticed to his satisfaction certain familiar landmarks. But soon he was in unknown territory and very varied and vast territory it was. The immense size of London always surprised him. He had had no inkling when he had interrupted Ginge's recitation of the stops on this route of how long the list would have been. Naively, he had supposed that Ginge would have named no more than two or three further places before the terminus, whereas in fact there would have been a dozen. As the conductor sang out, 'Church Street,' 'Notting Hill Gate,' 'Pembridge Road,' he felt a growing relief that Hathall had merely caught the bus to West Hampstead station.

This station was reached at last after about threequarters of an hour. The bus went on over a bridge above railway lines and past two more stations on the opposite side, West End Lane and another West Hampstead on some suburban line. It had been climbing ever since it left Kilburn and it went on climbing up narrow winding West End Lane till it reached West End Green. Wexford got off. The air was fresh here, not only fresh in comparison to that of Chelsea, but nearly as diesel-free as in Kingsmarkham. Surreptitiously, he consulted his guide. Dartmeet Avenue lay about a quarter of a mile to the east, and he was a little puzzled by this. Surely Hathall could have walked to West Hampstead station in five minutes and walked by the back doubles. Why catch a bus? Still, Ginge had seen him do it. Maybe he merely disliked walking.

Wexford found Dartmeet Avenue with ease. It was a hilly street like most of the streets round here and lined with fine tall houses built mostly of red brick, but some had been modernized and faced with stucco, their sash windows replaced by sheets of plain plate glass. Tall trees, now almost leafless, towered above roofs and pointed gables, and there were mature unpollarded trees growing in the pavements. Number 62 had a front garden that was all shrubbery and weeds. Three black plastic dustbins with 62 painted on their sides in white-wash stood in the side entrance. Wexford noted the phone-box where Ginge had kept his vigils and decided which of the bay windows must be Hathall's. Could anything be gained by calling on the landlord? He concluded that nothing could. The man would be bound to tell Hathall someone had been enquiring about him, would describe that someone, and then the fat would be in the fire. He turned away and walked slowly back to West End Green, looking about him as he did so for such nooks, crannies and convenient trees as might afford him shelter if he dared tail Hathall himself. Night closed in early now, the evenings were long and dark, and in a car . . .

461

The 28 bus sailed down Fortune Green Road as he reached the stop. It was a good frequent service. Wexford wondered, as he settled himself behind the driver, if Robert Hathall had ever sat on that very seat and looked out through this window upon the three stations and the radiating railway lines. Such ruminations verged on the obsessional, though, and that he must avoid. But it was impossible to refrain from wondering afresh why Hathall had caught the bus at all just to reach this point. The woman, when she came to Hathall's home, came by train. Perhaps Hathall didn't like the tube train, got sick of travelling to work by Tube, so that when he went to her home, he preferred the relaxation of a bus ride.

It took about ten minutes to get to Kilburn. Ginge, who was as sure to be found in the Countess of Castlemaine at noon as the sun is to rise at daybreak or the sound of thunder to follow the sight of lightning, was hunched on his bar stool. He was nursing a half of bitter but when he saw his patron he pushed the tankard away from him, the way a man leaves his spoon in his half-consumed soup when his steak arrives. Wexford ordered a Demon King by name and without description of its ingredients. The barman understood.

'He's got you on your toes, this bleeder, hasn't he?' Ginge moved to an alcove table. 'Always popping up to the Smoke, you are. You don't want to let it get on top of you. Once let a thing like that get a hold on you and you could end up in a bleeding bin.'

'Don't be so daft,' said Wexford, whose own wife had said much the same thing to him that morning, though in more refined terms. 'It won't be for much longer, anyway. This coming week ought to see an end of it. Now what I want you to do . . .'

'It won't be for *no* longer, Mr Wexford.' Ginge spoke with a kind of shrinking determination. 'You put me on this to spot him with a bird and I've spotted him with a bird. The rest's up to you.'

'Ginge,' Wexford began cajolingly, 'just to watch the station next week while I watch the house.'

'No,' said Ginge.

'You're a coward.'

'Cowardness,' said Ginge, exhibiting his usual difficulty in making his command of the spoken language match up to his mastery of the written, 'don't come into it.' He hesitated and said with what might have been modesty or shame, 'I've got a job.'

Wexford almost gasped. 'A *job?*' In former days this monosyllable had exclusively been employed by Ginge and his brother to denote a criminal exercise. 'You mean you've got paid work?'

'Not me. Not exactly.' Ginge contemplated his Demon King rather sadly and, lifting his glass, he sipped from it delicately and with a kind of nostalgia. *Sic transit gloria mundi* or it had been good while it lasted. 'The wife has. Bleeding barmaid. Evenings and Sunday dinnertimes.' He looked slightly embarrassed. 'Don't know what's got into her.'

'What I don't know is why it stops you working for me.'

'Anyone'd think,' said Ginge, 'you'd never had no bleeding family of your own. Someone's got to stay home and mind the kids, haven't they?'

Wexford managed to delay his outburst of mirth until he was out on the pavement. Laughter did him good, cleansing him of the feverish balked feeling Ginge's refusal to cooperate further had at first brought him. He could manage on his own now, he thought as once more he boarded the 28 bus, and manage for the future in his car. From his car he could watch West Hampshire station on Sunday. With luck, Hathall would meet the woman there as he had done on the previous Sunday, and once the woman was found, what would it matter that Hathall knew he had been followed? Who would reproach him for breaking the rules when his disobedience had resulted in that success?

463

But Hathall didn't meet the woman on Sunday, and as the week wore on Wexford wondered at the man's elusiveness. He stationed himself in Dartmeet Avenue every evening but he never saw Hathall and he only once saw evidence of occupancy of the room with the bay window. On the Monday, the Tuesday and the Wednesday he was there before six and he saw three people enter the house between six and seven. No sign of Hathall. For some reason, the traffic was particularly heavy on the Thursday evening. It was six-fifteen before he got to Dartmeet Avenue. Rain was falling steadily and the long hilly street was black and glittering with here and there on its surface the gilt glare of reflected lamplight. The place was deserted but for a cat which snaked from between the dusbins and vanished through a fissure in the garden wall. A light was on in a downstairs room and a feebler glow showed through the fanlight above the front door. Hathall's window was dark, but as Wexford put on the handbrake and switched off the ignition, the bay window suddenly became a brilliant yellow cube. Hathall was in, had arrived home perhaps a minute before Wexford's own arrival. For a few seconds the window blazed, then curtains were drawn across it by an invisible hand until all that could be seen were thin perpendicular lines of light like phosphorescent threads gleaming on the dim wet façade.

The excitement this sight had kindled in him cooled as an hour, two hours, went by and Hathall didn't appear. At half past nine a little elderly man emerged, routed out the cat from among the sodden weeds and carried it back into the house. As the front door closed on him, the light that rimmed Hathall's curtains went out. That alerted Wexford and he started to move the car to a less conspicuous position, but the front door remained closed, the window remained dark, and he realized that Hathall had retired early to bed.

Having brought Dora to London for a holiday, he remembered his duty to her and squired her about the West End shopping centres in the daytime. But Denise was so much more adept at doing this than he that on the Friday he deserted his wife and his nephew's wife for a less attractive woman who was no longer a wife at all.

The first thing he saw when he came to Eileen Hathall's house was her ex-husband's car parked on the garage drive, the car which Ginge said had long ago been sold. Had Ginge made a mistake about that? He drove on till he came to a call-box where he phoned Marcus Flower. Yes, Mr Hathall was in, said the voice of a Jane or a Julie or a Linda. If he would just hold the line . . . Instead of holding the line, he put the receiver back and within five minutes he was in Eileen Hathall's arid living room, sitting on a cushionless chair under the Spanish gypsy.

'He gave his car to Rosemary,' she said in answer to his question. 'She sees him sometimes at her gran's, and when she said she'd passed her test he gave her his car. He won't need it where he's going, will he?'

'Where is he going, Mrs Hathall?'

'Brazil.' She spat out the rough r and the sibilant as if the word were not the name of a country but of some loathsome reptile. Wexford felt a chill, a sudden anticipation that something bad was coming. It came. 'He's all fixed up,' she said, 'to go the day before Christmas Eve.'

In less than a month . . .

'Has he got a job there?' he said steadily.

'A very good position with a firm of international account-ants.' There was something pathetic about the pride she took in saying it. The man hated her, had humiliated her, would probably never see her again, yet for all that, she was bitterly proud of what he had achieved. 'You wouldn't believe the money he's getting. He told Rosemary and she told me. They're paying me from London, deducting what I get before it goes to him. He'll still have thousands and thousands a year to live on. And they're paying his fare, fixing it all up, got a house there waiting for him. He hasn't had to do a thing.'

Should he tell her Hathall wouldn't be going alone, wouldn't live in that house alone? She had grown stouter in the past year, her thick body – all bulges where there should be none – stuffed into salmon-pink wool. And she was permanently flushed as if she ran an endless race. Perhaps she did. A race to keep up with her daughter, keep pace with rage and leave the quiet dullness of misery behind. While he was hesitating, she said. 'Why d'you want to know? You think he killed that woman, don't you?'

'Do *you?*' he said boldly.

If she had been struck across the face her skin couldn't have crimsoned more deeply. It looked like flogged skin about to split and bleed. 'I wish he had!' she said on a harsh gasp, and she put up her hand, not to cover her eyes as he had at first thought, but her trembling mouth.

He drove back to London, to a fruitless Friday night vigil, an empty Saturday, a Sunday that might – just might – bring him what he desired.

December first, and once more pouring with rain. But this was no bad thing. It would clear the streets and make the chance of Hathall's peering into a suspicious-looking car less likely. By half past twelve he had parked as nearly opposite the station as he dared, for it wasn't only the chance of being spotted by Hathall that worried him, but also the risk of obstructing this narrow bottleneck. Rain drummed hard on the car roof, streamed down the gutter between the curb and the yellow painted line. But this rain was so heavy that, as it washed over the windscreen, it didn't obscure his view but had only a distorting effect as if there were a fault in the glass. He could see the station entrance quite clearly and about a hundred yards of West End Lane where it humped over the railway lines. Trains rattled unseen beneath him, 159 and 28 buses climbed and descended the hill. There were few people

about and yet it seemed as if a whole population were travelling, proceeding from unknown homes to unknown destinations
through the wet pallid gloom of this winter Sunday. The hands
of the dashboard clock crawled slowly through and past the
third quarter after twelve.

By now he was so used to waiting, resigned to sitting on
watch like a man who stalked some wary cunning animal, that
he felt a jolt of shock which was almost disbelief when at ten
to one he saw Hathall's figure in the distance. The glass played
tricks with him. He was like someone in a hall of mirrors, first
a skeletal giant, then a fat dwarf, but a single sweep of the
windscreen wipers brought him suddenly into clear focus. His
umbrella up, he was walking swiftly towards the station –
fortunately, on the opposite side of the road. He passed the
car without turning his head, and outside the station he
stopped, snapped the umbrella shut and open, shut, open and
shut, to shake off the water drops. Then he disappeared into
the entrance.

Wexford was in a dilemma. Was he meeting someone or
travelling himself? In daylight, even in this rain, he dared not
leave the car. A red train scuttled under the road and came
to a stop. He held his breath. The first people to get off the
train began to come out on to the pavement. One man put a
newspaper over his head and ran, a little knot of women
fluttered, struggling with umbrellas that wouldn't open. Three
opened simultaneously, a red one, a blue one and an orange
pagoda, blossoming suddenly in the greyness like flowers.
When they had lifted and danced off, what their brilliant
circles had hidden was revealed – a couple with their backs
to the street, a couple who stood close together but not
touching each other while the man opened a black umbrella
and enclosed them under its canopy.

She wore blue jeans and over them a white raincoat, the hood
of which was up. Wexford hadn't been able to catch a glimpse

of her face. They had set off as if they meant to walk it, but a taxi came splashing down with its For Hire light glowing orange like a cigarette end. Hathall hailed it and it bore them off northwards. Please God, thought Wexford, let it take them home and not to some restaurant. He knew he hadn't hope of tailing a London taxi-driver, and the cab had vanished before he was out into West End Lane and off.

And the journey up the hill was maddeningly slow. He was bogged down behind a 159 bus – a bus that wasn't red but painted all over with an advertisement for Dinky Toys which reminded him of Kidd's at Toxborough – and nearly ten minutes had passed before he drew up in front of the house in Dartmeet Avenue. The taxi had gone, but Hathall's light was on. Of course he'd have to put the light on at midday on such a day as this. Wondering with interest rather than fear if Hathall would hit him too, he went up the path and examined the bells. There were no names by the bell-pushes, just floor numbers. He pressed the first-floor bell and waited. It was possible Hathall wouldn't come down, would just refuse to answer it. In that case, he'd find someone else to let him in and he'd hammer on Hathall's room door.

This turned out to be unnecessary. Above his head the window opened and, stepping back, he looked up into Hathall's face. For a moment neither of them spoke. The rain dashed between them and they stared at each other through it while a variety of emotions crossed Hathall's features – astonishment, anger, cautiousness, but not, Wexford thought, fear. And all were succeeded by what looked strangely like satisfaction. But before he could speculate as to what this might mean, Hathall said coldly:

'I'll come down and let you in.'

Within fifteen seconds he had done so. He closed the door quietly, saying nothing, and pointed to the stairs. Wexford had never seen him so calm and suave. He seemed entirely relaxed. He looked younger and he looked triumphant.

'I should like you to introduce me to the lady you brought here in a taxi.'

Hathall didn't demur. He didn't speak. As they went up the stairs Wexford thought, has he hidden her? Sent her to some bathroom or up on to the top floor? His room door was on the latch and he pushed it open, allowing the chief inspector to precede him. Wexford walked in. The first thing he saw was her raincoat, spread out to dry over a chair back.

At first he didn't see her. The room was very small, no more than twelve feet by ten, and furnished as such places always are. There was a wardrobe that looked as if it had been manufactured round about the time of the Battle of Mons, a narrow bed with an Indian cotton cover, some wooden-armed chairs that are euphemistically known as 'fireside,' and pictures that had doubtless been painted by some relative of the landlord's. The light came from a dust-coated plastic sphere suspended from the pockmarked ceiling.

A canvas screen, canvas-coloured and hideous, shut off one corner of the room. Behind it, presumably, was a sink, for when Hathall gave a cautionary cough, she pushed it aside and came out, drying her hands on a tea towel. It wasn't a pretty face, just a very young one, heavy-featured, tough and confident. Thick black hair fell to her shoulders and her eyebrows were heavy and black like a man's. She wore a tee-shirt with a cardigan over it. Wexford had seen that face somewhere before, and he was wondering where when Hathall said:

'This is the "lady" you wanted to meet.' His triumph had changed to frank amusement and he was almost laughing. 'May I present my daughter, Rosemary?'

CHAPTER FIFTEEN

It was a long time since Wexford had experienced such an anticlimax. Coping with awkward situations wasn't usually a problem with him, but the shock of what Hathall had just said – combined with his realization that his own disobedience was now known – stunned him into silence. The girl didn't speak either after she had said a curt hello, but retreated behind the screen where she could be heard filling a kettle.

Hathall, who had been so withdrawn and aloof when Wexford first arrived, seemed to be getting the maximum possible enjoyment from his adversary's dismay. 'What's this visit in aid of?' he asked. 'Just looking up old acquaintances?'

In for a penny, in for a pound, thought Wexford, echoing Miss Marcovitch. 'I understand you're going to Brazil,' he said. 'Alone?'

'Can one go alone? There'll be about three hundred other people in the aircraft.' Wexford smarted under that one and Hathall saw him smart. 'I hoped Rosemary might go with me, but her school is here. Perhaps she'll join me in a few years' time.'

That fetched the girl out. She picked up her raincoat, hung it on a hanger and said, 'I haven't even been to Europe yet. I'm not burying myself in Brazil.'

Hathall shrugged at this typical sample of his family's ungraciousness, and said as brusquely, 'Satisfied?'

'I have to be, don't I, Mr Hathall?'

Was it his daughter's presence that kept his anger in check. He was almost mild, only a trace of his usual resentful querulousness sounding in his voice when he said, 'Well, if you'll excuse us, Rosemary and I have to get ourselves some lunch

which isn't the easiest thing in the world in this little hole. I'll
see you out.'

He closed the door instead of leaving it on the latch. It
was dark and quiet on the landing. Wexford waited for the
explosion of rage but it didn't come, and he was conscious
only of the man's eyes. They were the same height and their
eyes met on a level. Briefly, Hathall's showed white and staring
around hard black irises in which that curious red spark
glittered. They were at the head of the steep flight of stairs,
and as Wexford turned to descend them, he was aware of a
movement behind him, of Hathall's splayed hand rising. He
grasped the banister and swung down a couple of steps. Then
he made himself walk down slowly and steadily. Hathall didn't
move, but when Wexford reached the bottom and looked back,
he saw the raised hand lifted higher and the fingers closed in
a solemn and somehow portentous gesture of farewell.

'He was going to push me down those stairs,' Wexford said
to Howard. 'And I wouldn't have had much redress. He could
have said I'd forced my way into his room. God, what a mess
I've made of things! He's bound to put in another of his
complaints and I could lose my job.'

'Not without a pretty full enquiry, and I don't think Hathall
would want to appear at any enquiry.' Howard threw the
Sunday paper he had been reading on to the floor and turned
his thin bony face, his ice-blue penetrating eyes towards his
uncle. 'It wasn't his daughter all the time, Reg.'

'Wasn't it? I know you saw this woman with short fair
hair, but can you be sure it was Hathall you saw her with?'

'I'm sure.'

'You saw him once,' Wexford persisted. 'You saw him
twenty yards off for about ten seconds from a car *you were
driving*. If you had to go into court and swear that the man
you saw outside Marcus Flower was the same man you saw
in the garden of Bury Cottage, would you swear? If a man's
life depended on it, would you?'

'Capital punishment is no longer with us, Reg.'

'No, and neither you nor I – unlike many of our calling – would wish to see it back. But if it were with us, then would you?'

Howard hesitated. Wexford saw that hesitation and he felt tiredness creep through his body like a depression drug. Even a shred of doubt could dispel what little hope he now had left.

At last, 'No, I wouldn't,' Howard said flatly.

'I see.'

'Wait a minute, Reg. I'm not sure nowadays if I could even swear to a man's identity if my swearing to it might lead to his death. You're pressing me too hard. But I'm sure beyond a reasonable doubt, and I'll still say to you, yes, I saw Robert Hathall. I saw him outside the offices of Marcus Flower in Half Moon Street with a fair-haired woman.'

Wexford sighed. What difference did it make, after all? By his own blundering of that day he had put an end to all hope of following Hathall. Howard mistook his silence for doubt and said, 'If he isn't with her, where does he go all those evenings he's out? Where did he go on that bus?'

'Oh, I still believe he's with her. The daughter just goes there sometimes on Sundays. But what good does that do me? I can't follow him on a bus. He'll be looking for me now.'

'He'll think, you know, that seeing him with his daughter will put you off.'

'Maybe. Maybe he'll get reckless. So what? I can't conceal myself in a doorway and leap on a bus after him. Either the bus would go before I got on or he'd turn round and see me. Even if I got on without his seeing me . . .'

'Then someone else must do it,' said Howard firmly.

'Easy to say. My Chief Constable says no, and you won't cross swords with my Chief Constable by letting me have one of your blokes.'

'That's true, I won't.'

'Then we may as well give over talking about it. I'll go

back to Kingsmarkham and face the music – a bloody great symphony in Griswold sharp major – and Hathall can go to the sunny tropics.'

Howard got up and laid a hand on his shoulder. 'I will do it,' he said.

The awe had gone long ago, giving way to love and comradeship. But that 'I will do it,' spoken so lightly and pleasantly, brought back all the old humiliation and envy and awareness of the other's advantages. Wexford felt a hot dark flush suffuse his face. '*You?*' he said roughly, 'you yourself? You must be joking. You take rank over me, remember?'

'Don't be such a snob. What if I do? I'd like to do it. It'd be fun. I haven't done anything like that for years and years.'

'Would you really do that for me, Howard? What about your own work?'

'If I'm the god you make me out to be, don't you think I have some say in the hours I work? Of course I shan't be able to do it every night. There'll be the usual crises that come up from time to time and I'll have to stay late. But Kenbourne Vale won't degenerate into a sort of twentieth-century Bridewell just because I pop up to West Hampstead every so often.'

So on the following evening Chief Superintendent Howard Fortune left his office at a quarter to six and was at West End Green on the hour. He waited until half past seven. When his quarry didn't come, he made his way along Dartmeet Avenue and observed that there was no light on in the window his uncle had told him was Hathall's.

'I wonder if he's going to her straight from work?'

'Let's hope he's not going to make a habit of that. It'll be almost impossible to follow him in the rush hour. When does he give up this job of his?'

'God knows,' said Wexford, 'but he leaves for Brazil in precisely three weeks.'

One of those crises at which he had hinted prevented Howard from tailing Hathall on the following night, but he was free on the Wednesday and, changing his tactics, he got to Half Moon Street by five o'clock. An hour later, in Teresa Street, he told his uncle what had happened.

'The first person to come out of Marcus Flower was a seedy-looking guy with a toothbrush moustache. He had a girl with him and they went off in a Jaguar.'

'That'd be Jason Marcus and his betrothed,' said Wexford.

'Then two more girls and then – Hathall. I *was* right, Reg. It's the same man.'

'I shouldn't have doubted you.'

Howard shrugged. 'He got into the Tube and I lost him. But he wasn't going home. I know that.'

'How can you know?'

'If he'd been going home he'd have walked to Green Park station, gone one stop on the Piccadilly Lane to Piccadilly Circus or on the Victoria Line to Oxford Circus and changed on to the Bakerloo. He'd have walked south. But he walked north, and at first I thought he was going to get a bus home. But he went to Bond Street station. You'd never go to Bond Street if you meant to go to North-west London. Bond Street's only on the Central Line until the Fleet Line opens.'

'And the Central Line goes where?'

'Due east and due west. I followed him into the station but – well, you've seen our rush hours, Reg. I was a good dozen people behind him in the ticket queue. The thing was I had to be so damn careful he didn't get a look at me. He went down the escalator to the westbound platform – and I lost him.' Howard said apologetically, 'There were about five hundred people on the platform. I got stuck and I couldn't move. But it's proved one thing. D'you see what I mean?'

'I think so. We have to find where the west-bound Central Line route crosses the 28 bus route, and somewhere in that area lives our unknown woman.'

'I can tell you where that is straight off. The westbound Central Line route goes Bond Street, Marble Arch, Lancaster

Gate, Queensway, Notting Hill Gate, Holland Park, Shepherd's Bush, and so on. The southbound 28 route goes Golders Green, West Hampstead, Kilburn, Kilburn Park, Great Western Road, Pembridge Road, Notting Hill Gate, Church Street, on through Kensington and Fulham to here and ultimately to Wandsworth. So it has to be Notting Hill. She lives, along with half the roving population of London, somewhere in Notting Hill. Small progress, but better than nothing. Have you made any?'

Wexford, on tenterhooks for two days, had phoned Burden, expecting to hear that Griswold was out for his blood. But nothing was further from the truth. The Chief Constable had been 'buzzing around' Kingsmarkham, as Burden put it, tearing between there and Myringham where there was some consternation over a missing woman. But he had been in an excellent frame of mind, had asked where Wexford had gone for his holiday, and on being told London ('For the theatres and museums, you know, sir,' Burden had said) had asked facetiously why the chief inspector hadn't sent him a picture postcard of New Scotland Yard.

'Then Hathall hasn't complained,' said Howard thoughtfully.

'Doesn't look like it. If I were to be optimistic, I'd say he thinks it safer not to draw attention to himself.'

But it was December third . . . Twenty days to go. Dora had dragged her husband round the stores, doing the last of her Christmas shopping. He had carried her parcels, agreed that this was just the thing for Sheila and that was exactly what Sylvia's elder boy wanted, but all the time he was thinking, twenty days, twenty days . . . this year Christmas for him would be the season of Robert Hathall's getaway.

Howard seemed to read his thoughts. He was eating one of those enormous meals he consumed without putting on a pound. Taking a second helping of *charlotte russe*, he said, 'If only we could get him on something.'

'What d'you mean?'

'I don't know. Some little thing you could hold him on that would stop him leaving the country. Like shoplifting, say, or travelling on the Tube without a ticket.'

'He seems to be an honest man,' said Wexford bitterly, 'if you can call a murderer honest.'

His nephew scraped the dessert bowl. 'I suppose he *is* honest?'

'As far as I know, he is. Mr Butler would have told me if there's been a smell of dishonesty about him.'

'I daresay. Hathall was all right for money in those days. But he wasn't all right for money when he got married to Angela, was he? Yet, in spite of their having only fifteen pounds a week to live on, they started doing all right. You told me Somerset had seen them on a shopping spree and then dining at some expensive place. Where did that money come from, Reg?'

Pouring himself a glass of Chablis from the bottle by Howard's elbow, Wexford said, 'I've wondered about that. But I've never been able to come to any conclusion. It didn't seem relevant.'

'Everything's relevant in a murder case.'

'True.' Wexford was too grateful to his nephew to react huffily at this small admonition. 'I suppose I reckoned that if a man's always been honest he doesn't suddenly become dishonest in middle age.'

'That depends on the man. This man suddenly became an unfaithful husband in middle age. In fact, although he'd been monogamous since puberty, he seems to have turned into a positive womanizer in middle age. And he became a murderer. I don't suppose you're saying he killed anyone before, are you?' Howard pushed away his plate and started on the gruyère. 'There's one factor in all this I don't think you've taken into sufficient account. One personality.'

'Angela?'

476

'Angela. It was when he met her that he changed. Some would say she'd corrupted him. This is an outside chance – a very wayout idea altogether – but Angela had been up to a little fraud on her own, one you know about, possibly others you don't. Suppose she encouraged him into some sort of dishonesty.'

'Your saying that reminds me of something Mr Butler said. He said he overheard Angela tell his partner, Paul Craig, that he was in a good position to fiddle his Income Tax.'

'There you are then. They must have got that money from somewhere. It didn't grow on trees like the "miracle" plums.'

'There hasn't been a hint of anything,' said Wexford. 'It would have to be at Kidd's. Aveney didn't drop so much as a hint.'

'But you weren't asking him about money. You were asking him about women.' Howard got up from the table and pushed aside his chair. 'Let's go and join the ladies. If I were you I'd take a little trip to Toxborough tomorrow.'

CHAPTER SIXTEEN

The rectangular white box set on green lawns, the screen of saplings, leafless and pathetic in December, and inside, the warm cellulose smell and the turbaned women painting dolls to the theme music from *Doctor Zhivago*. Mr Aveney conducted Wexford through the workshops to the office of the personnel manager, talking the while in a shocked and rather indignant way.

'Cooking the books? We've never had anything like that here.'

'I'm not saying you have, Mr Aveney. I'm working in the dark,' said Wexford. 'Have you ever heard of the old payroll fiddle?'

'Well, yes, I *have*. It used to be done a lot in the forces. No one'd get away with it here.'

'Let's see, shall we?'

The personnel manager, a vague young man with fair bristly hair, was introduced as John Oldbury. His office was very untidy and he seemed somewhat distraught as if he had been caught in the middle of searching for something he knew he would never find. 'Messing about with the wages, d'you mean?' he said.

'Suppose you tell me how you work with the accountant to manage the payroll.'

Oldbury looked distractedly at Aveney, and Aveney nodded, giving an infinitesimal shrug. The personnel manager sat down heavily and pushed his fingers through his unruly hair. 'I'm not very good at explaining things,' he began. 'But I'll try. It's like this: when we get a new worker I sort of tell the accountant details about her and he works them out for her wages. No, I'll have to be more explicit. Say we take on a – well, we'll call her Joan Smith, Mrs Joan Smith.' Oldbury, thought

Wexford, was as unimaginative as he was inarticulate. 'I tell the accountant her name and her address – say . . .'

Seeing his total defeat, Wexford said, 'Twenty-four Gordon Road, Toxborough.'

'Oh, fine!' The personnel manager beamed his admiration. 'I tell him Mrs Joan Smith, of whatever-it-is Gordon Road, Toxborough . . .'

'Tell him by what means? Phone? A chit?'

'Well, either. Of course I keep a record. I haven't,' said Oldbury unnecessarily, 'got a very good memory. I tell him her name and her address and when she's starting and her hours and whatever, and he feeds all that into the computer and Bob's your uncle. And after that I do it every week for her overtime and – whatever.'

'And when she leaves you tell him that too?'

'Oh, sure.'

'They're always leaving. Chop and change, it's everlasting,' said Aveney.

'They're all paid in weekly wage packets?'

'Not all,' said Oldbury. 'You see, some of our ladies don't use their wages for – well, housekeeping. Their husbands are the – what's the word?'

'Breadwinners?'

'Ah, fine. Breadwinners. The ladies – some of them – keep their wages for holidays and sort of improving their homes and just saving up, I suppose.'

'Yes, I see. But so what?'

'Well,' said Oldbury triumphantly, '*they* don't get wage packets. Their wages are paid into a bank account – more likely the Post Office or a Trustee Savings Bank.'

'And if they are, you tell that to the accountant and he feeds it into his computer?'

'He does, yes.' Oldbury smiled delightedly at the realization he had made himself so clear. 'You're absolutely right. Quick thinking, if I may say so.'

'Not at all,' said Wexford, slightly stupefied by the man's zany charm. 'So the accountant could simply invent a woman and feed a fictitious name and address into the computer? Her wages would go into a bank account which the accountant – or, rather, his female accomplice – could draw on when they chose?'

'That,' said Oldbury severely, 'would be fraud.'

'It would indeed. But, since you keep records, we can easily verify if such a fraud has ever been committed.'

'Of course we can.' The personnel manager beamed again and trotted over to a filing cabinet whose open drawers were stuffed with crumpled documents. 'Nothing easier. We keep records for a whole year after one of our ladies has left us.'

A whole year . . . And Hathall had left them eighteen months before. Aveney took him back through the factory where the workers were now being lulled (or stimulated) by the voice of Tom Jones. 'John Oldbury' he said defensively, 'has got a very good psychology degree and he's marvellous with people.'

'I'm sure. You've both been very good. I apologize for taking up so much of your time.'

The interview had neither proved nor disproved Howard's theory. But since there were no records, what could be done? If the enquiry wasn't a clandestine one, if he had men at his disposal, he could send them round the local Trustee Savings Banks. But it was, and he hadn't. Yet he could see so clearly now how such a thing could have been done; the idea coming in the first place from Angela; the female accomplice brought in to impersonate the women Hathall had invented, and to draw money from the accounts. And then – yes, Hathall growing too fond of his henchwoman so that Angela became jealous. If he was right, everything was explainable, the deliberately contrived solitude of the Hathalls, their cloistral life, the money that enabled them to dine out and Hathall to buy presents for his daughter. And they would all have been in it together – until Angela realized the woman was more than an accomplice to her husband, more than a useful collector of revenues . . . What had she done? Broken up the affair and threatened that if it started again, she'd shop them both? That would have meant the end of Hathall's career. That would put paid to his job at Marcus Flower or any future accountancy job. So they had murdered her. They had killed Angela to be together, and knowing Kidd's kept records for only one year, to be safe forever from the risk of discovery . . .

Wexford drove slowly down the drive between the flat green lawns, and at the gateway to the main industrial estate road met another car coming in. Its driver was a uniformed police officer and its other occupant Chief Inspector Jack 'Brock' Lovat, a small snub-nosed man who wore small gold-rimmed glasses. The car slowed and Lovat wound his window down.

'What are you doing here?' Wexford asked.

'My job,' said Lovat simply.

His nickname derived from the fact that he kept three badgers, rescued from the diggers before badger-digging became an offence, in his back garden. And Wexford knew of old that it was useless questioning the head of Myringham CID about anything but this hobby of his. On that subject he was fulsome and enthusiastic. On all others – though he did his work in exemplary fashion – he was almost mute. You got a 'yes' or a 'no' out of him unless you were prepared to talk about setts and plantigrade quadrupeds.

'Since there are no badgers here,' Wexford said sarcastically, 'except possibly clockwork ones, I'll just ask this. Is your visit connected in any way with a man called Robert Hathall?'

'No,' said Lovat. Smiling closely, he waved his hand and told the driver to move on.

But for its new industries, Toxborough would by now have dwindled to a semi-deserted village with an elderly population. Industry had brought life, commerce, roads, ugliness, a community centre, a sports ground and a council estate. This last was traversed by a broad thoroughfare called Maynnot Way, where the concrete stilts of street lamps replaced the trees, and which had been named after the only old house that remained in it, Maynnot Hall. Wexford, who hadn't been this way for ten years when the concrete and the brick had first begun to spread across Toxborough's green fields, knew that somewhere, not too far from here, was a Trustee Savings Bank. At the second junction he turned left into Queen Elizabeth Avenue, and there it was, sandwiched between a betting shop and a place that sold cash-and-carry carpets.

The manager was a stiff pompous man who reacted sharply to Wexford's questions.

'Let you look at our books? Not without a warrant.'

'All right. But tell me this. If payments stop being made into an account and it's left empty or nearly empty, do you write to the holder and ask him or her if they want it closed?'

'We gave up the practice. If someone's only got fifteen pence in an account he's not going to waste money on a stamp saying he wants the account closed. Nor is he going to spend five pence on a bus fare to collect it. Right?'

'Would you check for me if any accounts held by women have had no payments made into them or withdrawals made from them since – well, last April or May twelvemonth? And if there are any, would you communicate with the holders?'

'Not,' said the manager firmly, 'unless this is an official police matter. I haven't got the staff.'

Neither, thought Wexford as he left the bank, had he. No staff, no funds, no encouragement; and still nothing but his own 'feelings' with which to convince Griswold that this was worth pursuing. Kidd's had a payroll, Hathall could have helped himself to money from it by the means of accounts held by fictitious women. Come to that, Kingsmarkham police station had a petty cash box and he, Wexford, could have helped himself out of it. There was about as much ground for suspicion in the latter case as in the former, and that was how the Chief Constable would see it.

'Another dead end,' he said to his nephew that night. 'But I understand how it all happened now. The Hathalls and the other woman work their fraud for a couple of years. The share-out of the loot takes place at Bury Cottage. Then Hathall gets his new job and there's no longer any need for the payroll fiddle. The other woman should fade out of the picture, but she doesn't because Hathall has fallen for her and wants to go on seeing her. You can imagine Angela's fury. It was *her* idea, she planned it, and it's led to this. She tells Hathall to give her up or she'll blow the whole thing, but Hathall can't. He pretends he has and all seems well between him and Angela, to the extent of Angela asking her mother-in-law to stay and cleaning up the cottage to impress her. In the afternoon Angela fetches her rival, perhaps to wind up the whole thing finally. The other woman strangles her as arranged, but leaves that print on the bath.'

'Admirable,' said Howard. 'I'm sure you're right.'

'And much good it does me. I may as well go home tomorrow. You're coming to us for Christmas?'

Howard patted his shoulder as he had done on the day he promised his vigilance. 'Christmas is a fortnight off. I'll keep on watching every free evening I get.'

At any rate, there was no summons from Griswold awaiting him. And nothing much had happened in Kingsmarkham during his absence. The home of the chairman of the rural council had been broken into. Six colour sets had been stolen from the television rental company in the High Street. Burden's son had been accepted by Reading University, subject to satisfactory A Levels. And Nancy Lake's house had been sold for a cool twenty-five thousand pounds. Some said she was moving to London, others that she was going abroad. Sergeant Martin had decorated the police station foyer with paper chains and mobiles of flying angels which the Chief Constable had ordered removed forthwith as they detracted from the dignity of Mid-Sussex.

'Funny thing Hathall didn't complain, wasn't it?'

'Lucky for you he didn't.' At ease now in his new glasses, Burden looked more severe and puritanical than ever. With a rather exasperated indrawing of breath, he said, 'You must give that up, you know.'

'Must? Little man, little man, *must* is not a word to be addressed to chief inspectors. Time was when you used to call me "sir." '

'And it was you asked me to stop. Remember?'

Wexford laughed. 'Let's go over to the Carousel and have a spot of lunch, and I'll tell you all about what I *must* give up.'

Antonio was delighted to see him back and offered him the speciality of the day – *moussaka*.

'I thought that was Greek.'

'The Greeks,' said Antonio, flinging out his hands, 'got it from us.'

'A reversal of the usual process. How interesting. I may as well have it, Antonio. And steak pie, which you got from *us*, for Mr Burden. Have I got thinner, Mike?'

'You're wasting away.'

'I haven't had a decent meal for a fortnight, what with chasing after that damned Hathall.' Wexford told him about it while they ate. 'Now do you believe?'

'Oh, I don't know. It's mostly in your head, isn't it? My daughter was telling me something the other day she got from school. About Galileo, it was. They made him recant what he'd said about the earth moving round the sun but he wouldn't give it up, and on his deathbed his last words were, "It does move." '

'I've heard it. What are you trying to prove? He was right. The earth does go round the sun. And on *my* deathbed I'll say, "He did do it." ' Wexford sighed. It was useless, may as well change the subject . . . 'I saw old Brock last week. He was as close as ever. Did he find his missing girl?'

'He's digging up Myringham Old Town for her.'

'As missing as that, is she?'

Burden gave Wexford's *moussaka* a suspicious look and a suspicious sniff, and attacked his own steak pie. 'He's pretty sure she'd dead and he's arrested her husband.'

'What, for murder?'

'No, not without the body. The bloke's got a record and he's holding him on a shop-breaking charge.'

'Christ!' Wexford exploded. 'Some people have all the luck.'

His eyes met Burden's, and the inspector gave him the kind of look we level at our friends when we begin to doubt their mental equilibrium. And Wexford said no more, breaking the silence only to ask after young John Burden's successes and prospects. But when they rose to go and a beaming Antonio had been congratulated on the cooking, 'When I retire or die, Antonio,' Wexford said, 'will you name a dish after me?'

The Italian crossed himself. 'Not to speak of such things, but yes, sure I will. *Lasagne* Wexford?'

'*Lasagne Galileo.*' Wexford laughed at the other's puzzlement. 'It sounds more Latin,' he said.

The High Street shops had their windows filled with glitter, and the great cedar outside the Dragon pub had orange and green and scarlet and blue light bulbs in its branches. In the toyshop window a *papier mâché* and cotton wool Santa Claus nodded and smiled and gyrated at an audience of small children who pressed their noses to the glass.

'Twelve more shopping days to Christmas,' said Burden.

'Oh, shut up,' Wexford snapped.

CHAPTER SEVENTEEN

A grey mist hung over the river, curtaining its opposite bank, shrouding the willows in veils of vapour, making colourless the hills and the leafless woods so that they appeared like a landscape in an out-of-focus monochrome photograph. On this side, the houses of the Old Town slept in the freezing mist, all their windows closed against it, their garden trees utterly still. The only motion was that of water drops falling gently and very slowly from threadlike branches. It was bitterly cold. As Wexford walked down past St. Luke's and Church House, it seemed wonderful to him that up there beyond those layers of cloud, miles of icy mist, must be a bright though distant sun. A few more days to the shortest day, the longest night. A few more days to the solstice when the sun would have moved to its extremest limit from this part of the earth. Or as he should put it, he thought, recalling Burden's snippet of pop education from the day before, when the ground on which he stood would have moved to its extremest limit of the sun . . .

He saw the police cars and police vans in River Lane before he saw any of the men who had driven them there or any signs of their purpose. They were parked all along the lane, fronting the row of almost derelict house whose owners had abandoned them and left them to be inhabited intermittently by the desperate homeless. Here and there, where the glass or even the frame of an ancient window had collapsed and gone, the cavity was patched with plastic sheeting. Against other windows hung bedspreads, sacks, rags, torn and soaking brown paper. But there were no squatters here now. Winter and the damp rising from the river had driven them to find other quarters, and the old houses, immeasurably more beautiful even now than any modern terrace, waited in the sour cold for new occupants or new purchasers. They were old but they were also very nearly immortal. No one might destroy them. All that could become of them was a slow disintegration into extreme decay.

An alley led between broken brick walls to the gardens which lay behind them, gardens which had become repositories of rubbish, rat-infested, and which sloped down to the river bank. Wexford made his way down this alley to a point where the wall had caved in, leaving a gap. A young police sergeant, standing just inside and holding a spade in his hand, barred his way and said, 'Sorry, sir. No one's allowed in here.'

'Don't you know me, Hutton?'

The sergeant looked again and, taken aback, said, 'It's Mr Wexford, isn't it? I beg your pardon, sir.'

Wexford said that was quite all right, and where was Chief Inspector Lovat to be found?

'Down where they're digging, sir. On the right-hand side at the bottom.'

'They're digging for this woman's body?'

'Mrs Morag Grey. She and her husband squatted here for a bit the summer before last. Mr Lovat thinks the husband may have buried her in this garden.'

'They lived *here*?' Wexford looked up at the sagging gable, shored up with a balk of timber. The leprous split plaster has scaled off in places, showing the bundles of wattle the house had been built of four hundred years before. A gaping doorway revealed interior walls which, slimy and running with water, were like those of a cave that the sea invades daily.

'It wouldn't be so bad in summer,' said Hutton by way of apology, 'and they weren't here for more than a couple of months.'

A great tangle of bushes, mud-spattered, under which lay empty cans and sodden newspaper, cut off the end of the garden. Wexford pushed his way through them into a waste-land. Four men were digging, and digging more than the three spits deep which is the gardener's rule. Mountains of earth, scattered with chalk splinters, were piled against the river wall. Lovat was sitting on this wall, his coat collar turned up, a thin damp cigarette stuck to his lower lip, watching them inscrutably.

'What makes you think she's here?'

'Got to be somewhere.' Lovat showed no surprise at his arrival but spread another sheet of newspaper on the wall for him to sit down. 'Nasty day,' he said.

'You think the husband killed her?' Wexford knew it was useless asking questions. You had to make statements and wait for Lovat to agree with them or refute them. 'You've got him on a shop-breaking charge. But you've got no body, just a missing woman. Someone must have made you take that seriously, and not Grey himself.'

'Her mother,' said Lovat.

'I see. Everyone thought she'd gone to her mother, and her mother thought she was elsewhere, but she didn't answer mother's letters. Grey's got a record, maybe living with another woman. Told a lot of lies. Am I right?'

'Yes.'

Wexford thought he had done his duty. It was a pity he knew so little about badgers, was even less interested in them than he was in the Grey affair. The icy mist was seeping through his clothes to his spine, chilling his whole body. 'Brock,' he said, 'will you do me a favour?'

Most people when asked that question reply that it all depends on what the favour is. But Lovat had virtues to offset his taciturnity. He took another crumpled cigarette from a damp and crumpled packet. 'Yes,' he said simply.

'You know that guy Hathall I'm always on about? I think he worked a payroll fiddle while he was with Kidd's at Toxborough. That's why I was there when we met the other day. But I've no authority to act. I'm pretty sure it was like this . . .' Wexford told him what he was pretty sure it was like.

'Would you get someone along to those Trustee Savings Banks and see if you can smell out any false accounts? And quick, Brock, because I've only got ten days.'

Lovat didn't ask why he only had ten days. He wiped his spectacles which the fog had misted and readjusted them on his red snub nose. Without looking at Wexford or showing the least interest, he fixed his eyes on the men and said, 'One way and another I've had a lot to do with digging in my time.'

Wexford made no response. Just at the moment he couldn't summon up much enthusiasm for a League-Against-Cruel-Sports homily. Nor did he repeat his request, which would only have annoyed Lovat, but sat silent in the damp cold listening to the sounds the spades made when they struck chalk, and the soft slump of earth lifted and slung heavily aside. Cans, waterlogged cartons, were lumped on to the growing heaps, to be followed by unearthed rose bushes, their roots scorpion-like and matted with wet soil. Was there a body under there? At any moment a spade might reveal, not a clod of ancient mortar or another mass of brown root, but a white and rotting human hand.

The mist was thickening over the almost stagnant water. Lovat threw his cigarette end into an oil-scummed puddle. 'Will do,' he said.

It was a relief to get away from the river and its miasma – the miasma that had once been thought of as a breeder of disease – and up into the fashionable part of the Old Town where he had parked his car. He was wiping its misted windscreen when he saw Nancy Lake, and he would have wondered what she was doing there had she not, at that moment, turned into a little baker's shop, famous for its home-baked bread and cakes. More than a year had passed since he had last seen her, and he had almost forgotten the sensation he had felt then, the catching of breath, the faint tremor in the heart. He felt it now as he saw the glass door close on her, the shop's warm orange glow receive her.

Although he was shivering now, his breath like smoke on the cold haze, he waited there for her on the kerb. And when she came out she rewarded him with one of her rich sweet smiles. 'Mr Wexford! There are policemen everywhere down here, but I didn't expect to see you.'

'I'm a policeman too. May I give you a lift back to Kingsmarkham?'

'Thank you, I'm not going back just now.' She wore a chinchilla coat that sparkled with fine drops. The cold which pinched other faces had coloured hers and brightened her eyes. 'But I'll come and sit in your car with you for five minutes, shall I?'

Someone, he thought, ought to invent a way of heating a car while the engine was switched off. But she didn't seem to feel the cold. She leaned towards him with the eagerness and the vitality of a young woman. 'Shall we share a cream cake?'

He shook his head. 'Bad for my figure, I'm afraid.'

'But you've got a lovely figure!'

Knowing that he shouldn't, that this was inviting a renewal of flirtation, he looked into those shining eyes and said, 'You are always saying things to me that no woman has said for half a lifetime.'

She laughed. 'Not always. How can it be "always" when I never see you?' She began to eat a cake. It was the kind of cake no one should attempt to eat without a plate, a fork and a napkin. She managed it with her bare fingers remarkably well, her small red tongue retrieving flecks of cream from her lips. 'I've sold my house,' she said. 'I'm moving out the day before Christmas Eve.'

The day before Christmas Eve ... 'They say that you're going abroad.'

'Do they? They've been saying things about me round here for twenty years and most of it has been a distortion of the truth. Do they say that my dream has come true at last?' She finished her cake, licked her fingers delicately. 'Now I must go. Once – Oh, it seems years ago – I asked you to come and have tea with me.'

'So you did,' he said.

'Will you come? Say – next Friday?' When he nodded, she said, 'And we'll have the last of the miracle jam.'

'I wish you'd tell me why you call it that.'

'I will, I will . . .' He held the car door open for her and she took the hand he held out. 'I'll tell you the story of my life. All shall be made clear. Till Friday, then.'

'Till Friday.' It was absurd, this feeling of excitement. You're old, he told himself sternly. She wants to give you plum jam and tell you the story of her life, that's all you're fit for now. And he watched her walk away until her grey fur had melted into the river mist and was gone.

'I can't follow him on the Tube, Reg. I've tried three times, but each night the crowds get worse with the pre-Christmas rush.'

'I can imagine,' said Wexford, who felt he never wanted to hear the word 'Christmas' again. He was more aware of the season's festive pressures than he had ever been in the past. Was Christmas more christmassy this year than usual? Or was it simply that he saw every card that flopped on to his front door mat, every hint of the coming celebrations, as a threat of failure? There was a bitter irony in the fact that this year they were going to fill the house with more people than ever before, both his daughters, his son-in-law, his two grandsons, Howard and Denise, Burden and his children. And Dora had already begun to put up the decorations. He had to hunch in his chair, the phone on his knees, to avoid prickling his face on the great bunch of holly that hung above his desk. 'That seems to be that then, doesn't it?' he said. 'Give it up, finish. Something may come out of the payroll thing. It's my last hope.'

Howard's voice sounded indignant. 'I didn't mean I want to give it up. I only meant that I can't do it that way.'

RUTH RENDELL

'What other way is there?'
'Why shouldn't I try to tail him from the other end?'
'The other end?'
'Last night after I'd lost him on the Tube, I went up to Dartmeet Avenue. You see, I'd reckoned he may stay all night with her some nights, but he doesn't always stay there. If he did, there'd be no point in his having a place of his own. And he didn't stay last night, Reg. He came home on the last 28 bus. So I thought, why shouldn't I also get on that last bus?'
'I must be getting thick in my old age,' said Wexford, 'but I don't see how that helps.'
'This is how. He'll get on at the stop nearest to her place, won't he? And once I find it I can wait at it the next night from five-thirty onwards. If he comes by bus I can follow him, if he comes by Tube it'll be harder, but there's still a good chance.'
Kilburn Park, Great Western Road, Pembridge Road, Church Street . . . Wexford sighed. 'There are dozens of stops,' he said.
'Not in Notting Hill, there aren't. And it has to be Notting Hill, remember. The last 28 bus crosses Notting Hill Gate at ten to eleven. Tomorrow night I'll be waiting for it in Church Street. I've got six more weekday evenings, Reg, six more watching nights to Christmas.'
'You shall have the breast of the turkey,' said his uncle, 'and the fifty-pence piece from the pudding.'
As he put the phone down, the doorbell rang and he heard the thin reedy voices of young carol singers.

'God rest you merry gentlemen,
Let nothing you dismay . . .'

CHAPTER EIGHTEEN

The Monday of the week before Christmas passed and the Tuesday came and there was nothing from Lovat. Very likely he was too busy with the Morag Grey case to make much effort. Her body hadn't beén found, and her husband, remanded in custody for a week, was due to appear in court again solely on the shop-breaking charge. Wexford phoned Myringham police station on Tuesday afternoon. It was Mr. Lovat's day off, Sergeant Hutton told him, and he wouldn't be found at home as he was attending something called the convention of the Society of Friends of the British Badger.

No word came from Howard. It wasn't awe that stopped Wexford phoning him. You don't harass someone who is doing you the enormous favour of giving up all his free time to gratify your obsession, pursue your chimera. You leave him alone and wait. *Chimera:* Monster, bogy, thing of fanciful conception. That was how the dictionary defined it, Wexford discovered, looking the word up in the solitude of his office. Thing of fanciful conception . . . Hathall was flesh and blood all right, but the woman? Only Howard had ever seen her, and Howard wasn't prepared to swear that Hathall – the monster, the bogy – had been her companion. Let nothing you dismay, Wexford told himself. Someone had made that handprint, someone had left those coarse dark hairs on Angela's bedroom floor.

And even if his chances of ever laying hands on her were now remote, growing more remote with each day that passed, he would still want to know how it had been done, fill in those gaps that still remained. He'd want to know where Hathall had met her. In the street, in a pub, as Howard had once suggested? Or had she originally been a friend of Angela's from those early London days before Hathall had been introduced to his second wife at that Hampstead party? Surely she must have lived in the vicinity of Toxborough or Myringham if hers had been the job of making withdrawals from those accounts. Or had that task been shared between her and Angela? Hathall had worked only part-time at Kidd's. On his day off, Angela might have used the car to collect.

Then there was the book on Celtic languages, another strange 'exhibit' in the case he hadn't even begun to account for. Celtic languages had some, not remote, connection with archaeology, but Angela had shown no interest in them while working at the library of the National Archaeologists' League. If the book wasn't relevant, why had Hathall been so upset by the sight of it in his, Wexford's hands?

But whatever he might deduce from the repeated examination of these facts, from carefully listing apparently unconnected pieces of information and trying to establish a link, the really important thing, the securing of Hathall before he left the country, depended now on finding evidence of that fraud. Putting those puzzle pieces together and making a picture of his chimera could wait until it was too late and Hathall was gone. That, he thought bitterly, would make an occupation for the long evenings of the New Year. And when he had still heard nothing from Lovat by Wednesday morning, he drove to Myringham to catch him in his own office, getting there by ten o'clock. Mr Lovat, he was told, was in court and wasn't expected back before lunch.

Wexford pushed his way through the crowds in Myringham's shopping precinct, climbing concrete steps, ascending and descending escalators – the whole lot strung with twinkling fairy lights in the shape of yellow and red daisies – and made his way into the magistrates' court. The public gallery was almost empty. He slid into a seat, looked round for Lovat, and spotted him sitting at the front almost under the Bench.

A pale-faced gangling man of about thirty was in the dock – according to the solicitor appearing for him, one Richard

George Grey, of no fixed abode. Ah, the husband of Morag. No wonder Lovat looked so anxious. But it didn't take long for Wexford to gather that the shop-breaking charge against Grey was based on very fragile evidence. The police, obviously, wanted a committal which it didn't look as if they would get. Grey's solicitor, youthful, suave and polished, was doing his best for his client, an effort that made Lovat's mouth turn down. With rare *schadenfreude*, Wexford found himself hoping Grey would get off. Why should he be the lucky one, able to hold a man until he had got enough evidence against him to charge him with the murder of his wife?

'And so you will appreciate, Your Worships, that my client has suffered from a series of grave misfortunes. Although he is not obliged to divulge to you any previous convictions, he wishes to do so, aware, no doubt, of how trivial you will find his one sole conviction to be. And of what does this single conviction consist? That, Your Worships, of being placed on probation for being found on enclosed premises at the tender age of seventeen.'

Wexford shifted along to allow for the entry of two elderly women with shopping bags. Their expressions were avid and they seemed to make themselves at home. This entertainment, he thought, was free, matutinal, and the real nittygritty stuff of life, three advantages it had over the cinema. Savouring Lovat's discomfiture, he listened as the solicitor went on.

'Apart from this, what do his *criminal proclivities* amount to? Oh, it is true that when he found himself destitute and without a roof over his head, he was driven to take refuge in a derelict house for which its rightful owner had no use and which was classified as *unfit for human habitation*. But this, as Your Worships are aware, is no crime. It is not even, as the law has stood for six hundred years, trespass. It is true too that he was dismissed by his previous employer for – he frankly admits, though no charge was brought – appropriating from his employer the negligible sum of two pounds fifty. As a result, he was obliged to leave his flat or tied cottage in Maynnot Hall, Toxborough, and as an even more serious result was deserted by his wife on the ground that she refused to live with a man whose honesty was not beyond reproach. This lady, whose whereabouts are not known and whose desertion has caused my client intense distress, seems to have something in common with the Myringham police, in particular that of hitting a man when he is down . . .'

There was a good deal more in the same vein. Wexford would have found it less boring, he thought, if he had heard more of the concrete evidence and less of this airy-fairy-pleading. But the evidence must have been thin and the identification of Grey shaky, for the magistrates returned after three minutes to dismiss the case. Lovat got up in disgust and Wexford rose to follow him. His elderly neighbours moved their shopping bags under protest, there was a press of people outside the court – a cloud of witnesses appearing for a grievous bodily harm case – and by the time he got through, Lovat was off in his car and not in the direction of the police station.

Well, he was fifteen miles north of Kingsmarkham, fifteen miles nearer London. Why waste those miles? Why not go on northwards for a last word with Eileen Hathall? Things could hardly be worse than they were. There was room only for improvement. And how would he feel if she were to tell him Hathall's emigration had been postponed, that he was staying a week, a fortnight, longer in London?

As he passed through Toxborough, the road taking him along Maynnot Way, a memory twitched at the back of his mind. Richard and Morag Grey had lived here once, had been servants presumably at Maynnot Hall – but it wasn't that. Yet it had something to do with what the young solicitor had said. Concentratedly, he reviewed the case, what he had come to think of as Hathall country, a landscape with figures. So many places and so many figures . . . Of all the personalities he had encountered or heard spoken of, one had been hinted at by the solicitor in his dramatic address to the Bench. But no name had been mentioned except Grey's . . . Yes, his wife. The lost woman, that was it. 'Deserted by his wife on the grounds that she refused to live with a man whose honesty was not beyond reproach.' But what did it remind him of? Way back in Hathall country, a year ago perhaps, or months or weeks, someone somewhere had spoken to him of a woman with a peculiar regard for honesty. The trouble was that he hadn't the slightest recollection of who that someone had been.

No effort of memory was required to identify Eileen Hathall's lunch guest. Wexford hadn't seen old Mrs Hathall for fifteen months and he was somewhat aghast to find her there. The ex-wife wouldn't tell the ex-husband of his call, but the mother would very likely tell the son. Never mind. It no longer mattered. Hathall was leaving the country in five days' time. A man who is fleeing his native land forever has no time for petty revenges and needless precautions.

And it seemed that Mrs Hathall, who was sitting at the table drinking an after-lunch cup of tea, was under a lucky misapprehension as to the cause of his visit. This tiresome policeman had called at a house where she was before; he was calling at a house where she was again. On each previous occasion he had wanted her son, therefore – 'You won't find him here,' she said in that gruff voice with its North Country undercurrent. 'He's busy getting himself ready for going abroad.'

Eileen met his questioning glance. 'He came here last night and said good-bye,' she said. Her voice sounded calm, almost complacent. And looking from one woman to the other, Wexford realized what had happened to them. Hathall, while living in England, had been to each of them a source of chronic bitterness, breeding in the mother a perpetual need to nag and harass, in the ex-wife resentment and humiliation. Hathall gone, Hathall so far away that he might as well be dead, would leave them at peace. Eileen would take on the status almost of a widow, and the old woman would have a ready-made respectable reason – her granddaughter's English education – as to why her son and daughter-in-law were parted.

'He's going on Monday?' he said.

Old Mrs Hathall nodded with a certain smugness. 'Don't suppose we shall ever set eyes on him again.' She finished her tea, got up and began to clear the table. The minute you finished a meal you cleared the remains of it away. That was the rule. Wexford saw her lift the lid from the teapot and contemplate its contents with an air of irritation, as if she regretted the wicked waste of throwing away half a pint of tea. And she indicated to Eileen with a little dumb show that there was more if she wanted it. Eileen shook her head and Mrs Hathall bore the pot away. That Wexford might have drunk it, might at least have been given the chance to refuse it, didn't seem to cross their minds. Eileen waited till her mother-in-law had left the room.

'I'm well rid of him,' she said. 'He'd no call to come here, I'm sure. I'd done without him for five years and I can do without him for the rest of my life. As far as I'm concerned, it's good riddance.'

It was as he had supposed. She was now able to pretend to herself that she had sent him away, that now Angela was gone she could have accompanied him to Brazil herself had she so chosen. 'Mum and me,' she said, surveying the bare room, unadorned by a single bunch of holly or paper streamer, 'Mum and me'll have a quiet Christmas by ourselves. Rosemary's going to her French pen-friend tomorrow and she won't be back till her school term starts. We'll be nice and quiet on our own.'

He almost shivered. The affinity between these women frightened him. Had Eileen married Hathall because he could bring her the mother she wanted? Had Mrs Hathall chosen Eileen for him because this was the daughter she needed?

'Mum's thinking of coming to live here with me,' she said as the old woman came plodding back. 'When Rosemary goes off to college, that is. No point in keeping up two homes, is there?'

A warmer, a more affectionate, woman might have reacted by smiling her gratification or by linking an arm with this ideal daughter-in-law. Mrs Hathall's small cold eyes flickered their approval over the barren room, resting briefly on Eileen's puffy face and crimped hair, while her mouth, rigid and down-turned, showed something like disappointment that she had no fault to find. 'Come along then, Eileen,' she said. 'We've got them dishes to do.'

They left Wexford to find his own way out. As he came from under the canopy that reminded him of a provincial railway station, the car that had been Hathall's turned into the drive, Rosemary at the wheel. The face that was an intelligent version of her grandmother's registered recognition but no polite expression of greeting, no smile.

'I hear you're going off to France for Christmas?'

She switched off the engine but otherwise she didn't move.

'I remember your saying once before that you'd never been out of England.'

'That's right.'

'Not even on a day trip to France with your school, Miss Hathall?'

'Oh, that,' she said with icy calm. 'That was the day Angela got herself strangled.' She made a quick chilling gesture of running one finger across her throat. 'I told my mother I was going with school. I didn't. I went out with a boy instead. Satisfied?'

'Not quite. You can drive, you've been able to drive for eighteen months. You disliked Angela and seem fond of your father . . .'

She interrupted him harshly. 'Fond of *him?* I can't stand the sight of any of them. My mother's a vegetable and the old woman's a cow. You don't know – no one knows – what they put me through, pulling me this way and that between them.' The words were heated but her voice didn't rise. 'I'm going to get away this year and none of them'll ever see me again for dust. Those two can live here together and one day they'll just die and no one'll find them for months.' Her hand went up to push a lock of coarse dark hair from her face, and he saw her fingertip, rosy red and quite smooth. 'Satisfied?' she said again.

'I am now.'

'Me kill Angela?' She gave a throaty laugh. 'There's others I'd kill first, I can tell you. Did you really think I'd killed her?'

'Not really,' said Wexford, 'but I'm sure you could have if you'd wanted to.'

He was rather pleased with this parting shot and thought of a few more *esprits d'escalier* as he drove off. It had only once before been his lot to confound a Hathall. He might, of course, have asked her if she had ever known a woman with a scarred fingertip, but it went against the grain with him to ask a daughter to betray her father, even such a daughter and such a father. He wasn't a medieval inquisitor or the pillar of a Fascist state.

Back at the police station he phoned Lovat who, naturally, was out and not expected to reappear till the following day. Howard wouldn't phone. If he had watched last night he had watched in vain, for Hathall had been making his farewells at Croydon.

Dora was icing the Christmas cake, placing in the centre of the white frosted circle a painted plaster Santa Claus and surrounding it with plaster robins, ornaments which came out each year from their silver paper wrappings and which had first been brought when Wexford's elder daughter was a baby.

'There! Doesn't it look nice?'

'Lovely,' said Wexford gloomily.

Dora said with calculated callousness, 'I shall be glad when that man's gone to wherever he's going and you're your normal self again.' She covered the cake and rinsed her hands. 'By the way, d'you remember once asking me about a woman called Lake? The one you said reminded you of George the Second?'

'I didn't say that,' said Wexford uneasily.

'Something like that. Well, I thought you might be interested to know she's getting married. To a man called Somerset. His wife died a couple of months ago. I imagine something has been going on there for years, but they kept it very dark. Quite a mystery. He can't have made any deathbed promises about only taking mistresses, can he? Oh, darling, I do wish you'd show a bit of interest sometimes and not look so perpetually fed up!'

CHAPTER NINETEEN

Thursday was his day off. Not that he would take a day off as he meant to run Lovat to earth – a fine metaphor, he thought, to use in connection with a protector of wildlife – but there was no reason for early rising. He had gone to sleep thinking what an old fool he was to suppose Nancy Lake fancied him when she was going to marry Somerset, and when morning came he was deep in a Hathall dream. This time it was totally nonsensical with Hathall and his woman embarking on to a flying 28 bus, and the phone ringing by his bed jerked him out of it at eight o'clock.

'I thought I'd get you before I left for work,' said Howard's voice. 'I've found the bus stop, Reg.'

That was more alerting than the alarm bell of the phone. 'Tell,' he said.

'I saw him leave Marcus Flower at five-thirty, and when he went up to Bond Street station I knew he'd be going to her. I had to go back to my own manor for a couple of hours, but I got down to the New King's Road by half past ten. God, it was easy. The whole exercise worked out better than I dared hope.

'I was sitting on one of the front seats downstairs, the near-side by the window. He wasn't at the stop at the top of Church Street or the next one just after Notting Hill Gate station. I knew if he was going to get on it would have to be soon and then, lo and behold, there he was all on his own at a request stop halfway up Pembridge Road. He went upstairs. I stayed on the bus and saw him get off at West End Green, and then,' Howard ended triumphantly, 'I went on to Golders Green and came home in a cab.'

'Howard, you are my only ally.'

'Well, you know what Chesterton said about that. I'll be at that bus stop from five-thirty onwards tonight and then we'll see.'

Wexford put on his dressing gown and went downstairs to find what Chesterton had said. 'There are no words to express the abyss between isolation and having one ally. It may be conceded to the mathematicians that four is twice two. But two is not twice one; two is two thousand times one . . .' He felt considerably cheered. Maybe he had no force of men at his disposal but he had Howard, the resolute, the infinitely reliable, the invincible, and together they were two thousand. Two thousand and one with Lovat. He must bathe and dress and get over to Myringham right away.

The head of Myringham CID was in, and with him Sergeant Hutton.

'Not a bad day,' said Lovat, peering through his funny little spectacles at the uniformly white, dull, sun-free sky.

Wexford thought it best to say nothing about Richard Grey. 'Did you get to work on that payroll thing?'

Lovat nodded very slowly and profoundly, but it was the sergeant who was appointed spokesman. 'We found one or two accounts which looked suspicious, sir. Three, to be precise. One was in the Trustee Savings Bank at Toxborough, one at Passingham St. John and one here. All had had regular payments made into them by Kidd and Co., and in all cases the payments and withdrawals ceased in March or April last year. The one in Myringham was in the name of a woman whose address turned out to be a sort of boarding house-cum-hotel. The people there don't remember her and we haven't been able to trace her. The one at Passingham turned out to be valid, all above board. The woman there worked at Kidd's, left in the March and just didn't bother to take the last thirty pee out of her account.'

'And the Toxborough account?'

'That's the difficulty, sir. It's in the name of a Mrs Mary

Lewis and the address is a Toxborough address, but the house is shut up and the people evidently away. The neighbours say they're called Kingsbury not Lewis, but they've taken in lodgers over the years and one of them could have been a Lewis. We just have to wait till the Kingsburys come back.'

'Do these neighbours know when they're coming back?'

'No,' said Lovat.

Does anyone ever go away the week before Christmas and not stay away till after Christmas? Wexford thought it unlikely. His day off stretched before him emptily. A year ago he had resolved to be patient, but the time had come when he was counting the hours rather than the days to Hathall's departure. Four days. Ninety-six hours. And that, he thought, must be the only instance when a large number sounds pitifully smaller than a small number. Ninety-six hours. Five thousand, seven hundred and sixty minutes. Nothing. It would be gone in the twinkling of an eye . . .

And the frustrating thing was that he had to waste those hours, those thousands of minutes, for there was nothing left for him personally to do. He could only go home and help Dora hang up more paper chains, arrange more coy bunches of mistletoe, plant the Christmas tree in its tub, speculate with her as to whether the turkey was small enough to lie on an oven shelf or big enough instead to be suspended by strings from the oven roof. And on Friday when only seventy-two hours remained (four thousand three hundred and twenty minutes) he went with Burden up to the police station canteen for the special Christmas dinner. He even put on a paper hat and pulled a cracker with Policewoman Polly Davies.

Ahead of him was his tea date with Nancy Lake. He nearly phoned her to cancel it, but he didn't do this, telling himself there were still one or two questions she could answer for him and that this was as good a way as any of using up some of those four thousand-odd minutes. By four o'clock he was in Wool Lane, not thinking about her at all, thinking how, eight months before, he had walked there with Howard, full of hope and energy and determination.

'We've been lovers for nineteen years,' she said. 'I'd been married for five and I'd come to live here with my husband, and one day when I was walking in the lane I met Mark. He was in his father's garden, picking plums. We knew its proper name, but we called it a miracle tree because it was a miracle for us.'

'The jam,' said Wexford, 'is very good.'

'Have some more.' She smiled at him across the table. The room where they were sitting was as bare as Eileen Hathall's and there were no Christmas decorations. But it wasn't barren or sterile or cold. He could see signs everywhere of the removal of a picture, a mirror, an ornament, and looking at her, listening to her, he could imagine the beauty and the character of those furnishings that were packed now, ready to be taken to her new home. The dark blue velvet curtains still hung at the French window, and she had drawn them to shut out the early mid-winter dusk. They made for her a sombre night sky background, and she glowed against them, her face a little flushed, the old diamond on her finger and the new diamond beside it, sparking rainbow fire from the light of the lamp at her side. 'Do you know,' she said suddenly, 'what it's like to be in love and have nowhere to go to make love?'

'I know it – vicariously.'

'We managed as best we could. My husband found out and then Mark couldn't come to Wool Lane any more. We'd tried not seeing each other and sometimes we kept it up for months, but it never worked.'

'Why didn't you marry? Neither of you had children.'

She took his empty cup and refilled it. As she passed it to him, her fingers just brushed his and he felt himself grow hot with something that was almost anger. As if it wasn't bad enough, he thought, her being there and looking like that

505

without all this sex talk as well. 'My husband died,' she said. 'We were going to marry. Then Mark's wife got ill and he couldn't leave her. It was impossible.'

He couldn't keep the sneering note out of his voice. 'So you remained faithful to each other and lived in hopes?'

'No, there were others – for me.' She looked at him steadily, and he found himself unable to return that look. 'Mark knew, and if he minded he never blamed me. How could he? I told you once, I felt like a distraction, something to – to divert him when he could be spared from his wife's bedside.'

'Was it she you meant when you asked me if it was wrong to wish for someone's death?'

'Of course. Who else? Did you think – did you think I was speaking of *Angela?*' Her gravity went and she was smiling again. 'Oh, my dear . . .! Shall I tell you something else? Two years ago when I was very bored and very lonely because Gwen Somerset was home from hospital and wouldn't let Mark out of her sight, I – I made advances to Robert Hathall. There's confession for you! And he wouldn't have me. He turned me down. I am not accustomed,' she said with mock pomposity, 'to being turned down.'

'I suppose not. Do you think I'm blind,' he said rather savagely, 'or a complete fool?'

'Just unapproachable. If you've finished, shall we go into the other room? It's more comfortable. I haven't yet stripped it of every vestige of me.'

His questions were answered, and there was no need now to ask where she had been when Angela died or where Somerset had been, or probe any of those mysteries about her and Somerset, which were mysteries no more. He might as well say good-bye and go, he thought, as he crossed the hall behind her and followed her into a warmer room of soft textures and deep rich colours, and where there seemed no hard surfaces, but only silk melting into velvet and velvet into brocade. Before she could close the door, he held out his hand to her, meaning to begin a little speech of thanks and farewell. But she took his hand in both of hers.

'I shall be gone on Monday,' she said, looking up into his face. 'The new people are moving in. We shan't meet again. I would promise you that, if you like.'

Up till then he had doubted her intentions towards him. There was no room for doubt now.

'Why should you think I want to be the last fling for a woman who is going to her first love?'

'Isn't it a compliment?'

He said, 'I'm an old man, and an old man who is taken in by compliments is pathetic.'

She flushed a little. 'I shall soon be an old woman. We could be pathetic together.' A rueful laugh shook her voice. 'Don't go yet. We can – talk. We've never really talked yet.'

'We have done nothing but talk,' said Wexford, but he didn't go. He let her lead him to the sofa and sit beside him and talk to him about Somerset and Somerset's wife and the nineteen years of secrecy and deception. Her hand rested in his, and as he relaxed and listened to her, he remembered the first time he had held it and what she had said when he had kept hold of it a fraction too long. At last she got up. He also rose and put that hand to his lips. 'I wish you happy,' he said. 'I hope you're going to be very happy.'

'I'm a little afraid, you know, of how it will be after so long. Do you understand what I mean?'

'Of course.' He spoke gently, all savagery gone, and when she asked him to have a drink with her he said, 'I'll drink *to* you and to your happiness.'

She put her arms round his neck and kissed him. The kiss was impulsive, light, over before he could respond to her or resist her. She was gone from the room for some minutes, more minutes than were needful to fetch drinks and glasses. He heard the sound of her footsteps overhead, and he guessed how she would be when she came back. So he had to decide what he should do, whether to go or stay. Gather ye rosebuds, roses, other men's flowers, while ye may? Or be an old man, dreaming dreams and being mindful of one's marriage vows?

The whole of his recent life seemed to him a long series of failures, of cowardice and caution. And yet the whole of his recent life had also been bent towards doing what he believed to be right and just. Perhaps, in the end, it came to the same thing.

At last he went out into the hall. He called her name, 'Nancy!', using that name for the first and only time, and when he moved to the foot of the stairs, he saw her at the head of them. The light there was soft and kind, unnecessarily kind, and she was as he had known she would be, as he had seen her in his fantasies – only better than that, better than his expectations.

He looked up at her in wondering appreciation, looked for long silent minutes. But by then he had made up his mind.

Only the unwise dwell on what is past with regret for rejected opportunity or nostalgia for chosen delight. He regretted nothing, for he had only done what any man of sense would have done in his position. His decision had been reached during those moments while she had been away from the room and he had stuck to that decision, confident he was acting according to his own standards and what was right for him. But he was astonished to find it was so late when he let himself into his own house, nearly eight o'clock. And at the recalling of his mind to time's passing, he was back to counting the minutes, back to calculating that only about three and a half thousand of them remained. Nancy's face faded, the warmth of her vanished. He marched into the kitchen where Dora was making yet another batch of mince pies and said rather brusquely, 'Has Howard phoned?'

She looked up. He had forgotten – he was always forgetting

– how astute she was. 'He wouldn't phone at this time, would he? It's last thing at night or first thing in the morning with him.'

'Yes, I know. But I'm strung up about this thing.'

'Indeed you are. You forgot to kiss me.'

So he kissed her, and the immediate past was switched off. No regrets, he reminded himself, no nostalgia, no introspection. And he took a mince pie and bit into the hot crisp crust.

'You'll get fat and gross and revolting.'

'Perhaps,' said Wexford thoughtfully, 'that wouldn't be such a bad thing – in moderation, of course.'

CHAPTER TWENTY

Sheila Wexford, the chief inspector's actress daughter, arrived on Saturday morning. It was good to see her in the flesh, her father said, instead of two-dimensionally and monotonally in her television serial. She pranced about the house arranging the cards more artistically and singing that she was dreaming of a white Christmas. It seemed, however, that it was going to be a foggy one. The long-range weather forecast had said it would be, and now the weather signs themselves fulfilled this prediction as a white morning mist shrouded the sun at noon and by evening was dense and yellowish.

The shortest day of the year. The Winter Solstice. It was arctic in light as well as in temperature, the fog closing out daylight at three and heralding seventeen hours of darkness. Along the streets lighted Christmas trees showed only as an amber blur in windows. God rest you merry, gentlemen, let nothing you dismay . . . Seventeen hours of darkness, thirty-six hours to go.

Howard had promised to phone and did so at ten. Hathall had been indoors alone at 62 Dartmeet Avenue since three. Howard was in the call-box opposite the house, but now he was going home. His six watching nights to Christmas were over – today's had been a bonus vigil, undertaken because he couldn't bear to be beaten and he was going home.

'I'll watch him tomorrow, Reg, for the last time.'

'Is there any point?'

'I shall feel I've done the job as thoroughly as it can be done.'

Hathall had been alone most of the day. Did that mean he had sent the woman on ahead of him? Wexford went to bed early and lay awake thinking of Christmas, thinking of himself and Howard retired to a quiet corner and holding their last inquest over what had happened, what else they could have done, what might have happened if on October second a year ago Griswold hadn't issued his ban.

On Sunday morning the fog began to lift. The vague hope Wexford had entertained that fog might force Hathall to postpone his departure faded as the sun appeared strong and bright by midday. He listened to the radio news but no airports were closed and no flights cancelled. And as the evening began with a bright sunset and a clear frosty sky – as if winter was already dying with the passing of the solstice – he knew he must resign himself to Hathall's escape. It was all over.

But though he could teach himself to avoid introspection where Nancy Lake was concerned, he couldn't help dwelling with regret and bitterness over the long period during which he and Robert Hathall had been adversaries. Things might have been very different if only he had guessed at that payroll fraud – if fraud there was – before. He should have known too that an angry paranoiac with much at stake wouldn't react passively to his clumsy probing and what that probing implied. But it was all over now and he would never know who the woman was. Sadly he thought of other questions that must remain unanswered. What was the reason for the presence in Bury Cottage of the Celtic languages book? Why had Hathall, who in middle life had come to enjoy sexual variety, repulsed such a woman as Nancy Lake? Why had his accomplice, in most ways so thorough and careful, left her handprint on, of all places, the side of the bath? And why had Angela, anxious to please her mother-in-law, desperate for a reconciliation, worn on the day of her visit the very clothes which had helped turn her mother-in-law against her?

It didn't cross his mind that, at this late stage, Howard would have any further success. Hathall's habit was to stay at home on Sundays, entertaining his mother or his daughter. And even though he had already said good-bye to them, there seemed no reason to suppose he would change his ways to the extent of going to Notting Hill and her, when they were leaving together on the following day. So when he lifted the receiver at eleven that Sunday night and heard the familiar voice, a little tired now and a little irritable, he thought at first Howard was phoning only to say at what time he and Denise would arrive on Christmas Eve. And when he understood the true reason for the call, that at last when it was too late, Howard was on the brink of accomplishing his task, he felt the sick despair of a man who doesn't want hope to come in and threaten his resignation.

'You saw her?' he said dully. 'You actually saw her?'

'I know how you're feeling, Reg, but I have to tell you. I couldn't keep it to myself. I saw him. I saw her. I saw them together. And I lost them.'

'Oh, *God*. My God, it's more than I can take.'

'Don't kill the messenger, Reg,' Howard said gently. 'Don't do a Cleopatra on me. I that do bring the news made not the match.'

'I'm not angry with you. How could I be after all you've done? I'm angry with – fate, I suppose. Tell me what happened.'

'I started watching the house in Dartmeet Avenue after lunch. I didn't know whether Hathall was in or not until I saw him come out and put a great sackful of rubbish into one of those dustbins. He was having a clear-out, packing, I expect, and throwing out what he didn't want. I sat there in the car, and I nearly went home when I saw his light go on at half past four.

'Maybe it would have been better if I had gone home. At least I couldn't have raised your hopes. He came out of the house at six, Reg, and walked down to West End Green. I followed him in the car and parked in Mill Lane – that's the street that runs westwards off Fortune Green Road. We both waited for about five minutes. The 28 bus didn't come and he got into a taxi instead.'

'You followed it?' said Wexford, admiration for a moment overcoming his bitterness.

'It's easier to follow a taxi than a bus. Buses keep stopping. Following a taxi in London on a Sunday night is a different matter from trying to do it by day in the rush hours. Anyway, the driver took more or less the same route as the bus. It dropped Hathall outside a pub in Pembridge Road.'

'Near that stop where you saw him get on the bus before?'

'Quite near, yes. I've been to that bus stop and the streets round about it every night this week, Reg. But he must have used the back street to get to her from Notting Hill Gate station. I never saw him once.'

'You went into this pub after him?'

'It's called the Rosy Cross and it was very crowded. He bought two drinks, gin for himself and pernod for her, although she hadn't come in yet. He managed to find two seats in a corner and he put his coat on one of them to keep it. Most of the time the crowd blocked my view of him, but I could see that glass of yellow pernod waiting on the table for her to come and drink it.

'Hathall was early or she was ten minutes late. I didn't know she'd come in till I saw a hand go round that yellow glass and the glass lifted up out of my sight. I moved then and pushed through the crowd to get a better look. It was the same woman I saw him with outside Marcus Flower, a pretty woman in her early thirties with dyed blonde cropped hair. No, don't ask. I didn't see her hand. I was too close for safety as it was. I think Hathall recognized me. God, he'd have to be blind not to by now, even with the care I've taken.

'They drank their drinks quite quickly and pushed their way out. She must live quite near there, but where she lives I can't tell you. It doesn't matter now, anyway. I saw them walking away when I came out and I was going to follow them on foot. A taxi came and they got into it. Hathall didn't even wait to tell the driver where he wanted to go. He just got in and must have given his instructions afterwards. He wasn't going to run the risk of being followed, and I couldn't follow them. The taxi went off up Pembridge Road and I lost them. I lost them and went home.

'The last of Robert Hathall, Reg. It was good while it lasted. I really thought – well, never mind. You were right all along the line and that, I'm afraid, must be your consolation.'

Wexford said good night to his nephew and that he would see him on Christmas Eve. An aircraft sounded overhead, coming out of Gatwick. He stood by his bedroom window and watched its white and red lights like meteors crossing the clear starlit sky. Just a few more hours and Hathall would be on such an aircraft. First thing in the morning? Or an afternoon flight? Or would he and she be going by night? He found he knew very little about extradition. It hadn't come in his way to know about it. And things had taken such strange turns lately that a country would probably bargain, would want concessions or some sort of exchange before releasing a foreign national. Besides, though you might get an extradition order if you had irrefutable evidence of murder, surely you wouldn't on a fraud charge. Deception, the charge would be, he thought, deception under Section 15 of the Theft Act of 1968. It suddenly seemed fantastic to contemplate putting all that political machinery in motion to fetch a man out of Brazil for helping himself to the funds of a plastic doll factory.

He thought of Crippen being apprehended in mid-Atlantic by a wireless message, of train robbers caught after long periods of freedom in the distant South, of films he had seen in which some criminal, at ease now and believing himself secure, felt the heavy hand of the law descend on his shoulder as he sat drinking wine in a sunny pavement café. It wasn't his world. He couldn't see himself, even in a minor capacity, taking part in exotic drama. Instead he saw Hathall flying away to freedom, to the life he had planned and had done murder to get, while in a week or two perhaps Brock Lovat was obliged to admit defeat because he had found no fraud or theft or deception but only a few vague hints of something underhand which Hathall might have been called to account for – if only Hathall had been there to answer.

The day had come.

Waking early, Wexford thought of Hathall waking early too. He had seen Howard the night before, had suspected he was still being followed, so wouldn't have dared spend the night with the woman or have her spend the night with him. Now he was washing at the sink in that nasty little room, taking a suit from the Battle of Mons wardrobe, shaving before packing his razor into the small hand-case he would take with him in the aircraft. Wexford could see the red granite face, more heavily flushed from its contact with the razor's edge, the thinning black hair slicked back with a wet comb. Now Hathall would be taking a last look at the ten by twelve cell which had been his home for nine months, and thinking with happy anticipation of the home that was to be his; now across to the call-box, at mid-winter daybreak, to check his flight with the airport and harangue the girl who spoke to him for not being prompt enough or efficient or considerate enough; now, lastly, a call to *her*, wherever she was, in the labyrinth of Notting Hill. No, perhaps one more call. To the taxi rank or car-hire place for the car that would take him and his luggage away forever . . .

Stop it, he told himself severely. Leave it. No more of this. This way madness – or at least an obsessional neurosis – lies. Christmas is coming, go to work, forget him. He took Dora a cup of tea and went to work.

In his office he went through the morning mail and stuck a few Christmas cards around. There was one from Nancy Lake, which he looked at thoughtfully for a moment or two

515

before putting it inside his desk. No less than five calendars had come, including one of the glossy nudes *genre*, the offering of a local garage. It brought to mind Ginge at West Hampstead station, the offices of Marcus Flower . . . Was he going crazy? What was happening to him when he let erotica bring to mind a murder hunt? Stop it. From his selection he chose a handsome and immensely dull calendar, twelve colour plates of Sussex scenes, and pinned it on to the wall next to the district map. The gift of a grateful garage he put into a new envelope, marked it *For Your Eyes Only* and had it sent down to Burden's office. That would set the prim inspector fulminating against current moral standards and divert his, Wexford's, mind from that bloody, unspeakable, triumphant, God-damned crook and fugitive, Robert Hathall.

Then he turned his attention to the matters that were at present concerning Kingsmarkham police. Five women in the town and two from outlying villages had complained of obscene telephone calls. The only extraordinary thing about that was that their caller had also been a woman. Wexford smiled a little to note the odd corners of life into which Women's Liberation was infiltrating. He smiled more grimly and with exasperation at Sergeant Martin's attempt to make an issue out of the activities of four small boys who had tied a length of string from a lamppost to a garden wall in an effort to trip up passersby. Why did they waste his time with this rubbish? Yet sometimes it is better to have one's time wasted than spent on hankering ever and ever after a vain thing . . .

His internal phone was bleeping. He lifted the receiver, expecting the voice of a self-righteous and indignant Burden.

'Chief Inspector Lovat to see you, sir. Shall I show him up?'

CHAPTER TWENTY-ONE

Lovat came in slowly, and with him his inevitable interpreter, his *fidus Achates*, Sergeant Hutton.

'Lovely day.'

'Be damned to the day,' said Wexford in a throaty voice because his heart and his blood pressure were behaving very strangely. 'Never mind the day. I wish it would bloody well snow, I wish . . .'

Hutton said quietly. 'If we might just sit down a while, sir? Mr Lovat has something to tell you which he thinks will interest you greatly. And since it was you put him on to it, it seemed only a matter of courtesy . . .'

'Sit down, do as you like, have a calendar, take one each. I know why you've come. But just tell me one thing. Can you get a man extradited for what you've found out? Because if you can't, you've had it. Hathall's going to Brazil today, and ten to one he's gone already.'

'Dear me,' said Lovat placidly.

Wexford nearly put his head in his hands. 'Well, can you?' he shouted.

'I'd better tell you what Mr Lovat *has* found, sir. We called at the home of Mr and Mrs Kingsbury again last night. They'd just returned. They'd been on a visit to their married daughter who was having a baby. No Mrs Mary Lewis has ever lodged with them and they have never had any connection with Kidd and Co. Moreover, on making further enquiries at the board-ing house Mr Lovat told you about, he could discover no evidence at all of the existence of the other so-called account holder.'

'So you've had a warrant sworn for Hathall's arrest?'

'Mr Lovat would like to talk to Robert Hathall, sir,' said

Hutton cautiously. 'I'm sure you'll agree we need a little more to go on. Apart from the – er, courtesy of the matter, we called on you for Hathall's present address.'

'His present address,' Wexford snapped, 'is probably about five miles up in the air above Madeira or wherever that damned plane flies.'

'Unfortunate,' said Lovat, shaking his head.

'Maybe he hasn't left, sir. If we could phone him?'

'I daresay you could if he had a phone and if he hasn't left.' Wexford looked in some despair at the clock. It was ten-thirty. 'Frankly, I don't know what to do. The only thing I can suggest is that we all get out to Millerton-*les-deux* – er, Hightrees Farm, and lay all this before the Chief Constable.'

'Good idea,' said Lovat. 'Many a fine night I've spent watching the badger setts there.'

Wexford could have kicked him.

He never knew what prompted him to ask the question. There was no sixth sense about it. Perhaps it was just that he thought he should have the facts of this fraud as straight in his mind as they were in Hutton's. But he did ask it, and afterwards he thanked God he had asked it then on the country lane drive to Millerton.

'The addresses of the account holders, sir? One was in the name of Mrs. Dorothy Carter of Ascot House, Myringham – that's the boardinghouse place – and the other of Mrs. Mary Lewis at 19 Maynnot Way, Toxborough.'

'Did you say Maynnot Way?' Wexford asked in a voice that sounded far away and unlike his own.

'That's right. It runs from the industrial estate to . . .'

'I know where it runs to, Sergeant. I also know who lived at Maynnot Hall in the middle of Maynnot Way.' He felt a constriction in his throat. 'Brock,' he said, 'what were you doing at Kidd's that day I met you at the gates?'

Lovat looked at Hutton and Hutton said, 'Mr Lovat was

pursuing his enquiries in connection with the disappearance of Morag Grey, sir. Morag Grey worked as a cleaner at Kidd's for a short while when her husband was gardener at the hall. Naturally, we explored every way open to us.'

'You haven't explored Maynnot Way enough.' Wexford almost gasped at the enormity of his discovery. His chimera, he thought, his thing of fanciful conception. 'Your Morag Grey isn't buried in anyone's garden. She's Robert Hathall's woman, she's going off to Brazil with him. My God, I can see it all . . . !' If only he had Howard beside him to explain all this to instead of the phlegmatic Lovat and this openmouthed sergeant. 'Listen,' he said. 'This Grey woman was Hathall's accomplice in the fraud. He met her when they both worked at Kidd's, and she and his wife had the job of making withdrawals from those accounts. No doubt, she thought up the name and address of Mrs Mary Lewis because she knew Maynnot Way and knew the Kingsburys let rooms. Hathall fell for her and she murdered Hathall's wife. She isn't dead, Brock, she's been living in London as Hathall's mistress ever since . . . When did she disappear?'

'As far as we know, in August or September of last year, sir,' said the sergeant, and he brought the car to a halt on the gravel outside Hightrees Farm.

For the sake of the reputation of Mid-Sussex, it would be most unfortunate for Hathall to escape. This, to Wexford's amazement, was the opinion of Charles Griswold. And he saw a faint flush of unease colour the statesmanlike face as the Chief Constable was forced to admit the theory was tenable.

'This is a little more than 'feeling,' I think, Reg,' he said, and it was he personally who phoned London Airport.

Wexford and Lovat and Hutton had to wait a long time before he came back. And when he did it was to say that Robert Hathall and a woman travelling as Mrs Hathall were on the passenger list of a flight leaving for Rio de Janeiro at twelve forty-five. The airport police would be instructed to hold them both on a charge of deception under the Theft Act, and a warrant had better be sworn at once.

'She must be travelling on his passport.'

'Or on Angela's,' Wexford said. 'He's still got it. I remember looking at it, but it was left with him in Bury Cottage.'

'No need to be bitter, Reg. Better late than never.'

'It happens, sir,' said Wexford very politely but with an edge to his voice, 'to be twenty to twelve now. I just hope we're in time.'

'Oh, he won't get out now,' Griswold said on a breezy note. 'They'll stop him at the airport where you can take yourselves forthwith. Forthwith, Reg. And tomorrow morning you can come over for a Christmas drink and tell me all about it.'

They went back to Kingsmarkham to pick up Burden. The inspector was in the foyer, peering through his glasses at the envelope he brandished, and angrily enquiring of a puzzled station sergeant who had had the effrontery to send him pornography for his exclusive perusal.

'Hathall?' he said when Wexford explained. 'You don't mean it. You're joking.'

'Get in the car, Mike, and I'll tell you on the way. No, Sergeant Hutton will tell *us* on the way. What have you got there? Art studies? Now I see why you needed glasses.'

Burden gave a snort of rage and was about to launch into a long explanation of his innocence, but Wexford cut him short. He didn't need diversions now. He had been waiting for this day, this moment, for fifteen months, and he could have shouted his triumph at the crisp blue air, the springlike sun. They left in two cars. The first contained Lovat and his driver and Polly Davies, the second Wexford, Burden and Sergeant Hutton with their driver.

'I want to know everything you can tell me about Morag Grey.'

'She was – well, is – a Scot, sir. From the northwest of Scotland, Ullapool. But there's not much work up there and she came south and went into service. She met Grey seven or eight years ago and married him and they got that job at Maynnot Hall.'

'What, he did the garden and she cleaned the place?'

'That's right. I don't quite know why as she seems to have been a cut above that sort of thing. According to her mother and – more to the point – according to her employer at the hall, she'd had a reasonable sort of education and was quite bright. Her mother says Grey had dragged her down.'

'How old is she and what does she look like?'

'She'd be about thirty-two now, sir. Thin, dark-haired, nothing special. She did some of the housework at the hall and did outside cleaning jobs as well. One of those was at Kidd's, in last March twelvemonth, but she only stayed two or three weeks. Then Grey got the sack for taking a couple of quid from his employer's wife's handbag. They had to leave their flat and go and squat in Myringham Old Town. But soon after that Morag turned him out. Grey says she found out the reason for their getting the push and wouldn't go on living with a thief. A likely story, I'm sure you'll agree, sir. But he insisted on it, despite the fact that he went straight from her to another woman who had a room about a mile away on the other side of Myringham.'

'It doesn't,' said Wexford thoughtfully, 'seem a likely story under the circumstances.'

'He says he spent the money he pinched on a present for her, a gilt snake necklace . . .'

'Ah.'

'Which may be true but doesn't prove much.'

'I wouldn't say that, Sergeant. What happened to her when she was left on her own?'

'We know very little about that. Squatters don't really have neighbours, they're an itinerant population. She had a series of cleaning jobs up until August and then she went on Social Security. All we know is that Morag told a woman in that row

of houses that she'd got a good job in the offing and would
be moving away. What that job was and where she was going
we never found out. No one saw her after the middle of
September. Grey came back around Christmas and took away
what possessions she'd left behind.'

'Didn't you say it was her mother who started the hue and
cry?'

'Morag had been a regular correspondent, and when her
mother got no answers to her letters she wrote to Grey. He
found the letters when he went back at Christmas and at last
he wrote back with some cock-and-bull story about thinking
his wife had gone to Scotland. Mother had never trusted
Richard Grey and she went to the police. She came down
here and we had to get an interpreter in on account of –
believe it or not – her speaking only Gaelic.'

Wexford, who at that moment felt, like the White Queen,
that he could have believed six impossible things before breakfast, said, 'Does Morag also – er, have the Gaelic?'

'Yes, sir, she does. She's bilingual.'

With a sigh Wexford sank back against the upholstery.
There were a few loose ends to be tied, a few small instances
of the unaccountable to be accounted for, but otherwise . . . He
closed his eyes. The car was going very slowly. Vaguely he
wondered, but without looking, if they were running into heavy
traffic as they approached London. It didn't matter. Hathall
would have been stopped by now, detained in some little side
room of the airport. Even if he hadn't been told why he wasn't
allowed to fly, he would know. He would know it was all over.
The car was almost stopping. Wexford opened his eyes and
seized Burden's arm. He wound down the window.

'See,' he said, pointing to the ground that now slid past
at a snail's pace. 'It does move. And that . . .' his arm went
upwards, skywards, '. . . that doesn't.'

'What doesn't?' said Burden. 'There's nothing to see. Look
for yourself. We're fog-bound.'

CHAPTER TWENTY-TWO

It was nearly four o'clock before they reached the airport. All aircraft were grounded, and Christmas holiday travelers filled the lounges while queues formed at enquiry desks. The fog was all-enveloping, fluffy like aerated snow, dense earthbound clouds of it, a white gas that set people coughing and covering their faces.

Hathall wasn't there.

The fog had begun to come down at Heathrow at eleven-thirty, but it had affected other parts of London earlier than that. Had he been among the hundreds who had phoned the airport from fog-bound outer suburbs to enquire if their flights would leave? There was no way of knowing. Wexford walked slowly and painstakingly through the lounges, from bar to restaurant, out on to the observation terraces, looking into every face, tired faces, indignant faces, bored faces. Hathall wasn't there.

'According to the weather forecast,' said Burden, 'the fog'll lift by evening.'

'And according to the long-range, it's going to be a white Christmas, a white fog Christmas. You and Polly stay here, Mike. Get on to the chief constable and fix it so that we have every exit watched, not just Heathrow.'

So Burden and Polly remained while Wexford and Lovat and Hutton began the long drive to Hampstead. It was very slow going. Streams of traffic, bound for the M1, blocked all the north-west roads as the fog, made tawny by the yellow overhead lights, cast a blinding pall over the city. The landmarks on the route, which by now were all too familiar, had lost their sharp outlines and become amorphous. The winding hills of Hampstead lay under a smoky shroud and the great trees of Hampstead loomed like black clouds before being swallowed up in paler vapour. They crawled into Dartmeet Avenue at ten minutes to seven and pulled up outside number 62. The house was in darkness, every window tight shut and dead black. The dustbins were dewed where the fog had condensed on them. Their lids were scattered, and a cat darted out from under one of them, a chicken bone in its mouth. As Wexford got out of the car, the fog caught at his throat. He thought of another foggy day in Myringham Old Town, of men digging in vain for a body that had never been there. He thought of how his whole pursuit of Hathall had been befogged by doubt and confusion and obstruction, and then he went up to the front door and rang the landlord's bell.

He had rung it twice more before a light showed through the pane of glass above the lintel. At last the door was opened by the same little elderly man Wexford had once before seen come out and fetch his cat. He was smoking a thin cigar and he showed neither surprise nor interest when the chief inspector said who he was and showed him his warrant card.

'Mr Hathall left last night,' he said.

'Last night?'

'That's right. To tell you the truth, I didn't expect him to go till this morning. He'd paid his rent up to tonight. But he got hold of me in a bit of hurry last night and said he'd decided to go, so it wasn't for me to argue, was it?'

The hall was icy cold, in spite of the oil heater which stood at the foot of the stairs, and the place reeked of burning oil and cigar smoke. Lovat rubbed his hands together, then held them out over the guttering blue and yellow flames.

'Mr Hathall came back here about eight last night in a taxi,' said the landlord. 'I was out in the front garden, calling my cat. He came up to me and said he wanted to vacate his room there and then.'

'How did he seem?' Wexford said urgently. 'Worried? Upset?'

'Nothing out of the way. He was never what you'd call a

pleasant chap. Always grumbling about something. We went up to his room for me to take the inventory. I always insist on that before I give them back their deposits. D'you want to go up now? There's nothing to see, but you can if you want.'

Wexford nodded and they mounted the stairs. The hall and the landing were lit by the kind of lights that go off automatically after two minutes, and they went off now before Hathall's door was reached. In the pitch dark the landlord cursed, fumbling for his keys and for the light switch. And Wexford, his nerves tautening again, let out a grunt of shock when something snaked along the banister rail and jumped for the landlord's shoulder. It was, of course, only the cat. The light went on, the key was found, and the door opened.

The room was stuffy and musty as well as cold. Wexford saw Hutton's lip curl as he glanced at the First World War wardrobe, the fireside chairs and the ugly paintings, as he thought no doubt of an inventory being taken of this Junk City rubbish. Thin blankets lay untidily folded on the bare mattress beside a bundle of nickel knives and forks secured with a rubber band, a whistling kettle with a string-bound handle and a plaster vase that still bore on its base the price ticket indicating that it had cost thirty-five pence.

The cat ran along the mantelpiece and leaped on to the screen. 'I knew there was something fishy about him, mind you,' said the landlord.

'How? What gave you that idea?'

He favoured Wexford with a rather contemptuous smile. 'I've seen you before, for one thing. I can spot a copper a mile off. And there was always folks watching him. I don't miss much, though I don't say much either. I spotted the little fellow with the ginger hair – made me laugh when he came here and said he was from the council – and the tall thin one that was always in a car.'

'Then you'll know,' Wexford said, swallowing his humiliation, 'why he was watched.'

'Not me. He never did nothing but come and go and have his mother to tea and grouse about the rent.'

'He never had a woman come here? A woman with short fair hair?'

'Not him. His mother and his daughter, that's all. That's who he told me they were, and I reckon it was true seeing they was the spitting image of him. Come on, puss, let's get back where it's warm.'

Turning wearily away, standing on the spot where Hathall had been on the point of flinging him down those stairs, Wexford said, 'You gave him back his deposit and he left. What time was that?'

'About nine.' The landing light went off again and again the landlord flicked the switch, muttering under his breath while the cat purred on his shoulder. 'He was going abroad somewhere, he said. There were a lot of labels on his cases but I didn't look close. I like to see what they're doing, you know, keep an eye till they're off the premises. He went over the road and made a phone call and then a taxi came and took him off.'

They went down into the smelly hall. The light went off and this time the landlord didn't switch it on. He closed the door on them quickly to keep out the fog.

'He could have gone last night,' said Wexford to Lovat. 'He could have crossed to Paris or Brussels or Amsterdam and flown from there.'

'But why should he?' Hutton objected. 'Why should he think we're on to him after all this time?'

Wexford didn't want to tell them, at this stage, about Howard's involvement or Howard's encounter with Hathall on the previous evening. But it had come sharply into his mind up in that cold deserted room. Hathall had seen Howard at about seven, had recognized this man who was tailing him, and soon after had given him the slip. The taxi he had got into had dropped the girl off and taken him back to Dartmeet Avenue where he had settled with his landlord, taken his luggage and gone. Gone where? Back to her first and then . . .? Wexford shrugged unhappily and went across the road to the call-box.

Burden's voice told him the airport was still fog-bound. The place was swarming with disappointed stranded would-be travellers, and swarming by now with anxious police. Hathall hadn't appeared. If he had phoned, along with hundreds of other callers, he hadn't given his name.

'But he knows we're on to him,' said Burden.

'What d'you mean?'

'D'you remember a chap called Aveney? Manager of Kidd's?'

'Of course I remember. What the hell is this?'

'He got a phone call from Hathall at his home at nine last night. Hathall wanted to know – asked in a roundabout way, mind you – if we'd been asking questions about him. And Aveney, the fool, said not about his wife, that was all over, but only looking into the books in case there was something fishy about the payroll.'

'How do we know all this?' Wexford asked dully.

'Aveney had second thoughts, wondered if he ought to have told him anything, though he knew our enquiries had come to nothing. Apparently, he tried to get hold of you this morning and when he couldn't he at last contacted Mr Griswold.'

That, then, was the phone call Hathall had made from the call-box in Dartmeet Avenue, this very call-box, after leaving the landlord and before getting into that taxi. That, coupled with his recognition of Howard, would have been enough to frighten the wits out of him. Wexford went back across the road and got into the car where Lovat was smoking one of his nasty little damp cigarettes.

'I think the fog's thinning, sir,' said Hutton.

'Maybe. What time is it?'

'Ten to eight. What do we do now? Get back to the airport or try and find Morag Grey's place?'

With patient sarcasm, Wexford said, 'I have been trying

to do that for nine months, Sergeant, the normal period of gestation, and I've brought forth nothing. Maybe you think you can do better in a couple of hours.'

'We could at least go back through Notting Hill, sir, instead of taking the quicker way by the North Circular.'

'Oh, do as you like,' Wexford snapped, and he flung himself into the corner as far as possible from Lovat and his cigarette which smelled as bad as the landlord's cigar. Badgers! Country coppers, he thought unfairly. Fools who couldn't make a simple charge like shopbreaking stick. What did Hutton think Notting Hill was? A village like Passingham St. John where everyone knew everyone else and would be all agog and raring to gossip because a neighbour had gone off to foreign parts?

They followed the 28 bus route. West End Lane, Quex Road, Kilburn High Road, Kilburn Park ... The fog was decreasing, moving now, lying here in dense patches, there shivering and thinning into streaks. And Christmas colours began to glitter through it, garish paper banners in windows, sharp little starry lights that winked on and off. Shirland Road, Great Western Road, Pembridge Villas, Pembridge Road ...

One of these, Wexford thought, sitting up, must be the bus stop where Howard had seen Hathall board the 28. Streets debouched everywhere, streets that led into other streets, into squares, into a vast multitudinously peopled hinterland. Let Hutton make what he could of ...

'Stop the car, will you?' he said quickly.

Pink light streamed across the roadway from the glazed doors of a public house. Wexford had seen its sign and remembered. The Rosy Cross. If they had been regular customers, if they had often met there, the licensee or a barman might recall them. Perhaps they had met there again last night before leaving or had gone back just to say good-bye. At least he would know. This way he might know for sure.

The interior was an inferno of light and noise and smoke.

The crowd was of a density and a conviviality usually only reached much later in the evening, but this was Christmas, the night before the Eve. Not only was every table occupied and every bar stool and place by the bar, but every square foot of floor space too where people stood packed, pressed against each other, their cigarettes sending spirals of smoke to mingle with the blue pall that hung between gently swaying paper chains and smarting screwed-up eyes. Wexford pushed his way to the bar. Two barmen and a girl were working it, serving drinks feverishly, wiping down the counter, slopping dirty glasses into a steaming sink.

'And the next?' called the older of the barmen, the licensee maybe. His face was red, his forehead gleaming with sweat and his grey hair plastered against it in wet curls. 'What's for you, sir?'

Wexford said, 'Police. I'm looking for a tall black-haired man, about forty-five, and a younger blonde woman.' His elbow was jostled and he felt a trickle of beer run down his wrist. 'They were in here last night. The name is . . .'

'They don't give their names. There were about five hundred people in here last night.

'I've reason to think they came in here regularly.'

The barman shrugged. 'I have to attend to my customers. Can you wait ten minutes?'

But Wexford thought he had waited long enough. Let it pass into other hands, he could do no more. Struggling through the press of people, he made again for the door, bemused by the colours and the lights and the smoke and the heady reek of liquor. There seemed to be coloured shapes everywhere, the circles of red and purple balloons, the shining translucent cones of liqueur bottles, the squares of stained window glass. His head swimming, he realized he hadn't eaten all day. Red and purple circles, orange and blue paper spheres, here a green glass square, there a bright yellow rectangle . . .

A bright yellow rectangle. His head cleared. He steadied

and stilled himself. Jammed between a man in a leather coat and a girl in a fur coat, he looked through a tiny space that wasn't cluttered by skirts and legs and chair legs and handbags, looked through the blue acrid smoke at that yellow rectangle which was liquid in a tall glass, and saw it raised by a hand and carried out of his sight.

Pernod. Not a popular drink in England. Ginge had drunk it mixed with Guinness as a Demon King. And one other, she that he sought, his chimera, his thing of fanciful conception, drank it diluted and yellowed by water. He moved slowly, pushing his way towards that corner table where she was, but he could get only within three yards of her. There were too many people. But now there was a space clear enough at eye level for him to see her, and he looked long and long, staring greedily as a man in love stares at the woman whose coming he has awaited for months on end.

She had a pretty face, tired and wan. Her eyes were smarting from the smoke and her cropped blonde hair showed half an inch of dark at the roots. She was alone, but the chair beside her was covered by a folded coat, a man's coat, and stacked against the wall behind her, piled at her feet and walling her in, were half a dozen suitcases. She lifted her glass again and sipped from it, not looking at him at all, but darting quick nervous glances towards a heavy mahogany door marked *Telephone and Toilets*. But Wexford lingered, looking his fill at his chimera made flesh, until hats and hair and faces converged and cut off his view.

He opened the mahogany door and slipped into a passage. Two more doors faced him, and at the end of the passage was a glass kiosk. Hathall was bent over the phone inside it, his back to Wexford. Phoning the airport, Wexford thought, phoning to see if his flight's on now the fog is lifting. He stepped into the men's lavatory, pulling the door to, waiting till he heard Hathall's footsteps pass along the passage.

The mahogany door swung and clicked shut. Wexford let a minute go by and then he too went back into the bar. The cases were gone, the yellow glass empty. Thrusting people aside, ignoring expostulation, he gained the street door and flung it open. Hathall and the woman were on the pavement edge, surrounded by their cases, waiting to hail a taxi.

Wexford flashed a glance at the car, caught Hutton's eye and raised his hand sharply, beckoning. Three of the car's doors opened simultaneously and the three policemen it had contained were on their feet, bounced on to the wet stone as if on springs. And then Hathall understood. He swung round to face them, his arm enclosing the woman in a protective but useless hold. The colour went out of his face, and in the light of the misted yellow lamps the jutting jaw, the sharp nose and the high forehead were greenish with terror and the final failure of his hopes. Wexford went up to him.

The woman said, 'We should have left last night, Bob,' and when he heard her accent, made strong by fear, he knew. He knew for sure. But he couldn't find his voice and, standing silent, he left it to Lovat to approach her and begin the words of the caution and the charge.

'Morag Grey . . .'

She brought her knuckles to her trembling lips, and Wexford saw the small L-shaped scar on her forefinger as he had seen it in his dreams.

CHAPTER TWENTY-THREE

Christmas Eve.

They had all arrived and Wexford's house was full. Upstairs, the two little grandsons were in bed. In the kitchen
Dora was again examining that turkey, consulting Denise this
time as to the all-important question of whether to hang it up
or lay it on the oven shelf. In the living room Sheila and her
sister were dressing the tree while Burden's teenage children
subjected the record player, which had to be in good order
for the following day, to a rather inexpert servicing. Burden
had taken Wexford's son-in-law down to the Dragon for a
drink.

'The dining room for us then,' said Wexford to his nephew.
The table was already laid for Christmas dinner, already
decorated with a handsome centrepiece. And the fire was laid
too, as sacrosanct as the table, but Wexford put a match to
the sticks. 'I shall get into trouble about that,' he said, 'but I
don't care. I don't care about anything now I've found her,
now *you*,' he added generously, 'and I have found her.'

'It was little or nothing I did,' said Howard. 'I never even
found where she was living. Presumably, you know now?'

'In Pembridge Road itself,' said Wexford. 'He only had
that miserable room but he paid the rent of a whole flat for
her. No doubt, he loves her, though the last thing I want is
to be sentimental about him.' He took a new bottle of whisky
from the sideboard, poured a glass for Howard and then,
recklessly, one for himself. 'Shall I tell you about it?'

'Is there much left to tell? Mike Burden's already filled me
in on the identity of the women, this Morag Grey. I tried to
stop him. I knew you'd want to tell me yourself.'

'Mike Burden,' said his uncle as the fire began to crackle

and blaze, 'had today off. I haven't seen him since I left him at London Airport yesterday afternoon. He hasn't filled you in, he doesn't know, unless – is it in the evening papers? The special court, I mean?'

'It wasn't in the early editions.'

'Then there is much left to tell.' Wexford drew the curtains against the fog which had returned in the afternoon. 'What did Mike say?'

'That it happened more or less the way you guessed, the three of them in the payroll fraud. Wasn't it that way?'

'My theory,' Wexford said, 'left far too many loopholes.' He pulled his armchair closer to the fire. 'Good to relax, isn't it? Aren't you glad you haven't got to get your tailing gear on and go off up to West End Green?'

'I'll say it again, I did very little. But at least I don't deserve to be kept in suspense.'

'True, and I won't keep you in it. There was a payroll fraud all right. Hathall set up at least two fictitious accounts, and maybe more soon after he joined Kidd's. He was pulling in a minimum of an extra thirty pounds a week for two years. But Morag Grey wasn't in on it. She wouldn't have helped anyone swindle a company. She was an honest woman. She was so honest she didn't even keep a pound note she found on an office floor, and so upright she wouldn't stay married to a man who'd stolen two pounds fifty. She couldn't have been in on it, still less have planned and collected from the Mary Lewis account because Hathall didn't meet her till the March. She was only at Kidd's for a couple of weeks and that was three months before Hathall left.'

'But Hathall was in love with her, surely? You said so yourself. And what other motive . . .?'

'Hathall was in love with his wife. Oh, I know we decided he's acquired amorous tastes, but what real evidence did we have of that?' With a slight self-consciousness too well covered for Howard to detect, Wexford said, 'If he was so susceptible,

533

why did he reject the advances of a certain very attractive neighbour of his? Why did he give everyone who knew him the impression of being an obsessively devoted husband?'

'You tell me,' Howard grinned. 'You'll be saying in a minute that Morag Grey didn't kill Angela Hathall.'

'That's right. She didn't. Angela Hathall killed Morag Grey.'

A wail rose from the record player in the next room. Small feet scuttled across the floor above and there was a violent crash from the kitchen. The noise drowned Howard's low exclamation.

'I was pretty surprised myself,' Wexford went on casually. 'I suppose I guessed when I found out yesterday about Morag Grey being so honest and only being at Kidd's for such a short while. Then when we arrested them and I heard her Australian accent I knew.'

Howard shook his head slowly in astonishment and wonder rather than disbelief. 'But the identification, Reg? How could he hope to get away with it?'

'He did get away with it for fifteen months. You see, the secretive isolated life they led in order to make the payroll scheme work was in their favour when they planned this murder. It wouldn't have done for Angela to get well known in case she was recognized as not being Mrs Lewis or Mrs Carter when she went to make withdrawals from those accounts. Hardly a soul knew her even by sight. Mrs Lake did, of course, and so did her cousin, Mark Somerset, but who on earth would have called on them to identify the body? The natural person was Angela's husband. And just in case there was any doubt, he took his mother with him, taking care she should see the body first. Angela had dressed Morag in her own clothes, those very clothes she was wearing on the only previous occasion her mother-in-law had seen her. That was a fine piece of psychology, Howard, thought up, I'm sure, by

Angela who planned all the intricacies of this business. It was old Mrs Hathall who phoned us, old Mrs Hathall who put doubt out of court by telling us her daughter-in-law had been found dead in Bury Cottage.

'Angela started cleaning the place weeks ahead to clean off *her own fingerprints.* No wonder she had rubber gloves and dusting gloves. It wouldn't have been too difficult a task, seeing she was alone all week without Hathall there to leave his own prints about. And if we queried such extreme cleanliness, what better reason for it than that she was getting the cottage perfect for old Mrs Hathall's visit?'

'Then the handprint and the L-shaped scar were hers?'

'Of course.' Wexford drank his whisky slowly, making it last. 'The prints we thought were hers were Morag's. The hair in the brush we thought was hers were Morag's. She must have brushed the dead girl's hair – nasty, that. The coarser dark hairs were Angela's. She didn't have to clean the car in the garage or at Wood Green. She could have cleaned it any time she chose in the previous week.'

'But why did she leave that one print?'

'I think I can guess at that. On the morning of the day Morag died, Angela was up early getting on with her cleaning. She was cleaning the bathroom, had perhaps taken off her rubber gloves and was about to put on the others to polish the floor, when the phone rang. Mrs Lake rang to ask if she could come over and pick the miracle plums. And Angela, naturally nervous, steadied herself with her bare hand on the side of the bath when she got up to answer the phone.

'Morag Grey spoke, and doubtless read, Gaelic. Hathall must have known that. So Angela found out her address – they would have been keeping a close eye on her – and wrote to her, or more probably called on her, to ask if she would give her some assistance into the research she was doing into Celtic languages. Morag, a domestic servant, can only have been flattered. And she was poor too, she needed money. This,

I think, was the good job she spoke of to her neighbour, and she gave up her cleaning work at this time, going on to the Social Security until Angela was ready for her to start.'

'But didn't she know Angela?'

'Why should she? Angela would have given her a false name, and I see no reason why she should have known Hathall's address. On the nineteenth of September Angela drove over to Myringham Old Town, collected her and drove her to Bury Cottage for a discussion on their future work. She took Morag upstairs to wash or go to the loo or comb her hair. And there she strangled her, Howard, with her own gilt snake necklace.

'After that it was simple. Dress Morag in the red shirt and the jeans, imprint a few mobile objects with her fingerprints brush her hair. Gloves on, take the car down that tunnel of a lane, away to London. Stay a night or two in a hotel till she could find a room, wait for time to go by till Hathall could join her.'

'But why, Reg? Why kill her?'

'She was an honest woman and she found out what Hathall was up to. She was no fool, Howard, but rather one of those people who have potential but lack drive. Both her former employer and her mother said she was a cut above the kind of work she was doing. Her feckless husband dragged her down. Who knows? Maybe she would have had the ability to advise a *genuine* etymologist on demotic Gaelic, and maybe she thought this was her chance, now she was rid of Grey, to better herself. Angela Hathall, when you come to think of it, is a very good psychologist.'

'I see all that,' said Howard, 'but how did Morag find out about the payroll fraud?'

'That,' Wexford said frankly, 'I don't know – yet. I'd guess Hathall stayed late one evening while she was working there, and I'd guess she overheard a phone conversation he had with Angela on that occasion. Perhaps Angela had suggested a false address to him and he called her to check up he'd got it right before he fed it into the computer. Don't forget Angela was the mainspring behind all this. You couldn't have been more right when you said she'd influenced and corrupted him. Hathall is just the sort of man to think of a cleaner as no more than a piece of furniture. But even if he'd spoken guardedly, that name, Mrs Mary Lewis, and that address, 19 Maynnot Way, would have alerted Morag. It was just down the road from where she and her husband lived and she knew no Mary Lewis lived there. And if, after that call, Hathall immediately began to feed the computer . . .'

'She blackmailed him?'

'I doubt it. She was an honest woman. But she'd have queried it, on the spot perhaps. Maybe she merely told him she'd overheard what he'd said and there was no Mary Lewis there, and if he'd seemed flustered – my God, you should see him when he's flustered! – she could have asked more and more questions until she had some hazy idea of what was actually going on.'

'They killed her for *that*?'

Wexford nodded. 'To you and me it seems a wretched motive. But to them? They would ever after have been in a panic of fear, for if Hathall's swindle were uncovered he'd lose his job, lose his new job at Marcus Flower, never get another job in the one field he was trained for. You have to remember what a paranoid pair they were. They expected to be persecuted and hounded, they suspected even the innocent and harmless of having a down on them.'

'You weren't innocent and harmless, Reg,' said Howard quietly.

'No, and perhaps I'm the only person who has ever truly persecuted Robert Hathall.' Wexford raised his almost empty glass. 'Happy Christmas,' he said. 'I shan't let Hathall's loss of liberty cloud the season for me. If anyone deserves to lose it, he does. Shall we join the others? I think I heard Mike come in with my son-in-law.'

The tree had been dressed. Sheila was jiving with John Burden to the thumping cacophony that issued from the record player. Having restored a sleepy little boy to his bed for the third time, Sylvia was wrapping the last of the presents, one of Kidd's Kits for Kids, a paint-box, a geographical globe, a picture book, a toy car. Wexford put an arm round his wife and an arm round Pat Burden and kissed them under the mistletoe. Laughing, he put his hand out to the globe and spun it. Three times it circled on its axis before Burden saw the point, and then he said:

'It does move. You were right. He did do it.'

'Well, you were right too,' said Wexford. 'He didn't murder his wife.' Seeing Burden's look of incredulity, he added, 'And now I suppose I shall have to tell the story all over again.'

A Sleeping Life

For Elaine and Leslie Gray,
with affection and gratitude

Those have most power to hurt us, that we love;
We lay our sleeping lives within their arms.
O, thou hast raised up mischief to his height,
And found one to outname thy other faults.

BEAUMONT AND FLETCHER: *The Maid's Tragedy*

CHAPTER ONE

Home early for once. Maybe he'd start getting home early regularly now August had begun, the silly season. Criminals as well as the law-abiding take their holidays in August. As he turned the car into his own road, Wexford remembered his grandsons would be there. Good. It would be light for another three hours, and he'd take Robin and Ben down to the river. Robin was always on about the river because his mother had read *The Wind in the Willows* to him, and his great desire was to see a water rat swimming.

Sylvia's car was parked outside the house. Odd, thought Wexford. He'd understood Dora was having the boys for the afternoon as well as the evening and that they'd be staying the night. As he edged his own car past his daughter's into the drive, she came running out of the house with a screaming Ben in her arms and six-year-old Robin looking truculent at her heels. Robin rushed up to his grandfather.

'You promised we could see the water rat!'

'So you can as far as I'm concerned and if there's one about. I thought you were staying the night.'

Sylvia's face was crimson, with rage or perhaps just from haste. It was very hot.

'Well, they're not. Thanks to my dear husband, nobody's going anywhere even though it does happen to be our wedding anniversary. Will you shut up, Ben! He's bringing a client home for dinner instead, if you please, and I of course as usual have to be the one to do the cooking and fetch the kids.'

'Leave them here,' said Wexford. 'Why not?'

'Yes, leave us here,' Robin shouted. '*Go on.*'

'Oh, no, that's out of the question. Why do you have to

543

encourage them, Dad? I'm taking them home and Neil can have the pleasure of putting them to bed for once.'

She thrust both children into the car and drove off. The windows of the car were all open, and the yells of the two little boys, for Robin had begun to back his brother up, vied with the roar of the ill-treated engine. Wexford shrugged and went indoors. Some sort of scene had evidently been taking place, but he knew his wife better than to suppose she would be much disturbed by it. True to his expectations, she was sitting placidly in the living room watching the tail end of a children's programme on television. A great many books had been pulled out of the shelves, and on a tower block of them sat a teddy bear.

'What's got into Sylvia?'

'Women's Lib,' said Dora Wexford. 'If Neil wants to bring a client home he ought to cook the meal. He ought to come home in the afternoon and clean the house and lay the table. She's taken the children home for the sole purpose of getting him to put them to bed. And she's taking care to stir them up on the way to make sure he has a hard time of it.'

'God. I always thought she was quite a sensible girl.'

'She's got a bee in her bonnet about it. It's been going on for months. You are the people, we are the others. You are the masters, we are the chattels.'

'Why haven't you told me about any of this?'

Dora switched off the television. 'You've been busy. You wouldn't have wanted to listen to all this nonsense when you got home. I've been getting it every day.'

Wexford raised his eyebrows. 'It's nonsense?'

'Well, not entirely, of course. Men still do have a better time of it in this world than women, it's still a man's world. I can understand she doesn't like being stuck at home with the boys, wasting her life, as she puts it, while Neil gets more and more successful in his career.' Dora smiled. 'And she says she got more A Levels than he did. I can understand she gets bored when people come and the men talk to Neil about architecture and the women talk to her about polishing the bedroom furniture. Oh, I can *understand* it.'

Her husband looked hard at her. 'You feel that way too?'

'Never you mind,' said Dora, laughing now. 'Let's forget our rather tiresome child. You're so early we might go out somewhere after we've eaten. Would you like to?'

'Love to.' He hesitated, said quickly, 'It's not threatening their marriage, is it? I've always thought of them as being so happy together.'

'We have to hope it'll pass. Anything we do or say would only make things worse, wouldn't it?'

'Of course. Now where shall we go? Cinema? Or how about the open-air theatre at Sewingbury?'

Before she could give him an answer, the phone rang.

'Sylvia,' she said. 'She's realized Ben left his teddy. You get it, darling. Oh, and Reg . . .? Would you say we'll drop it in on our way? I can't stand another session of the wounded wives tonight.'

Wexford lifted the receiver. It wasn't his daughter. Dora knew it wasn't even before he spoke. She knew that look. All he said was 'Yes' and 'Sure, I will', but she knew. He hung up and said, 'They don't all go on holiday in August. A body in a field not half a mile from here.'

'Is it . . .?'

'Not one of the people,' her husband said drily. 'One of the others.' He tightened the tie he had loosened, rolled down his shirtsleeves. 'I'll have to go straightaway. What'll you do? Stir up the telly so I have a hard time of it putting it to rights? You must regret marrying me.'

'No, but I'm working on it.'

Wexford laughed, kissed her and drove back the way he had come.

Kingsmarkham is a sizeable town somewhere in the middle of Sussex, much built-up now on the Stowerton and Sewingbury sides, though open and unspoilt country still remains at its northern end. There the High Street becomes the Pomfret Road, and there the pinewoods of Cheriton Forest clothe the hills.

Forest Road is the last street in the area to bear the postal address Kingsmarkham. It debouches directly from the Pomfret Road, but to reach it most of its few residents take the short cut from the end of the High Street by footpath across a field. Wexford parked his car at the point in Forest Road where this footpath entered it as an alley near the boundary fence of a pair of houses called Carlyle Villas. He swung into the alley and followed the footpath along a high privet hedge that bounded allotments. About a hundred yards ahead of him he could see a group of men gathered at the edge of a little copse.

Inspector Michael Burden was among them and so was Dr Crocker, the police doctor, and a couple of photographers. As Wexford approached, Burden came up to him and said something in a low voice. Wexford nodded. Without looking at the body, he went up to Detective Loring who stood a little apart with a younger man who looked pale and shaken.

'Mr Parker?'

'That's right.'

'I understand you found the body?'

Parker nodded. 'Well, my son did.'

He couldn't have been more than twenty-five himself.

'A *child*?' said Wexford.

'He doesn't realize. I hope not. He's only six.'

They sat down on a wooden seat the council had put there for pensioners to rest on. 'Tell me what happened.'

'I'd taken him round to my sister's, give the wife a bit of a break while she was putting the other two to bed. I live in one of the bungalows in Forest Road, Bella Vista, the one with the green roof. We were coming back, along the path here, and Nicky was playing with a ball. It went in the long grass under the hedge and he went to look for it. He said,

"Dad, there's a lady down there." I sort of knew, I don't know how. I went and looked and I – well, I know I shouldn't have, but I sort of pulled her coat over her chest. Nicky, you see, he's only six, there was – well, blood, a mess.'

'I do see,' said Wexford. 'You didn't move anything else?'

Parker shook his head. 'I told Nicky the lady was ill and we'd go home and phone the doctor. I said she'd be all right. I don't think he realized. I hope not. I got him home and phoned your people. Honestly, I wouldn't have touched her if I'd been on my own.'

'This was an exception, Mr Parker.' Wexford smiled at him. 'I'd have done the same in your place.'

'He won't have to . . .? I mean, there'll be an inquest, won't there? I mean, I'll have to go, I know that, but . . .'

'No, no. Good God, no. Get off home now and we'll see you again later. Thanks for your help.'

Parker got up off the seat, glanced at the photographers, the huddle round the body, then turned round. 'It's not for me to . . . Well, I mean, I do know who she is. Perhaps you don't . . .'

'No, we don't yet. Who is she?'

'Well, a Miss Comfrey. She didn't actually live here, her dad lives here.' Parker pointed back down the path. 'Carlyle Villas, the one with the blue paint. She must have been stopping there. Her dad's in hospital. He's an old man, he broke his hip, and she must have come down to see him.'

'Thanks, Mr Parker.'

Wexford crossed the sandy path, and Burden stepped aside for him to look down at the body. It was that of a middle-aged woman, biggish and gaunt. The face was coated with heavy make-up, clotted scarlet on the mouth, streaky blue on the crêpe eyelids, a ghastly ochreish layer on the planes of cheek and forehead. The grey eyes were wide and staring, and in them Wexford thought he saw – it must be his imagination – a sardonic gleam, a glare, even in death, of scorn.

A fringe of dark hair just showed under a tightly tied blue headscarf. The body was clothed in a blue and pink printed dress of some synthetic material, and the matching jacket had been drawn across the bodice. One of the high-heeled shoes had come off and hung suspended on a tangle of brambles. Across the hips lay a large scarlet handbag. There were no rings on the hands, no watch on either wrist, but a heavy necklace of red glass beads round the neck, and the nails, though short, were painted the same scarlet.

He knelt down and opened the handbag, covering his fingers with his handkerchief. Inside was a key ring with three keys on it, a box of matches, a packet of king-sized cigarettes from which four had been smoked, a lipstick, an old-fashioned powder compact, a wallet, in the bottom of the bag some loose change. No purse. No letters or documents. The wallet, which was an expensive new one of black leather, contained forty-two pounds. She hadn't been killed for the money she had on her.

There was nothing to give him a clue to her address, her occupation or even her identity. No credit card, no bank card, no cheque book.

He closed the bag and parted her jacket. The bodice of the dress was black with clotted blood, but plainly discernible in the dark matted mass were two cuts, the outward evidence of stab wounds.

CHAPTER TWO

Wexford moved away, and the doctor came back and knelt where he had knelt. He said to Loring:

'No sign of the weapon, I daresay?'

'No, sir, but we haven't made much of a search yet.'

'Well, get searching, you and Gates and Marwood. A knife of some sort.' The chances of it being there, he thought pessimistically, were slight. 'And when you haven't found it,' he said, 'you can do a house-to-house down Forest Road. Get all you can about her and her movements, but leave Parker and Carlyle Villas to me and Mr Burden.'

Back to Dr Crocker.

'How long has she been dead, Len?'

'Now, for God's sake, don't expect too much precision at this stage. Rigor's fully established, but the weather's been very hot, so its onset will have been more rapid. I'd say at least eighteen hours. Could be more.'

'OK.' Wexford jerked his head at Burden. 'There's nothing more here for us, Mike. Carlyle Villas and Parker next, I think.'

Michael Burden was properly of too high a rank to accompany a chief inspector on calls of inquiry. He did so because that was the way they worked, the way it worked. They had always done so, and always would, in spite of disapproving mutterings from the Chief Constable.

Two tall men. Nearly twenty years separated them, and once they had been so dissimilar in appearance as to provide that juxtaposition of incongruities which is the stuff of humour. But Wexford had lost his abundant fat and become almost a gaunt man, while Burden had always been lean. He was the better-looking of the two by far, with classical features that would have been handsome had they been less pinched by sour experience. Wexford was an ugly man, but his was the face that arrested the eye, compelled even the eyes of women, because it had in it so much lively intelligence and zest for life, so much vigour, and in spite of his seniority, so much more of the essence of youth.

Side by side, they walked along the footpath and down the alley into Forest Road, not speaking, for there was nothing yet to say. The woman was dead, but death by murder is in a way not an end but a beginning. The lives of the naturally dead may be buried with them. Hers would now gradually be exposed, event after event, obscure though she had been, until it took on the character of a celebrity's biography.

From the alley, they turned to the right and stood outside the pair of houses, cottages really, in front of which Wexford had parked his car. The houses shared a single gable, and in its apex was a plaster plaque bearing their name and the date of their construction: Carlyle Villas, 1902. Wexford knocked at the blue front door with little hope of getting an answer. There was none, and no one came when they rang the bell on the neighbouring front door, a far more trendy and ambitious affair of wrought iron and reeded glass.

Frustrated at this most promising port of call, they crossed the street. Forest Road was a cul-de-sac, ending in a stone wall, behind which meadows swelled and the forest sprawled. It contained about a dozen houses, apart from Carlyle Villas, a clutch of tiny cottages at the wall end, two or three newer bungalows, a squat grey stone lodge that had once stood at the gates of a long-vanished mansion. One of the bungalows, built at the period when Hollywood's influence penetrated even this corner of Sussex, had windows of curved glass and a roof of green pantiles. Bella Vista.

The child Nicky was still up, sitting with his mother in a living room that had the same sort of untidy look as the one Wexford had left an hour before. But if Parker hadn't introduced this girl as his wife, Wexford would have taken her for no more than an adolescent. She had the smooth brow and bunchy cheeks of a child, the silken hair, the innocent eyes. She must have been married at sixteen, though she looked no more than that now.

Parker said with ferocious winks, 'This gentleman's a doctor, come to tell us the poor lady's all right.'

Nicky buried his face in his mother's shoulder.

'Quite all right,' Wexford lied. 'She'll be fine.' They say the dead are well . . .

'You get along to Nanna's room then, Nicky, and she'll let you watch her TV.'

The tension lightened on his departure. 'Thanks,' said Parker. 'I only hope it isn't going to have a bad effect on him, poor kid.'

'Don't worry. He's too young to see newspapers, but you'll have to exercise a bit of censorship when it comes to the TV. Now, Mr Parker, I think you said Miss – er – Comfrey's father was in hospital. D'you know which hospital?'

'Stowerton. The infirmary. He had an accident last – when would it have been, Stell?'

'About May,' said Stella Parker. 'Miss Comfrey came down to see him, came in a taxi from the station, and when he saw her he rushed out of the house and fell over on the path and broke his hip. Just like that it happened. Her and the taxi-man, they took him to the hospital in the same taxi and he's been there ever since. I never saw it. Mrs Crown told me. Miss Comfrey's been down once to see him since. She never did come much, did she, Brian?'

'Not more than once or twice a year,' said Parker.

'I knew she was coming yesterday. Mrs Crown told me. I saw her in the Post Office and she said Rhoda'd phoned to say she was coming on account of old Mr Comfrey'd had a stroke. But I never saw her, didn't really know her to speak to.'

Burden said, 'Who is Mrs Crown?'

'Miss Comfrey's auntie. She lives in the next house to old Mr Comfrey. She's the one you want to see.'

'No doubt, but there's no one in.'

'I tell you what,' said Stella Parker who seemed to have twice her husband's grasp and intelligence, 'I don't want to put myself forward, but I do read detective books, and if it's sort of background stuff you want, you couldn't do better than talk to Brian's gran. She's lived here all her life, she was born in one of those cottages.'

'Your grandmother lives with you?'

'Helped us buy this place with her savings,' said Parker, 'and moved in with us. It works OK, doesn't it, Stell? She's a wonder, my gran.'

Wexford smiled and got up. 'I may want to talk to her but not tonight. You'll be notified about the inquest, Mr Parker. It shouldn't be too much of an ordeal. Now, d'you know when Mrs Crown will be home?'

'When the pubs turn out,' said Parker.

'I think the infirmary next, Mike,' said Wexford. 'From the vague sort of time Crocker gave us, it's beginning to look to me as if Rhoda Comfrey was killed on her way back from visiting her father in hospital. She'd have used that footpath as a short cut from the bus stop.'

'Visiting time at Stowerton's seven till eight in the evenings,' said Burden. 'We may be able to fix the time of death more accurately this way than by any post-mortem findings.'

'The pub-orientated aunt should help us there. If this old boy's *compos mentis*, we'll get his daughter's London address from him.'

'We'll also have to break the news,' said Burden.

Departing visitors were queueing at the bus stop outside Stowerton Royal Infirmary. Had Rhoda Comfrey queued there on the previous night? It was ten past eight.

A man in the porter's lodge told them that James Albert

Comfrey was a patient in Lytton Ward. They went along a corridor and up two flights of stairs. A pair of glass double doors, the entrance to Lytton Ward, were closed. As Wexford pushed them open, a young nurse of Malaysian or Thai origin popped up in their path and announced in a chirrup that they couldn't come in now.

'Police,' said Burden. 'We'd like to see the sister in charge.'

'If you please, my dear,' said Wexford, and the girl gave him a broad smile before hurrying off. 'Do you have to be so bloody rude, Mike?'

She came back with Sister Lynch, a tall dark-haired Irish-woman in her late twenties.

'What can I do for you gentlemen?' She listened, clicked her tongue as Wexford gave her the bare details. 'There's a terrible thing. A woman's not safe to walk abroad. And Miss Comfrey in here only last night to see her father.'

'We'll have to see him, Sister.'

'Not tonight you won't, Chief Inspector. I'm sure I'm sorry, but I couldn't allow it, not with the old gentlemen all settling down for the night. They'd none of them get a wink of sleep, and it's going off duty I am myself in ten minutes. I'll tell him myself tomorrow, though whether it'll sink in at all I doubt.'

'He's senile?'

'There's a word, Chief Inspector, that I'm never knowing the meaning of. Eighty-five he is, and he's had a major stroke. Mostly he sleeps. If that's to be senile, senile he is. You'll be wasting your valuable time seeing him. I'll break it to him as best I can. Now would there be anything else?'

'Miss Comfrey's home address, please.'

'Certainly.' Sister Lynch beckoned to a dark-skinned girl who had appeared, pushing a trolley of drugs. 'Would you get Miss Comfrey's home address from records, Nurse Mahmud?'

'Did you talk to Miss Comfrey last night, Sister?'

'No more than to say hallo and that the old gentleman was just the same. And I said good-bye to her too. She was talking to Mrs Wells and they left together. Mrs Wells's husband is in the next bed to Mr Comfrey. Here's the address you were wanting. Thank you, nurse. Number one, Carlyle Villas, Forest Road, Kingsmarkham.' Sister Lynch studied the card which had been handed to her. 'No phone I see.'

'I'm afraid you've got Mr Comfrey's address there,' said Wexford. 'It's his daughter's we want.'

'But that is his daughter's, his and his daughter's.'

Wexford shook his head. 'No. She lived in London.'

'It's the only one we have,' said Sister Lynch, a slight edge to her voice. 'As far as we know, Miss Comfrey lived in Kingsmarkham with her father.'

'Then I'm afraid you were misled. Suppose you had had to get in touch with her – for instance, if her father had taken a turn for the worse – how would you have done so?'

'Notified her by letter. Or sent a messenger.' Sister Lynch had begun to look huffy. He was questioning her efficiency. 'That wouldn't have been necessary. Miss Comfrey phoned in almost every day. Last Thursday, now, she phoned on the very day her father had his stroke.'

'And yet you say she hadn't a phone? Sister, I need that address. I shall have to see Mr Comfrey.'

Her eyes went to her watch and noted the time. She said very sharply, 'Aren't I telling you, the poor old gentleman's no more than a vegetable at all? As for giving you an address, you'd as likely get an answer out of my little dog.'

'Very well. In the absence of Miss Comfrey's address, I'll have Mrs Wells's please.' This was provided, and Wexford said. 'We'll come back tomorrow.'

'You must suit yourselves. And now I'll take my leave of you.'

Wexford murmured as they left, 'There is nothing you could take from me that I would more willingly part withal,' and then to Burden, who was smugly looking as if his early rudeness had been justified and he hoped his superior realized it, 'We'll get it from the aunt. Odd, though, isn't it, her not giving her home address to the hospital?'

'Oh, I don't know. Underhand, but not odd. These old people can be a terrible drag. And it's always the women who are expected to look after them. I mean, old Comfrey'll be let out some time and he won't be able to live on his own any more. A single woman and a daughter is a gift to all those busybody doctors and social workers. They'd seize on her. Wouldn't even consider expecting it of a son. If she gave them her real address they'd pounce on that as a convalescent home for the old boy.'

'You're the last person I thought I'd ever hear handing out Women's Lib propaganda,' said Wexford. 'Wonders will never cease. But doesn't it strike you that your theory only increases her chances of getting stuck with her father? They think she's on the spot, they think she lives with him already.'

'There'll be an explanation. It isn't important, is it?'

'It's a departure from the norm, and that makes it important to me. I think Mrs Wells next, Mike, and then back to Forest Road to wait for the aunt.

Mrs Wells was seventy years old, slow of speech and rather confused. She had seen and spoken to Rhoda Comfrey twice before on her previous visits to the hospital, once in May and once in July. On the evening before they had got on the bus together outside the hospital at eight-fifteen. What had they talked about? Mrs Wells thought it had mostly been about her husband's hip operation. Miss Comfrey hadn't said much, had seemed a bit nervous and uneasy. Worried about her father, Mrs Wells thought. No, she didn't know her London address, believed in fact that she lived in Forest Road where she had said she was returning. Mrs Wells had left the bus at the Kingsbrook Bridge, but her companion had remained on it, having a ticket to the next fare stage.

They returned to the police station. The weapon hadn't been found, and the house-to-house inquiry made by Loring, Marwood and Gates had produced negative results. No one in the cottages or the bungalows had heard or seen anything untoward on the previous evening. The inhabitants of the single detached house were away on holiday, and nobody had been working on the allotments. Rhoda Comfrey had been slightly known to everyone the three men had questioned, but only one had seen her on the previous day, and that had been when she left her father's house at six-twenty to catch the bus for Stowerton. Her London address was unknown to any of the residents of Forest Road.

'I want you to get back there,' Wexford said to Loring, 'and wait for Mrs Crown. I'm going home for an hour to get a bite to eat. When she comes in, call me on my home number.'

CHAPTER THREE

Dora had been sewing, but the work had been laid aside, and he found her reading a novel. She got up immediately and brought him a bowl of soup, chicken salad, some fruit. He seldom talked about work at home, unless things got very tough. Home was a haven – Oh, what know they of harbours that sail not on the sea? – and he had fallen in love with and married the kind of woman who would give him one. But did she mind? Did she see herself as the one who waited and served while he lived? He had never thought much about it. Thinking of it now reawakened the anxiety that had laid dormant for the past three hours, pushed out of mind by greater urgencies.

'Hear any more from Sylvia?' he said.

'Neil came round for the teddy bear. Ben wouldn't go to sleep without it.' She touched his arm, then rested her hand on his wrist. 'You mustn't worry about her. She's grown-up. She has to cope with her own problems.'

'Your son's your son,' said her husband, 'till he gets him a wife, but your daughter's your daughter the whole of your life.'

'There goes the phone.' She sighed, but not rebelliously. 'I have measured out my life in telephone bills.'

'Don't wait up for me,' said Wexford.

It was dark now, ten minutes to eleven, the wide sky covered all over with stars. And the moonlight was strong enough to cast bold shadows of tree and gate and pillar box along the length of Forest Road. A single street lamp shone up by the stone wall, and lights were on all over 2, Carlyle Villas, though the other houses were in darkness. He rang the bell on the reeded glass and wrought-iron front door.

'Mrs Crown?'

He had expected a negative answer because this woman was much younger than he had thought she would be. Only a few years older than he. But she said yes, she was, and asked him what he wanted. She smelt of gin and had about her the reckless air – no apparent fear of him or cautiousness or suspicion – that drink brings, though this might have been habitual with her. He told her who he was and she let him in. There, in a cluttered bizarre living room, he broke the news to her, speaking gently and considerately but all the time sensing that gentleness and consideration weren't needed here.

'Well, fancy,' she said. 'What a thing to happen! Rhoda, of all people. That's given me a bit of a shock, that has. A drink is called for. Want one?' Wexford shook his head. She helped herself from a gin bottle that stood on a limed oak sideboard whose surface was covered with drips and smears and ring marks. 'I won't make show of grief. We weren't close. Where did you say it happened? Down the footpath? You won't see me down there in a hurry, I can tell you.'

She was like the room they were in, small and over-dressed in bright colours and none too clean. The stretch nylon covers on her chairs were of a slightly duller yellow than the tight dress she wore, and unlike it, they were badly marked with cigarette burns. But all were disfigured with the same sort of liquor splashes and food stains. Mrs Crown's hair was of the same colour and texture as the dried grasses that stood everywhere in green and yellow vases, pale and thin and brittle but defiantly gold. She lit a cigarette and left it hanging in her mouth which was painted, as her niece's had been, to match her fingernails.

'I haven't yet been able to inform your brother,' Wexford said. 'It would appear he's not up to it.'

'Brother-in-*law*, if you don't mind,' said Mrs Crown. 'He's not my brother, the old devil.'

'Ah, yes,' said Wexford. 'Now, Mrs Crown, it's getting late

and I don't want to keep you up, but I'd like to know what you can tell me of Miss Comfrey's movements yesterday.

She stared at him, blowing smoke through her sharp nose. 'What's that got to do with some maniac stabbing her? Killed her for her money, didn't he? She was always loaded, was Rhoda.' Horrifyingly, she added, with a Wife of Bath look, remembering the old dance, 'Wouldn't be for sex, not so likely.'

Wexford didn't take her up on that one. He said repressively, 'You saw her yesterday?'

'She phoned me on Friday to say she'd be coming. Thought I might get bothered if I saw lights on next door, not expecting anyone to be there, if you see what I mean. God knows why she put herself out. I was amazed. Picked up the phone and she says, "Hallo, Lilian. I wonder if you know who this is?" Of course I knew. I'd know that deep voice of hers anywhere and that put-on accent. She never got that from her mum and dad. But you don't want to know all that. She came in a taxi yesterday about one. All dressed-up she was, but miserable as sin. She was always down in the mouth when she came here, made no secret she hated the place, far cry from the way she sounded on the phone, all cocky, if you know what I mean. Sure you won't have a drink? I think I'll have a drop more.'

A good deal more than a drop of neat gin in her glass, Lilian Crown perched on the sofa arm and swung her legs. The calves were shapeless with varicose veins, but she still kept the high instep, the dancing foot, of one who has led a riotous youth. 'She never came in here till a quarter past six. "Feel like coming with me, Lilian?" she said, knowing damn well I wouldn't. I told her I'd got a date with my gentleman friend, which was the honest truth, but I could tell she didn't like it, always was jealous. "When'll you be back?" she said. "I'll come in and tell you how he is." "All right," I said, doing my best to be pleasant, though I never had any time for him or her after my poor sister went. "I'll be in by ten," I said, but she never came and no lights came on. Gone straight back to London, I thought, knowing her, never dreaming a thing like that had happened.'

Wexford nodded. 'I'll very likely want to speak to you again, Mrs Crown. In the meantime, would you give me Miss Comfrey's London address?'

'I haven't got it.'

'You mean you don't *know* it?'

'That's what I mean. Look, I live next door to the old devil, sure I do, but that's convenience, that is. I came here for my sister's sake and after she went I just stopped on. But that doesn't mean we were close. As a matter of fact, him and me, we weren't on speaking terms. As for Rhoda — well, I won't speak ill of the dead. She was my sister's girl, when all's said and done, but we never did get on. She left home must be twenty years ago, and if I've set eyes on her a dozen times since, that's it. She'd no call to give me her address or her phone number, and I'm sure I wouldn't have asked for it. Look, if I'd got it I'd give it you, wouldn't I? I'd have no call not to.'

'At least, I suppose, you know what she did for a living?'

'In business, she was,' said Lilian Crown. 'Got her own business.' Bitterness pinched her face. 'Money stuck to Rhoda, always did. And she hung on to it. None of it came my way or *his*. He's a proper old devil but he's her dad, isn't he?'

A woman who had said she wouldn't speak ill of the dead . . . Wexford went home, building up in his mind a picture of what Rhoda Comfrey had been. A middle-aged, well-off, successful woman, probably self-employed; a woman who had disliked the town of her origins because it held for her painful associations; who liked her privacy and had kept, in so far as she could, her address to herself; a clever, cynical, hard-bitten woman, indifferent to this country world's opinion, and owing to her unpleasant old father no more than a bare duty. Still, it was too early for this sort of speculation. In the morning they would have a warrant to search Mr Comfrey's house, the address, the nature of her business, would be discovered; and Rhoda Comfrey's life unfold. Already Wexford had a feeling – one of those illogical intuitive feelings the Chief Constable so much disliked – that the motive for her murder lay in that London life.

Kingsmarkham Police station had been built about fifteen years before, and the conservative townsfolk had been shocked by the appearance of this stark white box with its flat roof and wide picture windows. But a decade and a half had tripled the size of the saplings around it so that now its severity was half-screened by birches and laburnums. Wexford had his office on the second floor; buttercup-yellow walls with maps on them and a decorous calendar of Sussex views, a new blue carpet, his own desk of dark red rosewood that belonged to him personally and not to the Mid-Sussex Constabulary. The big window afforded him a fine view of the High Street, of higgledy-piggledy rooftops, of green meadows beyond. This morning, Wednesday, August tenth, it was wide open and the air-conditioning switched off. Another lovely day, exactly what the clear sky and stars and bright moon of the previous night had promised.

Since he had looked in first thing in the morning and left again for Stowerton Royal Infirmary, the clothes Rhoda Comfrey had been wearing had been sent up and left on the desk. Wexford threw down beside them the early editions of the evening papers he had just picked up. Middle-aged spinsters, even when stabbed to death, were apparently not news, and neither paper had allotted to this murder more than a couple of paragraphs on an inside page. He sat down by the window to cool down, for the front aspect of the police station was still in shade.

James Albert Comfrey. They had drawn cretonne curtains

561

printed with flowers round the old man's bed. His hands moved like crabs, gnarled and crooked, across the sheet. Sometimes they plucked at a tuft of wool on the red blanket, then they parted and crawled back, only to begin again on their journey. His mouth was open, he breathed stertorously. In the strong, tough yet enfeebled face, Wexford had seen the lineaments of the daughter, the big nose, long upper lip and cliff-like chin.

'Like I said,' said Sister Lynch, 'it never meant a thing to him when I passed on the news. There's little that registers at all.'

'Mr Comfrey,' said Wexford, approaching the bed.

'Sure, and you may as well save your breath.'

'I'd like to have a look in that locker.'

'I can't have that,' said Sister Lynch.

'I have a warrant to search his house.' Wexford was beginning to lose his patience. 'D'you think I couldn't get one to search a cupboard?'

'What's my position going to be if there's a come-back?'

'You mean *he's* going to complain to the hospital board?' Without wasting any more time, Wexford had opened the lower part of the locker. It contained nothing but a pair of slippers and a rolled-up dressing-gown. Irish ire making itself apparent behind him in sharp exhalations, he shook out the dressing-gown and felt in its pockets. Nothing. He rolled it up again. An infringement of privacy? he thought. The gown was made of red towelling with 'Stowerton Infirmary' worked in white cotton on its hem. Perhaps James Comfrey no longer possessed anything of his own.

He did. In the drawer above the cupboard was a set of dentures in a plastic box and a pair of glasses. Impossible to imagine this man owning an address book. There was nothing of that sort in the drawer, nothing else at all but a scrap of folded tissue.

So he had come away, baulked and wondering. But the

house itself would yield that address, and if it didn't those newspaper accounts, meagre as they were, would rouse the London friends and acquaintances, employers of employees, who must by now have missed her.

He turned his attention to the clothes. It was going to be a day of groping through other people's possessions – such closets to search, such alcoves to importune! Rhoda Comfrey's dress and jacket, shoes and underwear, were unremarkable, the medium-priced garments of a woman who had retained a taste for bright colours and fussy trimmings into middle age. The shoes were a little distorted by feet that had spread. No perfume clung to the fabric of dress and slip. He was examining labels which told him only that the shoes came from one of a chain of shops whose name had been a household word for a quarter of a century, that the clothes might have been bought in any Oxford Street or Knightsbridge emporium, when there came a knock at the door.

The head of Dr Crocker appeared. 'What seems to be the trouble?' said the doctor very breezily.

They were lifelong friends, having known each other since their schooldays when Leonard Crocker had been in the first form and Reginald Wexford in the sixth. And it had sometimes been Wexford's job – how he had loathed it! – to shepherd home to the street next his own in Pomfret the mischievous recalcitrant infant. Now they were both getting on in years, but the mischievousness remained. Wexford was in no mood for it this morning.

'What d'you think?' he growled. 'Guess.'

Crocker walked over to the desk and picked up one of the shoes. 'The old man's my patient, you know.'

'No, I don't know. And I hope to God you haven't come here just to be mysterious about it. I've had some of that nonsense from you before. "The secrets of the confessional" and "a doctor's like a priest" and all that rubbish.'

Crocker ignored this. 'Old Comfrey used to come to my

surgery regularly every Tuesday night. Nothing wrong with him bar old age till he broke his hip. These old people, they like to come in for a chat. I just thought you might be interested.'

'I am, of course, if it's interesting.'

'Well, it's the daughter that's dead and he was always on about his daughter. How she'd left him all on his own since her mother died and neglected him and didn't come to see him from one year's end to the next. He was really quite articulate about it. Now, how did he describe her?'

'A thwart disnatured torment?'

The doctor raised his eyebrows. 'That's good, but it doesn't sound old Comfrey's style. I've heard it somewhere before.'

'Mm,' said Wexford. 'No doubt you have. But let's not go into the comminations of Lear on his thankless child. You will, of course, know the thankless child's address.'

'London.'

'Oh, really! If anyone else says that to me I'll put them on a charge for obstruction. You mean even *you* don't know where in London? For God's sake, Len, this old boy's eighty-five. Suppose you'd been called out to him and found him at death's door? How would you have got in touch with his next of kin?'

'He wasn't at death's door. People don't have deathbeds like that any more, Reg. They get ill, they linger, they go into hospital. The majority of people die in hospital these days. During the whole long painful process we'd have got her address.'

'Well, you didn't,' Wexford snapped. 'The hospital haven't got it now. How about that? I have to have that address.'

'It'll be at old Comfrey's place,' said Crocker easily.

'I just hope so. I'm going over there now to find it if it's findable.'

The doctor jumped down from his perch on the edge of the desk. With one of those flashbacks to his youth, to his schooldays, he said on an eager note, 'Can I come too?'

'I suppose so. But I don't want you cavorting about and getting in everyone's way.'

'Thanks very much,' said Crocker in mock dudgeon. 'Who do you think the popularity polls show to be the most respected members of the community? General practitioners.'

'I knew it wasn't cops,' said Wexford.

CHAPTER FOUR

The house smelt as he had thought it would, of the old person's animal-vegetable-mineral smell, sweat, cabbage and camphor.

'What did moths live on before man wore woollen clothes?'

'Sheep, I suppose,' said the doctor.

'But do sheep have moths?'

'God knows. This place is a real tip, isn't it?'

They were turning out drawers in the two downstairs rooms. Broken pens and pencils, dried-out ink bottles, sticking plaster, little glass jars full of pins, dead matches, nails, nuts and bolts, screws of thread; an assortment of keys, a pair of dirty socks full of holes, pennies and threepenny bits from the old currency, pieces of string, a broken watch, some marbles and some dried peas; a five-amp electric plug, milk bottle tops, the lid of a paint tin encrusted with blue from the front door, cigarette cards, picture hangers and an ancient shaving brush.

'Nice little breeding ground for anthrax,' said Crocker, and he pocketed a dozen or so boxes and bottles of pills that were ranged on top of the chest. 'I may as well dispose of this lot while I'm here. They won't chuck them out, no matter how often you tell them. Though why they should be so saving when they get them for free in the first place, I never will know.'

The footfalls of Burden, Loring and Gates could be heard overhead. Wexford knelt down, opened the bottom drawer. Underneath a lot of scattered mothballs, more socks redolent of cheesy mustiness, and a half-empty packet of birdseed, he found an oval picture frame lying face-downwards. He turned it over and looked at a photograph of a young woman with short dark hair, strong jaw, long upper lip, biggish nose.

'I suppose that's her,' he said to the doctor.

'Wouldn't know. I never saw her till she was dead and she didn't look much like that then. It's the spitting image of the old man, though, isn't it? It's her all right.'

Wexford said thoughtfully and a little sadly, remembering the over-made-up, raddled face, 'It does look like her. It's just that it was taken a long time ago.' And yet she hadn't looked sad. The dead face, if it were possible to say such a thing, had looked almost pleased with itself. 'We'll try upstairs,' he said.

There was no bathroom in the house, and the only lavatory was outside in the garden. The stairs were not carpeted but covered with linoleum. Burden came out of the front bedroom which was James Comfrey's.

'Proper old glory hole in there. D'you know, there's not a book in the house, and not a letter or a postcard either.'

'The spare room,' said Crocker.

It was a bleak little place, the walls papered in a print of faded pink and mauve sweet pea, the bare floorboards stained dark brown, the thin curtains whitish now but showing faintly the remains of a pink pattern. On the white cotton counterpane that covered the single bed lay a freshly pressed skirt in a navy-checked synthetic material, a blue nylon blouse and a pair of tights still in their plastic wrapping. Apart from a wall cupboard and a very small chest of drawers, there was no other furniture. On the chest was a small suitcase. Wexford looked inside it and found a pair of cream silk pyjamas of better quality than any of Rhoda Comfrey's daytime wear, sandals of the kind that consist only of a rubber sole and rubber thong, and a sponge bag. That was all. The cupboard was empty as were the drawers of the chest.

The closets had been searched and the alcoves importuned in vain.

Wexford said hotly to Crocker and Burden, 'This is unbelievable. She doesn't give her address to her aunt or the hospital where her father is or to her father's doctor or his neighbours. It's not written down anywhere in his house, he hasn't got it with him in the hospital. No doubt, it was in his head where it's now either locked in or knocked out. What the hell was she playing at?'

'Possum,' said the doctor.

Wexford gave a snort. 'I'm going across the road,' he said. 'Mind you leave the place as you found it. That means untidying anything you've tidied up.' He grinned snidely at Crocker. It made a change for him to order the doctor about, for the boot was usually on the other foot. 'And get Mrs Crown formally to identify the body, will you, Mike? I wish you joy of her.'

Nicky Parker opened the door of Bella Vista, his mother close behind him in the hall. Again the reassuring game was played for the child's benefit and Wexford passed off as a doctor. Well, why not? Weren't doctors the most respected members of the community? A baby was crying somewhere, and Stella Parker looked harassed.

'Would it be convenient,' he said politely, 'for me to have a chat with your – er – grandmother-in-law?'

She said she was sure it would, and Wexford was led through to a room at the back of the house. Sitting in an armchair, on her lap a colander containing peas that she was shelling, sat one of the oldest people he had ever seen in his life.

'Nana, this is the police inspector.'

'How do you do, Mrs –?'

'Nana's called Parker too, the same as us.'

She was surrounded by preparations for the family's lunch. On the floor, on one side of her chair, stood a saucepanful of potatoes in water, the bowl of peelings in water beside it. Four cooking apples awaited her attention. Pastry was made, kneaded, and set on a plate. This, apparently, was one of the ways in which she, at her extreme age, contributed to the household management. Wexford remembered how Parker had called his grandmother a wonder, and he began to see why.

For a moment she took no notice of him, exercising perhaps the privilege of matriarchal eld. Stella Parker left them and shut the door. The old woman split open the last of her pods, an enormous one, and said as if they were old acquaintances:

'When I was a girl they used to say, if you find nine peas in a pod put it over your door and the next man to come in will be your own true love.' She scattered the nine peas into the full colander, wiped her greened fingers on her apron.

'Did you ever do it?' said Wexford.

'What d'you say? Speak up.'

'Did you ever do it?'

'Not me. Didn't need to. I'd been engaged to Mr Parker since we was both fifteen. Sit down, young man. You're too tall to be on your legs.'

Wexford was amused and absurdly flattered. 'Mrs Parker . . .' he began on a bellow, but she interrupted him with what was very likely a favourite question.

'How old d'you think I am?'

There are only two periods in a woman's life when she hopes to be taken for older than she is, under sixteen and over ninety. In each case the error praises a certain achievement. But still he was wary.

She didn't wait for an answer. 'Ninety-two,' she said, 'and I still do the veg and make my own bed and do my room. And I looked after Brian and Nicky when Stell was in the hospital having Katrina. I was only eighty-nine then, though. Eleven children I've had and reared them all. Six of them gone now.' She levelled at him a girl's blue eyes in nests of wrinkles. 'It's not good to see your children go before you, young man.' Her face was white bone in a sheath of crumpled parchment. 'Brian's dad was my youngest, and he's been gone two years come November. Only fifty, he was. Still, Brian and Stell have been wonderful to me. They're a wonder, they are, the pair of them.' Her mind, drifting through the past, the ramifications of her family, returned to him, this stranger who must have come for something. 'What were you wanting? Police, Stell said.' She sat back, put the colander on the floor, and folded her hands. 'Rhoda Comfrey, is it?'

'Your grandson told you?'

''Course he did. Before he ever told you.' She was proud that she enjoyed the confidence of the young, and she smiled. But the smile was brief. Archaically, she said, 'She was wickedly murdered.'

'Yes, Mrs Parker. I believe you knew her well?'

'As well as my own children. She used to come and see me every time she come down here. Rather see me than her dad, she would.'

At last, he thought. 'Then you'll be able to tell me her address?'

'Speak up, will you?'

'Her address in London?'

'Don't know it. What'd I want to know that for? I've not written a letter in ten years and I've only been to London twice in my life.'

He had wasted his time coming here, and he couldn't afford to waste time.

'I can tell you all about her, though,' said Mrs Parker. 'Everything you'll want to know. And about the family. Nobody can tell you like I can. You've come to the right place for that.'

'Mrs Parker, I don't think . . .' That I care? That it matters? What he wanted at this stage was an address, not a biography, especially not one told with meanderings and digressions. But how to cut short without offence a woman of ninety-two whose deafness made interruption virtually impossible? He would have to listen and hope it wouldn't go on too long. Besides, she had already begun . . .

'They come here when Rhoda was a little mite. An only

child she was, and used to play with my two youngest. A poor feeble thing was Agnes Comfrey, didn't know how to stand up for herself, and Mr Comfrey was a real terror. I don't say he hit her or Rhoda, but he ruled them with a rod of iron just the same.' She rapped out sharply. 'You come across that Mrs Crown yet?'

'Yes,' said Wexford, 'But . . .' Oh, not the aunt, he thought, not the by-path. She hadn't heard him.

'You will. A crying scandal to the whole neighbourhood, she is. Used to come here visiting her sister when her first husband was alive. Before the war, that was, and she was a real fly-by-night even then, though she never took to drink till he was killed at Dunkirk. She had this baby about three months after – I daresay it was his all right, give her the benefit of the doubt – but it was one of them mongols, poor little love. John, they called him. Her and him come to live here with the Comfreys. Aggie used to come over to me in a terrible state of worry about what Lilian got up to and tried to keep dark, and Jim Comfrey threatening to throw her out.

'Well, the upshot of it was she met this Crown in the nick of time and they took the house next door when they was married on account of it had been empty all through the war. And d'you know what she done then?'

Wexford shook his head and stared at the pyramid of peas which were having a mesmeric effect on him.

'I'll tell you. She had little John put in a home. Have you ever heard the like, for a mother to do such a thing like that? Sweet affectionate little love he was too, the way them mongols are, and loved Rhoda, and she taking him out with her, not a bit ashamed.

'She'd have been how old then, Mrs Parker?' Wexford said for something to say. It was a mistake because he didn't really care, and he had to bawl it twice more before she heard.

'Twelve, she was, when he was born, and sixteen when Lilian had him put away. She was at the County High School, and Mr Comfrey wanted to take her away when she was fourteen like you could in them days. The headmistress herself, Miss Fowler that was, come to the house personally herself to beg him let Rhoda stay on, her being so bright. Well, he gave way for a bit, but he wasn't having her go on to no college, made her leave at sixteen, wanted her money, he said, the old skinflint.'

It was very hot, and the words began to roll over Wexford only half-heard. Just the very usual unhappy tale of the mean-spirited working-class parent who values cash in hand more than the career in the future. 'Got shop work – wanted to better herself, did Rhoda – always shut up in that back bedroom reading – taught herself French – went to typing classes –' How the hell was he going to get that address? Trace her through those clothes, those antique shoes? Not a hope. The sharp old voice cackled on. 'Nothing to look at – never had a boy – that Lilian always at her – "When you going to get yourself a boy-friend, Rhoda?" – got to be a secretary – poor thing, she used to get herself up like Lilian, flashy clothes and high heels and paint all over her face.' He'd have to get help from the Press: *Do You Know This Woman?* On the strength of that photograph? 'Aggie got cancer – never went to the doctor till it was too late – had an operation, but it wasn't no use – she passed on and poor Rhoda was left with the old man –'

Well, he wasn't going to allow publication of photos of her dead face, never had done that and never would. If only Mrs Parker would come to an end, if only she hadn't about twenty years still to go! 'And would have stayed, I daresay – been a slave to him – stayed for ever but for getting all that money – tied to him hand and foot –'

'What did you say?'

'I'm the one that's deaf, young man,' said Mrs Parker.

'I know, I'm sorry. But what was that about coming into money?'

'You want to listen when you're spoken to, not go off in day-dreams. She didn't come into money, she won it. On the pools, it was one of them office what-d'you-call-its.'

'Syndicates?'

'I daresay. Old Jim Comfrey, he thought he was in clover. 'My ship's come in,' he says to my eldest son. But he was wrong there. Rhoda upped and walked out on him, and so much for the house he was going to have and the car and all.'

'How much was it?'

'How much was what? What she won? Thousands and thousands. She never said and I wouldn't ask. She come round to my place one afternoon – I was living up the road then – and she'd got a big case all packed. Just thirty, she was, and twenty years ago nearly to the day. She had the same birthday as me, you see, August the fifth, and forty-two years between us. 'I'm leaving, Auntie Vi,' she says, 'going to London to seek my fortune,' and she gives me the address of some hotel and says would I have all her books packed up and sent on to her? Fat chance of that. Jim Comfrey burned the lot of them down the garden. I can see her now like it was yesterday, in them high heels she couldn't walk in properly and a dress all frills, and beads all over her and fingernails like she'd dipped them in red paint and . . .'

'You didn't see her yesterday, did you?' Wexford yelled rapidly. 'I mean, the day before yesterday?'

'No. Didn't know she was here. She'd have come, though, if it wasn't for some wicked . . .'

'What was she going to do in London, Mrs Parker?'

'Be a reporter on a paper. That's what she wanted. She was secretary to the editor of the *Gazette* and she used to write bits for them too. I told you all that only you wasn't listening.'

Puzzled, he said, 'But Mrs Crown said she was in business.'

'All I can say is, if you believe her you'll believe anything. Rhoda got to be a reporter and did well for herself, had a nice home, she used to tell me, and what with the money she'd won and her wages . . .'

He bellowed, 'What newspaper, d'you know? Whereabouts was this home of hers?'

Mrs Parker drew herself up, assuming a duchessy dignity. She said rather frigidly, 'Lord knows, I hope you'll never get to be deaf, young man. But maybe you'll never understand unless you do. Half the things folks say to you go over your head, and you can't keep stopping them to ask them what? Can you? They think you're going mental. Rhoda used to say she'd written a bit here and a bit there, and gone to this place or that, and bought things for her home and whatnot, and how nice it was and what nice friends she'd got. I liked to hear her talk, I liked her being friendly with an old woman, but I know better than to think I'm like to follow half the things she *said*.'

Defeated, flattened, bludgeoned and nearly stunned, Wexford got up. 'I must go, Mrs Parker.'

'I won't quarrel with that,' she said tartly and, showing no sign of fatigue, 'You've fair worn me out, roaring at me like a blooming bull.' She handed him the colander and the potatoes. 'You can make yourself useful and give these to Stell. And tell her to bring me in a pie dish.'

CHAPTER FIVE

Had she perhaps been a freelance journalist?

At the press conference Wexford gave that afternoon he asked this question of Harry Wild, of the *Kingsmarkham Courier*, and of the only reporter any national newspaper had bothered to send. Neither of them had heard of her in this connection, though Harry vaguely remembered a plain-featured dark girl called Comfrey, who twenty years before, had been secretary to the editor of the now defunct *Gazette*.

'And now,' Wexford said to Burden, 'we'll adjourn to the Olive for a well-earned drink. See if you can find Crocker. He's about somewhere, dying to get the low-down on the medical report.'

The doctor was found, and they made their way to the Olive and Dove where they sat outside at a table in the little garden. It had been the sort of summer that seldom occurs in England, the sort foreigners believe never occurs, though the Englishman of middle age can look back and truthfully assert that there have been three or four such in his lifetime. Weeks, months, of undimmed sunshine had pushed geraniums up to five feet and produced fuchsias of a size and profusion only generally seen inside a heated greenhouse. None of the three men wore a jacket, but the doctor alone sported a tee-shirt, a short-sleeved adolescent garment in which he made his rounds and entranced his female patients.

Wexford drank white wine, very dry and as cold as the Olive was able to produce it which, tonight, was around blood heat. The occasional beer was for when Crocker, a stern medical mentor, wasn't around. It was a while now since the chief inspector had suffered a mild thrombosis, but any excesses, as the doctor never tired of telling him, could easily lead to another.

He began by congratulating his friend on the accuracy of his on-the-spot estimate of the time of death. The eminent pathologist who had conducted the post-mortem had put it at between seven and nine-thirty.

'Eight-thirty's the most probable,' he said, 'on her way home from the bus stop.' He sipped his warm wine. 'She was a strong healthy woman – until someone put a knife in her. One stab wound pierced a lung and the other the left ventricle. No signs of disease, no abnormalities. Except one. I think in these days you could call it an abnormality.'

'What do you mean?' said Crocker.

'She was a virgin.'

Burden, that strait-laced puritan, jerked up his head. 'Good heavens, she was an unmarried woman, wasn't she? Things have come to a pretty pass, I must say, if a perfectly proper condition for a single woman is called abnormal.'

'I suppose you must say it, Mike,' said Wexford with a sigh, 'but I wish you wouldn't. I agree that a hundred years ago, fifty years ago, even twenty, such a thing wouldn't be unusual in a woman of fifty, but it is now.'

'Unusual in a woman of *fifteen*, if you ask me,' said the doctor.

'Look at it this way. She was only thirty when she left home, and that was just at the beginning of the stirrings of the permissive society. She had some money. Presumably, she lived alone without any kind of chaperonage. All right, she was never very attractive or charming, but she wasn't repulsive, she wasn't deformed. Isn't it very strange indeed that in those first ten years at least she never had one love affair, not even one adventure for the sake of the experience?'

'Frigid,' said Crocker. 'Everyone's supposed to be rolling about from bed to bed these days, but you'd be surprised how many people just aren't interested in sex. Women especially. Some of them put up a good showing, they really try, but they'd much rather be watching the TV.'

'So old Acton was right, was he? "A modest woman",' Wexford quoted, ' "seldom desires any sexual gratification for herself. She submits to her husband but only to please him and, but for the desire for maternity, would far rather be relieved from his attentions." '

Burden drained his glass and made a face like someone who had taken unpalatable medicine. He had been a policeman for longer than Rhoda Comfrey had been free of paternal ties, had seen human nature in every possible seamy or sordid aspect, yet his experience had scarcely at all altered his attitude towards sexual matters. He was still one of those people whose feelings about sex are grossly ambivalent. For him it was both dirty and holy. He had never read that quaint Victorian manual, Dr Acton's *Functions and Disorders of the Reproductive Organs*, male-orientated, prudish, repressive and biologically very wide of the mark, but it was for such as he that it had been written. Now, while Wexford and the doctor – who for some reason beyond his comprehension seemed to know the work well – were quoting from it with scathing laughter and casting up of eyes, he said brusquely, interrupting them:

'In my opinion, this has absolutely nothing to do with Rhoda Comfrey's murder.'

'Very likely not, Mike. It seems a small point when we don't even know where she lived or how she lived or who her friends were. But I hope all that will be solved tomorrow.'

'What's so special about tomorrow?'

'I think we shall see that this rather dull little backwoods killing will have moved from the inside pages to be frontpage news. I've been very frank with the newspapers – mostly via Harry Wild who'll scoop a packet in lineage – and I think I've given them the sort of thing they like. I've also given them that photograph, for what it's worth. I'll be very much surprised if tomorrow morning we don't see headlines such as "Murdered Woman Led Double Life" and "What Was Stabbed Woman's Secret?" '

RUTH RENDELL

'You mean,' said Burden, 'that some neighbour of hers or employer or the man who delivers her milk will see it and let us know?'

Wexford nodded. 'Something like that. I've given the Press a number for anyone with information to ring. You see, that neighbour or employer may have read about her death today without its occurring to them that we're still in ignorance of her address.'

The doctor went off to get fresh drinks. 'All the nuts will be on the blower,' said Burden. 'All the men whose wives ran away in 1956, all the paranoiacs and sensation-mongers.'

'That can't be helped. We have to sort out the sheep from the goats. God knows, we've done it before often enough.'

The newspapers, as he put it, did him proud. They went, as always, too far with headlines more bizarre than those he had predicted. If the photograph, touched up out of recognition, struck no chords, he was sure the text must. Rhoda Comfrey's past was there, the circumstances of her Kingsmarkham life, the history of her association with the old *Gazette*, the details of her father's illness. Mrs Parker and Mrs Crown had apparently not been so useless after all.

By nine the phone began to ring.

For Wexford, his personal phone had been ringing throughout the night, but those calls had been from newspapermen wanting more details and all ready to assure him that Rhoda Comfrey hadn't worked for *them*. In Fleet Street she was unknown. Reaching the station early, he set Loring to trying all the London local papers, while he himself waited for something to come from the special line. Every call that had the slightest hint of genuineness about it was to be relayed to him.

Burden, of course, had been right. All the nuts were on the blower. There was the spiritualist whose sister had died fifteen years before and who was certain Rhoda Comfrey must

578

have been that sister reincarnated; the son whose mother had abandoned him when he was twelve; the husband, newly released from a mental hospital, whose wife that he declared missing came and took the receiver from him with embarrassed apologies; the seer who offered to divine the dead woman's address from the aura of her clothes. None of these calls even reached Wexford's sanctum, though he was told of them. Personally he took the call from George Rowlands, former editor of the *Gazette*, who had nothing to tell him but that Rhoda had been a good secretary with the makings of a feature-writer. Every well-meant and apparently sane call he took, but the day passed without anything to justify his optimism. Friday came, and with it the inquest.

It was quickly adjourned, and nothing much came out of it but a reproof for Brian Parker from an unsympathetic coroner. This was a court, not a child guidance clinic, said the coroner, managing to imply that the paucity of evidence was somehow due to Parker's having rearranged Rhoda Comfrey's clothes.

The phone calls still came sporadically on the Saturday, but not one caller claimed to know Rhoda Comfrey by name or said he or she had lived next door to her or worked with her. No bank manager phoned to say she had an account at his bank, no landlord to say that she paid him rent.

'This,' said Wexford, 'is ridiculous. Am I supposed to believe she lived in a tent in Hyde Park?'

'Of course it has to be that she was living under an assumed name.' Burden stood at the window and watched the bus from Stowerton pause at the stop, let off a woman passenger not unlike Rhoda Comfrey, then move off towards Forest Road. 'I thought the papers were doing their usual hysterical stuff when they printed all that about her secret life.' He looked at Wexford, raising his eyebrows. 'I thought you were too.'

'My usual hysterical stuff. Thanks very much.'

'I meant melodramatic,' said Burden, as if that mitigated the censure. 'But they weren't. You weren't. Why would she behave like that?'

'For the usual melodramatic reason. Because she didn't want the people who knew Rhoda Comfrey to know what Rhoda Comfrey was up to. Espionage, drug-running, protection rackets, a call-girl ring. It's bound to be something like that.'

'Look, I didn't mean you always exaggerate. I've said I was wrong, haven't I? As a matter of fact, the call-girl idea did come into my mind. Only she was a bit old for that and nothing much to look at and – well . . .'

'Well, what? She was the only virgin prostitute in London, was she? It's a new line, Mike, it's an idea. It's a refreshing change in these dissolute times. I can think of all sorts of fascinating possibilities in that one, only I wouldn't like to burn your chaste ears. Shall we try to be realistic?'

'I always do,' said Burden gloomily. He sat down and rested his elbows on Wexford's desk. 'She's been dead since Monday night, and it's Sunday now and we don't even know where she lived. It seems hopeless.'

'That's not being realistic, that's defeatist. She can't be traced through her name or her description, therefore she must be traced by other means. In a negative sort of way, all this has shown us something. It's shown us that her murder is connected with that other life of hers. A secret life is almost always a life founded on something illicit or illegal. In the course of it she did something which gave someone a reason to kill her.'

'You mean we can't dismiss the secret life and concentrate on the circumstantial and concrete evidence we have?'

'Like what? No weapon, no witnesses, no smell of a motive?' Wexford hesitated and said more slowly, 'She seldom came back here, but she had been coming once or twice a year. The local people knew her by sight, knew who she was.

Therefore, I don't think this is a case of someone returning home after a long absence and being recognized – to put it melodramatically, Mike – by an old enemy. Nor was her real life here or her work or her interests or her involvements. Those, whatever they were, she left behind in London.'

'You don't think the circumstances point to local knowledge?'

'I don't. I say her killer knew she was coming here and followed her, though not, possibly, with premeditation to kill. He or she came from London, having known her in that other life of hers. So never mind the locals. We have to come to grips with the London life, and I've got an idea how to do it. Through that wallet she had in her handbag.'

'I'm listening,' said Burden with a sigh.

'I've got it here.' Wexford produced the wallet from a drawer in his desk. 'See the name printed in gold on the inside? Silk and Whitebeam.'

'Sorry, it doesn't mean a thing to me.'

'They're a very exclusive leather shop in Jermyn Street. That wallet's new. I think there's a chance they might remember who they sold it to, and I'm sending Loring up first thing in the morning to ask them. Rhoda Comfrey had a birthday last week. If she didn't buy it herself, I'm wondering what are the chances of someone else having bought it for her as a gift.'

'For a *woman*?'

'Why not? If she was in need of a wallet. Women carry banknotes as much as we do. The days of giving women a bottle of perfume or a brooch are passing, Mike. They are very nearly the people now. *Sic transit gloria mundi.*'

'*Sic transit gloria* Sunday, if you ask me,' said Burden.

Wexford laughed. His subordinate and friend could still surprise him.

CHAPTER SIX

As soon as he had let himself into his house, Dora came out from the kitchen, beckoned him into it and shut the door.

'Sylvia's here.'

There is nothing particularly odd or unusual about a married daughter visiting her mother on a Sunday afternoon, and Wexford said, 'Why shouldn't she be? What d'you mean?'

'She's left Neil. She just walked out after lunch and came here.'

'Are you saying she's seriously *left Neil*? Just like that? She's walked out on her husband and come home to mother? I can't believe it.'

'Darling, it's true. Apparently, they've been having a continuous quarrel ever since Wednesday night. He promised to take her to Paris for a week in September – his sister was going to have the children – and now he says he can't go, he's got to go to Sweden on business. Well, in the resulting row Sylvia said she couldn't stand it any longer, being at home all day with the children and never having a break, and he'd have to get an *au pair* so that she could go out and train for something. So he said – though I think she's exaggerating there – that he wasn't going to pay a girl wages to do what it was his wife's job to do. She'd only train for something and then not be able to get a job because of the unemployment. Anyway, all this developed into a great analysis of their marriage and the role men have made women play and how she was sacrificing her whole life. You can imagine. So this morning she told him that if she was only a nurse and a housekeeper she'd go and be a nurse and housekeeper with her parents – and here she is.'

'Where is she now?'

'In the living room, and Robin and Ben are in the garden.
I don't know how much they realize. Darling, don't be harsh
with her.'

'When have I ever been harsh with my children? I haven't
been harsh enough. I've always let them do exactly as they
liked. I should have put my foot down and not let her get
married when she was only eighteen.'

She was standing up with her back to him. She turned
round and said, 'Hallo, Dad.'

'This is a bad business, Sylvia.'

Wexford loved both his daughters dearly, but Sheila, the
younger, was his favourite. Sheila had the career, the tough
life, had been through the hardening process, and had remained soft and sweet. Also she looked like him, although he
was an ugly man and everyone called her beautiful. Sylvia's
hard classical features were those of his late mother-in-law,
and hers the Britannia bust and majestic bearing. She had led
the protected and sheltered existence in the town where she
had been born. But while Sheila would have run to him and
called him Pop and thrown her arms round him, this girl stood
staring at him with tragic calm, one marmoreal arm extended
along the mantelpiece.

'I don't suppose you want me here, Dad,' she said. 'I'd
nowhere else to go. I won't bother you for long. I'll get a job
and find somewhere for me and the boys to live.'

'Don't speak to me like that, Sylvia. Please don't. This is
your home. What have I ever said to make you speak to me
like that?'

She didn't move. Two great tears appeared in her eyes
and coursed slowly down her cheeks. Her father went up to
her and took her in his arms, wondering as he did so when
it was that he had last held her like this. Years ago, long before
she was married. At last she responded, and the hug he got
was vice-like, almost breath-crushing. He let her sob and gulp
into his shoulder, holding her close and murmuring to this

fugitive goddess, all magnificent five feet ten of her, much the same words that he had used twenty years before when she had fallen and cut her knee.

More negative results awaited him on Monday evening. The phone calls were still coming in, growing madder as time went by. No newspaper in the country knew of Rhoda Comfrey either as an employee or in a freelance capacity, no Press agency, no magazine, and she was not on record as a member of the National Union of Journalists.

Detective Constable Loring had left for London by an early train, bound for the leather shop in Jermyn Street. Wexford wished now that he had gone himself, for he was made irritable by this enforced inactivity and by thoughts of what he had left behind him at home. Tenderness he felt for Sylvia, but little sympathy. Robin and Ben had been told their father was going away on business and that this was why they were there, but although Ben accepted this, Robin perhaps knew better. He was old enough to have been affected by the preceding quarrels and to have understood much of what had been said. Without him and Ben, their mother would have been able to lead a free, worthwhile and profitable life. The little boy went about with a bewildered look. That damned water rat might have provided a diversion, but the beast was as elusive as ever.

And Neil had not come. Wexford had been sure his son-in-law would turn up, even if only for more recriminations and mud-slinging. He had neither come nor phoned. And Sylvia, who had said she didn't want him to come, that she never wanted to see him again, first moped over his absence, then harangued her parents for allowing her to marry him in the first place. Wexford had had a bad night because Dora had hardly slept, and in the small hours he had heard Sylvia pacing her bedroom or roving the house.

Loring came back at twelve, which was the earliest he could possibly have made it, and Wexford found himself perversely wishing he had been late so that he could have snapped at him. That was no way to go on. Pleasantly he said:

'Did you get any joy?'

'In a sort of way, sir. They recognized the wallet at once. It was the last of a line they had left. The customer bought it on Thursday, August fourth.'

'You call that a sort of way? I call it a bloody marvellous break.'

Loring looked pleased, though it was doubtful whether this was praise or even directed at him. 'Not Rhoda Comfrey, sir,' he said hastily. 'A man. Chap called Grenville West. He's a regular customer of Silk and Whitebeam. He's bought a lot of stuff from them in the past.'

'Did you get his address?'

'Twenty-two, Elm Green, London, West 15,' said Loring.

No expert on the metropolis, Wexford nevertheless knew a good deal of the geography of the London Borough of Kenbourne. And now, in his mind's eye, he saw Elm Green that lay half a mile from the great cemetery. Half an acre or so of turf with elm trees on it, a white-painted fence bordering two sides of it, and facing the green, a row of late-Georgian houses, some with their ground floors converted into shops. A pretty place, islanded in sprawling, squalid Kenbourne which, like the curate's egg and all London boroughs, was good in parts.

It was a piece of luck for him that this first possible London acquaintance – friend, surely – of Rhoda Comfrey had been located here. He would get help, meet with no obstruction, for his old nephew, his dead sister's son, was head of Kenbourne Vale CID. That Chief Superintendent Howard Fortune was at present away on holiday in the Canary Islands was a pity but no real hindrance. Several members of Howard's team were known to him. They were old friends.

By two Stevens, his driver, was heading the car towards London. Wexford relaxed, feeling his confidence returning,

Sylvia and her troubles pushed to the back of his mind, and he felt stimulated by the prospect before him when Stevens set him down outside Kenbourne Vale Police Station.

'Inspector Baker in?'

It was amusing, really. If anyone had told him, those few years before, that the day would come when he would actually be asking for Baker, wanting to see him, he would have laughed with resentful scorn. For Baker had been the reverse of pleasant to him when, convalescing after his thrombosis with Howard and Denise, he had helped solve the cemetery murder. But Howard, Wexford thought secretly, would have refused that word 'helped', would have said his uncle had done all that solving on his own. And that had marked the beginning of Baker's respect and friendship. After that, there had been no more barbs about rustic policemen and interference and ignorance of London thugs.

His request was answered in the affirmative, and two minutes later he was being shown down one of those bottle-green painted corridors to the inspector's office with its view of a brewery. Baker got up and came to him delightedly, hand outstretched.

'This is a pleasant surprise, Reg!'

It was getting on for two years since Wexford had seen him. In that time, he thought, there had been more remarkable changes, and not just in the man's manner towards himself. He looked years younger, he looked happy. Only the harsh corncrake voice with its faint cockney intonation remained the same.

'It's good to see you, Michael.' Baker shared Burden's Christian name. How that had once riled him! 'How are you? You're looking fine. What's the news.'

'Well, you'll know Mr Fortune's away in Tenerife. Things are fairly quiet here, thank God. Your old friend Sergeant Clements is somewhere about, he'll be glad to see you. Sit down and I'll have some tea sent up.' There was a framed photograph of a fair-haired, gentle-looking woman on the desk.

Baker saw Wexford looking at it. 'My wife,' he said, self-conscious, proud, a little embarrassed. 'I don't know if Mr Fortune mentioned I'd got married —' a tiny hesitation '— again?'

Yes, Howard had, of course, but he had forgotten. The new ease of manner, the happiness, were explained. Michael Baker had once been married to a girl who had become pregnant by another man and who had left him for that other man. Finding that out from Howard had marked the beginnings of his toleration of Baker's rudeness and his thinly veiled insults.

'Congratulations. I'm delighted.'

'Yes, well . . .' Awkwardness brought out shades of Baker's old acerbity. 'You didn't come here to talk about my domestic bliss. You came about this Rose — no, Rhoda — Comfrey. Am I right?'

Wexford said on a surge of hope, 'You know her? You've got some . . .?'

'Wouldn't I have been in touch if I had? No, but I read the papers. I don't suppose you've got much else on your mind at the moment, have you?'

Sylvia, Sylvia . . . 'No, not much.' The tea came, and he told Baker about the wallet and Grenville West.

'I do know *him*. Well, not to say "know". He's what you might call our contribution to the arts. They put bits about him in the local paper from time to time. Come on, Reg, I always think of you as so damned intellectual. Don't tell me you've never heard of Grenville West?'

'Well, I haven't. What does he do?'

'I daresay he's not that famous. He writes books, historical novels. I can't say I've ever set eyes on him, but I've read one of his books — bit above my head — and I can tell you a bit about him from what I've seen in the paper. In his late thirties, dark-haired chap, smokes a pipe — they put his photo on his book jackets. You know those old houses facing the Green? He lives in a flat in one of them over a wine bar.'

Having courteously refused Baker's offer of assistance, sent his regards to Sergeant Clements, and promised to return later, he set off up Kenbourne High Street. The heat that was pleasant, acceptable in the country, made of this London suburb a furnace that seemed to be burning smelly refuse. A greyish haze obscured the sun. He wondered why the Green looked different, barer somehow, and bigger. Then he noticed the stumps where the trees had been. So Dutch Elm disease denuded London as well as the country . . .

He crossed the grass where black children and one white child were playing ball, where two Indian women in saris, their hair in long braids, walked slowly and gracefully as if they carried invisible pots on their heads. The wine bar had been discreetly designed not to mar the long elegant façade, as had the other shops in this row, and the sign over its bow window announced in dull gold letters: Vivian's Vineyard. The occasional slender tree grew out of the pavement, and some of the houses had window boxes with geraniums and petunias in them. Across the house next door to the bar rambled the vines of an *ipomaea*, the Morning Glory, its trumpet flowers open and glowing a brilliant blue. This might have been some corner of Chelsea or Hampstead. If you kept your eyes steady, if you didn't look south to the gasworks or east to St Biddulph's Hospital, if you didn't smell the smoky, diesel-y stench, it might even have been Kingsmarkham.

He rang repeatedly at the door beside the shop window, but no one came. Grenville West was out. What now? It was nearly five and, according to the notice on the shop door, the Vineyard opened at five. He sat down on one of the benches on the Green to wait until it did.

Presently a pale-skinned negroid girl came out, peered up and down the street and went back in again, turning the sign to 'Open'. Wexford followed her and found himself in a dim cavern, light coming only from some bulbs behind the bar itself and from heavily shaded Chianti-bottle lamps on the tables. The window was curtained in brown and silver and the curtains were fast drawn. On a high stool, under the most powerful of the lamps, the pale Negress had seated herself to leaf through a magazine.

He asked her for a glass of white wine, and then if the owner or manager or proprietor was about.

'You want Vic?'

'I expect I do if he's the boss.'

'I'll fetch him.'

She came back with a man who looked in his early forties. 'Victor Vivian. What can I do for you?'

Wexford showed him his warrant card and explained. Vivian seemed rather cheered by the unexpected excitement, while the girl opened enormous eyes and stared.

'Take a pew,' said Vivian not ineptly, for the place had the gloom of a chapel devoted to some esoteric cult. But there was nothing priestly about its proprietor. He wore jeans and a garment somewhere between a tee-shirt and a windcheater with a picture on it of peasant girls treading out the grape harvest. 'Gren's away. Went off on holiday to France, you know – let's see now – last Sunday week. He always goes to France for a month at this time of the year.'

'You own the house?'

'Not to say "own", you know. I mean, Notbourne Properties own it. I've got the under-lease.'

He was going to be an 'I mean-er' and 'you know-er'. Wexford could feel it coming. Still, such people usually talked a lot and were seldom discreet. 'You know him well?'

'We're old mates, Gren and me, you know. He's been here fourteen years and a damn good tenant. I mean, he does all his repairs himself and it's handy, you know, having someone always on the premises when the bar's closed. Most evenings he'll drop in here for a drink, you know, and then as often as not I'll have a quick one with him, up in his place, I mean, after we've knocked off for the night, and then, you know . . .'

RUTH RENDELL

Wexford cut this useless flow short. 'It's not Mr West I'm primarily interested in. I'm trying to trace the address of someone who may have been a friend of his. You've read of the murder of Miss Rhoda Comfrey?'

Vivian gave a schoolboy whistle. 'The old girl who was stabbed? You mean she was a friend of Gren's? Oh, I doubt that, I mean, I doubt that very much. I mean, she was fifty, wasn't she? Gren's not forty, I mean, I doubt if he's more than thirty-eight or thirty-nine. Younger than me, you know.'

'I wasn't suggesting the relationship was a sexual one, Mr Vivian. They could just have been friends.'

This possibility was apparently beyond Vivian's comprehension, and he ignored it. 'Gren's got a girl-friend. Nice little thing, you know, worships the ground he treads on.' A sly wink was levelled at Wexford. 'He's a wily bird, though, is old Gren. Keeps her at arm's length a bit. Afraid she might get him to the altar, you know, or that's my guess, I mean. Polly something-or-other, she's called, blonde – I mean, she can't be more than twenty-four or five. Came to do his typing, you know, and now she hangs on like the proverbial limpet. Have another drink? On the house, I mean.'

'No, thank you, I won't.' Wexford produced the photograph and the wallet. 'You've never seen this woman? She'd changed a lot, she didn't look much like that any more, I'm afraid.'

Vivian shook his head and his beard waggled. He had a variety of intense facial contortions, all stereotyped and suggesting the kind a ham actor acquired to express astonishment, sagacity, knowingness and suspicion. 'I've never seen her here or with Gren, you know,' he said, switching on the one that indicated disappointed bewilderment. 'Funny, though, I mean, there's something familiar about the face. Something, you know, I can't put a finger on it. Maybe it'll come back.' As Wexford's hopes leapt, Vivian crushed them. 'This picture wasn't in the papers, was it? I mean, could that be where I've seen her before?'

'It could.'

Two people came into the bar, bringing with them a momentary blaze of sunshine before the door closed again. Vivian waved in their direction, then, turning back, gave a low whistle. 'I say! That isn't old Gren's wallet, is it?'

Vague memories of Latin lessons came back to Wexford, of forms in which to put questions expecting the answer no. All Vivian's questions seemed to expect the answer no, perhaps so that he could whistle and put on his astounded face when he got a yes.

'Well, is it?'

'Now wait a minute. I mean, this one's new, isn't it? You caught me out for a minute, you know. Gren's got one like it, only a bit knocked around, I mean. Just like that, only a bit battered. Not new, I mean.'

And he had taken it with him to France, Wexford thought. He was making slow progress, but he kept trying. 'This woman was almost certainly living under an assumed name, Mr Vivian. never mind the name or the face. Did Mr West ever mention to you any woman friend he had who was older than himself?'

'There was his agent, his – what-d'you-call-it?' – literary agent. I can't remember her name. Mrs Something, you know. Got a husband living, I'm sure of that. I mean, it wouldn't be her, would it?'

'I'm afraid not. Can you tell me Mr West's address in France?'

'He's touring about, you know. Somewhere in the south, that's all I can tell you. Getting back to this woman, I'm racking my brains, but I can't come up with anyone. I mean, people chat to you about this and that, especially in my job, I mean, and a lot of it goes in one ear and out the other. Old Gren goes about a lot, great walker, likes his beer, likes to have a walk about Soho at night. For the pubs, I mean, nothing nasty, I don't mean that. He's got his drinking pals, you know, and he may have talked of some woman, but I wouldn't have the faintest idea about her name or where she lives, would I? I mean, I'm sorry I can't be of more help. But you know how it is, I mean, you don't think anyone's going to ask, I mean, it doesn't cross your mind, does it?'

As Wexford rose to go, he was unable to resist the temptation.

'I know what you mean,' he said.

CHAPTER SEVEN

'You're not having much luck,' said Baker over a fresh pot of tea. 'I'll tell you what I'll do. I'll have someone go through the Kenbourne street directory for you. If he did know her, she might have been living only a stone's throw away.'

'Not as Rhoda Comfrey. But it's very good of you, Michael.'

Stevens was waiting for him, but they hadn't got far along Kenbourne High Street when Wexford noticed a large newish public library on the opposite side. It would close, he guessed, at six, and it was a quarter to now. He told Stevens to drop him and park the car as best he could in this jungle of buses and container lorries and double yellow lines, and then he got out and jay-walked in most unpoliceman-like fashion across the road.

On the forecourt stood a bronze of a mid-nineteenth-century gentleman in a frock-coat. 'Edward Edwards' said a plaque at its feet, that and no more, as if the name ought to be as familiar as Victoria R or William Ewart Gladstone. It wasn't familiar to Wexford and he had no time to waste wondering about it.

He went on into the library and its large fiction section, and there he was, rubbing shoulders with Rebecca and Morris. Three of Grenville West's novels were in, *Killed With Kindness*, *The Venetian Courtesan*, *Fair Wind to Alicante*, and each was marked on the spine with an H for Historical. The first title appealed to him most and he took the book from the shelf and looked at the publisher's blurb on the front inside flap of the jacket.

'Once again,' he read, 'Mr West astonishes us with his virtuosity in taking the plot and characters of an Elizabethan drama and clothing them in his fine rich prose. This time it is Mistress Nan Frankford, from Thomas Heywood's *A Woman Killed with Kindness*, who holds the stage. At first a loving and faithful wife, she is seduced by her husband's trusted friend, and it is her remorse and Frankford's curious generosity which contribute to the originality of this compelling book. Mr West sticks closely to Heywood's plot, but he shows us what Heywood had no need to attempt for his contemporary audience, a vivid picture of domestic life in late sixteenth-century England with its passions, its cruelties, its conventions and its customs. A different world is unfolded before us, and we are soon aware that we are being guided through its halls, its knot gardens and its unspoilt pastoral countryside by a master of his subject.'

Hmm, thought Wexford, not for him. If *Killed With kindness* was from Heywood's play of almost identical title, *The Venetian Courtesan* was very likely based on Webster's *The White Devil* and *Fair Wind to Alicante* – on what? Wexford had a quick look at the blurb inside the jacket of that one and saw that its original was *The Changeling* of Middleton and Rowley.

A clever idea, he thought, for those who liked that sort of thing. It didn't look as if the author went in for too much intellectual stuff, but concentrated on the blood, thunder and passion which, from the point of view of his sales, was wise of him. There was a lot of Elizabethan and Jacobean plays, hundreds probably, so the possibilities of West going on till he was seventy or so seemed limitless.

Killed With Kindness had been published three years before. He turned to the back of the jacket. There Grenville West was portrayed in tweeds with a pipe in his mouth. He wore glasses and had a thick fringe of dark hair. The face wasn't very interesting but the photographer's lighting effects were masterful.

Under the picture was a biography:

'Grenville West was born in London. He has a degree in

history. His varied career has led him from teaching through freelance journalism, with short spells as a courier, barman and antique dealer, to becoming a highly successful writer of historical romance. In the twelve years since his first book, *Her Grace of Amalfi*, was published, he has delighted his readers with nine more novels of which several have been translated into French, German and Italian. His novels also appear in the United States and are regularly issued in paper-back.

'*Apes in Hell* was made into a successful television play, and *Arden's Wife* has been serialized for radio.

'Mr West is a francophile who spends most of his holidays in France, has a French car and enjoys French cooking. He is 35 years old, lives in London and is unmarried.'

On the face of it, Wexford thought, the man would appear to have little in common with Rhoda Comfrey. But then he didn't really know much about Rhoda Comfrey, did he? Maybe she too had been a francophile. Mrs Parker had told him, that when a young woman, she had taught herself French. And there was firm evidence that she had wanted to write and had tried her hand at journalism. It was possible that West had met her at a meeting of one of those literary societies, formed by amateurs who aspire to have their work published, and who had invited him to address them. Then why keep the relationship dark? In saying that there was nothing unpleasant in West's secretiveness, Vivian had only succeeded in suggesting that there was.

The library was about to close. Wexford went out and made a face at Edward Edwards who looked superciliously back at him. Stevens was waiting for him on the pavement, and together they walked back to the car which had necessarily been parked a quarter of a mile away.

He had made a mental note of the name of West's publishers, Carlyon Brent, of London, New York and Sydney. Would they tell him anything if he called them? He had a feeling they would be cagily discreet.

'I don't see what you're hoping to get, anyway,' said Burden in the morning. 'He's not going to have told his publishers who he gives birthday presents to, is he?'

'I'm thinking about this girl, this Polly something or other,' Wexford said. 'If she does his typing in his flat, which it seems as if she does, it's likely she also answers his phone. A sort of secretary, in fact. Therefore, someone at his publishers may be in the habit of speaking to her. Or, at any rate, it's possible West will have told them her name.'

Their offices were located in Russell Square. He dialled the number and was put through to someone he was told was Mr West's editor.

'Oliver Hampton speaking.' A dry cool public-school voice.

He listened while Wexford went somewhat awkwardly into his explanation. The awkwardness was occasioned not by Hampton's interruptions – he didn't interrupt – but by a strong extra-aural perception, carried along fifty miles of wires, that the man at the other end was incredulous, amazed and even offended.

At last Hampton said, 'I couldn't possibly give you any information of that nature about one of my authors.' The information 'of that nature' had merely been an address at which West could be written to or spoken to, or, failing that, the name of his typist. 'Frankly, I don't know who you are. I only know who you say you are.'

'In that case, Mr Hampton, I will give you a number for you to phone my Chief Constable and check.'

'I'm sorry, but I'm extremely busy. In point of fact, I have no idea where Mr West is at this moment except that he is somewhere in the South of France. What I will do is give you the number of his agent if that would help.'

Wexford said it might and noted the number down. Mrs Brenda Nunn, of Field and Bray, Literary Agents. This would be the woman Vivian had said was middle-aged and with a husband living. She was more talkative than Hampton and less suspicious, and she satisfied herself on his *bona fides* by calling him back at Kingsmarkham Police Station.

'Well, now we've done all that,' she said, 'I'm afraid I really can't be much help to you. I don't have an address for Mr West in France and I'd never heard of Rhoda Comfrey till I read about her in the papers. I do know the name of this girl who works for him. I've spoken to her on the phone. It's – well, it's Polly Flinders.'

'It's *what?*'

'I know. Now you can see why it stuck in my mind. Actually, it's Pauline Flinders – heaven knows what her parents were thinking about – but Grenville – er, Mr West – refers to her as Polly. I've no idea where she lives.'

Next Wexford phoned Baker. The search of the electoral register had brought to light no Comfrey in the parliamentary constituency of Kenbourne Vale. Would Baker do the same for him in respect of a Miss Pauline Flinders? Baker would, with pleasure. The name seemed to afford him no amusement or even interest. However, he was anxious to help, and in addition would send a man to Kenbourne Green to inquire in all the local shops and of Grenville West's neighbours.

'It's all so vague,' said Dr Crocker who came to join them for lunch at the Carousel Café. 'Even if the Comfrey woman was going under another name in London, this girl would have recognized her from the description in the papers. The photograph, unlike as it is, would have meant something to her. She'd have been in touch, she'd have read all your appeals.'

'So therefore doesn't it look as if she didn't because she has something to hide?'

'It looks to me,' said Burden, 'as if she just didn't know her.'

Waiting to hear from Baker, Wexford tried to make some sort of reasonable pattern of it. Rhoda Comfrey, who, for some unknown motive, called herself something else in London, had been a fan and admirer of Grenville West, had become his friend. Perhaps she performed certain services for him in connection with his work. She might – and Wexford was rather pleased with this notion – run a photocopying agency. That would fit in with what Mrs Crown had told him. Suppose she had made copies of manuscripts for West free of charge, and he, in gratitude, had given her a rather special birthday present? After all, according to old Mrs Parker, she had become fifty years old on 5 August. In some countries, Wexford knew, the fiftieth birthday was looked on as a landmark of great significance, an anniversary worthy of particular note. He had bought the wallet on the fourth, given it to her on the fifth, left for his holiday on the seventh, and she had come down to Kingsmarkham on the eighth. None of this got him nearer finding the identity of her murderer, but that was a long way off yet, he thought gloomily.

Into the midst of these reflections the phone rang.

'We've found her,' said the voice of Baker. 'Or we've found where she lives. She was in the register. West Kenbourne, All Souls Grove, number fifteen, flat one. Patel, Malina N. and Flinders, Pauline J. No number in the phone book for either of them, so I sent Dinehart round, and a woman upstairs said your Flinders usually comes in around half-four. D'you want us to see her for you? It's easily done.'

'No, thanks, Michael, I'll come up.'

Happiness hadn't eroded all the encrusting sourness from Baker's nature. He was still quick to sense a snub where no snub was intended, still looking always for an effusively expressed appreciation. 'Suit yourself,' he said gruffly. 'D'you know how to find All Souls Grove?' Implicit in his tone was the suggestion that this country bumpkin might be able to find a haystack or even a needle in one, but not a street delineated in every London guide. 'Turn right out of Kenbourne Lane Tube station into Magdalen Hill, right again into Balliol Street, and it's the second on the left after Oriel Mews.'

Forebearing to point out that with his rank he did rate a

car and a driver, Wexford said only, 'I'm most grateful, Michael, you're very good,' but he was too late.

'All in a day's work,' said Baker and put the phone down hard.

Wexford had sometimes wondered why it is that a plain woman so often chooses to live with, or share a flat with, or be companioned by, a beautiful woman. Perhaps choice does not enter into it; perhaps the pressure comes from the other side, from the beautiful one whose looks are set off by the contrast, while the ill-favoured one is too shy, too humble and too accustomed to her place to resist.

In this case, the contrast was very marked. Beauty had opened the front door to him, beauty in a peacock-green sari with little gold ornaments, and on hands of a fineness and delicacy seldom seen in Western women, the width across the broadest part less than three inches, rings of gold and ivory. An exquisite small face, the skin a smoky gold, peeped at him from a cloud of silky black hair.

'Miss Patel?'

She nodded, and nodded again rather sagely when he showed her his warrant card.

'I'd like to see Miss Flinders, please.'

The flat, on the ground floor, was the usual furnished place. Big rooms divided with improvised matchwood walls, old reject furniture, girls' clutter everywhere – clothes and magazines, pinned-up posters, strings of beads hanging from a door handle, half-burned coloured candles in saucers. The other girl, the one he had come to see, turned slowly from having been hunched over a typewriter. An ashtray beside her was piled with stubs. He found himself thinking:

> Little Polly Flinders
> Sat among the cinders,
> Warming her pretty little toes . . .

As it happened, her feet were bare under the long cotton skirt, and they were good feet, shapely and long. Perhaps, altogether, she wouldn't have been so bad if he hadn't seen Malina Patel first. She wouldn't have been bad at all but for that awful stoop, assumed no doubt in an attempt to reduce her height, though it was less than his Sylvia's, and but for the two prominent incisors in her upper jaw. Odd, he thought, in someone of her years, child of the age of orthodontics.

She came up to him, unsmiling and wary, and Malina Patel went softly away, having not spoken a word. He plunged straight into the middle of things.

'No doubt you've read the papers, Miss Flinders, and seen about the murder of a Miss Rhoda Comfrey. This photograph was in the papers. Imagine it, if you can, aged by about twenty years and its owner using another name.'

She looked at the photograph and he watched her. He could make nothing of her expression, it seemed quite blank.

'Do you think you have ever seen her? In, let us say, the company of Mr Grenville West?'

A flush coloured her face unbecomingly. Victor Vivian had described her as a blonde, and that word is very evocative, implying beauty and a glamorous femininity, a kind of Marilyn Monroe-ishness. Pauline Flinders was not at all like that. Her fairness was just an absence of colour, the eyes a watery pale grey, the hair almost white. Her blush was vivid and patchy under that pale skin, and he supposed it was his mention of the man's name that had caused it. Not guilty knowledge, though, but love.

'I've never seen her,' she said, and then, 'Why do you think Grenville knew her?'

He wasn't going to answer that yet. She kept looking towards the door as if she were afraid the other girl would come back. Because her flat-mate had teased her about her feelings for the novelist?

'You're Mr West's secretary, I believe?'

'I had an advertisement in the local paper saying I'd do typing for people. He phoned me. That was about two years ago. I did a manuscript for him and he liked it and I started sort of working for him part-time.' She had a graceless way of speaking, in a low dull monotone.

'So you answered his phone, no doubt, and met his friends. Was there anyone among his friends who might possibly have been this woman?'

'Oh, no, no one.' She sounded certain beyond a doubt, and she added fatuously, with a lover's obsessiveness, 'Grenville's in France. I had a card from him.' Why wasn't it on the mantelpiece? As she slipped the postcard out from under a pile of papers beside her typewriter, Wexford thought he knew the answer to that one too. She didn't want to be teased about it.

A coloured picture of Annecy, and 'Annecy' was clearly discernible on the otherwise smudged postmark. 'Greeting from France, little Polly Flinders, the sunshine, the food, the air and the *bel aujourd'hui*. I shan't want to come back. But I shall – So, see you. G. W.' Typical of one of those literary blokes, he thought, but not, surely, the communication of a lover. Why had she shown it to him with its mention of her whimsical nickname? Because it was all she had?

He brought out the wallet and laid it down beside the postcard. What he wanted was for her to shriek, turn pale, cry out, 'Where did you get that?' – demolish the structure of ignorance he fancied she might carefully have built up. She did nothing but stare at it with that same guarded expression.

'Have you ever seen this before, Miss Flinders?'

She looked at it inside and out. 'It looks like Grenville's wallet,' she said, 'the one he lost.'

'Lost?' said Wexford.

She seemed to gain self-confidence and her voice some

animation. 'He was coming back from the West End on a bus, and when he came in he said he'd left the wallet on the bus. That must have been Thursday or Friday week. Where did you find it?'

'In Miss Rhoda Comfrey's handbag.' He spoke slowly and heavily. So that was the answer. No connection, no relationship between author and admiring fan, no fiftieth birthday present. She had found it on a bus and kept it. 'Did Mr West report his loss?'

When she was silent she tried to cover her protruding teeth, as people with this defect do, by pushing her lower lip out over them. Now the teeth appeared again. They caused her to lisp a little. 'He asked me to but I didn't. I didn't exactly forget. But someone told me the police don't really like you reporting things you've lost or found. A policeman my mother knows told her it makes too much paperwork.'

He believed her. Who knew better than he that the police are not angels in uniform, sacrificing themselves to the public good? Leaving her to return to her typewriter, he went out into the big gloomy hall of the house. The flat door opened again behind him and Malina Patel appeared with a flash bright as a kingfisher. Her accent, as English and as prettily correct as his Sheila's surprised him nearly as much as what she said.

'Polly was here with me all the evening on the eighth. She was helping me to make a dress, she was cutting it out' Her smile was mischievous and her teeth perfect. 'You're a detective, aren't you?'

'That's right.'

'What a freaky thing to be. I've never seen one before except on the TV.' She spoke as if he were some rare animal, an eland perhaps. 'Do people give you a lot of money? Like "Fifty thousand dollars to find my daughter, she's all the world to me" that kind of thing?'

'I'm afraid not, Miss Patel.'

He could have sworn she was mocking her friend's dull

naivety. The lovely face became guileless, the eyes opened hugely.

'When you first came to the door,' she said, 'I thought you might be a bailiff. We had one of those before when we hadn't paid the rates.'

CHAPTER EIGHT

A red-hot evening in Kenbourne Vale, a dusty dying sun. The reek of cumin came to him from Kemal's Kebab House, beer and sweat from the Waterlily pub. All the eating and drinking places had their doors wide open, propped back. Children of all ages, all colours, pure races and mixed races, sat on flights of steps or rode two-and three-wheelers on hard pavements and up and down narrow stuffy alleys. An old woman, drunk or just old and sick, squatted in the entrance to a betting shop. There was nothing green and organic to be seen unless you counted the lettuces, stuffed tight into boxes outside a green-grocer's, and they looked as much like plastic as their wrappings.

One thing to be thankful for was that now he need not come back to Kenbourne Vale ever again if he didn't want to. The trail had gone cold, about the only thing that had this evening. Sitting in the car on the road back to Kingsmarkham, he thought about it. At first Malina Patel's behaviour had puzzled him. Why had she come out voluntarily to provide herself or Polly Flinders with an unasked-for alibi? Because she was a tease and a humorist, he now reflected, and in her beauty dwelt with wit. Everything she had said to him had been calculated to amuse – and how she herself had smiled at the time! – all that about telly detectives and bailiffs. Very funny and charming from such a pretty girl. But no wonder Polly kept the postcard hidden and feared her overhearing their conversation. He could imagine the Indian girl's comments.

But if she hadn't been listening at the door how the hell had she known what he had come for? Easy. The woman upstairs had told her. One of Baker's men – that none too reliable Dinehart probably – had been round earlier in the day and let slip not only that the Kingsmarkham police wanted to talk to Polly but why they had wanted to talk to her. Malina would have read the papers, noted the date of Rhoda Comfrey's death. He remembered how closely and somehow complacently she had looked at his warrant card. Rather a naughty girl she was, playing detective stories and trying to throw cats among pigeons to perplex him and tease her flat-mate.

Ah, well, it was over now. Rhoda Comfrey had found that wallet on a bus or in the street, and he was back where he started.

Just before nine he walked into his own house. Dora was out, as he had known she would be, baby-sitting for Burden's sister-in-law, Sylvia nowhere to be seen or heard. In the middle of the staircase sat Robin in pyjamas.

'It's too hot to go to sleep. You aren't tired, are you, Grandad?'

'Not really,' said Wexford who was.

'Granny said you would be but I know you, don't I? I said to Granny that you'd want some fresh air.'

'River air? Put some clothes on, then, and tell Mummy where you're going.'

Twilight had come to the water meadows. 'Dusk is a very good time for water rats,' said Robin. 'Dusk.' He seemed to like the word and repeated it over and over as they walked along the river bank. Above the sluggish flow of the Kingsbrook gnats danced in lazy clouds. But the heat was not oppressive, the air was sweet and a refreshment to a London-jaded spirit.

However, 'I'm afraid we've had it for tonight,' Wexford said as the darkness began to deepen.

Robin took his hand. 'Yes, we'd better go back because my daddy's coming. I thought he was in Sweden but he's not. I expect we'll go home tomorrow. Not tonight because Ben's asleep.'

Wexford didn't know what answer to make. And when they came into the hall he heard from behind the closed door of the living room the angry but lowered voices of his daughter and son-in-law. Robin made no move towards that door. He looked at it, looked away, and rubbed his fists across his tired eyes.

'I'll see you into bed,' said his grandfather and lifted him more than usually tenderly in his arms.

In the morning they phoned him from Stowerton Royal Infirmary. They thought the police would wish to know that Mr James Comfrey had 'passed away' during the night, and since his daughter was dead, whom should they get in touch with?

'Mrs Lilian Crown,' he said, and then he thought he might as well go and see her himself. There was little else to do.

She was out. In Kingsmarkham the pubs open at ten on market day. To Bella Vista then. Today its name, its veridian roof and its sun-trap windows were justified. Light and heat beat down with equal force from a sky of the same hard dark blue as the late Mr Comfrey's front door.

'He's gone then,' the old woman said. News travels fast in these quiet backwoods places. During the hour that had passed since Wexford had been told the news, Mrs Crown also had been told and had informed at least some of her neighbours. 'It's a terrible thing to die, young man, and have no one shed a tear for you.'

She was stringing beans today, slicing them into long thin strips as few young housewives can be bothered to do. 'I daresay it'd have been a relief to poor Rhoda. Whatever'd she have done, I used to ask myself, if they'd turned him out of there and she'd had to look after him? Nursed her mother devotedly, she did, used to have to take time off work and all, but there was love there of course, and not a word of appreciation from old Jim.' The vital, youthful eyes fixed piercingly on him. 'Who'll get the money?'

'The money, Mrs Parker?'

'Rhoda's money. It'd have gone to him, being next of kin. I know that. Who'll get it now? That's what I'd like to know.'

This aspect hadn't occurred to him. 'Maybe there isn't any money. Few working people these days have much in the way of savings.'

'Speak up, will you?'

Wexford repeated what he had said, and Mrs Parker gave a scornful cackle.

"Course there's money. She got that lot from her pools win, didn't she? Wouldn't have blued that, not Rhoda, she wasn't one of your spendthrifts. I reckon you lot have been sitting about twiddling your thumbs or you'd have got to the bottom of it by now. A house there'll be somewhere, filled up with good furniture, and a nice little sum in shares too. D'you want to know what I think? It'll all go to Lilian Crown.'

Rather unwillingly he considered what she had said. But would it go to Mrs Crown? Possibly, but for that intervening heir, James Comfrey. If she had had anything to leave and if she had died intestate, James Comfrey had for nine days been in possession of his daughter's property. But a sister-in-law wouldn't automatically inherit from him, though her son, the mongol, if he were still alive . . . A nephew by marriage? He knew little of the law relating to inheritance, and it hardly seemed relevant now.

'Mrs Parker,' he said, pitching his voice loud, 'you're quite right when you say we haven't got very far. But we do know Miss Comfrey was living under an assumed name, a false name. Do you follow me?' She nodded impatiently. 'Now when people do that, they often choose a name that's familiar to them, a mother's maiden name, for instance, or the name of some relative or childhood friend.'

'Whyever would she do that?'

'Perhaps only because her own name had very unpleasant associations for her. Do you know what her mother's maiden name was?'

Mrs Parker had it ready. 'Crawford. Agnes and Lilian Crawford, they was. Change the name and not the letter, change for worse and not for better. Poor Agnes changed for worse all right, and the same applies to that Lilian, though it wasn't a C for her the first time. Crown left her and he's got another wife somewhere, I daresay, for all she says he's dead.

'So she might have been calling herself Crawford?' He was speaking his thoughts aloud. 'Or Parker, since she was so fond of you. Or Rowlands after the editor of the old *Gazette*.' This spoken reverie had scarcely been audible to Mrs Parker, and he bawled out his last suggestion. 'Or Crown?'

'Not Crown. She hadn't no time for that Lilian. And no wonder, always mocking her and telling her to get herself a man.' The old face contorted and Mrs Parker put up her fists as the aged do, recalling that far distant childhood when such a gesture was natural. 'Why'd she call herself anything but her rightful name? She was a good woman was Rhoda, never did anything wrong nor underhand in her whole life.'

Could you truthfully say that of anyone? Not, certainly, of Rhoda Comfrey who had stolen something she must have known would be precious to its owner, and whose life could be described as a masterpiece of underhandedness.

'I'll go out this way, Mrs Parker,' he said, opening the french window to the garden because he didn't want to encounter Nicky.

'Mind you shut it behind you. They can talk about heat all they like, but my hands and feet are always cold like yours'll be, young man, when you get to my age.'

There was no sign of Mrs Crown. He hadn't checked her movements on the night in question, but was it within the bounds of possibility that she had killed her niece? The motive was very tenuous, unless she knew of the existence of a will. Certainly there might be a will, deposited with a firm of solicitors who were unaware of the testator's death, but Rhoda Comfrey would never have left anything to the aunt she so disliked. Besides, that little stick of a woman wouldn't have had the physical strength . . .

His car, its windows closed and its doors locked for safety's sake, was oven-hot inside, the steering wheel almost too hot to hold. Driving back, he was glad he was a thin man now so that at least the trickling sweat didn't make him look like a pork carcase in the preliminary stages of roasting.

Before the sun came round, he closed the windows in his office and pulled down the blinds. Somewhere or other he had read that that was what they did in hot countries rather than let the air in. Up to a point it worked. Apart from a short break for lunch in the canteen, he sat up there for the rest of the day, thinking, thinking. He couldn't remember any previous case that had come his way in which, after nine days, he had had no possible suspect, could see no glimmer of a motive, or knew less about the victim's private life. Hours of thinking got him no further than to conclude that the killing had been, wildly incongruous though it seemed, a crime of passion, that it had been unpremeditated, and that Mrs Parker had allowed affection to sway her assessment of Rhoda Comfrey's character.

'Where's your mother?' said Wexford, finding his daughter alone.

'Upstairs, reading bedtime stories.'

'Sylvia,' he said, 'I've been busy, I'm still very busy, but I hope there'll never be a time when I've got too much on my hands to think about my children. Is there anything I can do to help? When I'm not being a policeman that's what I'm here for.'

She hung her head. Large and statuesque, she had a face designed, it seemed, to register the noble virtues, courage and fortitude. She was patience on a monument, smiling at grief. Yet she had never known grief, and in her life hardly any courage or fortitude had ever been called for.

'Wouldn't you like to talk about it?' he said.

The strong shoulders lifted. 'We can't change the facts. I'm a woman and that's to be a second-rate citizen.'

'You didn't used to feel like this.'

'Oh, Dad, what's the use of talking like that? People change. We don't hold the same opinions all our lives. If I say I read a lot of books and went to some meetings, you'll only say what Neil says, that I shouldn't have read them and I shouldn't have gone.'

'Maybe I shall and maybe I'd be right if what you've read has turned you from a happy woman into an unhappy one and is breaking up your marriage. Are you less of a second-rate citizen here with your parents than at home with your husband?'

'I shall be if I get a job, if I start training for something now.'

Her father forbore to tell her that he hardly cared for the idea of her attending some college or course while her mother was left to care for Robin and Ben. Instead he asked her if she didn't think that to be a woman had certain advantages. 'If you get a flat tyre,' he said, 'the chances are in five minutes some chap'll stop and change the wheel for you for no more reason than that you've got a good figure and a nice smile. But if it was me I could stand there flagging them down for twenty-four hours without a hope in hell of even getting the loan of a jack.'

'Because I'm pretty!' she said fiercely, and he almost laughed, the adjective was so inept. Her eyes flashed, she looked like a Medea. 'D'you know what that means? Whistles, yes, but no respect. Stupid compliments but never a sensible remark as from one human being to another.'

'Come now, you're exaggerating.'

'I am not, Dad. Look, I'll give you an example. A couple of weeks ago Neil backed the car into the gatepost and I took it to the garage to get a new rear bumper and light. When the mechanics had done whistling at me, d'you know what the manager said? "You ladies," he said, "I bet he had a thing or two to say when he saw what you'd done." *He took it for granted* I'd done it because I'm a woman. And when I corrected him he couldn't talk seriously about it. Just flirtatiousness and silly cracks and I was to explain this and that to Neil. "His motor", he said, and to tell *him* this, that and the other. I know as much about cars as Neil, it's as much my car as his.' She stopped and flushed. 'No, it isn't, though!' she burst out. 'It isn't! And it isn't as much my house as his. My children aren't even as much mine as his, he's their legal guardian. My God, my life isn't as much mine as his!'

'I think we'd better have a drink,' said her father, 'and you calm down a bit and tell me just what your grievances against Neil are. Who knows? I may be able to be your intermediary.'

Thus he found himself, a couple of hours later, closeted with his son-in-law in the house which he had, in former times, delighted to visit because it was noisy and warm and filled, it had seemed to him, with love. Now it was dusty, chilly and silent. Neil said he had had his dinner but, from the evidence, Wexford thought it had taken a liquid and spirituous form.

'Of course I want her back, Reg, and my kids. I love her, you know that. But I can't meet her conditions. I won't. I'm to have some wretched *au pair* here which'll mean the boys moving in together, pay her a salary I can ill afford, just so that Syl can go off and train for some profession that's already overcrowded. She's a damn good wife and mother, or she was. I don't see any reason to employ someone to do the things she does so well while she trains for something she may not do well at all. Have a drink?'

'No, thanks.'

'Well, I will, and you needn't tell me I've had too much already. I know it. The point is, why can't she go on doing her job while I do mine? I don't say hers is less important than mine. I don't say she's inferior and when she says others say so I think that's all in her head. But I'm not paying her a wage for doing what other women have done since time immemorial for love. Right? I'm not going to jeopardize my career by cancelling trips abroad, or exhaust myself cleaning the place and bathing the kids when I get home after a long day. I'll dry the dishes, OK, I'll see she gets any labour-saving equipment she wants, but I'd like to know just who needs the liberation if I'm to work all day and all night while she footles around at some college for God knows how many years. I wish I was a woman, I can tell you, no money worries, no real responsibility, no slogging off to an office day in and day out for forty years.'

'You don't wish that, you know.'

'I almost have done this week.' Neil threw out a despairing hand at the chaos surrounding him. 'I don't know how to do housework. I can't cook, but I can earn a decent living. Why the hell can't she do the one and I do the other like we used to? I could wring those damned Women's Libbers' necks. I love her, Reg. There's never been anyone else for either of us. We row, of course we do, that's healthy in a marriage, but we love each other and we've got two super kids. Doesn't it seem crazy that a sort of political thing, an impersonal thing, could split up two people like us?'

'It's not impersonal to her,' said Wexford sadly. 'Couldn't you compromise, Neil? Couldn't you get a woman in just for a year till Ben goes to school?'

'Couldn't she wait just for a year till Ben goes to school? OK, so marriage is supposed to be give and take. It seems to me I do all the giving and she does all the taking.'

'And she says it's the other way about. I'll go now, Neil.' Wexford laid his hand on his son-in-law's arm. 'Don't drink too much. It's not the answer.'

'Isn't it? Sorry, Reg, but I've every intention tonight of getting smashed out of my mind.'

Wexford said nothing to his daughter when he got home, and she asked him no questions. She was sitting by the still open french window, cuddling close to her Ben who had awakened and cried, and reading with mutinous concentration a book called *Woman and the Sexist Plot*.

CHAPTER NINE

Ben passed a fractious night and awoke at seven with a sore throat. Sylvia and her mother were discussing whether to send for Dr Crocker or take Ben to the surgery when Wexford had to leave for work. The last thing he expected was that he himself would be spending the morning in a doctor's surgery, for he saw the day ahead as a repetition of the day before, to be passed in fretful inertia behind drawn blinds.

He was a little late getting in. Burden was waiting for him, impatiently pacing the office.

'We've had some luck. A doctor's just phoned in. He's got a practice in London and he says Rhoda Comfrey was on his list, she was one of his patients.'

'My God. At last. Why didn't he call us sooner?'

'Like so many of them, he was away on holiday. In the South of France, oddly enough. Didn't know a thing about it till he got back last night and saw one of last week's newspapers.'

'I suppose you said we'd want to see him?'

Burden nodded. 'He expects to have seen the last of his surgery patients by eleven and he'll wait in for us. I said I thought we could be there soon after that.' He referred to the notes he had taken. 'He's a Dr Christopher Lomond and he's in practice at a place called Midsomer Road, Parish Oak, London, W19.'

'Never heard of it,' said Wexford. 'But come to that, I've only just about heard of Stroud Green and Nunhead and Earlsfield. All those lost villages swallowed up in . . . What are you grinning at?'

'I know where it is. I looked it up. It may be W19 but it's still part of your favourite beauty spot, the London Borough of Kenbourne.'

'Back again,' said Wexford. 'I might have known it. And what's more, Stevens has gone down with the flu − flu in August! − so unless you feel like playing dodgem cars, it's train for us.'

Though unlikely to be anyone's favourite beauty spot, the district in which they found themselves was undoubtedly the best part of Kenbourne. It lay some couple of miles to the north of Elm Green and Kenbourne High Street and the library, and it was one of those 'nice' suburbs which sprang up to cover open country between the two world wars. The tube station was called Parish Oak, and from there they were directed to catch a bus which took them up a long hilly avenue, flanked by substantial houses whose front gardens had been docked for road-widening. Directly from it, at the top, debouched Midsomer Road, a street of comfortable-looking semi-detached houses, not unlike Wexford's own, where cars were tucked away into garages, doorsteps held neat little plastic containers for milk bottles, and dogs were confined behind wrought-iron gates.

Dr Lomond's surgery was in a flat-roofed annexe attached to the side of number sixty-one. They were shown in immediately by a receptionist, and the doctor was waiting for them, a short youngish man with a cheerful pink face.

'I didn't recognize Miss Comfrey from that newspaper photograph,' he said, 'but I thought I remembered the name and when I looked at the photo again I saw a sort of resemblance. So I checked with my records. Rhoda Agnes Comfrey, 6 Princevale Road, Parish Oak.'

'So she hadn't often come to you, Doctor?' said Wexford.

'Only came to me once. That was last September. It's often the way, you know. They don't bother to register with a doctor till they think they've got something wrong with them. She had herself put on my list and she came straight in.'

Burden said tentatively, 'Would you object to telling us what was wrong with her?'

The doctor laughed breezily. 'I don't think so. The poor woman's dead, after all. She thought she'd got appendicitis because she'd got pains on the right side of the abdomen. I examined her, but she didn't react to the tests and she hadn't any other symptoms, so I thought it was more likely to be indigestion and I told her to keep off alcohol and fried foods. If it persisted she was to come back and I'd give her a letter to the hospital. But she was very much against the idea of hospital and I wasn't surprised when she didn't come back. Look, I've got a sort of dossier thing here on her. I have one for all my patients.'

He read from a card: ' "Rhoda Agnes Comfrey. Age forty-nine. No history of disease, apart from usual childhood ailments. No surgery. Smoker –" I told her to give that up, by the way. "Social drinker" ' That can mean anything. "Formerly registered with Dr Castle of Glebe Road, Kingsmarkham, Sussex." '

'And he died last year,' said Wexford. 'You've been a great help, Doctor. Can I trouble you to tell a stranger in these parts where Princevale Road might be?'

'Half way down that hill you came up from the station. It turns off on the same side as this just above the block of shops.'

Wexford and Burden walked slowly back to the avenue which they now noted was called Montfort Hill.

'Funny, isn't it?' said Wexford. 'We know everyone else must have known her under an assumed name, but not her doctor, I wonder why not.'

'Too risky?'

'What's the risk? In English law one can call oneself what one likes. What you call yourself *is* your name. People think you have to change your name by deed poll but you don't. I could call myself Waterford tomorrow and you could call yourself Fardel without infringing a hairsbreadth of the law.'

Looking puzzled, Burden said, 'I suppose so. Look, I see the Waterford thing, but why Fardel?'

'You grunt and sweat under a weary life, don't you? Never mind, forget it. We won't go to Princevale Road immediately. First I want to introduce you to some friends of mine.'

Baker seemed to have forgotten his cause for offence and greeted Wexford cordially.

'Michael Baker, meet Mike Burden, and this, Mike, is Sergeant Clements.'

Once, though not for more than a few hours, Wexford had suspected the rubicund baby-faced sergeant of murder to be certain of the undisputed guardianship of his adopted son. It always made him feel a little guilty to remember that, even though that suspicion had never been spoken aloud. But the memory – how could he have entertained such ideas about this pillar of integrity? – had made him careful, in every subsequent conversation, to show kindness to Clements and not fail to ask after young James and the small sister chosen for him. However, the sergeant was too conscious of his subordinate rank to raise domestic matters now, and Wexford was glad of it for other reasons. He, in turn, would have been asked for an account of his grandsons, at present a sore and embarrassing subject.

'Princevale Road?' said Baker. 'Very pleasant district. Unless I'm much mistaken, number six is one of a block of what they call town houses, modern sort of places with a lot of glass and weatherboarding.'

'Excuse me, sir,' Clements said eagerly, 'but unless *I'm* much mistaken we were called to break-in down there a few months back. I'll nip downstairs and do a bit of checking.'

Baker seemed pleased to have guests and something to relieve the tedium of August in Kenbourne Vale. 'How about a spot of lunch at the Grand Duke, Reg? And then we could all get along there, if you've no objection.'

Anxious to do nothing which might upset the prickly Baker, who was a man of whom it might be said that one should not touch his ears, Wexford said that he and Burden would be

617

most gratified, adding to Baker's evident satisfaction, that he didn't know how they would get on without his help.

The sergeant came back, puffed up with news.

'The occupant is a Mrs Farriner,' he said. 'She's away on holiday. It wasn't her place that was broken into, it was next door but one, but apparently she's got a lot of valuable stuff and she came in here before she went away last Saturday week to ask us to keep an eye on the house for her.'

'Should put it on safe deposit,' Baker began to grumble. 'What's the use of getting us to . . .'

Wexford interrupted him. He couldn't help himself. 'How old is she, Sergeant? What does she look like?'

'I've not seen her myself, sir. Middle-aged, I believe, and a widow or maybe divorced. Dinehart knows her.'

'Then get Dinehart to look at that photo, will you?'

'You don't mean you think Mrs Farriner could be that Comfrey woman, sir?'

'Why not?' said Wexford.

But Dinehart was unable to say one way or another. Certainly Mrs Farriner was a big tall woman with dark hair who lived alone. As to her looking like that girl in the picture – well, people change a lot in twenty years. He wouldn't like to commit himself.

Wexford was tense with excitement. Why hadn't he thought of that before? All the time he was frustrated or crossed by people being away on holiday, and yet he had never considered that Rhoda Comfrey might not have been missed by friends and neighbours because they *expected* her to be absent from her home. They supposed a Mrs Farriner to be at some resort, going under the name by which they knew her, so why connect her with a Miss Comfrey who had been found murdered in a Sussex town?

In the Grand Duke, an old-fashioned pub that had surely once been a country inn, they served themselves from the cold table. Wexford felt too keyed-up to eat much. Dealing diplomatically with people like Baker might be a social obligation, but it involved wasting a great deal of time. The others seemed to be taking what he saw as a major break-through far more placidly than he could. Even Burden showed a marked lack of enthusiasm.

'Doesn't it strike you as odd,' he said, 'that a woman like this Mrs Farriner, well-off enough to live where she lives and have all that valuable stuff, should keep a wallet she presumably found on a bus?'

'There's nowt so strange as folk,' said Wexford.

'Maybe, but it was you told me that any departure from the norm is important. I can imagine the Rhoda Comfrey *we* know doing it, but not this Mrs Farriner from what we know of her. Therefore it seems unlikely to me that they're one and the same.'

'Well, we're not going to find out by sitting here feeding our faces,' said Wexford crossly.

To his astonishment, Baker agreed with him. 'You're quite right. Drink up, then, and we'll get going.'

Ascending Montfort Hill on the bus, Wexford hadn't noticed the little row of five or six shops on the left-hand side. This time, in the car, his attention was only drawn to them by the fact of Burden giving them such an intense scrutiny. But he said nothing. At the moment he felt rather riled with Burden. The name of the street which turned off immediately beyond these shops was lettered in black on a white board, Princevale Road, W19, and Burden eyed this with similar interest, craning his neck to look back when they had passed it.

At the very end of the street – or perhaps, from the numbering, the very beginning – stood a row of six terraced houses. They looked less than ten years old and differed completely in style from the detached mock-Tudor, each with a generous front garden, that characterized Princevale Road. Wexford supposed that they had been built on ground left vacant after the demolition of some isolated old house. They were a sign of the times, of scarcity of land and builders' greed. But they were handsome enough for all that, three floors high, boarded in red cedar between the wide plateglass windows. Each had its own garage, integrated and occupying part of the ground floor, each having a different coloured front door, orange, olive, blue, chocolate, yellow and lime. Number six, at this end of the block, had the typical invitation-to-burglars look a house takes on when its affluent and prideful owner is away. All the windows were shut, all the curtains drawn back with perfect symmetry. An empty milk bottle rack stood on the doorstep, and there were no bottles, full or empty, beside it. Stuck through the letterbox and protruding from it were a fistful of letters and circulars in brown envelopes. So much for police surveillance, Wexford thought to himself.

It was rather unwillingly that he now relinquished a share of the investigating to Baker and Clements, though he knew Baker's efficiency. The hard-faced inspector and his sergeant went off to ring at the door of number one. With Burden beside him, Wexford approached the house next door to the empty one.

Mrs Cohen at number five was a handsome Jewess in her early forties. Her house was stuffed with ornaments, the wallpaper flocked crimson on gold, gold on cream. There were photographs about of nearly grown-up children, a buxom daughter in a bridesmaid's dress, a son at his bar mitzvah.

'Mrs Farriner's a very charming nice person. What I call a brave woman, self-supporting, you know. Yes, she's divorced. Some no-good husband in the background, I believe, though she's never told me the details and I wouldn't ask. She's got a lovely little boutique down at Montfort Circus. I've had some really exquisite things from her and she's let me have them at cost. That's what I call neighbourly. Oh, no, it couldn't be' – looking at the photograph '– not *murdered*. Not a false name, that's not Rose's nature. Rose Farriner, that's her name. I

mean, it's laughable what you're saying. Of course I know
where she is. First she went off to see her mother who's in a
very nice nursing home somewhere in the country, and then
she was going on to the Lake District. No, I haven't had a
card from her, I wouldn't expect it.'

The next house was the one which had been burgled, and
Mrs Elliott, when they had explained who they were, promptly
assumed that there had been another break-in. She was at
least sixty, a jumpy nervous woman who had never been in
Rose Farriner's house or entertained her in her own. But she
knew of the existence of the dress shop, knew that Mrs Farriner
was away and had remarked that she sometimes went away
for weekends, in her view a dangerous proceeding with so
many thieves about. The photograph was shown to her and
she became intensely frightened. No, she couldn't say if Mrs
Farriner had looked like that when young. It was evident that
the idea of even hazarding an identification terrified her, and
it seemed as if by so doing she feared to put her own life in
jeopardy.

'Rhoda,' said Wexford to Burden, 'means a rose. It's Greek
for rose. She tells people she's going to visit her mother in a
nursing home. What are the chances she's shifted the facts,
and mother is father and the nursing home's a hospital?'

Baker and Clements met them outside the gate of number
three. They too had been told of mother and the nursing
home, of the dress shop, and they too had met only with
doubt and bewilderment over the photograph. Together the
four of them approached the last, the chocolate coloured, front
door.

Mrs Delano was very young, a fragile pallid blonde with
a pale blond baby, at present asleep in its pram in the porch.

'Rose Farriner's somewhere around forty or fifty,' she
said as if one of those ages was much the same as the other
and all the same to her. She looked closely at the photograph, turned even paler. 'I saw the papers, it never crossed

my mind. It could be her. I can't imagine now why I didn't see it before.'

In the display window on the left side of the shop door was the trendy gear for the very young: denim jeans and waistcoats, tee-shirts, long striped socks. The other window interested Wexford more, for the clothes on show in it belonged in much the same category as those worn by Rhoda Comfrey when she met her death. Red, white and navy were the predominating colours. The dresses and coats were aimed at a comfortably-off middle-aged market. They were 'smart' – a word he knew would never be used by his daughters or by anyone under forty-five. And among them, trailing from an open sleeve to a scent bottle, suspended from a vase to the neck of a crimson sweater, were strings of glass beads.

A woman of about thirty came up to attend to them. She said her name was Mrs Moss and she was in charge while Rose Farriner was away. Her manner astonished, suspicious cautious – all to be expected in the circumstances. Again the photograph was studied and again doubt was expressed. She had worked for Mrs Farriner for only six months and knew her only in her business capacity.

'Do you know what part of the country Mrs Farriner originally came from?' Burden asked her.

'Mrs Farriner's never discussed private things with me.'

'Would you say she's a secretive person?'

Mrs Moss tossed her head. 'I really don't know. We aren't always gossiping to each other, if that's what you mean. She doesn't know any more about me than I know about her.'

Wexford said suddenly, 'Has she ever had appendicitis?'

'Has she *what*?'

'Has she had her appendix out? It's the kind of thing one often does know about people.'

Mrs Moss looked as if she were about to retort that she really couldn't say, but something in Wexford's serious and ponderous gaze seemed to inhibit her. 'I oughtn't to tell you things like that. It's a breach of confidence.'

'You're aware as to whom we think Mrs Farriner really is or was. I think you're being obstructive.'

'But she can't be that woman! She's in the Lake District. She'll be back in the shop on Monday.'

'Will she? Have you had a card from her? A phone call?'

'Of course I haven't. Why should I? I know she's coming home on Saturday.'

'I'll be as frank with you,' Wexford said, 'as I hope you'll be with me. If Mrs Rose Farriner has had her appendix removed she cannot be Miss Rhoda Comfrey. There was no scar from an appendicectomy on Miss Comfrey's body. On the other hand, if she has not, the chances of her having been Miss Comfrey are very strong. We have to know.'

'All right,' said Mrs Moss, 'I'll tell you. It must have been about six months ago, about February or March. Mrs Farriner took a few days off work. It was food poisoning, but when she came back she did say she'd thought at first it was a grumbling appendix because – well, because she'd had trouble like that before.'

CHAPTER TEN

The heat danced in waving mirages on the white roadway. Traffic kept up a ceaseless swirl round Montfort Circus, and there was headache-provoking noise, a blinding glare from sunlight flashing off chrome and glass. Wexford and Baker took refuge in the car which Clements had imperiously parked on a double yellow band.

'We'll have to get into that house, Michael.'

Baker said thoughtfully, 'Of course we do have a key . . .' His eye caught Wexford's. He looked away. 'No, that's out of the question. It'll have to be done on a warrant. Leave it to me, Reg, I'll see what can be done.'

Burden and Clements stood out on the pavement, deep in conversation. Well aware of Burden's prudishness and also of Clement's deep-rooted disapproval of pretty well all persons under twenty-five – which augured ill for James and Angela in the future – Wexford had nevertheless supposed that they would have little in common. He had been wrong. They were discussing, like old duennas, the indecent appearance of the young housewife who had opened the door of number two Princevale Road dressed only in a bikini. Wexford gave the inspector a discourteous and peremptory tap on the shoulder.

'Come on, John Knox. I want to catch the four-thirty-five back to Sussex, home and beauty.'

Burden looked injured, and when they had said good-bye and were crossing the Circus to Parish Oak station, remarked that Clements was a very nice chap.

'Very true,' sneered Wexford with Miss Austen, 'and this is a very nice day and we are taking a very nice walk.'

Having no notion of what he meant but suspecting he was being got at, Burden ignored this and said they would never get a warrant on that evidence.

'What d'you mean, on that evidence? To my mind, its conclusive. You didn't expect one of those women to come out with the whole story, did you? "Oh, yes, Rose told me in confidence her real name's Comfrey." Look at the facts. A woman of fifty goes to a doctor with what she thinks may be appendicitis. She gives the name of Comfrey and her address as 6 Princevale Road, Parish Oak. The only occupant of that house is a woman of around fifty called Rose Farriner. Six months later Rose Farriner is again talking of a possible appendicitis. Rhoda Comfrey is dead, Rose Farriner has disappeared. Rhoda Comfrey was comfortably-off, probably had her own business. According to Mrs Parker, she was interested in dress. Rose Farriner is well-off, has her own dress shop. Rose Farriner has a sick old mother living in a nursing home in the country. Rhoda Comfrey had a sick old father in a hospital in the country. Isn't that conclusive?'

Burden walked up and down the platform, looking gloomily at posters for pale blue movies. 'I don't know. I just think we'll have trouble getting a warrant.'

'There's something else bothering you, isn't there?'

'Yes there is. It's a way-out thing. Look, it's the sort of thing that usually troubles you, not me. It's the sort of thing I usually scoff at, to tell you the truth.'

'Well, what the hell is it? You might as well tell me.'

Burden banged the palm of his hand with his fist. His expression was that of a man who, sceptical, practical, down-to-earth, hesitates from a fear of being laughed at to confess that he has seen a ghost. 'It was when we were driving up Montford Hill and we passed those shops, and I thought it hadn't really been worth getting a bus up that first time, it not being so far from the station to the doctor's place. And then I sort of noticed the shops and the name of the street facing us and . . . Look, it's stupid, forget it. Frankly, the more I think about it the more I can see I was just reading something into nothing. Forget it.'

'*Forget it?* After all that build-up? Are you crazy?'

'I'm sorry, sir,' said Burden very stiffly, 'but I don't approve of police work being based on silly conjectures and the sort of rubbish women call intuition. As you say, we have some very firm and conclusive facts to go on. No doubt, I was being unduly pessimistic about that warrant. Of course we'll get one.'

An explosion of wrath rose in Wexford with a fresh eruption of sweat. 'You're a real pain in the arse,' he snapped, but the rattle of the incoming train drowned his words.

His temper was not improved by Friday morning's newspaper. 'Police Chief Flummoxed by Comfrey Case' said a headline running across four columns at the foot of page one. And there, amid the text, was a photograph of himself, the block for which they had presumably had on file since the days when he had been a fat man. Piggy features glowered above three chins. He glowered at himself in the bathroom mirror and, thanks to Robin running in and out and shouting that grandad had got his picture in the paper, cut himself shaving the chicken skin where the three chins used to be.

He drove to Forest Road and let himself into the late James Comfrey's house with Rhoda Comfrey's key. There were two other keys on the ring, and one of them, he was almost sure, would open Rose Farriner's front door. At the moment, though, he was keeping that to himself for comparison with the one in the possession of Kenbourne police only if the obtaining of the warrant were held up. For if they weren't identical – and, in the light of Rhoda Comfrey's extreme secrecy about her country life in town and her town life in the country, it was likely enough they wouldn't be – he might as well say good-bye to the chance of that warrant here and now. But he did wonder about the third key. To the shop door perhaps? He walked into the living room, insufferably musty now, that Crocker had called a real tip, and flung open the window.

From the drawers which had been re-filled with their

muddled and apparently useless assortment of string and pins and mothballs and coins he collected all the keys that lay amongst it. Fifteen, he counted. Three Yale keys, one Norlond, one stamped RST, one FGW Ltd., seven rusted or otherwise corroded implements for opening the locks of back doors or privy doors or garden gates, a car ignition key and a smaller one, the kind that is used for locking the boot of a car. On both of these last were stamped the Citröen double chevron. They had not been together in the same drawer and to neither of them was attached the usual leather tag.

A violent pounding on the front door made him jump. He went out and opened it and saw Lilian Crown standing there.

'Oh, it's you', she said. 'Thought it might be kids got in. Or squatters. Never know these days, do you?'

She wore red trousers and a tee-shirt which would have been better suited to Robin. Brash fearlessness is not a quality generally associated with old women, especially those of her social stratum. Timidity, awe of authority, a need for self-effacement so often get the upper hand after the climacteric – as Sylvia might have pointed out to him with woeful examples – but they had not triumphed over Mrs Crown. She had the boldness of youth, and this surely not induced by gin at ten in the morning.

'Come in, Mrs Crown,' he said, and he shut the door firmly behind her. She trotted about, sniffing.

'What a pong! Haven't been in here for ten years.' She wrote something in the dust on top of the chest of drawers and let out a girlish giggle.

His hands full of keys, he said, 'Does the name Farriner mean anything to you?'

'Can't say it does.' She tossed her dried grass hair and lit a cigarette. She had come to check that the house hadn't been invaded by vandals, come from only next-door, but she had brought her cigarettes with her and a box of matches. To have a companionable smoke with squatters? She was amazing.

'I suppose your niece had a car,' he said, and he held up the two small keys.

'Never brought it here if she did. And she would've. Never missed a chance of showing off.' Her habit of omitting pronouns from her otherwise not particularly economical speech irritated him. He said rather sharply, 'Then whom do these keys belong to?'

'No good asking me. If she'd got a car left up in London, what's she leave her keys about down here for? Oh, no, that car'd have been parked outside for all the world to see. Couldn't get herself a man, so she was always showing what she could get. Wonder who'll get her money? Won't be me, though, not so likely.'

She blew a blast of smoke into his face, and he retreated, coughing.

'I'd like to know more about that phone call Miss Comfrey made to you on the Friday evening.'

'Like what? said Mrs Crown, smoke issuing dragon-like from her nostrils.

'Exactly what you said to each other. You answered the phone and she said, "Hallo, Lilian. I wonder if you know who this is." Is that right?' Mrs Crown nodded. 'Then what?' Wexford said. 'What time was it?'

'About seven. I said hallo and she said what you've said. In a real put-on voice, all deep and la-di-da. "Of course I know," I said. "If you want to know about your dad," I said, "you'd best get on to the hospital," "Oh, I know all about that," she said. "I'm going away on holiday," she said, "but I'll come down for a couple of days first." '

'You're sure she said that about a holiday?' Wexford interrupted.

' 'Course I'm sure. There's nothing wrong with my memory. Tell you another thing. She called me darling. I was amazed. "I'll come down for a couple of days first, darling," she said. Mind you, there was someone else with her while she was phoning. I know what she was up to. She'd got some woman there with her and she wanted her to think she was talking to a man.'

'But she called you Lilian.

'That's not to say the woman was in there with her when she started talking, is it? No, if you want to know what I think, she'd got some friend in the place with her, and this friend came in after she'd started talking, so she put in that "darling" to make her think she'd got a boy-friend she was going to see. I'm positive, I knew Rhoda. She said it again, or sort of "My dear", she said. "Thought you might be worried if you saw lights on, my dear. I'll come in and see you after I've been to the infirmary." And then whoever it was must have gone out again, I heard a door slam. Her voice went very low after that and she just said in her usual way, "See you Monday then. Good-bye." '

'You didn't wish her Many Happy Returns of the day?'

If a spider had shoulders they would have looked like Lilian Crown's. She shrugged them up and down, up and down, like a marionette. 'Old Mother Parker told me afterwards it was her birthday. You can't expect me to remember a thing like that. I knew it was in August sometime. Sweet fifty and never been kissed!'

'That's all, Mrs Crown,' said Wexford distastefully and escorted her back to the front door. Sometimes he thought how nice it would be to be a judge so that one could boldly and publicly rebuke people. With his sleeve he rubbed out of the dust the arrowed heart – B loves L – she had drawn there, wondering as he did so if B were the 'gentleman friend' she went drinking with, and wondering too about incidence of adolescent souls lingering on in mangy old carcases.

He made the phone call from home.

'I can tell you that here and now,' said Baker. 'Dinehart happened to mention it. Rose Farriner runs a Citröen. Any help to you?'

RUTH RENDELL

'I think so, Michael. Any news of my Chief Constable's get-together with your Super?'

'You'll have to be patient a bit longer, Reg.'

Wexford promised he would be. The air was clearing. Rhoda Comfrey Farriner had made that call to her aunt from Princevale Road on the evening of her birthday when, not unnaturally, she had had a friend with her. A woman, as Lilian Crown had supposed? No, he thought, a man. Late in life, she had at last found herself a man whom she had been attempting to inspire with jealousy. He couldn't imagine why. But never mind. That man, whoever he was, had indeed been inspired, had heard enough to tell him where Rhoda Rose Comfrey Farriner was going on Monday. Wexford had no doubt that that listener had been her killer.

It had been a crime of passion. Adolescent souls linger on, as Mrs Crown had shown him, in ageing bodies. Not in everyone does the heyday in the blood grow tame. Had he not himself even recently, good husband though he tried to be, longed wistfully for the sensation of being again in love? Hankered for the feeling of it and murmured to himself the words of Stendhal – though it might be with the ugliest kitchen-maid in Paris, as long as he loved her and she returned his ardour . . .

The girl who sat in the foyer of Kingsmarkham Police Station was attracting considerable attention. Sergeant Camb had given her a cup of tea, and two young detective constables had asked her if she was quite comfortable and was she sure there was nothing they could do to help her? Loring had wondered if it would cost him his job were he to take her up to the canteen for a sandwich or the cheese on toast Chief Inspector Wexford called Fuzz Fondue. The girl looked nervous and upset. She had with her a newspaper at which she kept staring in an appalled way, but she would tell no one what she wanted, only that she must see Wexford.

630

Her colouring was exotic. There is an orchid, not pink or green or gold, but of a waxen and delicate beige, shaded with sepia, and this girl's face had the hue of such an orchid. Her features looked as if drawn in charcoal on oriental silk, and her hair was black silk, massy and very finely spun. For her country-women the sari had been designed, and she walked as if she were accustomed to wearing a sari, though for this visit she was in Western dress, a blue skirt and a white cotton shirt.

'Why is he such a long time?' she said to Loring, and Loring who was a romantic young man thought that it was in just such a tone that the Shunamite had said to the watchman: Have ye seen him whom my soul loveth?

'He's a busy man,' he said. 'but I'm sure he won't be long.' And for the first time he wished he were ugly old Wexford who could entertain such a visitor in seclusion.

And then, at half past twelve, Wexford walked in.

'Good morning, Miss Patel.'

'You remember me!'

Loring had the answer to that one ready. Who could forget her, once seen? Wexford said only that he did remember her, that he had a good memory for faces, and then poor Loring was sharply dismissed with the comment that if he had nothing to do the chief inspector could soon remedy that. He watched beauty and the beast disappear into the lift.

'What can I do for you, Miss Patel?'

She sat down in the chair he offered her. 'You're going to be very angry with me. I've done something awful. No, really, I'm afraid to tell you. I've been so frightened ever since I saw the paper. I got on the first train. You're all so nice to me, everyone was so nice, and I know it's going to change and it won't be nice at all when I tell you.'

Wexford eyed her reflectively. He remembered that he had put her down as a humorist and a tease, but now her wit had deserted her. She seemed genuinely upset. He decided to try a little humour himself and perhaps put her more at ease.

'I haven't eaten any young women for months now,' he said, 'and, believe me, I make it a rule never to eat them on Fridays.'

She didn't smile. She gave a gulp and burst into tears.

CHAPTER ELEVEN

He could hardly comfort her as he would have comforted his Sylvia or his Sheila whom he would have taken in his arms. So he picked up the phone and asked for someone to bring up coffee and sandwiches for two, and remarked as much to himself as to her that he wouldn't be able to get angry when he had his mouth full.

Crying did nothing to spoil her face. She wiped her eyes, sniffed and said, 'You *are* nice. And I've been such an idiot. I must be absolutely out of my tree.'

'I doubt it. D'you feel like beginning or d'you want your coffee first?'

'I'll get it over.'

Should he tell her he was no longer interested in Grenville West, for it must have been he she had come about, or let it go? Might as well hear what it was.

'I told you a deliberate lie,' she said.

He raised his eyebrows. 'You aren't the first to do that by a long chalk. I could be in the *Guinness Book of Records* as the man who's had more deliberate lies told him than anyone else on earth.'

'But I told this one. I'm so ashamed.'

The coffee arrived and a plate of ham sandwiches. She took one and held it but didn't begin to eat. 'It was about Polly,' she said. 'Polly never goes out in the evenings alone, but *never*. If she goes to Grenville's he always runs her home or puts her in a taxi. She had a horrible thing happen about a year back. She was walking along in the dark and a man came up behind her and put his arms round her. She screamed and kicked him and he ran off, but after that she was afraid to be out alone in the dark. She says if people were allowed to have guns in this country she'd have one.'

Wexford said gently, 'Your deliberate lie, Miss Patel? I think you're stalling.'

'I know I am. Oh, dear. Well, I told you Polly was at home with me that Monday evening, but she wasn't. She went out before I got home from work and she came back alone – oh, I don't know, after I was in bed. Anyway, the next day I asked her where she'd been because I knew Grenville was away, and she said she'd got fed up with Grenville and she'd been out with someone else. Well, I knew she'd been unhappy about him for a long time, Grenville, I mean. She wanted to go and live with him. Actually, she wanted to marry him, but he wouldn't even kiss her.' Malina Patel gave a little shudder. 'Ooh, I wouldn't have wanted him to kiss me! There's something really funny about him, something queer – I don't mean gay-queer, or I don't *think* so – but something sort of hard to . . .'

'On with your story, please, Miss Patel!'

'I'm sorry. So what I was going to say was that Polly had met this man who was married and that Monday they'd been to some motel and had a room there for the evening. And she said this man of hers was afraid of his wife finding out, she'd put a private detective on him, and if that detective came round, would I say she'd been at home with me?'

'*You thought I was a private detective?*'

'Yes! I told you I was mad. I told Polly I'd do what she said if a detective came, and a detective did come. It didn't seem so very awful, you see, because it's not a crime, sleeping with someone else's husband, is it? It's not very nice but it's not a crime. I mean, not against the law.'

Wexford did his best to suppress his laughter and succeeded fairly well. Those remarks of hers, then, which he had thought witty and made at his expense, had in fact come from a genuine innocence. If she wasn't so pretty and so sweet, he would have been inclined to call her – it seemed sacrilege – downright stupid.

She ate a sandwich and took a gulp of coffee.

'And I was glad Polly had got someone after being so miserable about Grenville. And I thought private detectives are awful people, snooping and prying and getting paid for doing dirty things like that. So I thought it didn't really matter telling a lie to that sort of person.'

This time Wexford had to let his laughter go. She looked at him dubiously over the top of her coffee cup.

'Have you ever known any private detectives, Miss Patel?'

'No but I've seen lots of them in films.'

'Which enabled you to identify me with such ease? Seriously, though . . .' He stopped smiling. 'Miss Flinders knew who I was. Didn't she tell you afterwards?'

It was the crucial question, and on her answer depended whether he accompanied her at once back to Kenbourne Vale or allowed her to go alone.

'Of course she did! But I was too stupid to see. She said you hadn't come about the man and the motel at all, but it was something to do with Grenville and that wallet he'd lost and she was going to tell me a whole lot more, but I wouldn't *listen*. I was going out, you see, I was late already, and I was sick of hearing her on and on about Grenville. And she tried again to tell me the next day, only I said not to go on about Grenville, please, I'd rather hear about her new man, and she hasn't mentioned him – Grenville, I mean – since.'

He seized on one point. 'You knew before that the wallet had been lost, then?'

'Oh, yes! She'd been full of it. Long before she told me about the motel and the man and the private detective. Poor Grenville had lost his wallet on a bus and he'd asked her to tell the police but she hadn't because she thought they wouldn't be able to do anything. That was *days* before she went to the motel.'

He believed her. His case for indentifying Rhoda Comfrey as Rose Farriner was strengthened. What further questions he asked Malina Patel would be for his amusement only.

'May I ask what made you come and tell me the awful truth?'

'Your picture in the paper. I saw it this morning and I recognized you.'

From *that* picture? Frivolous inquiries may lead to humiliation as well as amusement.

'Polly had already gone out. I wished I'd listened to her before. I suddenly realized it had all been to do with that murdered woman, and I realized who you were and everything. I felt awful. I didn't go to work. I phoned and said I'd got gastro-enteritis which was another lie, I'm afraid, and I left a note for Polly saying I was going to see my mother who was ill, and then I got the train and came here. I've told so many lies now I've almost forgotten who I've told what.'

Wexford said, 'When you've had more practice you'll learn how to avoid that. Make sure to tell the same lie.'

'You don't mean it!'

'No, Miss Patel, I don't. And don't tell lies to the police, will you? We usually find out. I expect we should have found this one out, only we're no longer very interested in that line of inquiry. Another cup of coffee?'

She shook her head. 'You've been awfully nice to me.'

'You don't go to prison till next time,' said Wexford. 'What they call a suspended sentence. Come on, I'll take you downstairs and we'll see if we can fix you up with a lift to the station. I have an idea Constable Loring has to go that way.'

Large innocent eyes of a doe or calf met his. 'I'm afraid I'm being an awful lot of trouble.'

'Not a bit of it,' Wexford said breezily. 'He'll bear it with the utmost fortitude, believe me.'

Once again he got home early with a free evening ahead. Such a thing rarely happened to him in the middle of a murder case. There was nothing to do but wait and wonder. Though not to select or discard from a list of suspects, for he had none, nor attempt to read hidden meanings and calculated falsehoods between the lines of witnesses' statements. He had no witnesses. All he had were four keys and a missing car; a wallet that beyond all doubt now had been lost on a bus; and a tale of a phone call overheard by a man who, against all reasonable probability, loved withered middle-aged gawky Rhoda Comfrey so intensely that he had killed her from jealousy.

Not a very promising collection of objects and negativities and conjectures.

The river was golden in the evening light, having on its shallow rippling surface a patina like that on beaten bronze. There were dragonflies in pale blue or speckled armour, and the willow trailed his hoar leaves in the grassy stream.

'Wouldn't it be nice,' said Robin, 'if the river went through your garden?'

'My garden would have to be half a mile longer,' said Wexford.

Water rats having failed to appear, the little boys had taken off sandals and socks and were paddling. It was fortunate that Wexford, rather against his will, had consented to remove his own shoes, roll up his trousers and join them. For Ben, playing boats with a log of willow wood, leant over too far and toppled in up to his neck. His grandfather had him out before he had time to utter a wail.

'Good thing it's so warm. You'll dry off on the way back.'

'Grandad carry.'

Robin looked anything but displeased. 'There'll be an awful row.'

'Not when you tell them how brave grandad jumped in and saved your brother's life.'

'Come *on*. It's only about six inches deep. He'll get in a row and so will you. You know what women are.'

But there was no row, or rather, no fresh row to succeed that already taking place. How it had begun Wexford didn't know, but as he and the boys came up to the french windows he heard his wife say with, for her, uncommon tartness, 'Personally, I think you've got far more than you deserved, Sylvia. A good husband, a lovely home and two fine healthy sons. D'you think you've ever done anything to merit more than that?'

Sylvia jumped up. Wexford thought she was going to shout some retort at her mother, but at that moment, seeing her mudstained child, she seized him in her arms and rushed away upstairs with him. Robin, staring in silence, at last followed her, his thumb in his mouth, a habit Wexford thought he had got out of years before.

'And you tell me not to be harsh with her!'

'It's not very pleasant,' said Dora, not looking at him, 'to have your own daughter tell you a woman without a career is a useless encumbrance when she gets past fifty. When her looks have gone. Her husband only stays with her out of duty and because someone's got to support her,'

He was aghast. She had turned away because her eyes had filled with tears. He wondered when he had last seen her cry. Not since her own father died, not for fifteen years.

The second woman to cry over him that day. Coffee and sandwiches were hardly the answer here, though a hug might have been. Instead he said laconically, 'I often think if I were a bachelor now at my age, and you were single – which, of course, you wouldn't be – I'd ask you to marry me.'

She managed a smile. 'Oh, Mr Wexford, this is so sudden. Will you give me time to think it over?'

'No,' he said. 'Sorry. We're going out to celebrate our engagement.' He touched her shoulder. 'Come on. Now. We'll go and have a nice dinner somewhere and then we'll go to the pictures. You needn't tell Sylvia. We'll just sneak out.'

'We can't!'

'We're going to.'

So they dined at the Olive and Dove, she in an old cotton dress and he in his water-rat-watching clothes. And then they saw a film in which no one got murdered or even got married, still less had children or grandchildren, but in which all the characters lived in Paris and drank heavily and made love all day long. It was half past eleven when they got back, and Wexford had the curious feeling, as Sylvia came out into the hall to meet them, that they were young lovers again and she the parent. As if she would say: Where had they been and what sort of a time was this to come home? Of course she didn't.

'The Chief Constable's been on the phone for you, Dad.'

'What time was that?' said Wexford.

'About eight and then again at ten.'

'I can't phone him now. It'll have to wait till the morning.'

Sharing the initials and, to some extent, the appearance of the late General de Gaulle, Charles Griswold lived in a converted farmhouse in the village of Millerton – Millerton *Les-Deux-Églises*, Wexford called it privately. Wexford was far from being his favourite officer. He regarded him as an eccentric and one who used methods of the kind Burden had denounced on Parish Oak station platform.

'I hoped to get hold of you last night,' he said coldly when Wexford presented himself at Hightrees Farm at nine-thirty on Saturday morning.

'I took my wife out, sir.'

Griswold did not exactly think that policemen shouldn't have wives. He had one himself, she was about the place now, though some said he had more or less mislaid her decades ago. But that females of any kind should so intrude as to have to be taken out displeased him exceedingly. He made no comment. His big forehead rucked up into a frown.

'I sent for you to tell you that this warrant has been sworn. The matter is in the hands of the Kenbourne police. Super-intendent Rittifer foresees entering the house tomorrow morning, and it is entirely by his courtesy that you and another officer may accompany him.'

It's my case, Wexford thought resentfully. She was killed in my manor. Oh, Howard, why the hell do you have to be in Tenerife now? Aloud he said, not very politely:

'Why not today?'

'Because it's my belief the damned woman'll turn up today, the way she's supposed to.'

'She won't, sir. She's Rhoda Comfrey.'

'Rittifer thinks so too. I may as well tell you that if it rested on your notions alone the obtaining of this warrant wouldn't have my support. I know you. Half the time you're basing your inquiries on a lot of damn-fool intuitions and *feelings*.'

'Not this time, sir. One woman has positively identified Rhoda Comfrey as Rose Farriner from the photograph. She is the right age, she disappeared at the right time. She complained of appendicits symptoms only a few months after we know Rhoda Comfrey went to a doctor with such symptoms. She . . .'

'All right, Reg.' The Chief Constable delivered the kind of dismissive shot of which only he was capable. 'I won't say you know your own business best because I don't think you do.'

CHAPTER TWELVE

The courtesy of Superintendent Rittifer did not extend to his putting in an appearance at Princevale Road. No blame to him for that, Wexford thought. He wouldn't have done so either in the superintendent's position and on a fine Sunday afternoon. For it was two by the time they got there, he and Burden with Baker and Sergeant Clements.

Because it was a Sunday they had come up in Burden's car and the traffic hadn't been too bad. Now that the time had come he was beginning to have qualms, the seeds of which had been well sown by Burden and the Chief Constable. The very thing which had first put him on to Rose Farriner now troubled him. Why should she go to a doctor and give only to him the name of Rhoda Comfrey while everyone else knew her as Rose Farriner? And a local doctor too, one who lived no more than a quarter of a mile away, who might easily and innocently mention that other name to those not supposed to know it. Then there were the clothes in which Rhoda Comfrey's body had been dressed. He remembered thinking that his own wife wouldn't have worn them even in the days when they were poor. They had been of the same sort of colours as those sold in the Montfort Circus boutique, but had they been of anything like the same standard? Would Mrs Cohen have wanted to get them at cost and have described them as 'exquisite'? How shaky too had been that single identification, made by a very young woman who looked anaemic and neurotic, who might even be suffering from some kind of post-natal hysteria.

Could Burden have been right about the wallet? He got out of the car and looked up at the house. Even from their linings he could see that the curtains were of the kind that cost a hundred pounds for a set. The windows were double-glazed, the orange and white paintwork fresh. A bay tree stood in a tub by the front door. He had seen a bay tree like that in a garden centre priced at twenty-five pounds. Would a woman who could afford all that steal a wallet? Perhaps, if she were leading a double life, had two disparate personalities inside that strong gaunt body. Besides, the wallet had been stolen, and from a bus that passed through Kenbourne Vale . . .

Before Baker could insert the key Mrs Farriner had given Dinehart, Wexford tested out the two which had been on Rhoda Comfrey's ring. Neither fitted.

'That's a bit of a turn-up for the books,' said Burden.

'Not necessarily. I should have brought all the keys that were in that drawer.' Wexford could see Baker didn't like it, but he unlocked the door just the same and they went in.

Insufferably hot and stuffy inside. The temperature in the hall must have been over eighty and the air smelt strongly. Not of mothballs and dust and sweat, though, but of pine-scented cleansers and polish and those deodorizers which, instead of deodorizing, merely provide a smell of their own. Wexford opened the door to the garage. It was empty. Clean towels hung in the yellow and white shower room and there was an unused cake of yellow soap on the washbasin. The only other room on this floor was carpeted in black, and black and white geometrically patterned curtains hung at its french window. Otherwise, it contained nothing but two black armchairs, a glass coffee table and a television set.

They went upstairs, bypassing for the time being the first floor, and mounting to the top. Here were three bedrooms and a bathroom. One of these bedrooms was totally empty, a second, adjoining it, furnished with a single bed, a wardrobe and a dressing table. Everything was extremely clean and sterile-looking, the wastepaper baskets emptied, the flower vases empty and dry. Again, in this bathroom, there were fresh towels hanging. A medicine chest contained aspirins, nasal spray, sticking plaster, a small bottle of antiseptic. Wexford was beginning to wonder if Rhoda Comfrey had ever stamped anything with her personality, but the sight of the principal bedroom changed his mind.

It was large and luxurious. Looking about him, he recalled that spare room in Carlyle Villas. Since then she had come a long way. The bed was oval, its cover made of some sort of beige-coloured furry material, with furry beige pillows piled at its head. A chocolate-coloured carpet, deep-piled, one wall all mirror, one all glass overlooking the street, one filled with built-in cupboards and dressing table counter, the fourth entirely hung with brown glass beads, strings of them from ceiling to floor. On the glass counter stood bottles of French perfume, a pomander and a crystal tray containing silver brushes.

They looked at the clothes in the cupboards. Dresses and coats and evening gowns hung there in profusion, and all were not only as different from those on Rhoda Comfrey's body as a diamond is different from a ring in a cracker, but of considerably higher quality than those in Mrs Farriner's shop.

On the middle floor the living room was L-shaped, the kitchen occupying the space between the arms of the L. A refrigerator was still running on a low mark to preserve two pounds of butter, some plastic-wrapped vegetables and a dozen eggs.

Cream-coloured carpet in the main room, coffee-coloured walls, abstract paintings, a dark red leather suite – real leather, not fake. Ornaments, excluded elsewhere, abounded here. There was a good deal of Chinese porcelain, a bowl that Wexford thought might be Sung, a painting of squat peasants and yellow birds and red and purple splashes that surely couldn't be a Chagall original – or could it?

'No wonder she wanted us to keep an eye on it,' said Baker, and Clements began on a little homily, needless in this company, on the imprudence of householders, the flimsiness of locks and the general fecklessness of people who had more money than they knew what to do with.

Wexford cut him short. 'That's what I'm interested in.' He pointed to a long teak writing desk in which were four drawers and on top of which stood a white telephone. He pictured Rhoda Comfrey phoning her aunt from there, her companion coming in from the kitchen perhaps with ice for drinks. Dr Lomond had warned her to keep off alcohol. There was plenty of it here in the sideboard, quite an exotic variety, Barcardi and Pernod and Campari as well as the usual whisky and gin. He opened the top drawer in the desk.

A cardboard folder marked 'Car' held an insurance policy covering the Citroën, a registration document and a manufacturer's handbook. No driving licence. In another, marked 'House', a second policy and a mass of services bill counterfoils. There was a third folder, marked 'Finance', but it held only a paying-in book from Barclays Bank, Montfort Circus, W19.

'And yet she didn't have a cheque-book or a credit card on her,' Wexford remarked more or less to himself.

Writing paper in the second drawer, with the address of the house on it in a rather ornate script. Under the box was a personal phone directory. Wexford turned to C for Comfrey, F for father, D for dad, H for hospital, S for Stowerton, and back to C for Crown. Nothing . . .

Burden said in a curiously high voice, 'There's some more stuff here.' He had pulled out the drawer in a low table that stood under the window. Wexford moved over to him. A car door banged outside in the street.

'You ought to look at this,' Burden said, and he held out a document. But before Wexford could take it there was a sound from below as of the front door being pushed open.

'Not expecting any more of your people, are you?' Wexford said to Baker.

Baker didn't answer him. He and the sergeant went to the head of the stairs. They moved like burglars surprised in the course of robbery, and 'burglars' was the first word spoken by the woman who came running up the stairs and stopped dead in front of them.

'Burglars! Don't tell me there's been a break-in!'

She looked round her at the open drawers, the disarranged ornaments. 'Mrs Cohen said the police were in the house. I couldn't believe it, not on the very day I come home.' A man had followed her. 'Oh, Bernard, look, my God! For heaven's sake, what's happened?'

In a hollow voice, Baker said, 'It's quite all right, madam, nothing has been taken, there's been no break-in. I'm afraid we owe you an apology.'

She was a tall well-built woman who looked about forty but might have been older. She was handsome, dark, heavily made-up, and she was dressed in expensively tailored denim jeans and waistcoat with a red silk shirt. The man with her seemed younger, a blond burly man with a rugged face.

'What are you doing with my birth certificate?' She said to Burden.

He handed it to her meekly along with a certificate of a divorce decree. Her face registered many things, mainly disbelief and nervous bewilderment. Wexford said:

'You are Mrs Rose Farriner?'

'Well, of course I am. Who did you think I was?'

He told her. He told her who he was and why they were there.

'Lot of bloody nonsense,' said the man called Bernard. 'If you want to make an issue of this, Rosie, you can count on my support. I never heard of such a thing.'

Mrs Farriner sat down. She looked at the photograph of Rhoda Comfrey, she looked at the newspaper Wexford gave her.

'I think I'd like a drink, Bernard. Whisky, please. I thought you were here because burglars had got in and now you say

you thought *I* was this woman. What did you say your name
was? Wexford? Well, Mr Wexford, I am forty-one years old,
not fifty, my father has been dead for nine years and I've
never been to Kingsmarkham in my life. Thanks, Bernard.
That's better. It was a shock, you know. My God, I don't
understand how you could make a mistake like that.' She
passed the documents to Wexford who read them in silence.

Rosemary Julia Golbourne, born forty-one years before in
Northampton. The other piece of paper, which was a certificate making a decree nisi absolute, showed that the marriage
which had taken place between Rosemary Julia Golbourne and
Godfrey Farriner at Christ Church, Lancaster Gate, in April
1959 had been dissolved fourteen years later at Kenbourne
Country Court.

'Had you delayed another week,' said Mrs Farriner, 'I
should have been able to show you my second marriage
certificate.' The blond man rested his hand on her shoulder
and glowered at Wexford.

'I can only apologize very profoundly, Mrs Farriner, and
assure you we have done no damage and that everything will
be restored as it was.'

'Yes, but look here, that's all very well,' said Bernard. 'You
come into my future wife's home, break in more or less, go
through her private papers, and all because . . .'

But Mrs Farriner had begun to laugh. 'Oh, it's so ridiculous!
A secret life, a mystery woman. And that photograph! Would
you like to see what I looked like when I was thirty? For God's
sake, there's a picture in that drawer.' There was. A pretty girl
with dark brown curls, a smiling wide-eyed face only a little
softer and smoother than the same face now. 'Oh, I shouldn't
laugh. That poor creature. But to mix me up with some old
spinster who got herself mugged down a country lane!'

'I must say you take it very well, Rosie.'

Mrs Farriner looked at Wexford. She stopped laughing. He
thought she was a nice woman, if insensitive. 'I shan't take it

further, if that's what you're worrying about,' she said. 'I shan't complain to the Home Secretary. I mean, now I've got over the shock, it'll be something to dine out on, won't it? And now I'll go and make us all some coffee.'

Wexford wasn't over the shock. He refused Baker's offer of a lift to Victoria. Burden and he walked slowly along the pavement. Well-mannered as were the residents of Princevale Road, a good many of Mrs Farriner's neighbours had come out to watch their departure. What some of them were afterwards to call a 'police raid' had made their weekend, though they pretended as they watched that they were clipping their hedges or admonishing their children.

The sun shone strongly on Kenbourne Tudor, on subtly coloured paintwork and unsubtly coloured flowers, petunias striped and quartered like flags, green plush lawns where sprinklers fountained. Wexford felt hollow inside. He felt that hollow sickness that follows exclusively the making of some hideous howler or *faux pas*.

'There'll be an awful row,' said Burden unhelpfully, using the very words Robin had used two days before.

'I suppose so. I should have listened to you.'

'Well . . . I didn't say much. It was just that I had this feeling all the time, and you know how I distrust "feelings".'

Wexford was silent. They had come to the end of the street where it joined Montfort Hill. There he said, 'What was the feeling? I suppose you can tell me now.'

'You've asked me at exactly the right point, OK, I'll tell you. It struck me the first time we passed this spot.' Burden led the chief inspector a little way down Montfort Hill, away from the bus stop they had been making for. 'We'll suppose Rhoda Comfrey is on her way to Dr Lomond's, whose name she's got out of the phone book. She isn't exactly sure where Midsomer Road is, so she doesn't get the bus, she walks from Parish Oak station.

'For some reason which we don't know she doesn't want
to give Dr Lomond her true address, so she has to give him a
false one, and one that's within the area of his practice. So far
she hasn't thought one up. But she passes these shops and looks
up at that tobacconist, and what's the first thing she sees?'

Wexford looked up. 'A board advertising Wall's ice cream.
My God, Mike, a hanging sign for Player's Number Six
cigarettes. Was that what your feeling was about. Was that
why you kept looking back that first time we came in the car?
She sees the number six, and then that black and white street
sign for Princevale Road?'

Burden nodded unhappily.

'I believe you're right, Mike. It's the way people do behave.
It could happen almost unconsciously. Dr Lomond's receptionist asks her for her address when she comes to register and
she comes out with number six, Princevale Road.' Wexford
struck his forehead with the heel of his hand. 'I ought to have
seen it! I've come across something like it before, and here in
Kenbourne Vale, years ago. A girl called herself Loveday
because she'd seen the name on a shop.' He turned on Burden.
'Mike, you should have told me about this, you should have
told me last week.'

'Would you have believed me if I had?'

Hot-tempered though he might be, Wexford was a fair
man. 'I might've – but I'd have wanted to get into that house
just the same.'

Burden shrugged. 'We're back to square one, aren't we?'

CHAPTER THIRTEEN

There was no point in delaying. He went straight to Hightrees Farm. Griswold listened to him with an expression of lip-curling disgust. In the middle of Wexford's account he helped himself to a brandy and soda, but he offered nothing to his subordinate.

When it was ended he said, 'Do you ever read the newspapers?'

'Yes, sir. Of course.'

'Have you ever noticed how gradually over the past ten years or so the Press have been ramming it home to people that their basic freedoms are constantly under threat? And who comes in for most of the shit-throwing? The police. You've just given them a big helping of it on a plate, haven't you? All ready for throwing tomorrow morning.'

'I don't believe Mrs Farriner will tell the Press, sir.'

'She'll tell her friends, won't she? Some busybody dogooder will get hold of it.' The Chief Constable, who referred to Mid-Sussex as the General had been in the habit of referring to *la belle France*, with jealousy and with reverence, said, 'Understand, I will not have the hitherto unspotted record of the Mid-Sussex Constabulary smeared all over by the gutter Press. I will not have it endangered by one foolish man who acts on psychology and not on circumstantial evidence.'

Wexford smarted under that one. 'Foolish man' was hard to take. And he smarted more when Griswold went on, even though he now called him Reg which meant there would be no immediate retribution.

'This woman's been dead for two weeks, Reg, and as far as you've got, she might as well have dropped from Mars. She might as well have popped off in a space ship every time she left Kingsmarkham.' I'm beginning to think she did, Wexford thought, though he said nothing aloud. 'You know I don't care to call the Yard in unless I must. By the end of this coming week I'll have to if my own men can't do better than this. It seems to me . . .' and he gave Wexford a ponderous bull-like glare '. . . that all you can do is get your picture in the papers like some poove of a film actor.'

Sylvia sat in the dining room, the table covered with application forms for jobs and courses.

'You've picked the wrong time of year,' her father said, picking up a form that applied for entry to the University of London. 'Their term starts next month.'

'The idea is I get a job to fill in the year and start doing my degree next year. I have to get a grant, you see.'

'My dear, you don't stand a chance. They'll assess you on Neil's salary. At least, I suppose so. He's your husband.'

'Maybe he won't be by then. Oh, I'm so sick of you men ruling the world! It's not fair just taking it for granted my husband pays for me like he'd pay for a child.'

'Just as fair as taking it for granted the taxpayers will. I know you're not interested in my views or your mother's, but I'm going to give you mine just the same. The way the world still is, women have to prove they're as capable as men. Well, you prove it. Do an external degree or a degree by correspondence and in something that's likely to lead to a good job. It'll take you five years and by that time the boys'll be off your hands. Then when you're thirty-five you and Neil will be two professional people with full-times jobs and a servant you both pay for. Nobody'll treat you like a chattel or a furniture polisher then. You'll see.'

She pondered, looking sullen. Very slowly she began filling in the section of a form headed 'Qualifications'. The list of them, Wexford noted sadly, was sparse. She scrawled a line through *Mr/Mrs/Miss* and wrote *Ms.* Her head came up and the abundant hair flew out.

'I'm glad I've got boys. I'd feel sick with despair for them if they were girls. Didn't you want a son?'

'I suppose I did before Sheila was born. But after she was born I didn't give it another thought.'

'Didn't you think what we'd suffer? You're aware and sensitive, Dad. Didn't you think how we'd be exploited and humiliated by men and *used?*'

It was too much. There she sat, tall and powerful, blooming with health, the youthful hue sitting on her skin like morning dew, a large diamond cluster sparkling on her hand, her hair scented with St Laurent's *Rive Gauche*. Her sister, described by critics as one of England's most promising young actresses, had a big flat of her own in St John's Wood where, it had often seemed to her father, she sweetly exploited and used all the men who frequented it.

'I couldn't send you back, could I?' he snapped. 'I couldn't give God back your entrance ticket and ask for a male variety instead. I know exactly what Freud felt when he said there was one question that would always puzzle him. What is it that women want?'

'To be people,' she said.

He snorted and walked out. The Crockers and a couple of neighbours were coming in for drinks. The doctor hustled Wexford upstairs and produced his sphygmomanometer.

'You look rotten, Reg. What's the matter with you?'

'That's for you to say. How's my blood pressure?'

'Not bad. Is it Sylvia?'

He hated explaining why his daughter and the children were in the house. People categorize others into the limited compartments their imaginations permit. They assumed that either Sylvia or her husband had been unfaithful or that Neil had been cruel. He couldn't spell it all out, but just had to watch the speculating gleam in their eyes and take their pity.

'Partly,' he said, 'and it's this Comfrey case. I dream about her, Len. I rack my brains, such as they are, about her. And

I've made a crazy mistake. Griswold half-crucified me this afternoon, called me a foolish man.'

'We all have to fail, Reg,' said Crocker like a liberal headmaster.

'There was a sort of sardonic gleam in her eyes when we found her. I don't know if you noticed. I feel as if she's laughing at me from beyond the grave. Hysterical, eh? That's what Mike says I am.'

But Mike didn't say it again. He knew when to tread warily with the chief inspector, though Wexford had become a little less glum when there was nothing in the papers on Monday or Tuesday about the Farriner fiasco.

'And that business wasn't all vanity and vexation of spirit,' he said. 'We've learnt one thing from it. The disappearance of Rhoda Comfrey, alias whatever, may not have been re-marked by her neighbours because they expect her to be away on holiday. So we have to wait and hope a while longer that someone from outside will still come to us.'

'Why should they at this stage?'

'Exactly because it is at this stage. How long do the majority of people go on holiday for?'

'A fortnight,' said Burden promptly.

Wexford nodded. 'So those friends and neighbours who knew her under an assumed name would have expected her back last Saturday. Now they wouldn't have been much con-cerned if she wasn't back by Saturday, but by Monday when she doesn't answer her phone, when she doesn't turn up for whatever work she does? By today?'

'You've got a point there.'

'God knows, every newspaper reader in the country must be aware we still don't know her London identity. The Press has rammed it home hard enough. Wouldn't it be nice, Mike, if at this very moment some public-spirited citizen were to be walking into a nick somewhere in north or west London to say she's worried because her boss or the woman next door hasn't come back from Majorca?'

Burden always took Wexford's figurative little flights of fancy literally. 'She couldn't have been going there, wouldn't have had a passport.'

'As Rhoda Comfrey she might have. Besides, there are all sorts of little tricks you can get up to with passports. You're not going to tell me a woman who's fooled us like this for two weeks couldn't have got herself a dozen false passports if she'd wanted them.'

'Anyway, she didn't go to Majorca. She came here and got herself stabbed.' Burden went to the window and said wonderingly, 'There's a cloud up there.'

'No bigger than a man's hand, I daresay.'

'Bigger than that,' said Burden, not recognizing this quotation from the Book of Kings. 'In fact, there are quite a lot of them.' And he made a remark seldom uttered by Englishmen in a tone of hope, still less of astonishment. 'It's going to rain.'

The room went very dark and they had to switch the light on. Then a golden tree of forked lightning sprang out of the forest, splitting the purple sky. A great rolling clap of thunder sent them retreating from where they had been watching the beginnings of this storm, and Burden closed the windows.

At last the rain came, but sluggishly at first in the way rain always does come when it has held off for weeks, slow intermittent plops of it. Wexford remembered how Sylvia, when she was a tiny child, had believed until corrected that the rain was contained up there in a bag which someone punctured and then finally sliced open. He sat down at his desk and again phoned the Missing Persons Bureau, but no one had been reported missing who could remotely be identified as Rhoda Comfrey.

It was still only the middle of the afternoon. Plenty of time for the public-spirited citizen's anxiety and tension to mount until . . . Today was the day, surely, when that would happen if it was going to happen. The bag was sliced open and rain crashed in a cataract against the glass, bringing with it a sudden drop in the temperature. Wexford actually shivered; for the first time in weeks he felt cold, and he put on his jacket. He found himself seeing the storm as an omen, this break in the weather signifying another break. Nonsense, of course, the superstition of a foolish man. He had thought he had had breaks before, hadn't he? Two of them, and both had come to nothing.

By six there had come in no phone calls relevant to Rhoda Comfrey, but still he waited, although it was not necessary for him to be there. He waited until seven, until half past, by which time all the exciting pyrotechnics of the storm were over and the rain fell dully and steadily. At a quarter to eight, losing faith in his omen, in the importance of this day above other days – it had been one of the dreariest he had spent for a long time – he drove home through the grey rain.

CHAPTER FOURTEEN

It was like a winter's evening. Except at night, the french windows had not been closed since the end of July and now it was August twenty third. Tonight they were not only closed, but the long velvet curtains were drawn across them.

'I thought of lighting a coal fire,' said Dora who had switched on one bar of the electric heater.

'You've got quite enough to do without that.' Child-minding, Wexford thought, cooking meals for five instead of two. 'Where's Sylvia gone?' he snapped.

'To see Neil, I think. She said something earlier about presenting him with a final ultimatum.'

Wexford made an impatient gesture. He began to walk about the room, then sat down again because pacing can only provoke irritation in one's companion. Dora said:

'What is it, darling? I hate to see you like this.'

He shrugged. 'I ought to rise above it. There's a story told about St Ignatius of Loyola. Someone asked him what he would do if the Pope decided to dissolve the Society of Jesus on the morrow, and he said, "Ten minutes at my orisons and it would be all the same to me." I wish I could be like that.'

She smiled. 'I won't ask you if you want to talk about it.'

'Wouldn't do any good. I've talked about it to the point of exhaustion – the Comfrey case, that is. As for Sylvia, is there anything we haven't said? I suppose there'll be a divorce and she'll live here with the boys. I told her this was her home and of course I meant it. I read somewhere the other day that one in three marriages now come to grief, and hers is going to be one of them. That's all. It just doesn't make me feel very happy.'

The phone rang, and with a sigh Dora got up to answer it.

'I'll get it,' Wexford said, almost pouncing on the receiver. The voice of Dora's sister calling from Wales as she mostly did on a mid-week evening. He said, yes, there had been a storm and, yes, it was still raining, and then he handed the phone to Dora, deflated. Two weeks before, just a bit earlier than this, he had received the call that told him of the discovery of Rhoda Comfrey's body. He had been confident then, full of hope, it had seemed simple.

Through layers of irrelevant facts, information about people he would never see again and whom he need not have troubled to question, through a mind-clogging jumble of trivia, a gaunt harsh face looked up at him out of his memory, the eyes still holding that indefinable expression. She had been fifty and ugly and shapeless and ill-dressed, but someone had killed her from passion and in revenge. Some man who loved her had believed her to be coming here to meet another man. It was inconceivable but it must be so. Stabbing in those circumstances is always a crime of passion, the culmination of a jealousy or a rage or an anguish that suddenly explodes. No one kills in that way because he expects to inherit by his victim's death, or thereby to achieve some other practical advantage . . .

'They had the storm in Pembroke this morning,' said Dora, coming back.

'Fantastic,' said her husband, and then quickly, 'Sorry, I shouldn't snipe at you. Is there anything on the television?'

She consulted the paper. 'I think I know your tastes by now. If I suggested any of this lot I might get that vase chucked at me. Why don't you read something?'

'What is there?'

'Library books. Sylvia's and mine. They're all down there by your chair.'

He humped the stack of them on to his lap. It was easy to sort out which were Sylvia's. Apart from *Woman and the Sexist Plot*, there was Simone de Beauvoir's *The Second Sex* and Mary Wollstonecraft's *A Vindication of the Rights of Woman*.

Dora's were a detective story, a biography of Marie Antoinette and Grenville West's *Apes in Hell*. His reaction was to repudiate this last, for it reminded him too forcibly of his first mistake. Women's Lib as seen through the eyes of Shelley's mother-in-law would almost have been preferable. But that sort of behaviour was what Burden called hysterical.

'What's this like?'

'Not bad,' said Dora. 'I'm sure it's very well researched. As far as I'm concerned, the title's way-out, quite meaningless.'

'It probably refers to an idea the Elizabethans had about unmarried women. According to them, they were destined to lead apes in hell.'

'How very odd. You'd better read it. It's based on some play called *The Maid's Tragedy*.'

But Wexford, having looked at the portrait of its author, pipe in mouth, on the back of the jacket, turned to Marie Antoinette. For the next hour he tried to concentrate on the childhood and youth of the doomed Queen of France, but it was too real for him, too factual. These events had taken place, they were history. What he needed tonight was total escape. A detective story, however bizarre, however removed from the actualities of detection, was the last thing to give it to him. By the time Dora had brought in the tray with the coffee things, he had again picked up *Apes in Hell*.

Grenville West's biography was no longer of interest to him, but he was one of those people who, before reading a novel, like to acquaint themselves with that short summary of the plot publishers generally display on the front flap of the jacket and sometimes in the preliminary pages. After all, if this précis presents too awful an augury one need read no further. But in this instance the jacket flap had been obscured by the library's own covering of the book, so he turned the first few pages.

Apparently, it was West's third novel, having been preceded by *Her Grace of Amalfi* and *Arden's Wife*. The plot summary informed him that the author's source had been Beaumont and Fletcher's *The Maid's Tragedy*, a Jacobean drama set in classical Rhodes. West, however, had shifted the setting to the England of his favourite half-timbering and knot gardens, and with an author's omnipotent conjuring trick – his publisher's panegyric, this – had transformed kings and princes into a seventeenth-century aristocracy. Not a bad idea, Wexford thought, and one which Beaumont and Fletcher might themselves have latched on to if writing about one's contemporaries and fellow nationals had been more in favour at the time.

Might as well see what it was like. He turned the page, and his fingers rested on the open pages, his breath held. Then he gave a gasp.

'What on earth is it?' said Dora.

He made her no answer. He was looking at two lines of type in italics on an otherwise blank sheet. The dedication.

For Rhoda Comfrey, without whom this book could never have been written.

CHAPTER FIFTEEN

'Our first red herring,' Burden said.

'Only it wasn't a red herring. If this isn't proof West knew her I don't know what would be. He's known her for years, Mike. This book was published ten years ago.'

It was a cool clean day. The rain had washed roofs and pavements and had left behind it a thin mist, and the thermometer on Wexford's wall recorded a sane and satisfactory sixty-five degrees. Burden was back to a normal-weight suit. He stood by the window, closed against the mist, examining *Apes in Hell* with a severe and censorious expression.

'What a load of rubbish,' was his verdict. He had read the plot summary. 'Ten years ago, yes,' he said. 'That Hampton guy, his publisher, why didn't he tell you West had dedicated a book to this woman?'

'Maybe he'd forgotten or he'd never known. I don't know anything about publishing, Mike. They call Hampton West's editor, but for all I know an editor may never see a writer's dedication. In any case, I refuse to believe that a perfectly respectable and no doubt disinterested man like Hampton was involved in a plot to conceal from me West's friendship with Rhoda Comfrey. And the same goes for his literary agent and for Vivian and Polly Flinders. They simply didn't know about the dedication.'

'It's a funny thing about the wallet, isn't it?' said Burden after a pause. 'He must have given it to her. The alternative is inconceivable.'

'The alternative being that he lost it and it was found by chance and deliberately kept by a friend of his? That's impossible, but there's a possibility between those two alternatives, that he left it behind in her house or flat or wherever

659

she lived and she, knowing he was to be away for a month, just kept it for him.'

'And *used* it? I don't think much of that idea. Besides, those two girls told you he lost it, and that he asked this Polly to report the loss to the police.'

'Are they both lying then?' said Wexford. 'Why should they lie?'

Burden didn't answer him. 'You'll have him fetched back now, of course.'

'I shall try. I've already had a word with the French police. Commissaire Laquin in Marseilles. We worked together on a case once, if you remember. He's a nice chap.'

'I'd like to have heard that conversation.'

Wexford said rather coldly, 'He speaks excellent English. If West's in the South of France he'll find him. It shouldn't be too difficult even if he's moving from one hotel to another. He must be producing his passport wherever he goes.'

Burden rubbed his chin, gave Wexford the sidelong look that presages a daring or even outrageous suggestion. 'Pity we can't get into West's flat.'

'Are you insane? D'you want to see me back on the beat or in the sort of employment Malina Patel marked out for me? Christ, Mike, I can just see us rifling through West's papers and have him come walking in in the middle of it.'

'OK, OK. You're getting this Laquin to send West home? Suppose he won't come? He may think it a bit thin, fetching him back from his holiday merely because he knew someone who got herself murdered.'

'Laquin will ask him to accompany him to a police station and then he'll phone me so that I can speak to West. That'll be a start. If West can give me Rhoda Comfrey's London address he may not need to come home. We'll see. We can't take any steps to enforce his return, Mike. As far as we know, he's committed no offence and it's quite possible he hasn't seen an English newspaper since he left this country. It's more than likely, if he's that much of a francophile.'

Given to *non sequiturs* this morning, Burden said, 'Why couldn't this book have been written without her?'

'It only means she helped him in some way. Did some research for him, I daresay, which may mean she worked in a library. One thing, this dedication seems to show West had no intention of concealing their friendship.'

'Let's hope not. So you're going to glue yourself to this phone for the next few days, are you?'

'No,' Wexford retorted. 'You are. I've got other things to do.'

The first should have been to question those girls, but that would have to wait until they were both home in the evening. The second perhaps to visit Silk and Whitebeam in Jermyn Street and discover in detail the circumstances of the purchase of that wallet. And yet wouldn't all be made plain when West was found? Wexford had a feeling – what anathema that would have been to the Chief Constable – that West was not going to be easily found.

He sent Loring back to the leather shop and Bryant to inquiring of every library in London as to whether any female member of their staff had not returned to work after a holiday as she should have done. Then he took himself to Forest Road.

Young Mrs Parker with a baby on her hip and old Mrs Parker with a potato peeler in her hand looked at *Apes in Hell* not so much as if it were an historical novel as any hysterical novelty. Babies and beans might be all in the day's work to them. Books were not.

'A friend of Miss Comfrey's?' said Stella Parker at last. It seemed beyond her comprehension that anyone she knew or had known could also be acquainted with the famous. Grenville West was famous in her eyes simply because he had his name in print and had written things which got into print. She repeated what she had said, this time without the interrogative note, accepting the incredible just as she accepted nuclear fission or the fact that potatoes now cost fifteen pence a pound. 'A friend of Miss Comfrey's. Well!'

Her grandmother-in-law was less easily surprised. 'Rhoda was a go-getter. I shouldn't wonder if she'd known the Prime Minister.'

'But do you know for a fact that she was a friend of Grenville West's?'

'Speak up.'

'He wants to know,' said Stella Parker, 'if you know if she knew him, Nanna.'

'Me? How should I know. The only West I ever come across was that Lilian.'

Wexford bent over her. 'Mrs Crown?'

'That's right. Her first husband's name was West. She was Mrs West when she first come here to live with Agnes. And poor little John, he was called West too, of course he was. I thought I told you that, young man, when we was talking about names that time.'

'I didn't ask you,' said Wexford.

West is a common name. So he thought as he waited in the car for Lilian Crown to come home from the pub. But if Grenville West should turn out to be some connection by marriage of Rhoda Comfrey's how much more feasible would any acquaintance between them be. If, for instance, they called each other cousin as many people do with no true blood tie to justify it. Their meeting, their casual affection, would then be explained. And might she not have called herself West, preferring this common though euphonious name over the rarer Comfrey?

Lilian Crown arrived home on the arm of an elderly man whom she did not attempt to introduce to Wexford. They were neither of them drunk, that is to say unsteady on their feet or slurred in their speech, but each reeked of liquor, Lilian Crown of spirits and the old man of strong ale. There was even a dampish look about them, due no doubt to the humid weather, but suggesting rather that they had been dipped into vats of their favourite tipple.

Mrs Crown evidently wanted her friend to accompany her and Wexford into the house, but he refused with awed prot-estations and frenetic wobblings of his head. Her thin shoulders went up and she made a monkey face at him.

'OK, be like that.' She didn't say good-bye to him but marched into the house, leaving Wexford to follow her. He found her already seated on the food-stained sofa, tearing open a fresh packet of cigarettes.

'What is it this time?'

He knew he was being over-sensitive with this woman, who was herself totally insensitive. But it was difficult for him, even at his age and after his experiences, to imagine a woman whose only child was a cripple and an idiot not to have had her whole life blighted by her misfortune. And although he sensed that she might answer any question he asked her about her son with indifference, he still hoped to avoid asking her. Perhaps it was for himself and not for her that he felt this way, perhaps he was, even now, vulnerable to man's or woman's, inhumanity.

'You were Mrs West, I believe,' he said, 'before you married for the second time?'

'That's right. Ron – Mr West, that is – got himself killed at Dunkirk.' She put it in such a way as to imply that her first husband had deliberately placed himself as the target for a German machine-gun or aircraft. 'What's that got to do with Rhoda?'

'I'll explain that in a moment, if you don't mind. Mr West had relatives, I suppose?'

'Of course he did. His mum didn't find him under a gooseberry bush. Two brothers and a sister he had.'

'Mrs Crown, I have good reason to be interested in anyone connected with your late niece who bears the name of West. Did these people have children? Do you know where they are now?' Would she, when she hadn't known the address of her own niece? But very likely they had no reason to be secretive.

'Ethel, the sister, she never spoke a word to me after I married Ron. Gave herself a lot of mighty fine airs, for all her dad was only a farm labourer. Married a Mr Murdoch, poor devil, and I reckon they'd both be over eighty now if they're not dead. The brothers was Len and Sidney, but Sidney got killed in the war like Ron. Len was all right, I got on OK with Len.' Mrs Crown said this wonderingly, as if she had surprised herself by admitting that she got on with anyone connected to her by blood or by marriage. 'Him and his wife, they still send me Christmas cards.'

'Have they any children?'

Mrs Crown lit another cigarette from the stub of the last, and Wexford got a blast of smoke in his face. 'Not to say *children*. They'll be in their late thirties by now. Leslie and Charley, they're called.' The favour in which she held the parents did not apparently extend to their sons. 'I got an invite to Leslie's wedding, but he treated me like dirt, acted like he didn't know who I was. Don't know if Charley's married, wouldn't be bothered to ask. He's a teacher, fancies himself a cut above his people, I can tell you.'

'So as far as you know there isn't a *Grenville* West among them?'

Like Mrs Parker, Lilian Crown had evidently set him down as stupid. They were both the sort of people who assume authority, any sort of authority, to be omniscient, to know all sorts of private and obscure details of their own families and concerns as well as they know them themselves. This authority did not, and therefore this authority must be stupid. Mrs Crown cast up her eyes.

'Of course there is. They're all called Grenville, aren't they? It's like a family name, though what right a farm labourer thinks he's got giving his boys a fancy handle like that I never will know.'

'Mrs Crown,' said Wexford, his head swimming, 'what do you mean, they're all called Grenville?'

She reeled it off rapidly, a list of names. 'Ronald Grenville West, Leonard Grenville West, Sidney Grenville West, Leslie Grenville West, Charles Grenville West.'

'And these people,' he said, half-stunned by it, 'your niece Rhoda knew them?'

'May have come across Leslie and Charley when they was little kids, I daresay. She'd have been a lot older.'

He had written the names down. He looked at what he had written. Addresses now, and Mrs Crown was able, remarkably, to provide them or some of them. The parents lived at Myfleet, a village not far from Kingsmarkham, the son Leslie over the county boundary in Kent. She didn't know the whereabouts of Charley, but his school was in South London, so his father said, which meant he must live down there somewhere, didn't it?

And now he had to ask it, as tactfully as he could. For if every male of the West family . . .

'And that is all?' he said almost timorously. 'There's no one else called Grenville West?'

'Don't think so. Not that I recall.' She fixed him with a hard stare. 'Except my boy, of course, but that wouldn't count, him not being normal. Been in a home for the backward like since he was so high. He's called John Grenville West, for what it's worth.'

CHAPTER SIXTEEN

No word came from Commissaire Laquin that day. But Loring's inquiries were more fruitful, clearing up at last the matter
of the wallet.

'Those girls weren't lying,' Wexford said to Burden. 'He
did lose a wallet on a bus, but it was his *old* one he lost. That's
what he told the assistant at Silk and Whitebeam when he
went on Thursday, 4 August, to replace it with a new one.'

'And yet it was the new one we found in the possession of
Rhoda Comfrey.'

'Mike, I'm inclined to believe that the old one did turn up
and he gave her the new one, maybe on the Saturday when
it was too late to tell Polly Flinders. She told him she had
reached the age of fifty the day before, and he said OK, have
this for a present.'

'You think he was a sort of cousin of hers?'

'I do, though I don't quite see yet how it can help us. All
these people on the list have been checked out. Two of them,
in any case, are dead. One is in an institution at Myringham,
the Abbotts Palmer Hospital. One is seventy-two years old.
One had emigrated with his wife to Australia. The last of
them, Charles Grenville West, is a teacher, has been married
for five years and lives in Carshalton. The father, also John
Grenville West, talks of cousins and second cousins who may
bear the name, but he's doddery and vague. He can't tell us
the whereabouts of any of them. I shall try this Charles.'

Almost the first thing Wexford noticed when he was shown
into Charles Grenville West's living room was a shelf of books
with familiar titles: *Arden's Wife, Apes in Hell, Her Grace of Amalfi,
Fair Wind to Alicante, Killed with Kindness*. They had pride of

place in the bookcase and were well cared for. The whole room was well cared for, and the neat little house itself, and smiling, unsuspicious, cooperative Mr and Mrs West.

On the phone he had told Charles West only that he would like to talk to him about the death of a family connection of his, and West had said he had never met Rhoda Comfrey – well, he might have seen her when he was a baby – but Wexford would be welcome to call just the same. And now Wexford, having accepted a glass of beer, having replied to kind inquiries about the long journey he had made, looked again at the books, pointed to them and said:

'Your namesake would appear to be a favourite author of yours.'

West took down *Fair Wind to Alicante*. 'It was the name that first got me reading them,' he said, 'and then I liked them for themselves. I kept wondering if we were related.' He turned to the back of the jacket and the author's photograph. 'I thought I could see a family resemblance, but I expect that was imagination or wishful thinking, because the photo's not very clear, is it? And then there were things in the books, I mean in the ones with an English setting...'

'What sort of things?' Wexford spoke rather sharply. His tone wasn't one to give offence, but rather to show Charles West that these questions were relevant to the murder.

'Well, for instance, in *Killed with Kindness* he describes a manor house that's obviously based on Clythorpe Manor near Myringham. The maze is described and the long gallery. I've been in the house, I know it well. My grandmother was in service there before she married.' Charles West smiled. 'My people were all very humble farm workers and the women were all in service, but they'd lived in that part of Sussex for generations, and it did make me wonder if Grenville West was one of us, some sort of cousin, because he seemed to know the countryside so well. I asked my father but he said the family was so huge and with so many ramifications.'

'I wonder you didn't write to Grenville West and ask *him*,' said Wexford.

'Oh, I did. I wrote to him care of his publishers and I got a very nice letter back. Would you like to see it? I've got it somewhere.' He went to the door and called out, 'Darling, d'you think you could find that letter from Grenville West? But he's not a relation,' he said to Wexford. 'You'll see what he says in the letter.'

Mrs West brought it in. The paper was headed with the Elm Green address. 'Dear Mr West,' Wexford read. 'Thank you for your letter. It gives me great pleasure that you have enjoyed my novels, and I hope you will be equally pleased with *Sir Bounteous*, which is to be published next month and which is based on Middleton's *A Mad World, My Masters*.

'This novel also has an English setting or, more precisely, a Sussex setting. I am very attached to your native county and I am sorry to have to tell you that it is not mine, nor can I trace any connection between your ancestry and mine. I was born in London. My father's family came originally from Lancashire and my mother's from the West Country. Grenville was my mother's maiden name.

'So, much as I should have liked to discover some cousins – as an only child of two only children, I have scarcely any living relatives – I must disappoint myself and perhaps you too.

'With best wishes,

'Yours sincerely,

'Grenville West.'

With the exception, of course, of the signature, it was typewritten. Wexford handed it back with a shrug. Whatever the information, or lack of it, had done for the author and for Charles West, it had certainly disappointed him. But there was something odd about it, something he couldn't quite put his finger on. The style was a little pretentious with a whisper of arrogance, and in the calculated leading from paragraph to paragraph, the almost too elegant elision of the professional writer. That wasn't odd, though, that wasn't odd at all . . . He was growing tired of all these hints, these 'feelings', these pluckings at his mind and at the *fingerspitzengefühl* he seemed to have lost. No other case had ever been so full of whispers that led nowhere. He despised himself for not hearing and understanding them, but whatever Griswold might say, he knew they were sound and true.

'A very nice letter,' he said dully. Except, he would have liked to add, that most of it is a carefully spun fabric of lies.

There was one more Grenville West to see, the one who dragged out his life in the Abbotts Palmer Hospital. Wexford tried to picture what that man would be like now, and his mind sickened. Besides, he knew he had only contemplated going there to keep himself away from the police station, away from hearing that Laquin had nothing for him, that Griswold had called in the Yard over his head, for it was getting to the end of the week now, it was Thursday.

That was no attitude for a responsible police officer to take. He went in. The weather was hot and muggy again, and he felt he had gone back a week in time, for there, waiting for him again, was Malina Patel.

An exquisite little hand was placed on his sleeve, limpid eyes looked earnestly up at him. She seemed tinier and more fragile than ever. 'I've brought Polly with me.'

Wexford remembered their previous encounters. The first time he had seen her as a provocative tease, the second as an enchanting fool. But now an uneasiness began to overcome his susceptibility. She gave the impression of trying hard to be good, of acting always on impulse, of a dotty and delightful innocence. But was innocent dottiness compatible with such careful dressing, calculated to stun? Could that sweet guilelessness be natural? He cursed those susceptibilities of his, for they made his voice soft and gallant when he said:

'Have you now? Then where is she?'

'In the loo. She said she felt sick and one of the policemen showed her where the loo was.'

'All right. Someone will show you both up to my office when she's feeling better.'

Burden was there before him. 'It would seem, according to your pal, that the whole of France is now being scoured for our missing author. He hasn't been in Annecy, whatever your little nursery rhyme friend may say.'

'She's on her way up now, perhaps to elucidate.'

The two girls came in. Pauline Flinders' face was greenish from nausea, her lower lip trembling under the ugly prominent teeth. She wore faded frayed jeans and a shirt which looked as if they had been picked out of a crumpled heap on a bedroom floor. Malina too wore jeans, of toffee-brown silk, stitched in white, and a white clinging sweater and gold medallions on a long gold chain.

'I made her come,' said Malina. 'She was in an awful state. I thought she'd been really ill.' And she sat down, having given Burden a shy sidelong smile.

'What is it, Miss Flinders?' Wexford said gently.

'Tell him, Polly. You promised you would. It's silly to come all this way for nothing.'

Polly Flinders lifted her head. She said rapidly, in a monotone, 'I haven't had a card from Grenville. That was last year's. The postmark was smudged and I thought you wouldn't know, and you didn't know.'

The explosion of wrath she perhaps expected didn't come. Wexford merely nodded. 'You also thought I wouldn't know he knew Rhoda Comfrey. But he had known her for years, hadn't he?'

Breathlessly, Polly said, 'She helped him with his books. She was there in his flat a lot. But I don't know where she lived. I never asked, I didn't want to know. About the postcard, I . . .'

670

'Never mind the postcard. Were you and Miss Comfrey in Mr West's flat on the evening of August fifth?' A nod answered him and a choking sound like a sob. 'And you both overheard her make a phone call from there, saying where she would be on the Monday?'

'Yes, but . . .'

'Tell him the truth, Polly. Tell him everything and it'll be all right.'

'Very well, Miss Patel, I'll do the prompting.' He hadn't taken his eyes from the other girl, and now he said to her, 'Have you any idea of Mr West's present whereabouts? No? I think you told me the lie about the postcard because you were afraid for Mr West, believing him to have had something to do with Miss Comfrey's death.'

She gave him an eager pathetic nod, her hands clenched.

'I don't think we'll talk any more now,' he said. 'I'll come and see you tomorrow evening. That will give you plenty of time to get into a calmer frame of mind.' Malina looked disappointed, less so when he went on, 'I shall want you to give me the name of the man with whom you spent that Monday evening. Will you think about that?'

Again she said yes, a sorrowful and despairing monosyllable, and then Burden took them both away, returning to say, 'Rhoda Comfrey was blackmailing West. I wonder why we didn't think of that before.'

'Because it isn't a very bright idea. I can see how someone might succeed in blackmailing *her*. She had a secret life she genuinely wanted kept secret. But West?'

'West,' said Burden repressively, 'is almost certainly homosexual. Why else reject Polly? Why else mooch about Soho at night? Why hobnob with all those blokes in bars? And why, most of all, have a long-standing friendship with an older woman on a completely platonic basis? That's the sort of thing these queers do. They like to know women, but it's got to be *safe* women, married ones or women much older than they are.'

Wexford wondered why he hadn't thought of that. Once again he had come up against Burden's solid common sense. And hadn't his own 'feelings' also been hinting at it when he read the letter to Charles West?

He jeered mildly just the same. 'So this long-standing friend suddenly takes it into her head to blackmail him, does she? After ten years? Threatens to expose his gay goings-on, I suppose.' He had never liked the word 'queer'. 'Why should he care? It's nothing these days. He probably advertises his – his inversion in *Gay News*.'

'Does he? Then why doesn't your Indian lady friend know about it? Why doesn't his agent or Vivian or Polly? It mightn't do him any good with his readership if ordinary decent people were to find what he gets up to in London at night. It wouldn't with me, I can tell you.'

'Since when have you been one of his readers?'

Burden looked a little shamefaced as he always did when confessing to any even mild intellectual lapse. 'Since yesterday morning,' he admitted. 'Got to do something while I'm being a phone operator, haven't I? I sent Loring out to get me two of them in paperback. I thought they'd be above my head, but they weren't. Quite enjoyable, lively sort of stuff, really, and the last thing you'd feel is that their author's homosexual.'

'But you say he is.'

'And he wants to keep it dark. He's queer but he's still thinking of settling down with Polly – they do that when they get middle-aged – and Rhoda mightn't have liked the idea of only being able to see him with a wife around. So she threatens to spill the beans unless he gives Polly up. And there's your motive.'

'It doesn't account for how he happens to have the same name as a whole tribe of her aunt's relatives.'

'Look,' said Burden, 'your Charles West wrote to him, thinking he might be a cousin. Why shouldn't Rhoda have done the same thing years ago, say after she'd read his first book? Charles West didn't pursue it, but she may have done. That could be the reason for their becoming friends in the first place, and then the friendship was strengthened by Rhoda doing research for him for that book that's dedicated to her. The name is relevant only in that it brought them together.'

'I just hope,' said Wexford, 'that tomorrow will bring West and us together.'

Robin came up and opened the car door for him.

'Thanks very much,' said Wexford. 'You're the new hall porter, are you? I suppose you want a tip.' He handed over the ices he had bought on the way home. 'One for your brother, mind.'

'I'll never be able to do it again,' said Robin.

'Why's that? School starting? You'll still get in before I do.'

'We're going home, Grandad. Daddy's coming for us at seven.'

To the child Wexford couldn't express what he felt. There was only one thing he could say, and in spite of his longing to be alone once more with Dora in peace and quiet and orderliness, it was true. 'I shall miss you.'

'Yes,' said Robin complacently. Happy children set a high valuation on themselves. They expect to be loved and missed. 'And we never saw the water rat.'

'There'll be other times. You're not going to the North Pole.'

The little boy laughed inordinately at that one. Wexford sent him off to find Ben and hand the ice over, and then he let himself into the house. Sylvia was upstairs packing. He put his arm round her shoulder, turned her face towards him.

'Well, my dear, so you and Neil have settled your differences?'

'I don't know about that. Not exactly. Only he's said he'll give me all the support I need in taking a degree if I start next year. And he's – he's bought a dishwasher!' She gave a little half-ashamed laugh. 'But that's not why I'm going back.'

'I think I know why.'

She pulled away from him, turning her head. For all her height and her majestic carriage, there was something shy and gauche about her. 'I can't live without him, Dad,' she said. 'I've missed him dreadfully.'

'That's the only good reason for going back, isn't it?'

'The other thing – well, you can say women are equal to men but you can't give them men's position in the world. Because that's in men's minds and it'll take hundreds of years to change it.' She came out with a word that was unfamiliar to her wellread father. 'One would just have to practise aeonism,' she said.

What had she been reading now? Before he could ask her, the boys came in.

'We could have a last try for the water rat, Grandad.'

'Oh, Robin! Grandad's tired and Daddy's coming for us in an hour.'

'An hour,' said Robin with a six-year-old's view of time, 'is ever so long.'

So they went off together, the three of them, over the hill and across the meadow to the Kingsbrook. It was damp and misty and still, the willows bluish amorphous shadows, every blade of grass glistening with water drops. The river had risen and was flowing fast, the only thing in nature that moved.

'Grandad carry,' said Ben somewhat earlier in the expedition than usual.

But as Wexford bent down to lift him up, something apart from the river moved. A little way to the right of them, in the opposite bank, a pair of bright eyes showed themselves at the mouth of a hole.

'Ssh,' Wexford whispered. 'Keep absolutely still.'

The water rat emerged slowly. It was not at all rat-like but handsome and almost rotund with spiky fur the colour of sealskin and a round alert face. It approached the water with slow stealth but entered it swiftly and began to swim, spreading and stretching its body, towards the bank on the side where they stood. And when it reached the bank it paused and looked straight at them seemingly without fear, before scurrying off into the thick green rushes.

Robin waited until it had disappeared. Then he danced up and down with delight. 'We saw the water rat! We saw the water rat!'

'Ben wants to see Daddy! Ben want to go home! Poor Ben's feet are cold!'

'Aren't you pleased we saw the water rat, Grandad?'

'Very pleased,' said Wexford, wishing that his own quest might come to so simple and satisfying an end.

CHAPTER SEVENTEEN

Grenville West's elusiveness could no longer be put down to chance. He was on the run and no doubt had been for nearly three weeks now. Everything pointed to his being the killer of Rhoda Comfrey, and by Friday morning Wexford saw that the case had grown too big for him, beyond the reach of his net. Far from hoping to dissuade the Chief Constable from carrying out his threat, he saw the inevitability of calling in Scotland Yard and also the resources of Interpol. But his call to the Chief Constable left him feeling a little flat, and the harsh voice of Michael Baker, phoning from Kenbourne Vale, made him realize only that now he must begin confessing failure.

Baker asked him how he was, referred to their 'red faces' over the Farriner business, then said:

'I don't suppose you're still interested in that chap Grenville West, are you?'

To Wexford it had seemed as if the whole world must be hunting for him, and yet here was Baker speaking as if the man were still a red herring, incongruously trailed across some enormously more significant scent.

'Am I still interested! Why?'

'Ah,' said Baker. 'Better come up to the Smoke then. It'd take too long to go into details on the phone, but the gist is that West's car's been found in an hotel garage not far from here, and West left the hotel last Monday fortnight without paying his bill.'

Wexford didn't need to ask any more now. He remembered to express effusive gratitude, and within not much more than an hour he was sitting opposite Baker at Kenbourne Vale

Police Station, Stevens having recovered from his flu or perhaps only his antipathy to London traffic.

'I'll give you a broad outline,' said Baker, 'and then we'll go over to the Trieste Hotel and see the manager. We got a call from him this morning and I sent Clements up there. West checked in on the evening of Sunday, August seventh, and parked his car, a red Citroën, in one of the hotel's lock-up garages. When he didn't appear to pay his bill on Wednesday morning, a chambermaid told Hetherington – that's the manager – that his bed hadn't been slept in for two nights.'

'Didn't he do anything about it?' Wexford put in.

'Not then. He says he knew who West was, had his address and had no reason to distrust him. Besides, he'd left a suitcase with clothes in it in his room and his car in the garage. But when it got to the end of the week he phoned West's home, and getting no reply sent someone round to Elm Green. You can go on from there, Sergeant, you talked to the man.'

Clements, who had come in while Baker was speaking, greeted Wexford with a funny little half-bow. 'Well, sir, this Hetherington, who's a real smoothie but not, I reckon, up to anything he shouldn't be, found out from the girl in that wine bar place where West was, and he wasn't too pleased. But he calculated West would write to him from France.'

'Which didn't happen?'

'No, sir. Hetherington didn't hear a word and he got to feeling pretty sore about it. Then, he says, it struck him the girl had said a motoring holiday, which seemed fishy since West's car was still at the Trieste. Also West had gone off with his room key and hadn't left an ignition key with the hotel. Hetherington began to feel a bit worried, said he suspected foul play, though he didn't get on to us. Instead he went through West's case and found an address book. He got the phone numbers of West's publishers and his agent and Miss Flinders and he phoned them all. None of them could help him, they all said West was in France, so this morning, at long last, he phoned us.'

They were driven up to North Kenbourne, round Montfort Circus and down a long street of lofty houses. Wexford noted that Undine Road was within easy walking distance of Parish Oak tube station, and not far therefore from Princevale Road and Dr Lomond's surgery. Formerly the Trieste Hotel had been a gigantic family house, but its balconies and turrets and jutting gables had been masked with new brickwork or weather-boarding, and its windows enlarged and glazed with plain glass. Mr Hetherington also seemed to have been smoothed out, his sleek fair hair, pink china skin and creaseless suit. He presented as spruce an appearance compared with the four policemen as his hotel did with its neighbours. His careful grooming reminded Wexford of Burden's fastidiousness, though the inspector never quite had the look of having been sprayed all over with satin-finish lacquer.

He took them into his office, a luxurious place that opened off a white-carpeted, redwood panelled hallway in which very large houseplants stood about on Corinthian columns.

Neither Baker nor Clements were the sort of men to go in for specious courtesies or obsequious apology. In his rough way, Baker said, 'You'll have to tell the whole story again, sir. We're taking a serious view.'

'My pleasure.' Hetherington flashed a smile that bore witness to his daily use of dental floss, and held it steadily as if for unseen cameras. 'I'm feeling considerable concern about Mr West myself. I feel convinced something dreadful has happened. Do please sit down.' He eyed Wexford's raincoat uncertainly, ushered him away from the white upholstered chair in which he had been about to sit, and into a duncol-oured one. He said, 'You'll be more comfortable there, I think,' as to a caller of low social status directed to the servants' entrance. 'Now where shall I begin?'

'At the beginning,' said Wexford with perfect gravity. 'Go on to the end and then stop.'

This time he got an even more uncertain look. 'The beginning,' said Hetherington, 'would be on the Saturday, Saturday the sixth. Mr West telephoned and asked if he could have a room for three nights, the Sunday, Monday and Tuesday. Naturally, that would usually be an impossible request in August, but it so happened that a very charming lady from Minneapolis who stays with us regularly every year had cancelled on account of . . .' He caught Wexford's eye, stern censor of snobbish digression. 'Yes, well, as I say, it happened to be possible and I told Mr West he could have Mrs Gruber's room. He arrived at seven on the Sunday and signed the register. I have it here.'

Wexford and Baker looked at it. It was signed 'Grenville West' and the Elm Green address was given. Certain that the manager was incapable of obeying his injunction, Wexford said:

'He had been here before, I think?'

'Oh, yes, once before.'

'Mr Hetherington, weren't you surprised that a man who lived within what is almost walking distance of the hotel should want to stay here?'

'Surprised?' said Hetherington. 'Certainly not. Why should I be? What business was it of mine? I shouldn't be *surprised* if a gentleman who lived next door wanted to stay in the hotel.'

He took the register away from them. While his back was turned Clements murmured with kindly indulgence, 'It happens a lot, sir. Men have tiffs with their wives or forget their keys.'

Maybe, Wexford thought, but in those cases they don't book their night's refuge some fifteen hours in advance. Even if the others didn't find it odd, he did. He asked Hetherington if West had brought much luggage.

'A suitcase. He may have had a handbag as well.' Although Hetherington was strictly correct in employing this word, the rather quaint usage made Wexford want to repeat, in Lady Bracknell's outraged echo, 'A handbag?' But he only raised his eyebrows, and Hetherington said, 'He asked if he could garage his car – he didn't want to leave it on the hardtop parking – so I let him have number five which happened to be vacant. He put the car away himself.' There was a small hesitation. 'As a matter of fact, it was a little odd now I come to think of it. I offered to get the car garaged for him and asked for his key, but he insisted on doing it himself.'

'When did you last see him?' Baker asked.

'I never saw him again. He ordered breakfast in his room on the Monday morning. No one seemed to have seen him go out. I expected him to vacate his room by noon on Wednesday but he didn't appear to pay his bill.' Hetherington paused, then went on to tell the story broadly as Wexford had heard it from Clements. When he had finished Wexford asked him what had become of West's room key.

'Heaven knows. We do stress that our guests hand in their keys at reception when they go out, we make them too heavy to be comfortably carried in a pocket, but it's of no avail. They will take them out with them. We lose hundreds. I have his suitcase here. No doubt you will wish to examine the contents.'

For some moments Wexford had been regarding a suitcase which, standing under Hetherington's desk, he had guessed to be the luggage West had left behind him. It was of brown leather, not new but of good quality and stamped inside the lid with the name and crest of Silk and Whitebeam, Jermyn Street. Baker opened it. Inside were a pair of brown whipcord slacks, a yellow roll-neck shirt, a stone-coloured lightweight pullover, a pair of white underpants, brown socks and leather sandals.

'Those were the clothes he arrived in,' said Hetherington, his concern for West temporarily displaced by distaste for anyone who would wear trousers with a shiny seat and a pullover with a frayed cuff.

'How about this address book?' said Baker.

'Here.'

The entries of names, addresses and phone numbers were sparse. Field and Bray, Literary Agents; Mrs Brenda Nunn's personal address and phone number; several numbers and extensions for West's publishers; Vivian's Vineyard; Polly Flinders; Kenbourne Town Hall; a number for emergency calls to the North Thames Gas Board; London Electricity; the London Library and Kenbourne Public Library, High Road Branch; some French names and numbers and places – and Crown, Lilian, with the Kingsmarkham telephone number of Rhoda Comfrey's aunt.

Wexford said, 'Where's the car now?'

'Still in number five garage. I couldn't move it, could I? I hadn't the means.'

I wonder if I have, thought Wexford. They trooped out to the row of garages. The red Citroën looked as if it had been well maintained and it was immaculately polished. The licence plates showed that it was three years old. The doors were locked and so was the boot.

'We'll get that open,' Baker said. 'Should have a key to fit, or we'll get one. It won't take long.'

Wexford felt through the jangling mass in his pocket. Two keys marked with a double chevron. 'Try these,' he said.

The keys fitted.

There was nothing inside the car but a neat stack of maps of Western Europe on the dashboard shelf. The contents of the boot were more rewarding. Two more brown leather suitcases, larger than the one West had left in his room, and labelled 'Grenville West, Hotel Casimir, Rue Victor Hugo, Paris'. Both were locked, but the opening of suitcases is child's play.

'To hell with warrants,' Wexford said out of range of Hetherington's hearing. 'Can we have these taken back to the nick?'

'Surely,' said Baker, and to Hetherington in the grating tones of admonition that made him unpopular with the public and colleagues alike, 'You've wasted our time and the tax-payers' money by delaying like this. Frankly, you haven't a hope in hell of getting that bill paid.'

Loring drove the car back with Baker beside him, while Wexford went with Clements. A lunchtime traffic jam held the police car up, Clements taking this opportunity during a lull in events to expound on lack of public cooperation, laxity that amounted to obstruction, and Hetherington's hair which he averred had been bleached. At last Wexford managed to get him off this – anyone whose conversation consists in continual denunciation is wearying to listen to – and on to James and Angela. By the time they got to the police station both cases had been opened and were displayed in the centre of the floor of Baker's drab and gloomy sanctum.

The cases were full of clothes, some of which had evidently been bought new for West's holiday. In a leather bag was a battery-operated electric shaver, a tube of suntan cream and an aerosol of insect repellant, but no toothbrush, toothpaste, soap, sponge or flannel, cologne or after-shave.

'If he's a homosexual,' said Wexford, 'these are rather odd omissions. I should have expected a fastidious interest in his personal appearance. Doesn't he even clean his teeth?'

'Maybe he's got false ones.'

'Which he scrubs at night with the hotel nailbrush and the hotel soap?'

Baker had brought to light a large brown envelope, sealed. 'Ah, the documents.' But there was something else inside apart from papers. Carefully, Baker slit the envelope open and pulled out a key to which was attached a heavy wood and metal tag, the metal part engraved with the name of the Trieste Hotel and the number of the room West had occupied for one night.

'How about this?' said Baker. 'He isn't in France, he never left the country.'

What he handed to Wexford was a British passport, issued according to its cover to Mr J.G. West.

CHAPTER EIGHTEEN

Wexford opened the passport at page one.

The name of the bearer was given as Mr John Grenville West and his national status as that of a citizen of the United Kingdom and Colonies. Page two gave West's profession as a novelist, his place of birth as Myringham, Sussex, his date of birth 9 September 1940, his country of residence as the United Kingdom, his height as five feet nine, and the colour of his eyes as grey. In the space allotted to the bearer's usual signature, he had signed it 'Grenville West'.

The photograph facing this description was a typical passport photograph and showed an apparent lunatic or psychopath with a lock of dark hair grimly falling to meet a pair of black-framed glasses. At the time it was taken West had sported a moustache.

Page four told Wexford that the passport had been issued five years before in London, and on half a dozen of the subsequent pages were stamps showing entries to and exists from France, Belgium, Holland, Germany, Italy, Turkey and the United States, and there was also a visa for the United States. West, he noted, had left the country at least twelve times in those five years.

'He meant to go this time,' said Baker. 'Why didn't he go? And where is he?'

Wexford didn't answer him. He said to Loring:

'I want you to go now, as fast as you can make it, to the Registry of Births and look this chap West up. You get the volume for the year 1940, then the section with September in, then all the Wests. Have you got that? There'll be a lot of them but it's unlikely there'll be more than one John Grenville West born on 9 September. I want his mother's name and his father's.'

Loring went. Baker was going through the remaining contents of the envelope. 'A cheque-book,' he said, 'a Eurocard and an American Express card, travellers' cheques signed by West, roughly a thousand francs. . . . He meant to come back for this lot all right, Reg.'

'Of course he did. There's a camera here under some of these clothes, nice little Pentax.' Suddenly Wexford wished Burden were with him. He had reached one of those points in a case when, to clear his mind and dispel some of this frustration, he needed Burden and only Burden. For rough argument with no punches pulled, for a free exchange of insults with no offence taken if such words as 'hysterical' or 'prudish' were hurled in the heat of the moment. Baker was a very inadequate substitute. Wexford wondered how he would react to some high-flown quotation, let alone to being called a pain in the arse. But needs must when the devil drives. Choosing his words carefully, toning down his personality, he outlined to Baker Burden's theory.

'Hardly germane to this inquiry,' said Baker, and Wexford's mind went back years to when he and the inspector had first met and when he had used those very words. 'All this motive business. Never mind motive. Never mind whether West was this Comfrey woman's second cousin or, for that matter, her grandmother's brother-in-law.' A bigtoothed laugh at this witticism. 'It's all irrelevant. If I may say so, Reg —' Like all who take offence easily, Baker never minded giving offence to others or even noticed he was giving it '— if I may say so, you prefer the trees to the wood. Ought to have been one of these novelist chappies yourself. Plain facts aren't your cup of tea at all.'

Wexford took the insult — for it is highly insulting to be told that one would be better at some profession other than that which one has practised for forty years — without a word. He chuckled to himself at Baker's mixed metaphors, sylvan and refective. Was refective the word? Did it mean what he thought it did, pertaining to mealtimes? There was another word he had meant to look up. It was there, but not quite there, on the tip of his tongue, the edge of his memory. He needed a big dictionary, not that potty little *Concise Oxford* which, in any case, Sheila had appropriated long ago . . .

'Plain facts, Reg,' Baker was saying. 'The principal plain fact is that West scarpered on the day your Comfrey got killed. I call that evidence of guilt. He meant to come back to the Trieste and slip off to France but something happened to scare him off.'

'Like what?'

'Like being seen by someone where he shouldn't have been. That's like what. That's obvious. Look at that passport. West wasn't born in London, he was born somewhere down in your neck of the woods. There'll be those around who'll know him, recognize him.' Baker spoke as if the whole of Sussex were a small rural spot, his last sentence having a *Wind in the Willows* flavour about it as if West had been the Mole and subject to the scrutiny of many bright eyes peering from the boles of trees. 'That's where these second cousins and grandmother's whatsits come in. One of them saw him, so off into hiding he went.'

'Under the protection, presumably, of another of them?'

'Could be,' said Baker seriously. 'But we might just as well stop speculating and go get us a spot of lunch. You can't do any more. I can't do any more. You can't find him. I can't find him. We leave him and his gear to the Yard, and that's that. Now how about a snack at the Hospital Arms?'

'Would you mind if we went to Vivian's Vineyard instead, Michael?'

With some casting up of eyes and pursing of lips, Baker agreed. His expression was that of a man who allows a friend with an addiction one last drink or cigarette. So on the way to Elm Green Wexford was obliged to argue it out with himself. It seemed apparent that West had booked into the

Trieste to establish an alibi, but it was a poor sort of alibi since he had signed the register in his own name. Baker would have said that all criminals are fools. Wexford knew this was often not so, and especially not so in the case of the author of books praised by critics for their historical accuracy, their breadth of vision and their fidelity to their models. He had not meant to kill her, this was no premeditated crime. On the face of it, the booking into the Trieste looked like an attempt at establishing an alibi, but it was not. For some other purpose West had stayed there. For some other reason he had gone to Kingsmarkham. How had his car keys come into Rhoda Comfrey's possession? And who was he? Who was he? Baker called that irrelevant, yet Wexford knew now the whole case and its final solution hung upon it, upon West's true identity and his lineage.

It was true that he couldn't see the wood for the trees, but not that he preferred the latter. Here the trees would only coalesce into a wood when he could have each one before him individually and then, at last, fuse them. He walked in a whispering forest, little voices speaking to him on all sides, hinting and pleading – 'Don't you see now? Can't you put together what he has said and she has said and what I am saying?'

Wexford shook himself. He wasn't in a whispering wood but crossing Elm Green where the trees had all been cut down, and Baker was regarding him as if he had read in a medical journal that staring fixedly at nothing, as Wexford had been doing, may symptomize a condition akin to epilepsy.

'You OK, Reg?'

'Fine,' said Wexford with a sigh, and they went into the brown murk of Vivian's Vineyard. The girl with the pale brown face sat on a high stool behind the bar, swinging long brown legs, chatting desultorily to three young men in what was probably blue denim, though in here it too looked brown. The whole scene might have been a sepia photograph.

Baker had given their order when Victor Vivian appeared from the back with a wine bottle in each hand.

'Hallo, hallo, hallo!' He came over to their table and sat down in the vacant chair. Today the tee-shirt he wore was printed all over with a map of the vineyards of France, the area where his heart was being covered by Burgundy and the Auvergne.

'What's happened to old Gren, then? I didn't know a thing about it, you know, till Rita here gave me the low-down. I mean, told me there was this hotel chap after him in a real tizz, you know.'

Baker wouldn't have replied to this but Wexford did. 'Mr West didn't go to France,' he said. 'He's still in this country. Have you any idea where he might go?'

Vivian whistled. He whistled like the captain of the team in the *Boy's Own Paper.* 'I say! Correct me if I'm wrong, you know, but I'm getting your drift. I mean, it's serious, isn't it? I mean, I wasn't born yesterday.'

From a physical point of view this was apparent, though less so from Vivian's mental capacity. Not for the first time Wexford wondered how a man of West's education and intelligence could have borne to spend more than two minutes in this company unless he had been obliged to. What had West seen in him? What had he seen, for that matter, in Polly Flinders, dowdy and desperate, or in the unprepossessing, graceless Rhoda Comfrey?

'You reckon old Gren's on the run?'

The girl put two salads, a basket of rolls and two glasses of wine in front of them. Wexford said, 'You told me Mr West came here fourteen years ago. Where did he come from?'

'Couldn't tell you that, you know. I mean, I didn't come here myself till a matter of five years back. Gren was here. *In situ,* I mean.'

'You never talked about the past? About his early life?'

Vivian shook his head, his beard waggling. 'I'm not one

to push myself in where I'm not wanted, you know. Gren never talked about any family. I mean, he may have said he'd lost his parents, I think he did say that, you know, I think so.'

'He never told you where he'd been born?'

Baker was looking impatient. If it is possible to eat ham and tomatoes with an exasperated air, he was doing so. And he maintained a total disapproving silence.

Vivian said vaguely, 'People don't, you know. I mean, I reckon Rita here was born in Jamaica, but I don't know, you know. I don't go about telling people where I was born. Gren may have been born in France, you know, France wouldn't surprise me.' He banged his chest. 'Old Gren brought me this tee-shirt back from his last hols, you know. Always a thoughtful sort of chap. I mean, I don't like to think of him in trouble, I don't at all.'

'Did you see him leave for this holiday of his? I mean . . .' How easy it was to pick up the habit! 'When he left here on Sunday, the seventh?'

'Sure I did. He popped in the bar. About half-six it was, you know. "I'm just off, Vic," he says. He wouldn't have a drink, you know, on account of having a long drive ahead of him. I mean, his car was parked out here in the street, you know, and I went out and saw him off. "Back on September fourth," he says, and I remember I thought to myself, his birthday's round about then, I thought, eighth or the ninth, you know, and I thought I'd look that up and check and have a bottle of champers for him.'

'Can you also remember what he was wearing?'

'Gren's not a snappy dresser, you know. I mean, he went in for those roll-neck jobs, seemed to like them, never a collar and tie if he could get away with it. His old yellow one, that's what he was wearing, you know, and a sweater and kind of dark-coloured trousers. Never one for the gear like me, you know. I'd have sworn he went to France, I mean I'd have taken my oath on it. This is beyond me, frankly, you know.

I'm lost. When I think he called out to me, "I'll be in Paris by midnight, Vic," in that funny high voice of his, and he never went there at all – well, I go cold all over, you know. I mean, I don't know what to think.'

Baker could stand no more. Abruptly he said, 'We'll have the bill, please.'

'Sure, yes, right away. Rita! When he turns up – well, if there's anything I can do, you know, any sort of help I can give, you can take that as read, you know. I mean, this has knocked me sideways.'

It was evident that Baker thought the representatives of the Mid-Sussex Constabulary would return to their rural burrow almost at once. He had even looked up the time of a suitable train from Victoria and offered a car to take them there. Wexford hardened himself to hints – there were so many other hints he would have softened to if he had known how – and marched boldly back into the police station where Loring sat patiently waiting for him.

'Well?'

'Well, sir, I've found him.' Loring referred to his notes. 'The birth was registered at Myringham. In the county,' he said earnestly, 'of Sussex. 9 September 1940. John Grenville West. His father's name is given as Ronald Grenville West and his mother's name as Lilian West, born Crawford.'

CHAPTER NINETEEN

Little John. Sweet affectionate little love, the way them mongols are . . . Mrs Parker's voice was among the whisperers. He could hear it clearly in the receiver of his mind, and hear too Lilian Crown's, brash and tough and uncaring. Been in a home for the backward like since he was so high . . .

'I looked up the parents too, sir, just to be on the safe side. Ronald West's parents were John Grenville West and Mary Ann West, and Ronald's birth was also registered in Myringham in 1914. The mother, Lilian West, was the daughter of William and Agnes Crawford, and her birth was registered in Canterbury in 1917. Ronald and Lilian West were married in Myringham in 1937.'

'You're sure there's no other John Grenville West born on that date and registered at Myringham?'

How could there be? Such a coincidence would evince the supernatural.

'Quite sure, sir,' said Loring.

'I know who this man is. He's mentally retarded. He's been in an institution for the greater part of his life.' Wexford was uncertain whom he was addressing. Not Baker or Loring or the baffled Clements. Perhaps only himself. 'It can't be!' he said.

'It is, sir,' said Loring, not following, anxious only that his thoroughness should not be questioned.

Wexford turned from him and buried his face in his hands. Burden would have called this hysterical or maybe just melodramatic. For Wexford, at this moment, it was the only possible way of being alone. Fantastic pictures came to him of a normal child being classified as abnormal so that his mother, in order to make a desired marriage, might be rid of him. Of that child somehow acquiring an education, of being adopted but retaining his true name. Then why should Lilian Crown have concealed it?

He jumped up. 'Michael, may I use your phone?'

'Sure you can, Reg.'

Baker had ceased to hint, had stopped his impatient fidgeting. Wexford knew what he was thinking. It was as if there had been placed before him, though invisible to others, a manual of advice to ambitious policemen. Always humour the whims of your chief's uncle, even though in your considered opinion the old boy is off his rocker. The uses of nepotism must always be borne in mind when looking to promotion.

Burden's voice, from down there in the green country, sounded sane and practical and encouraging.

'Mike, could you get over to the Abbotts Palmer Hospital? Go there, don't phone. I could do that myself. They have, or had, an inmate called John Grenville West. See him if you can.'

'Will do,' said Burden. 'Is he seeable? What I'm trying to say is, is he some sort of complete wreck or is he capable of communicating?'

'If he's who he seems to be, he's more than capable of communicating, in which case he won't be there. But I'm not sending you on a wild goose chase. You have to find out when he entered the institution, when he left and how. Everything you can about him, OK? And if you find he's not there but was cured, if that's possible, and went out into the world, confront the man's mother with it, will you? You may have to get tough with her. Get tough. Find out if she knew he was Grenville West, the author, and why the hell she didn't tell us.'

'Am I going to find out who his mother is?'

'Mrs Lilian Crown, 2 Carlyle Villas, Forest Road.'

'Right,' said Burden.

'I'll be here. I'd come back myself, only I want to wait in Kenbourne till Polly Flinders gets home this evening.'

Baker accepted this last so philosophically as to send down for coffee. Wexford took pity on him.

'Thanks, Michael, but I'm going to take myself off for a walk.' He said to Loring, 'You can get over to All Soul Grove and find out when the Flinders girl is expected home. If Miss Patel is taking another of her days off, I daresay you won't find the work too arduous.'

He went out into the hazy sunshine. Sluggishly people walked, idled on street corners. It seemed strange to him, as it always does to us when we are in a state of turbulence, that the rest of humanity was unaffected. He that is giddy thinks the world turns round. Giddiness exactly described his present condition, but it was a giddiness of the mind, and he walked steadily and slowly along Kenbourne High Road. At the cemetery gate he turned into the great necropolis. Along the aisles, between the serried tombs, he walked, and sat down at last on a toppled gravestone. On a warm summer's day there is no solitude to be found on a green or in a park, but one may always be sure of being alone in the corner of a cemetery. The dead themselves seem to decree silence, while the atmosphere of the place and its very nature are repellent to most people.

Very carefully and methodically he assembled the facts, letting the whispers wait. West had been cagey about his past, had made few friends, and those he had were somehow unsuitable and of an intellect unequal to his own. He gave his publishers and his readers his birthplace as London, though his passport and the registration of his birth showed he had been born in Sussex. His knowledge of the Sussex countryside and its great houses also showed a familiarity with that county. No one seemed to know anything of his life up to fourteen years before, and when he had first come to Elm Green and two years before his book was published. Not to his neighbour and intimate friend did he ever speak of his origins, and to one other bearer of the name Grenville West he had denied any connection with the family.

Why?

Because he had something to keep hidden, while Rhoda Comfrey was similarly secretive because she had her blackmailing activities to keep hidden. Put the two together and what do you get? A threat on the part of the blackmailer to disclose something. Not perhaps that West was homosexual – Wexford could not really be persuaded that these days this was of much significance – but that he had never been to a university (as his biography claimed he had), never been a teacher or a courier or a freelance journalist, been indeed nothing till the age of twenty-four when he had somehow emerged from a home for the mentally handicapped.

As his first cousin, Rhoda Comfrey would have known it; from her it could never have been kept as it had been kept from others. Had she used it as a final weapon – Burden's theory here being quite tenable – when she saw herself losing her cousin to Polly Flinders? West had overheard that phone call made by her to his own mother, even though she had called Lilian Crown 'darling' to put him off the scent. Had he assumed that she meant to see his mother and wrest from her the details of his early childhood, the opinions of doctors, all Mrs Crown's knowledge of the child's incarceration in that place and his subsequent release?

Here, then, was a motive for the murder. West had booked into the Trieste Hotel because it was simpler to allow Polly Flinders and Victor Vivian to believe him already in France. But that he had booked in his own name and for three nights showed surely that he had never intended to kill his cousin. Rather he had meant to use those three days for argument with Rhoda and to attempt to dissuade her from her intention.

But how had he done it? Not the murder, that might be clear enough, that unpremeditated killing in a fit of angry despair. How had he contrived in the first place such an escape and then undergone such a metamorphosis? Allowing for the fact that he might originally have been unjustly placed in the Abbotts Palmer or its predecessor, how had he surmounted his terrible difficulties? Throughout his childhood and early youth he must have been there, and if not in fact retarded, retardation would surely have been assumed for some years so that education would have been withheld and his intellect dulled and impeded by the society of his fellow inmates. Yet at the age of twenty-five or-six he had written and published a novel which revealed a learned knowledge of the Elizabethan drama, of history and of the English usage of the period.

If, that is, he were he.

It couldn't be, as Wexford had said to Loring, and yet it must be. For though John Grenville West might not be the author's real name, though he might be a suitable pseudonym by chance have alighted on it – inventing it, so to speak, himself – other aspects were beyond the possibility of coincidence. True, the chance use of this name (instead, for example, of his real one which might be absurd or dysphonious) could have brought him and Rhoda together, the cousinship at first having been assumed on her part as Charles West had also assumed it. But he could not by chance have also chosen her cousin's birthday and parentage. It must be that John Grenville West, the novelist, the francophile, the traveller, was also John Grenville West, the retarded child his mother had put away when he was six years old. From this dismal state, from this position in the world . . .

He stopped. The words he had used touched a bell and rang it. Again he was up in the spare bedroom with his daughter, and Sylvia was talking about men and women and time, saying something about men's position in the world. And after that she had said this position could only be attained by practising something or other. Deism? No, of course not. Aeolism? Didn't that mean being long-winded? Anyway, it wasn't that, she hadn't said that. What had she said?

He tried placing one letter of the alphabet after another to follow the diphthong and the O, and settled at last with absolute conviction for 'aeonism'. Which must have something to do with aeons. So she had only meant that, in order for sexual equality to be perfected, those who desired it would have to transcend the natural course of time.

He felt disappointed and let down, because, with a curious shiver in that heat, he had felt he had found the key. The word had not been entirely new to him. He fancied he had heard it before, long before Sylvia spoke it, and it had not meant transcending time at all.

Well, he wasn't getting very far cogitating like this. He might as well go back. It was after five, and by now Burden might have got results. He left the cemetery as they were about to close the gates and got a suspicious look from the keeper who had been unaware of his presence inside. But outside the library he thought of that elusive word again. He had a large vocabulary because in his youth he had always made a point of looking up words whose meaning he didn't know. It was a good rule and not one reserved to the young.

This was the place for which Grenville West had a ticket and where Wexford himself had first found his books. Now he spared them a glance on his way to the reference room. Four were in, including *Apes in Hell*, beneath whose covers Rhoda Comfrey's name lurked with such seeming innocence.

The library had only one English dictionary, the *Shorter Oxford* in two bulky volumes. Wexford took the first one of these down, sat at the table and opened it. 'Aeolism' was not given, and he found that 'aeolistic' meant what he thought it did and that it was an invention of Swift's. 'Aeon' was there – 'an age, or the whole duration of the world, or of the universe; an immeasurable period of time; eternity'. 'Aeonian' too and 'aeonial', but no 'aeonism'.

Could Sylvia have made it up, or was it perhaps the etymologically doubtful brain-child of one of her favourite

Women's Lib writers? That wouldn't account for his certainty that he had himself previously come across it. He replaced the heavy tome and crossed the street to the Police Station.

Baker was on the phone when he walked in, chatting with such tenderness and such absorption that Wexford guessed he could only be talking to his wife. But the conversation, though it appeared only to have been about whether he would prefer fried to boiled potatoes for his dinner and whether he would be home by six or could make it by ten to, put him in great good humour. No, no calls had come in for Wexford. Loring had not returned, and he, Baker, thought it would be a good idea for the two of them to adjourn at once to the Grand Duke. Provided, of course, that this didn't delay him from getting home by ten to six.

'I'd better stay here, Michael,' Wexford said rather awkwardly, 'if that's all right with you.'

'Be my guest, Reg. Here's your young chap now.'

Loring was shown in by Sergeant Clements. 'She came in at half past four, sir. I told her to expect you some time after six-thirty.'

He had no idea what he would say to her, though he might have if only Burden would phone. The word still haunted him. 'Would you mind if I made a call?' he said to Baker.

Humouring him had now become Baker's line. 'I said to be my guest, Reg. Do what you like.' His wife and the fried potatoes enticed him irresistibly. 'I'll be off then.' With stoical resignation, he added, 'I daresay we'll be seeing a good deal of each other in the next few days.'

Wexford dialled Sylvia's number. It was Robin who answered.

'Daddy's taken Mummy up to London to see Auntie Sheila in a play.'

The Merchant of Venice at the National. She was playing Jessica, and her father had seen her in the part a month before. Another of those whispers hissed at him from the text – 'But love is blind, and lovers cannot see the pretty follies that themselves commit.' To the boy he said:

'Who's with you, then? Grandma?'

'We've got a sitter,' said Robin. 'For Ben,' he added.

'See you,' said Wexford just as laconically, and put the receiver back. Clements was still there, looking, he thought, rather odiously sentimental. 'Sergeant,' he said, 'would you by any chance have a dictionary in this place?'

'Plenty of them, sir. Urdu, Bengali, Hindi, you name it, we've got it. Have to have on account of all these immigrants. Of course we do employ interpreters, and a nice packet they make out of it, but even they don't know all the words. And just as well, if you ask me. We've got French too and German and Italian for our Common Market customers, and common is the word. Oh, yes, we've got more Dick, Tom and Marias, as my old father used to call them, than they've got down the library.'

Wexford controlled an impulse to throw the phone at him. 'Would you have an *English* dictionary?'

He was almost sure Clements would say this wasn't necessary as they all spoke English, whatever the *hoi polloi* might do. But to his surprise he was told that they did and Clements would fetch it for him, his pleasure.

He hadn't been gone half a minute when the switchboard, with many time-wasting inquiries, at last put through a call from Burden. He sounded as if the afternoon had afforded him work that had been more distressing than arduous.

'Sorry I've been so long. I'm not so tough as I think I am. But, God, the sights you see in these places. What it boils down to is that John Grenville West left the Abbotts Palmer when he was twenty . . .'

'*What?*'

'Don't get excited,' Burden said wearily. 'Only because they hadn't the facilities for looking after him properly. He isn't a mongol at all, whatever your Mrs Parker said. He was born with serious brain damage and one leg shorter than the other. Reading between the lines, from what they said and didn't say, I gather this was the result of his mother's attempt to procure an abortion.'

Wexford said nothing. The horror was all in Burden's voice already.

'Don't let anyone ever tell me,' said the inspector savagely, 'that it was wrong to legalize abortion.'

Wexford knew better than to say at this moment that it was Burden who had always told himself, and others, that. 'Where is he now?'

'In a place near Eastbourne. I went there. He's been nothing more than a vegetable for eighteen years. I suppose the Crown woman was too ashamed to tell you. I've just come from her. She said it was ever so sad, wasn't it, and offered me a gin.'

CHAPTER TWENTY

The dictionaries Clements brought him, staggering under their weight, turned out to be the *Shorter Oxford* in its old vast single volume and *Webster's International* in two volumes.

'There's a mighty lot of words in those, sir. I doubt if anyone's taken a look at them since we had that nasty black magic business in the cemetery a couple of years back and I couldn't for the life of me remember how to spell mediaeval.'

It was the associative process which had led Rhoda Comfrey to give Dr Lomond her address as 6 Princevale Road, and that same process that had brought Sylvia's obscure expression back to Wexford's mind. Now it began to operate again as he was looking through the *Addenda and Corrigenda* to the *Shorter Oxford*.

'Mediaeval?' he said. 'You mean you weren't sure whether there was a diphthong or not?' The sergeant's puzzled frown made him say hastily, 'You weren't sure whether it was spelt i, a, e or i, e, was that it?'

'Exactly, sir.' Clements' need to put the world right – or to castigate the world – extended even to criticizing lexicographers. 'I don't know why we can't have simplified spelling, get rid of all these unnecessary letters. They only confuse schoolkids, I know they did me. I well remember when I was about twelve . . .'

Wexford wasn't listening to him. Clements went on talking, being the kind of person who would never have interrupted anyone when he was speaking, but didn't think twice about assaulting a man's ears while he was reading.

'. . . And day after day I got kept in after school for mixing up "there" and "their", if you know what I mean, and my father said . . .'

Diphthongs, thought Wexford. Of course. That ae was just

an anglicization of Greek eeta, wasn't it, or from the Latin which had a lot of ae's in it? And often these days the diphthong was changed to a single e, as in modern spelling of mediaeval. So his word, Sylvia's word, might appear among the E's and not the A's at all. He heaved the thick wedge of pages back to the E section. 'Eolienne' – 'a fine dress farbric' ... 'Eosin' – 'a red dye-stuff' ...

Maybe Sylvia's word had never had a diphthong, maybe it didn't come from Greek or Latin at all, but from a name or a place. That wasn't going to help him, though, if it wasn't in the dictionaries. Wild ideas came to him of getting hold of Sylvia here and now, of calling a taxi and having it take him down over the river to the National Theatre, finding her before the curtain went up in three-quarters of an hour's time ... But there was still another dictionary.

'Harassment, now,' the sergeant was saying. 'There's a word I've never been able to spell, though I always say over to myself, "possesses possesses five s's".'

Webster's International. He didn't want it to be international, only sufficiently comprehensive. The E section. 'Eocene', 'Eolienne' – and there it was.

'Found what you're looking for, sir?' said Clements.

Wexford leant back with a sigh and let the heavy volume fall shut. 'I've found, Sergeant, what I've been looking for for three weeks.'

Rather warily, Malina Patel admitted them to the flat. Was it for Loring's benefit that she had dressed up in harem trousers and a jacket of some glossy white stuff, heavily embroidered? Her black hair was looped up in complicated coils and fastened with gold pins.

'Polly's in an awful state,' she said confidingly. 'I can't do anything with her. When I told her you were coming I thought she was going to faint, and then she cried so terribly. I didn't know what to do.'

Perhaps, Wexford thought, you could have been a friend

to her and comforted her, not spent surely a full hour making yourself look like something out of a seraglio. There was no time now, though, to dwell on forms of hypocrisy, on those who will seek to present themselves as pillars of virtue and archetypes of beauty even at times of grave crisis.

Making use of those fine eyes – could she even cry at will? – she said sweetly, 'But I don't suppose you want to talk to me, do you? I think Polly will be up to seeing you. She's in there. I said to her that everything would be all right if she just told the truth, and then you wouldn't frighten her. Please don't frighten her, will you?'

Already the magic was working on Loring who looked quite limp. It had ceased to work on Wexford.

'I'd rather frighten you, Miss Patel,' he said. Her eyelashes fluttered at him. 'And you're wrong if you think I don't want to talk to you. Let us go in here.'

He opened a door at random. On the other side of it was a squalid and filthy kitchen, smelling of strong spices and of decay, as if someone had been currying meat and vegetables that were already rotten. The sink was stacked up to the level of the taps with unwashed dishes. She took up her stand in front of the sink, too small to hide it, a self-righteous but not entirely easy smile on her lips.

'You're very free with your advice,' he said. 'Do you find in your experience that people take it?'

'I was only trying to help,' she said, slipping into her little girl role. 'It was good advice, wasn't it?'

'You didn't take my good advice.'

'I don't know what you mean.'

'Not to lie to the police. The scope of the truth, Miss Patel, is very adequately covered by the words of the oath one takes in the witness box. I swear to tell the truth, the whole truth and nothing but the truth. After I had warned you, you obeyed – as far as I know – the first injunction and the third but not the second. You left out a vital piece of truth.'

702

She seized on only one point. 'I'm not going into any witness box!'

'Oh, yes you will. One thing you may be sure of is that you will. Yesterday morning you received a phone call, didn't you? From the manager of the Trieste Hotel.'

She said sullenly, 'Polly did.'

'And when Miss Flinders realized that Mr West's car had been found, you told her that the police would be bound to find out. Did you advise her to tell us? Did you remember my advice to you? No. You suggested that the best thing would be to bring her to us with the old story that your conscience had been troubling you.'

She shifted her position, and the movement sent the dirty plates subsiding over the edge of the bowl.

'When did you first know the facts, Miss Patel?'

A flood of self-justification came from her. Her voice lost its soft prettiness and took on a near-cockney inflexion. She was shrill.

'What, that Polly hadn't been in a motel with a married man? Not till last night. I didn't, I tell you, I didn't till last night. She was in an awful state and she'd been crying all day, and she said I can't tell him that man's address because there isn't a man. And that made me laugh because Polly's never had a real boy-friend all the time I've known her, and I said, "You made it up?" And she said she had. And I said, "I bet Grenville never kissed you either, did he?" So she cried some more and . . .' The faces of the two men told her she had gone too far. She seemed to remember the personality she wished to present and to grab at it in the nick of time. 'I knew you'd find out because the police always did, you said. I warned her you'd come, and then what was she going to say?'

'I meant,' Wexford tried, 'when did you know where Miss Flinders had truly been that night?'

Anxiety gone – he wasn't really cross, men would never really be cross with her – she smiled the amazed smile of someone on whom a great revelatory light has shone. 'What a weird thing! I never thought about that.'

No, she had never thought about that. About her own attractions and her winning charm she had thought, about establishing her own ascendancy and placing her friend in a foolish light, about what she called her conscience she had thought, but never about the aim of all these inquiries. What a curiously inept and deceiving term Freud had coined, Wexford reflected, when he named the conscience the superego!

'It never occurred to you then that a girl who never went out alone after dark must have had some very good reason for being out alone all that evening and half the night? You didn't think of that aspect? You had forgotten perhaps that that was the evening of Rhoda Comfrey's murder?'

She shook her head guilelessly. 'No, I didn't think about it. It couldn't have had anything to do with me or Polly.'

Wexford looked at her steadily. She looked back at him, her fingers beginning to pick at the gold embroideries on the tunic whose whiteness set off her orchid skin. At last the seriousness of his gaze affected her, forcing her to use whatever powers of reasoning she had. The whole pretty sweet silly façade broke, and she let out a shattering scream.

'Christ,' said Loring.

She began to scream hysterically, throwing back her head. The heroine, Wexford thought unsympathetically, going mad in white satin. 'Oh, slap her face or something,' he said and walked out into the hall.

Apart from the screeches, and now the choking sounds and sobs from the kitchen, the flat was quite silent. It struck him that Pauline Flinders must be in the grip of some over-powering emotion, or stunned into a fugue, not to have reacted to those screams and come out to inquire. He looked forward with dread and with distaste to the task ahead of him.

All the other doors were closed. He tapped on the one that led to the living room where he had interviewed her before. She didn't speak, but opened the door and looked at him with great sorrow and hopelessness. Everything she wore and everything about her seemed to drag her down, the flopping hair, the stooping shoulders, the loose overblouse and the long skirt, compelling the eye of the beholder also to droop and fall.

Today there was no script on the table, no paper in the typewriter. No book or magazine lay open. She had been sitting there waiting – for how many hours? – paralysed, capable of no action.

'Sit down, Miss Flinders,' he said. It was horrible to have to torture her, but if he was to get what he wanted he had no choice. 'Don't try to find excuses for not telling me the name of the man you spent the evening of August eighth with. I know there was no man.'

She tensed at that and darted him a look of terror, and he knew why. But he let it pass. Out of pity for her, his mind was working quickly, examining this which was so fresh to him, so recently realized, trying to get enough grasp on it to decide whether the whole truth need come out. But even at this stage, with half the facts still to be understood, he knew he couldn't comfort her with that one.

She hunched in a chair, the pale hair curtaining her face. 'You were afraid to go out alone at night,' he said, 'and for good reason. You were once attacked in the dark by a man, weren't you, and very badly frightened?'

The hair shivered, her bent body nodded.

'You wished it were legal in this country for people to carry guns for protection. It's illegal too to carry knives but knives are easier to come by. How long is it, Miss Flinders, since you have been carrying a knife in your handbag?'

She murmured, 'Nearly a year.'

'A flick knife, I suppose. The kind with a concealed blade that appears when you press a projection on the hilt. Where is that knife now?'

'I threw it into the canal at Kenbourne Lock.'

Never before had he so much wished he could leave someone in her position alone. He opened the door and called to Loring to come in. The girl bunched her lips over her teeth, straightened her shoulders, her face very white.

'Let us at least try to be comfortable,' said Wexford, and he motioned her to sit beside him on the sofa while Loring took the chair she had vacated. 'I'm going to tell you a story.' He chose his words carefully. 'I'm going to tell you how this case appears.'

'There was a woman of thirty called Rhoda Comfrey who came from Kingsmarkham in Sussex to London where she lived for some time on the income from a football pools win, a sum which I think must have been in the region of ten thousand pounds.

'When the money began to run out she supplemented it with an income derived from blackmail, and she called herself West, Mrs West, because the name Comfrey and her single status were distasteful to her. After some time she met a young man, a foreigner, who had no right to be in this country but who, like Joseph Conrad before him, wanted to live here and write his books in English. Rhoda Comfrey offered him an identity and a history, a mother and father, a family and a birth certificate. He was to take the name of someone who would never need national insurance or a passport because he had been and always would be in an institution for the mentally handicapped – her cousin, John Grenville West. This the young man did.

'The secret bound them together in a long uneasy friendship. He dedicated his third novel to her, for it was certain that without her that book would never have been written. He would not have been here to write it. Was he Russian perhaps? Or some other kind of Slav? Whatever he was, seeking asylum, she gave him the identity of a real person who would never need to use his reality and who was himself in an asylum of a different kind.

'And what did she get from him? A young and personable man to be her escort and her companion. He was homosexual, of course, she knew that. All the better. She was not a highly sexed woman. It was not love and satisfaction she wanted, but a man to show off to observers.

'How disconcerting for her, therefore, when he took on a young girl to type his manuscripts for him, and that young girl fell in love with him . . .'

Polly Flinders made a sound of pain, a single soft 'Ah!', perhaps irrepressible. Wexford paused, then went on.

'He wasn't in love with her. But he was growing older, he was nearly middle-aged. What sort of dignified future has a homosexual who follows the kind of life-style he had been following into his forties? He decided to marry, to settle down – at least superficially – to add another line to that biography of his on the back of his books.

'Perhaps he hadn't considered what this would mean to the woman who had created him and received his confidences. It was not she, twelve years his senior, he intended marrying, but a girl half her age. To stop him, she threatened to expose his true nationality, his illegalities and his homosexual conduct. He had no choice but to kill her.'

Wexford looked at Polly Flinders who was looking hard at him.

'But it wasn't quite like that, was it?' he said.

CHAPTER TWENTY-ONE

While he was speaking a change had gradually come over her. She was suffering still but she was no longer tortured with fear. She had settled into a kind of resigned repose until, at his last sentence, apprehensiveness came back. But she said nothing, only nodding her head and then shaking it, as if she wished to please him, to agree with him, but was doubtful whether he wanted a yes or a no.

'Of course he had a choice,' Wexford went on. 'He could have married and left her to go ahead. His readers would have felt nothing but sympathy with a man who wanted asylum in this country, even though he had used illegal means to get it. And there was not the slightest chance of his being deported after so long. As for his homosexuality, who but the most old-fashioned would care? Besides, the fact of his marriage would have put paid to any such aspersions. And where and how would Rhoda Comfrey have published it? In some semi-underground magazine most of his readers would never see? In a gossip column where it would have to be written with many circumlocutions to avoid libel? Even if he didn't feel that *any* publicity is good publicity, he still had a choice. He could have agreed to her demands. Marriage for him was only an expedient, not a matter of passion.'

The girl showed no sign that these words had hurt her. She listened calmly, and now her hands lay folded in her lap. It was as if she were hearing what she wanted to hear but had hardly dared hope she would. Her pallor, though, was more than usually marked. Wexford was reminded of how he had once read in some legend or fairy story of a girl so fair and with skin so transparent, that when she drank the course the red wine followed could be seen as it ran down her throat.

But Polly Flinders was in no legend or fairy story – or even nursery rhyme – and her dry bunched lips looked parched for wine or love.

'It was for this reason,' he said, 'that someone else was alarmed – the girl he could so easily be prevented from marrying. She loved him and wanted to marry him, but she knew that this older woman had far more influence over him than she did.

'August fifth was Rhoda Comfrey's birthday. Grenville West showed her – and showed the girl too – how little malice or resentment he felt towards her by giving her an expensive wallet for a birthday present. Indicating, surely, that he meant to let her rule him? That evening they were all together, the three of them, in Grenville West's flat, and Rhoda Comfrey asked if she might make a phone call. Now when a guest does that, a polite host leaves the room so that the person making the call may be private. You and Mr West left the room, didn't you, Miss Flinders? But perhaps the door was left open.

'She was only telephoning her aunt to say she was going to visit her father in Stowerton Infirmary on the following Monday, but to impress you and Mr West she made it appear as if she were talking to a man. You were uninterested in that aspect of it, but you were intrigued to find out where she would be on the Monday. In the country where you could locate her as you never could on her own in London.'

He paused, deciding to say nothing about the Trieste Hotel and West's disappearance, guessing that she would be thankful for his name to be omitted.

'On the evening of Monday, August eighth, you went to Stowerton, having found out when visiting time was. You saw Miss Comfrey get on to a bus with another woman, and you got on to it too, without letting her see you. You left the bus at the stop where she left it and followed her across the footpath – intending what? Not to kill her then. I think you wished only to be alone with her to ask why and to try to dissuade her from interfering between you and Mr West.

'But she laughed at you, or was patronizing, or something of that sort. She said something hurtful and cruel, and driven beyond endurance, you stabbed her. Am I right, Miss Flinders?'

Loring sat up stiffly, bracing himself, waiting perhaps for more screams. Polly Flinders only nodded. She looked calm and thoughtful as if she had been asked for verbal confirmation of some action, and not even a reprehensible action, she had performed years before. Then she sighed.

'Yes, that's right. I killed her. I stabbed her and wiped the knife on the grass and got on another bus and then a train and came home. I threw the knife into Kenbourne Lock on the way back. I did it just like you said.' She hesitated, added steadily, 'And why you said.'

Wexford got up. It was all very civilized and easy and casual. He could tell what Loring was thinking. There had been provocation, no real intent, no premeditation. The girl realized all this and that she would get off with three or four years, so better confess it now and put an end to the anxiety that had nearly broken her. Get it over and have peace, with no involvement for Grenville West.

'Pauline Flinders,' he said, 'you are charged with the murder on August eighth of Rhoda Agnes Comfrey. You are not obliged to say anything in answer to the charge, but anything you do say may be taken down and used in evidence.'

'I don't want to say anything,' she said. 'Do I have to go with you now?'

'It seems,' said Burden when Wexford phoned him, 'a bit of a sell.'

'You want more melodrama? You want hysterics?'

'Not exactly that. Oh, I don't know. There seems to have been so many oddities in this case, and what it boils down to is that it was this girl all along. She killed the woman just because she was coming between her and West.' Wexford said nothing. 'I suppose she *did* kill her? She's not confessing in an attempt to protect West?'

'Oh, she killed her all right. No doubt about that. In her statement she's given us the most precise circumstantial account of times, the geography of the Forest Road area, what Rhoda Comfrey was wearing and even the fact that the London train, the nine-twenty-four Kingsmarkham to Victoria, was ten minutes late that night. Tomorrow Rittifer will have Kenbourne Lock dragged and we'll find that knife.'

'And West himself had nothing to do with it?'

'He had everything to do with it. Without him there'd have been no problem. He was the motive. I'm tired now, Mike, and I've got another call to make. I'll tell you the rest after the special court tomorrow.'

His other call was to Michael Baker. A woman with a soft voice and a slight North Country accent answered. 'It's for you, darling,' she called out, and Baker called back, 'Coming, darling.' His voice roughened, crackling down the phone when he heard who it was, and implicit in his tone was the question, 'Do you know what time it is?' though he didn't actually say this. But when Wexford had told him the bare facts he became immediately cocky and rather took the line that he had predicted such an outcome all along.

'I knew you were wasting your time with all those names and dates and birth certificates, Reg. I told you so.' Wexford had never heard anyone utter those words in seriousness before, and had he felt less tired and sick he would have laughed. 'Well, all's well that ends well, eh?'

'I daresay. Good night, Michael.'

Maybe it was because he forgot to add something on the lines of his eternal gratitude for all the assistance rendered him by Kenbourne police that Baker dropped the receiver without another word. Or, rather, without more than a fatuous cry of

'Just coming, sweetheart,' which he hardly supposed could be addressed to him.

Dora was in bed, sitting up reading the Marie Antoinette book. He sat down beside her and kicked off his shoes.

'So it's all over, is it?' she said.

'I've behaved very badly,' he muttered. 'I've strung that wretched girl along and told her lies and accepted lies from her just to get a confession. I've got a horrible job. She still thinks she's got away with it.'

'Darling,' Dora said gently, 'you do realize I haven't the least idea what you're talking about?'

'Yes, in a way I'm talking to myself. Maybe being married is talking to oneself with one's other self listening.'

'That's one of the nicest things you've ever said to me.'

He went into the bathroom and looked at his ugly face in the glass, at the bags under his tired eyes and the wrinkles and the white stubble on his chin that made him look like an old man.

'I am alone the villain of the earth,' he said to the face in the glass, 'and feel I am so most.'

In court on Saturday morning, Pauline Flinders was charged with the murder of Rhoda Comfrey, committed for trial and remanded in custody.

After it was over Wexford avoided the Chief Constable – it was supposed to be his day off, wasn't it? – and gave Burden the slip and pretended not to see Dr Crocker, and got into his own car and drove to Myringham. What he had to do, would spend most of the day doing, could only be done in Myringham.

He drove over the Kingsbrook Bridge and through the old town to the centre. There he parked on the top floor of the multi-storey car park, for Myringham was given over to shoppers' cars on Saturdays, and went down in the lift to enter the building on the opposite side of the street.

In marble this time, Edward Edwards, a book in his hand, looked vaguely at him. Wexford paused to read what was engraved on the plinth and then went in, the glass doors opening of their own accord to admit him.

CHAPTER TWENTY-TWO

For years before it became a hotel – for centuries even – the Olive and Dove had been a coaching inn where the traveller might not get a bedroom or, come to that, a bed to himself, but might be reasonably sure of securing a private parlour. Many of these parlours, oak-panelled, low-ceilinged cubby-holes, still remained, opening out of passages that led away from the bar and the lounge bar, though they were private no longer but available to any first-comer. In the smallest of them where there was only one table, two chairs and a settle, Burden sat at eight o'clock on Sunday evening, waiting for the chief inspector to come and keep the appointment he had made himself. He waited impatiently, making his half-pint of bitter last, because to leave the room now for another drink would be to invite invasion. Coats thrown over tables imply no reservation in the Olive at weekends. Besides, he had no coat. It was too warm.

Then at ten past, when the bitter was down to its last inch, Wexford walked in with a tankard in each hand.

'You're lucky I found you at all, hidden away like this,' he said. 'This is for plotters or lovers.'

'I thought you'd like a bit of privacy.'

'Maybe you're right. I am Sir Oracle, and when I ope my lips let no dog bark.'

Burden raised his tankard and said, 'Cheers! This dog's going to bark. I want to know where West is, why he stayed in that hotel, who he is, come to that, and why I had to spend Friday afternoon inspecting mental hospitals. That's for a start. I want to know why, on your admission, you told that girl two entirely false stories and where you spent yesterday.'

'They weren't entirely false,' said Wexford mildly. 'They had elements of the truth. I knew by then that she had killed

714

Rhoda Comfrey because there was no one else who could have done so. But I also knew that if I presented her with the absolute truth at that point, she would have been unable to answer me and not only should I not have got a confession, but she would very likely have become incoherent and perhaps have collapsed. What was true was that she was in love with Grenville West, that she wanted to marry him, that she overheard a phone conversation and that she stabbed Rhoda Comfrey to death on the evening of August eighth. All the rest, the motive, the lead up to the murder and the characters of the protagonists to a great degree – all that was false. But it was a version acceptable to her and one which she might not have dreamed could be fabricated. The sad thing for her is that the truth must inevitably be revealed and has, in fact, already been revealed in the report I wrote yesterday for Griswold.

'I spent yesterday in the new public library in Myringham, in the reference section, reading Havelock Ellis, a biography of the Chevalier d'Eon, and bits of the life histories of Isabelle Eberhardt, James Miranda Barry and Martha Jane Burke – if those names mean anything to you.'

'There's no need to be patronizing,' said Burden. 'They don't.'

Wexford wasn't feeling very light-hearted, but he couldn't, even in these circumstances, resist teasing Burden who was already looking irritable and aggrieved.

'Oh, and Edward Edwards,' he said. 'Know who Edward Edwards was? The Father of Public Libraries, it said underneath his statue. Apparently, he was instrumental in getting some bill through Parliament in 1850 and . . .'

'For God's sake,' Burden exploded, 'can't you get on to West? What's this Edwards got to do with West?'

'Not much. He stands outside libraries and West's books are inside.'

'Then where is West? Or are you saying he's going to turn

up now he's read in the paper that one of his girl-friends has murdered the other one?'

'He won't turn up.'

'Why won't he?' Burden said slowly. 'Look, d'you mean there were two people involved in murdering Rhoda Comfrey? West as well as the girl?'

'No. West is dead. He never went back to the Trieste Hotel because he was dead.'

'I need another drink,' said Burden. In the doorway he turned round and said scathingly, 'I suppose Polly Flinders bumped him off too?'

'Yes,' said Wexford. 'Of course.'

The Olive was getting crowded and Burden was more than five minutes fetching their beer. 'My God,' he said, 'who d'you think's out there? Griswold. He didn't see me. At least, I don't think so.'

'Then you'd better make that one last. I'm not running the risk of bumping into him.'

Burden sat down again, his eye on the doorway which held no door. He leant across the table, his elbows on it. 'She can't have. What became of the body?'

Wexford didn't answer him directly. 'Does the word eonism mean anything to you?'

'No more than all those names you flung at me just now. Wait a minute, though. An aeon means a long time, an age. An aeonist is — let's see — is someone who studies changes over long periods of time.'

'No. I thought something like that too. It has nothing to do with aeons, there's no a in it. Havelock Ellis coined the word in a book published in 1928 called *Studies in the Psychology of Sex, Eonism and other Studies*. He took the name from that of the Chevalier d'Eon, Charles Eon de Beaumont, who died in this country in the early part of the nineteenth century...' Wexford paused and said, '... Having masqueraded for thirty-three years as a woman.'

'Rhoda Comfrey masqueraded for twenty years as a man. When I agreed that Pauline Flinders had murdered Grenville West, I meant that she had murdered him in the body of Rhoda Comfrey. Rhoda Comfrey and Grenville West were one and the same.'

'That's not possible,' said Burden. 'People would have known or at least suspected.' Intently staring at Wexford's face, he was oblivious of the long bulky shadow that had been cast across the table and his own face.

Wexford turned round, said, 'Good evening, sir,' and smiled pleasantly. It was Burden who, realizing, got to his feet.

'Sit down, Mike, sit down,' said the Chief Constable, casting upon Wexford a look that implied he would have liked the opportunity to tell him to sit down also. 'May I join you? Or is the chief inspector here indulging his well-known habit of telling a tale with the minimum of celerity and the maximum of suspense? I should hate to interrupt before the climax was reached.'

In a stifled voice, Burden said, 'The climax was reached just as you came in, sir. Can I get you a drink?'

'Thank you, but I have one.' Griswold produced, from where he had been holding it, for some reason, against his trouser leg, a very small glass of dry sherry. 'And now I too would like to hear this wonderful exposition, though I have the advantage over you, Mike, of having read a condensed version. I heard your last words. Perhaps you'll repeat them.'

'I said she couldn't have got away with it. Anyone she knew well would have known.'

'Well, Reg?' Griswold sat down on the settle next to Burden. 'I hope my presence won't embarrass you. Will you go on?'

'Certainly I will, sir.' Wexford considered saying he wasn't easily embarrassed but thought better of it. 'I think the answer to that question is that she took care, as we have seen, only to know *well* not very sensitive or intelligent people. But even so, Malina Patel had noticed there was something odd about Grenville West, and she said she wouldn't have liked him to kiss her. Even Victor Vivian spoke of a "funny high voice" while, incidentally, Mrs Crown said that Rhoda's voice was deep. I think it probable that such people as Oliver Hampton and Mrs Nunn did know, or rather, if they didn't know she was a woman, they suspected Grenville West of being of ambivalent sex, of being physically a hermaphrodite, or maybe an effeminate homosexual. But would they have told me? When I questioned them I suspected West of nothing more than being acquainted with Rhoda Comfrey. They are discreet people, who were connected with West in a professional capacity. As for those men Rhoda consorted with in bars, they wouldn't have been a bunch of conservative suburbanites. They'd have accepted her as just another oddity in a world of freaks.

'Before you came in, sir, I mentioned three names. Isabelle Eberhardt, James Miranda Barry and Martha Jane Burke. What they had in common was that they were all eonists. Isabelle Eberhardt became a nomad in the North African desert where she was in the habit of sporadically passing herself off as male. James Barry went to medical school as a boy in the days before girls were eligible to do so, and served for a lifetime as an army doctor in the British colonies. After her death she was found to be a woman, and a woman who had had a child. The last named is better known as Calamity Jane who lived with men as a man, chewed tobacco, was proficient in the use of arms, and was only discovered to be a woman while she was taking part in a military campaign against the Sioux.

'The Chevalier d'Eon was a physically normal man who successfully posed as a female for thirty years. For half that period he lived with a woman friend called Marie Cole who never doubted for a moment that he also was a woman. She nursed him through his last illness and didn't learn he was a man until after his death. I will quote to you Marie Cole's reaction to the discovery from the words of the Notary Public, Doctors' Commons, 1810: "She did not recover from the shock for many hours."

'So you can see that Rhoda Comfrey had precedent for what she did, and that the lives of these predecessors of hers show that cross-dressing succeeds in its aim. Many people are totally deceived by it, others speculate or doubt, but the subject's true sex is often not detected until he or she become ill or wounded, or until, as in Rhoda's case, death supervenes.'

The Chief Constable shook his head, as one who wonders rather than denies. 'What put you on to it, Reg?'

'My daughters. One saying a woman would have to be an eonist to get a man's rights, and the other dressing as a man on the stage. Oh, and Grenville West's letter to Charles West – that had the feel of having been written by a woman. And Rhoda's fingernails painted but clipped short. And Rhoda having a toothbrush in her luggage at Kingsmarkham and West not having one in his holiday cases. All feelings, I'm afraid, sir.'

'That's all very well,' said Burden, 'but what about the age question? Rhoda Comfrey was fifty and West was thirty-eight.'

'She had a very good reason for fixing her age as twelve years less than her true one. I'll go into that in a minute. But also you must remember that she saw herself as having lost her youth and those best years. This was a way of regaining them. Now think what are the signs of youth in men and women. A woman's subcutaneous fat begins to decline at fifty or thereabouts, but a man never has very much of it. So even a young man may have a hard face, lined especially under the eyes without looking older than he is. A woman's youthful looks largely depend on her having no lines. Here, as elsewhere, we apply a different standard for the sexes. You're what, Mike? In your early forties? Put a wig and make-up on you and you'll look an old hag, but cut off the hair of a woman of your age, dress her in a man's suit, and she could pass for thirty. My daughter Sheila's twenty-four, but when she puts on doublet and hose for Jessica in *The Merchant of Venice* she looks sixteen.'

Remarkably, it was the Chief Constable who supported him. 'Quite true. Think of Crippen's mistress, Ethel Le Neve. She was a mature woman, but when she tried to escape across the Atlantic disguised in men's clothes she was taken for a youth. And by the way, Reg, you might have added Maria Marten, the Red Barn victim, to your list. She left her father's house disguised as a farm labourer, though I believe transvestism was against the law at the time.'

'In seventeenth-century France,' said Wexford, 'men, at any rate, were executed for it.'

'Hmm. You have been doing your homework. Get on with the story, will you?'

Wexford proceeded: 'Nature had not been kind to Rhoda as a woman. She had a plain face and a large nose and she was large-framed and flat-chested. She was what people call "mannish", though incidentally no one did in this case. As a young girl she tried wearing ultra-feminine clothes to make herself more attractive. She copied her aunt because she saw that her aunt got results. She, however, did not, and she must have come to see her femaleness as a grave disadvantage. Because she was female she had been denied an education and was expected to be a drudge. All her miseries came from being a woman, and she had none of a woman's advantages over a man. My daughter Sylvia complains that men are attentive to her because of her physical attractions but accord her no respect as a person. Rhoda had no physical attractions so, because she was a woman, she received neither attention nor respect. No doubt she would have stayed at home and become an embittered old maid, but for a piece of luck. She won a large sum of money in an office football pools syndicate. Where she first lived in London and whether as a man or a woman, I don't know and I don't think it's relevant. She began to write. Did she at this time cease to wear those unsuitable clothes and take to trousers and sweaters and jackets instead? Who knows? Perhaps, dressed like that, she was once or twice mistaken for a man, and that gave her the idea. Or what is more likely, she took to men's clothes because, as Havelock Ellis says, cross-dressing fulfilled a deep demand of her nature.

'It must have been then that she assumed a man's name, and perhaps this was when she submitted her first manuscript to a publisher. It was then or never, wasn't it? If she was going to have a career and come into the public eye there must be no ambivalence of sex.

'By posing – or passing – as a man she had everything to gain: the respect of her fellows, a personal feeling of the rightness of it for her, the freedom to go where she chose and do what she liked, to walk about after dark in safety, to hobnob with men in bars on an equal footing. And she had very little to lose. Only the chance of forming close intimate friendships, for this she would not dare to do – except with unobservant fools like Vivian.'

'Well,' said Burden, 'I've just about recovered from the shock, unlike Marie Cole who took some hours. But there's something else strikes me she had to lose.'

He looked with some awkwardness in the direction of the Chief Constable, and Griswold, without waiting for him to say it, barked, 'Her sexuality, eh? How about that?'

'Len Crocker said at the start of this case that some people are very low-sexed. And if I may again quote Havelock Ellis, eonists often have an almost asexual disposition. "In people", he says, "with this psychic anomaly, physical sexual urge seems often subnormal." Rhoda Comfrey, who had had no sexual experience, must have decided it was well worth sacrificing the possibility – the remote possibility – of ever forming a satisfactory sexual relationship for what she had to gain. I am sure she did sacrifice it and became a man whom other men and women just thought rather odd.

'And she took pains to be as masculine as she could be. She dressed plainly, she used no colognes or toilet waters, she carried an electric shaver, though we must suppose it was never used. Because she couldn't grow an Adam's apple she wore high necklines to cover her neck, and because she couldn't achieve on her forehead an M-line, she always wore a lock of hair falling over her brow.'

'What d'you mean?' said Burden. 'An M-line?'

'Look in the mirror,' said Wexford.

The three men got up and confronted themselves in the ornamented glass on the wall above their table. 'See,' said Wexford, putting his own hands up to his scanty hairline, and the other two perceived how their hair receded in two triangles at the temples. 'All men,' he said, 'have to some degree, but no woman does. Her hairline is oval in shape. But for Rhoda Comfrey these were small matters and easily dealt with. It was only when she paid a rare visit to Kingsmarkham to see her father that she was obliged to go back to being a woman. Oh, and on one other occasion. No wonder people said she was happy in London and miserable in the country. For her, dressing as a woman was very much what it would be like for a normal man to be forced into drag.

'But she played it in character, or in her old character, dressing fussily, wearing heavy make-up, painting her finger-nails which, however, she couldn't grow long for the purpose. For these visits she kept women's underclothes and an old pair of stiletto-heeled shoes. When you come to think of it, she might buy a woman's dress without trying it on, but hardly a pair of shoes.'

'But you said,' put in Griswold, 'that there were other occasions when she went back to being a woman.'

'I said there was one, sir. She might deceive her friends and her acquaintances. They weren't going to subject her to a physical examination. She had been a patient of old Dr Castle in Kingsmarkham, though I imagine she was a strong healthy woman who seldom needed medical attention. Last year, however, he died, but when she suspected she had appendicitis, she had to go to a doctor. Even the most cursory examination would have revealed she was no man, so to Dr Lomond she went reluctantly as a woman, giving her true name and an address she thought up on the way. Hence the Farriner confusion.

'That was a year ago, by which time she had already met Polly Flinders – and Polly Flinders had fallen in love with her.'

CHAPTER TWENTY-THREE

'Everything points to Rhoda Comfrey's having been aware of the girl's feelings,' Wexford went on, 'and to some extent to her having encouraged them. She let her act as her secretary instead of just an occasional typist, took her into the wine bar for drinks, drove her home if she was kept late at Elm Green, sent her whimsical postcards. What she did not do, and probably felt she was behaving ethically in not doing – although I daresay she didn't want to either – was show her the least demonstrative affection.'

'It was cruel and unjustifiable all the same,' said Burden.

'I think it was natural,' Wexford said hesitantly. 'I think it was very *human*. After all, look at it from Rhoda's point of view. As a girl of twenty-five she hadn't been remotely attractive to men. Mustn't it have enormously gratified her to know that at fifty she had someone of twenty-five in love with her? A poor obtuse innocent creature perhaps, but still a young human being in love with her. A poor ill-favoured thing, but mine own. Who else had ever really loved her? Her mother, long ago. Mrs Parker? This was a love of a different kind, and the kind everyone wants once in a lifetime.'

Griswold had started to look impatient. 'All right, Reg, all right. Get back to the nitty-gritty, can't you? You're a policeman, not a shrink.'

'Well, for the nitty-gritty, sir, we have to come to a month or so ago. Rhoda was planning to go on holiday, but her father had had a stroke. She meant to go, no doubt about that, but perhaps she ought to see the old man first and find out how the land lay.'

'What d'you mean by that?'

'I mean that if he was very seriously incapacitated she

would know that her greatest fear, that her father might have to be parked on her one day, would be groundless and she could go off to France with a light heart. But she had to go down there and find out, even though this would mean putting off her holiday for a day or two. Never mind. That was no great inconvenience. She phoned her aunt to tell her she would be coming and when she did so Polly Flinders was in the flat, but not all the time in the room.

'Now, if no one else did, Polly knew that Grenville West had once or twice before disappeared mysteriously at week-ends. I think we can assume that Rhoda rather enjoyed keeping her in the dark about that, and guessed she was giving her cause for jealousy. On that Friday evening Polly had very likely been troublesome – she may, for instance, have wanted West to take her away on holiday with him – and Rhoda vented her annoyance by calling Lilian Crown "darling". Polly overheard, as she was meant to overhear, and believed that West was involved with another woman living in the country. No doubt she asked questions, but was told it was no business of hers, so she determined to go to Stowerton on the Monday and find out for herself what was going on.'

Burden interrupted him. 'Why didn't Rhoda or West or whatever we're going to call him or her – it gets a bit complicated – go to Kingsmarkham that day? Then there wouldn't have been any need to postpone the holiday. Where does the Trieste Hotel come in?'

'Think about it,' said Wexford. 'Walk out of Elm Green in make-up and high-heeled shoes and a dress?'

'I should have thought a public lavatory . . .' Burden stopped himself proceeding further with this gaffe, but not in time to prevent Griswold's hoot of laughter.

'How does he manage to go in the Gents' and come out of the Ladies', Mike?'

Wexford didn't feel like laughing. He had never been amused by drag or the idea of it, and now the humorous aspects of this particular case of cross-dressing seemed to him quenched by its consequences. 'She used hotels for the change-over,' he said rather coldly, 'and usually hotels in some distant part of London. But this time she had left it too late to pick and choose, especially with the tourist season as its height. On that Saturday she must have tried to book in at a number of hotels without success. The only one which could take her was the Trieste which she had used once before – on the occasion of the visit to Dr Lomond. You can see, Mike, how she walked out of the Trieste on that day, crossed Montfort Circus, went up Montfort Hill, and chose an address from a street name and an advertisement.

'So back to the Trieste she went, with her car packed up for the French holiday and allowing Vivian to believe she was leaving directly for France. The car was left in a garage at the hotel with her passport and French currency locked up in the boot. On her person she retained the car keys and her new wallet, and these went into her handbag when on the following day she left the hotel as Rhoda Comfrey.'

'That must have been as bad as walking out of Elm Green. Suppose she'd been seen?'

'By whom? An hotel servant? She says she's calling on her friend, Mr West. It would have been easy enough to mingle with the other guests or conceal herself in a cloakroom, say, if Hetherington had appeared. As a respectable middle-aged lady, she'd hardly have been suspected of being there for what you'd call an immoral purpose.'

'Hotels don't take much notice of that these days,' said the Chief Constable easily. Forgetting perhaps that it was he who had told Wexford to get back to the nitty-gritty, he said, 'This passport, though. I'm still not clear about it. I see she had to have a man's name and a man's identity, but why that one? She could have changed her name by deed poll or kept Comfrey and used one of those Christian names that will do for either sex. Leslie, for instance, or Cecil.'

'Deed poll means a certain amount of publicity, sir. But I don't think that was entirely the reason. She needed a passport. Of course she could have used some ambiguous Christian name for that. And with her birth certificate and her change of name document she could have submitted to the Passport Office a photograph that gave no particular indication of whether she was male or female . . .'

'Exactly,' said Griswold. 'A British passport isn't required to state the holder's home address or marital status or,' he added with some triumph, 'the holder's sex.'

'No, sir, not in so many words. If the holder is accompanied by a child, that child must be declared as male or female, but not the holder. Yet on the cover and on page one the holder's *style* is shown. It wouldn't have helped her much, would it, to have a man's Christian name and a man's photograph but be described as *Miss* Cecil Comfrey?'

'You're a shrewd man, Reg,' said the Chief Constable.

Wexford said laconically, 'Thanks,' and remembered that it wasn't long since that same voice had called him a foolish one. 'Instead she chose to acquire and submit the birth certificate of a man who would never need a passport because he would never, in any conceivable circumstances, be able to leave this country. She chose to assume the identity of her mentally defective and crippled first cousin. And to him, I discovered yesterday, she left everything of which she died possessed and her royalties as long as they continue.'

'They won't do poor John West much good,' said Burden. 'What happened when Polly encountered Rhoda on the Monday evening?'

Not much caring what reaction he would get, Wexford said, 'At the beginning of *Apes in Hell*, two lines are quoted from Beaumont and Fletcher's play:

Those have most power to hurt us, that we love;
We lay our sleeping lives within their arms.

727

'Rhoda wrote that book long before she met Polly. I wonder if she ever thought what they really meant or ever thought about them again. Possibly she did. Possibly she understood that Polly had laid her sleeping life within her arms, and that though she might have to repudiate the girl, she must never let her know the true state of affairs. For eonists, Ellis tells us, are often "educated, sensitive, refined and reserved".

'On that Monday evening Polly came to the gates of Stowerton Infirmary prepared to see something which would make her upset and unhappy. She expected to see West either with another woman or on his way to see another woman. At first she didn't see West at all. She joined the bus queue, watching a much bedizened middle-aged woman who was in conversation with an old woman. When did she realize? I don't know. It may be that at first she took Rhoda for some relative of West's, even perhaps a sister. But one of the things we can never disguise is the way we walk. Rhoda never attempted to disguise her voice. Polly got on the bus and went upstairs, feeling that the unbelievable was happening. But she followed Rhoda and they met on that footpath.

'What she saw when they confronted each other must have been enough to cause a temporary loss of reason. Remember she had come, prepared to be distressed, but nothing had prepared her for this. Marie Cole's shock would have been nothing to hers. She saw, in fact, a travesty in the true meaning of the word, and she stabbed to death an abomination.'

Griswold looked embarrassed. 'Pity she couldn't have seen it for what it was, a lucky escape for her.'

'I think she saw it as the end of the world,' Wexford said sombrely. 'It was only later on that she came to feel anything would be preferable to having it known she'd been in love with a man who was no man at all. And that's why she agreed to my story.'

'Cheer up, Reg,' said the Chief Constable. 'We're used to

your breaking the rules. You always do.' He laughed, adding, 'The end justifies the means,' as if this aphorism were invariably accepted by all as pithy truth instead of having for centuries occasioned controversy. 'Let's all have another drink before they shut up shop.'

'Not for me, sir,' said Wexford. 'Good night.' And he walked out into the dark and went home, leaving his superior planning reprisals and his subordinate affectionately incensed.

STATEHOOD AND
SELF-DETERMINATION

The concepts of statehood and self-determination provide the normative structure on which the international legal order is ultimately premised. As a system of law founded upon the issue of territorial control, ascertaining and determining which entities are entitled to the privileges of statehood continues to be one of the most difficult and complex matters in international law. Moreover, although the process of decolonization is almost complete, the principle of self-determination has raised new challenges for the metropolitan territories of established states, including the extent to which 'internal' self-determination guarantees additional rights for minority and other groups. As the controversies surrounding remedial secession have revealed, the territorial integrity of a state can be questioned if there are serious and persistent breaches of the human rights of its citizens. This volume brings together such debates to reflect further on the current state of international law regarding these fundamental issues.

PROFESSOR DUNCAN FRENCH is Head of the Law School and Professor of International Law at the University of Lincoln, UK.

STATEHOOD AND SELF-DETERMINATION

Reconciling Tradition and Modernity
in International Law

Edited by
DUNCAN FRENCH

CAMBRIDGE
UNIVERSITY PRESS

CAMBRIDGE UNIVERSITY PRESS
Cambridge, New York, Melbourne, Madrid, Cape Town,
Singapore, São Paulo, Delhi, Mexico City

Cambridge University Press
The Edinburgh Building, Cambridge CB2 8RU, UK

Published in the United States of America by Cambridge University Press, New York

www.cambridge.org
Information on this title: www.cambridge.org/9781107029330

First published 2013

Printed and bound in the United Kingdom by the MPG Books Group

A catalogue record for this publication is available from the British Library

Library of Congress Cataloguing in Publication data
Statehood and self-determination : reconciling tradition and modernity in international law /
Edited by Duncan French.
p.   cm.
Includes index.
ISBN 978-1-107-02933-0
1. Self-determination, National.   2. Recognition (International law)
3. Sovereignty.   4. Legitimacy of governments.   5. Newly independent states.
I. French, Duncan.
KZ4041.S75   2013
341.26–dc23
2012028833

ISBN 978-1-107-02933-0 Hardback

CONTENTS

CONTRIBUTORS

JESSICA ALMQVIST is a lecturer in public international law and international relations in the faculty of law, Autonomous University of Madrid. She has a Ph.D. in Law from the European University Institute (2002). She has previously been a researcher on the Project on International Courts and Tribunals, Center on International Cooperation, New York (2002–4), Adjunct Professor, New School, New York (2003–4), researcher at the Foundation for International Relations and External Dialogue in Madrid (2004–6), and also at the Center for Political and Constitutional Studies, Madrid (2006–9).

GRACE BOLTON is a D.Phil. candidate in international relations at St. Antony's College, Oxford University, where she is examining remedial secession in theory and practice since 1945. In 2010, she obtained her M.Phil. in International Relations (Oxon.) and co-edited a special issue of *St. Antony's International Review* entitled 'Secession, Sovereignty and the Quest for Legitimacy'. Her research focuses on international responses to self-determination conflicts, EU enlargement and neighbourhood policy, and post-conflict state-building.

MARTIN DAWIDOWICZ Ph.D. is currently an associate at LALIVE, Geneva, where he specializes in public international law and investment treaty arbitration. Previously, he worked as Consultant in the UN Office of Legal Affairs (Codification Division) in New York and taught public international law at Oxford University, among other positions held. He has published on various topics of international law in a number of leading journals and publications, including the *British Yearbook of International Law*.

ERIC DE BRABANDERE Ph.D. is Associate Professor of Public International Law at the Grotius Centre for International Legal Studies at Leiden University. He is also a Visiting Professor at the Université Catholique de Lille (France) and a member of the Board of Editors of the *Leiden Journal of International Law* and the *Revue belge de droit international*. He previously worked as an attorney-at-law at the Brussels Bar and at Ghent University. His areas of expertise include international dispute settlement, international (investment) arbitration and general international law.

KATHERINE DEL MAR is a Ph.D. candidate in international law at the Graduate Institute of International and Development Studies, Geneva. She was Adviser to the Republic of Serbia in the advisory proceedings before the International Court of Justice in *Accordance with International Law of the Unilateral Declaration of Independence in Respect of Kosovo.*

MALGOSIA FITZMAURICE holds a Chair of Public International Law at Queen Mary University of London. She is an editor-in-chief of the *International Community Law Review* and one of the editors of *Queen Mary Studies in International Law,* published by Martinus Nijhoff Publishers. She is also a Nippon Foundation Professor of Marine Environmental Law at the International Maritime Law Institute of the International Maritime Organisation in Malta. Her research interests are the law of treaties, international environmental law, settlement of environmental disputes and indigenous peoples. She has published widely on all of these subjects.

DUNCAN FRENCH is Head of the University of Lincoln Law School and Professor of International Law. He was previously Professor of International Law at the University of Sheffield, where he hosted the 2011 International Law Association British Branch conference on 'States, peoples and minorities: whither the nation in international law?', at which the chapters in this volume were originally presented. Recent work includes edited collections on global justice and sustainable development, international dispute settlement and the criminological and legal consequences of climate change, and papers on such varied topics as Antarctica, governance of the deep seabed, EU/Caribbean treaty arrangements on foreign direct investment, and the development of complaint and grievance mechanisms in international law.

GLEIDER I. HERNÁNDEZ is Lecturer in Law at the University of Durham. From 2007 to 2010, he served as law clerk to Judges Bruno Simma and Peter

Tomka of the International Court of Justice. He completed his D.Phil. at Wadham College, Oxford and holds an LL.M. from Leiden University, and LL.B. and BCL degrees from McGill University.

JACKSON NYAMUYA MAOGOTO holds a Bachelor of Laws with First Class Honours from Moi University (Kenya) and postgraduate degrees from the University of Cambridge (Masters in Law), University of Technology Sydney (Masters in Law) and University of Melbourne (Doctorate in Law). He is currently a senior lecturer at the University of Manchester, UK. His international law interests encompass the fields of international criminal law, international humanitarian and human rights law, use of force and peace-keeping, space law, counter-terrorism and private military corporations.

TAMAR MEGIDDO is a JSD student at New York University School of Law. She received her Bachelor's degree in Law and the Humanities from the Hebrew University of Jerusalem (2009) and her LL.M. in International Legal Studies from NYU School of Law (2012). Her publications include a first Hebrew *Guide to the Convention on the Elimination of All Forms of Discrimination Against Women* (2011) (co-authored with Ruth Halperin-Kaddari).

ZOHAR NEVO is an Israeli attorney with Yigal Arnon & Co., where his practice focuses on matters involving corporate and commercial law. He received his LL.B. from the Faculty of Law at Hebrew University and an MBA from the School of Business Administration at Hebrew University. He is also interested in public international law and was a recipient of the Fritz & Margaret Oberlander Award for excellence in international law.

ALEXANDROS X. M. NTOVAS advocate (Athens), doctoral grantee in public international law, is lecturer in law at the University of Southampton Law School, UK. He has studied law, political analysis and international relations in Greece, England, Belgium and the Netherlands. He researches, teaches and practises in several substantive areas and levels of public and administrative law.

JADRANKA PETROVIC Ph.D. teaches international law and business law-related units in the Department of Business Law and Taxation, Monash University. Her research interests include international legal protection of cultural property and several other areas of international law, such as international humanitarian law, international criminal law, international human rights law and international dispute resolution. She is the author of *The Old Bridge of Mostar and Increasing Respect for Cultural Property in Armed Conflict* (Brill, 2012).

YAËL RONEN Ph.D. is senior lecturer in Sha'arei Mishpat College in Israel and academic editor of the *Israel Law Review*. She received her Ph.D. at the University of Cambridge in 2006. Prior to embarking on an academic career she served as a diplomat and lawyer in the Israeli Foreign Service for nine years. Her areas of interest include statehood and territorial status, the laws of armed conflict, international human rights law and international criminal law, as well as the intersection between these topics. Among her books are *Transition from Illegal Regimes under International Law* (Cambridge University Press, 2011) and *The Iran Nuclear Issue* (Hart, 2010).

KATJA L. H. SAMUEL Ph.D. is a barrister, and lecturer at Reading University, UK, who specializes in human rights, rule of law and security-related matters, in particular counter-terrorism. Her research interests also include the Organisation of Islamic Cooperation and the influences of Islamic law, especially their influences upon international law-making, peace and security.

MOHAMMAD SHAHABUDDIN achieved LL.B. and LL.M. degrees from the University of Dhaka, and completed his Ph.D. in International Law at SOAS, University of London. He also studied at the Yokohama National University in Japan for the degree of Master of International and Business Law. He is currently the Chairman of the Department of Law & Justice at Jahangirnagar University in Bangladesh. He is also the Assistant Director (Research) of Bangladesh Institute of Law and International Affairs (BILIA).

KELLY STATHOPOULOU is a Ph.D. candidate at the University of Nottingham, UK, where she also teaches EU law as a part-time tutor. Her doctoral thesis examines the relationship between African intrastate peace agreements and self-determination. She previously studied law in Athens (LL.B., National and Kapodistrian University of Athens), Utrecht and Sheffield (joint LL.M. in Conflict and Security Law, Utrecht University and Sheffield University).

CHARLOTTE STEINORTH is Assistant Professor at the Legal Studies Department of the Central European University, Budapest. Before joining CEU in 2012, she was a research fellow at the Max Planck Institute for Comparative Public Law and International Law in Heidelberg. After studies in law and political science at Paris II, she obtained an LL.M. and a Ph.D. from the London School of Economics, for which she was recipient of the Olive Stone Memorial Scholarship. Her research focuses on international human rights law, migration law and democratization and international law.

JAMES SUMMERS Ph.D. is a lecturer in international law at the University of Lancaster. He is the author of a number of works on self-determination. His book *Peoples and International Law* was published in 2007 by Martinus Nijhoff. A second edition is currently being prepared for publication in 2013. He recently edited a book on the legal controversy surrounding Kosovo's declaration of independence, *Kosovo: A Precedent?* (Martinus Nijhoff, 2011). He is currently working on a textbook on international law.

MAI TAHA is an SJD (doctoral) candidate at the University of Toronto, Faculty of Law. She received her LL.M. from the University of Toronto and her M.A. in International Human Rights Law from the American University in Cairo. She was previously a legal adviser for refugees in Egypt, as well as holding positions at the International Criminal Court and the British Institute for International and Comparative Law. Her research focuses on public international law, international legal history and labour law.

JURE VIDMAR is Leverhulme Trust Early Career Fellow at the Faculty of Law, University of Oxford, where he also teaches public international law. He was recently also a visiting fellow at the Institute for International and Comparative Law in Africa, University of Pretoria. His publications have mainly addressed the issues of statehood, self-determination, international delimitation, democratic theory, political participation and norm conflicts in international law. He recently co-edited (with Erika de Wet) *Hierarchy in International Law: The Place of Human Rights* (Oxford, 2012). He is also an editor of the *Hague Yearbook of International Law*.

JACQUI ZALCBERG is a lecturer in law at Humboldt University, Faculty of Law, Berlin, where she established, coordinates and teaches the Human Rights Law Clinic. She holds an LL.M. from Columbia University, where she was the Charles B. Bretzfelder Fellow in International Law, and received her B.A./LL.B. (Hons.) from Monash University, Australia. Her focus is on the rights of indigenous peoples in international law, and she has worked on a range of indigenous rights cases in a variety of international, regional and domestic courts, including as legal adviser to the UN Special Rapporteur on the rights of indigenous peoples.

Self-determination has formed part of the vocabulary of international law since the Treaty of Versailles and the formation of the League of Nations. Its influence has not been constant, but has waxed and waned according to circumstances. Following the virtual completion of the decolonization process (Western Sahara and Palestine two notable exceptions), the 'first generation' of self-determination has largely run its course. But the principle has not lapsed or been deprived of all continuing value, even if its relevance to cases such as the dissolution of the former Yugoslavia remains equivocal and contested.

Thus, the international law on statehood and the principle of self-determination provide a normative framework that supports the classic conception of the international legal order as shaped by and constituted of states. From a distance, it appears enduring, even basal. But quiet waters run deep, and the declarative effect of statehood and self-determination masks significant ongoing uncertainties, as well as disguising the difficulties inherent in applying these doctrines to novel and persistent factual situations. This is revealed in the International Court of Justice's 2010 Advisory Opinion on Kosovo, over which a vibrant debate continues. The questions raised – and mostly left unanswered – by the Court reveal yet again the contested role of international law in governing many communities' desires for autonomy and self-government, either within their state or beyond it.

This volume explores these issues through a wide-ranging discussion of many of the principal challenges, including the disputed doctrine of remedial secession, the rights of indigenous peoples, continued concerns over the diplomatic tool of recognition, and ongoing difficulties with self-determination. Equally, the volume balances general principle with instances of local circumstance and historical example. As the introduction notes, international law is enriched (if not made any more certain) by connection with the complexities of individual situations. Ultimately, the law on statehood and self-determination must be viewed as being in a constant process of change, seeking to balance the precepts of the past with the diverse claims of peoples and communities.

The essays assembled by Professor French represent an ambitious attempt to resolve some current issues surrounding self-determination and sovereignty, including the disputed doctrine of remedial secession, the rights of indigenous peoples, the role of non-state entities and the unresolved, protean difficulties within self-determination itself. The result is a volume of some significance, assembling an array of problems concerning statehood and self-determination to be solved by reference to a central idea – the shared belief in the capacity of international law to evolve, adapt and provide principled solutions. The result is a work in which the value of the whole exceeds that of its (already worthy) constituent parts.

James Crawford
Whewell Professor of International Law
Cambridge
26 June 2012

PREFACE

Issues of statehood, territory and self-determination continue to provide both a framework for, and the broad narrative of, international law in the twenty-first century? Though international law's capacity to regulate ever more complex areas of state, individual and even corporate activity (at least indirectly) is remarkable and has often been noted, continued disputes over such a foundational matter as territorial sovereignty, and the increasingly persistent assertion of further, more limited, rights within and without such sovereignty should themselves not go unnoticed. Though international law now plays an undoubtedly more flexible, adaptive and technical role in the political, social and economic life of states, some of the core principles and assumptions on which international law rests remain open to significant debate and challenge.

Perhaps this has always been the case. Nevertheless, as political situations arise, new complexities in international law emerge. As the International Court's 2010 Advisory Opinion in *Accordance with international law of the unilateral declaration of independence in respect of Kosovo* revealed – partially by way of its reasoning, but principally by what it did not say – there remain many aspects of international law for which we have little in the way of consensus; in this case, unilateral declarations of independence, remedial secession and the outer parameters of self-determination in a post-colonial setting, *inter alia*.

Within this context, there are several sub-themes that one might mention, and to which this preface can only briefly allude. These include, in no particular order, the doctrine and practice of recognition, the rights of indigenous peoples and other minorities, the role of third parties (including international organizations) in matters of state creation and state building, the symbiosis between culture, identity and nationhood in both concurrently upholding and undermining the fundamental basis of the 'nation state', and the countervailing (though certainly not conflicting) pressures of federalism, regionalism and supranationalism. Perhaps above all, there is the matter of the overarching relevance, application and implementation of legal principle in shaping, determining and resolving complex factual situations.

This volume – as full as it is – cannot hope to do justice to all these issues in the same depth. Nevertheless, what it can (and hopefully does) do is to provide the reader with detailed and reasoned analyses of many of the key debates, as well as highlighting examples from across the globe of various instances of where international legal principle is affecting (and is potentially being affected by) local circumstances. It has often been said that facts shape the law, and indeed one of the most noticeable things is the interplay of local and global politics in framing issues of territorial sovereignty.

Moreover, what this volume reveals, above all else, is a truth that international lawyers would be wise not to ignore; namely, that to be meaningful, international law needs to continue to make a difference. Consequently, international lawyers must be aware not just of the global *locus* of the discipline, but also of the many diverse, and often local, settings in which 'our' rules and processes potentially impact. With discussion of situations as far afield as Greenland, New Caledonia, Somaliland, Taiwan, as well as Kosovo, amongst others, the collection is hopefully both contextual in content as well as being international in focus. Equally, as numerous chapters reveal, the past is not a foreign country but, if understood correctly, it can help us to reflect on – often very similar – issues that still resonate in the present day.

The chapters in this collection were amongst those presented at the 2011 International Law Association British Branch annual conference held at the University of Sheffield, when I was there as Professor of International Law and Director of the Sheffield Centre for International and European Law. It thus seems only fitting that I should thank Sarah Beedham, Lisa Burns and Harriet Godfrey of that School of Law's research support office, who worked so hard to ensure that the conference occurred efficiently. Equally, I would like to acknowledge the support of Tawhida Ahmed, Ali Bohm, Russell Buchan, Paul James Cardwell, Richard Collins, Nathan Cooper, Scarlett McArdle, Andreas Rühmkorf, and Kate Wilkinson, both prior to, and during, the conference.

Particular thanks need to go to the contributors who have worked remarkably steadfastly in meeting the deadlines that I imposed, responding to my many demands on their time. But ultimately, this collection would not have been completed without the support of the staff at Cambridge University Press. Such thanks is not given as a matter of polite protocol, but out of real and sincere gratitude; completing this collection whilst at the same time taking up post as a head of school would have not been possible otherwise.

This book is dedicated to my children, Anna, Jacob, Matthew and Rebecca, whose interaction so often reminds me of the diplomacy, negotiation tactics and the occasional use of force of states.

TABLE OF CASES

Treaties and other international agreements

Other major documents by jurisdiction or organisation

LIST OF PRINCIPAL ABBREVIATIONS

AHLC	Ad Hoc Liaison Committee for Assistance to the Palestinians
AO	Autonomous Oblasts
ARSIWA	Articles on Responsibility of States for Internationally Wrongful Acts 2001
ASEAN	Association of Southeast Asian Nations
ASSR	Autonomous Soviet Socialist Republics
AU	African Union
CAR	Central African Republic
CCCE	*Conseil Consultatif Coutumier Environnemental*
CERD	Committee on the Elimination of Racial Discrimination
CIS	Commonwealth of Independent States
CSCE	Conference on Security and Co-operation in Europe
CSS	Comprehensive Proposal for the Kosovo Status Settlement
DPRK	Democratic People's Republic of Korea
DRC	Democratic Republic of the Congo
EC	European Community/European Communities
ECE	Eastern and Central European (States) (see Chapter 16)
ECOWAS	Economic Community of West African States
EFTA	European Free Trade Association
EMRIP	Expert Mechanism on the Rights of Indigenous Peoples
EU	European Union
EULEX	European Union Rule of Law Mission
FLNKS	*Front de Liberation Nationale Kanak et Socialist*
FPA	Fisheries Partnership Agreement
FRG	Federal Republic of Germany
GA Res.	UN General Assembly Resolution
HRC	Human Rights Committee
ICC	International Criminal Court
ICCPR	International Covenant on Civil and Political Rights 1966
ICESCR	International Covenant on Economic, Social and Cultural Rights 1966
ICJ	International Court of Justice
ICSID	International Centre for Settlement of Investment Disputes
IDPs	internally displaced persons
IGAD	Intergovernmental Authority on Development

xlvii

IIFFMCG	Independent International Fact-finding Mission on the Conflict in Georgia
ILA	International Law Association
ILC	International Law Commission
ILM	International Legal Materials
ILO	International Labour Organization
IMF	International Monetary Fund
KLA	Kosovo Liberation Army
LNTS	League of Nations Treaty Series
MFN	most-favoured nation
NAMMCO	North Atlantic Marine Mammal Commission
NATO	North Atlantic Treaty Organization
NGO	non-governmental organization
NSA	non-state actor
NSGT	non-self-governing territory
OAU	Organization of African Unity
OIC	Organization of Islamic Cooperation (formerly the Organization of the Islamic Conference)
OSCE	Organization for Security and Co-operation in Europe
PA	Palestinian Authority
PBC	Peacebuilding Commission
PCIJ	Permanent Court of International Justice
PISG	Provisional Institutions of Self-Government (in Kosovo)
PLO	Palestine Liberation Organization
PNA	Palestinian National Authority
PRC	People's Republic of China
RCPR	*Rassemblement Pour la Caledonie dans la Republique*
RIAA	Reports of International Arbitral Awards
R-UMP	*Rassemblement–UMP*
SADC	Southern African Development Community
SC Res.	UN Security Council Resolution
SFTG	Somali Federal Transitional Government
SRSG	Special Representative of the UN Secretary-General
SSR	Soviet Socialist Republics
TWAIL	third world approaches to international law
UC	*Union Calédonienne*
UDHR	Universal Declaration of Human Rights 1948
UIDHR	Universal Islamic Declaration of Human Rights 1981
UN	United Nations
UNCED	United Nations Conference on Environment and Development 1992
UNDRIP	United Nations Declaration on the Rights of Indigenous Peoples 2007
UNESCO	United Nations Educational, Scientific and Cultural Organization

UNHCR	United Nations High Commissioner for Refugees/UN Refugee Agency
UNMIK	United Nations Interim Administration Mission in Kosovo
UNOMIG	United Nations Observer Mission in Georgia
UNOSEK	Office of the Special Envoy of the Secretary-General of the United Nations for the future status process for Kosovo
UNSG	United Nations Secretary-General
UNTAET	United Nations Transitional Administration in East Timor
UNTS	United Nations Treaty Series
VCLT	Vienna Convention on the Law of Treaties 1969
WTO	World Trade Organization

~

Introduction

DUNCAN FRENCH

In international law there are few issues that better epitomize the combination of law, fact and power more enigmatically than the question of statehood. The state is the most fundamental unit of the international legal order, but it also sits at the apex of most of the paradoxes that distinguish, and thus frame, international law. Of course, it is not the fact of territorial statehood *per se* that ensures either its fundamental character or its complexity; rather, it is the characterization of sovereignty that flows from this territorial fact. As Judge Huber memorably recorded in his award in *Island of Palmas*, '[i]ndependence in regard to a portion of a globe is the right to exercise therein, to the exclusion of any other state, the functions of a state'.[1] Ignoring the inherent circularity of this proposition, and recognizing that sovereignty is to be understood in this context in both its functional and its elemental state, it remains the case that, above all else, it is from statehood and the characterization of its ensuing sovereignty that all else in international law has historically flowed.

Thus, it is in statehood that one seeks to find a seamless amalgam of legal doctrine and social reality. As all traditional legal analyses of the creation of states tell us, effective control of territory and people remains the hallmark of what constitutes a state.[2] Legal rules may appear to impose certain constraints upon the achievement of statehood – still not better exemplified than by article 1 of the 1933 Montevideo Convention on Rights and Duties of States[3] – but the extent to which they were ever intended to do other than merely reflect

---

[1] Award of 4 April 1928, 11 RIAA 831, 838.
[2] J. Crawford, *The Creation of States in International Law* (Oxford University Press, 2006, 2nd edn), p. 46: 'they [referring to the usually-employed criteria of statehood] are based on the principle of effectiveness among territorial units'. Nevertheless, see also ibid., p. 37: 'there has long been no generally accepted and *satisfactory* legal definition of statehood' (emphasis added).
[3] (1934) 165 LNTS 19.

the factual constituents of statehood rather than seek to impose a normative imprimatur upon its achievement has always been, and remains, unclear.

True, in cases of factual uncertainty, political contestation or diplomatic doubt, the law is turned to as a guide, but it often remains just that – a guide. With no central organizing agency either to prescribe the specific conditions of, or to determine the attainment or otherwise of the requirements of, statehood, international law on this issue remains notionally mandatory, apparently persuasive, but ultimately contingent upon claim and response. To highlight this point, one need only reflect that one almost never talks in terms of the legality or the illegality of statehood in normal circumstances; the law of statehood encapsulates a process not readily classified within the dichotomy of compliance and breach. Rather, statehood is the assessment of a conglomeration of facts through manifold legal prisms, which can either be focused and narrow or broad and all-encompassing, such variations dependent upon whether statehood is viewed – usually *a priori* – as acceptable or impermissible in any given situation.

Even in the most egregious examples of 'unlawful' statehood, it is the mechanism (or process) of acquisition that is viewed in illegal terms (for instance, the illegal use of force) and not the statehood, in and of itself. Such process-illegality may, of course, impact upon the legitimacy of the acquisition; one might note, for instance, the widespread acceptance of the doctrine of non-recognition of aggressively acquired territory.[4] But beyond the most blatant examples, illegality seems inapposite when coming to a judgement (invariably political) whether the various factors of statehood have been met.

Law bestows rights, privileges (as well as duties and obligations) upon states, but its role in their creation remains more subtle and nuanced. This is not to suggest international law is merely a veneer; a turn to realism in the face of the structural weakness of the international legal system. It is not to question the relevance of international law. Rather, it requires scholars to consider the extent of its part (the contribution of

---

[4] *Legal Consequences of the Construction of a Wall in the Occupied Palestinian Territory*, ICJ Report (2004) 136, 171: 'On 24 October 1970, the General Assembly adopted resolution 2625 (XXV), entitled "Declaration on Principles of International Law concerning Friendly Relations and Co-operation among States" . . . in which it emphasized that "No territorial acquisition resulting from the threat or use of force shall be recognized as legal." As the Court stated in its Judgment in the case concerning *Military and Paramilitary Activities in and against Nicaragua (Nicaragua v. United States of America)*, the principles as to the use of force incorporated in the Charter reflect customary international law. . .the same is true of its corollary entailing the illegality of territorial acquisition resulting from the threat or use of force.'

international law). Though statehood is capable of being described by law, it is much less certain that it is *governed* by it. This is not to dismiss the customary framework around the 'Montevideo criteria' as just a postscript to political decision-making – 'political' here being an assemblage of both the internal considerations of the putative state and the diplomatic deliberations of the international community in response thereto – but to recognize the partiality that such a normative understanding brings. The international law of statehood has provided us with the fullest understanding of what entities must do to be accepted as a state, but it remains a *legal* understanding of a much more complex social and political process. To that extent, it is inchoate. But this should not lead us to become fatalistic; international law has much to offer the wider debate, as the chapters in this volume testify.

However, as the International Court of Justice (ICJ)'s 2010 Advisory Opinion on Kosovo's unilateral declaration of independence[5] has revealed, the discipline of international law suffers when the subject matter is approached not just formally, but overly and overtly formalistically. In the attempt to ensure the advisory opinion maintained a careful balance between the diverse views of states, the ICJ sought not only to legalize the situation (i.e. to impose a framework of law onto the factual state of affairs) – which, in itself, though difficult, is not contentious – but went further, and idealized the role of law in this situation. In other words, the Court seemed to read into the situation a legal understanding that had little bearing upon what role law had actually played in the process, or on the behaviour and opinions of the key protagonists. It was this *ex post facto* interpretation that would disconnect the precepts of law from fact and, for many, reduce its overall credibility.

Nevertheless, the tendency and wish to conceive of statehood in legal terms continues to reflect a more fundamental and genuine aspiration, namely, to rebalance political considerations and normative understandings. When statehood is unquestioned and unquestionable, such an aspiration would appear to be easily met; there is a natural symmetry between law (as reflected by satisfaction of the principle of effective control) and fact. Though even this, as noted below, can be a mirage caused by the dominance of the state as the principal territorial entity, which fails to reflect a wider range of imperatives and calls for

---

[5] *Accordance with International Law of the Unilateral Declaration of Independence by the Provisional Institutions of Self-Government of Kosovo* (Advisory Opinion of 22 July 2010).

brief history of S.D. overleaf

intro with x

representation, including from indigenous peoples, minorities, intra- or cross-state peoples, and sub-national territorial units.

However, when statehood is unclear, not yet achieved or disputed – as was the case with Kosovo prior to the Court's judgment and remains subsequently – the disjunct between law and fact, and law's invariably peripheral role in resolving such situations, becomes the more glaring. Though the desire for law is not misconceived, its application to any given situation will, however, usually frustrate. In particular, the continued hope of some to devise a more legal doctrine of recognition as the means of providing law and certainty when little of either is apparent is a misunderstanding of that doctrine, at least as it can currently be employed by states. 'Misuse' as a term would, however, be inappropriate here as it suggests, in the usual course of events, a wrong interpretation; but only in the most obvious of circumstances could that be said to be so.

But this perspective of 'unquestioned-versus-disputed statehood' as a binary tension is ultimately false; certainly it is now, if it has not always been so. Even if one accepts the view that states *qua* states are, in their purest form, 'the formal agent for its population internationally',[6] Knop is surely right to note that this can be constructed as many 'different shades':

> [i]n some cases, international law certifies no more than the state's effective control over its population. In other cases, the creation of the state through an exercise of self-determination makes the state an agent chosen freely by a people. In yet others, international law engineers democracy and even differentiated forms and rights of representation for certain groups within the state.[7]

Thus, statehood as a legal form cannot truly be understood today without an appreciation of the myriad of alternatives, complexities, competing demands, and just 'different shades' that would seem to challenge the supremacy of the state as the paradigm legal form in international law, even if some of these other *collectivities* (for want of a better phrase to sum up everything from minority groups to non-recognized states) continue to view statehood as an aspirational form.

To be sure, self-determination receives particular attention in this volume as a principal driver of such change, having both historically

---

[6] K. Knop, 'Statehood: Territory, People, Government' in J. Crawford and M. Koskenniemi (eds), *The Cambridge Companion to International Law* (Cambridge University Press, 2012), p. 107.
[7] Ibid.

reoriented (through not the rejection, but rather the amplification of) the Westphalian model, as well as presenting newer and equally complex challenges to the metropolitan territory of pre-existing states. To that extent, self-determination – now seemingly tied by some to the much more contentious notion of remedial secession in the face of persistent and substantive human rights abuses and/or fundamental denials of self-governance – lies at the heart of any modern discussion of statehood. Indeed, it has been taken up and utilized in differing contexts of indigenous peoples and minority rights, though not without some historical precedent. Thus, as statehood is both a potential outcome of self-determination, but is also concomitantly a constraint thereon, it would be artificial to separate completely the one from the other. For practical reasons, this edited collection has separate parts, with the first focusing on statehood and recognition and the second on self-determination – and each certainly has its own sphere of separate interest – but much like an ill-conceived Venn diagram, the overlap is significant and forever changing.

Thus, it should be apparent that attention to these other forms is as interesting for what they tell us about statehood as they do about themselves. Philip Allott once wrote: '[a]t the end of the pre-modern period, it could not have been predicted with any justifiable sense of certainty that one particular form of social organization would come to dominate all the others . . . It would not have been possible to foresee the overwhelming power which the concept of the state would acquire within social reality-for-itself, subjecting all other forms of subordinate society to itself'.[8]

Whether other forms of society are still subordinated in quite the same way (even in the relatively short time since those words were written), and how one conceives of bundles of rights that attach to groups *vis-à-vis* the state, are thus issues that this work explores. Moreover, though it is only right to eschew an unduly hierarchical and systematic understanding of the varying participants in the international order, the challenge to the state is not just from below – or across, if one considers recognition as a matter of diplomacy – but also from what it means for states to be members of international organizations, and how that in turn impacts upon their own sovereignty.

[8] P. Allott, *Eunomia: New Order for a New World* (Oxford University Press, 1990 (paperback edn, 2001)), paragraph 12.48.

The authors in this volume bring their own perspective to these questions, as well as raising other matters pertinent to the general theme. The remainder of this Introduction will thus seek to provide further discussion of these chapters. But an additional point may be necessary, and that is the relationship between the generality of law and the specifics of local fact. A richness in many of the chapters is the focus given to particular geographical contexts; not necessarily as template examples, or metaphors, but sometimes simply as incidences of how law and fact intervene in very specific situations. It is hoped that the depth of detail contained therein will supplement and substantiate other chapters which equally focus on the position in general international law. It is through the combination of the two that this collection of essays generates fresh insight.

The book is divided into three parts; as already noted, Part I focuses upon statehood and recognition and Part II reflects upon the increasingly diverse context presented by self-determination (and indicates that this has perhaps always been the case). Part III then highlights the continuing complexity of the state in international affairs, being both the principal means of collating, however imperfectly, a nation's longing for history, tradition and culture – ultimately its sense of corporate belonging – whilst at the same time providing the singularly paradoxical conduit through which many of the new challenges and modalities of governance and self-organization are cascaded, filtered and given effect within the international system.

Part I: Statehood and recognition

Part I begins by recognizing that while statehood is an aspirational form for many territorial entities, there may be political reasons why, in some instances, this status has not – or has not yet – been sought by an entity itself. As Ronen notes, Taiwan is the most obvious example in this category, though there are others, such as the Commonwealth of Puerto Rico and perhaps, until its 2011 submission to the United Nations (UN), the Palestinian Authority. Regardless of whether the objective grounds of statehood have been achieved – territory, people and government – there has usually been either a clear political decision not to seek independence, or ambiguity as to its present and future intentions. Certainly, in some instances, there is the genuine concern that 'a declaration of independence might trigger a chain of events which would challenge the factual premises' of the very basis of the claim to statehood. Nevertheless, the existence of so-called quasi-states is not unproblematic both for themselves and for the international community, particularly (as the chapter reveals) as regards the rules relating to the use of force and self-defence. Ronen also considers whether an entity can be a 'state-for-a-limited-purpose' within a particular international regime, for instance, the International Criminal Court, but again such a purely functional approach is not without both practical and conceptual difficulties. The chapter concludes that in all of this debate '[t]he point of departure ... must be that the distinction between states and other entities, including quasi-states, cannot be dispensed with off-handedly'.

Chapter 2 moves the discussion forward to focus upon one of the key aspects of the 2010 Kosovo Advisory Opinion, namely, the legality of unilateral declarations of independence. Vidmar considers which aspects of unilateral declarations make them subject to the purview of international law and thus, consequently, in what situations they might be described in dichotomous terms as being either legal or illegal. In particular, and this is worthy of quotation at length:

> unilateral declarations of independence are issued in the sphere of international legal neutrality, so long as such declarations do not attempt to consolidate an illegal territorial situation, created by a breach of certain fundamental norms of international law, in particular those of *jus cogens* character.

Vidmar notes that the *unilateral* nature of such declarations neither prohibits their issuance nor precludes their acceptance under general international law. But this is far from saying they are inconsequential; rather, the more interesting question to ask is, who has authored the text – a selection of random individuals or 'representatives of an entity which meets, or is capable of meeting, the effectiveness standards presumed under the Montevideo criteria'? In the latter case, such declarations will be much more than just 'ink on paper', and thus are capable of having international legal effects, be they lawful or unlawful.

Del Mar, in Chapter 3, analyses another feature of the Advisory Opinion, namely, remedial secession. She sees great risk in accepting remedial secession as a means of resolving human rights and humanitarian crises within states. Not only is the doctrine not recognized in the *lex lata* (and she very explicitly repudiates any argument based on the savings clause found in the provisions on self-determination in the 1970 Declaration of Friendly Relations), but equally she argues that there are very strong reasons why the doctrine should not find a place in the international law of the future. Setting to one side the practical questions of who might be entitled to benefit from remedial secession, what level of seriousness a breach must attain and at what moment in time secession might be permitted – all questions Del Mar highlights as revealing the doctrine's inadequacy – the real difficulty is the mismatch between the undoubted moral horror of extreme human rights abuses and the solution that remedial secession provides. As she notes, 'a State is a legal entity, not a human rights solution ... remedial secession shifts the debate to a secessionist cause, and away from the real issues, namely the absence of an effective "human rights culture" in the State concerned'.

Discussion of remedial secession continues in Chapter 4, where the situation in Kosovo is set next to, and contrasted with, the situations in Abkhazia and South Ossetia both prior to and after the conflict in 2008. Bolton argues that in each case, such secession attempts went through three distinct phases – what she terms the constitutional phase, the bellicose phase and the remedial phase. During the constitutional phase, the international community sought to maintain the integrity of the pre-existing state and promote alternative, more limited, forms of autonomy and self-government as a means of reconciling the differing claims. When this failed, the bellicose phase saw the secessionist arguments convert into intra-state (and inter-state) conflict, where *de facto* separation between parent state and territorial entity occurs. Finally, Bolton suggests that during the remedial stage there are certain 'remedial conditions', which must be met if remedial secession (despite its continued contestation in international legal argument) is to be considered as a legitimate response. Indeed, recognizing the potential misuse of the doctrine, as was arguably the case with Russian intervention in, and subsequent recognition of, South Ossetia and Abkhazia, the present aim must be to discern those conditions which permit remedial secession as a remedy of last resort. While Bolton is certainly more willing to consider the final necessity of remedial secession, nevertheless there remain concerns as to its abuse, best expressed in the rhetorical question she asks in her conclusion: 'whose interests are served by remedial secession?'

Though both Chapters 3 and 4 deal with matters raised – if not necessarily responded to – by the ICJ in the 2010 Advisory Opinion, Chapter 5 considers much more specifically the reasoning of the Court in that judgment. Indeed, Ntovas very explicitly seeks to move away from the general issues raised by the Court to consider the *lex specialis* of UN

Security Resolution 1244 (1999) and the Constitutional Framework for Provisional Self-Government established thereunder. He argues that there is a fundamental paradox at the heart of the Advisory Opinion, which cannot simply be wished away. Indeed, the paradox flows from the Court's own reasoning, namely, that whilst the declaration of independence did not violate the *lex specialis*, the *lex specialis* remained in force on the day of the issuance of the declaration and indeed subsequently. As Ntovas notes,

> [t]he oxymoronic conclusion must be that since the date of the declaration . . . Kosovo has enjoyed two notionally distinct yet concurrent legal orders, and this gives rise to a specific conceptual difficulty regarding a conflict of legal orders, since both refer to precisely the same territorial entity with mutual exclusivity.

Contrary to the views expressed by certain judges in their own opinions, the Court invariably sought to avoid what the legal effects of its own judgment were; he quotes Judge Bennouna, who very succinctly asks: '[b]ut then what legal order governed the authors and the declaration itself?' Ntovas concludes by wondering whether the 'strained reasoning' of the Court – so as to avoid being ensnared by certain legal difficulties in the question presented to it – has actually harmed its own judicial character. Ultimately, acceptance of the Court's opinion is not premised on the authority of the Court, however pre-eminent, but on the intrinsic merit of its reasoning; and on this matter and as regards this Advisory Opinion, many remain unconvinced.

This view as to the limited contribution the Court's judgment made to the international community's response to the situation of Kosovo is noted in Chapter 6, where Almqvist considers the role of recognition in determining a final status for Kosovo. She argues that the ICJ along with the other 'UN-based multilateral mechanisms' – in which she also includes the General Assembly and the Security Council – have not been able to constrain what she terms the 'politics of recognition'. Rather, the international community's very mixed and divided response to Kosovo's unilateral declaration of independence indicates once again that states retain a high degree of national discretion on the question of whether to recognize putative states, thus highlighting the little that international institutions can do to 'foster[. . .] common ground'. For Almqvist, this is confirmation of the long history of political and diplomatic division on such matters, and the unevenness that this inevitably creates:

> [i]n stark contrast with the idea of a standard procedure, the corrobo-
> ration of these politics implies the absence of guarantees of foreseeability
> or certainty about the prospects of actually gaining the status of state-
> hood. Neither does it offer any guarantees of equal treatment and fairness
> across different cases and communities with similar aspirations.

Almqvist raises the prospect – though no more than that – of fresh insights into how the UN can play a role in recognition if, and when, a vote is moved on the submission of Palestine for UN membership. As Chapter 7 notes, an increasing number of states have already recognized it in anticipation of the membership application. Others, that have not gone so far, have nevertheless upgraded their missions and/or strength-ened their links with the Palestinian Authority. Nevertheless, at the same time, the United States is opposed to a unilateral application to the UN and would instead prefer a return to the negotiation table with Israel. In light of this, in their chapter, Megiddo and Nevo seek to provide a balanced assessment of whether the conditions for statehood – be that the Montevideo criteria, the principle of self-determination, as well as other considerations – can yet be said to have been met. Building on a previous assessment undertaken a few years previously, the authors now see a Palestinian case for statehood as having a much stronger basis. Economic development and institutional state building continues, and though the question whether negotiations have truly reached a stalemate is strongly debated (and even the glimmer of still further negotiations is likely to delay many of the key players from currently recognizing a Palestinian state), many that have recently recognized Palestine have either expressly or implicitly done so precisely because they no longer feel that successful completion of negotiations with Israel is a compul-sory precursor to statehood. Thus, Megiddo and Nevo feel confident enough to say that 'an independent State of Palestine may very well be recognised ... in the near future'. There certainly does now seem a groundswell of inevitability about Palestinian statehood; whether Kosovo is an antecedent as to what political will can accomplish is perhaps a more controversial issue.

A territorial entity which remains as hopeful for a similar assessment, but politically is much less likely to secure it, is Somaliland. Chapter 8 provides a historical overview of how Somaliland has found itself in this rather curious legal no-man's land; of possessing the stability Somalia does not, but not its formal status. As Maogoto notes, 'Somaliland offers a tricky legal problem but also an opportunity. States should exercise their voice by recognising Somaliland.' This is not just a political call, but also a deeply practical one. As he notes, 'an active role on the part of the state in international relations is consistent with a sovereign's duties and responsibilities to its citizenry'. There may be small signs of change; the 2012 London Conference on Somalia saw Somaliland acknowledged, at least procedurally, as distinct from Somalia. Whether that is enough to begin a process that will end in formal recognition is unlikely – as Maogoto notes, such recognition 'may prove a difficult adjustment for political processes still entrenched in dual social contract relationships of yester-decades'. And this seems an apt conclusion, more generally, for Part I, if one reflects that despite developments, the formal conditions of statehood and the policy-driven tool of recognition, when considered in concert, continue to ensure the exclusivity of the state (and the inferiority, or even the non-existence, of the non-state) in international affairs.

Part II: Self-determination

The second part of the volume draws out a range of issues that arise from consideration of self-determination, which reveal the principle's breadth, various uncertainties that continue to surround even its most elemental features, aspects of its historical application which had perhaps previously been downplayed and, more generally, how as a principle of international law it is still being actively utilized within discrete domestic contexts to greater or lesser effect. Of note is the rhetorical (but politically not insignificant) employment of self-determination above and beyond its strict legal application. Indeed, now that it has found its way into the lexicon of the rights of indigenous peoples, self-determination can slowly be seen as acquiring a distinct and increasingly autonomous meaning, somewhat detached from that originally assigned to it. Nevertheless, the core challenges remain. And as Chapter 9 highlights, one of the many unanswered questions goes to the very heart of the debate over the principle, namely, when one talks of the internal and external dimensions of self-determination, to what, in fact, is one referring? Summers suggests that internal and external self-determination (as, for instance, used by the Canadian Supreme Court in its 1997 judgment on the speculative matter of Quebec secession) provides self-determination with a more manageable content and thus allows the principle to be categorized in more easily understood terms. But he goes on to suggest that, in fact, internal and external self-determination as discrete concepts do not have definite meaning, but that much will depend upon the 'unit' to which they are applied; be that peoples,

sovereign states, political units (such as sub-national entities) within a
sovereign state, or territorial entities distinct from a sovereign state. For
each, what constitutes internal and external self-determination may have
very different appearances and alternate consequences, and it would
be wholly erroneous to try to classify too neatly which outcomes fall
into which respective category. Instead, the chapter purposely seeks to
highlight the complexity and discursive nature of the concepts. As
Summers notes,

> these perspectives can operate simultaneously across different elements
> of a self-determination process. As a result, it is argued that there is no
> single understanding of internal and external self-determination, rather,
> a range of perspectives. To focus on one actor may be to overlook the role
> of others in the process.

However, whereas constructive ambiguity can be essential and
indeed profitable in political discourse between different units of self-
determination in a genuine search for progress, self-determination is
also a legal rule as well as a legal principle, and as such it must have the
normative strength to constrain behaviour that is clearly at variance with
its precepts. Chapter 10 explores a particularly infamous failure of self-
determination, namely, Western Sahara. As Dawidowicz reveals, not
only have the people of Western Sahara not yet been freely able to
exercise their right to self-determination, but '[w]orse still, it appears
that important actors in the international community may effectively be
forestalling the effective exercise of this basic right'. Particular focus of
the chapter is the Fisheries Partnership Agreement between the
European Union (EU) and Morocco which, because of its failure to
exclude the waters of Western Sahara, has thus consequently permitted
the exploitation of the natural resources in that maritime territory and
without explicit regard to the interests of the people most clearly entitled
to benefit. And though in December 2011 the European Parliament
refused to give its consent to an extension to the agreement precisely
because of these concerns over its international legality, risks remain. As
Dawidowicz rather colourfully, but no less inaccurately, notes, '[w]ith
the efflux of time, even the hardest of rocks will eventually wither and
disintegrate into grains of sand. A similar process can be observed in
international law.'

However, if Western Sahara is a classic tale of (regrettably unfinished)
self-determination, Chapter 11 presents an alternative perspective,
focusing as it does on African intrastate peace agreements. Admittedly,

its focus on the texts rather than difficulties in implementation invariably means a more optimistic analysis of the success of these agreements than might otherwise be the case. But it is not Stathopoulou's aim to review their success; rather, she explores the extent to which self-determination has been used in the negotiation of the agreements (the process), in the final text (the substance of the principle) and, significantly, the involvement of the wider international community in the intrastate peace process. As the chapter makes clear, intrastate peace agreements are a curious form of instrument, the status and characterization of which is altogether unclear; 'being in the grey area where international law meets (pre)national law'. The strict legal relevance of self-determination is often set to one side in place of a more political appreciation of the term, to allow the emergence of new internal structures, usually with the participation of previous combatants, within the existing state. Thus self-determination becomes an important element in ensuring a reconfiguration of a state's power structures and institutions, rather than 'the withering of the state'. Perhaps because of this, and especially when considering the role of third parties and the wider international community in such politically charged processes, 'self-determination, though relevant, seems to be articulated in rather general terms'. However, notwithstanding this uncertainty, Stathopoulou sees significant potential for self-determination within the context of intrastate agreements:

> self-determination has three normative functions: as affirming duties in the case of gaps and silences in the agreements, as interpretive in the case of unclear undertakings, and as evaluative by being a general standard for appraising international involvement. Thus, even where the precise contours of the rule of self-determination remain uncertain, the principle can nevertheless assist even in the most difficult peace-building processes.

This rather broader understanding of self-determination is mirrored in the altogether different context considered in Chapter 12, which seeks to place the international legal principles surrounding self-determination next to religious norms on a similar theme, in particular the Islamic principle of *jihad* as properly understood. As Samuel notes, one should eschew the usual assumption that religious norms are merely 'aspirational' in effect or that they simply underpin political and/or theological justifications for self-determination struggles. Rather, she makes the undoubtedly more difficult claim that religious norms such as *jihad* and the Islamic understanding of justice 'may lie at the very core of the substance, interpretation, and application of such principles'. But this in turn raises the normative question as to whether the meaning and scope of self-determination as an international legal principle equates with similar concepts in Islamic law. Undoubtedly there is similarity and overlap, particularly as international law and Islamic law would both seem to support the rights of peoples to self-determination, and indeed both would consider such rights as peremptory. However, where they differ most explicitly are the 'triggers' that justify the recourse to self-determination and the justifications on the use of force by third parties in support thereof. This is not to suggest impossible contradiction – Judge Trindade in the Kosovo Advisory Opinion, for instance, on the issue of 'triggers' took a significantly broader approach to when self-determination is justifiable in general international law – but what this chapter encourages us to do is not to dismiss religious norms as inconsequential or lacking 'law and policy-making importance'.

Recognizing that self-determination continues to be conceptually, politically and even religiously debated should alert us also to the inevitability that historical practice surrounding self-determination was not of some pure form, but rather, has always been framed via a deeply political discourse. Chapter 13 identifies one particular incidence that has received significantly less attention than the well-reported post-1945 decolonization process, namely, the Mosul dispute which occupied the League of Nations in the 1920s. As Taha notes, 'it is imperative to engage with, and contest, the history that normalized the marriage between emancipation and national self-determination'. Of particular significance for Taha is the 'blind spots in legal scholarship', especially in the semi-periphery of neither North nor South where 'the "Arab" story has rarely been told'. In a detailed analysis of the evolution of the Mosul dispute and how it was handled by the leading protagonists within and outside the Council of the League of Nations, issues of regional nationalism, European imperialism and the assertion of capital interests are shown as all having played a part in the uneasy resolution of the dispute. As Taha says, 'European colonialism was still present, but the relationship was characterized by more sophistication than simply imperial imposition in the near East'. Self-determination is thus revealed as both contested and contextual, providing neither a definite response nor significant guidance beyond the factual and political prism of the immediate situation. Moreover, on a point that has wider relevance for the remainder of Part II, 'historical agency and participation were not able to buffer the larger structure that sought to defy agency at its most intrinsic and popular level'.

This theme of a tension existing between structure and popular agency can indeed be seen in Chapter 14, where Fitzmaurice reviews recent developments in the internationally proclaimed rights of indigenous peoples, but goes on to wonder how far that has actually generated greater protection and self-autonomy for them. The adoption of the 2007 UN Declaration on the Rights of Indigenous Peoples was undoubtedly a milestone in the international community's complex understanding of, and approach to, indigenous peoples. In particular, the reliance on the language of self-determination to concretize and strengthen still further the rights of indigenous peoples – though for a long time resisted by some – is a significant step forward. Nevertheless, as Fitzmaurice argues, though such international language is important in 'defin[ing] the general parameters and legal terms of the right of self-determination . . . in practical terms, however, it has had its shortcomings and limitations, as it cannot capture the diversity contained within national systems'. Undertaking an analysis of the situation of Greenland, and its ongoing and changing relationship with the metropolitan territory of Denmark, Fitzmaurice reveals the nuances, complexities and perhaps even idiosyncrasies that a national approach to self-determination, self-governance and autonomy is able to devise. Nevertheless, in her final analysis, Fitzmaurice returns to the question as to the overall value of the UN Declaration and states that it 'did not really bring anything new to the debate'. On the other hand, '[d]omestic law . . . is rich with possibility'.

In keeping with this attention to local circumstance, Chapter 15 focuses on the development of colonial and municipal processes in securing greater rights and opportunities for the Kanak of New Caledonia. Again, though the international rights provide the backdrop, the narrative is very particular to that situation. Zalcberg presents the self-determination struggle of the Kanak against changing French policies and approaches, as well as the very different priorities of the settler communities. Occasional militancy and political participation – common features of many self-determination struggles – have been features of the Kanak movement, not only against political structures, but increasingly also against commercial imperatives, in this case, of nickel mining. Zalcberg does not seek to present a rose-coloured portrayal of the current situation of the Kanak, but equally feels it appropriate to highlight some of the more innovative development and participation aspects of the emerging relationship between the indigenous peoples and the mining corporation. Nevertheless, 'the creation of new political structures, in part through the demands of self-determination, presents both challenges and threats to the indigenous peoples'. Engagement with (and within) the current system and preserving collective self-identity are in continuous tension for indigenous peoples, and it is a tension that is often misunderstood by the host/controlling state and others, but though it is a common theme for indigenous peoples, quite how it plays out in any particular situation will vary according to local circumstance.

The final chapter of Part II returns to the issue of agency and structure and, as with Chapter 13, again focuses on the period immediately after World War I, this time to consider what protection was given *to* minorities in Eastern Europe during the inter-war years. As is well known, a complex system of minority protection treaties was agreed, supervised by the League of Nations and on which the Permanent Court of International Justice had significant opportunity over the years for judicial analysis and comment. But this was no instance of political participation by the minorities themselves – viewed very much as non-Western European 'other' – as the protection scheme was devised *for* them, and its ambition was little more than regional stability. Indeed, as Shahabuddin notes, when placed alongside the more ambitious tenets of self-determination that were originally part of Woodrow Wilson's Fourteen Points, the minority protection treaties were a shallow form of autonomy: 'a fallback position where the principle of self-determination in the conservative sense could not be applied'. Moreover, the limitations of the scheme were not simply its failure to prevent the rise of Nazi hegemonic interest in German minorities in Eastern Europe in the 1930s, but that from the outset 'a significant characteristic of the interwar minority protection mechanism ... [was that] it actually avoided any general recognition of minority rights'. Self-determination has been one of the greatest developments in international law – infusing moral claim and political necessity – but it has never been an easy panacea, as these chapters highlight.

Part III: Tradition, opportunities and challenges: the changing nature of the state

Part III of the volume focuses on a range of traditional and modern challenges to the state, reflecting all the complexities and ambiguities that the state still represents. As a microcosm of these tensions, Chapter 17 explores the extent to which culture and tradition continue to be at the very heart of both national identity and statehood. Petrovic analyses the importance of cultural heritage to peoples and states and equally, within the context of the example she gives (namely, the destruction of the Old Bridge of Mostar during the Yugoslav conflict of the early 1990s), the extent to which damage to cultural property is a very poignant physical and symbolic component of the wider conflict against a particular people and their sense of identity. Cultural property, of course, has an inherent contradiction – that contradiction coming out most clearly in its purposeful destruction – because, as Petrovic notes, '[a]lthough they are precious to all humanity, objects of cultural property are often among the first wilful targets in armed conflicts'. Cultural property (certainly the most prized) thus has both international and local meaning, bestowing upon the international community a common interest in its protection, whilst at the same time this being very much secondary to the significance such property has for the peoples and the state in which it is located. And so was the situation with the destruction of the Old Bridge of Mostar, where the damage was aimed at the very heart – geographically, emotionally and morally – of that community and that people. Nevertheless, the international community, both through the *ad hoc* criminal tribunal for the former Yugoslavia which has had occasion to consider a war crime for the damage and the financial support given to rebuild the bridge, has shown global solidarity. As Petrovic concludes, '[w]hile the bridge was primarily rebuilt to re-establish broken interethnic links within a particular nation, the reconstruction project was "international" in character ... The universal value of the Bridge was reinforced ... by the fact that the case was before an international tribunal'.

The chapter following may seem very removed from such matters of tradition and cultural sensitivities – focusing as it does on increasing supranationalism within (some) international organizations and the extent to which state sovereignty is challenged thereby – but, in fact, there is significant resonance between them. Both chapters recognize the now almost insoluble relationship between the state and the international sphere and both, though each in its own way, note the changing nature of the state so that it is no longer the exclusive mechanism by which the local is reconciled with the international. As De Brabandere says:

> [t]he tendency to rely more on a form of legitimacy which depends on the consent of the population, however, clearly shows that in certain institutions, the consent of states as the primary legitimating factor is being complemented by the consent and/or control by the population directly affected by measures taken by that organisation.

For De Brabandere, this is a notable, but not invariably radical, departure from the *status quo*. Indeed, the existence of supranational governance need not be considered a diminution of the state at all, so as long as such organizations 'are viewed as deriving their legitimacy from the powers that have been conferred to them by the member states of that organisation'. Thus, while popular legitimacy must be considered a shift in where authority ultimately lies, international and regional organizations (even the most far-advanced in this respect, namely, the EU) are a long way from justifying their existence, their authority or their powers on popular approval alone. As De Brabandere concludes, such popular legitimacy is very much 'still in its infancy' and even then 'it is doubtful whether this form of legitimacy will ever be able to fully replace state-centred legitimacy'.

This sense of development – if still inchoate – also comes across very strikingly in Chapter 19 as Steinorth explores the extent to which notions of democracy and liberal governance have found their way into the rhetoric and operational practices of certain international organizations, in this case the UN and the World Bank. Though such ideals remain contested in intergovernmental political discourse, these international organizations have sought to engage with the promotion of democracy and good governance not as matters of principle, but as more efficient means of achieving their pre-existing mandates. As Steinorth notes, 'they have adopted an instrumental approach given the perceived factual benefits that liberal democracy has for the achievement of peace and development'. In particular, the World Bank – which is explicitly mandated *not* to take political considerations into account in its economic deliberations – is able to endorse an ideal such as good governance as it would appear to possess a 'technocratic apolitical character'. The concept 'does not name what or whose concept of "good" it purports to promote, but presents "good" simply as a "self-evident" qualification of governance'. But despite this instrumentality, Steinorth feels that such developments cannot occur without potential longer-term implications: '[such] considerable practice of promoting a particular form of domestic order sits uneasily with international law's tolerance of diversity, signalling the turning away from a pluralistic conception of world community'.

However, almost as an antidote to the perception that democracy is increasingly viewed (at least instrumentally) as universal, Chapter 20 reminds us that democracies come in all shapes and sizes – and, indeed, divisions. In particular, Hernández highlights how federalism breaks down the unitary nature of the state to reveal a complexity of structures, processes and checks-and-balances between even the most similar examples of the form. Using the United States, Canada, Australia, Germany, Switzerland, and Belgium as his principal examples – the first three being federal states with no express conferral of express treaty-making powers on its sub-national entities, the latter three being federal states which do grant (limited) treaty-making powers – Hernández reveals a multitude of differences between otherwise similar democratic states. Belgium, as will be widely known, is a particularly interesting example where the 'complete parallelism between [its] governmental orders', including in treaty-making, creates a dynamic that is almost without exception in international relations and domestic constitutive theory. Though the chapter focuses on the treaty-making powers of sub-national entities as an attribute of wider state sovereignty, the very distribution of such power – however framed and however tightly regulated it might be – is itself indicative of the need for greater appreciation of the more general place of sub-national entities within the international order. This question can be narrowly perceived, raising the doctrinal issue of concurrent international legal personalities within a state, but equally it can also be considered, more broadly, as to whether it is a first step in disaggregating the functions of the state in international law. But one should not discount the resilience of the (federal) state in international legal theory – or, as was said at the outset of this Introduction, that the state remains at the 'apex' of the international system – for as Hernández notes:

> [e]ven if a State wishes, within its own constitutional arrangements, to allow its component units to exercise the sovereign prerogative of entering into treaties, the treaty-making power of such units derives from the basic competence of the sovereign State, as a whole, to conclude treaties . . . reference by international law to a State's domestic constitutional arrangements would serve to reinforce its sovereignty in international law, rather than to disperse it.

Conclusion

In conclusion, one might reasonably recall the seminal statement of principle made by Judge Dillard in *Western Sahara*: 'It is for the people to determine the destiny of the territory and not the territory the destiny of the people.'[9] Taking it out of its immediate context of non-self-governing territories and self-determination, for which it had much

---

[9] *Western Sahara*, ICJ Report (1975), Sep. Op. Judge Dillard, p. 122.

relevance, how far should – or could – such a statement still prove to be a genuine aspiration for international law and international relations? As this volume explores, remedial secession remains deeply controversial, the rights of indigenous peoples and other minorities in their own self-government and (in the case of the former) over natural resources and land is still subject to much ambiguity and domestic variation, recognition as a tool of states is jealously guarded and arbitrarily applied and, more generally, the paradigm of the state is revealing itself to be flexible enough to withstand changing expectations, increasingly intrusive obligations and the evolution of a diverse array of internal (federal) and supranational modalities of governance.

Of course, Judge Dillard did not intend his statement to apply as a mantra across all situations; it was located within the particular context of its time and its setting. But what can perhaps be taken from it, however cautiously, is that nothing remains immutable and, in particular, that structural formations should never be considered as beyond change. This is not to favour constant and continuous upheaval, or even to make a comment as to the legality or otherwise of remedial secession as a doctrine of last resort, but the point is rather more wide-ranging; that states, quasi-states, territorial entities that want statehood, and those territorial entities that do not are becoming increasingly less unitary in nature and monolithic in character. For the international lawyer, this behoves us to understand the frustrating complexity of specific circumstance and localized detail; overarching principles and rules of general application are necessary and useful, but they will not provide the totality of the structures that different communities and peoples have always needed to find a way to live within and without.

PART I

Statehood and recognition

Entities that can be states but do not claim to be

YAËL RONEN[*]

I. Introduction

The international community is based on categories of participants; and despite warnings on the demise of the Westphalian system, states remain the dominant category in the international legal order,[1] holding rights and obligations in the widest array of international legal fields. What distinguishes statehood as a type of personality in international law is its universality – all entities which are states share a determined set of rights and duties, powers and immunities, which have developed through practice and are regarded as an acceptable basis for international interaction.

International law also regulates the participation in international relations of other categories of international persons, whose powers, rights and obligations reflect their respective spheres of operation.[2] For example, the laws of armed conflict apply to certain groups engaged in military operations; individuals are the holders of human rights and are legally accountable under international criminal law. The content of the international personality of actors other than states cannot be demarcated definitively in the abstract, since 'non-state actor' (NSA) is not a

---

[*] I am grateful to Robert Barnidge, Jean d'Aspremont, James Crawford, Duncan French, James Green, Guy Harpaz, Robert McCorquodale, Marko Milanovic, Yuval Shany and Colin Warbrick for their helpful comments. The usual disclaimers apply. NB: The bulk of this chapter was completed before the Palestinian Authority submitted an application for UN membership and the Prosecutor of the ICC published his decision regarding the situation in Palestine.

[1] A. C. Cutler, 'Critical Reflections on the Westphalian Assumptions of International Law and Organization: A Crisis of Legitimacy' (2001) 27 *Journal of International Studies* 133, 140.

[2] *Reparation for Injuries Suffered in the Service of the United Nations* (Advisory Opinion), [1949] ICJ Reports 174, 182: 'Under international law, the Organization must be deemed to have those powers which, though not expressly provided in the Charter, are conferred upon it by necessary implication as being essential to the performance of its duties.'

positive characterization, only a negative one.[3] The exact scope of a particular NSA's personality is therefore a matter for *ad hoc* analysis, by reference to the exact legal context in which the NSA operates. For example, rights of individuals may depend upon whether or not they are within the jurisdiction of a state party to a particular human rights treaty.

An important factor in the delineation of an actor's international rights and obligations might be territorial control, since the latter is a condition for the exercise of many powers. For example, the applicability of non-international conflicts under Additional Protocol II of the Geneva Conventions depends on the armed group's exercise of control over a part of the territory in which the conflict takes place. Such control indicates a degree of stability that is necessary for the armed group to be capable of effectively applying the rules of the Protocol.[4] Generally, however, territoriality is still very much associated with the notion of statehood, which is the epitome of effective control over territory, in the sense that there is a presumption of statehood and sovereignty when an entity exercises effective territorial control.

Quasi-states are a specific category of NSAs, identified by their similarity to states, including territorial control, and thus by the potential to exercise the full panoply of powers, rights and obligations of states. At the same time, quasi-states in this chapter are defined precisely by their voluntary self-exclusion from the category of states. The premise of this chapter is that statehood cannot be regarded as purely an objective status; quasi-states can, and do, exercise powers in an effective manner similar to that of states, but since formally they are not states, they may be exempt from the obligations and constraints which international law places on states. The measure of their personality must be assessed against the legal context in which they operate, which, largely speaking, will depend upon consent of other actors, mainly states.

The gap between capacity and status becomes difficult when responsibility depends on formal status. In such cases, quasi-states may enjoy a capacity that is unrestrained by responsibility. This disparity may place a strain on the system, particularly if the disparity hinges on the quasi-state's

---

[3] A phenomenon termed the 'not-a-cat' syndrome, by P. Alston, 'The "Not-a-Cat" Syndrome: Can the International Human Rights Regime Accommodate Non-State Actors?' in P. Alston (ed.), *Non-state Actors and Human Rights* (Oxford University Press, 2005), pp. 3–4.

[4] International Committee of the Red Cross, *Commentary on the Additional Protocols of 8 June 1977 to the Geneva Conventions of 12 August 1949* (ICRC/Martinus Nijhoff, Dordrecht, 1987), para. 4467. See also A. Clapham, *Human Rights Obligations of Non-State Actors* (Oxford University Press, 2006), pp. 36, 41–2.

own discretion (namely, its political choice not to declare statehood). This chapter explores the possibility of bridging the gap between capacity and status by bringing quasi-state into the category of states notwithstanding the absence of a formal claim of statehood on their part. At the same time, it should be borne in mind that in the absence of statehood, quasi-states are also excluded from a host of rules that benefit only states, such as participation in international organizations and state immunity. Accordingly, when contemplating a change in the status of quasi-states, the consequences of that change must be considered in their entirety.

The chapter proceeds as follows: Section II introduces a number of quasi-states. Section III demonstrates some difficulties that emerge when quasi-states act in a manner comparable to that of states, but without being bound by the same obligations as states. Section IV examines whether and how the gap between the effective operation of quasi-states and their legal status can be bridged. It considers whether quasi-states should be harnessed into the legal regime applicable to states; what the trigger for such harnessing should be; and whether statehood is an all-or-nothing notion or a divisible one, so that a quasi-state can be bound by the legal regime applicable to states on an *ad hoc* basis, in some areas of law even if not in others.

II.   The entities in question

Quasi-states are entities that fulfil the traditional requisites for statehood, which, as prescribed by the mainstream theory on statehood, is preconditioned on effectiveness: a permanent population in a defined territory, under an effective government.[5] In addition, quasi-states as defined in this chapter, do not claim to be states.[6] A prime example of a quasi-state was, until September 2011, the political entity in the Palestinian territories,[7] where an effective government (the Palestinian

---

[5] Montevideo Convention on Rights and Duties of States, 26 December 1933, 165 LNTS 19, Article 1. The 'capacity to enter into relations with other states' is a consequence of statehood rather than a criterion for it. Moreover, it is no longer an exclusive prerogative of states, J. Crawford, *The Creation of States in International Law* (2nd edn, Clarendon Press, Oxford, 2006), p. 61.

[6] This chapter does not address the matter of entities purporting to be states but which have failed to obtain recognition as such. Some of the analysis might nonetheless be applicable to entities that have been refused recognition as states on political grounds (such as Somaliland in northern Somalia).

[7] That is, until it formally applied for UN membership, UN Doc A/66/371-S/2011/592 (23 September 2011).

Authority) exercises authority over a population in a defined territory (even if its boundaries are controversial). There are clearly core geographical and functional areas in which the Palestinian Authority, and even more so Hamas, operate effectively and to the exclusion of Israel. The conflict between the Palestinian Authority and Hamas may raise the question of who precisely is the government of the Palestinian territories, but for present purposes this need not be decided. Should the Palestinian Authority declare statehood,[8] there is little doubt that its declaration could (and probably would) be regarded as constituting a new state. To avoid confusion, this chapter refers to the 'Palestinian Authority' rather than to 'Palestine', the latter term serving at present either as the formal UN designation for the Palestine Liberation Organization (PLO) as a non-state entity,[9] or as an expression of a political aspiration of statehood.

Another entity which may fall within the category of quasi-states is Taiwan. The population on the islands of Formosa and the Pescadores is governed by an effective government to the exclusion of others, but Taiwan is not generally considered a state. Crawford posits that this is precisely because it still has not unequivocally asserted its separation from the People's Republic of China (PRC).[10] Others hold that if Taiwan declares statehood, extending recognition to it would not be a straightforward matter legally, because it would involve policy choices relating to the balance between the prohibition on the use of force and the right to self-determination.[11] Taiwan has diplomatic relations with 23 states, mostly small states and micro-states (12 in Latin America and the Caribbean, 4 in Africa, 6 in Oceania, and the Holy See).[12] However,

---

[8] In September 2011 the Palestinian Authority applied for UN state membership. At the time of writing, the request is pending before the Security Council. The Palestinian Authority's application unambiguously claims statehood: UN General Assembly, Application of Palestine for Admission to Membership in the United Nations, UN Doc A/66/371-S/2011/592 (23 September 2011). However, there has been no declaration of independence by the Palestinian Authority.

[9] UN General Assembly Resolution 43/177 (15 December 1988).

[10] Crawford, *The Creation of States*, p. 219.

[11] For literature on the status of Taiwan see ibid., p. 211, but also Brad R. Roth, 'The Entity that Dare not Speak its Name: Unrecognized Taiwan as a Right-Bearer in the International Legal Order' (2009) 4 *East Asia Law Review* 91, 100.

[12] Palau, Tuvalu, Marshall Islands, Solomon Islands, Kiribati, Nauru, Guatemala, Paraguay, St. Vincent and the Grenadines, Belize, El Salvador, Haiti, Nicaragua, Dominican Republic, Burkina Faso, Sao Tome and Principe, Swaziland and the Gambia. Republic of China, Ministry of Foreign Affairs, www.mofa.gov.tw/webapp/ct. asp?xItem=32618&CtNode=1865&mp=6.

since these states do not have relations with the PRC, it appears that they regard Taiwan not as a state independent of the PRC, but as the legitimate government of mainland China. Taiwan also maintains representative offices in over 50 states.[13] It has full membership in 32 intergovernmental organizations and in their subsidiary bodies, as well as observer status in 19 others;[14] however, in many of these, its membership is based either on its pre-1971 status as the government of Mainland China, or on the fact that these organizations allow participation of non-states.[15]

Needless to say, in the cases of both the Palestinian Authority and Taiwan, a declaration of independence might trigger a chain of events which would challenge the factual premises of the preceding discussion: if Israel or China resort to force, for example, the effective control of the two quasi-states might be put into question even before statehood is established.

The Commonwealth of Puerto Rico[16] is a territory under US sovereignty. It is governed by a 1952 constitution adopted under US legislation, and exercises 'a measure of autonomy comparable to that possessed by the States'.[17] Following the adoption of the constitution, Puerto Rico was removed from the UN list of the non-self-governing territories, where it had been listed until then.[18] Relations between Puerto Rico and the United States are defined by the US Constitution and the Puerto Rican Federal Relations Act. The policy of the US executive has long been that Puerto Rico's status should be decided by the people of Puerto Rico.[19] Since 1952 the residents of Puerto Rico have carried out three referenda on the future status of the territory, repeatedly indicating preference for some version of commonwealth over statehood within

---

[13] Republic of China, Government Information Office, Embassies, Consulates and Missions Abroad, www.taiwanembassy.org/dept.asp?mp=1&codemeta=locationIDE.

[14] Republic of China, Ministry of Foreign Affairs, www.mofa.gov.tw/webapp/ct.asp?xItem=51335&CtNode=2254&mp=6.

[15] E.g. the World Health Assembly (WHA), which invited Taiwan to participate as observer in May 2009. Observer status at the WHA is also available to non-governmental Organizations (NGOs). Jacques deLisle, 'Taiwan in the World Health Assembly: A Victory, With Limits', Brookings Northeast Asia Commentary No. 29, www.brookings.edu/opinions/2009/05_taiwan_delisle.aspx.

[16] In Spanish: Estado Libre Asociado de Puerto Rico (free associated state of Puerto Rico).

[17] *Examining Bd. v. Flores de Otero*, 426 US 572, 597 (1976).

[18] UN General Assembly Resolution 748(XIII) (27 November 1953).

[19] Report by the President's Task Force on Puerto Rico's Status ('Task Force Report') (March 2011), www.whitehouse.gov/sites/default/files/uploads/Puerto_Rico_Task_Force_Report.pdf 18.

the federal US constitutional system and independence.[20] If Puerto Rico declares itself independent, even unilaterally, from an international legal perspective there is no reason to deny it recognition as a state.

Recent history offers examples of former quasi-states which have eventually become states. One example is Andorra, which until 1993[21] maintained a special relationship with both France and Spain: it was not under either of its neighbours' jurisdictions, nor did its relations with them follow the normal pattern of inter-state relations. When the question of Andorra's status arose tangentially before the European Court of Human Rights in 1992, the Court considered Andorra a 'European country' rather than a 'European state', but further noted that 'the development of the institutions of Andorra, if continued, might allow Andorra to "join the international community"'.[22] It is arguable that even at the time of that pronouncement, Andorra fulfilled the factual requisites of statehood.

Prior to declaring independence in August 2008, South Ossetia may also have qualified as a quasi-state as defined here, given its effective operation separately from Georgia[23] since the break-up of the Soviet Union in 1991 (through the growing apparatus of a small state with an elected parliament and president, military and police forces and various

---

[20] Although controversy over the terms of this status resulted in the majority of participants in the referendum of 1998 rejecting all options, including commonwealth, ibid.

[21] In 1993 the Principality of Andorra entered into the Treaty of Good Neighbourliness, Friendship and Co-operation between the Kingdom of Spain, the French Republic and the Principality of Andorra (1872 UNTS 195), under which the former two recognized it as a sovereign state (Article 1). Andorra subsequently joined the UN as a member state.

[22] A 'European country', as distinguished from a 'European state', can become an 'associate member' of the Council of Europe, Statute of the Council of Europe, London, 5 May 1949, 87 UNTS 103 (1951), Articles 5, 4; *Drozd and Janousek* v. *France and Spain*, App. No. 12747/87 Judgment (Merits) of 26 June 1992, para. 88. In 1950, the Federal Republic of Germany (FRG), and then French-occupied Saarland became associate members. The FRG became a full member in 1951, while the Saarland withdrew from its associate membership in 1956 after joining the FRG in 1955. At the time of writing there are no associate members in the Council of Europe.

[23] This statement assumes that recognition of South Ossetian independence would not have violated Georgia's right to self-determination and territorial integrity. The Independent International Fact-Finding Mission on the Conflict in Georgia also found that South Ossetia did not fulfil the requisite of effective government, and concluded that it was 'from the perspective of international law – thus not a state-like entity, but only an entity short of statehood', Report of the Independent International Fact-Finding Mission on the Conflict in Georgia ('Georgia Fact-Finding Report') (September 2009), vol. 2, p. 134, www.ceiig.ch/Report.html. The analysis by the Mission is nonetheless open to dispute, on grounds that will not be explored here.

ministries).[24] According to the European Union (EU)'s Independent International Fact-Finding Mission on the Conflict in Georgia, until 2008 South Ossetia had not unambiguously and consistently claimed to be a state, oscillating between demands for recognition as a sovereign and independent state, and advocating unification with North Ossetia through integration into Russia.[25]

Of the quasi-states noted above, some are exceptional in that they are (or were) operating on territory not within the sovereignty of a state. This is clear with respect to the Palestinian Authority and Andorra, but is also the case with regard to Taiwan, at least according to some views. This kind of quasi-state presents particular challenges to the international legal system. While the chapter is not limited to these quasi-states, it focuses on the challenges that they present.

There are many reasons for quasi-states to refrain from declaring statehood. For example, common wisdom suggests that historically the Palestinian reluctance to declare statehood stemmed from concern that this would weaken their bargaining position vis-à-vis Israel and the international support which they enjoy.[26] Taiwan refrains from declaring statehood for fear that this would result in a military attack by the PRC.[27] Residents of Puerto Rico appear to prefer commonwealth status over independence because the former entitles them to US citizenship, a right to unrestricted travel to the United States and economic aid, all of which may have to be renounced if Puerto Rico opts for independence.[28] These considerations are not related, at least not directly, to specific obligations that would be incumbent upon these quasi-states if they declare statehood. They are political choices which may not be second-guessed. At the same time, unilateral political choices should not, by themselves, obstruct the entry into operation of legal consequences, if those are merited by the existence of a particular factual situation, such as the existence of an effectively governed population in a defined territory. Therefore the absence of a claim to statehood may be only

---

[24] C. Waters, 'Law in Places that Don't Exist' (2006) 34 Denver *Journal of International Law and Policy* 401, 405.

[25] Georgia Fact-Finding Report, p. 129. This statement seems to be contradicted by the chronology provided by the fact-finding mission itself, p. 129, n 10.

[26] Y. Ronen, 'ICC Jurisdiction over Acts Committed in the Gaza Strip: Article 12(3) of the ICC Statute and Non-state Entities' (2010) 8 *Journal of International Criminal Justice* 3, 15–16; B. Ravid, 'Palestinian leadership divided over plan to seek UN recognition', *Ha'aretz* (9 June 2011), www.haaretz.com/print-edition/news/palestinian-leadership-divided-over-plan-to-seek-un-recognition-1.366679.

[27] Crawford, *The Creation of States*, p. 219, n. 78.   [28] Task Force Report.

one of various factors in determining an entity's rights, obligations
and status.

III. The significance of state-like conduct by quasi-states

The legitimacy of international law[29] derives in large part from its
reciprocal operation, either within specific regimes or as a pre-legal,
political concept, namely, the expectation that participants who operate
similarly be bound by similar obligations. Another underlying concept of
international law is that with power come obligations.[30] These expectations are thwarted when entities who act similarly to states are exempt
from the obligations that attach to statehood; or when, despite non-state
status, they benefit from legal powers otherwise reserved to states.

A quasi-state can act in a manner similar to that of a state in a variety
of ways. It may attempt to carry out an act which is reserved to states.
If such an act depends on acceptance by other states in order to have
legal consequences, legally it presents only a limited challenge to the
maintenance of the powers and obligations equilibrium. For example, if
a quasi-state attempts to accede to a treaty, states parties to the treaty
can refuse to accept such accession. This was the response of the
General Committee of the General Assembly of the United Nations
to the application of Taiwan for membership in 2007. The General
Committee decided not to include the application on the General
Assembly's agenda,[31] on the ground that in accordance with
General Assembly resolution 2758(XXVI),[32] the United Nations (UN)
considered Taiwan, for all intents and purposes, to be an integral part of

---

[29] 'Legitimacy' being understood as a basis for compliance separate from coercion, self-interest
or rational persuasion. D. Bodansky, 'The Concept of Legitimacy in International Law', UGA
Legal Studies Research Paper No. 07–013, 8. Available at http://ssrn.com/abstract=1033542.

[30] With respect to the human rights obligations of states outside their sovereign territory,
this was affirmed in the European Court of Human Rights judgment in *Al-Skeini and
Others* v. *the UK*, Application No. 55721/07 [2011] ECHR 1093 (7 July 2011), para. 137:
'It is clear that, whenever the State through its agents exercises control and authority
over an individual, . . . the State is under an obligation under Article 1 to secure to that
individual the rights and freedoms under Section 1 of the Convention'; and more
generally in the concurring opinion of Judge Bonello: 'Extraterritorially, a Contracting
State is obliged to ensure the observance of all those human rights which *it is in a
position to ensure*' (para. 32) (emphasis in original).

[31] UN Doc. A/BUR/62/SR.1, 4–8.

[32] UN General Assembly Resolution 2758(XXVI) (25 October 1971), expelling the representatives of Chang Kai-shek in favour of the PRC.

the PRC.[33] Once rejected, the application lost all potential to disrupt the UN legal order, in which only states can be members.

A quasi-state may also purport to perform an act which states carry out unilaterally, but which has international legal consequences. Examples could include the conferral of nationality on individuals under the quasi-state's effective control, or the establishment of a maritime zone, and subsequent prevention of entry or detention and prosecution of entrants into it. While the legal effect of such a conferral does not depend entirely on international consent, since it will have effect between the quasi-state and the individuals subject to its control, states can respond to it and determine its legal consequences when matters arise such as diplomatic protection, espousal of claims or assertion of criminal jurisdiction.

A different challenge arises when a quasi-state conducts itself in an area which is regulated under international law only insofar as states are concerned. It may use force, confiscate property, hold individuals in detention, conduct trials, or perform other acts of governance. The question in this case is not whether to give effect to the quasi-state's conduct, since such conduct is beyond the control of states, and to wish it away would be futile; but whether to subject the quasi-state to the regulation by international law of the consequences of its conduct, as if that conduct had been that of a state.

The participation of quasi-states in political, military, economic and other relations in a manner similar to states – but not under the legal regime applicable to states – presents a challenge to the international legal order because of the disparity between an entity's powers and its obligations and responsibilities. The following sections illustrate some challenges resulting from the fact that international law does not, at present, take full account of the potential involvement of quasi-states in international interaction and their exercise of powers associated in law with statehood.[34]

---

[33] The Under-Secretary-General for Legal Affairs, cited by the representative of St. Vincent and the Grenadines, UN Doc. A/BUR/62/SR.1 p.5.

[34] The issues we now proceed to discuss are not an exhaustive list of legal fields in which inter-state relations differ from the relations between states and NSAs. It is a brief recapitulation of matters that may be particularly pertinent in the circumstances relating to quasi-states. The analysis also does not address the difficulty of accountability through formal international legal institutions. This notorious weakness of international law also concerns states, although admittedly to a lesser extent than NSAs.

Readers may notice the absence of the laws of armed conflict from the present analysis. These laws distinguish between inter-state conflicts, which are governed by

1. The laws on the use of force

Ius ad bellum regulates the exercise of powers which are ordinarily regarded as falling within the monopoly of the state, and are regulated with respect to inter-state relations. The use of force by quasi-states is therefore a matter of uncertainty. The International Court of Justice (ICJ) has stated that the prohibition on the use of force under UN Charter Article 2(4) applies to states in their international relations.[35] In contrast, domestic use of force is regulated by domestic law and international human rights law. The normative framework is less clear with respect to use of force between a state and a quasi-state, particularly if the latter acts from territory that is not under the sovereignty of any state. *Prima facie*, Article 2(4) does not apply to the relations between a state and a quasi-state.[36] Perhaps such application can be grounded in the customary *ius ad bellum*, which, according to the ICJ, persists even after the adoption of the UN Charter, and differs in content from the treaty-based rules, including with respect to the meaning of 'armed attack', which authorizes the exercise of the 'inherent right' of self-defence.[37] There is merit in the

the law on international armed conflict, and intra-state conflicts, which are governed by the law on non-international armed conflict. (When the quasi-state is not part of the state, it is not clear how the conflict should be classified, but under the present state of the law, one paradigm or the other must apply).

This dilemma has led some scholars to suggest either an abandonment of the distinction, or at least the finding of common ground to all armed conflicts; G. Corn and E. Talbot Jensen, 'Transnational Armed Conflict: A "Principled" Approach to the Regulation of Counter-Terror Combat Operations' (2009) 42 *Israel Law Review* 46, propose fundamental principles that should apply in any conflict, regardless of its classification; R. S. Schöndorff, 'Extra-State Armed Conflicts: Is there a Need for a New Legal Regime?' (2005) 37 *New York University Journal of International Law and Politics* 1, proposes introducing the category of 'extra-state armed conflict' to the law of armed conflict. However, the question is not whether different laws apply in different conflicts, but whether the political choice of the quasi-state puts the state party to the conflict at a disadvantage. Since both the laws of international armed conflict and those of non-international armed conflict operate reciprocally, any advantage gained by a quasi-state from maintaining non-statehood also accrues to the adversary state. Accordingly, the distinction between the two types of conflicts actually allows the maintenance of symmetry of powers and responsibilities between the parties.

[35] *Accordance with International Law of the Unilateral Declaration of Independence by the Provisional Institutions of Self-Government of Kosovo* (Advisory Opinion of 22 July 2010), [80].

[36] Y. Dinstein, *War, Aggression and Self-Defence* (4th edn, Cambridge University Press, 2005), p. 204.

[37] *Military and Paramilitary Activities in and against Nicaragua* (*Nicaragua v. US*), Merits, Judgment, [1986] ICJ Reports 14, 92–3, [175]–[176] (27 June 1986).

argument that quasi-states, particularly those not within sovereign territory, *ought* to be bound by the prohibition on the use of force. If peace and security are core values that underpin the international order, it is only reasonable to expect that the use of force by NSAs should also be prohibited.[38] Thus, for example, it seems incongruous that Taiwan be permitted to use force against Japan, or that the Palestinians may attack Jordan.

However, there are conceptual problems in regarding quasi-states as bound by the prohibition on the use of force: the expansion of international law to actors other than states does not occur *ipso facto*. It requires state action.[39] Yet, as a matter of doctrine there has been no expansion of the *ius ad bellum* to actors other than states. There is also little practice to support this as *lex lata*. When North Korea used military force against the Republic of Korea in 1950, Security Council action taken against it was advanced specifically on grounds of a 'breach of the peace' rather than 'aggression',[40] a term reserved to use of force by states. More recently, one might mention the statement of the Independent International Fact-Finding Mission on the Conflict in Georgia, solicited by the EU, that 'the use of force by secessionist groups is in any case illegal under international law'.[41] Yet the South Ossetian case is problematic as support for this proposition, on two counts. First, in the circumstances before the Mission, a prohibition on use of force by South Ossetia against Georgia emanated from specific undertakings by the parties to the conflict. Second, the conflict was essentially domestic; there was no reason why the recourse to force should have been examined in terms of international law in the first place.

A particularly imbalanced but prevalent proposition is that even if a prohibition on the use of force applies to NSAs, international law exceptionally *permits* the use of force by an NSA (including a quasi-state) and by states assisting it, when that force is used in an endeavour to realize the right to self-determination of a people deprived of that right.[42]

---

[38] For arguments on this, see N. Tsagourias, 'Non-State Actors in International Peace and Security: Non-State Actors and the Use of Force' in J. d'Aspremont (ed.), *Participants in the International Legal System: Multiple Perspectives on Non-state Actors in International Law* (Routledge, London and New York, 2011) p. 326.

[39] C. Warbrick, 'States and Recognition in International Law' in M. Evans (ed.), *International Law* (Oxford University Press, 2003), pp. 205, 206.

[40] Crawford, *The Creation of States*, p. 470. Security Resolutions 82(1950) UN Doc. S/1501 (25 June 1950), 83(1950) UN Doc. S/1511 (27 June 1950), 84(1950) UN Doc. S/1588 (7 July 1950).

[41] Georgia Fact-Finding Report, p. 279.

[42] UN General Assembly Resolution 2625(XXV) (24 October 1970).

Various legal bases have been offered for this assertion, such as that the *ius cogens* character of the right to self-determination trumps any prohibition on the use of force by a people entitled to exercise the right (while UN Charter Article 2(4) continues to apply to the state involved in the dispute),[43] or that colonialism and related phenomena constitute a permanent armed attack against which self-defence would be admissible (thereby implicitly acknowledging that some prohibition must exist if an excuse of self-defence is required).[44]

If there is no international legal prohibition on the use of force by NSAs (including quasi-states), one might argue that there is also no international legal prohibition on the use of force by a state against an NSA. However, the argument of reciprocal non-application of the prohibition fails on both normative and positive grounds. First, the prohibition on use of force by states is not based on a notion of reciprocity, but on the perception that use of force constitutes a threat to international peace and security. It is for this reason that the prohibition on the use of force has been widely elevated to the rank of *ius cogens*.[45] Accordingly, it may be regarded as applying not only in inter-state relations, but in any cross-border dispute, regardless of whether the state's adversary is itself a state or not.

As a matter of positive law, the question of a prohibition on the use of force by a state against an NSA is subsumed in the literature into the question whether there is a right of self-defence against an NSA. Invariably, this question is analysed in terms of the use of force in self-defence against an NSA acting from the territory of another state. In *Congo v. Uganda*, the ICJ noted that it did not need to address the question whether international law provides for a right to self-defence against an NSA,[46] implying that it was not a clear case. This finding is

---

[43] C. Gray, 'The Charter Limitations on the Use of Force: Theory and Practice' in V. Lowe, A. Roberts, J. Welsh and D. Zaum (eds), *The United Nations Security Council and War* (Oxford University Press, 2008), pp. 86, 95; Tsagourias, 'Non-State Actors', p. 326.

[44] P. Malanczuk, 'Countermeasures and Self-Defence as Circumstances Precluding Wrongfulness in the International Law Commission's Draft Articles on State Responsibility' in M. Spinedi and B. Simma (eds), *United Nations Codification of State Responsibility* (Oceana Publications, New York, 1987), pp. 197, 252.

[45] J. A. Green, 'Questioning the Peremptory Status of the Prohibition of the Use of Force' (2011) *Michigan Journal of International Law* 215, 221. Green contests this view on the ground that the uncertainty surrounding the law on the use of force hinders any characterization of the prohibition of its use as a *jus cogens* norm, as well as because it is unclear whether there is enough evidence to establish that the prohibition is peremptory in nature.

[46] *Armed Activities on the Territory of the Congo (Democratic Republic of the Congo v. Uganda)*, Judgment [2005] ICJ Reports 168 [147] ('*Congo v. Uganda*').

contested both from within the Court[47] and in the literature,[48] as well as by some practice.[49] This framing of the question, however, obfuscates the question whether a state is bound by the prohibition on the use of force against an NSA in the first place. When the action in self-defence against an NSA entails military action against the territory of a 'host' state, there is no doubt that the prohibition on using force underlies the situation, since it applies between the two states. But there is practically no consideration of self-defence against an NSA acting not from within the territory of a state, let alone consideration whether an underlying prohibition exists. Thus, Security Council Resolution 1860(2009),[50] which called for the immediate withdrawal of Israeli forces from Gaza during

[47] Ibid., Separate Opinion of Judge Kooijmans, [26]–[31], Separate Opinion of Judge Simma, [4]–[15], Declaration of Judge Koroma, [9]. Even the judges who dissented in *Congo* v. *Uganda* from the ICJ's jurisprudence, namely, that there is no right to self-defence against an NSA, took it for granted that the armed attack by the NSA emanated from the territory of another state.

[48] For arguments in support of a right to self-defence against an NSA, see Dinstein, *War, Aggression and Self-Defence*, pp. 204–8, 247; M. Schmitt, 'Counter-Terrorism and the Use of Force in International Law' (2003) 79 *International Law Studies* 7, 33–4; R. Müllerson, 'Jus ad Bellum and International Terrorism' (2003) 79 *International Law Studies* 75, 112; S. A. Barbour and Z. A. Salzman, '"The Tangled Web": The Right of Self-Defense against Non-State Actors in the Armed Activities Case' (2008) 40 *New York University Journal of International Law and Politics* 53. For reservations as to a right to self-defence in response to an attack that is not attributable in any way to a state, see E. P. J. Myjer and N. D. White, 'The Twin Towers Attack: An Unlimited Right to Self-Defence?' (2002) 7 *Journal of Conflict and Security Law* 1, 7; C. Gray, 'President Obama's 2010 United States National Security Strategy and International Law on the Use of Force' (2011)10 *Chinese Journal of International Law* 35, 46; J. Green, *The International Court of Justice and Self-Defence in International Law* (Hart, Oxford, 2009), pp. 44–51. See also K. N Trapp, 'Back to Basics: Necessity, Proportionality and the Right of Self-Defence Against Non-State Terrorist Actors' (2007) 56 *International and Comparative Law Quarterly* 141.

[49] Security Council Resolutions 1368(2001), 1373(2001); for a review of state practice, see C. J. Tams, 'The Use of Force against Terrorists' (2009) 20 *European Journal of International Law* 359. But see T. Ruys and S. Verhoeven, 'Attacks by Private Actors and the Right of Self-Defence' (2005) *Journal of Conflict and Security Law* 289, 312, for arguments on the limited value of the resolutions as authorities for a right to self-defence against NSAs. The Independent International Fact-Finding Mission on the Conflict in Georgia posited that 'if the use of force is prohibited in the relations between a state and an entity short of statehood, then self-defence must be available to both sides as well'. Notably, the Mission was concerned with whether the NSA can avail itself of the right to self-defence; again, since international law does not regulate intra-state use of force, the comment was beside the point; any prohibition on the use of force – and exception to it – in the relations between Georgia and South Ossetia, was based on reciprocal undertakings: Georgia Fact-Finding Report, pp. 241–2.

[50] Security Council Resolution 1860(2009) (8 January 2009).

Operation Cast Lead, made no mention of Hamas's involvement in the conflict, weakening Israel's claim for applying *ius ad bellum*.[51] In January 2009, a group of international legal experts published a letter in the London *Times*, which declared simply that 'Israel's actions [against the Gaza Strip] amount to aggression, not self-defence.'[52] Earlier, in the *Wall* Advisory Opinion, the ICJ stated that the right to self-defence under UN Charter Article 51 only applies in the relations between states.[53] The Court did not find it necessary to distinguish between quasi-states and other NSAs. In neither the *Wall* Advisory Opinion nor the *Congo* v. *Uganda* judgment did the ICJ examine whether a prohibition on the use of force applied that entailed an exceptional justification if force is used. One might argue that any discussion of the right to self-defence implies that an underlying prohibition against the use of force applies. Yet as noted by Judge Tomka in *Congo* v. *Uganda*, the ICJ has reversed the order of its analysis so that the consideration of self-defence precedes that of the prohibition of the use of force.[54] Thus, it cannot be regarded as implying an underlying prohibition. Arguably, in the *Wall* Advisory Opinion, the unavailability to Israel of a right to self-defence against Palestinian armed groups was inconsequential, because the Court also concerned itself not with whether Israel had violated the prohibition on the use of force, but with the laws of armed conflict. In contrast, in *Congo* v. *Uganda*, the international responsibility of Uganda hinged on the unavailability of self-defence.

---

[51] This is in contradistinction to Security Council Resolution 1701(2006), which terminated the Second Lebanon War in 2006 and referred explicitly to Hezbollah. I. Rosenzweig and Y. Shany, 'Armed Conflict in Gaza – The General Jus ad Bellum Framework', Israel Democracy Institute, Terrorism and Democracy Newsletter Issue No. 2, www.idi.org.il/sites/english/ResearchAndPrograms/NationalSecurityandDemocracy/Terrorism_and_Democracy/Newsletters/Pages/2nd%20newsletter/1/Armed_Conflict_in_Gaza.aspx.

[52] *Sunday Times*, 'Israel's bombardment of Gaza is not self-defence – it's a war crime' (11 January 2009). Given the experts' view that the Gaza Strip remains under occupation, one might have expected the matter to be addressed entirely from the perspective of *ius in bello*. Clearly this was not the intention of the experts, who twice referred to 'aggression' by Israel and to the use of force not being 'necessary', both concepts of *ius ad bellum* rather than of *ius in bello*.

[53] *Legal Consequences of the Construction of a Wall in the Occupied Palestinian Territory*, Advisory Opinion, [2004] ICJ Reports 136, [139]. The Court added that an obstacle to the reliance on self-defence by a state was also that the force was used from territory within the effective control of the victim state itself.

[54] *Congo* v. *Uganda*, Declaration of Judge Tomka, [10].

The immediate implication of the ICJ's statements appears to be that the right of a state to respond to an attack by an NSA (whether acting from the territory of another state or otherwise) is limited as compared with its right to self-defence against an armed attack emanating from a state, even though an NSA can have the same military capacity as a state.[55] To mitigate this outcome, it has been suggested that the broad right to self-defence under customary law, unlike under UN Charter Article 51, does encompass action against NSAs,[56] or that even if a right of self-defence does not accrue as such,[57] a state's resort to the use of force may still be excusable under different doctrines, such as necessity as a circumstance precluding wrongfulness under international law, or armed countermeasures.[58] Reliance on necessity encounters various obstacles. First, even if a plea of necessity may be invoked with respect to conduct regulated by primary rules,[59] it is only acceptable if it does not

---

[55] Tsagourias, 'Non-State Actors', p. 326. A similar argument was put forward by the Israeli Supreme Court with regard to the application of the laws of international armed conflict to a transnational NSA: HCJ 769/02 *The Public Committee against Torture in Israel and Another* v. *the Government of Israel and Others*, the Supreme Court Sitting as the High Court of Justice (11 December 2005), noting that 'the fact that the terrorist organizations and their members do not act in the name of a state does not turn the struggle against them into a purely internal state conflict. Indeed, in today's reality, a terrorist organization is likely to have considerable military capabilities. At times they have military capabilities that exceed those of states. Confrontation with those dangers cannot be restricted within the state and its penal law. Confronting the dangers of terrorism constitutes a part of the international law dealing with armed conflicts of international character' [21].

[56] R. Turner, 'Commentary – *Ius ad Bellum*' (2003) 79 *International Law Studies* 129, 131–2; S. Rosenne, 'Self-defence and the Non-use of Force; Some Random Thoughts' in his *Essays on International Law and Practice* (Martinus Nijhoff Publishers, Leiden, Boston, 2007), pp. 633, 642.

[57] The international legal experts' letter of January 2009 states that 'the firing of rockets by Hamas into Israel and suicide bombings [. . .] are also contrary to international humanitarian law and are war crimes. Israel has a right to take reasonable and proportionate means to protect its civilian population from such attacks'. The basis under which Israel may act to protect its civilian population remains unclear, including whether it is within the *ius ad bellum* or the *ius in bello*. Since the letter attributes to Hamas only violations of *ius in bello*, presumably this is also the context for Israel's right to protect its civilian population. *Sunday Times*, 'Israel's bombardment of Gaza is not self-defence'.

[58] For treatment of this possibility, see Christian J. Tams, 'The Use of Force against Terrorists' (2009) 20 *European Journal of International Law* 372; Malanczuk, 'Countermeasures and Self-Defence', pp. 264–5.

[59] Draft Articles on Responsibility of States for Internationally Wrongful Acts, UN Doc. A/56/10 (2001), Article 25 Commentary para. 21 ('ILC Draft Articles'). The question is, of course, whether use of force in the relations between a state and an NSA *is* regulated by the primary rules.

'seriously impair an essential interest of . . . the international community as a whole'.[60] Since the use of force invariably impairs such an essential interest, it is doubtful that necessity can excuse the use of force. By the same token, necessity cannot be invoked if the prohibition on the use of force is a peremptory norm. Another limitation of necessity as an excuse is that unlike self-defence,[61] it does not permit collective action.[62] As for countermeasures, suffice to mention that they do not permit the use of force where it is otherwise prohibited, so they do not permit it where a right to self-defence does not exist independently.[63] With respect to both necessity and countermeasures, the International Law Commission (ILC) Draft Articles on Responsibility of States for Internationally Wrongful Acts stipulate that they do not prejudice any right arising from the international responsibility of a state which may accrue directly to any person or entity other than a state.[64] Thus, the right (or absence thereof) of NSAs to use force in self-defence remains a matter regulated by the primary rules, and the possibility of an NSA invoking state responsibility under the Articles has not been discounted.[65]

More generally, the ICJ's jurisprudence[66] implies that the use of force between a state and a quasi-state is regulated by different *ius ad bellum* rules from those governing the use of force between states. The quasi-state is not bound by the prohibition on the use of force, or is bound to a lesser extent. The effect of this is that the means available to a victim state are more limited when attacked by a quasi-state than when attacked by another state. Despite the fact that quasi-states evidently have the military capacity associated with statehood, a quasi-state can unilaterally withhold from the established state the right to exercise the right to self-defence in its full sense, by not claiming to be a state.[67]

---

[60] Ibid., Article 25(1)(b).

[61] For example, the UK attacks on Al Qaeda in 2001 onwards were perceived as collective self-defence in assistance of the United States. NATO and the OAS also invoked the right to collective self-defence, M. Schmitt, 'Counter-Terrorism and the Use of Force in International Law' (2003) 79 *International Law Studies* 7, 14, 17, 25.

[62] For additional arguments against reliance on necessity, see T. Ruys and S. Verhoeven, 'Attacks by Private Actors and the Right of Self-Defence' (2005) *Journal of Conflict and Security Law 289*, 308–9.

[63] ILC Draft Articles, Article 50(1)(b). For a discussion of views on the prevalence of this position, see 'Countermeasures and Self-Defence', pp. 229–30.

[64] ILC Draft Articles, Article 33(2).   [65] Ibid., Article 33, Commentary para. 4.

[66] Dinstein, *War, Aggression and Self-Defence*, p. 204; N. Lubell, *Extraterritorial Use of Force Against Non-State Actors* (Oxford University Press, 2010), pp. 32–5.

[67] For present purposes, questions relating to the responsibility to protect can be set aside.

2. International human rights law

International human rights law is an area in which quasi-states exercise power without necessarily being bound by the commensurate obligations, since obligations under international human rights law are traditionally imposed only on states. Until the late 1990s, the notion that the conduct of a NSA could affect human rights was not widespread. This perception has changed with the expansion of the scope of international human rights law, and with the expansion of the competences and areas of operation of international organizations such as the EU and the UN through its peacekeeping forces and territorial administrations.[68] Since the law has not developed at the same pace, the regulation of NSAs' conduct under international human rights has not followed their capacity to harm individuals with the same severity as states. There are various human rights standards developed for NSAs, without particular reference to territorial control, enforceable through non-legal means. But blurring the line between legal obligations and standards *de lege ferenda* might backfire by weakening the obligatory character of human rights.[69] This is not to say that NSAs could never be bound by international human rights law, as the law is in a constant flux;[70] but change comes slowly. An instructive example is the 2011 US Court of Appeals case where the responsibility of the Palestinian Authority for torture as a violation of international human rights law was discussed. The Court followed jurisprudence from 1984, according to which there was 'insufficient consensus . . . that torture by private actors violates international law',[71] noting that '[i]n 2011 it remains the case that appellants have shown us no such consensus'.[72] The Court candidly admitted what may be the true bar to holding an NSA responsible for torture under international law, namely, that this 'could open the doors of the federal courts to claims against nonstate actors anywhere in the world alleged to have cruelly treated any alien'.[73] While

---

[68] A. Reinisch, 'The Changing International Legal Framework for Dealing with Non-State Actors' in Alston (ed.), *Non-state Actors and Human Rights*, pp. 37, 62.

[69] Ibid., p. 69.

[70] For a review of the development of human rights responsibilities of NSAs see Alston (ed.), *Non-State Actors and Human Rights*.

[71] *Tel-Oren* v. *Libyan Arab Republic*, 726 F.2d 774 (D.C. Cir. 1984), 732 note 20.

[72] United States Court of Appeals for the District of Columbia Circuit No. 10–7024 *Ali Mahmud Ali Shaf and Others* v. *Palestinian Authority* (14 June 2011), 15–16. The Court distinguished torture from piracy and other international prohibitions such as genocide, for which responsibility can lie with NSAs.

[73] Ibid., 11.

proffered specifically in the context of US civil torts jurisdiction, this rationale is applicable more generally to domestic courts, which are the primary forum for invocation of violations of international law by NSAs. The Court did not address the fact that at issue was an NSA of a particular kind – a quasi-state enjoying territorial control and governmental authority and, moreover, established through an international instrument[74] and holding international status.

At present there is a disparity between the power of NSAs over individuals and their legal obligations towards them, particularly when the NSAs exercise territorial control.[75] This disparity also has implications vis-à-vis states: although international human rights law is not essentially an adversarial regime and therefore the question of reciprocity in the case of violation does not arise as a legal matter, politically, the asymmetry between states and quasi-states can be problematic; particularly when they are involved in a direct conflict, the state may be bound by international human rights law towards the population of the quasi-state,[76] but not vice versa. This asymmetry does not affect the legal obligations of the state party, but it weakens the legitimacy of the human rights regime.[77]

4.   International criminal law

In the context of international criminal law, the conduct of quasi-states does not raise immediate questions on the relationship between power and responsibility. This is because, for the most part, individual responsibility is not dependent on state or organizational affiliation. Indeed, international criminal law has developed in part as a reaction to the limitations of enforcement of the international legal order through state

---

[74] Israeli-Palestinian Interim Agreement on the West Bank and the Gaza Strip, signed 28 September 1995, (1997) 36 *International Legal Materials* 557.

[75] E.g. the non-accountability of the UN as reflected in *Behrami and Behrami* v. *France, Saramati* v. *France, Germany and Norway*, App. Nos. 71412/01 and 78166/01, Grand Chamber, Decision (2 May 2007).

[76] The requisites for extraterritorial responsibility under international human rights law are controversial, but at a minimum, responsibility incurs where there is effective territorial control: *Al-Skeini and Others* v. *the UK*; M. Milanovic, *Extraterritorial Application of Human Rights Treaties; Law, Principles, and Policy* (Oxford University Press, 2011), pp. 135–73.

[77] Empirical research indicates that states' decisions on joining human rights treaties are governed largely by domestic factors. For a succinct summary of findings, see B. A. Simmons, *Mobilizing for Human Rights: International Law in Domestic Politics* (Cambridge University Press, 2009), pp. 108–10.

responsibility.[78] International criminal law is thus often hailed as a regime that applies equally to all individuals, regardless of whether they are organs of a state. The difference between states and quasi-states is also not of significance, in that international criminal law does not purport to accommodate expectations of states to reciprocity or symmetry.[79] There are, however, exceptions, where statehood remains a fundamental element in both substantive and procedural criminal law. For example, the crime of aggression, as formulated for the purposes of the International Criminal Court (ICC), is applicable only to persons acting on behalf of states.[80] Accordingly, a first use of force by a quasi-state would not generate the same individual responsibility as it would if that entity were regarded as a state.[81] Yet if quasi-states exercise exclusive control over population, are capable of devising and executing policies, and use force, their leaders may be guilty of acts which are in substance international crimes. Similarly, the customary legal obligation under Common Article 1 of the Geneva Conventions to ensure respect for international humanitarian law, namely, to investigate allegations of war crimes over which states have jurisdiction, and, if appropriate, to prosecute the suspects,[82] seems to apply only to states. The

---

[78] Interim Report of the Commission of Experts Established Pursuant to Security Council Resolution 780(1992), UN Doc. S/25274 (26 January 1993), para. 320.

[79] Indeed, if the identity of the adversary was pertinent, one would also need to take account of the privileges of state organs which non-state organs do not enjoy, such as personal immunity.

[80] ICC Article 8bis, Definition of Aggression, UN General Assembly Resolution 3314 (XXIX) (14 December 1974), Article 1. Individual criminal responsibility for aggression under the ICC Statute has yet to become operative. However, it is significant here for two reasons: first, that the foundations for a distinction between leaders of states and of quasi-states has been established; second, that the adoption of the substantive provisions on the crime of aggression may consolidate its status as a customary norm, in which case the crime can be legitimately enforced by domestic authorities, unencumbered by the procedural limitations of the ICC. States may have constitutional constraints on direct application of customary criminal law, see *R v. Jones (Appellant) (On Appeal from the Court of Appeal (Criminal Division))* [2006] UKHL 16 (29 March 2006), per Lord Bingham of Cornhill [20]–[23] and Lord Mance [102]–[105].

[81] Again, in a conflict between a state and a quasi-state, *prima facie* Article 2(4) does not apply and therefore the crime of aggression would not apply to the state's organs. However, this conclusion should be qualified for a number of reasons: first, the prohibition on states under Article 2(4) has possibly grown also to non-international use of force; second, symmetry or reciprocity is irrelevant. If use of force justifies an international criminal sanction, it should not matter who uses it. That the state's organs are also exempt may offer symmetry, but not world order.

[82] J.-M. Henckaerts and L. Doswald-Beck, *Customary International Humanitarian Law, Volume I: Rules* (Cambridge University Press, ICRC, 2005), Rule 158, pp. 607–11; see

exemption of NSAs from the obligation to ensure respect for the laws of armed conflict disregards the fact that their effective governance may well be the background against which the violation of the laws of armed conflict is possible (particularly if committed on a large scale).[83] Consequently, when a criminal process follows a conflict[84] in which a state and a quasi-state are involved, holding some participants criminally responsible but not others, runs the risk of undermining the legitimacy of the mechanism as a means of ensuring international peace and security.

A different context of state-centrism in international criminal law is the institutional mechanism for criminal enforcement, embodied principally in the ICC Statute.[85] First, international criminal law is essentially reliant on domestic courts, with the ICC mechanism formalizing their precedence over international tribunals. This puts states, which are presumed to possess operational legal systems, under greater pressure than quasi-states to conduct proceedings. An entirely different institutional aspect is that since action within the ICC mechanism has legal rather than physical effect, the acts of a quasi-state – such as purporting to grant the ICC jurisdiction – would have no effect unless accepted by other states or by ICC organs (depending on the context). International practice nonetheless reveals that there may be a political interest in giving legal effect to an act even when legally it can be easily rejected.

---

also Protocol Additional to the Geneva Conventions of 12 August 1949, and Relating to the Protection of Victims of International Armed Conflicts (Protocol I) (adopted 8 June 1977, entered into force 7 December 1978) 1125 UNTS 3, Articles 1, 89. C. Kreß and K. Prost, 'Article 87' in O. Triffterer (ed.), *Commentary on the Rome Statute of the International Criminal Court* (2nd edn., C.H. Beck, Hart, Nomos, München, 2008), pp. 1517, 1523 and sources cited in n. 18.

[83] According to the Report of the United Nations Fact Finding Mission on the Gaza Conflict (the *Goldstone Report*), any authority exercising government-like functions in the Gaza Strip is responsible for ensuring effective measures for accountability for violations of international human rights law and international humanitarian law committed by armed groups acting in or from the Gaza Strip, para. 1633, p. 509. The Mission did not articulate the legal basis for such responsibility: UN Doc. A/HRC/12/48 (15 September 2009).

[84] International criminal law is often triggered by conflicts involving two or more parties (e.g., violations of the laws of armed conflict by definition require an armed conflict), but it can apply also in non-armed-conflict situations.

[85] Even jurisdiction based on referral from the Security Council is, essentially, based on consent of states, although not the ones directly implicated in the alleged crime.

IV.   Bridging the gap

1.   Introduction

As the previous section illustrates, the exclusion of quasi-states from the law applicable to states creates potential imbalances between a quasi-state's capacity and its accountability for abuse of its power. It also undermines the legitimacy of legal regimes which are designed on the basis of a political expectation of exclusivity to states or of reciprocity among regime participants.

There are different means of bridging the gap between the capacity of a quasi-state to act as a state and its formal status as a non-state. One means may be by extending the law presently applicable to states to quasi-states. Some areas of law are more conducive to such extension than others. For example, there is a growing interest in imposing obligations under international human rights law directly on NSAs, where those have the capacity to carry out acts that are tantamount to violations of human rights. This interest emanates both from states and from the NSAs themselves. For many NSAs, participation in the international human rights regime, at least on a voluntary basis, signifies a step towards international legitimation.[86] States, which perceive international human rights law as imposing obligations unaccompanied by direct benefits, may regard the imposition of human rights obligations on NSAs as a means of exempting themselves from responsibility,[87] without prejudicing any immediate interests.

In other areas of law, however, states may have reservations with respect to expanding the law to entities outside their political system.[88] For example, states have initially objected to the application of the laws of armed conflict in domestic conflicts, inter alia because this was perceived as legitimating guerilla movements. Similarly, states involved in domestic conflicts are less likely to accept an expansion of the right to self-defence such that it would apply in their relations with NSAs and to the latter's benefit.

---

[86] Hence the proposal to extend unilateral deeds of commitment such as the Geneva Call to cover human rights obligations, Clapham, *Human Rights Obligations*, pp. 291–4.

[87] E.g. *HN v. Netherlands (Ministry of Defence and Ministry of Foreign Affairs)*, First Instance Judgment, Decision No. LJN: BF0181, Case No. 265615, ILDC 1092 (NL 2008), 10 September 2008, DC (The Hague) (holding that attribution of acts and omissions by Dutchbat to the UN excluded attribution of the same conduct to the state). Revised on appeal.

[88] C. Warbrick, 'States and Recognition in International Law' in M. Evans (ed.), *International Law* (Oxford University Press, 2003), pp. 205, 213.

In these areas, it is interesting to explore a process in the converse direction: to regard a particular quasi-state as a state in order to subject it to the law applicable to states. This route may also raise objection on the ground that it implies legitimation of the existence of the quasi-state. Yet an important difference should be noted between expanding the coverage of the law and regarding a specific quasi-state as a state: expansion of the law in one area but not in others may result in the legitimacy-without-accountability that states are reluctant to offer. In contrast, if a quasi-state is regarded as a state, it is saddled not only with rights and powers, but also with at least some of the obligations of states. This accountability may mitigate the bitter pill of legitimacy. The following sections consider a number of routes by which such an outcome can be achieved.

2.   'If it walks like a duck . . .': imposing statehood on quasi-states

Where a quasi-state is capable of acting like a state, and performs acts that are only regulated for states or are regulated differently for states and for quasi-states, it may be useful to attribute statehood to it even in the absence of a claim on its part ('imposing statehood'), so that it be required to comply with the international rules commensurate with its capacity.[89]

A preliminary question is whether imposition of statehood on a quasi-state is a *desirable* means of bridging the gap between capability and obligation, given that it may create unexpected costs to the international community. The dilemma here evokes the conundrum of non-recognition: non-recognition is a policy aimed at deterring a wrongdoing state from pursuing its course of action. However, non-recognition may actually make it easier for that state to pursue the illegal act,[90] while recognition, exceptional and even to a limited extent, enables a measure of effective monitoring of the wrongdoing state's conduct. Similarly, rather than attempt to ignore the challenges presented by quasi-states, it may be preferable to contain their disruptive effect. At the same time, elevating a quasi-state to state status calls for also endowing it with the benefits of statehood, such as immunity from claims and membership in

---

[89] See also M. Sassòli, 'The Implementation of International Humanitarian Law: Current and Inherent Challenges' (2007) 10 *Yearbook of International Humanitarian Law* 45, 63.

[90] On the effectiveness of non-recognition as a means of inducing reversion to legal conduct, see Y. Ronen, *Transition from Illegal Regimes under International Law* (Cambridge University Press, 2011).

international organizations.[91] While it is not possible to calculate the benefits of this trade-off *in abstracto*, they may inform the debate over the desirability of imposing statehood in individual instances.

The notion of imposing statehood implies that the existence of a state is not conditional upon a claim by an aspirant entity, but upon the fulfilment of objective requisites of statehood. This is in line with the definition of a state under the Montevideo Convention,[92] which enumerates four requisites. Those have occasionally been complemented by additional ones,[93] but interestingly, the requisite of 'a claim of statehood' has never appeared on the list.[94] This may be explained by the fact that debates over statehood do not characteristically begin until there is a claim to that effect. But in rare occasions such as those considered here, the question arises with full force: does statehood hinge on a claim? Again, analogy from the debate over the role of recognition may be helpful in responding to this question: doctrine and practice generally reject the most reductionist version of the constitutive theory (namely, that an entity is not a state unless so recognized), inter alia on the ground that this theory allows any state to exempt itself from legal obligations towards an entity merely by unilaterally repudiating that entity's status.[95] By analogy, the requirement of an express claim of statehood enables a quasi-state to exempt itself from legal obligations that ought to apply to it in view of its effective functioning as a state, merely by unilaterally avoiding statehood. To avoid this, it should be possible to attribute statehood to eligible entities even in the absence of a claim on their part. This is analogous to the prevailing declaratory theory on recognition,[96] according to which statehood is a legal status

---

[91] On the possibility of a functionally-tailored status, see below.

[92] Montevideo Convention on Rights and Duties of States, Article 1.

[93] Crawford, *The Creation of States*, pp. 89–95, T. D. Grant, 'Defining Statehood: The Montevideo Convention and its Discontents' (1999) 37 *Columbia Journal of Transnational Law* 403, 434–51.

[94] Exceptionally, the US Restatement (Third) of Foreign Relations Law in the United States has added a claim of statehood as a requisite for recognition, American Law Institute, *Restatement of the Law (Third): The Foreign Relations Law of the United Nations*, section 201 comment f. According to Grant (ibid., p. 439) this addition was triggered by practice regarding Taiwan.

[95] Roth, 'The Entity that dare not Speak its Name', 104–5. I. Brownlie, *Principles of Public International Law* (6th edn, Oxford University Press, 2003), pp. 87–8. There are other grounds for preferring the declaratory theory, such as the conceptual difficulty in partial recognition under the constitutive theory.

[96] J. Dugard and D. Raič, 'The Role of Recognition in the Law and Practice of Secession' in M. G. Kohen (ed.), *Secession: International Law Perspectives* (Cambridge University Press, 2006), pp. 94, 98.

attaching to a certain state of affairs by virtue of certain rules or practices,[97] irrespective of whether that status is recognized by other states or not.

The notion of statehood as an objective status that does not depend on a claim is attractive, but it is not free of difficulty. For one, it may run counter to the principles of self-determination and territorial integrity. The right of peoples to freely determine their political status also includes the freedom to maintain their status as less than statehood. It could reasonably also include the right not to determine *any* status. Certainly, it includes the right of a people not to have any political status *imposed* on it. Where the quasi-state is not a self-determination unit, imposition of statehood might not violate any right to self-determination; but in such a case, more likely than not the quasi-state would be a secessionist entity within the territory of a state. In the ordinary situation, i.e. of conflicts over sovereignty in a given territory, a claim of statehood has an important and direct evidentiary value in countering claims of intervention in domestic affairs. It creates a presumption of successful secession by the quasi-state, in which case recognition of the new state is permissible. Without a claim to create this presumption, imposition of statehood risks constituting an illegal intervention in the domestic affairs of the parent state and a violation of its right to territorial integrity.

Considerations of second order also make the imposition of statehood improbable. Imposing statehood on an entity that does not wish to be regarded as such may be a self-deluding exercise, since the entity is unlikely to embrace the new regime imposed on it. Furthermore, established states are loath to see the emergence of new states, and are unlikely to engage in an exercise of voluntarily admitting the existence of new states, especially if the latter object to such a move. In conclusion, it seems that normative as well as practical considerations make a claim of statehood an indispensable condition for attribution of full statehood to quasi-states.[98]

---

[97] Crawford, *The Creation of States*, p. 5.

[98] 'A government is only recognized for what it claims to be', D. P. O'Connell, 'The Status of Formosa and the Chinese Recognition Problem' (1956) 50 *American Journal of International Law* 405, 415; see also A. Pellet, 'Le droit international a l'aube du XXIème siècle' (La société internationale contemporaine – Permanence et tendances nouvelles), in *Cours Euro-méditerranéens Bancaja de Droit International*, Vol. I (Pampelune, Aranzadi, 1998), pp. 19, 51.

3.   Implicit claims of statehood

If statehood cannot be attributed to a quasi-state unless it makes a claim to that effect, the question arises as to the extent to which acts of a quasi-state may be regarded as implicit claims of statehood. The notion of an implicit claim of statehood is relevant with respect to acts that only states are capable of carrying out. For example, since only a state can join the UN, an application under UN Charter Article 4 constitutes an implicit claim of statehood.[99] In contrast, use of armed force by a quasi-state may be regulated only for states, but not only states can engage in it. There is therefore no reason to assume that use of force by a quasi-state is an implicit claim of statehood.

Crawford posits that '[c]laims to statehood are not to be inferred from statements or actions short of explicit declaration.'[100] Such a narrow position is unwarranted. Again an analogy from the doctrine and practice regarding recognition may be helpful: recognition of statehood may be inferred from acts that are performed only in relations with other states, even if such acts are not accompanied or preceded by an express statement of recognition.[101] Thus, if the establishment of diplomatic relations with an entity is regarded as an implicit recognition of statehood, why should a request for such relations by a quasi-state not be construed as an implicit claim of statehood? Or, if acceptance of the opposability of a claim to territorial waters is regarded as an implicit recognition of statehood,[102] why should the claim itself not be regarded as an implicit assertion of statehood?

---

[99] The original members of the UN included some clearly non-state entities, such as the Ukraine and India. However, accepted members must be states.

[100] Crawford, *The Creation of States*, p. 211.

[101] Montevideo Convention Article 7 provides that: 'The recognition of a state may be express or tacit. The latter results from any act which implies the intention of recognizing the new state.' If recognition is not constitutive of the state, then there is less need for it to be express. For views on this, see W. T. Worster, 'Law, Politics, and the Conception of the State in State Recognition Theory' (2009) 27 *Boston University International Law Journal* 115, 139–40.

[102] In 1968 the United States declared that although it adhered to a three-mile rule of international law concerning territorial waters, the orders of its ships 'was to stay well clear of the twelve-mile limit which the North Korean authorities have by long practice followed'. Crawford regards this acceptance of the North Korean 12 nautical miles territorial sea claim (UN Doc. S/PV.1388 (26 January 1968), 5–6, para. 64) as an implicit recognition of the DPRK's statehood. Crawford, *The Creation of States*, pp. 471–2.

If the purpose of accepting implicit claims of statehood as effective is to minimize the phenomenon of quasi-states, a lenient approach is appropriate in interpreting such claims, so long as they are unequivocal. Yet practice reveals that even an act seemingly reserved only to states can be performed in a manner which leaves the intentions of its authors ambiguous. To the extent that quasi-states actively strive to benefit from their state-like status without submitting to the entire regime applicable to states, it is not surprising that their acts display such ambiguity.

One example concerns a declaration submitted by the Palestinian Authority to the ICC, purporting to grant the Court jurisdiction over crimes allegedly committed in the Palestinian territories. Under the ICC Statute, such a declaration could only be presented by a 'state', hence the debate on whether Palestine was a state or not. The Palestinian declaration uses the term 'PNA' (Palestinian National Authority), which invokes a governmental apparatus established by an Israeli-PLO agreement,[103] premised on the non-sovereignty of the PNA. Since this term acknowledges a non-state status, its use is irreconcilable with a claim to statehood. More generally, the recurrent demands, threats and plans by the PLO and the Palestinian Authority to announce the establishment of a sovereign and independent state[104] rebut any presumption that a claim of statehood has already been made implicitly.[105]

Similarly, the Taiwanese application to the UN is a masterpiece of ambiguity. From 1993 until 2007 Taiwan made a yearly application to join the UN. In 2007 it did so for the first time under the name 'Taiwan'. The application for 'participation in the United Nations'[106] had been drafted sufficiently vaguely so as to avoid a charge that it constituted a claim of statehood. It used terminology such as 'the 23 million people of

---

[103] Israeli-Palestinian Interim Agreement. The Agreement refers to the 'Palestinian Authority' rather than the 'Palestinian National Authority'.

[104] E.g. Al Jazeera, 'Palestinian PM hails UN "birth certificate"' (13 April 2011), http://english.aljazeera.net/news/europe/2011/04/2011413194451168413.html.

[105] On the claim that an explicit declaration of statehood has already been made in 1988, see Ronen, 'ICC Jurisdiction', 11–13.

[106] Request for the inclusion of a supplementary item in the agenda of the sixty-second session, Urging the Security Council to process Taiwan's membership application pursuant to rules 59 and 60 of the provisional rules of procedure of the Security Council and Article 4 of the Charter of the United Nations, Letter dated 13 August 2007 from the representatives of Belize, Burkina Faso, the Gambia, Honduras, Malawi, the Marshall Islands, Nauru, Palau, Saint Kitts and Nevis, Saint Vincent and the Grenadines, Sao Tome and Principe, Solomon Islands, Swaziland and Tuvalu to the United Nations addressed to the President of the General Assembly, UN Doc. A/62/193 (19 July 2007), Annex I.

Taiwan' and 'the beautiful land of Taiwan', with only the request for 'admission of Taiwan as a member of the United Nations under Article 4 of the Charter of the United Nations' indicating that at issue was a bid for status independent of, rather than as a competing government of, Mainland China.[107]

That the Taiwanese application was intentionally drafted vaguely is all the more evident when it is compared with talking points issued by Taiwan (and circulated by the states supporting the application), drafted in terms that leave no doubt that at issue is a claim of statehood. The talking points note that 'Since Taiwan has all the qualifications (a permanent population, a defined territory, government, capacity to enter relations with the other states) for a sovereign state as laid out in the "Montevideo Convention on the Rights and Duties of States", it has the right to apply for full UN membership as per Article 4 of the UN Charter.'[108] It is impossible to read this statement as anything but a claim of statehood. These requisites refer exclusively to territories under the control of the government of Taiwan, removing any doubt that at issue is a bid for membership independently of the PRC, and contrary to the One China principle. Even after the rejection of its application, Taiwan's president declared that 'the people of Taiwan consider their nation to be an independent sovereign country . . . Taiwan and the PRC are two separate sovereign countries . . . Therefore, Taiwan has the full right to become a member of the UN.'

Following the failure of the bid for membership, Taiwan reverted to formulae that cloud the issue: in 2008, simultaneous referenda were held in Taiwan (with inconclusive results), one advocating an application for new UN membership under the name 'Taiwan', the other advocating an application for the restoration of UN membership under the name 'Republic of China', 'Taiwan' or other appropriate name.[109] The existence of the two options indicates that any claim by Taiwan to statehood cannot be said to be unequivocal. In the lead-up to the referenda, the

---

[107] Ibid.

[108] Ministry of Foreign Affairs, Republic of China (Taiwan), 'Talking points for Taiwan's UN Membership Application', 10 August 2007, www.mofa.gov.tw/webapp/ct.asp? xItem=26680&ctNode=1878&mp=6.

[109] Both referenda failed because the number of votes fell well short of the minimum participation necessary to validate the outcome for any decision: Government Information Office, Republic of China (Taiwan), 'The Significance of the March 22 Referendums', 22 March 2008, www.gio.gov.tw/ct.asp?xItem=36471&ctNode=2462& mp=807.

president of Taiwan noted that the referenda had 'no bearing on the
issues of unification versus independence, and do[...] not constitute a
change to the status quo in the Taiwan Strait'.[110] It is likely that such
statements were intended to obscure the question of Taiwan's claim,
given the negative impact of a potential claim of independence on its
relations with the United States and Western European powers.

The language of the 2007 application was not so veiled as to have
prevented the UN from considering the Taiwanese application on the
merits, if it had wanted to. It was nonetheless sufficiently vague that
when the application failed, Taiwan could deny having declared statehood.[111] In the circumstances, no state had any interest in attributing
statehood to Taiwan against its own wish. But if there had been such
interest, could Taiwan have denied that it had claimed to be a state? Is the
Palestinian Authority estopped from denying its claim to statehood after
it purported to submit to the ICC Prosecutor a declaration available only
to states?

In considering the possibility of inferring a claim of statehood from a
particular act, the scope of the inference must be acknowledged: if the
interpretation of an act as an implicit claim of statehood comes before an
international institution with limited jurisdiction, any determination on
its part would only apply within its jurisdiction.[112] To take the
Palestinian declaration as an example, if the ICC Prosecutor had decided
to admit it, legally this acknowledgement of Palestinian statehood would

---

[110] Government Information Office, Republic of China (Taiwan), Associated Press
Interview with President Chen, 14 December 2007, www.gio.gov.tw/ct.asp?xItem=
35436&ctNode=2462&mp=807.

[111] On 31 July the President of Taiwan sent letters to the UN Secretary-General and the
President of the Security Council expressing regret that Taiwan's membership bid was
rejected by the secretariat. The letters mention that 'The people of Taiwan wish to join
the United Nations' and that Taiwan 'is an independent sovereign nation'. The term
'state' is patently absent: Ministry of Foreign Affairs, Republic of China (Taiwan),
President Chen Shui-bian's Letters to UN Secretary-General Ban Ki-moon and UN
Security Council President Wang Guangya, 31 July 2007, www.mofa.gov.tw/webapp/ct.
asp?xItem=26682&ctNode=2248&mp=6.

[112] Since the completion of this chapter, UNESCO has admitted Palestine as a member
state, illustrating the operation in practice of the statehood-for-a-limited-purpose
notion: Admission of Palestine as a Member of UNESCO, UNESCO Doc. 36C/
Resolution 76 (31 October 2011). For a similar claim with regard to attribution of
conduct to a state, see the reasoning of the ICJ for rejecting the International Criminal
Tribunal for the Former Yugoslavia (ICTY)'s adoption of the 'overall control' test in
*Application of the Convention on the Prevention and Punishment of the Crime of
Genocide (Bosnia and Herzegovina v. Serbia and Montenegro)*, Judgment, [2007] ICJ
Reports, 43.

have been valid *only for the purposes of the ICC statute*.[113] States or other organizations might rely on such an acknowledgement, but that would be a political choice, rather than a legal consequence. A similar argument has even been put forward in the past with respect to admission to the UN, namely, that recognition of statehood for the purpose of UN Charter Article 4 does not have a binding effect under general international law.[114] This brings to the fore the question whether statehood is divisible so as to be available for a limited purpose or in a limited context.

4. *Statehood-for-a-limited-purpose*

As noted earlier, a quasi-state purporting to act as a state may be regarded as implicitly claiming statehood if its intention is unambiguous. However, even if certain conduct is too ambiguous to be regarded as a general claim of statehood, it has been suggested that in a specific context it may generate the same consequences as a state's conduct, on the ground that the quasi-state can be regarded as a state within the limited context in which it acts.

The statehood-for-a-limited-purpose proposition is based on a 'functional approach', which advocates putting the emphasis on 'an attempt to correlate rules of law with the forms of human activity which they purport to regulate or from which they spring',[115] in order to reduce political divisions by decoupling authority from sovereignty and

---

[113] Since the completion of this chapter, the ICC Prosecutor has published its decision on the Situation in Palestine, essentially refusing to accept the Palestinian declaration as that of a state: ICC, Situation in Palestine, www.icc-cpi.int/NR/rdonlyres/C6162BBF-FEB9%964FAF-AFA9%96836106D2694A/284387/SituationinPalestine030412ENG.pdf. In the debate over the proper treatment of the Palestinian declaration to the ICC, it has been argued that the Palestinian Authority could and should be regarded as a state for the limited purpose of granting the ICC jurisdiction through Article 12(3). Y. Shany, 'In Defence of Functional Interpretation of Article 12(3) of the Rome Statute, A Response to Yaël Ronen' (2010) 8 *Journal of International Criminal Justice* 329, 336–9; A. Pellet, 'The Palestinian Declaration and the Jurisdiction of the International Criminal Court' (2010) 8 *Journal of International Criminal Justice* 981, 983–8. The political weight of such an acknowledgement could be much wider, of course: Ronen, 'ICC Jurisdiction', 24.

[114] For an exposition (and rejection) of this argument, see H. W. Briggs, 'Community Interest in the Emergence of New States: The Problem of Recognition' (1950) 44 *Proceedings of the American Society of International Law* 169, 175.

[115] Remarks of Professor Phillip Jessup, in Proceedings of the Third Conference of Teachers of International Law (Washington DC: Carnegie Endowment, 1928) p. 134, cited in Steve Charnovitz, 'What is International Economic Law?' (2011) 14 *Journal of International Economic Law* 3, 6–7.

allocating it according to function.[116] It is claimed that quasi-states on numerous occasions have been treated as states for certain purposes, on the ground that they possess the features of a state that are relevant to that regime. Shany mentions the fact that Taiwan, Puerto Rico and the PLO/Palestine have been allowed to participate in the work of a fair number of international organizations and to sign a number of international treaties. He also notes the participation of the PLO and of the authors of the Kosovo declaration of independence in advisory proceedings before the ICJ.[117] In the same vein, Pellet lists a variety of NSAs participating in international legal relations, including individuals standing trial before international criminal courts, companies involved in investment adjudication, non-state armed entities, microstates and international organizations, as well as specific entities such as pre-1993 Andorra and the Order of Malta.[118] Gowlland-Debbas notes the membership of Byelorussia, the Ukraine and India in the UN as early as in 1945, when they were still under Soviet and British sovereignty, respectively.[119]

Before examining the desirability of a purpose-related statehood, two observations are in order regarding the evidence on international practice. First, the numerous examples demonstrate the endowment of various NSAs with legal personality. But with the exception of the membership of non-states in the UN, in none of the examples was an NSA endowed with the personality *of a state*, even tentatively. The question at hand, it should be recalled, is not whether there are participants in international legal relations other than fully-fledged states (of course there are), but whether an entity could be classified under the category of states (or, indeed, any other category) for one purpose, but excluded from it for others.[120] None of the examples support such a proposition. Rather, these are examples in which the law applicable to

[116] W. Mattlie, *The Logic of Regional Integration: Europe and Beyond* (Cambridge University Press, 1999), pp. 21–3.
[117] Shany, 'In Defence', 334–5.   [118] Pellet, 'The Palestinian Declaration', 983–5.
[119] V. Gowlland-Debbas, 'Note on the Legal Effects of Palestine's Declaration under Article 12(3) of the ICC Statute' (20 October 2010), www.icc-cpi.int/NR/rdonlyres/56368E8B-2FBB-4CFB-88 AB-98D105F2C56F/282610/PalestineGowllandDebbas.pdf, para. 3.
[120] Pellet notes a decision of an ICSID tribunal which postulates that the criteria for determining whether a body is a state entity (similar to state organ) for jurisdictional purposes may differ from the criteria for determining that it is a state entity for substantive purposes. However, at issue in that case was attribution of a body to the state rather than recognition of the state itself. The question of dual entities is different from that of statehood: ICSID, *Maffezini* v. *Spain*, Case N8 ARB/97/7, Decision of the Tribunal on Objections to Jurisdiction, 25 January 2000, ICSID *Review - Foreign*

states has already been extended to apply to NSAs either generally (as in the case of participation in advisory proceedings in the ICJ) or with specific NSAs in mind. Thus, treaties which include certain international organizations participating in international treaties as 'states', expressly define the term 'state' as inclusive of additional entities. This is a short-hand technique to avoid the need to insert wording such as 'and regional integration organization within the limits of their competence' alongside every appearance of the word 'state'.[121] The adoption of the definition of 'state' which encompasses certain organizations is much the same as permitting treaty membership to 'independent customs territories',[122] a category which allows World Trade Organization (WTO) membership of Taiwan, Hong Kong or Macao without addressing the question of their statehood. The choice between the two techniques reflects political prefer-ences rather than legal ones. Both reflect the expanding legal personality of international organizations, but can hardly be interpreted as rendering the relevant entities 'states', even for the purpose of the treaties in question. Similarly, participation in ICJ advisory proceedings is not restricted to states, and thus the participation of the PLO or the authors of the Kosovo declaration in the written or oral proceedings is not indicative of state-like status.[123] In short, it is international regimes that are expanding beyond states, rather than NSAs being regarded as states-for-limited-purposes. The line between the two may be thin, but it is bright.

A second reservation as to the value of the alleged practice as evidence of a functional approach is that any expansion of the term 'state' to encompass entities other than states has only been made in explicit drafting of international instruments, i.e. expressly and only between consenting states. Interpreting the term 'state' as extending to NSAs where there has been no explicit consensual expansion, on a case-by-case basis and on the basis of policy considerations that are often

---

Investment Law Journal, 27–28, paragraphs 74–75; Pellet, 'The Palestinian Declaration', 987.

[121] To take the example of the Convention on the Rights of Persons with Disabilities, UN Doc. A/RES/61/106 (13 December 2006), Article 44.

[122] The General Agreement on Tariffs and Trade (GATT 1947), Article XXIV.

[123] Although, admittedly, the criteria for participation in advisory proceedings (ICJ Statute Article 66) do not easily accommodate either the PLO or the authors of the Kosovo declaration. For an analysis of their participation see Y. Ronen, 'Participation of Non-State Actors in ICJ Proceedings' (2012) 10 *The Law and Practice of International Courts and Tribunals* 27, arguing that the grounds for allowing the participation of these NSAs is not that they have achieved quasi-state status, but the fact that the dispute which triggered the advisory proceedings has implications for their future status.

disputed, stretches the functional approach too far. In conclusion, inter-national practice does not substantiate statehood for a limited purpose as a matter of *lex lata*.

The principal question, however, is whether there are any policy justifications for adopting the functional approach to statehood. Although stated in general terms, the functional approach originated in, and is widely associated with, the integration process in Europe post-World War II.[124] It is effective when it is consent based, in the pursuit of common goals. Importing it to a non-cooperative environment, where the definition of goals and their desirability are controversial, requires special justification.

One justification for giving legal effect to state-reserved acts per-formed by a quasi-state would be if it provided third parties with benefits perceived as desirable, and of which they would otherwise be deprived. For example, if a quasi-state purports to grant nationality to persons under its territorial control that are otherwise stateless, there may be merit in acknowledging such a grant so as to allow these individuals the benefit of diplomatic protection, or, conversely, of refugee status. Another justification might be the pursuit of a common international interest, particularly if it cannot be achieved otherwise. One such interest is reflected in the international criminal system, developed 'to confirm and endorse the most elementary principles of morality'.[125] If a func-tional approach to statehood is adopted, the matter becomes one of delineating the 'limited purpose'. For example, should a grant of nation-ality as proposed above be given effect only in the context of diplomatic protection, or also for other purposes that are nationality-related and reserved to states, such as the power to assert criminal jurisdiction?

A guiding principle in applying a functional approach is that with power comes responsibility. Thus, if a quasi-state is recognized as a state for a limited purpose, its powers and rights should be accompanied by the commensurate obligations and vice versa. In this context a distinc-tion is appropriate between regimes based on contractual reciprocity and those where the high ideals which inspired the regime provide, by virtue of the common will of the parties, the foundation and measure of all its

---

[124] M. Hirsch, 'The Sociology of International Economic Law: Sociological Analysis of the Regulation of Regional Agreements in the World Trading System' (2008) 19 *European Journal of International Law* 277, 286.

[125] *Reservations to the Convention on Genocide* (Advisory Opinion) [1951] ICJ Reports 15, 23.

provisions.[126] In regimes based on contractual reciprocity, identifying the corresponding rights and obligations is relatively easy, although there may also be unarticulated links. In legal regimes not based on reciprocity, it is not always possible to identify an obligation that corresponds to the power or right asserted; nor, for that matter, is it always possible to define certain conduct as the exercise of a right. Here the unique character of the ICC Statute is apparent: states parties provide each other, on a reciprocal basis, with powers and rights vis-à-vis third parties – individuals. These third parties did not participate in the creation of the regime, and thus their expectations with respect to the operation of the regime are not accounted for. Nor does the exercise by states of powers under the Statute create a direct obligation towards any other party or person. For example, the granting of jurisdiction to the ICC under ICC Statute Article 12(3) with respect to acts committed on a quasi-state's territory is a power to which no obligation corresponds directly, although it may expose the population associated with a quasi-state to prosecution by the ICC.[127]

It is tempting to argue that if a regime is not based on reciprocity in performance, inclusion of quasi-states in it is even less intrusive and there is all the more room to adopt a functional approach and to allow the quasi-state to perform the state-reserved act. However, it is not enough to cite a high moral objective – such as maintenance of global peace and security, or the eradication of impunity – in order to remove all obstacles to inclusion of quasi-states in a state-reserved regime. Few objectives are pursued without reservation or qualification. For example, the founding states of the UN would not have undertaken obligations under the Charter if they had not secured themselves permanent membership in the Security Council and the veto power to guarantee their interest. By the same token, the eradication of impunity under the ICC Statute is also circumscribed by substantive and procedural rights of the defendant, guaranteed through obligations undertaken by the states parties to the ICC Statute, either within the regime or outside it. Furthermore, the jurisdiction of the ICC is very limited in comparison with what the pursuit of accountability would have implied: the ICC does not have universal jurisdiction, but is subject to stringent control by state interests. In short, the apparent absence of a corresponding obligation

---

[126] Ibid.

[127] Assuming that pursuant to interpreting 'state' in Article 12(3) as inclusive of quasi-states, the term 'national' in Article 12(2)(b) will be interpreted as inclusive of residents.

does not of itself justify an unbridled expansion of the mechanism. Moreover, while the provisions of the ICC Statute do not easily reveal this, the environment of the ICC is imbued with expectations of political reciprocity. Thus, for example, Rule 44(2) of the ICC Rules on Procedure and Evidence prevents a one-sided declaration under Article 12(3) aimed at the adversary, while sheltering the declaring state's nationals or territory. Accordingly, even in the absence of responsibility accruing directly from the exercise of a specific legal power, and of a legal structure of reciprocity, the ICC mechanism reflects a delicate balance of political power. Manipulating one element in this balance contrary to the expectations of states disrupts the entire regime, even if no particular right or obligation is directly affected.

One might argue that any imbalance in the participation of a quasi-state within a particular regime can be avoided, if the entire regime is applied to it. For example, the acceptance of a declaration by a quasi-state under ICC Statute Article 12(3) could be accompanied by, or conditioned upon, cooperation of the quasi-state with the Court under Part 9, a duty which presently applies only to states. This does not, however, settle the difficulty inherent in a partial application of the law. It merely shifts it from intra-regime to inter-regime divisibility. For example, application of the entire ICC regime (including Part 9, for example) to a quasi-state does not resolve the question whether the quasi-state should be bound by international human rights standards within its own criminal jurisdiction; by the obligation to cooperate with the ICC if a UN Security Council resolution so demands; or by the customary international law obligation to ensure respect of international humanitarian law.[128] Again, the interrelation between various bodies of law renders the divisibility of law difficult to implement.

In short, the absence of a directly corresponding obligation does not make the participation of quasi-states in the regime inconsequential, but possibly the contrary: such participation would disrupt the conceptual foundation of the regime to which the states parties subscribed, which cannot be disaggregated by extracting particular obligations for the quasi-states to comply with.

Interestingly, most of the literature advocating the functional approach does not consider the need to ensure an equilibrium, either

---

[128] Part 9 of the ICC Statute on cooperation with the Court applies directly only to states parties, but customary law obligations and appropriate UN Security Council resolutions are binding upon all states: Kreß and Prost, 'Articles 87', p. 1523.

within the regime where recognition of statehood for a purpose is proposed, or with respect to the various areas in which quasi-states operate.[129] This is partly because for many regimes, including the ICC, reciprocity is not formally an important value. Yet, as argued here, even these regimes are based on an equilibrium of rights, powers and obligations; and it is precisely in these regimes that a partial application to quasi-states of rights or powers runs the risk of creating an imbalance. Regimes based on reciprocity are more likely to contain inherent mechanisms for adjustment when the equilibrium is disrupted, such as the remedies available for breach of treaties. Rigid structural regimes that are based on unilateral measures do not contain the same flexibility. Changing single elements in these regimes does not automatically set off a process of adjustment, but risks leaving the regimes skewed.

In addition, considering a quasi-state as a state for a limited purpose may raise the same problem as imposing statehood in general, namely, impracticality. Unlike the imposition of statehood across the board despite the absence of a claim by the quasi-state, attributing statehood for a limited purpose on the basis of an act of the quasi-state in that area can be assumed to meet the quasi-state's intention; but there is no reason to assume compliance by the quasi-state with law that it did not sub-scribe to. In addition, accepting the quasi-state's act in the limited context in which it aims to act would also encounter the objection from established states that it provides the quasi-states with legitimacy without responsibility. Consequently, in the choice between using a purported act by a quasi-state as grounds for imposing on it a wider scope of law normally applicable only to states, and simply denying the legal effect of the act, the latter may be the better choice. While neither course of action would respond to the immediate interests of the quasi-state, the latter would respond more accurately to its expectations than an upgrade of status, and would avoid problems of compliance.

---

[129] Pellet, 'The Palestinian Declaration'; Errol Mendes, 'Statehood and Palestine for the Purposes of Article 12(3) of the ICC Statute, A Contrary Perspective (30 March 2010) www.icc-cpi.int/NR/rdonlyres/D3C77FA6-9DEE-45B1-ACC0-B41706BB41E5/281876/OTPErrolMendesNewSTATEHOODANDPALESTINEFORTHEPURPOS.pdf; Shany, 'In Defence'. An exception is the position paper by Al Haq, which states cryptically that 'the PA is in many respects operating as a state, is being held to international legal obligations typically binding upon states, and has an internationally recognised aspiration to full statehood', Al Haq, 'Position paper on issues arising from the PA submission of a Declaration to the Prosecutor of the ICC under article 12(3) of the Rome Statute' (14 December 2009) paragraph 40, www.alhaq.org/etemplate.php?id=494.

Finally, opening up the possibility of statehood for a limited purpose may have profound negative implications for the prospective formulation of new regimes. If, regardless of the terminology used, there is no guarantee that a regime reserved to states remains so, the willingness of states to undertake new commitments would be severely curtailed, since they would be deterred by the possibility that the circle of participants expand beyond and contrary to their initial expectation.

V.   Conclusion

The apparent exclusion of quasi-states from the law applicable to states creates a variety of potential imbalances, since the gap between quasi-state's capacity and their status stands in the way of holding them accountable for abuse of their power. It also undermines the legitimacy of various legal regimes which are premised on a political expectation of exclusivity to states or of reciprocity among regime participants. To clarify, the argument here is not that the consent of a specific state is compromised in a specific instance. Rather, it is that the legitimacy of international law or of a particular legal regime as a consent-based system is undermined if the legitimate premises of that consent (i.e. reciprocity or responsibility) are proven false in practice, and there is not even an attempt to sustain them as legal fiction.

There are different means by which the fundamental premises of international law can be promoted. This chapter explored the proposition that where an entity functions as a state, it should be upgraded to that status even if it does not claim it. The chapter rejects the notion of imposed statehood contrary to the quasi-state's choice, on both normative and practical grounds. It proposes that acts of a quasi-state in the realm reserved to states in some cases can serve as implicit claims of statehood which can substantiate recognition of statehood. Finally, it examines whether the same acts justify recognition of statehood for a limited purpose, under a functional approach.

The attempt to offset the powers of quasi-states with commensurate responsibilities, whether by imposing status or by expanding their obligations, can become a circular process, through which the rights and powers of quasi-states also become thicker. Ultimately, this may result in a greater role for quasi-states than the international community is prepared for.

There is no one-stop solution to the challenges presented by NSAs in general and by quasi-states in particular. Not only are the factual circumstances of each quasi-state significant, but the legal regime with respect to which the matter arises is also of importance. Particular difficulties arise in the context of regimes which are not based on reciprocal obligations and state interests, but on the interests of the international community as a whole. In some instances, pursuit of the international interest may justify flexibility in the application of the law, extending it also to quasi-states, or, most exceptionally, regarding a quasi-state as a state for a particular purpose. In other instances, such policy would run counter to the fundamentals of the legal regime, thus weakening it rather than reinforcing its impact. The point of departure for any policy, however, must be that the distinction between states and other entities, including quasi-states, cannot be dispensed with off-handedly.

Unilateral declarations of independence in international law

JURE VIDMAR

I. Introduction

Unilateral claims for independence conflict with the principle of territorial integrity of states, which protects the parent state of the independence-seeking entity.[1] With regard to legal effects of the principle of territorial integrity, some scholars and governments have argued that by virtue of this principle, international law absolutely prohibits unilateral secession.[2] This interpretation is problematic.[3] However, if it were

---

[1] See The Declaration on Principles of International Law Concerning Friendly Relations and Co-operation Among States in Accordance with the Charter of the United Nations (hereinafter The Declaration on Principles of International Law), GA Res. 2625 (24 October 1970), 121, annex, principle 5, para. 7.

[2] Consider the following argument: 'As soon as the principle of territorial integrity applies, it necessarily outlaws secession without the consent of the parent state. Such understanding avoids systemic inconsistency under which international law would guarantee territorial integrity yet would not prohibit secession.' A. Orakhelashvili, 'Statehood, Recognition and the United Nations System: A Unilateral Declaration of Independence in Kosovo' (2009) 12 *Max Planck Yearbook of United Nations Law* 1, 13. See also ICJ, Accordance with International Law of the Unilateral Declaration of Independence by the Provisional Institutions of Self-Government of Kosovo, public sitting held on Friday 11 December 2009, CR 2009/33, 17, para. 5 (argument of Nguyen Anh on behalf of Vietnam), arguing that territorial integrity of states is a norm of *jus cogens*.

[3] See A. Peters, 'Statehood after 1989: *Effectivités* between Legality and Virtuality' (2010) *Proceedings of the European Society of International Law*, 8, SSRN version, at http://papers.ssrn.com/sol3/papers.cfm?abstract_id=1720904, arguing, *inter alia*, that the principle of territorial integrity of states in contemporary international law is 'no end in itself, but only has an instrumental value . . . the protection of territorial integrity can not [*sic*.] function as an absolute legal barrier to statehood'. See also, *Reference re Secession of Quebec* [1998] 2 SCR 217 (Supreme Court of Canada) (hereinafter the *Quebec* case), para. 155, where the Court argued that '[t]he ultimate success of . . . [unilateral] secession would be dependent on recognition by the international community'.

accepted, would it mean that international law directly prohibits unilateral declarations of independence or only acceptance of such declarations by foreign states? In the contrary view, declarations of independence fall entirely outside the purview of international legal regulation.[4] What is important is what happens afterwards – whether or not such a declaration is accepted by the international community.[5]

The present chapter seeks to demonstrate that neither of the two competing explanations is accurate. The central argument of the chapter is that the question of international legal regulation of declarations of independence is separate from the question of the regulation of their unilateral character. International law is neutral *only* with regard to the *unilateral character* of declarations of independence; this neutrality does not apply to such declarations in general.

Section II argues that a declaration of independence properly so-called can only be issued by the effective authorities of an entity which is capable of meeting the effectiveness standards presumed under the Montevideo

---

[4] This line was advanced in a number of pleadings, for example, before the ICJ in the *Kosovo* Advisory Opinion. Consider the following illustrative arguments: 'A declaration of independence . . . constitutes a *purely internal legal* act and not an international legal act.' See ICJ, Accordance with International Law of the Unilateral Declaration of Independence by the Provisional Institutions of Self-Government of Kosovo, public sitting held on Friday 4 December 2009, CR 2009/28, 27, para. 31 (argument of Jean d'Aspremont on behalf of Burundi, emphasis in original); 'A declaration [of independence] issued by persons within a State is a collection of words writ in water . . . What matters is what is done subsequently, especially the reaction of the international community.' See ICJ, Accordance with International Law of the Unilateral Declaration of Independence by the Provisional Institutions of Self-Government of Kosovo, public sitting held on Thursday 10 December 2009, CR 2009/32, 47, para. 6 (argument of James Crawford on behalf of the United Kingdom); 'State practice confirms that the adoption of a declaration of independence, or similar legal acts, frequently occurs during the creation of a new State. As such, this very act – the act of declaring independence – is legally neutral.' See ICJ, Accordance with International Law of the Unilateral Declaration of Independence by the Provisional Institutions of Self-Government of Kosovo, public sitting held on Monday 7 December 2009, CR 2009/29, 52, para. 11 (argument of Andreja Metelko-Zgombic on behalf of Croatia). However, a different argument was made on behalf of the United States, for example, where it was acknowledged that declarations of independence do not entirely fall outside of the purview of international law: 'We do not deny that international law may regulate particular declarations of independence, if they are conjoined with illegal uses of force or violate other peremptory norms, such as the prohibition against apartheid.' See ICJ, Accordance with International Law of the Unilateral Declaration of Independence by the Provisional Institutions of Self-Government of Kosovo, Public sitting held on Tuesday 8 December 2009, CR 2009/30, 30, para. 20 (argument of Hongju Koh on behalf of the United States).

[5] Ibid. (see the argument of James Crawford on behalf of the United Kingdom).

criteria for statehood.[6] Section III establishes a difference between illegality of declarations of independence and the unilateral character of such declarations. It shows that under certain circumstances a declaration of independence may be illegal under international law. Section IV considers the unilateral character of declarations of independence in relation to the principle of territorial integrity of states. It demonstrates that this principle has both inter- and intra-state implications, yet it does not render illegal either issuing or accepting a unilateral declaration of independence. Section V provides conclusions and demonstrates that, while declarations of independence are capable of violating general international law, a violation does not stem from the unilateral character of such declarations.

II.   Declarations of independence and effectiveness

In a number of pleadings before the International Court of Justice (ICJ) in the *Kosovo* Advisory Opinion, it was essentially argued that a declaration of independence is no more than 'ink on paper'.[7] In this interpretation, declarations of independence cannot be either a legal or an illegal act internationally;[8] they simply fall outside the purview of international law.[9] The applicable rules of international law come into the

---

[6] The traditional statehood criteria are spelled out in the Montevideo Convention on Rights and Duties of States, see 1933 Convention on Rights and Duties of States, adopted by the Seventh International Conference of American States, 165 LNTS 19 (1933). Article 1 provides: 'The State as a person of international law should possess the following qualifications: (a) a permanent population; (b) a defined territory; (c) government; and (d) capacity to enter into relations with other states.' It is commonly accepted that these criteria reflect customary international law. See, e.g., D. Raič, *Statehood and the Law of Self-Determination* (Kluwer, The Hague, 2002), p. 24. These criteria are said essentially to be based on the principle of *effectiveness* and are inadequate in the contemporary international law of statehood. Arguments have been made that the effectiveness-based criteria have been supplemented by a set of additional criteria based on legality. Practice of states and UN organs suggests that a state may not emerge as a result of illegal use of force, in breach of the right of self-determination, and/or in pursuance of racist policies. See J. Crawford, *The Creation of States in International Law* (2nd edn, Oxford University Press, 2006), p. 220; J. Dugard, *Recognition and the United Nations* (Grotius Publishing, Cambridge, 1987), pp. 135–7 and 152–61. Another sector of scholarship, however, still attaches central importance to the effectiveness-based Montevideo criteria and rejects the concept of the additional statehood criteria, with the argument that these constitute recognition requirements rather than statehood criteria. See S. Talmon, 'The Constitutive versus the Declaratory Doctrine of Recognition: Tertium Non Datur?' (2004) 75 *BYIL* 101, 126.

[7] See n. 4 above.   [8] Ibid.

[9] See H. Hannum, 'The Advisory Opinion on Kosovo: An Opportunity Lost, or a Poisoned Chalice Refused?' (2011) 24 *LJIL* 155, 156, arguing that the question of whether a

picture only at the next stage where a declaration of independence is or is not accepted by the international community.[10] In this view, only the question of *acceptance* of a declaration of independence is (partly) regulated by international law. It is a matter of the law of state responsibility that under some circumstances a declaration of independence must not be accepted.[11] At the same time, international law does not foresee any circumstances in which states would be under an obligation to accept a declaration of independence.

However, the argument that declarations of independence are not a concern of international law ignores the importance of the identity of the authors of a particular declaration.[12] Indeed, if the author of the present chapter declared independence for Scotland, it could hardly be argued that he intended to disrupt the territorial integrity of the United Kingdom or to create a new state without the support of the will of the people, i.e. in violation of the right of self-determination of the people of Scotland.[13] From the aspect of international law, this declaration of independence would be no more than 'ink on paper', certainly not illegal, but definitely legally irrelevant. However, does this mean that all declarations of independence are legally irrelevant internationally? Moreover, does this mean that declarations of independence cannot be illegal under certain circumstances? This section will clarify when declarations of independence are legally relevant, more precisely, when they are a concern of international law. The question of potential illegality of declarations of independence will be dealt with below.

Declarations of independence change, or intend to change, the legal status of the territory whose independence they are declaring. The

declaration of independence is in accordance with international law 'is equivalent to asking whether the decision of the United Kingdom to make drivers drive on the left side of the road rather than the right is in accordance with international law. The answer in both cases is clear: international law simply does not address the issue.'

[10] See n. 4 above.   [11] See nn. 51–4 below.

[12] Cf. M. Kohen and K. Del Mar, 'The Kosovo Advisory Opinion and UNSCR 1244 (1999): A Declaration of "Independence from International Law"?' (2011) 24 *LJIL* 109, 110, arguing that not all declarations of independence are issued in 'an international legal vacuum' and suggesting that one should pay attention to the question of who are the authors of a particular declaration of independence.

[13] It must be noted that there is a possibility that a referendum on Scottish independence will take place in 2014. If the will of the Scottish people favoured independence and the Scottish Parliament declare independence without the United Kingdom's agreement, this would not automatically create an independent Scotland. However, such a declaration would not be illegal and would indicate Scotland's attempt at unilateral secession. For more on the possibility of Scotland's independence, see BBC, 'Scottish Independence: Referendum Question Set Out' (25 January 2012), at www.bbc.co.uk/news/uk-scotland-scotland-politics-16702392.

question of whether such a declaration changes or only intends to change the legal status will depend on the mode of state creation. Where state creation is consensual, an entity may become a state at the moment of declaration of independence. This explanation is reinforced by the prevailing position in contemporary international law that recognition is a declaratory and not a constitutive act.[14] In the very moment when an entity declares independence the new state is not (yet) recognised. However, this is not a problem if recognition is declaratory and not necessary for an entity to become a state. Thus, it seems to be accepted doctrinally that a declaration of independence may instantly change the legal status of a territory.

In 2006, Montenegro declared independence in accordance with Article 60 of the Constitution of the State Union of Serbia and Montenegro, which provided for a clear mechanism for secession.[15] In this clear case the statehood criteria were met and there was no competing claim for territorial integrity of the parent state. The declaration of independence, adopted by the Montenegrin Parliament,[16] thus instantly created a new state.[17] This declaration of independence was therefore not only 'ink on paper', but a legal instrument with immediate domestic and international effects.

But sometimes a declaration of independence will not instantly create a new state or even lead to a state creation at all,[18] yet it may still fall within the ambit of international law. Clearly, a hypothetical declaration of independence of Scotland issued by the author of this chapter would not be a concern of international law, but what about the declaration of independence of Southern Rhodesia, issued by the racist government of

---

[14] For an overview on the 'great debate' between the constitutive and the declaratory theories, see T. Grant, *The Recognition of States: Law and Practice in Debate and Evolution* (Praeger, Westport, 1999), pp. 1–18.

[15] Article 60 of the Constitution of the State Union of Serbia and Montenegro (2003), *inter alia*, provided: 'After the end of the period of three years, member-states shall have the right to begin the process of a change of the status of the state or to secede from the State Union of Serbia and Montenegro' Article 60, The Constitution of the State Union of Serbia and Montenegro (2003)(author's translation).

[16] The Montenegrin Parliament declared independence on 3 June 2006. See Declaration of Independence of the Republic of Montenegro, *Official Gazette* of the Republic of Montenegro No. 36/06 (3 June 2006).

[17] The fact that the legal status of Montenegro was not disputed is, *inter alia*, confirmed by its prompt admission to UN membership. Indeed, Montenegro was admitted to the UN on 28 June 2006, less than a month after its declaration of independence: GA Res. 60/264 (28 June 2006).

[18] Cf. Crawford, *The Creation of States*.

Ian Smith?[19] This declaration of independence was addressed and condemned in United Nations (UN) Security Council and General Assembly resolutions and was considered to be issued by an illegal authority.[20] It is thus difficult to accept that international law was not concerned with this declaration at all. It is discussed below whether this situation suggests that a declaration of independence may be an unlawful act under international law. At this point, however, the chapter turns to the question of where the difference lies between Southern Rhodesia's declaration of independence, issued by the Smith government, and a potential declaration of independence of Scotland. The difference is that the Smith government of Southern Rhodesia was in effective control of that entity. Indeed, it is not disputed that Southern Rhodesia actually met the Montevideo criteria for statehood.[21] On the other hand, it is very unlikely that the UN organs would ever deal with a hypothetical declaration of independence of Scotland issued by the author of this chapter. This 'declaration of independence' would have no consequences, either for the international community, or for the people of Scotland. It is thus *effectiveness* which leads to the difference between quasi-declarations of independence, which are merely 'ink on paper', and declarations of independence properly so-called, which are capable of having legal effect; only the former, not the latter, fall outside regulation in international law.

An analogy can be drawn with treaty law. If person A and person B conclude a 'treaty' by way of which they 'create' obligations for states X and Y, this is only considered to be a signed but not yet ratified treaty governed by the regime of international law of treaties if A and B *are* representatives of states X and Y. Without representativeness this 'treaty' would be irrelevant for international law and merely 'ink on paper'. Of significance here is the concept of 'full powers', which is defined in Article 2(c) of the 1969 Vienna Convention on the Law of Treaties as 'a document emanating from the competent authority of a State designating a person or persons to represent the State for negotiating, adopting or authenticating the text of a treaty, for expressing the consent of the State to be bound by a treaty, or for accomplishing any other act with respect to a treaty'.[22]

---

[19] See GA Res. 1747 (XVI) (27 June 1962); GA Res. 2022 (XX) (5 November 1965); GA Res. 2024 (XX) (11 November 1965); SC Res. 202 (6 May 1965); SC Res. 216 (12 November 1965); SC Res. 217 (20 November 1965); SC Res. 277 (18 March 1970).

[20] For example, Resolution 217 condemned 'the usurpation of power by a racist settler minority in Southern Rhodesia'. SC Res. 217, para. 3. See also Raič, Statehood, p. 134.

[21] See, e.g., Dugard, *Recognition*, p. 91.

[22] Article 2(c), Vienna Convention on the Law of Treaties (1969).

The concept of 'full powers' in treaty law illustrates that international law presupposes that an act has legal relevance only if issued by the competent authority, and that the individual or group who acted need to be representatives of that authority. By analogy, international law cannot disregard the difference between declarations of independence issued by a random group of people and declarations of independence issued by representatives of the effective authorities of the territory whose independence they are declaring.

Moreover, the requirement for government is one of the Montevideo statehood criteria.[23] A government not only needs to exist, but also needs to be effective.[24] The reason for this requirement is that effective governments speak and act on behalf of states. The concept of a state in international law thus presupposes that not just anyone is capable of acting on behalf of states. Thus, when it comes to declarations of independence, only those matter which are issued by the authorities capable of acting on behalf of the effective government of a (future) state.

The logic of 'effective authorities', albeit with some problems, is also adopted in the recent *Kosovo* Advisory Opinion. The ICJ held that the unilateral declaration of independence of Kosovo was not issued by the organs of Kosovo's self-governing institutions, but that those who issued the declaration acted 'as persons who acted together in their capacity as representatives of the people of Kosovo outside the framework of the interim administration'.[25] This position is somewhat controversial, as it derives the representativeness of those who declared independence from their posts in the institutions of self-government and yet establishes that they acted outside of the institutions of self-government.[26] Despite this controversy, it is notable that the ICJ did not see the declaration of

---

[23] See n. 6 above.

[24] See A. Aust, *Handbook of International Law* (Cambridge University Press, 2005), pp. 136–7, arguing: 'There must be a central government operation as a political body within the law of the land and in effective control over the territory.'

[25] *Accordance with International Law of the Unilateral Declaration of Independence in Respect of Kosovo (Request for Advisory Opinion)*, Advisory Opinion of 22 July 2010, ICJ Reports (2010), para. 109 (hereinafter *Kosovo* Advisory Opinion).

[26] The ICJ argued that the authors of Kosovo's declaration of independence 'acted together in their capacity as representatives of the people of Kosovo'. Ibid., para 109. The capacity to act as representatives was thus evidently rooted in the fact that this was not a random group of individuals, but a group of postholders in Kosovo's institutions of self-government. But the ICJ went on to argue that this group acted 'outside the framework of the interim administration' (ibid.). The ICJ thus derived 'representativeness' from the institutions of self-government, yet for the purpose of the declaration of independence it separated the representatives from these institutions and treated them as if they were a

independence as issued by a random group of people, but rather, by those who are entitled to act on behalf of Kosovo and its people. Even if the authors of the declaration, in the ICJ's controversial view, acted outside the organs of self-government, they occupied posts in the effective government of Kosovo.

This section shows that one needs to differentiate between quasi-declarations of independence issued by random groups and declarations of independence properly so-called, which are issued by representative authorities of the effective entity in question and cannot conceptually fall outside the purview of international law. Now it must be considered how international law regulates declarations of independence and in what circumstances such declarations may be unlawful. Illegality has been argued to stem from the unilateral character of a declaration of independence, i.e. from (an attempted) disruption of the territorial integrity of a parent state.[27] Moreover, illegality of a declaration of independence may also stem from violation of certain fundamental norms of international law, most notably those of peremptory character.[28] These issues will be considered in turn.

III.   Separating the illegality and unilateral character of declarations of independence

When addressing the question of the potential illegality of Kosovo's unilateral declaration of independence, the ICJ, *inter alia*, made the following observation:

> [T]he illegality attached to [some other] declarations of independence . . . stemmed not from the unilateral character of these declarations as such, but from the fact that they were, or would have been, connected with the unlawful use of force or other egregious violations of norms of general international law, in particular those of a peremptory character *(jus cogens)*.[29]

Two conclusions follow from this observation. First, the Court rejected the view that international law prohibits issuing *unilateral* declarations of independence. Second, in so doing, the Court also seems to have rejected the view that international law does not regulate declarations of independence at all, and suggested that under some circumstances a

---

group of random individuals. For more, see J. Vidmar, 'The Kosovo Advisory Opinion Scrutinized' (2011) 24 *LJIL* 355, 359–61.

[27] See n. 1 above.   [28] See *Kosovo* Advisory Opinion, para. 81.   [29] Ibid.

declaration of independence may be illegal under international law. This section initially considers that suggestion. Subsequently, it turns to the position that the illegality cannot stem from the unilateral character of declarations of independence.

In paragraph 81, the Court was referring narrowly to declarations of independence 'being connected with' certain violations, and not to the emergence of states or to the obligation to withhold recognition. It thus follows that, in certain circumstances, a declaration of independence itself, not only its acceptance, may be illegal. The ICJ thereby adopted the position expressed by the United States in the pleadings before the Court: 'We do not deny that international law may regulate particular declarations of independence, if they are conjoined with illegal uses of force or violate other peremptory norms, such as the prohibition against apartheid.'[30] This position is partly contrary to the view of secession as being 'a legally neutral act the consequences of which are regulated internationally'.[31] It is more precise to say that international law is only neutral with respect to the unilateral character of a declaration of independence, while the declaration may still be illegal under international law on other grounds.

At this point exactly what constitutes a circumstance in which a declaration of independence is issued in violation of certain fundamental norms of international law, in particular those of *jus cogens* character needs to be clarified.[32]

In a narrow interpretation, a declaration of independence would need to be a direct consequence of a breach of a norm of this character.[33] However the ICJ interpreted a breach of *jus cogens* by a declaration of

---

[30] See ICJ, Accordance with International Law of the Unilateral Declaration of Independence by the Provisional Institutions of Self-Government of Kosovo, public sitting held on Tuesday 8 December 2009, CR 2009/30, 30, para. 20 (argument of Hongju Koh on behalf of the United States).

[31] Crawford, *The Creation of States*, p. 390.

[32] Cf. *Kosovo* Advisory Opinion, para. 81.

[33] Talmon, for example, argues that very few *jus cogens* norms could be relevant in the context of the law of statehood. In his view, claims to statehood or territory usually do not "arise from acts of genocide, torture or slavery". S. Talmon, 'The Duty not to "Recognize as Lawful" a Situation Created by the Illegal Use of Force or other Serious Breaches of a Jus Cogens Obligation: An Obligation without Real Substance?' in C. Tomuschat and J.-M. Thouvenin (eds), *The Fundamental Rules of the International Legal Order: Jus Cogens and Obligations Erga Omnes* (Nijhoff, Leiden, 2006), pp. 101, 107. Talmon then continues: 'With regard to situations created by genocide, torture, crimes against humanity and other serious breaches of a *jus cogens* norm there is no practice of non-recognition on which to draw. This is not surprising as these situations,

independence more broadly. The Court noted that in some situations declarations of independence 'were, or would have been, *connected with*' certain egregious violations of international law, in particular those of *jus cogens* character.[34] The context of this statement suggests that the wording 'connected with' should be understood broadly, as an attempt at consolidation of an effective situation created in violation of a certain fundamental norm of international law. In other words, a declaration of independence is issued in violation of international law where it attempts to *consolidate* an unlawful effective territorial situation.

The argument in paragraph 81 of the *Kosovo* Advisory Opinion was made with reference to Security Council and General Assembly resolutions dealing with Southern Rhodesia, the South African Homelands and Northern Cyprus. These resolutions indeed made several references to 'illegal declarations of independence'.[35] Prior to paragraph 81 of the *Kosovo* Advisory Opinion, it was possible to explain these references as resulting from the use of imprecise language, which could be seen as a consequence of diplomatic drafting of these resolutions. But now we have the authority of the ICJ's advisory opinion, which clearly suggests that a declaration of independence itself, and not only its acceptance, may be illegal under international law.

While a declaration of independence is capable of being unlawful under international law, it follows from paragraph 81 of the *Kosovo* Advisory Opinion that unlawfulness cannot be seen as a consequence of its unilateral character.[36] In other words, the principle of territorial integrity of states does not generate a norm which would absolutely prohibit declaring independence against the wishes of the parent state. But in reaching this conclusion, the ICJ made a controversial assumption in the preceding paragraph 80, arguing that 'the scope of the principle of territorial integrity is confined to the sphere of relations between States'.[37] Since independence is by definition declared by an entity which is not (yet) a state, its declaration of independence conceptually falls outside of the scope of the principle of territorial integrity.

---

as a rule, do not automatically give rise to any legal consequences which are capable of being denied by other states'. Ibid., p. 120.

[34] *Kosovo* Advisory Opinion, para. 81 (emphasis added).

[35] See SC Res. 541 (18 November 1983) (Northern Cyprus); SC Res. 216 (12 November 1965), SC Res. 217 (20 November 1965) (Southern Rhodesia); GA Res. 31/6 A (26 October 1976), GA Res. 32/105 N (14 December 1977), GA Res. 34/93 G (12 December 1979) (dealing with Transkei, Bophuthatswana and Venda).

[36] See *Kosovo* Advisory Opinion, para. 81.   [37] Ibid., para. 80.

The Court here referred to Article 2(4) of the UN Charter and to the second elaboration of the principle of territorial integrity in the Declaration on Principles of International Law.[38] Both authorities do indeed make references to territorial integrity and international relations. However, Article 2(4) mentions territorial integrity in the context of the use of force, not in the context of unilateral secession. Moreover, when invoking the principle of territorial integrity within the Declaration on Principles of International Law, the Court ignored the preceding first elaboration of the principle, which is made in the context of limitations on the right of self-determination.[39]

In light of the ICJ's choice to avoid any pronouncement on self-determination in the context of Kosovo, it is not difficult to see the reason why the Court chose to ignore the operation of the principle of territorial integrity in the context of this right. Yet it is questionable whether this position is consistent with international law.

IV. Territorial integrity of states and unilateral declarations of independence

The previous section showed that illegality and the unilateral character of declarations of independence are separate issues. Certain violations of norms of international law, in particular those of *jus cogens* character, may render a declaration of independence illegal. But illegality does not stem from the unilateral character of declarations of independence. According to the ICJ in the *Kosovo* Advisory Opinion, this is because the principle of territorial integrity applies only between states, while declarations of independence are, by definition, issued by a non-state actor. This section, however, shows that the principle of territorial integrity has both intra- and inter-state dimensions. It argues that the intra-state dimension of the principle of territorial integrity accommodates the neutrality of international law with regard to unilateral declarations of independence. Subsequently, the chapter considers whether the inter-state dimension of the principle prohibits international acceptance of a unilateral declaration of independence.

---

[38] Declaration on Principles of International Law, GA Res. 2625 (24 October 1970), annex, principle 5.

[39] See ibid.

1. The territorial integrity of states and 'internal' self-determination

It has been established earlier in this chapter that the issuing of a unilateral declaration of independence by the competent authorities of an entity signifies an attempt at unilateral secession. However, international law is not entirely silent on such attempts. The first elaboration of the principle of territorial integrity of states in the Declaration on Principles of International law provides:

> Nothing in the foregoing paragraphs [referring to the right of self-determination] shall be construed as authorizing or encouraging any action which would dismember or impair, totally or in part, the territorial integrity or political unity of sovereign and independent States conducting themselves in compliance with the principle of equal rights and self-determination of peoples as described above and thus possessed of a government representing the whole people belonging to the territory without distinction as to race, creed or colour.[40]

The Declaration on Principles of International Law is reflective of customary international law[41] and the principle of territorial integrity of states may thus generate certain customary norms, but it is questionable as to the content and scope of these norms and whether they are capable of rendering a unilateral declaration of independence illegal under international law.

The above-quoted elaboration is made in the context of the right of self-determination.[42] This right is codified in the common Article 1 of the International Covenant on Civil and Political Rights (ICCPR) and the International Covenant on Economic, Social and Cultural Rights (ICESCR).[43] While the right applies to all peoples, not only those subjected to colonialism,

> the right of self-determination is not an absolute right without any limitations. Its purpose is not directly to protect the personal or physical integrity of individuals or groups as is the purpose of the absolute rights and, unlike the absolute rights, the exercise of this right can involve major structural and institutional changes to a State and must affect, often significantly, most groups and individuals in that State and beyond that

---

[40] Ibid.   [41] *Kosovo* Advisory Opinion, para. 80.
[42] See Declaration on principles of International law, annex, principle 5.
[43] Article 1, International Covenant on Civil and Political Rights (ICCPR) and International Covenant on Economic, Social and Cultural Rights (ICESCR).

State, often significantly. Therefore, the nature of the right does require
some limitations to be implied on its exercise.[44]

Indeed, outside the colonial context, it is generally accepted that the right
of self-determination does not mean 'a right to independence'.
A plausible reason for a distinction between colonial and non-colonial
situations in this context can be found in the principle of territorial
integrity of states. As argued by Fox, in the process of decolonisation
'the only territorial relationship to be altered was that with the metropolitan power. Achieving independence . . . did not come at the expense
of another sovereign state's territory or that of an adjacent colony.'[45] It
follows that a state's metropolitan territory is protected by the principle
of territorial integrity of states, while its colonial possessions are not.
Therefore, colonial powers could not invoke this principle to limit the
right of self-determination of colonial peoples. The situation is different
when non-colonial peoples are concerned.

The above-mentioned limitation clause in the Declaration on
Principles of International Law restricts the exercise of the right of self-
determination in non-colonial situations to the internal mode, i.e. within
the international borders of an existing parent state. This was affirmed by
the Supreme Court of Canada in the *Quebec* case:

> The recognized sources of international law establish that the right to
> self-determination of a people is normally fulfilled through internal self-
> determination – a people's pursuit of its political, economic, social and
> cultural development within the framework of an existing state.[46]

But does this mean that in contemporary international law the right of
self-determination can only be exercised internally, unless consent of the
parent state for a new state creation is given? In other words, does the
principle of territorial integrity of states generate a norm prohibitory of a
unilateral declaration of independence? The elaboration of the principle
of territorial integrity of states in the Declaration on Principles of
International Law employs very careful language: dismemberment or
impairment of the territorial integrity of a sovereign state is not 'authorised' or 'encouraged', but the Declaration does not say it is prohibited.[47]

---

[44] R. McCorquodale, 'Self-Determination: A Human Rights Approach' (1994) 43 ICLQ
857, 875–6.
[45] G. Fox, 'Self-Determination in the Post-Cold War Era: A New Internal Focus' (1994–5)
16 *Michigan Journal of International Law* 733, 736.
[46] The *Quebec* case, para. 126.
[47] See Declaration on Principles of International Law, annex, principle 5.

In this vein, the Supreme Court of Canada held in the *Quebec* case that an attempt at unilateral secession could not be ruled out, and could still lead to creation of a new state.[48] Further, in the *Kosovo* Advisory Opinion, the ICJ also recalled extensive practice of state creations upon an initial issuing of a *unilateral* declaration of independence, and such state creations were not considered to be illegal simply because consent of the parent state was absent.[49]

It thus follows that no rule of general international law prohibits issuing a declaration of independence *unilaterally*, i.e. without consent of the parent state, and the right of self-determination may be consummated in its external mode, even without approval of the parent state. But the reason for this is not that the principle of territorial integrity would exclusively apply in relations between states, as was wrongly identified by the ICJ in the *Kosovo* Advisory Opinion. Indeed, the first elaboration of the principle of territorial integrity of states clearly limits the right of peoples to self-determination. The beneficiaries of this right are peoples within states, and not states acting internationally. However, the language used in the elaboration of the principle of territorial integrity reflects the neutrality of international law in relation to the unilateral character of a declaration of independence and does not prohibit this kind of declaration. The operation of the principle of territorial integrity of states in international relations nevertheless remains important and how this operation interlinks with unilateral declarations of independence needs to be considered.

---

[48] The *Quebec* case, para. 155.

[49] See *Kosovo* Advisory Opinion, para. 79, where the Court argued: 'During the eighteenth, nineteenth and early twentieth centuries, there were numerous instances of declarations of independence, often strenuously opposed by the State from which independence was being declared. Sometimes a declaration resulted in the creation of a new State, at others it did not. In no case, however, does the practice of States as a whole suggest that the act of promulgating the declaration was regarded as contrary to international law. On the contrary, State practice during this period points clearly to the conclusion that international law contained no prohibition of declarations of independence. During the second half of the twentieth century, the international law of self-determination developed in such a way as to create a right to independence for the peoples of non-self-governing territories and peoples subject to alien subjugation, domination and exploitation. . . A great many new States have come into existence as a result of the exercise of this right. There were, however, also instances of declarations of independence outside this context. The practice of States in these latter cases does not point to the emergence in international law of a new rule prohibiting the making of a declaration of independence in such cases.'

2. The territorial integrity of states and obligations
for third states

In relation to the obligation of states in respect of territorial integrity of other states, the second elaboration of the principle of territorial integrity of states in the Declaration on Principles of International Law provides: 'Every State shall refrain from any action aimed at the partial or total disruption of the national unity and territorial integrity of any other State or country.'[50] This is a notable expansion if compared to Article 2(4) of the UN Charter, which is confined to the context of the use of force. Since the emergence of a new state disrupts the territorial integrity of its parent state, the elaboration could be interpreted as being creative of an obligation to withhold recognition of an entity seeking unilateral secession.

Contemporary international law acknowledges an obligation to withhold recognition of an illegally emerged effective entity even if, in principle, it meets the Montevideo statehood criteria.[51] This obligation has been developed in the practice of states and UN organs and has also been adopted in the International Law Commission (ILC) Articles.[52] Article 41(2) of the ILC Articles provides that 'no State shall recognize as lawful a situation created by a serious breach [of *jus cogens*] nor render aid or assistance in maintaining that situation'.[53] It further specifies that states owe an obligation *erga omnes* to withhold formal or implied recognition of an effective territorial situation created in breach of *jus cogens*.[54] In this context, it must be noted that according to the Commentary to the ILC Articles on State Responsibility, the prohibition

---

[50] See Declaration on Principles of International Law, annex, principle 5.

[51] Talmon, 'The Constitutive versus the Declaratory', p. 148, argues that '[n]on-recognition *as a State* in response to a violation of international law has, in contrast to the politically motivated non-recognition *of a State*, a clearly defined scope. In the case of non-recognition as a State, it is not the individual State's subjective will to recognize . . . but the objective legal status of "State" that is at issue' (emphases in original). And Crawford, *The Creation of States*, p. 160, argues that when the illegality in question is substantial, 'States have a duty under customary international law not to recognize the act as legal. The norm in question must be one of the limited number of peremptory norms or, at any rate, a substantive rule of general international law, so that the illegality is one that involves the international community as a whole and not just particular States.'

[52] ILC Articles on Responsibility of States for Internationally Wrongful Acts, Articles 40 and 41; UN Doc. A/RES/56/83 (hereinafter ILC Articles on State Responsibility).

[53] Ibid., Article 41(2).

[54] Commentary to Article 40, Report of the ILC; UN Doc. A/56/10 (2001), 283.

of illegal use of force, the right of self-determination and the prohibition of racial discrimination are norms of *jus cogens* character.[55] Although the association of illegality in the context of the obligation to withhold recognition with the concept of *jus cogens* remains somewhat controversial,[56] it has been cautiously acknowledged by the ICJ in the *Kosovo* Advisory Opinion.[57] However, what is more important at this point is to recall that international law clearly demands that under some circumstances states owe an obligation *erga omnes* to withhold recognition. At the same time, nothing in the doctrine or non-recognition practice suggests that an obligation to withhold recognition applies when independence is declared without the consent of a parent state, or that an obligation owed *erga omnes* would apply because of the unilateral character of a declaration of independence. Indeed, the principle of territorial integrity of states cannot be seen as an absolute right, or even as a norm of *jus cogens*.[58] This position is further supported by the doctrine of remedial secession.

This doctrine is based on an inverted reading of the first elaboration of the principle of territorial integrity of states in the Declaration on Principles of International Law. According to this reading, a state which does not have 'a government representing the whole people belonging to the territory without distinction as to race, creed or colour'[59] cannot invoke the principle of territorial integrity of states in order to limit the peoples' right of self-determination to the exercise of this right in its internal mode.[60] Some authors see remedial secession as a *right* of oppressed peoples.[61] Yet international law *de lege lata* does not suggest

---

[55] Commentary to Article 41, Report of the ILC; UN Doc. A/56/10 (2001), 286–90.

[56] Talmon, 'The Constitutive versus the Declaratory', p. 103.

[57] *Kosovo* Advisory Opinion, para. 81.   [58] See Peters, 'Statehood after 1989', 8.

[59] See Declaration on Principles of International Law, annex, principle 5.

[60] For a thorough account of the academic support for 'remedial secession', see A. Tancredi, 'A Normative "Due Process" in the Creation of States Through Secession' in M. Kohen (ed), *Secession: International Law Perspectives* (Cambridge University Press 2006), pp. 171, 176.

[61] See, e.g., A. Buchanan, *Justice, Legitimacy, and Self-Determination* (Oxford University Press, 2004), p. 335, arguing: 'If the state persists in serious injustices toward a group, and the group's forming its own independent political unit is a remedy of last resort for these injustices, then the group ought to be acknowledged by the international community to have the claim-right to repudiate the authority of the state and to attempt to establish its own independent political unit.'

intro

that independence would be an entitlement in any situation other than classical 'salt water' colonialism.[62] In this context, Shaw argues that:

> such a major change in legal principle cannot be introduced by way of an ambiguous subordinate clause, especially when the principle of territorial integrity has always been accepted and proclaimed as a core principle of international law, and is indeed placed before the qualifying clause in the provision in question.[63]

He then continues by arguing that 'recognition may be more forthcoming where the secession has occurred as a consequence of violations of human rights'.[64] This explanation falls close to the position of the Supreme Court of Canada in the *Quebec* case in relation to unilateral secessions,[65] and indeed, also relates factually to some interpretations of the justification for Kosovo's indepedence.

In the end, remedial secession under contemporary international law is still (an attempt at) unilateral secession: neither prohibited, nor an entitlement. However, when oppression is in question, foreign states may find the claim to independence to be more legitimate and are more likely to grant recognition in such circumstances. Thus, in international law *de lege lata*, the doctrine of remedial secession can only be given effect through recognition. While secession is never an entitlement under international law, this doctrine may be seen as an example where foreign states are not precluded from granting recognition of (an attempt at) unilateral secession. This is not to say that states are ever under an obligation to grant recognition.[66] What is argued at this point is rather that states are not under a legal obligation to withhold it where a declaration of independence was issued unilaterally.

Thus, unilateral declarations of independence are issued in the sphere of international legal neutrality, so long as such declarations do not attempt to consolidate an illegal territorial situation, created by a breach of certain fundamental norms of international law, in particular those of *jus cogens* character. As long as a declaration of independence is *only*

[62] See generally, J. Vidmar, 'Remedial Secession in International Law: Theory and (Lack of) Practice' (2010) 6 *St Antony's International Review* 37, 37–56.
[63] M. Shaw, 'Peoples, Territorialism and Boundaries' (1997) 8 *EJIL* 478, 483.   [64] Ibid.
[65] See n. 48 above.
[66] An obligation to grant recognition was advocated by Hersch Lauterpacht, but the existence of such an obligation was never accepted in either doctrine or (state) practice. See H. Lauterpacht, *Recognition in International Law* (Cambridge University Press, 1948), pp. 12–24.

unilateral, either issuing or accepting such declaration does not lead to any illegality under international law.

V. Conclusion

Under some circumstances a declaration of independence is an act capable of instantly changing the legal status of a territory.[67] In other circumstances, however, it will create a legal situation of an attempt at unilateral secession. Thus, it should not be presumed that declarations of independence by definition fall outside of regulation by international law. Indeed practice of states and UN organs shows that in some circumstances a declaration of independence itself, and not only its acceptance, will be considered unlawful under international law.

As the ICJ pointed out in the *Kosovo* Advisory Opinion, illegality of declarations of independence stems 'from the fact that ... [such declarations] were, or would have been, connected with the unlawful use of force or other egregious violations of norms of general international law, in particular those of a peremptory character *(jus cogens)*'.[68] It was shown that a declaration of independence is unlawful where it attempts to consolidate an effective territorial situation created in breach of a norm of this character.

The conclusion that declarations of independence do not fall entirely outside the purview of international law needs to be qualified with two caveats. First, general international law is neutral with regard to the unilateral character of declarations of independence. In other words, the principle of territorial integrity of states does not generate a prohibition of either declaring independence unilaterally or accepting such a declaration. Territorial integrity of states is a principle in international law which, *inter alia*, imposes limitations on the right of self-determination,[69] but it is not an absolute right of states or even a norm of *jus cogens*,[70] as Vietnam put it in the pleadings in the *Kosovo* Advisory Opinion before the ICJ.[71]

Second, only a declaration of independence issued by the representatives of an entity which meets, or is capable of meeting, the effectiveness standards presumed under the Montevideo criteria for statehood can have the status of a declaration of independence under international

---

[67] See nn. 15–17 above.   [68] *Kosovo* Advisory Opinion, para. 81.
[69] See McCorquodale, 'Self-determination', 875–6.
[70] For a good analysis of this issue, see Peters, 'Statehood after 1989', 8.   [71] See n. 2 above.

law.[72] It is often argued that as far as international law is concerned, a declaration of independence is no more than 'ink on paper'.[73] This is indeed true when such declarations are issued by individuals who cannot speak on behalf of a (potentially) effective entity. However, this chapter has shown that where a declaration of independence is issued by the representatives of a (potentially) effective entity (even in the controversial case of Kosovo, which the ICJ categorised as acting outside the interim machinery of government), such a declaration is not merely 'ink on paper', issued by random individuals, but an act regulated by international law and capable of being (un)lawful.

[72] See nn. 23–5 above.   [73] See nn. 4 and 7 above.

The myth of remedial secession

KATHERINE DEL MAR[*]

I. Introduction

This chapter addresses a contested legal basis for the creation of a new State under international law: remedial secession. According to different formulations of the doctrine of remedial secession, a minority[1] (or a 'people' who have a right to 'internal self-determination'[2]), which is located on an identifiable part of a State's territory, is transformed into a 'people' who have a right to exercise ('external') self-determination and secede that territory from the State in question as a last resort to address gross violations of human rights perpetrated against them by the government.[3] In other words, once a certain threshold of violations has been perpetrated by the government against a collective of individuals located on an identifiable part of the territory of the State, the right for this collective of individuals to secede that territory is triggered.

Remedial secession is a legal myth: secession is not a remedy recognized in international law for violations committed by a State.[4] Its

[*] I am grateful to Professor Paola Gaeta and Professor Marcelo Kohen for their comments on earlier versions of this chapter.
[1] K. Doehring, 'Self-determination' in B. Simma (ed.), *The Charter of the United Nations: A Commentary*, 2nd edn (Oxford University Press, New York, 2002), vol. I, p. 58, § 37.
[2] A. Cassese, *Self-determination of Peoples: A Legal Reappraisal* (Cambridge University Press, 1995), p. 120.
[3] The term 'secession' is understood narrowly in this chapter to mean 'the creation of a new independent entity through the separation of part of the territory and population of an existing State, without the consent of the latter': M. Kohen, 'Introduction', in M. Kohen (ed.), *Secession: International Law Perspectives* (Cambridge University Press, New York, 2006), pp. 1–20, p. 3; see also, M. Kohen, 'Secession – A Legal Approach', in W. Kälin, R. Kolb, C. Spenlé and M. Voyaume (eds), *International Law, Conflict and Development: The Emergence of a Holistic Approach in International Affairs* (Martinus Nijhoff Publishers, Leiden/Boston, 2010), pp. 3–17, p. 5.
[4] International Law Commission, *Responsibility for States of Internationally Wrongful Acts* (2001), *YBILC*, vol. II (Part Two).

existence in international law is questionable, as evidenced by the positions adopted by States before the International Court of Justice in the
advisory proceedings on the *Accordance with international law of
the unilateral declaration of independence in respect of Kosovo*, and by
the difference of opinion evident among members of the Court. Its very
purpose is uncertain insofar as it purports to 'remedy' gross human
rights violations through the separation of part of an existing State's
territory and the population located thereon from the remainder of the
State's territory and population. Rather than providing a 'remedy',
remedial secession constitutes an acknowledgement of the inability of
the international community to prevent extreme ethnic violence, and its
invocation as a 'last resort' amounts to a renunciation of the utility of
human rights and other international legal rules in such situations.

Importantly, remedial secession does not address the core issues at stake.
The response to a temporary, albeit egregious, human rights situation that
the doctrine offers is permanent division among different parts of a population through the establishment of new international borders. Rather
than remedying the human rights situation by ensuring greater compliance
through the establishment and/or strengthening of a 'human rights culture'
in the State in question, an implementation of the doctrine would repro-
duce a similar starting point on a smaller scale: a new State in which
minorities are present, and in which the ethnic tensions remain unresolved.

It is one thing to argue that a government may lose its legitimacy if it
fails to live up to its fundamental commitments. As the 2011 revolution
in Libya demonstrates, a government which not only fails to protect its
citizens, but turns violently against them, loses legitimacy in the eyes of
the domestic population and the international community, and it may
trigger a collective international military response undertaken to protect
the civilian population at risk.[5] However, while a government may lose

---

[5] UNSC Resolution 1973 of 17 March 2011. An analysis of 'humanitarian intervention' and
the 'responsibility to protect' is beyond the scope of this chapter. On the latter notion –
which is broader than uses of military force – see Report of the High-level Panel on
Threats, Challenges and Change, *A More Secure World: Our Shared Responsibility*, 2
December 2004, UN doc. A/59/565; Report of the UN Secretary-General, *In Larger
Freedom: Towards Development, Security and Human Rights for All*, 21 March 2005,
UN doc. A/59/2005; UNGA Resolution 60/1, 24 October 2005, 'World Summit
Outcome'; UNSC Resolution 1674 (2006), 28 April 2006, 'Protection of Civilians in
Armed Conflict'; UN Secretary-General, *Implementing the Responsibility to Protect.
Report of the Secretary-General*, 12 January 2009, UN doc. A/63/677; UN Secretary-
General, *Report of the Secretary-General on the Protection of Civilians in Armed Conflict*,
29 May 2009, UN doc. S/2009/277; UNGA Resolution 63/308, 14 September 2009, 'The

legitimacy at both the domestic and international levels, it is quite another thing to argue that such a loss of legitimacy on the part of a government is transformed into a legal right of the victimized population to secede territory from the State.

This chapter first addresses the legal myth of the doctrine of remedial secession in Section II. As the *Kosovo* advisory proceedings before the International Court of Justice make clear, remedial secession remains highly controversial. Two arguments are challenged: that remedial secession forms part of the international law of self-determination; and that the legal basis of remedial secession is the saving clause contained in the 1970 Declaration on Friendly Relations. Section III examines some of the problems of implementing remedial secession. The identification of a 'people' who can exercise remedial secession and the identification of a critical date pose difficulties for an application of the doctrine in practice. Finally, Section IV questions the moral value of remedial secession. Despite its doubtful existence in international law, remedial secession is sometimes portrayed as an appropriate form of redress in response to extreme ethnic violence perpetrated by a government against a minority. While one can readily agree that 'something' must be done in such situations, it does not follow that this 'something' is secession, even as a last resort.

II. Legal myth of the doctrine of remedial secession

It was argued by some participants during the course of the *Kosovo* advisory proceedings before the International Court of Justice that the population of Kosovo – or an ethnically identifiable part of that population[6] – has a right to secede territory from Serbia because of the events that occurred on that territory, including various forms of discrimination, and culminating in particularly egregious violations committed against ethnic Albanians by the Yugoslav government during the armed conflict in the 1990s. On the basis of the characterization of the events that transpired in Kosovo, it was argued by some participants that this situation presents the requisite factual elements triggering an application of the doctrine of remedial secession.

Responsibility to Protect'; UNSC Resolution 1970, 26 February 2011, 'Peace and Security in Africa'.

[6] International Court of Justice, *Accordance with international law of the unilateral declaration of independence in respect of Kosovo*, advisory proceedings (hereinafter '*Kosovo* advisory proceedings'), Written Statement of Albania, paras. 75 and 79.

The *Kosovo* advisory proceedings are noteworthy in two respects in relation to the doctrine of remedial secession. The written and oral phases of the proceedings demonstrate that States are clearly divided on the existence of remedial secession in international law. While some participants advocated for the existence of the doctrine, and its application to Kosovo, others either refrained from addressing the question, or expressly rejected the doctrine. For its part, the International Court of Justice took care not to acknowledge the existence of the doctrine in international law when it noted that the issue was beyond the scope of the question posed by the United Nations (UN) General Assembly. Only two judges accepted the existence of the doctrine, which they addressed in their Separate Opinions. They were Judge Cançado Trindade[7] and Judge Yusuf.[8]

Of the five permanent members of the UN Security Council – all of which participated in the advisory proceedings – only the Russian Federation implicitly supported the doctrine of remedial secession and contended that it did not apply to Kosovo.[9] This may be explained by reference to the position adopted by the Russian Federation vis-à-vis the purported secession of South Ossetia and Abkhazia. Although France, the United Kingdom and the United States of America had each recognized an independent Republic of Kosovo prior to the commencement of the advisory proceedings, they did not expressly endorse remedial secession. The United Kingdom cautiously left open the possibility for the Court to find in favour of an exercise of ('external') self-determination *in extremis*, but it did not go so far as to endorse remedial secession.[10] China expressly rejected the doctrine, noting that it 'does not believe there is such a right under international law'.[11]

Other States also made clear their rejection of the doctrine of remedial secession. They were Azerbaijan,[12] the Republic of Cyprus,[13] Iran,[14]

---

[7] International Court of Justice, *Accordance with international law of the unilateral declaration of independence in respect of Kosovo*, Advisory Opinion of 22 July 2010 (hereinafter '*Kosovo* Advisory Opinion'), Separate Opinion of Judge Cançado Trindade, p. 53, para. 175.

[8] *Ibid.*, Separate Opinion of Judge Yusuf, pp. 3–4, para. 11.

[9] *Kosovo* advisory proceedings, Verbatim Record, 8 December 2009, CR 2009/30, p. 44, paras. 20–2 (Gevorgian).

[10] *Ibid.*, 10 December 2009, CR 2009/32, p. 54, para. 29 (Crawford).

[11] *Ibid.*, 7 December 2009, CR 2009/29, p. 35, para. 23 (Xue).

[12] *Ibid.*, 3 December 2009, CR 2009/27, p. 24, para. 40 (Mehdiyev).

[13] *Ibid.*, 7 December 2009, CR 2009/29, pp. 47–8, paras. 58–61 (Droushiotis).

[14] *Ibid.*, Written Statement of Iran, p. 6, para. 4.1.

Romania, Serbia,[15] Slovakia[16] and Spain.[17] Romania cited the doctrine negatively, noting that 'the "remedial secession" theory is not yet established in international law and is still wanting meaningful State practice',[18] and it argued that in any event the doctrine did not apply to the facts in question.[19] Slovakia noted that the human rights violations in Kosovo had already been addressed under international law:

> The Slovak Republic by no means disputes the serious violations of international law in the past by the Federal Republic of Yugoslavia in its treatment of the Kosovars. However, officials individually responsible have been indicted and prosecuted for criminal violations of international law in Kosovo at the International Criminal Tribunal for Former Yugoslavia. To trace a right to change the status of Kosovo back to the events of 1999 does not comport with the law. There is no authority for a rule of law which allows the 'punishment' of States, especially by something as a loss of territory, for breaches of the law.[20]

The participants who supported the doctrine of remedial secession before the Court included Albania,[21] Estonia,[22] Finland, Germany, Ireland,[23] the Netherlands,[24] Poland[25] and Switzerland. Many States in support of the secession of Kosovo based their arguments on an enlarged understanding of self-determination that encompasses a characterization of the situation in Kosovo. Finland argued for secession to apply in situations of 'abnormality, or rupture, or revolution, war, alien subjugation or the absence of a meaningful prospect for a functioning internal self-determination regime'.[26] Similarly, Germany advocated for the secession of Kosovo on the basis of a denial of 'internal' self-determination.[27] Switzerland argued *inter alia* that secession in the case of Kosovo was

[15] *Ibid.*, Written Comments of Serbia, 14 July 2009, pp. 142–5.
[16] *Ibid.*, Written Statement of Slovakia, para. 28.
[17] *Ibid.*, Verbatim Record, 8 December 2009, CR 2009/30, p. 17, paras. 37–44 (Escobar Hernández).
[18] *Ibid.*, Written Statement of Romania, p. 40, para. 138.
[19] *Ibid.*, Verbatim Record, 10 December 2009, CR 2009/32, p. 33, para. 23 (Dinsecu).
[20] *Ibid.*, Written Statement of Slovakia, para. 28.
[21] *Ibid.*, Verbatim Record, 2 December 2009, CR 2009/26, pp. 22–3, para. 15 (Gill).
[22] *Ibid.*, Written Statement by Estonia, p. 6, para. 2.1.
[23] *Ibid.*, Written Statement of Ireland, p. 9, para. 30.
[24] *Ibid.*, Verbatim Record, 10 December 2009, CR 2009/32, p. 15, paras. 27–8 (Lijnzaad).
[25] *Ibid.*, Written Statement of Poland, p. 25, para. 6.5; Written Comments of the Authors, p. 157, para. 8.40.
[26] *Ibid.*, Written Statement by Finland, p. 4, para. 9.
[27] *Ibid.*, Written Statement by Germany, pp. 33–5.

lawful on the basis of the saving clause contained in principle 5, paragraph 7, of the Declaration on Friendly Relations.[28]

The Court's position with respect to these conflicting arguments was to consider that it was beyond the scope of the question it was asked by the General Assembly for it to address the 'existence of any right of "remedial secession"'.[29] Nevertheless, the Court made clear that it was sensitive to the precarious nature of the doctrine. It thus adopted a very cautious approach when addressing the question in passing. It is worth quoting the Court in full:

> A number of participants in the present proceedings have claimed, although in almost every instance only as a secondary argument, that the population of Kosovo has the right to create an independent State either as a manifestation of a right to self-determination or pursuant to what they described as a right of 'remedial secession' in the face of the situation in Kosovo.
>
> The Court has already noted (see paragraph 79 of the advisory proceedings) that one of the major developments of international law during the second half of the twentieth century has been the evolution of the right of self-determination. Whether, outside the context of non-self-governing territories and peoples subject to alien subjugation, domination and exploitation, the international law of self-determination confers upon part of the population of an existing State a right to separate from that State is, however, a subject on which radically different views were expressed by those taking part in the proceedings and expressing a position on the question. Similar differences existed regarding whether international law provides for a right of 'remedial secession' and, if so, in what circumstances. There was also a sharp difference of views as to whether the circumstances which some participants maintained would give rise to a right of 'remedial secession' were actually present in Kosovo.[30]

From the *Kosovo* advisory proceedings, it is evident that this most recent opportunity for States to give voice to their opinions concerning the existence of the doctrine of remedial secession in general, and its application to the case of Kosovo more specifically, demonstrates that the doctrine remains on the normative sidelines of international law. In light of this recent practice, this section considers two arguments for the existence of a right to remedial secession in international law. The first

---

[28] *Ibid.*, Written Statement of Switzerland, p. 16, paras. 62–3.
[29] *Kosovo* Advisory Opinion, para. 83.   [30] *Ibid.*, para. 82.

concerns the right of self-determination, in both its 'external' and 'internal' dimensions. It is submitted that remedial secession does not form part of international law on self-determination. The second argument relates to the saving clause contained in principle 5, paragraph 7, of the Declaration on Friendly Relations annexed to UN General Assembly resolution 2625 (XXV). It is demonstrated that this provision does not constitute the legal basis for the doctrine of remedial secession.

1. Remedial secession does not form part of the international law of self-determination

The doctrine of remedial secession is often discussed in relation to self-determination. Marc Weller semantically conjoins remedial secession with self-determination by employing the expression 'remedial self-determination' to argue that 'persistent and discriminatory exclusion from governance of a constitutionally relevant or recognised segment of the population gives rise to a right to remedial self-determination'.[31] It is submitted that remedial secession does not form part of the international law of self-determination. The 'right of self-determination' refers to two very different notions that differ both in terms of the content of the right, and in relation to the holder of the right. Remedial secession confusingly purports theoretically to link these two notions in defining its own normative contours.

The first right to self-determination, which is sometimes called the right to 'external' self-determination, refers to the right to complete independence of a narrowly defined 'people'. The modes of implementing 'external' self-determination are the emergence of an independent State, free association with an independent State, integration with an independent State, or the open-ended possibility of 'the emergence into any other political status freely determined by a people'.[32] The outcome of an exercise of 'external' self-determination must be a manifestation of the free will of a 'people'. Judge Sir Muhammad Zafrulla noted in this respect that arrangements that provide a 'people' entitled to ('external') self-determination with 'some kind of autonomy and local

---

[31] M. Weller, *Escaping the Self-determination Trap* (Martinus Nijhoff Publishers, Leiden, 2008), p. 59.

[32] UN General Assembly resolution 2625 (XXV). See also *Western Sahara, Advisory Opinion*, ICJ. Reports 1975, p. 33. The first three modes of implementation of 'external' self-determination were earlier laid out in UN General Assembly resolution 1514 (XV). See also *ibid.*, p. 32.

self-government'[33] would constitute 'a denial of self-determination as envisaged in the Charter of the United Nations'.[34]

With respect to the narrowly defined holder of a right of ('external') self-determination, the Court stated in the *Kosovo* Advisory Opinion that '[d]uring the second half of the twentieth century, the international law of self-determination developed in such a way as to create a right to independence for *the peoples of non-self-governing territories and peoples subject to alien subjugation, domination and exploitation*'.[35] As international practice demonstrates, 'peoples' is a narrowly defined legal category in the context of 'external' self-determination. It refers to the population in territories that were placed under the Mandate system of the League of Nations,[36] later the International Trusteeship System within the framework of the UN,[37] and 'non-self-governing territories' under Charter XI of the UN Charter. The UN General Assembly has developed a methodology for identifying 'non-self-governing territories' in its resolution 1541 (XVI).[38] 'Peoples' with a right to exercise

---

[33] International Court of Justice, *Legal Consequences for States of the Continued Presence of South Africa in Namibia (South West Africa) notwithstanding Security Council Resolution 276 (1970)*, Pleadings, Oral Arguments, Documents, vol. II, p. 585 (de Villiers).

[34] *Legal Consequences for States of the Continued Presence of South Africa in Namibia (South West Africa) notwithstanding Security Council Resolution 276 (1970)*, Advisory Opinion, ICJ Reports 1971, Declaration of President Sir Muhammad Zafrulla, p. 63.

[35] *Kosovo* Advisory Opinion, p. 30, para. 79 (emphasis added). See also *Legal Consequences for States of the Continued Presence of South Africa in Namibia (South West Africa) notwithstanding Security Council Resolution 276 (1970)*, Advisory Opinion, ICJ Reports 1971, pp. 31–2, paras. 52–3; *East Timor (Portugal* v. *Australia)*, Judgment, ICJ Reports 1995, p. 102, para. 29; *Legal Consequences of the Construction of a Wall in the Occupied Palestinian Territory*, Advisory Opinion, ICJ Reports 2004, pp. 171–2, para. 88.

[36] Article 22 of the Covenant of the League of Nations.

[37] Chapters XII and XIII of the Charter of the UN.

[38] Principles which should guide Members in determining the information called for in Article 73e of the Charter of the UN, annexed to UN General Assembly resolution 1541 (XVI). According to Principle IV: '*Prima facie* there is an obligation to transmit information in respect of a territory which is geographically separate and is distinct ethnically and/or culturally from the country administering it.' Principle V provides further: 'Once it has been established that such a *prima facie* case of geographical and ethnical or cultural distinctness of a territory exits, other elements may be brought into consideration. These additional elements may be *inter alia*, of an administrative, political, juridical, economic or historical nature. If they affect the relationship between the metropolitan State and the territory concerned in a manner which arbitrarily places the latter in a position or status of subordination, they support the presumption that there is an obligation to transmit information under Article 73e of the Charter.'

('external') self-determination arguably also include a population under foreign military occupation.[39]

Outside the context of decolonization, international law may recognize the right of a 'people' to exercise 'external' self-determination where such a right for an identified group of individuals within a State is consecrated in the domestic law of the State. A right to exercise 'external' self-determination for identified 'peoples' was recognized in the constitutions of the Federal People's Republic of Yugoslavia, later the Socialist Federal Republic of Yugoslavia, the break-up of which amounted to instances of dissolution, not secession. It should be stressed that the 1946 Constitution of the Federal People's Republic of Yugoslavia, recognized the national groups of Serbs, Croats, Slovenes, Macedonians and Montenegrins, each with the right to secede territory from the federal State they had formed.[40] Kosovo was designated as an autonomous region within the federal unit of the Republic of Serbia,[41] not as a separate federal unit, and therefore – unlike the other federal units – it does not have a right to exercise ('external') self-determination.

By contrast, the right of so-called 'internal' self-determination is a different creature altogether. This right of self-determinations refers to 'the choice of a system of governance and the administration of the functions of governance according to the will of the governed'.[42] In general, the holder of the right of 'internal' self-determination is the whole population of a State. In this respect, the International Covenant on Civil and Political Rights (ICCPR) and the International Covenant on Economic, Social and Cultural Rights (ICESCR) refer to the right of self-determination of 'all peoples'.[43] The mode of implementation of 'internal'

---

[39] Article 1(4) of Protocol Additional (I) to the Geneva Conventions of 12 August 1949, and Relating to the Protection of Victims on International Armed Conflicts, 8 June 1977, entered into force 7 December 1979, 1125 UNTS 3.

[40] *Kosovo* advisory proceedings, Written Statement of Serbia, 15 April 2009, para. 148.

[41] *Ibid.*, para. 150. Similarly, in the 1963 Federal Constitution of the Socialist Federal Republic of Yugoslavia, Kosovo was designated as an autonomous province within the federal republic of Serbia: *ibid.*, paras. 158 and 159. The 1974 Federal Constitution also designated Kosovo as an autonomous province of Serbia: *ibid.*, para. 173.

[42] M. Weller, 'Why the Legal Rules on Self-determination Do Not Resolve Self-determination Disputes', in M. Weller and N. Metzger (eds), *Settling Self-Determination Disputes* (Martinus Nijhoff Publishers, Leiden, 2008), pp. 17–46, p. 20.

[43] International Covenant on Civil and Political Rights, 16 December 1966, entered into force 23 March 1978, 999 UNTS 171, Article 1; International Covenant on Economic, Social and Cultural Rights, 16 December 1966, entered into force 3 January 1976, 993 UNTS 3, Article 1.

self-determination is the 'right of every citizen to take part in the conduct of public affairs at any level',[44] free from outside interference.

In some situations, a group of citizens within a State may participate in representative government in a particular way by enjoying some degree of self-government and autonomy within the institutional framework of the State. For example, indigenous peoples enjoy a right to ('internal') self-determination, exercisable within a State. Article 4 of the UN Declaration on the Rights of Indigenous Peoples provides that '[i]ndigenous peoples, in exercising their right to self-determination, have the right to autonomy or self-government in matters relating to their internal and local affairs, as well as ways and means for financing their autonomous functions'.[45] The same Declaration is careful to stipulate in Article 46, paragraph 1, that:

> Nothing in this Declaration may be interpreted as implying for any State, people, group, or person any right to engage in any activity or to perform any act contrary to the Charter of the United Nations or construed as authorizing or encouraging any action which would dismember or impair, totally or in part, the territorial integrity or political unity of sovereign and independent States.[46]

'Internal' self-determination should not be confused with minority rights, even though both apply within a State, and neither concerns the secession of territory. The Human Rights Committee took pains to distinguish ('internal') self-determination, set out in Article 1 of the ICCPR, from minority rights under Article 27. It noted in its General Comment No. 23 that

> [t]he Covenant draws a distinction between the right to self-determination and the rights protected under article 27. The former is expressed to be a right belonging to peoples and is dealt with in a separate part (Part I) of the Covenant ... Article 27, on the other hand, relates to rights conferred on individuals as such ... The enjoyment of the rights to which article 27 relates does not prejudice the sovereignty and territorial integrity of a State party.[47] Concretely, this may mean that a population – and not a minority – on part of a State's territory may exercise 'internal'

---

[44] UN doc. A/51/18, 1 January 1996.
[45] United Nations Declaration on the Rights of Indigenous Peoples, annexed to UN General Assembly resolution 61/295, 13 September 2007, Article 4.
[46] Ibid., Article 46, paragraph 1.
[47] Human Rights Committee, General Comment No. 23, 'The rights of minorities (Art. 27)', 4 August 1994, CCPR/C/21/Rev.1/Add.5.

self-determination through a certain degree of autonomy and self-governance ithin the State. Members of a minority within a State enjoy minority rights, but these do not encompass the right of 'internal' self-determination. ← e.g population of Scotland.

Remedial secession is a doctrinal invention that effectively purports to link 'internal' self-determination and 'external' self-determination by arguing that a serious failure to exercise the former right of self-determination must be 'remedied' by an exercise of the latter. This attempt to theoretically fasten together two very different legal notions is misleading. It constitutes an attempt to bridge two notions that have very different modes of implementation, and that each respectively apply *ratione personae* to very different groups of individuals. 'External' self-determination unquestionably applies to a narrowly defined 'people', namely, peoples of non-self-governing territories and peoples subjected to alien subjugation, domination and exploitation, and arguably also to peoples subjected to foreign military occupation; it does not apply to minorities within a State, regardless of whether or not a minority has been the victim of gross human rights violations perpetrated against them by the State. By contrast, 'internal' self-determination applies to the population of a State as a whole – and to indigenous peoples within a State – and it is unrelated to the secession of territory.

To argue that the same collectives of individuals who have a right to exercise 'internal' self-determination should also have a right to exercise 'external' self-determination if the former right is violated in a serious way has been formulated in two distinct arguments. Advocates of remedial secession argue either that (1) remedial secession by minorities in such circumstances is simply an *extension* of a traditional understanding of ('external') self-determination; or (2) remedial secession in some form has *always constituted* part of international law on ('external') self-determination. These arguments are each considered in turn.

With respect to the argument that remedial secession constitutes an extension of a traditional understanding of ('external') self-determination, Judge Cançado Trindade stated in his Separate Opinion to the *Kosovo* Advisory Opinion that:

 The principle of self-determination has survived decolonization, in order to face nowadays new and violent manifestations of systematic oppression of peoples ... It is immaterial whether, in the framework of these new experiments, self-determination is given the qualification of 'remedial', or another qualification. The fact remains that people cannot be targeted for atrocities, cannot live under systematic oppression. The

principle of self-determination applies in new situations of systematic
oppression, subjugation and tyranny.[48]

Similarly, Judge Yusuf argued that in situations in which a right to
'internal' self-determination has been denied, or where such persons
are subjected to discrimination, persecution and egregious violations of
human rights or humanitarian law, an ethnically or racially distinct
group within a State could secede territory in an exercise of 'external'
self-determination. He noted that '[u]nder such exceptional circumstances, the right of peoples to self-determination may support a claim
to separate statehood provided it meets the conditions prescribed by
international law, in a specific situation, taking into account the historical context'.[49] Judge Yusuf thought that these conditions could have
been met in the case of Kosovo.[50]

This argument in favour of extending the right to 'external' self-
determination to other collectives of individuals is based on analogy.
The analogy advanced is that minorities on an identifiable part of a
State's territory, who have been subjected to systematic exclusion and
oppression, find themselves in similar circumstances to 'peoples' subject
to alien subjugation, domination and exploitation, thereby giving rise to
a right to independence. It could be argued that the two situations are
analogous, because both present a collective of individuals who desire to
self-govern without interference, but who are prevented from doing so,
and the individual members of this collective are subjected to egregious
human rights violations by the government in power.

There is nothing peculiar about arguing by analogy in law, and with
respect to identifying a unit of self-determination more particularly.
James Crawford wrote '[a] legal principle of self-determination is analogy'.[51] That said, to argue that a minority has a right to 'external' self-
determination is pushing the bounds of analogy too far. Analogy is a
form of reasoning that is just as much about recognizing similarities as it
is about taking care also to recognize differences. It has been noted in this
respect that:

> [i]f rightly pursued, [analogy] is employed, at once, both in generalizing
> and discriminating; in the acute perception at once of points of agree-
> ment and points of difference. The acmé of the philosophical power is

---

[48] *Kosovo* Advisory Opinion, Separate Opinion of Judge Cançado Trindade, p. 53, para. 175.
[49] *Ibid.*, Separate Opinion of Judge Yusuf, pp. 3–4, para. 11.   [50] *Ibid.*, p. 4, para. 13.
[51] J. Crawford, *The Creation of States in International Law*, 2nd edn (Oxford University Press, New York, 2006), p. 115.

displayed in the perfect cooperation of these two opposite proceedings. We must study to combine in such a way as not to merge real differences; and so to distinguish as not to divert the eye from the real correspondence.[52]

An argument based on analogy of human rights violations suffered by minorities, with the right to 'external' self-determination of a 'people', focuses too intently on apparent similarities and fails to see important differences. Human rights violations coupled with a secessionist claim is not analogous to an exercise of 'external' self-determination by peoples in the context of decolonization or foreign occupation. The former is a question of protecting human rights of individuals within a State, regardless of whether these individuals have secessionist aspirations; the latter is about the right of a recognized 'people' to independence free from external interference.

An important difference is that both 'external' and 'internal' self-determination do not single out persons based on ethnicity, religion, race or a similar distinguishing feature as the holders of a right (with the unique exception of indigenous populations who have a right to 'internal' – not 'external' – self-determination); self-determination applies to the whole of a population on identifiable territory designated as a 'people'. Otherwise it would serve to discriminate against individuals living on the same territory from others on the basis of ethnic, religious, racial or other objectively identifiable grounds. Moreover, the absence of clear criteria for identifying a unit that has a right to 'remedial self-determination' means that to extend self-determination in this manner would be detrimental to stability in international relations and open to potential abuse. An analysis of some of the criteria for an application of remedial secession is discussed in Section III *infra*.

According to the second argument, remedial secession has always constituted part and parcel of the law on self-determination. It is in the context of this argument that the *Åland Islands* case has recently been 're-discovered' as the ultimate authority.[53] This case concerned a claim by an ethnic Swedish minority in Finland to secede territory and be incorporated into Sweden, a claim that was rejected. The celebrated

---

[52] R. Dickson Hampden, *Course of Lectures: Introduction to the Study of Moral Philosophy*, delivered in the University of Oxford in Lent Term MDCCCXXXV (B. Fellowes, London, 1835), lecture V, pp. 178–9.

[53] Weller, *Escaping the Self-determination Trap*, p. 59.

obiter dictum of the Commission of Rapporteurs from the Åland case that is relied upon to argue that remedial secession has always constituted part of the right of ('external') self-determination provides as follows: '[t]he separation of a minority from the State of which it forms a part and its incorporation in another State can only be considered as an altogether exceptional solution, a last resort when the State lacks the will or the power to enact and apply just and effective guarantees.'[54]

On the basis of this passage, Marc Weller argues that '[f]ailure to grant autonomy and human and minority rights provisions might therefore be constitutive of a right to self-determination'.[55] Similarly, Martti Koskenniemi, appearing on behalf of Finland in the *Kosovo* advisory proceedings, stated before the Court, albeit in very cautious terms:

> I suggest ... that instead of us, here, imaging a new rule [of remedial secession], it is better to think of this as part of the traditional law of self-determination that was always to be balanced against territorial integrity and contained the possibility of its application, as the *Aaland Islands* case demonstrates, through an external solution.[56]

It is curious to rely on the statement of the Rapporteurs to argue in favour of remedial secession when the Rapporteurs stated in the same Report that:

> To concede to minorities, either of language or religion, or to any fractions of a population the right of withdrawing from the community to which they belong, because it is their wish or good pleasure, would be to destroy order and stability within States and to inaugurate anarchy in international life; it would be to uphold a theory incompatible with the very idea of the State as a territorial and political unity.[57]

It is also peculiar to rely on the statement of the Rapporteurs to argue that remedial secession has always formed part of the right of 'external' self-determination, when the Commission itself questioned the very existence of self-determination in its 1921 Report, noting that '[t]his principle [of self-determination] is not, properly speaking a rule of international law and the League of Nations has not entered it in its

---

[54] Report Presented to the Council of the League of Nations by the Commission of Rapporteurs, League of Nations doc. B.7.21/68/106 (1921), p. 28.

[55] Weller, *Escaping the Self-determination Trap*, p. 60.

[56] *Kosovo* advisory proceedings, Verbatim Record, 8 December 2009, CR 2009/30, p. 62, para. 23 (Koskenniemi).

[57] Report Presented to the Council of the League of Nations by the Commission of Rapporteurs, League of Nations doc. B.7.21/68/106 (1921), p. 28.

Covenant ... It is a principle of justice and of liberty, expressed by a vague and general formula which has given rise to most varied interpretations and differences of opinion.'[58] Nowadays, the right to 'external' self-determination is unquestionably established, but it does not apply to minorities within a State.'[59]

UKRAINE - build up the illegality ↓ mode of exc. S.D

2. Myth that the legal basis of remedial secession is the saving clause contained in the Declaration on Friendly Relations

An additional argument frequently made in furtherance of the contention that remedial secession constitutes part and parcel of the international law of self-determination, is that the saving clause contained in principle 5, paragraph 7, of the Declaration on Friendly Relations constitutes the legal basis of remedial secession. In this vein, James Crawford suggests that the saving clause may assist in identifying a unit of self-determination in 'extreme cases of oppression' in line with the wording of the clause.[60] Others have been more forthright. Karl Doehring argues on the basis of the saving clause that '[i]t is therefore well arguable that discrimination against ethnic minorities could potentially give rise to a right of secession'.[61] Antonio Cassese considered that 'the contention could be made that the Declaration on Friendly Relations *links external self-determination to internal self-determination in exceptional circumstances.*'[62]

The saving clause provides:

> nothing in the foregoing paragraphs shall be construed as authorizing or encouraging any action which would dismember or impair, totally or in part, the territorial integrity or political unity of sovereign and independent States conducting themselves in compliance with the principle of equal rights and self-determination of peoples as described above and thus possessed of a government representing the whole people belonging to the territory without distinction as to race, creed, or color.[63]

This saving clause has been read *a contrario* in order to argue that 'if a government does not represent the whole people it is illegitimate and thus in violation of the principle of self-determination, and this

---

[58] Ibid., p. 27.   [59] Crawford, *The Creation of States in International Law*, p. 111.
[60] *Ibid.*, p. 119.   [61] Doehring, 'Self-determination', p. 58, § 37.
[62] Cassese, *Self-determination of Peoples*, p. 120 (emphasis in original).
[63] Friendly Relations Declaration annexed to UN General Assembly resolution 2625 (XXV), 24 October 1970, principle 5, paragraph 7.

illegitimate character serves in turn to legitimise "action which would dismember or impair, totally or in part, the territorial integrity or political unity" of the sovereign and independent State.'[64] In other words, it has been read backwards, to argue that the description of States conducting themselves in accordance with equal rights and ('internal') self-determination is a condition for the respect of the territorial integrity and political unity of States. This reading *a contrario* of the saving clause was endorsed by Judge Yusuf, who considered that:

> the saving clause in its latter part implies that if a State fails to comport itself in accordance with the principle of equal rights and self-determination of peoples, an exceptional situation may arise whereby the ethnically or racially distinct group denied internal self-determination may claim a right of external self-determination or separation from the State which could effectively put into question the State's territorial unity and sovereignty.[65]

There is no basis for such an argument on a good faith reading of the saving clause. It is evident from the words themselves that the purpose of the provision is to ensure that no preceding provision should be construed as authorizing the secession of territory, and not the opposite meaning. That the purpose of the provision is to safeguard the territorial integrity of States is also evident from the *travaux préparatoires*.[66] Furthermore, the words 'as described above' in the saving clause is a reference to the use of self-determination laid down in principle 5 of the Declaration on Friendly Relations, i.e. colonial situations, alien occupation and racist regimes. A straightforward reading of the saving clause that interprets the provision as a narrowing down of the preceding clauses, rather than as a broad tail, is thus in order. As Marc Weller has noted, 'the generally negative phrasing of this provision confirms that it was meant to restrict the application of the principle thus

---

[64] L. Buchheit, *Secession: The Legitimacy of Self-Determination* (Yale University Press, New Haven/London, 1978), p. 93.

[65] *Kosovo* Advisory Opinion, Separate Opinion of Judge Yusuf, p. 4, para. 12.

[66] For example, see the statement by Mr. Arangio-Ruiz (Italy), UN General Assembly, 1970 Special Committee on Principles of International Law Concerning Friendly Relations and Co-operation among States, Summary Records of the One Hundred and Tenth to One Hundred and Fourteenth Meeting held at Palais des Nations, Geneva, from 31 March to 1 May 1970, UN doc. A/AC.125/SR.110–114, p. 22. James Summers notes that '[t]he drafting, in fact, reveals virtually no positive intention to establish any rights for minorities to secede under any circumstances': James Summers, 'The Right of Self-Determination and Nationalism in International Law' (2005) 12 *International Journal on Minority and Group Rights* 325–54, at 335.

enunciated, rather than expanding its application'.[67] It is therefore problematic to contend that the saving clause is the legal basis of a right of remedial secession, because such an argument is grounded on an overly expansive reading of a clause that is clearly restrictive in meaning.

III.   Problems relating to the practical implementation of remedial secession

If we temporarily suspend our judgment on the existence of remedial secession as part of international law, and turn our attention to analysing the issues that arise in the potential implementation of this doctrine in practice, it quickly becomes evident that there are some overwhelming practical difficulties. Two requirements for a potential exercise of remedial secession are discussed in this section: (a) identifying a 'people' who have a right to exercise remedial secession; and (b) determining the critical date for an exercise of remedial secession.

Before analysing the practical difficulties encountered in the implementation of these two requirements, a brief note on the criteria for an exercise of remedial secession is first in order. Although the idea of remedial secession has been fleshed out in legal scholarship, the criteria necessary for an exercise of the doctrine remain elusive. In this respect, a curious argument presented during the *Kosovo* advisory proceedings by some participants was the idea that Kosovo is a so-called '*sui generis* case'.[68]

Many participants in favour of the secession of Kosovo chose to characterize its recent history in such a way as to argue that the case of Kosovo was like no other; that secession in these circumstances should not be seen as a 'precedent' for analogous situations. In short, instead of formulating criteria for the universal application of remedial secession, it was argued by some participants that the situation in Kosovo was so unique as to give rise to secession as a one-off exception.

---

[67] Weller, *Escaping the Self-determination Trap*, pp. 61–2 (emphasis in original).

[68] *Kosovo* advisory proceedings, Written Statement of Albania, p. 49, para. 95; Written Statement of Denmark, p. 6, para. 2.4; Written Statement of Estonia, p. 11, para. 2.2; Written Statement of France, p. 41; Written Statement of Germany, p. 26; Written Statement of Ireland, p. 12, para. 34; Written Statement of Japan, p. 5; Written Statement of Latvia, p. 2, para. 8; Written Statement of Luxembourg, p. 3, para. 5; Written Statement of Maldives, p. 1; Written Statement of Poland, p. 22, para. 5.1; Written Statement of Slovenia, p. 2.

There were no shortage of criteria proposed for an application of remedial secession.[69] The problem is that the lists of requirements proposed by different participants constituted a series of one-sided historical accounts of the events that transpired in Kosovo, rather than criteria for future applications of the doctrine. In other words, the reasons given for an application of remedial secession were descriptive rather than normative. This approach can be explained by the danger to stability in international relations that the formulation of general criteria for remedial secession would pose. Egypt argued in this respect that 'the adoption of generalized criteria [for remedial secession] would be detrimental and pose genuine threats to international peace and security, which would be an undesired result as per the UN Charter'.[70]

The argument in favour of the *sui generis* nature of the situation of Kosovo evidences from the outset the problems that arise when a right to secede territory is advanced in favour of minorities. The challenge for advocates of remedial secession is to identify criteria to rein in a potential over-use and abuse of the doctrine. Even then, these imposed restrictions are not without their own inherent problems, as evidenced in the following two sections.

1. Identifying a 'people' who can exercise remedial secession

A key problem for a potential application of the doctrine is the identification of a 'people' who can exercise remedial secession. Advocates of the doctrine acknowledge that not just anyone has the right to remedial secession. Only those persons who are identifiable as a 'people', that is, a minority on identifiable territory who have a right to exercise so-called 'internal' self-determination, and who have been the victim of gross human rights violations perpetrated by the State against them, are considered as having a right to remedial secession. As Judge Yusuf noted:

> Surely, there is no general positive right under international law which entitles all ethically or racially distinct groups within existing States to claim separate statehood, as opposed to the specific right of external self-determination which is recognized by international law in favour of the

---

[69] See, for example, *Kosovo* advisory proceedings, Written Statement of Estonia, p. 12; Written Statement of France, p. 41; Written Statement of Germany, p. 27; Written Statement of Ireland, p. 10, para. 33; Written Statement of Japan, pp. 6–8; Written Statement of Luxembourg, p. 4, para. 6; Written Statement of Poland, p. 22, para. 5.2; Written Statement of the United Kingdom of 17 April 2009, pp. 11–14, para. 0.22.

[70] *Ibid.*, Written Statement of Egypt, p. 19, para. 74.

peoples of non-self-governing territories and peoples under alien subjugation, domination and exploitation. Thus a racially or ethnically
distinct group within a State, even if it qualifies as a people for the
purposes of ['internal'] self-determination, does not have the right to
unilateral secession simply because it wishes to create its own separate
State, through this might be the wish of the entire group. The availability
of such a general right in international law would reduce to naught the
territorial sovereignty and integrity of States and would lead to interminable conflicts and chaos in international relations.[71]

However, outside the context of decolonization, and a right to self-
determination for an identified 'people' consecrated in the constitution
of a State and recognized by international law, there are no criteria for the
identification of a 'people' who have the right to exercise self-determination.
Judge Cançado Trindade considered in his Separate Opinion that 'it
would not be necessary to indulge in semantics of what constitutes a
'people'. . . This is a point which has admittedly been defying international
legal doctrine to date.'[72] He nevertheless turned his hand to proposing some
criteria:

> What is clear to me is that, for its configuration, there is conjunction of
> factors, of an objective as well as subjective character, such as traditions
> and culture, ethnicity, historical ties and heritage, language, religion,
> sense of identity or kinship, the will to constitute a people; these are all
> *factual*, not *legal*, elements, which usually overlap each other.[73]

For Judge Cançado Trindade there is something objectively held in
common by a group of individuals, as well as a subjective affinity, that
defines the group as a 'people'. While some of these proposed criteria
hold good for the identification of a minority within a State, such criteria
alone are insufficient for the purpose of identifying a so-called 'people'
who can exercise remedial secession. This is because the identification of
a 'people' who have a right to remedial secession is more complex than
the identification of a 'people' who have a right to exercise ('external')
self-determination, both within and outside the contexts of decolonization and foreign occupation.

The identification of a 'people' who have a right to remedial secession
would constitute a three-stage process. The first stage is the identification

---

[71] *Kosovo* Advisory Opinion, Separate Opinion of Judge Yusuf, p. 3, para. 10.
[72] *Ibid.*, Separate Opinion of Judge Cançado Trindade, p. 68, para. 228.   [73] *Ibid.*

of a minority within the population of a State, which appears to be the requirement principally addressed by Judge Cançado Trindade. The second stage is the identification of this 'minority' on a distinguishable part of State territory; not all minorities against whom serious violations are committed can theoretically secede territory if the members of the minority are widely dispersed throughout a territory without any clear concentration or connection to specific territory. The third stage of the identification of this 'people' is premised on the egregious violations of human rights that this group has endured as the trigger for remedial secession. As Cyprus noted during the *Kosovo* advisory proceedings, '[t]his "right of secession of last resort" would thus make a "people" of the "victim" part of the population'.[74] It is this third stage of identifying a 'people' who can exercise remedial secession that will be considered here.

The identification of a 'people' based on gross violations of human rights raises a number of practical problems. One such problem is proving the occurrence of human rights violations of a seriousness to warrant remedial secession. In situations involving human rights abuses perpetrated by a government against its own citizens, difficulties arise in obtaining evidence that may only be in the hands of the government against which such allegations are made. This difficulty is exacerbated where violations are occurring in an ongoing armed conflict. These are not new problems for proving human rights violations, or violations of international humanitarian law. The particular difficulty presented in the context of a claim of a right to remedial secession concerns the identity of the assessor of such evidence.

Secessionist entities rely on the support of other States for the success of their enterprise. Such support in the form of recognition of a new State is necessary for the uncontroversial creation of a State by secession.[75] The characterization of events within a State by other States, justifying an exercise of remedial secession, raises concerns. As a result of the black and white manner with which events may be painted by some States in furtherance of their support for the creation of a new State, individual criminal justice may prove difficult to implement equally with respect to all persons alleged to have committed core international crimes. As the

---

[74] *Kosovo* advisory proceedings, Written Statement of the Republic of Cyprus, 17 April 2009, para. 142.

[75] The constitutive and declaratory schools of thought with respect to the legal effect of recognition are not discussed in this chapter. See J. Dugard and D. Raič, 'The Role of Recognition in the Law and Practice of Secession', in Kohen (ed.), *Secession: International Law Perspectives*, pp. 94–137, at pp. 97–9.

report by Rapporteur Dick Marty for the Council of Europe on the 'Inhuman treatment of people and illicit trafficking in human organs in Kosovo' makes clear, although – undoubtedly – the most egregious violations were perpetrated against ethnic Albanians by the Yugoslav government, violations occurred on both sides of the ethnic armed conflict:

> The crimes committed by the Serb forces have been documented, denounced and, to the extent possible, tried in courts of law ... None of these historical events could be cast in doubt today. However, what emerged in parallel was a climate and a tendency to view these events and acts through a lens that depicted everything as rather too clear-cut: on one side the Serbs, who were seen as the evil oppressors, and on the other side the Kosovar Albanians, who were seen as the innocent victims ... The basic essence of justice demands that everyone be treated in the same way. Moreover, the duty to find the truth and administer justice must be discharged in order for genuine peace to be restored, and for the different communities to be reconciled and begin living and working together.[76]

Rapporteur Marty went on to note that this perception of events in black and white terms of oppressor/victim to a large degree was due to the attitude adopted by some States on the basis of their relationship with the Kosovo Liberation Army (KLA):

> Western counties that engaged themselves in Kosovo had refrained from a direct intervention on the ground, preferring recourse to air strikes, and had thus taken on the KLA as their indispensable ally for ground operations. The international actors chose to turn a blind eye to the war crimes of the KLA, placing a premium instead on achieving some degree of short-term stability.[77]

Historical accounts can be manipulated in the furtherance of short-term political goals. In some instances, this may be detrimental to securing criminal prosecutions and implementing human rights in the longer term.

The possibility for other States to characterize events that transpire between a secessionist entity and the government within the same State in a particular way in order to buttress the political position they have

[76] Council of Europe: Parliamentary Assembly, *Inhuman Treatment of People and Illicit Trafficking in Human Organs in Kosovo*, 7 January 2011, doc. 12462, available at www.unhcr.org/refworld/docid/4d874ec52.html, p. 6, para. 6.
[77] *Ibid.*, para. 7.

taken vis-à-vis the existence of a new State, raises the question of potential abuse of the doctrine of remedial secession. In this vein, the purported secession of South Ossetia and Abkhazia from Georgia on the basis of an exercise of remedial secession proved an uncomfortable invocation of the doctrine by the Russian Federation for advocates of remedial secession. Advocates of remedial secession have been cautious in recognizing the claimed independence of South Ossetia and Abkhazia as instances of remedial secession. While some scholars are willing to invoke the Russian Federation's reliance on the argument of remedial secession as an example of further State practice in support of the doctrine, they will not commit themselves to considering the doctrine to have been correctly applied in the case of South Ossetia and Abkhazia.[78] For its part, the Independent Fact-Finding Mission on the Conflict in Georgia stated in 2008 that '[i]nternational law does not recognise a right to unilaterally create a new state on the principle of self-determination outside the colonial context and apartheid'.[79]

It must be stressed that remedial secession – occurring as it would in instances where the consent of the parent State is not forthcoming – must be accompanied by strong support from other States in the form of recognition of the new State, to be successful. The issue of the necessary recognition of the new State from other States that is required for an exercise of remedial secession to succeed raises a further concern. This is that the doctrine of remedial secession may be used as a political tool clothed as a legal mechanism to justify interference in the internal affairs of States. This is not to suggest that gross human rights violations and serious international humanitarian law violations that occur within a State are not of international concern – clearly they are. Rather, it is to suggest that the doctrine of remedial secession provides a window of opportunity for some States to characterize events in such a way as to justify the support they provide to armed secessionist groups within a State, in violation of the principle of non-interference.[80]

---

[78] Weller, *Escaping the Self-determination Trap*, p. 68.

[79] Independent International Fact-finding Mission on the Conflict in Georgia, report available online at www.ceiig.ch, vol. I, p. 17, para. 11.

[80] Declaration on the Inadmissibility of Intervention in the Domestic Affairs of States and the Protection of their Independence and Sovereignty, annexed to UN General Assembly resolution 2131 (XX); Principle 3 contained in the Declaration on the Principles of International Law concerning Friendly Relations and Co-operation among States, annexed to UN General Assembly resolution 2625 (XXV); *Military and Paramilitary Activities in and against Nicaragua (Nicaragua v. United States of America)*, Merits, Judgment, ICJ Reports 1986, pp. 106–9, paras. 202–7.

An interesting point was made in this respect by Argentina during the oral phase of the *Kosovo* advisory proceedings. Referring to a public statement made by Sir John Sawers on behalf of the United Kingdom, to the effect that the unilateral declaration of independence by the authors of the declaration had been undertaken 'in co-ordination' with other States,[81] Argentina argued that there was evidence of a coordinated effort on the part of some States to support a secessionist movement in Serbia. According to Argentina, such coordination by States with a secessionist entity within another State would constitute a violation of the principle not to interfere in the internal affairs of a State.[82] The Court in the *Kosovo* Advisory Opinion did not address this point.

2. Identification of the critical date for an exercise of remedial secession

In a well-known formulation of the doctrine of remedial secession provided by Lee Buchheit in his 1978 treatise entitled *Secession: The Legitimacy of Self-Determination*, the *ultimum remedium* requirement for an application of remedial secession is stressed:

> Remedial secession envisions a scheme by which, corresponding to the various degrees of oppression inflicted upon a particular group by its governing State, international law recognizes a continuum of remedies ranging from protection of individual rights, to minority rights, and ending with secession as the *ultimate remedy*.[83]

Participants who advocated for remedial secession before the International Court of Justice in the *Kosovo* advisory proceedings also took care to emphasize its 'last resort' nature. It was an element that was also underscored by Judge Yusuf, who considered that '[a]ll possible remedies for the realization of internal self-determination must be exhausted before the issue is removed from the domestic jurisdiction of the State which had hitherto exercised sovereignty over the territory inhabited by the people making the claim.'[84] That remedial secession is a

---

[81] Sir John Sawers (United Kingdom), 8 October 2008, UN doc. A/63/PV.22, p. 3.

[82] *Kosovo* advisory proceedings, Verbatim Record, 2 December 2009, CR 2009/26, p. 35, para. 10 (Ruiz Cerutti).

[83] Buchheit, *Secession: The Legitimacy of Self-Determination*, p. 222 (emphasis in original).

[84] *Kosovo* Advisory Opinion, Separate Opinion of Judge Yusuf, p. 5, para. 16.

'last resort' in turn raises a question of timing: when is the critical date for exercising remedial secession?

It appears that remedial secession is not triggered until particularly serious violations have been perpetrated. This is understandable. Otherwise, the secession of territory from the parent State may appear disproportionate to the human rights violations alleged. It is recalled in this respect that Kosovo adopted a series of unilateral declarations of independence in 1991.[85] These declarations of independence were adopted in response to a perception by ethnic Albanians in Kosovo that the realization of 'internal' self-determination was not possible. Albania was the only State to recognize Kosovo as an independent State at this moment in time. Clearly, the human rights abuses alleged in 1991 were not sufficiently serious in the eyes of other States to warrant an exercise of remedial secession.

The requirement for particularly gross human rights violations to occur before remedial secession may be successfully invoked, begs the following question: how soon after the particularly serious violations begin occurring is remedial secession triggered? It is recalled that the North Atlantic Treaty Organization (NATO) intervention in Yugoslavia occurred in the late 1990s. The declaration of independence that was the subject of the *Kosovo* advisory proceedings was issued roughly a decade later, on 17 February 2008. Some States considered this claim of remedial secession too late. The Russian Federation argued before the International Court of Justice – in an attempt to distinguish its position in favour of the secession of South Ossetia and Abkhazia on the one hand, from its rejection of the secession of Kosovo, on the other – that '[i]f ever the situation in Kosovo came close to the criteria of remedial secession, that was in the spring of the year 1999. Yet, even at that time the international community reaffirmed the territorial integrity of the FRY'.[86] For its part, Romania considered that a claim of remedial secession could not be premised on facts that had occurred a decade beforehand.[87]

[85] *Kosovo* advisory proceedings, Written Contribution of the Authors of the unilateral declaration of independence, 17 April 2009, paras. 3.30, 3.32. The text of the declaration of independence of 22 October 1991 is reproduced in H. Krieger (ed.), *The Kosovo Conflict and International Law: An Analytical Documentation 1974–1999* (Cambridge University Press, 2001), pp. 12–13.
[86] *Kosovo* advisory proceedings, Verbatim Record, 8 December 2009, CR 2009/30, p. 44, para. 20 (Gevorgian).
[87] *Ibid.*, Verbatim Record, 10 December 2009, CR 2009/32, p. 35, para. 28 (Dinescu).

Attempts to identify the critical date for an exercise of remedial secession bring to light profound cracks in the doctrine. It is evident that the critical date marks the moment in time when there is recognition of the serious failure of the State in question to implement fundamental human rights, and a failure of the international community of States to prevent the occurrence of particularly egregious violations. In this respect, remedial secession by its own definition is a response that comes too late.

What if the State in question remedies the situation internally following the occurrence of particularly egregious violations, or takes important steps in this direction following a regime change? Is a minority's right to remedial secession no longer applicable in an improved human rights situation? According to Germany, it is possible that '[a] situation may change, repression may cease, the constitutional structure of the State in which the group in question is living may change, and for example federalize or decentralize, and so on. Whether or not such changes make the right to "external" self-determination disappear must be judged on the merits of each case, taking into account the severity of the situation prior to those changes.'[88] This argument emphasizes the continuing relevance of past human rights abuses in order to assess the current status quo. It thereby places a premium on punishing a State for past atrocities to the detriment of the population concerned, whose human rights may now be better implemented. This is a peculiar argument, given that it is the latter occurrence – an improvement in the implementation of human rights – that secession purports to attain.

The very invocation of remedial secession is problematic, because a secessionist cause is elevated to a value above all others. The promise of statehood 'some time in the future' to a collective of individuals, and regardless of the actual human rights situation on the ground, undermines any possibility for different parts of a population to reconcile in the future. The implementation of human rights is not limited to action taken by a government; it equally requires a population to be responsive. However, if the improvement of the human rights situation is detrimental to the future secession of territory, it is difficult to see what would motivate a victimized population to assist a new government in addressing past atrocities with a view to achieving reconciliation within a State.

[88] *Kosovo* advisory proceedings, Written Statement of Germany, p. 35.

IV.   Misguided moral value of remedial secession

Underlying the doctrine of remedial secession is a compelling story: after a period of severe discrimination in the State in which they are citizens and resident, culminating in particularly egregious violations, a minority is able to free itself from its oppressed existence under the cruel regime in power, and begin a new liberated future of self-governance. It is a persuasive account. Indeed, it is not difficult to find general agreement on the point that egregious violations committed by a government against a minority that take the form of core international crimes, and following a period of serious maltreatment, represent in some way 'the last straw'; that at this moment, 'enough is enough'. The difference of opinion lies in what one considers to be the appropriate response to such a situation. It is submitted that it does not follow that secession is the appropriate response. It is argued that the invocation of secession in such circumstances is misguided.

A central moral argument that underpins the doctrine of remedial secession is the idea that a minority should be allowed to self-govern. Andre Liebich calls it 'the principle of self-rule as an irreducible value'.[89] In the context of the doctrine of remedial secession, this idea takes its strongest form in the argument that by virtue of the fact that a minority has been prevented from exercising some form of self-government or autonomy in the spheres of executive, legislative and judicial powers, within the constitutive and legislative framework of the State in question, or at the very least from participating in representative government, this minority should have a right to secede territory. Thus, rather than arguing that the status quo should be reinstated or improved, advocates of remedial secession argue that the past failure in the implementation of human rights triggers the absolute right to secede territory as a 'remedy'.

While self-governance and autonomy may be a recognized mode of 'internal' self-determination for part of a population within a State, such a right of 'internal' self-determination is not recognized for a minority. It would be problematic if this were the case, because such an approach would have a discriminatory effect. The very idea of a nation – in the sense of a 'nation-State' – as a racial or ethnic community 'entails some exclusiveness of attitude towards those deemed not to possess the

[89] A. Liebich, 'Must Nations Become States?', *Nationalities Papers*, 31 (2003), pp. 453–69, at p. 457.

relevant ethnic identity'.[90] Although there may be concentrations of minorities on different parts of a State's territory, it is the ethnically heterogeneous population as a whole on all parts of a State's territory that have a right to 'internal' self-determination (with the exception of indigenous peoples). This right to 'internal' self-determination in turn should not be misconstrued to mean self-governance in the form of a new State created for this purpose. It means self-governance within the international boundaries of an existing State.

The argument put forward here is premised on a long-term, global picture of what international society should look like. It is submitted that it is not desirable to amalgamate the notion of a State with the notion of a minority (or 'nation' where this term is understood to refer to a racial or ethnic group). Andre Liebich argues in this respect that the political unit of a State should not correspond to cultural units, and that where such a correlation already appears to exist, this is the result of coincidence valid at some moments in time in some parts of the world, rather than as a result of a functional imperative.[91] Reference can also be made to the writings of Judge Dame Rosalyn Higgins, who described her outlook of international society as follows:

> Because I believe in diversity, and plurality, and tolerance, and mutual respect, I favour multilateralism and multinationalism. The use of force is appalling, indiscriminate barbarity unforgivable. But the move to uninational and unicultural states that constitutes postmodern tribalism is profoundly illiberal. The attempt to legitimise these tendencies by the misapplication of legal terms runs the risk of harming the very values that international law is meant to promote.[92]

Shared ethnic and racial characteristics may play some role in building a particular 'national' identity of a State's population. However, a 'nation' in the sense of a group of individuals who share similar racial and ethnic characteristics should not constitute the principal building block of modern States. The citizens of a State can have a sense of 'national' identity that is not contingent on ethnic or racial grounds. Sir Neil MacCormick explained that 'nation' can also be understood in civic terms, to mean one that 'is constituted by a sense of common belonging

[90] N. MacCormick, *Questioning Sovereignty: Law, State, and Nation in the European Commonwealth* (Oxford University Press, New York, 1999), p. 171.

[91] Liebich, 'Must Nations Become States?', p. 462.

[92] R. Higgins, 'Postmodern Tribalism and the Right to Secession', in C. Brölmann, R. Lefeber and M. Ziek (eds), *Peoples and Minorities in International Law* (Martinus Nijhoff Publishers, Dordrecht, 1993), pp. 29–35, p. 35.

among those who share civic institutions, with no exclusiveness towards
any person or group willing to participate in them'.[93]

There are good arguments for turning away from the idea of a nation-
State as a legal entity encompassing ethnically or racially similar individuals. Jeremy Waldron offers a compelling argument for the idea that
rather than forming political communities on the basis of ethnic, religious, linguistic or cultural affinity, we should advocate for States that are
'formed not on account of any special affinity or trust, but rather on
account of the potential conflict that this proximity to one another is
likely to engender. People should join in political community with those
they are most likely to fight.'[94] Waldron's argument is intriguing precisely because it challenges the assumption that political communities –
including the macro political community of a State – should be premised
on 'special affinity' among individuals, manifested by objective characteristics they hold in common with one another, such as race and
ethnicity.

From a more practical perspective, would the human rights of the
population be better protected by virtue of the creation of a new State? Of
immediate significance is that the population that was a minority in the
parent State would now be the majority in the new State, and the inverse
would also be the case. In this respect, it has been remarked that
'[s]ecession seldom solves the human problem to which it is addressed,
namely the need to buttress the identity and enhance the security of the
breakaway population. The reason is that it creates disenfranchised
minority groups trapped within the new State.'[95] The main result of
secession is a turning of the tables from one disenfranchised group of
individuals to another.

If the underlying ethnic tensions have not been resolved, it is difficult
to see in what way the human rights situation would immediately
improve. Rather, the identity of the more marginalized and victimized
parts of the population would simply shift from one ethnic group to
another, in line with the new balance of ethnic groups in power. And if
fundamental human rights of the new minorities were not respected,

---

[93] MacCormick, *Questioning Sovereignty*, p. 170.
[94] J. Waldron, 'The Principle of Proximity', New York University, School of Law, Public
Law & Legal Theory Research Paper Series, Working Paper No. 11–08, January 2011,
available at: http://ssrn.com/abstract=1742413, p. 1.
[95] J. Mayall, 'Nationalism, Self-determination, and the Doctrine of Territorial Unity', in
M. Weller and N. Metzger (eds), *Settling Self-Determination Disputes* (Martinus Nijhoff
Publishers, Leiden, 2008), pp. 5–16, p. 10.

would the new State be willing to accept that a situation triggering an application of remedial secession may present itself on its own territory with respect to its minorities? Some scholars have expressed doubt in this regard.[96]

It is highly problematic to create a new State in the circumstances to which the doctrine of remedial secession purports to apply. The reason is that the root causes of the humanitarian dilemma, namely, tensions among different segments of a population resulting in human rights violations, would remain unresolved. These underlying causes would simply be repackaged in the form of two States, rather than one. The root causes may even be exacerbated through the establishment of international boundaries separating parts of the population from one another, because distance can create more misunderstandings; separation can lead to greater distrust.

V. Conclusion

Following the *Kosovo* advisory proceedings, it is evident that remedial secession is not an accepted basis for the creation of new States under international law. Kosovo was championed by advocates of remedial secession as the clearest example of an application of the doctrine. However, as evidenced by the conflicting positions adopted by States before the International Court of Justice, and the reticence of the Court even to acknowledge the existence of the doctrine, remedial secession does not apply to Kosovo, and the very existence of the doctrine in international law is questionable. Consequently, it is not the case that 'there is a clear trend towards the acceptance of remedial self-determination'.[97] Following the Advisory Opinion rendered by the Court, the existence of the doctrine in international law has been cast into further doubt.

The doctrine of remedial secession is premised on the idea that the institutional clothing of a new State is the best form of protection for a minority, the members of which have been denied the exercise of a right to 'internal' self-determination, and against whom other gross human rights violations have been committed. But a State is a legal entity, not a human rights solution. A State has the potential, and in many cases the ability, to protect its population. It also has legal obligations incumbent

---

[96] Liebich, 'Must Nations Become States?', p. 458.
[97] Weller, *Escaping the Self-determination Trap*, p. 64.

on it to do so. At the same time, a State has the potential to do the exact opposite, and the powers at the disposal of a State mean that a government can be a particularly brutal perpetrator of gross human rights violations. The creation of a new State *per se* is not a 'remedy'.

Problematically, the doctrine of remedial secession shifts the debate to a secessionist cause, and away from the real issues, namely, the absence of an effective 'human rights culture' in the State concerned, and the underlying ethnic tensions that would remain intact following the secession of part of a State's territory on which new minorities would be present. These underlying ethnic tensions may even be exacerbated by the application of the doctrine in some situations. Rather than resolve the ethnic conflict, remedial secession reinforces the root causes; instead of implementing human rights, it renounces their utility. Remedial secession proposes a drastic response to a serious humanitarian crisis, and it is not difficult to agree that 'something' must be done in such situations. However, this 'something' is not secession, and this 'something' should have been done long before the outbreak of extreme violence. Remedial secession is not a remedy; it is a poor apology.

International responses to the secession attempts of Kosovo, Abkhazia and South Ossetia 1989–2009

GRACE BOLTON

I. Introduction

The contrast in international responses to the secession attempts of Kosovo, Abkhazia and South Ossetia in the early 1990s and 2008 is striking. While the international community disregarded the sovereignty claims of these entities during the early 1990s, a number of states re-evaluated their claims to independence fifteen years after the collapse of the federations. This chapter argues that to understand the attempted secessions of these entities, it is necessary to examine three distinct phases: a constitutional phase, a bellicose phase and a remedial phase. During the first phase, the international community refused to consider the independence claims emanating from autonomous entities, ostensibly to limit fragmentation and to promote stability. Following the recognition of the 'constituent republics', autonomous entities were effectively 'trapped' within the internationally-recognized, 'territorial integrity' of the successor states. During the bellicose phase, the unaddressed grievances of the autonomous entities developed into intra-state conflict, resulting in protracted internal destabilization with significant humanitarian implications (including human rights violations and ethnic cleansing) and leading to the *de facto* separation of certain autonomous entities from their host republics.

During the 'remedial phase', this chapter argues that a subtle evolution within legal and normative thinking on the responsibility of a host state to protect minorities lends credence to the doctrine of remedial secession – a series of conditions which may allow for secession as a 'remedy of last resort'. As will be explored in detail, this doctrine was invoked by most of the states that recognized Kosovo following its Declaration of Independence from Serbia on 17 February 2008. Similarly, Russia invoked these conditions to justify its recognition of Abkhazia and South Ossetia, two weeks after the August 2008 war in Georgia. Accordingly, the main contribution of this chapter is to identify a set of 'remedial conditions' that may facilitate (or block) the recognition of secessionist entities and to examine their political instrumentalization within the cases of Kosovo, Abkhazia and South Osseita. While most scholarship to date focuses on debating the existence (or non-existence) of remedial secession in international law, this chapter explores the political uses and abuses of this contested legal doctrine.

II.   The bellicose phase and the remedial conditions

During the constitutional phase, the independence claims put forward by the 'autonomous entities' were tragically underestimated. During the bellicose phase, the unaddressed grievances of the autonomous entities such as Abkhazia, Nagorno-Karabakh, South Ossetia, Transdniestria and Chechnya resulted in protracted conflicts with significant human-itarian implications (including human rights violations and ethnic cleansing) and leading to the *de facto* separation of certain autonomous entities from their host republics. This can be seen clearly in relation to Abkhazia, South Ossetia and Kosovo.

When the Republic of Georgia was admitted to the United Nations (UN) in August 1992, the Georgian authorities were struggling to control two separatist regions, Abkhazia and South Ossetia. War followed in South Ossetia in 1991–2 and in Abkhazia in 1992–4, resulting in wide-spread ethnic cleansing and the *de facto* separation of these entities from Georgia.[1] Meanwhile, in Kosovo, the escalation of Serbian state-sponsored violence against the Albanian population led to the 1999 North Atlantic Treaty Organization (NATO) intervention, the international administra-tion of Kosovo and, ultimately, Kosovo's *de facto* secession from Serbia.[2] As these conflicts unfolded within the 'territorial integrity' of the recently recognized host states, scholars began re-examining the literature on unilateral secession considering whether a qualified right to secession can arise as a last resort to remedy human rights violations.

---

[1] See S. Cornell, *Small Nations and Great Powers: A Study of Ethnopolitical Conflict in the Caucasus* (London: Routledge, 2000), pp. 153–62.

[2] See M. Weller, *Contested Statehood: Kosovo's Struggle for Independence* (Oxford University Press, 2008).

The theoretical basis for 'remedial secession' is located in international law and normative theory, reflecting the increased salience of human rights considerations during state creation. A number of legal scholars explicitly discuss the doctrine of remedial secession,[3] often described more technically as 'a qualified right to unilateral secession', the purported legal basis for which stems from the enshrinement of the right of self-determination. The 1970 UN Declaration on Friendly Relations addresses *inter alia* self-determination, and proponents of the remedial secession doctrine claim that an inverted reading of the 'safeguard clause' of Principle V gives rise to the doctrine. According to this inverted reading, a state which does not conduct itself 'in compliance with the principle of equal rights and self-determination of peoples' and is not 'possessed of a government representing the whole people belonging to the territory without distinction' is not protected by the safeguard clause and may be exposed to actions which, in the name of the principle of self-determination, may 'dismember or impair, totally or in part, its territorial integrity or political unity'.[4]

Based on an analysis of the 1970 *travaux préparatoires*, Cassese argues that the Declaration on Friendly Relations 'links external self-determination to internal self-determination in exceptional circumstances'.[5] Jure Vidmar recently investigated the application of the doctrine in Bangladesh, the Baltic Republics and Kosovo. He suggests that remedial secession has the following function in international law: although not a legal entitlement, remedial secession confers political and normative legitimacy on oppressed secessionist groups and may encourage states to recognize their independence.[6]

Parallel to the growing consideration of remedial secession in legal doctrine, normative theories of secession are a product of the post-Cold War era, and were undoubtedly shaped by that era. Allen Buchanan 'launched' the contemporary debate about 'the morality of secession in 1991',[7] but his

---

[3] See D. Raic, *Statehood and the Law of Self-Determination* (Leiden: Brill, 2002); L. Buchheit, *Secession: The Legitimacy of Self-Determination* (New Haven, CT: Yale University Press, 1978); Weller, *Contested Statehood*.

[4] E. J. de Aréchaga, 'International Law in the Past Third of a Century', (1978) 159 *Recueil des cours*, 110.

[5] A. Cassese, *Self-determination of Peoples: A Legal Appraisal* (Cambridge University Press, 1995).

[6] J. Vidmar, 'Remedial Secession in International Law: Theory and (Lack of) Practice', (2010) 6 *St. Antony's International Review*, 43.

[7] M. Margaret (ed.), *National Self-Determination and Secession* (Oxford University Press, 1998), p. 34.

initial theories were superseded by his 2004 work, where he proposes a justice-based re-organization of international law, incorporating a 'just cause' theory of secession as a 'remedial right only'.[8]

Following a systhesis of the legal and philosophical writings on 'remedial secession', the following conditions are identified as conditions that facilitate (or block) 'remedial secession':[9]

(1) violations of autonomy agreements by the host state;
(2) unjust annexation of territory;
(3) human rights abuses perpetrated by the host state;
(4) international intervention to mediate a status outcome;
(5) support of powerful countries; and
(6) exhaustion of negotiations.

These six 'remedial conditions' will now be explored in relation to Kosovo, Abkhazia and South Ossetia in order to explore the uses, abuses and limitations of the doctrine.

1.   Tracing remedial secession in Kosovo 1989–2009

During the period in consideration, Kosovo demonstrates a number of features that correspond to the 'remedial conditions'.

1.1   The abolition of autonomy and a sustained denial of internal self-determination

The abolition of autonomy is one of the key remedial conditions identified by Buchanan[10] and carries legal significance, as certain legal scholars consider the right to (internal) self-determination as a right *jus cogens*. Furthermore, Cassese argues that the 1970 Declaration safeguard clause indicates that the denial of internal self-determination may convert into an external right of self-determination.[11] Kosovo presents a clear case of the abolition of autonomy, particularly in view of Kosovo's 'quasi-republican status' under the 1974 Constitution of Yugoslavia. The gradual centralization of power in Belgrade from 1988 to 1990 introduced constitutional amendments to reduce the competencies of the

---

[8] A. Buchanan, *Justice, Legitimacy and Self-Determination: Moral Foundations for International Law* (Oxford University Press, 2004).

[9] G. Bolton, *International Responses to the Secession Attempts of Kosovo, Abkhazia and South Ossetia 1989–2009*, unpublished M.Phil. thesis, University of Oxford (2010).

[10] Buchanan, *Justice, Legitimacy and Self-Determination*, pp. 351–3.

[11] Cassese, *Self-determination of Peoples*.

Kosovo Assembly, until the Serbian authorities dissolved both the Assembly and the Government, thereby removing 'the last vestiges of Kosovo's autonomous status'.[12]

However, the significance of the violation of autonomy agreements is unclear. During the 1990s, UN General Assembly resolutions repeated demands for the restoration of Kosovo's autonomy, but politicians were unwilling to raise the issue at international conferences on Yugoslavia in 1991, 1992 and 1995, due to Serbia's insistence that Kosovo was an 'internal' matter.[13] By 1999, the UN Secretary-General saw the violation of Kosovo's autonomy as the 'root cause of the crisis':

> Before there was a humanitarian catastrophe in Kosovo, there was a human rights catastrophe. Before there was a human rights catastrophe, there was a political catastrophe: the deliberate, systematic and violent disenfranchisement of the Kosovar Albanian people.[14]

Accordingly, the abolition of autonomy, or the denial of internal self-determination is a significant remedial condition – particularly in combination with other factors.

1.2   Human rights violations during the 1990s

David Raic rightly identifies human rights abuses as the 'catalytic agent' for remedial secession, but the challenge is to identify appropriate thresholds.[15] Following the abolition of Kosovo's autonomy, a number of discriminatory laws were introduced, prohibiting Albanians from the unauthorized sale of private property and restricting Albanian language education.[16] During the 1990s, international monitoring bodies such as the CSCE and the UN Special Rapporteur for Human Rights chronicled the discrimination suffered by Kosovo-Albanians. Accordingly, the UN General Assembly (UNGA) adopted twelve resolutions between 1992 and 1998, summarizing the findings of the monitoring mechanisms and condemning Federal Republic of Yugoslavia (FRY)/Serbian abuses of

---

[12] N. Malcolm, *Kosovo: A Short History* (Oxford University Press, 2002), p. 246.

[13] R. Caplan, *Europe and the Recognition of New States in Yugoslavia* (Cambridge University Press, 2005), p. 140.

[14] UN Information Service, 'Secretary-General Addresses High-Level Meeting on Balkans', SG/SM/6992, 14 May 1999.

[15] Raic, *Statehood and the Law of Self-Determination*, p. 372.

[16] M. Weller, *The Crisis in Kosovo 1989–1999*, International Documents and Analysis, Vol. I, Documents and Analysis Publishing Ltd (Cambridge University Press, 1999), pp. 62–3.

human rights in Kosovo. A frequently-repeated operative clause
condemned:

> the large-scale repression by the police and military of the Federal
> Republic of Yugoslavia against the defenceless ethnic Albanian popula-
> tion and the discrimination against the ethnic Albanians in the admin-
> istrative and judiciary branches of government, education, health care
> and employment, aimed at forcing ethnic Albanians to leave.[17]

In winter 1995, Milošević made it clear that discussing Kosovo at Dayton
would destroy any chance of a settlement in Bosnia-Herzegovina.[18]
Kosovo-Albanians saw the Dayton Agreement as a 'betrayal', particularly
in view of the decision to lift sanctions on the FRY, despite the human
rights situation in Kosovo.[19] This discredited Ibrahim Rugova, the
Kosovo-Albanian leader, and his policy of passive resistance, creating
increased support for the Kosovo Liberation Army (KLA). During 1996,
the KLA developed a strategy of targeting Serbian police stations and army
sites, as well as Albanian 'collaborators'. This in turn provoked Serb
counter-attacks, which increasingly targeted civilians and entire
Albanian communities, who looked to the KLA for protection.

In March 1998, US Envoy Robert Gelbard announced that the KLA
was 'a terrorist group'.[20] Possibly emboldened by this, the Serbian regime
launched aggressive 'counter-terrorist' operations, surrounding villages
and 'liquidating' groups of up to fifty people at a time, including women
and children.[21] The escalation of violence transformed the Kosovo issue
'from a human rights problem into a humanitarian crisis'.[22] In June
1998, the European Union (EU) condemned the 'wide-spread house-
burning and indiscriminate artillery attacks of whole villages [indicat-
ing] a new level of aggression on the part of the Serbian security forces'
and viewed these practices as 'a new wave of ethnic cleansing'.[23] By
September 1998, the UN Secretary-General concluded that 'the level of

---

[17] UN General Assembly Resolution, Situation of Human Rights in Kosovo, 49/204,
A/RES/49/204, 13 March 1995.
[18] R. Holbroke, *To End a War* (New York: Random House, 1998), p. 370.
[19] M. Weller, *Peace Lost: The Failure of Conflict Prevention in Kosovo* (Leiden: Brill, 2008),
p. 131.
[20] R. Caplan, 'International Diplomacy and the Crisis in Kosovo', *International Affairs*, 74
(1998), 753.
[21] UNHCR Field Operation Report, April 1998, in Weller, *Crisis in Kosovo*, p. 259.
[22] Weller, *Contested Statehood*, p. 66.
[23] EU, *Declaration by the European Union on Kosovo*, 98/56/CFSP, 11 June 1998.

destruction points clearly to an indiscriminate and disproportionate use of force against civilian populations'.[24]

The UN Security Council adopted three resolutions in 1998, calling for an 'enhanced status for Kosovo, a substantially greater degree of autonomy and meaningful self-determination'.[25] Accordingly, US Ambassador Hill was tasked with mediating a political solution. The Rambouillet Accords were drafted by 23 February 1998 and provided for wide powers of self-government for Kosovo, respecting the territorial integrity of the FRY for three years before holding a referendum on status.[26] While representatives of the Kosovo-Albanians signed the Accords, the FRY and Serbia refused to sign, prompting NATO's military campaign against the FRY on 24 March 1999.[27]

On 24 March 1999, US President Bill Clinton explained his reasons for intervening in Kosovo:

> In 1989 Serbia's leader Slobodan Milošević ... stripped Kosovo of the constitutional autonomy its people enjoyed, thus denying them their right to speak their language, run their schools, shape their daily lives. For years, Kosovars struggled peacefully to get their rights back. When President Milošević sent his troops and police to crush them, the struggle grew violent ... As the Kosovars were saying yes to peace [at Rambouillet], Serbia stationed 40,000 troops in and around Kosovo ... Now they've started moving from village to village, shelling civilians and torching their houses ... This is not war in the traditional sense. It is an attack by tanks and artillery on a largely defensless people, whose leaders already have agreed to peace [at Rambouillet]. Ending this tragedy is a moral imperative.[28]

Here Clinton clearly invokes remedial conditions, as well as the moral imperative to act. A decade later, the same arguments were made in the UN Security Council meeting that discussed Kosovo's Declaration of Independence.[29] The UK attached particular significance to the cumulative effect of Belgrade's actions, explaining that Resolution 1244

[24] Report of the Secretary-General, prepared pursuant to Security Council Resolution 1160 (1998) and 1199 (1998), S/1998/912, 3 October 1998.
[25] See UN Security Council Resolutions 1160 (1998); 1199 (1998); and 1203 (1998).
[26] Interim Agreement for Peace and Self-Government in Kosovo, Rambouillet, 23 February 1999.
[27] J. Vidmar, 'International Legal Responses to Kosovo's Declaration of Independence', (2009) 42 *Vanderbilt Journal of Transnational Law*, 793.
[28] President Clinton Addresses Nation on Yugoslavia Strike, 24 March 1999.
[29] United Kingdom of Great Britain and Northern Ireland; United States, UNSC Meeting-Record, S/PV.5839, 18 February 2008.

'deprived Belgrade of the exercise of authority in Kosovo' not just because the 'then regime in Belgrade ... unilaterally deprived Kosovo of its powers of self-government' but since it 'tried in 1999 to expel the majority population from the territory of Kosovo'.[30]

From this analysis, it seems that, in the immediate post-Cold War period, revoking autonomy and pursuing discriminatory policies was not a sufficient cause to remove authority: evidence of more extensive suffering and human rights violations was needed to justify intervention and *de facto* secession.

1.3   International intervention

Kosovo's experience of international administration and status negotiations illustrates the remaining conditions of remedial secession. UN Security Council (UNSC) Resolution 1244 (1999) was the founding document of the post-war order in Kosovo. Despite the resolution's preambular commitment to the territorial integrity of the FRY, Vidmar emphasizes that the 'operative paragraphs created a situation that is not easily reconciled with the principle of territorial integrity'.[31] The resolution demanded that the FRY end 'violence and repression in Kosovo' and withdraw from Kosovo 'all military, police and paramilitary forces'.[32] In addition, the Council authorized the deployment, under UN auspices, of 'international civil and security presences'. The civil presence was mandated to 'promote the establishment, pending a final settlement, of substantial autonomy and self-government in Kosovo' as well as 'facilitating a political process designed to determine Kosovo's future status'.[33]

In accordance with Resolution 1244, the UN Interim Administration Mission in Kosovo (UNMIK) was established, which vested supreme authority over legislative, executive and judicial bodies in the Special Representative of the Secretary-General (SRSG). In 2001, UNMIK introduced the 'Constitutional Framework for Provisional Self-Government', which aimed to establish a 'comprehensive legal framework for self-government for Kosovo'.[34] The SRSG was mandated to 'facilitate the transfer of powers and responsibilities' to the Provisional Institutions of Self-Government (PISG) including: the Assembly; the President of

---

[30] *Ibid.*, 12.   [31] Vidmar, 'International Legal Responses', 796.
[32] UN Security Council Resolution 1244 (1999), 10 June 1999.   [33] *Ibid.*
[34] UNMIK Regulation 2001/9, Constitutional Framework for Provisional Self-Government in Kosovo, 15 May 2001.

Kosovo; the Government; the Courts. This gradual process began in 2002 and UNMIK completed the transfer of the prescribed PISG responsibilities by the end of 2003.[35] In March 2004, UNMIK unveiled the complex 'Kosovo Standards Implementation Plan', to achieve the benchmarks that SRSG Michael Steiner believed 'should be achieved before launching a discussion on status'.[36]

While Kosovo's politicians were increasingly frustrated by this complex policy, popular frustration with the delayed status rose. On 16 March 2004, riots erupted in Kosovo as over 51,000 people participated in more than 33 separate incidents across the Country, resulting in 19 fatalities (8 Serbs, 11 Albanians).[37] The Organization for Security and Co-operation in Europe (OSCE) chronicled 954 people injured, 4,100 people displaced, 4,550 houses and 27 Orthodox churches and monasteries burnt.[38] At the emergency UNSC meeting on 18 March, Serbia described the riots as 'ethnic cleansing'.[39] However, this term was not used by the other countries present, which condemned the violence, emphasizing the need to adhere to the 'standards before status' process.[40]

In the following months, Belgrade claimed that the riots exposed Kosovo's unsuitability for statehood.[41] In response, Albin Kurti, leader of the pro-independence 'Vetevendosje' (Self-Determination) movement, commented that 'much is made of the outbreak of violence in March as an example of Kosova's unpreparedness for self-determination . . . Kosova's unresolved status is the root cause of the inter-communal tensions and resultant instability'.[42] Reaching a similar conclusion, the UN Secretary-General (UNSG) viewed the March riots as the failure of UNMIK and commissioned a comprehensive re-evaluation of UN strategy in Kosovo. Following the recommendation of Ambassador Kai Eide's reports, the UNSC authorized the initiation of the future status process

---

[35] Report of the Secretary-General on the United Nations Interim Administration Mission in Kosovo, S/2004/71, 26 January 2004, para. 5.

[36] UN Security Council Meeting Record, S/PV.4518, 24 April 2002, 3.

[37] J. Ker-Lindsay, 'From Autonomy to Independence: The Evolution of International Thinking on Kosovo, 1998–2005', (2009) 11 *Journal of Balkan and Near Eastern Studies*, 150.

[38] OSCE Mission in Kosovo, 'Human Rights Challenges following the March Riots in 2004', 4.

[39] Serbia, UN Security Council Meeting Record, S/PV.4928, 18 March 2004, 3.

[40] Germany, *ibid.*, 15.

[41] I. King and W. Mason, *Peace at Any Price: How the World Failed Kosovo* (New York: Cornell University Press, 2006), p. 190.

[42] 'Time for determined international action on Kosovo', *The Irish Times* (5 January 2005).

and Martti Ahtisaari was appointed as UN Special Envoy for Kosovo (UNOSEK) to oversee the process.[43]

1.4   The exhaustion of negotiations

In order for secession to be presented as a remedy of last resort, all judicial and political mechanisms should be exhausted. In practice, this revolves around the 'exhaustion of negotiations'. Kosovo's Future Status negotiations occurred in two different phases. First, the Vienna Negotiations were convened between February 2006 and March 2007, and Ahtisaari made his recommendation and proposal at the end of this phase. When Serbia and Russia called for renewed negotiations, an additional Troika-led round was held between August and December 2007.

Following the Vienna Negotiations, Ahtisaari presented his proposal to the two parties in February 2007. Weller explains that 'Kosovo embraced the proposal in principle, offering modest suggestions for amendment.'[44] In contrast, Serbian Prime Minister Kostunica rejected the agreement and called on Ahtisaari to re-engage in negotiations on the basis of the 'substantive autonomy model'.[45] Significantly, the call for more discussions was also echoed by the Russian Government.[46] Nonetheless, Ahtisaari claimed that 'the potential of negotiations is exhausted'.[47] Ahtisaari sent his Comprehensive Proposal and a separate Recommendation to the UNSG, who fully endorsed both documents and presented them to the Security Council on 26 March 2007.[48]

Concerning Kosovo's future status, Ahtisaari recommended 'independence, supervised initially by the international community'. In justifying his position, Ahtisaari clearly invoked the remedial conditions:

> After years of peaceful resistance to Milošević's policies of oppression – the revocation of Kosovo's autonomy, the systematic discrimination against the vast Albanian majority in Kosovo and their effective elimination from public life – Kosovo-Albanians eventually responded with armed resistance. Belgrade's reinforced and brutal repression followed, involving the tragic loss of civilian lives and the displacement and expulsion on a massive scale of Kosovo-Albanians from their homes,

---

[43] Weller, *Contested Statehood*, p. 189.   [44] *Ibid.*, p. 210.   [45] *Ibid.*, p. 211.
[46] J. Ker-Lindsay, *Kosovo: The Path to Contested Statehood in the Baltans* (London: I.B. Tauris, 2009), p. 63.
[47] UNOSEK Press Conference, 10 March 2007.
[48] Report of the Special Envoy of the Secretary-General on Kosovo's future status, S/2007/168, 26 March 2007.

and from Kosovo. The dramatic deterioration of the situation on the ground prompted the intervention of the North Atlantic Treaty Organization (NATO), culminating in the adoption of resolution 1244 (1999).[49]

Ahtisaari also emphasized the effect of international adminstration:

> For the past eight years, Kosovo and Serbia have been governed in complete separation ... [UNMIK's] assumption of all legislative, executive and judicial authority throughout Kosovo, has created a situation in which Serbia has not exercised any governing authority over Kosovo.[50]

In his Comprehensive Proposal for the Kosovo Status Settlement (CSS), Ahtisaari outlined prescriptions for Kosovo's future status, including constitutional, economic and security provisions. Ahtisaari's CSS also described the supervisory role envisaged for the international presence, until all 'authority vested in UNMIK shall be transferred en bloc to the authorities of Kosovo'.[51] Ahtisaari's CSS met a divided response. While the Quint lobbied the Security Council in favour of a draft resolution to endorse the Ahtisaari package, Serbia and Russia insisted on holding a new round of negotiations. This highlights the difficulty of establishing a threshold for the exhaustion of negotiations.

Between August and December 2007, a troika of senior diplomats from Russia, the United States and the EU held a new round of status talks. Serbia took full advantage of the opportunity to start negotiations afresh and supported autonomy, offering Kosovo 'most competencies and symbols that are normally reserved only for sovereign countries'.[52] Kosovo reiterated its demands for independence, having negotiated Ahtisaari's CSS in good faith as the 'definitive settlement'.[53] On 7 December, the troika informed the Secretary-General that 'neither side was willing to cede its position on the basic question of sovereignty'.[54] Emerging from a UNSC meeting on the Troika report, the United States and certain EU states issued a joint statement 'that the potential for a negotiated solution is now exhausted'.[55] Media reports suggested that these countries had decided to implement the Ahtisaari

---

[49] *Ibid.*, 3.   [50] *Ibid.*

[51] Report of the Special Envoy of the Secretary-General on Kosovo's future status, 9.

[52] Weller, *Contested Statehood*, pp. 225–7.   [53] *Ibid.*, 223.

[54] Report of the EU/US/Russia Troika on Kosovo, 4 December 2007.

[55] Comments to the media by the Permanent Representatives of Belgium, France, Italy, United Kingdom, United States of America, Slovakia and Germany on the situation in Kosovo, text at www.un.org/webcast/stakeout2007.html.

Plan without a Security Council resolution, and forecast Kosovo's imminent unilateral declaration of independence.[56]

1.5   Normative undertaking from the seceding entity

Convened in an extraordinary meeting on 17 February 2008, members of the Kosovo Assembly adopted a Declaration of Independence. This document draws on both constitutional aspects and remedial justifications, referring both to the dissolution of Yugoslavia and the experience of discrimination, human rights abuses and international administration. The Declaration observed that 'Kosovo is a special case arising from Yugoslavia's non-consensual breakup and is not a precedent for any other situation.' The Preamble expressed gratitude that 'in 1999 the world intervened, thereby removing Belgrade's governance over Kosovo'.[57] Regarding the final status negotiations, it regretted 'that no mutually acceptable status was possible, in spite of the good faith engagement of [Kosovo] leaders'.[58] Although declaring Kosovo 'an independent and sovereign state', the authors of the Declaration undertook to 'cooperate fully with [international] presences' and to 'accept fully . . . the Ahtisaari plan'. Reflecting the remedial condition of committing to protect minority rights, the Declaration undertook 'to protect and promote the rights of all communities in Kosovo . . . and their effective participation in political and decision-making processes'.

Although Kosovo's Declaration concluded with an undertaking to 'contribute to relations of friendship and cooperation with the Republic of Serbia', Serbia's National Assembly reacted to Kosovo's unilateral Declaration of Independence with great hostility, claiming that it 'represent[s] a violent and unilateral secession'. It is interesting to note that Serbia immediately labelled Kosovo's action as 'secession', whereas Kosovo's Declaration maintained that independence brought 'to an end the process of Yugoslavia's violent dissolution'.[59]

1.6   Support of powerful countries

The Security Council convened on 18 February to discuss Kosovo. As a forum for countries to state their positions, this debate allows us to consider the position of powerful countries towards Kosovo's independence. Both Serbia and Russia requested that the Secretary-General

---

[56] Vidmar, 'International Legal Responses to Kosovo's Declaration of Independence', 803.
[57] Kosovo Declaration of Independence, 17 February 2008.   [58] *Ibid.*   [59] *Ibid.*

instruct his Special Representative in Kosovo to declare the act of secession 'null and void'.[60]

During the Security Council debate, aspects of the Kosovo case were raised, which reflect the remedial secession conditions. Concerning constitutional status, Panama emphasized that 'Kosovo enjoyed an autonomy very much like the autonomy of the old republics of greater Yugoslavia, and an attempt was made to deprive it of that autonomy.'[61] Costa Rica announced its recognition of Kosovo in response 'to the will of the people of Kosovo – a people who find it impossible to live together with the Serb majority in the same country after the 1998 campaign of ethnic cleansing'.[62] The United States also described this policy as 'ethnic cleansing' and explained that, in response to 'that humanitarian disaster and clear threats to international peace and security, NATO led a military intervention that stopped the violence and brought peace to Kosovo'.[63] The United Kingdom (UK) agreed that 'the events of 1999 shape the events we see now'[64] and emphasized that the new regime in Belgrade has 'a duty to help resolve the problems caused by Milošević, and they must accept that the legacy of Milošević's oppression and violence has made it impossible for Kosovo to return to control by Belgrade'.[65] Concerning the conditions of last resort, Belgium, the UK and Italy emphasized that 'the potential for reaching a negotiated solution has been exhausted'.[66]

In anticipation of these arguments, Serbian President, Boris Tadić, stated that: 'Since 1999, 250,000 Serbs and other non-Albanians have been expelled from Kosovo. In mid-March 2004, militant and extremist members of the Albanian community in Kosovo burned 35 Churches and Monasteries and 800 houses in only three days, while another 5,000 Serbs and other non-Albanians fled their homes. Is the independence of Kosovo a just reward for all the things that I have enumerated?'[67] Both Serbia and Russia voiced concern about Kosovo's potential to become a 'precedent', with Tadić claiming that 'there are dozens of other Kosovos in the world, and all of them are lying in wait for Kosovo's act of secession to become a reality and to be established as an acceptable norm'.[68] In response, many countries emphasized the unique historical circumstances surrounding the Kosovo issue, including Belgium, Indonesia, Croatia, the UK, the United States and France.

---

[60] Russia, UN Security Council Meeting Record, S/PV.5839, 18 February 2008. 7.
[61] Panama, *ibid.*, 21.   [62] Costa Rica, *ibid.*, 17.   [63] United States, *ibid.*
[64] UK, *ibid.*, 12.   [65] *Ibid.*, 13.   [66] Italy, *ibid.*, 9.   [67] Serbia, *ibid.*, 4.   [68] *Ibid.*, 5.

The above analysis also illustrates the divergence between Russia and the rest of the Contact Group, reflecting two different theoretical positions. First, Russia supported Belgrade's position, invoking the principles of the 'classical international system' concerning the sovereignty and territorial integrity of states.[69] By contrast, the United States, UK and France demonstrated a normative shift towards making state sovereignty conditional on respect for human rights.[70] When the International Court announced its Advisory Opinion on the legality of the unilateral declaration of independence in Kosovo on 22 July 2010, it acknowledged that a number of participants raised the remedial secession doctrine, in 'every instance only as a secondary argument' describing it as a subject on which 'radically different views were expressed', but emphasized that remedial secession was 'beyond the scope of the question posed by the General Assembly'.[71] The limited consideration of remedial secession in the Advisory Opinion, as well as the Dissenting Opinions, has been explored elsewhere and is beyond the scope of this chapter.[72] Of significance, most countries that have recognized Kosovo have invoked some of the remedial conditions.[73] As we will now see, Russia also invoked the remedial conditions to justify its recognition of Abkhazia and South Ossetia, but these arguments have attracted little or no international support.

2. Abkhazia and South Ossetia: Russia's (mis)application of remedial secession

In August 2008, the 'frozen' conflict in South Ossetia escalated into open war between Georgia and Russia. On 26 August 2008, Russia recognized the independence of Abkhazia and South Ossetia. On the same day, Russian President Dimity Medvedev issued a public statement justifying Russia's recognition.[74] The statement, which refers to a series of historical and

---

[69] Weller, *Contested Statehood*, p. 191.

[70] J. M. Welsh (ed.), *Humanitarian Intervention and International Relations* (Oxford University Press, 2006), p. 2.

[71] ICJ, 'Accordance with International Law of the Unilateral Declaration of Independence by the Provisional Institutions of Self-Government of Kosovo', Advisory Opinion, 22 July 2010, para. 83.

[72] See article in the same volume by Katherine Del Mar, 'The Myth of Remedial Secession'.

[73] See G. Bolton and G. Visoka, *Recognizing Kosovo's Independence: Remedial Secession or Earned Sovereignty?*, Occasional Paper, No. 11/10, SESSOX, University of Oxford (2010). See also Chapter 3 above.

[74] Statement by Russian President Dmitry Medvedev, 26 August 2008, (Medvedev Recogniton Speech) www.un.int/russia/new/MainRoot/docs/off_news/260808/newen2.htm.

contemporary events in Abkhazia, South Ossetia and Georgia, is all the more remarkable for its invocation of the remedial conditions:

> [Georgian President] Saakashvili opted for genocide to accomplish his political objectives. By doing so he himself dashed all the hopes for the peaceful coexistence of Ossetians, Abkhazians and Georgians in a single state. The peoples of South Ossetia and Abkhazia have several times spoken out at referendums in favour of independence for their republics. It is our understanding that after what has happened in Tskhinval and what has been planned for Abkhazia they have the right to decide their destiny by themselves.[75]

Medvedev's recognition statement makes reference to several remedial conditions, including human rights abuses – claiming that the Georgians aimed to 'ethnically cleanse' the Abkhaz and the South Ossetians between 1990 and 1994, and again in 2008 – the internationalization of the conflict, the exhaustion of negotiations and assurances of the democratic authority of the Abkhaz and South Ossetian authorities. This section will consider the applicability of the remedial conditions to Abkhazia and South Ossetia, and gauge the extent to which Russia's invocation of the remedial conditions constitutes the use or abuse of the doctrine. A final section examines the impact of Kosovo's independence on Russian policy towards Abkhazia and South Ossetia.

2.1   Contested sovereignties 1989–91: the abolition of autonomy?

Within the ethno-territorial hierarchy of the Union of Soviet Socialist Republics (USSR), the Soviet Socialist Republics (SSRs, or 'Union Republics') were most powerful, followed respectively by Autonomous Soviet Socialist Republics (ASSRs), Autonomous Oblasts (AOs) and 'autonomous districts' (*okrugs*).[76] South Ossetia was an AO of the Soviet Union created within the Georgian SSR in 1922, a status it retained until the Georgian SSR revoked its autonomy in December 1990. From 1921 to 1931, Abkhazia was an SSR in confederation with the Georgian SSR. In 1931, the Abkhazia SSR was abolished and transformed into the Abkhaz ASSR within the Georgian SSR, a status it retained until 1991. With the weakening of the Soviet Union, a series of nationalist groups asserted the respective claims of Georgians, Abkhaz and South Ossetians, unleashing a

---

[75] *Ibid.*
[76] E. Walker, *Dissolution: Sovereignty and the Breakup of the Soviet Union* (Oxford University Press, 2003), p. 2.

cycle of actions and reactions.[77] In response, Georgian nationalist leader Zviad Gamsakhurdia based his 1990 electoral campaign on 'the rights of Georgians in Abkhazia and South Ossetia', increasing tensions among Georgia's ethnic minorities.[78] Medvedev referred to this period as Gamsakhurdia's 'Georgia for Georgians' campaign.[79]

Although not addressed by Medvedev, the violation of autonomy agreements merits consideration. In preparation for their multi-party elections, the Georgian authorities introduced a law to prevent regional parties from participating.[80] Considering this a ruse to exclude their national movement from the elections, South Ossetia's Regional Soviet declared South Ossetia's sovereignty as a Soviet Democratic Republic within the USSR on 20 September 1990.[81] Following this, the Georgian Parliament abolished the autonomy of South Ossetia and instituted a state of emergency in the region, which resulted in war.[82] In January 1991, Georgia was declared a unitary state with no internal boundaries, implicitly abolishing the autonomous status of all three autonomous entities of the country.[83] In March 1991, voters in Abkhazia and South Ossetia voted overwhelmingly (98.6% and 99%, respectively) in favour of Gorbachev's Union Treaty, while refusing to participate in Georgia's separate independence referendum.

A detailed assessment of violations of autonomy agreements is complicated by the 'war of laws' between the Abkhaz and Georgian authorities. During 1992, the revival of Georgia's pre-Soviet 1921 Constitution, which did not define Abkhazia's autonomous status clearly, prompted the Abkhaz Supreme Soviet to declare sovereignty as the 'Republic of Abkhazia', and to reinstate the 1925 draft constitution.[84] However, this declaration was not intended as a proclamation of independence, as the 1925 Constitution provided for a federative relationship between 'two equal republics'.[85] Nonetheless, the Georgian

[77] Independent International Fact-Finding Mission on the Conflict in Georgia (IIFFMCG), 71–3.
[78] Cornell, *Small Nations and Great Powers*, pp. 150–1.
[79] Medvedev Recognition Speech, 26 August 2008.
[80] Cornell, *Small Nations and Great Powers*, p. 155.
[81] Declaration of State Sovereignty of the Soviet Democratic Republic of South Ossetia, (20 September 1990), available at www.rrc.ge/law/dekl_1990_09_20_e.htm?lawid=1194&lng_3=en.
[82] Cornell, *Small Nations and Great Powers*, p. 155.   [83] *Ibid.*, p. 153.
[84] Raič, *Statehood and the Law of Self-Determination*, p. 381
[85] T. Potier, *Conflict in Nagorno-Karabakh, Abkhazia and South Ossetia: A Legal Appraisal* (The Hague: Kluwer Law International, 2001), p. 11.

Parliament annulled the Abkhazian decision.[86] This created a complex situation of overlapping and contested sovereignty over the territory of Abkhazia. As recently as August 2008, Russia argued in the UNSC that there were 'two States on the territory of the Georgian Soviet Socialist Republic that were no longer connected to one another: Georgia, which declared its secession from the Soviet Union as an independent State, and Abkhazia, which continued to be an integral part of the Soviet Union'.[87]

2.2 'Ethnic cleansing' and the 1991–4 wars

The doctrine of collective non-recognition holds that 'states may be under an obligation to refrain from recognising entities' that are created in violation of 'essential rules of the international community', including the prohibition of the use of force by states, the right to self-determination, the prohibition of apartheid or the prohibition of genocide and ethnic cleansing.[88] In contrast, the remedial position holds that victims of ethnic cleansing may have a right to secession as a remedy of last resort. Accordingly, accusations of 'ethnic cleansing' carry major implications for aspirant states. In his speech, Medvedev claimed that ethnic cleansing occured twice: between 1990 and 1994 and during the 2008 war. He accused Gamsakhurdia of attempting to implement his Georgia for Georgians policy 'through the annihilation of a whole people' ordering 'attacks on the cities of Sukhum and Tskhinval', stating that these wars resulted in 'thousands of people killed, dozens of thousands of refugees and devastated villages'. In view of the gravity of these accusations, it is necessary to ascertain whether the abuses invoked by Medvedev represent an objective evaluation of the suffering.

The war in South Ossetia lasted from January 1991 to June 1992, producing over 1,000 casualties and 110,000 refugees.[89] Official Georgian sources claim that about 60,000 Ossets left Georgia for North Ossetia, but this was not well catalogued by the international community.[90] As a result, attention focused on the high-profile plight of Georgian refugees. Although the figures vary considerably, one source claims that

---

[86] *Ibid.*
[87] Russia, UN Security Council Meeting Report, S/PV.5969, 28 August 2008, 18.
[88] M. Weller, *Escaping the Self-Determination Trap* (Berlin, Brill, 2009), p. 40.
[89] N. S. MacFarlane, 'On the Front Lines in the Near Aboard: The CIS and the OSCE in Georgia's Civil Wars' (1997) 18 *Third World Quarterly*, 512.
[90] *Ibid.*

23,000 ethnic Georgians fled from South Ossetia.[91] Since this figure represents most of South Ossetia's pre-war Georgian population, accusations of 'ethnic cleansing' emanated from Tbilisi. The situation in South Ossetia was not addressed by any UN resolutions before Georgia was admitted as a member on 6 July 1992.[92]

In August 1992, Georgian troops entered eastern Abkhazia, to restore communications links. However on experiencing resistance, they pressed onward into Sukhumi, attacked the Abkhaz Parliament and drove the Abkhaz out of Sukhumi.[93] The war in Abkhazia lasted until 14 May 1994 and displaced approximately 350,000 of Abkhazia's 540,000 inhabitants.[94] Abkhazia's ethnic composition changed dramatically: by February 1995 the proportion of ethnic Georgians decreased from 45 per cent of the pre-war population to less than 5 per cent, while the Abkhaz minority of 17 per cent increased its proportion to 50 per cent.[95]

It is important to emphasize that the ethnicity targeted for displacement reflected the relative strength of the warring parties during different phases of the conflict.[96] During the first phase, Georgian forces controlled the territory, and ethnic Abkhaz were the main victims.[97] Human Rights Watch chronicled 'gross intimidation by Georgian forces for the purpose of terrorizing, robbing and driving the Abkhaz population out of their homes'.[98] In autumn 1992, the Abkhaz gained the upper hand and displaced ethnic Georgians, with the UN Refugee Agency (UNHCR) estimating that Abkhaz forces expelled 250,000 ethnic Georgians from the region.[99]

In October 1993, a UNSC fact-finding mission confirmed this two-phase analysis and concluded that 'civilians of all ethnic groups have been victims'.[100] Georgia submitted a government report to the UN

---

[91] Human Rights Watch, 'Russia: The Ingush-Ossetian Conflict in the Prigorodnyi Region', May 1996.

[92] UN Security Council Resolution 793 (1992), 30 November 1992.

[93] MacFarlane, 'On the Front Lines in the Near Aboard', 514.

[94] UNHCR Information Bulletin, July 1994, 4.

[95] E. Mooney, 'Internal Displacement and the Conflict in Abkhazia', (1996) 3 *International Journal on Group Rights*, 198.

[96] UNHCR's Operational experience with internally displaced persons (Geneva, 1994), 39.

[97] *Ibid.*

[98] Human Rights Watch, 'Georgia/Abkhazia: Violations of the Laws of War and Russia's role in the conflict', March 1995, 20.

[99] UNHCR's Operational experience with internally displaced persons (Geneva, 1994), 39.

[100] Report of the Secretary-General's fact-finding mission to investigate human rights violations in Abkhazia, Republic of Georgia, UN Doc. S/2679S, 1993, para. 52.

Secretary-General, claiming that 'the Abkhaz and their accomplices premeditated the genocide of the Georgian population'.[101] Although a 1994 UNHCR report described 'ethnic cleansing',[102] the UNSC adopted more neutral language, condemning 'attempts to change the demographic composition of Abkhazia'.[103] By contrast, states at the 1994 summit of the OSCE 'reiterated their strong support for the sovereignty and territorial integrity of Georgia' and 'expressed further concern over "ethnic cleansing", the massive expulsion of people, predominantly Georgian'.[104] Accordingly, the position that the Abkhaz created an ethnically homogenous territory as a result of ethnic cleansing severely undermined international support for Abkhazia's claim for independence. This represents an inversion of the remedial condition of human rights violations, as perpetrated by the seceding entity on members of the host state.

2.3 The extent of international intervention in Abkhazia and South Ossetia

Following the conflicts in the 1990s, Medvedev claimed that Russia came forward as a 'mediator and peacekeeper ... invariably guided by the recognition of Georgia's territorial integrity'.[105] This claim is undermined by the fact that the conflicts were facilitated by Russian funds and military hardware.[106] Accordingly, MacFarlane argues that Russia's political involvement reflected its hegemonic aspirations in the 'near abroad'.[107] Immediate responsibility for peacekeeping was devolved to the Commonwealth of Independent States (CIS) in Abkhazia and to Russia in South Ossetia.[108] Therefore, Russia established itself simultaneously as a mediator and 'as a participant in the conflict with an extremely ambivalent role'.[109] Consequently, Western actors adopted a

---

[101] Letter dated 24 February 1994 from the Permanent Representative of Georgia to the United Nations, addressed to the Secretary-General, S/1994/225, 26 February 1994.

[102] UNHCR's Operational experience with internally displaced persons (Geneva, 1994), 39.

[103] UN Security Council Resolution 896 (1994), S/RES/896, 31 January 1994.

[104] CSCE Budapest Document, 'Towards a Genuine Partnership in a New Era', 6 December 1994.

[105] Medvedev Recognition Speech, 26 August 2008.

[106] MacFarlane, 'On the front lines in the near aboard', 520–2.   [107] Ibid.

[108] Ibid., 514.

[109] S. Stewart, 'The Role of the United Nations in the Georgian-Abkhazian Conflict', (2003) 2 Journal of Ethnopolitics and Minority Issues in Europe, 12.

cautious, minimalist position towards the conflicts as Russian influence increased the risks of Western intervention.[110]

Concerning an international multilateral presence, the Conference on Security and Cooperation in Europe (CSCE, renamed the OSCE in 1995), ran a mission in Georgia from 1992, with a primary responsibility in South Ossetia, until its mandate failed to be renewed in June 2009. The main international actor in the Abkhaz arena was the United Nations Observer Mission in Georgia (UNOMIG). Established in August 1993, UNOMIG's mandate gradually expanded to include 'overseeing the implementation of the [Abkhaz] ceasefire agreement, monitoring the conduct of the CIS peacekeeping forces' and coordinating the negotiations as part of the 'Geneva Peace process'.[111] Following the 2008 conflict, as stated above, UNOMIG's mandate was not renewed in June 2009. The UN High Commissioner for Refugees (UNHCR) was mandated with negotiating return for internally displaced persons (IDPs).[112] Although the role of the EU was initially limited to aid provision during the 1990s, it became increasingly active after 2003. The EU Monitoring Mission (EUMM) deployed to Georgia in September 2008, which monitors compliance with the six-point plan, and promotes normalization, stabilization and the return of IDPs.[113] Of note, these instances of external involvement in Georgia were not as broad or extensive in their mandate as UNMIK's international adminstration in Kosovo.

2.4   International mediation and the exhaustion of negotiations

While the mediation process for both entities was often characterized by periods of relative inactivity during more than fifteen years of engagement, some trends are identifiable. During the 1990s, priority was given to mediating a resolution for Abkhazia.[114] International and regional mediation identified the 'self-governance of Abkhazia and South Ossetia within a federal Georgia' as the key objective and presented the parties with a number of variations on federalism.[115] Goals within Abkhazia and South Ossetia changed over time. It was often unclear whether

---

[110]   R. Fawn and S. N. Cummings, 'Interests over Norms in Western Policy towards the Caucasus: How Abkhazia is No One's Kosovo', (2001) 10 *European Security*, 100.

[111]   Stewart, 'The Role of the United Nations in the Georgian-Abkhazian Conflict', 3.

[112]   *Ibid.*, 13.

[113]   Legal basis of the European Union Monitoring Mission, available at www.eumm.eu/en/about_eumm/legalbasis.

[114]   IIFFMCG, 121.   [115]   *Ibid.*, 119.

South Ossetia desired integration with Russia or outright independence. Meanwhile, Abkhazia desired a form of confederation with Georgia, including a right to secede, before declaring its independence in 1999, whereupon its position hardened. The Georgian Government initially insisted upon maintaining its territorial integrity. Georgia came to favour 'asymmetrical federalism', according to which Abkhazia would receive a higher level of self-government than South Ossetia.[116] Tbilisi justified this distinction arguing that the Ossetians have a homeland outside Georgia – the North Ossetian Republic in the Russian Federation.

The Abkhaz had little faith in the UN-sponsored Georgian–Abkhaz peace process, as the UN *a priori* favoured the territorial integrity of Georgia.[117] In Resolution 1255 (1999) the Security Council called for proposals 'on the distribution of constitutional competences between Tbilisi and Sukhumi as part of a comprehensive settlement'.[118] Fearing the reaffirmation of Georgian territorial integrity during this process, the Republic of Abkhazia issued the Act of State Independence in October 1999, following a referendum.[119] However, the international community gave this declaration little attention. At its 1999 summit, the OSCE reaffirmed 'strong support for the sovereignty and territorial integrity of Georgia' and described as 'unacceptable and illegitimate' the 'so-called presidential elections and referendum in Abkhazia, Georgia'.[120] In November 1999, Dieter Boden became SRSG and promptly outlined 'Basic principles for the distribution of constitutional competences between Tbilisi and Sukhumi', within a federal agreement. Although this was the focus of UN status mediation for Abkhazia for several years, the Abkhaz leaders refused even to receive the Boden Document for consideration.[121]

Following the 'Rose Revolution' in November 2003, the new Georgian President Saakashvili embarked on a series of initiatives to resolve the conflicts in Abkhazia and South Ossetia. Addressing the UNGA annual session in 2004, Saakashvili proposed a new three-stage 'settlement plan' to include: confidence-building and the return of refugees/IDPs; demilitarization of the conflict areas; and offering the breakaway regions the

---

[116] *Ibid.*
[117] Stewart, 'The Role of the United Nations in the Georgian-Abkhazian Conflict', 14.
[118] UN Security Council Resolution 1255(1999), S/RES/1255, 30 July 1999.
[119] Text at en.wikisource.org/wiki/Act_of_State_Independence_of_the_Republic_of_Abkhazia.
[120] OSCE, *Istanbul Declaration 1999*, September 1999, 49. [121] IIFFMCG, 88.

'broadest form of autonomy' with international guarantees.[122]
Saakashvili outlined that his goal was to 'peacefully re-incorporate
South Ossetia and Abkhazia' into a 'prosperous, tolerant and successful
Georgian state'.[123] Since there was a general feeling that the conflict in
South Ossetia was easier to resolve, Tbilisi's diplomatic efforts concen-
trated predominantly on South Ossetia between 2004 and 2007.[124]

The Kosovo future status talks began in early 2006, and Russian
President Putin began drawing parallels. In a national broadcast, he
asked: 'If people believe that Kosovo can be granted full independence,
why then should we deny it to Abkhazia and South Ossetia?'[125] Russia's
'universalist' position on Kosovo prompted Georgia to establish
'Georgian administrations' in South Ossetia and Abkhazia during
2006.[126] Aiming to make Russian recognition of the two separatist
provinces more difficult, the Georgian Parliament passed a resolution
calling for the suspension of Russian peacekeeping operations in the
provinces.[127]

In 2008, increasing recognition of Kosovo's independence spurred on
developments in the Caucasus. Russia's *Duma* stated that Kosovo's
independence gives Russia the right to forge new relationships with
self-proclaimed states and lifted long-standing economic sanctions on
Abkhazia in March, urging other CIS countries to follow suit.[128] In early
March 2008, South Ossetia and Abkhazia issued separate statements
requesting international recognition.[129] Significantly, Abkhazia's
Statement invoked many of the remedial conditions. The statement
emphasized the suffering of the Abkhaz people following Abkhazia's
incorporation into Georgia in 1931, including the 'destruction of the
political and intellectual elite of the Abkhaz people', the 'policy of
Georgianisation' and the 'policy of assimilation and resettlement'.[130]
Considering the events in the 1990s, the statement criticized Georgia's
'armed aggression against Abkhazia'. Concerning status negotiations,
the Statement claims that all Abkhaz efforts 'were completely blocked by
the authorities of Georgia'. Invoking the normative conditions, the statement explained that 'democratic institutions, civil society, [and] an

---

[122] *Ibid.*   [123] *Ibid.*   [124] *Ibid.,* 121.
[125] RFE/RL, 'Russia: Putin Calls For "Universal Principles" in Resolving Frozen Conflicts',
2 February 2006.
[126] IIFFMCG, 123.   [127] *Ibid.,* 114.   [128] *Ibid.*
[129] *Statement of the People's Assembly of the Parliament of the Republic of Abkhazia,* 7
March 2008. Available at www.unpo.org/article/7935.
[130] *Ibid.*

effective legal system successfully operate' in Abkhazia, where 'every effort is made for the protection of human rights and freedoms' to protect the identity and development of ethnic minorities in Abkhazia. Finally, the Abkhaz Statement claimed that international recognition of Abkhazia's independence 'will serve peace and stability in the Caucasus'.[131]

Following this appeal, in March 2008 the EU External Relations Commissioner, Benita Ferrero-Waldner, addressed a news conference and confirmed that 'there is a growing preoccupation and anxiety that Russia may be paving the way for recognition of Abkhazia', but that 'Georgia's territorial integrity has always been clearly supported by the EU.'[132] In late March, President Saakashvili offered the Abkhaz 'unlimited autonomy, wide federalism and very serious representation in the central governmental bodies of Georgia'.[133] However, the Abkhaz leaders refused to receive the document from UNOMIG, claiming that Saakashvili's proposal was merely 'part of propaganda ahead of the NATO summit in Bucharest'.[134] At that NATO summit in April 2008, the question of Georgia's membership was raised, pending review in December 2008.[135] According to Georgian commentators, the prospect of NATO membership provided Russia with an incentive to destabilize Georgia.[136]

2.5 The August 2008 War in South Ossetia

The 2009 Independent International Fact-Finding Mission on the Conflict in Georgia (IIFFMCG), concluded that:

> The shelling of Tskhinvali by the Georgian armed forces during the night of 7 to 8 August 2008 marked the beginning of the large-scale armed conflict in Georgia, yet it was only the culminating point of a long period of increasing tensions, provocations and incidents.[137]

The report pointed out that the conflict 'developed into a combined inter-state and intra-state conflict, opposing Georgian and Russian forces at one level of confrontation as well as South Ossetians together

---

[131] *Ibid.*   [132] Reuters, 'EU concerned at Russian moves on Abkhazia', 10 March 2008.
[133] Crisis Group, *Georgia and Russia: Clashing over Abkhazia*, 5 June 2008, 20.
[134] *Ibid.*
[135] 'NATO denies Georgia and Ukraine', 3 April 2008, http://news.bbc.co.uk/1/hi/world/europe/7328276.stm.
[136] Interview at the Georgian Foundation for Strategic and International Studies (September 2009).
[137] IIFFMCG, 11.

with Abkhaz fighters and the Georgians at another'.[138] Another theatre of hostility opened on the western flank, where Abkhaz forces, supported by 9,000 Russian troops, captured the upper Kodori Valley in Abkhazia.[139] Following the five-day war:

> The Georgian side claimed losses of 170 servicemen, 14 policemen and 228 civilians and 1,747 persons wounded. The Russian side claimed losses of 67 servicemen and 283 wounded. The South Ossetians spoke of 365 persons killed, which probably included both servicemen and civilians. Altogether about 850 persons lost their lives ... more than 100,000 civilians fled their homes.[140]

On 12 August 2008, French President Nicolas Sarkozy brokered a cease-fire agreement between Medvedev and Saakashvili.[141] Significantly, point six of the agreement envisaged 'the opening of international discussions on the modalities of security and stability of South Ossetia and Abkhazia'.[142] The commitment to this point undermines Russia's claim that negotiations were 'exhausted' when it recognized Abkhazia and South Ossetia two weeks later.

The Abkhaz and South Ossetian authorities lobbied Moscow for recognition, describing Georgian actions in South Ossetia as 'a Caucasian Stalingrad'.[143] Accordingly, the Russian Federation Council and State *Duma* called upon Medvedev to recognize the independence of the two regions and establish diplomatic relations. Medvedev issued the decrees of recognition on 26 August 2008, and although his statement invoked several remedial conditions to justify recognition, this preliminary analysis suggests that this statement represents an abuse of the doctrine of remedial secession.

2.6   International responses to Russia's recognition

On 28 August, the UNSC convened to discuss 'the situation in Georgia'. In a clear restatement of the remedial arguments put forward by Medvedev, Russia explained that recognition reflected Russia's 'responsibility for ensuring the survival of their brotherly peoples in the face of the aggressive and chauvinistic policy of Tbilisi'.[144] Russia invoked

[138] *Ibid.*, 10.   [139] *Ibid.*, 11.   [140] *Ibid.*, 5.   [141] *Ibid.*, 11.
[142] For text of the Six Point Plan, see www.civil.ge/eng/article.php?id=19069.
[143] 'Russian upper house seeks independence for Georgian rebel regions' (RIA Novosti, 25 August 2008), available at http://en.rian.ru/russia/20080825/116254039.html.
[144] Russia, UN Security Council Meeting Record, S/PV.5969, 28 August 2008, 7.

Georgia's violation of autonomy, describing how 'Gamsakhurdia ...
annulled the existence of entities on Georgian territory.'[145] Describing
Gamsakhurdia's 'Georgia for Georgians' policy, Russia described the
'bloodshed of the early 1990s', emphasizing that Georgia's actions constituted 'genocide'.[146] Moving on to discuss the 'aggressive attack on
South Ossetia on the night of 8 August 2008', Russia claimed that
'Saakashvili himself put an end to the territorial integrity of Georgia by
using crude and blatant military force against people whom ... he
wanted to see as part of his State.'[147] Then Russia alluded to a remedy
of last resort against host state abuse: 'Saakashvili left them [Abkhazia
and South Ossetia] no other choice but to provide for their own security
and to seek to exercise the right to self-determination as independent
States.'[148]

Georgia immediately challenged the crux of Russia's arguments.
Beginning with the 1992–4 Abkhaz war, Georgia described the plight of
the ethnic Georgian IDPs and refugees 'who became the targets of brutal
ethnic cleansing and persecution'.[149] Drawing on previous international
support, Georgia emphasized that 'ethnic cleansing was confirmed and
recognized at the summits of the OSCE held in 1994, 1996 and 1998 and in
UN resolutions'.[150] It stated that these events were replicated in 2008 'in
the Tskhinvali region' where 'over 150,000 people [became] IDPs and
refugees'.[151] Georgia emphasized that 'both separatist regimes' refuse 'to
allow the ethnically Georgian population to return to their homes' and
claimed these actions 'are part of a systematic plan to ethnically cleanse
Georgians from the Tskhinvali region, as previously happened in
Abkhazia'.[152] Georgia emphasized that 'the recognition of the separatist
regimes by the Russian Federation constitutes nothing less than full and
unequivocal support for the separatist insurgents, who are the direct
perpetrators of ethnic cleansing.'[153] Here, Georgia invoked the collective
non-recognition of statehood created through ethnic cleansing.

But did Russia's invocation of remedial secession convince the other
Security Council members? Noting that Russia justified its recognition
'based on the need to prevent humanitarian catastrophe', the UK emphasized that 'what we have seen in recent weeks is ethnic Georgians being
pressured to flee from their homes in South Ossetia and Abkhazia'.[154]
The United States questioned Russia's 'pre-emptive' recognition of

---

[145] *Ibid.* [146] *Ibid.*, 8. [147] *Ibid.* [148] *Ibid.* [149] Georgia, *ibid.*, 4. [150] *Ibid.*
[151] *Ibid.*, 5. [152] *Ibid.* [153] *Ibid.* [154] *Ibid.*, 12.

Abkhazia, pointing out that 'Abkhazia does not border South Ossetia. . . . There was no humanitarian crisis to address.'[155]

The exhaustion of negotiations was also questioned by a number of states. While Russia argued that Saakashvili's rule was characterized by 'total inflexibility and unceasing provocation', which drove the 'last nail into the coffin of the negotiating process',[156] Georgia also pointed out that Russia 'disregarded its commitments with respect to the six-point ceasefire plan' of 12 August and reaffirmed its willingness to negotiate.[157] The UK emphasized that 'future arrangements in South Ossetia and Abkhazia can be agreed only through international negotiations involving all the parties, as envisaged in point 6 of the six-point plan'.[158] These positions suggest that negotiations cannot be considered 'exhausted', as only a fortnight had passed since the six-point plan and Georgia remained willing to negotiate. The United States concluded that Russia's recognition was 'a political act that challenges the post-Soviet borders for the first time since the former Soviet republics gained their independence'.[159]

Since Russia's recognition in August 2008, Abkhazia and South Ossetia have only attracted the recognition of five other countries. Venezuela's President Chavez stated that 'We support Russia. Russia has all the right to defend their own [sic.] interest.'[160] Nicaragua recognized the entities, stating that it 'fully supports the Russian government's position'.[161] Following Nauru's recognition in December 2009, a Russian newspaper reported that it received $50 million from Russia in return.[162] In 2011, Vanuatu and Tuvalu also recognized Abkhazia and South Ossetia. The above comments suggest that countries have recognized Abkhazia and South Ossetia for political and/or financial reasons. No country invoked the remedial secession criteria, apart from Russia, which can be understood as an abuse of the doctrine of remedial secession.

III. Conclusion

As outlined in this chapter, international responses to the secession attempts of Kosovo, Abkhazia and South Ossetia can be analysed

---

[155] United States, *ibid.*, 15.   [156] Russia, *ibid.*, 8.   [157] Georgia, *ibid.*, 6.
[158] France, *ibid.*, 9; UK, *ibid.*, 12.   [159] United States, *ibid.*, 15.
[160] Venezuela Recognizes South Ossetia and Abkhazia Independence, 31 August 2008, www.novinite.com/view_news.php?id=96574.
[161] Nicaragua recognizes South Ossetia and Abkhazia (RIA Novosti, 4 September 2008, http://en.rian.ru/world/20080904/116538071.htmlVenezuela.
[162] *Ibid.*

according to three major phases: constitutional, bellicose and remedial. The 'remedial phase' was characterized by efforts to remedy the contested territories and was initially limited to mechanisms such as autonomy, federalism but ultimately gave rise to the question of whether secession can be considered 'a remedy of last resort'. Having outlined a series of 'remedial conditions' that facilitate (or block) secession, the chapter considered the invocation and applicability of these conditions in Kosovo, Abkhazia and South Ossetia. Following this empirical investigation, the findings are summarized in Table 4.1, and the nature and operation of the 'remedial conditions' are discussed thematically.

Concerning the violation of autonomy agreements, Kosovo presents a clear case of the abolition of autonomy, as Belgrade introduced constitutional amendments to reduce the competencies of the Kosovo Assembly, and finally abolished the Assembly in July 1990. Similarly, the Georgian authorities abolished the autonomy of South Ossetia in September 1990 and declared Georgia a unitary state with no internal boundaries in January 1991. This condition was often invoked in both cases. Concerning the unjust annexation of territory, certain historical arguments could be made, but the unjust annexation of territory is not the most salient condition in these cases. Indeed, this condition is generally problematic, as many states could contest their borders, claiming they arise from past unjust conquest or annexation.

Human rights abuses are considered the 'catalytic agent' for remedial secession, but the challenge is to identify appropriate thresholds.[163] Kosovo illustrated the gradual deterioration of human rights, beginning with a number of discriminatory laws and practices during the early 1990s. During the bellicose phase, the perpetration of ethnic cleansing in Kosovo, Abkhazia and South Ossetia had significant implications for the statehood aspirations of these peoples. While international condemnation of the ethnic cleansing of some 350,000 Georgians from Abkhazia contributed to the collective non-recognition of Abkhazia, international outcry against the Serbian authorities, who perpetrated ethnic cleansing and violations of human rights against the Kosovo-Albanians crossed the threshold to prompt NATO military intervention and the international administration of Kosovo. Accordingly, human rights abuses are invoked extensively, reinforcing the shift from 'sovereignty as authority over territory' towards 'sovereignty as responsibility', which may be giving rise to two concepts that are closely related. The

---

[163] Raič, *Statehood and the Law of Self-Determination*, p. 372.

Table 4.1: *The invocation of remedial conditions in Kosovo, Abkhazia and South Ossetia*

Remedial conditions	Kosovo		Abkhazia		South Ossetia	
	2008 Declaration of Independence	International Response*	2008 Request for Recognition	Russian Recognition^	Factual Situation^ñ	Russian Recognition^
Abolition of autonomy	Present	Invoked	Present	Invoked	Present	Invoked
Persistent and serious violation of human rights	Present	Invoked	Present	Invoked	Present	Invoked
Unjust annexation of territory	Absent	Partial reference	Absent	Absent	Absent	Absent
International intervention/ presence	Extensive	UN/OSCE/EU	Limited	CIS/UN	Limited	CIS/OSCE
Support of powerful countries	Present	The 'Quint' of US, UK, France Germany and Italy	Limited	Russia	Limited	Russia
Exhaustion of negotiations	Present	Invoked	Invoked	Invoked	Invoked	Invoked

Source: Table created by the author.

* Generalized from 91 countries that have recognized Kosovo.

^ The other countries that have recognized Abkhazia and South Ossetia did not invoke any of these criteria.

ñ Due to the lack of statements from South Ossetia, the factual situation is considered.

first – humanitarian intervention – empowers external actors to intervene in the state and to prevent human rights abuses. The second – remedial secession – could empower an oppressed people to claim secession as a remedy of last resort following serious and persistent human rights abuses, which may empower the international community to recognize their independence.

The level and form of international intervention is a significant condition. In Georgia, Russia played a central role, leading the CIS peacekeeping. The OSCE had primary responsibility in South Ossetia, while UNOMIG monitored the implementation of the ceasefire agreement, monitored the CIS peacekeepers and coordinated negotiations as part of the Geneva peace process. As the mandate for the OSCE and UNOMIG was not renewed in 2009, the EUMM now monitors compliance with the ceasefire, while promoting normalization, stabilization and the return of IDPs. In Kosovo, by contrast, Resolution 1244 effectively removed Serbia's functional sovereignty and mandated UNMIK to supervise legislative, executive and judicial power, while facilitating the transfer of powers to Kosovo's Provisional Institutions of Self-Government. In these instances, we see that international intervention serves to stabilize the situation on the ground and create an environment for a negotiated outcome. Equally, intervention often serves to reinforce the ceasefire status quo, so states may be more hesitant to agree to future international administrations. It is difficult to establish a threshold for the exhaustion of negotiations, but both cases demonstrate the need to convince the international community that all rounds of negotiations have been taken seriously.

The support of powerful countries is a significant factor when considering remedial secession. Russia's opposition to Kosovo's independence led it to diverge from the Contact Group position, leaving a 'Quint' of western powers to support Kosovo's independence. The split widened when Russia recognized Abkhazia and South Ossetia, a move condemned by the Quint. This split paralysed the Security Council on serveral occasions: Russia's threat to veto the 2007 draft resolution on Kosovo and its veto also precluded the renewal of the mandates for the UN and OSCE presence in Georgia in 2009. The prominence of such powerful coalitions highlights the strategic dimension of these conflicts. It is no coincidence that the (Western) Quint countries recognize Kosovo. Similarly, Russia's recognition of Abkhazia and South Ossetia serves the strategic purpose of expanding Russia's interest in the 'near abroad'. This leaves us with the question: whose interests are served by remedial secession? Conceived as a doctrine to empower an oppressed people to secede as a remedy of last resort, remedial secession now risks being instrumentalized by powerful countries, who assert their power over vulnerable peoples. While the various aspects of remedial secession are questioned by international lawyers, it will be equally important to engage with international relations scholarship to explore (and minimize) the *political* uses and abuses of this contentious doctrine.

The paradox of Kosovo's parallel legal orders in the reasoning of the Court's Advisory Opinion

ALEXANDROS X. M. NTOVAS[*]

I. Introduction

In 2008, the General Assembly of the United Nations (UN) requested an advisory opinion from the International Court of Justice on whether the unilateral declaration of independence of Kosovo was in accordance with international law. It will be recalled that the question was worded in the following terms: 'Is the unilateral declaration of independence by the Provisional Institutions of Self-Government of Kosovo in accordance with international law?'.[1] To the question posed, the Court rendered its judicial Opinion in negative form, by concluding that the declaration of independence did not violate either general or *lex specialis* international law.[2] Thenceforth, the reasoning of the Court has been criticised as to the manner in which it discharged the first limb of the question regarding the compatibility of the declaration with general international law. Being implicitly premised on the so-called *Lotus*

[*] The author wishes to acknowledge the very helpful comments generously provided by the editor of this book, and by Dr James Maclean and Dr Alun Gibbs for general comments on earlier drafts of this chapter. Any errors are to the author's alone. This chapter reflects a detailed version of the author's argument, 'The Paradox of Kosovo's Parallel Legal Orders', which appeared on 12 September 2010 at internationallawobserver.eu, with the kind assistance of Dr Gentian Zyberi and Mr Dominik Zimmerman, Research Fellow at the Max Planck Institute for Comparative Public Law and International Law.
[1] A/RES/63/2 'Request for an advisory opinion of the International Court of Justice on whether the unilateral declaration of independence of Kosovo is in accordance with international law', adopted 8 October 2008 by a recorded vote of 77 in favour to 6 against, with 74 abstentions.
[2] *Accordance with international law of the unilateral declaration of independence in respect of Kosovo*, Advisory Opinion ICJ (22 July 2010) General List No. 141, paragraph 122 (hereinafter *Kosovo* Advisory Opinion).

principle,[3] and furthermore remaining silent on other issues drawing on the very substance of the question,[4] the *Kosovo* Advisory Opinion has been viewed as if it 'might not enter into the judicial history of the Court for its answer to this question, but rather for what it did not say'.[5] In this respect, it has been very insightfully noted that the Court's reasoning was 'essentially an argument that combin[ed] legal positivism with political realism',[6] with that uneasy combination most probably being responsible for what has been viewed elsewhere 'as clumsy reasoning' arising from 'a tortuous exercise of avoiding from commenting on complex and difficult legal issues, with its only objective of not stumbling into *non liquet*'.[7]

The purpose of this chapter is to draw attention to the internal consistency of the Court's reasoning in the context of the question's second limb – *i.e.* the *lex specialis* international law, in considering particularly the extent to which the Court creates a paradox through its attempt, on the one hand, to recognise that Kosovo was subject to the legal order of the UN Security Council Resolution 1244 (1999) and the Constitutional Framework for Provisional Self-Government established thereunder[8] – as this 'was still in force and applicable as at 17 February 2008' – and its finding, on the other, that the unilateral declaration neither violated general international law nor the applicable *lex specialis*

---

[3] *Case of S.S. Lotus*, PCIJ, Series A. No. 10, Judgment of 7 September 1927. Apropos the inapt application of the principle as considered by the minority of the Court, see the Declaration of Judge Simma, *passim*. This particular aspect of the Court's ruling has been extensively discussed in the literature and therefore will not be considered here. Indicatively, see A. Peters, 'Does Kosovo Lie in the *Lotus*-Land of Freedom?', (2011) 24 *Leiden Journal of International Law*, 95. *Contra.* see J. d'Aspremont, 'The Creation of States before the International Court of Justice: Which (Il)Legality?', at p. 5 (The Hague Justice Portal (1 October 2010), available at haguejusticeportal.net/eCache/DEF/12/090. htm, last accessed October 2010).

[4] *E.g.*, among other underlying aspects of the question, see the issue of remedial secession; *q.v.*, Theodore Christakis, 'The ICJ Advisory Opinion on Kosovo: Has International Law something to say about Secession?' (2011) 24 *Leiden Journal of International Law*, 73; and T. Burri, 'The Kosovo Opinion and Secession: The Sounds of Silence and Missing Links' (2010) 11 *German Law Journal*, 881. For an exposition of the problematic nature of the doctrine of remedial secession in the aftermath of the *Kosovo* Advisory Opinion, see Chapter 3 above.

[5] B. Arp, 'The ICJ Advisory Opinion on the Accordance with International Law of the Unilateral Declaration of Independence in Respect of Kosovo and the International Protection of Minorities', (2010) 11 *German Law Journal*, 847.

[6] R. Falk, 'The Kosovo Advisory Opinion: Conflict Resolution and Precedent', (2011) 105 *American Journal of International Law*, at 54.

[7] Arp, 'The ICJ Advisory Opinion', at 847.   [8] *Kosovo* Advisory Opinion, paragraph 91.

and, as such, its content is valid under international law.[9] The oxy-moronic conclusion must be that since the date of the declaration – 17 February 2008 – Kosovo has enjoyed two notionally distinct yet con-current legal orders, and this gives rise to a specific conceptual difficulty regarding a conflict of legal orders, since both refer to precisely the same territorial entity with mutual exclusivity.

The above theoretical paradox emanating from the Court's own legal reasoning thus provides a focus for the present analysis. This conflict will be demonstrated in particular by exposing the unfortunateness of the Court's argument as to its categorical premise that 'Resolution 1244 (1999) . . . does not preclude the issuance of the declaration of independence of 17 February 2008 because the two instruments operate on a different level.'[10] The Court comes to this conclusion through a meth-odologically questionable process of reasoning in order to avoid address-ing the consequential conflict of legal orders. In other words, while on the one hand the Court noticeably identified the attendant issue of the Declaration's legal consequences, on the other it awkwardly excluded such issues from further consideration. As will be analysed later in this chapter, it is precisely this deliberate omission of the Court to attest the validity of its categorical premise that subsequently creates the distorted reality of the paradoxical legal orders. Thus, it will be submitted here that the main argument of the Court departed not from a premise of which the validity has been proved, but from one which is only presupposed, or assumed to be true. Even though such reasoning can initially be allowed in the process of constructing an argument,[11] the validity of the final conclusion inevitably rests in its entirety on the extent that the original assumption is proved to be valid. Otherwise, the whole argument degen-erates into the fallacy of circular absurdity, whereby the conclusion assumes the premise and the premise has been assumed to lead precisely to that conclusion – *i.e., petitio principii circulus in probando*. In this regard, in the past the Court itself has notably avoided developing its reasoning upon hypothetical arguments.[12] Therefore, it will be argued here that the reasoning developed by the Court is so inconsistent, and

[9] *Ibid.*, paragraph 122.   [10] *Ibid.*, paragraph 114.
[11] On the qualitative differentiation between presupposed and proved premises in the legal paradigm, refer to A. Peczenik, *On Law and Reason* (London: Springer, 2009), at p. 124*ff.*
[12] An argument of this sort can be seen in the *Case concerning the Northern Cameroons*, where the Applicant suggested that a judgment of the Court in its favour would, or at any rate might, have a legal effect or possible legal application, inasmuch as it might be made the basis of further proceedings before either the Court itself or some other international

thus unconvincing, that it is difficult not to perceive it as having swerved into something of a judicial fallacy. In order to analyse the consistency of such reasoning, the remainder of the chapter, before considering the details of the Court's judgment, will first briefly discuss the respective legal orders as they appear in its Opinion.

II.   The international legal order of Kosovo

The Court begins its analysis with an examination of the legal nature of United Nations Security Council (UNSC) Resolution 1244 (1999), identifying relevant legal obligations under international law on the basis of the UN Charter's Chapter VII.[13] In brief,[14] Resolution 1244 (1999) authorises the UN Secretary-General to establish an international civil presence in Kosovo to provide an interim administration (hereinafter referred to as UNMIK), and appoint a Special Representative to control its implementation.[15] The *ratio legis* of the Resolution's paragraph 10 in particular reflects the central principle envisaged in the *Agreement on the Principles (Peace Plan) to Move Towards a Resolution of the Kosovo Crisis*, which was presented to the leadership of the Federal Republic of Yugoslavia by Martti Ahtisaari (the President of Finland at the time) representing the European Union (EU), and Viktor Chernomyrdin, special envoy of the President of the Russian Federation.[16] Under the authority vested in the Special Representative of the Secretary-General, UNMIK assumes quasi-sovereign competencies to exert all legislative

---

tribunal. The Court declined jurisdiction on the basis of it being impossible in that case to render a judgment capable of effective application. The untenable legal nature of such argument was articulated expressly in the concurring Separate Opinion of Judge Sir Gerald Fitzmaurice, who viewed that 'whether this would be the case can only be entirely speculative, and the Court could not in any event render a judgment on a hypothetical basis of this kind'; *q.v.*, ICJ Reports 1963, p. 15, at p. 107.

[13] *Kosovo* Advisory Opinion, paragraph 85 *et seq.*

[14] The international legal order applicable to the entity of Kosovo has been the subject of extensive scholarship, of which the accuracy makes it unnecessary to present here an in-depth analysis. See, among others, C. Stahn, *The Law and Practice of International Territorial Administration* (Cambridge University Press, 2008), at pp. 310–32 and 549; and R. Wilde, *International Territorial Administration* (Oxford University Press, 2008), *passim*. For a brief assessment thereof, see A. Yannis, 'The UN as Government in Kosovo', (2004) 10 *Global Governance*, 67.

[15] UNSC Resolution 1244 (1999), paragraphs 10 and 11, respectively.

[16] *Q.v.*, S/1999/649 'Letter dated 7 June 1999 from the Permanent Representative of Germany to the United Nations Addressed to the President of the Security Council'. On the background of the Agreement, see B.C. Harzl, 'Conflicting Perceptions: Russia, the West and Kosovo' (2008) 33 *Review of Central and East European Law*, at 511–13.

and executive functions with respect to Kosovo, including the administration of the judiciary.[17] Indicatively, in UNMIK/Reg./1999/1 it is further provided that 'in the performance of the duties entrusted to the interim administration under [R]resolution 1244 (1999), UNMIK will, as necessary, issue legislative acts in the form of regulations'. Moreover, particular attention must be drawn to the stipulation that 'such regulations will remain in force until repealed by UNMIK or superseded by such rules as are subsequently issued by the institutions established under a political settlement, as provided for in [R]esolution 1244 (1999)'.[18]

Pursuant to further the authority consigned to the Special Representative under Resolution 1244 (1999), and in fulfilment of its provisions stipulating the establishment and development of meaningful self-government in Kosovo pending a final solution,[19] he promulgated the 'Constitutional Framework for Provisional Self-Government'. As the Court attested, 'the Constitutional Framework ... [was] created pursuant to resolution 1244 (1999), which is applicable only in Kosovo and the purpose of which is to regulate, during the interim phase established by resolution 1244 (1999), matters which would ordinarily be the subject of internal, rather than international, law.'[20] Notably, on the legal nature of the UNMIK regulations, and by extension, that of the Constitutional Framework, the Court also observed, that these:

> [were] adopted by the Special Representative of the Secretary-General on the basis of the authority derived from Security Council resolution 1244 (1999) ... and thus ultimately from the United Nations Charter. The Constitutional Framework derives its binding force from the binding character of resolution 1244 (1999) and thus from international law. In that sense it therefore possesses an international legal character.[21]

On the above international legal basis, the '[e]ntity of Kosovo' is expressly placed 'under interim international administration', as an undivided

---

[17] UNMIK/Reg./1999/1 (of 25 July) Section 1, paragraph 1.   [18] *Ibid.*, Section 4.

[19] UNMIK/Reg./2001/9 (of 15 May), as subsequently amended by regulations 2002/9 (of 3 May) and 2007/29 (of 4 October). For a thorough commentary thereof, see C. Stahn, 'Constitution without a State? Kosovo under the United Nations Constitutional Framework for Self-Government', (2001) 14 *Leiden Journal of International Law*, 531; and A. Orakhelashvili, 'Statehood, Recognition and the United Nations System: A Unilateral Declaration of Independence in Kosovo', pp. 1–44, in A. von Bogdandy and R. Wolfrum (eds), *Max Planck Yearbook of United Nations Law, Volume 12* (Brill, 2008).

[20] *Kosovo* Advisory Opinion, paragraph 89.   [21] *Ibid.*, paragraph 88.

territory wherein the 'Provisional Institutions of Self-Government' – founded by[22] and acting within[23] the *Constitutional Framework* – shall exercise their responsibilities democratically in accordance with UNSC Resolution 1244 (1999).[24] Moreover, under this international legal order, the Special Representative retains extensive public authority[25] to oversee the *Provisional Institutions* and ensure the full implementation of the afore-mentioned resolution, including also the assumption of appropriate meas-ures whenever actions of the institutions are inconsistent either with that resolution or the *Constitutional Framework*.[26] Interestingly, these sovereign powers and responsibilities are not only reserved exclusively for the Special Representative but their exercise bears directly on the attributive elements of Kosovo's international legal personality;[27] *e.g.* the conclusion of interna-tional agreements and the conduct of external relations, including with States and international organisations, as may be necessary for the imple-mentation of its mandate.[28]

---

[22] See M. Riegner, 'The Two Faces of the Internationalized *pouvoir constituant*: Independence and Constitution-Making under External Influence in Kosovo', (2010) 2 *Goettingen Journal of International Law*, 1035.

[23] On the gradual institutional development of the provisional bodies of governance within the applicable international legal regime, see M. Brand, *The Development of Kosovo Institutions and the Transition of Authority from UNMIK to Local Self-Government* (Centre for Applied Studies in International Negotiations: Geneva, 2003).

[24] *Constitutional Framework for Provisional Self-Government*, Chapter 1. *Videlicet*, under paragraph 5, the aforementioned Institutions are: (a) Assembly; (b) President of Kosovo; (c) Government; (d) Courts; and (e) Other bodies and institutions set forth in the Constitutional Framework.

[25] On the basis of UNMIK/Reg./1999/1.

[26] *Constitutional Framework*, Chapter 12. For instance, in accordance with Chapter 8, para-graph 1 *lit.*(b), the authority of the Special Representative of the Secretary-General extends even into: 'Dissolving the Assembly and calling for new elections in circumstances where the Provisional Institutions of Self-Government are deemed to act in a manner which is not in conformity with UNSCR 1244(1999), or in the exercise of the [S]pecial Representative's responsibilities under that Resolution. The [S]pecial Representative shall exercise this power after consultation with the President of Kosovo.' In addition, it may be recalled that the Constitutional Framework takes precedence over any law of the Assembly in the case of conflict; *q.v.*, Chapter 14, paragraph 1.

[27] Among others, Muharremi concedes to the fact that 'Kosovo's formal and real inde-pendence are a matter of concern given the mandate of UNMIK under Resolution 1244 to exercise administrative authority over Kosovo and the extensive powers of the International Civilian Representative and the EU Rule of Law Mission.'; *q.v.*, R. Muharremi, 'Kosovo's Declaration of Independence: Self-Determination and Sovereignty Revisited', (2008) 33 *Review of Central and East European Law*, at 428 *et seq.*

[28] Constitutional Framework, Chapter 8, paragraph 1 *lit.*(m) and (o); examples of such treaties include the UNMIK/FTA/2003/1 'Free Trade Agreement between UNMIK on

Having outlined the extant international legal order that applies to the entity of Kosovo, it is now important to consider the declared legal order which emanates from the Declaration of Independence. This is not an attempt to appraise or in any other way qualify one legal order against the other, but the sole purpose for doing so is merely to expose that the two orders present a mutually exclusive claim on the same territorial entity.[29]

III. The declared legal order of Kosovo

Following the collapse of the international multilateral negotiations led by the UN Secretary-General's Special Envoy on the *Comprehensive Proposal for the Kosovo Status Settlement*,[30] a unilateral declaration of independence was issued in Pristina on 17 February 2008 by the 'democratically-elected leaders of [Kosovo's] people'.[31] Soon after, the Assembly of Kosovo also adopted its own constitution, which became effective on 15 June 2008.[32] Of interest here are the main stipulations contained in both of these legal documents, which will be reviewed, first, through the prism of the establishing legal order, and subsequently in their relation to the existing international legal order of UNSC Resolution 1244 (1999).

On 17 February 2008, Kosovo proclaimed itself 'an independent and sovereign state',[33] asserting its international borders on the basis of those

behalf of the Provisional Institutions of Self-Government in Kosovo and The Council of Ministers of the Republic of Albania' (4 July 2003), and UNMIK/FTA/2005/1 'Interim Free Trade Agreement between UNMIK on behalf of the Provisional Institutions of Self-Government in Kosovo and the Government of FYROM' (31 August 2005).

[29] For a more in-depth analysis of the two legal orders exposing their awkward coexistence, see B. Knoll, 'From Benchmarking to Final Status? Kosovo and the Problem of an International Administration's Open-Ended Mandate', (2005) 16 *European Journal Of International Law*, 637.

[30] The *Kosovo Declaration of Independence* in its preamble characteristically 'Recall[ed] the years of internationally sponsored negotiations between Belgrade and Pristina over the question of our future political status; Regretting that no mutually acceptable status outcome was possible, in spite of the good-faith engagement of our leaders.' See, H. H. Perritt, 'Final Status for Kosovo', (2005) 80 *Chicago Kent Law Review*, 3. For a more cautious approach thereto, see R.J. Vogel, 'Dependent on Arrival: Kosovo's Status Settlement and the New Constitution', (2008) 17 *International Affairs Review*, 1.

[31] *Kosovo Declaration of Independence*, paragraph 1.

[32] *Constitution of the Republic of Kosovo*, Article 162.

[33] *Kosovo Declaration of Independence*, paragraph 1. On the belief in the achieved statehood, see the public pronouncements made in the formal session of the Assembly on the occasion of the first anniversary of Independence of Kosovo by then President Jakup

envisioned in Annex VIII of the *Comprehensive Proposal*.[34] The Kosovar Constitution reaffirms explicitly in this respect that 'the Republic of Kosovo is an independent, sovereign, democratic, unique and indivisible state'[35] with a 'sovereignty and territorial integrity . . . intact, inalienable, indivisible and protected by all means provided in [its] Constitution and the law'.[36] Remarkably, the avowed sovereignty was viewed as emanating directly from the people of Kosovo, since 'the Republic of Kosovo is a State of its citizens'.[37] However, under the specific circumstances, this raises the question of the territorial application of UNSC Resolution 1244 (1999), insofar as the international legal order established there-under assumed the suspended sovereign functions of Serbia.

Consonant with the attributes of such proclaimed statehood, the Declaration immediately asserted all international obligations of Kosovo, including, most notably, 'those concluded on [its] behalf by UNMIK and treaty and other obligations of the former Socialist Federal Republic of Yugoslavia to which [it is] bound as a former constituent part'.[38] In this respect, the way that the constitution addresses the essential issue of continuity of international agreements and applicability of earlier legislation is particularly revealing. With respect to former sources of obligations, it is provided that these will continue to be respected until either they have been renegotiated, withdrawn from, or superseded by new international agreements or acts covering the same subject areas and adopted pursuant to the constitutional procedure.[39] In this context, the constitution also established the Assembly as the sole institution of the Republic of Kosovo capable of ratifying international treaties[40] and responsible for overseeing foreign policy.[41] The constitution further endorses Kosovo's international legal personality,

---

Krasniqi, viewing 'independence of Kosovo [being] a legal and irreversible reality', and the Prime Minister of the Republic of Kosovo, Hashim Thaçi, stating that 'nine years of transition have passed, full of challenges, but successful. Today is the first anniversary of our proud, independent, sovereign and free state'; *q.v.*, Republica Kosova, Skup-ština – Republica e Kosovës, Kuvendi (17 February 2009) available at assembly-kosova.org/, last accessed June 2011.

[34] *Kosovo Declaration of Independence*, paragraph 8.
[35] *Constitution of the Republic of Kosovo*, Article 1.   [36] *Ibid.*, Article 2, paragraph 2.
[37] *Ibid.*, Article 1.   [38] *Kosovo Declaration of Independence*, paragraph 9.
[39] *Constitution of the Republic of Kosovo*, Article 145, paragraph 1.
[40] *Ibid.*, Article 65, paragraph 4. In conjunction with Article 18, paragraph 1, the Assembly exerts the prerogative of exclusive legislation with regard to treaties relating to territory, peace, alliances, political and military issues; fundamental rights and freedoms; membership in international organizations, and the undertaking of financial obligations.
[41] *Ibid.*, Article 65, paragraph 12.

in recognising its ability to 'conclude international agreements and become a member of international organizations'.[42]

Nevertheless, the above constitutional claims pose a challenge to the territorial application of UNMIC regulations and the Constitutional Framework which derive their legal authority and legitimacy directly from UNSC Resolution 1244 (1999). For example, regarding obligations stemming from prior domestic legislation, the constitution also provides that insofar as they conform to its provisions, they should remain applicable until repealed, superseded or amended.[43] This is sensible, since the constitution, as the highest legal act of the Republic of Kosovo, enjoys supremacy over all laws and other legal acts.[44] The constitution stipulates succinctly, in a provision regulating the applicability of international law to the internal legal system, that 'legally binding norms of international law have superiority over the laws of the Republic of Kosovo',[45] something that follows from the general, yet more comprehensive constitutional stipulation, that 'the Republic of Kosovo shall respect international law'.[46]

In approaching this, however, it should be borne in mind that the Kosovar Constitution reflects essentially a unilateral implementation of the UN Secretary-General Special Envoy's Comprehensive Proposal for the Status Settlement, which in principle envisaged independence for Kosovo supervised by the international community.[47] Nevertheless, it will

---

[42] *Ibid.*, Article 17, paragraph 1. Article 18 further stipulates the pertinent constitutional procedure for the ratification of international agreements. The eighth operative paragraph of the *Kosovo Declaration of Independence* had also proclaimed full international legal personality in stating that: 'With independence comes the duty of responsible membership in the international community. We accept fully this duty and shall abide by the principles of the United Nations Charter, the Helsinki Final Act, other acts of the Organization on Security and Cooperation in Europe, and the international legal obligations and principles of international comity that mark the relations among states.'

[43] *Ibid.*, Article 145, paragraph 2.

[44] *Ibid.*, Article 16, paragraph 1. Paragraph 4 further provides that 'every person and entity in the Republic of Kosovo is subject to the provisions of the Constitution'. See further J. Marko, 'The New Kosovo Constitution in a Regional Comparative Perspective', (2008) 33 *Review of Central and East European Law*, 437.

[45] *Ibid.*, Article 19, paragraph 2. Article 22 in providing expressly only for the direct applicability of certain international treaties guaranteeing human rights and fundamental freedoms gives priority to the latter in the case of conflict, over provisions of laws and other acts of public institutions.

[46] *Ibid.*, Article 16, paragraph 3. N.B., this stipulation is provided within the article of constitutional supremacy.

[47] S/2007/168.Add.1, 'Letter dated 26 March 2007 from the Secretary-General addressed to the President of the Security Council (Addendum: Comprehensive Proposal for the Kosovo Status Settlement)'.

be recalled that this plan was never endorsed by the UNSC as no action to effect it was taken. The unilateral implementation of the Status Settlement is explicit in the text of the declaration, where the opening operative paragraph stipulates quite clearly that 'this declaration reflects the will of our people and it is in full accordance with the recommendations of UN Special Envoy Martti Ahtisaari and his Comprehensive Proposal, thereby accepting in full 'the obligations for Kosovo contained in the Ahtisaari Plan, and ... those obligations including through priority adoption of the legislation included in its Annex XII'.[48] Furthermore, the declaration incongruously appears to qualify the proposed legal order in the Status Settlement against that of the international legal order of the UNMIK Constitutional Framework, and by extension the application of the Resolution, in affirming categorically that 'Kosovo shall be legally bound to comply with the provisions contained in this Declaration, including, especially, the obligations for it under the Ahtisaari Plan. In all of these matters, we shall act consistent with principles of international law and resolutions of the Security Council of the United Nations, including resolution 1244 (1999).'[49]

The constitution effected the above stipulations through its final and transitional provisions, incorporating by reference the relevant arrangements under the Status Settlement and providing for the latter's precedence over all other legal provisions in Kosovo.[50] More specifically, in accordance with Article 15 of the Status Settlement, by a 120-day transition period during which UNMIK should continue to exercise its mandate in accordance with relevant UNSC resolutions.[51] Accordingly, to the extent they were not inconsistent with the Status Settlement,[52] the Constitutional Framework and other applicable laws should have remained in effect until the end of the transition period or the adoption of the constitution by the Assembly.[53] Either way, the mandate of UNMIK would be deemed to have expired, and

---

[48] *Kosovo Declaration of Independence*, paragraph 3.   [49] *Ibid.*, paragraph 12.

[50] *Constitution of the Republic of Kosovo*, Article 143, paragraph 2. Remarkably, in doing so, paragraph 3 provides that even 'if there are inconsistencies between the provisions of this Constitution, laws or other legal acts of the Republic of Kosovo and the provisions of the said Settlement, the latter shall prevail.' However, this concession was to apply only within the initially planned 120-day transition.

[51] *Comprehensive Proposal*, Article 15 'Transitional Arrangements and Final Provisions', paragraph 1 *lit.*(a). Given that the *Constitution of the Republic of Kosovo* effectively incorporated the Status Settlement, the transitional period shall be assumed to have commenced from the entry into force of the former, (*i.e*, 15 June 2008) in accordance with Article 162 of the constitution.

[52] *Comprehensive Proposal*, Article 15, paragraph 1 *lit.*(b).

[53] *Ibid.*, *lit.*(c) in conjunction with *lit.*(d).

all legislative and executive authority previously vested in it transferred en bloc to the governing authorities of Kosovo.[54] Consequently, according to the Status Settlement, and thus the constitution, 'UNMIK Regulations promulgated by the [Special Representative of the Secretary-General] ... pursuant to UNSC Resolution 1244 ... shall continue to apply ... until their validity expires, or until they are revoked or replaced by legislation regulating the same subject matter in accordance with the provisions of this Settlement.'[55]

IV. The paradox of parallel legal orders

In light of all of this, the final conclusion reached by the Court that 'the adoption of the declaration of independence of 17 February 2008 did not violate ... Security Council resolution 1244 (1999) or the Constitutional Framework',[56] makes it difficult to escape the oxymoronic conclusion that since the date of declaration Kosovo – at least theoretically – enjoys in terms of legitimacy, two distinctive yet concurrent legal orders.

The implication of the Court's finding, on the one hand, is that of the proclaimed sovereign order emanating from the Declaration of Independence. Surely it can be countered that the Court patently did not rule on the operational legality of the proclaimed domestic regime. But what, then, is the effect and the very purpose of the *Kosovo Advisory Opinion* in finding that a declaration which irreversibly asserts independence and full sovereignty over the territory in question does not violate the obligations applicable to that territory's international law? Responding to such argument, one need only recall the *ratio* in a case where the Court was presented with the opportunity to examine its ability to render a judgment incapable of effective application. Viewing that notwithstanding that its judicial function is to state the law, but nevertheless '[pronouncing] only in connection with concrete cases where there exists at the time of the adjudication an actual controversy involving a conflict of legal interests between the parties', the Court determined that '[its] judgment must have some practical consequence in the sense that it can affect existing legal rights or obligations of the parties, thus removing uncertainty from their legal relations'.[57] In that

---

[54] *Ibid., lit.*(g).   [55] *Ibid.*, Article 15, paragraph 2, sub-paragraph 1.
[56] *Kosovo* Advisory Opinion, paragraph 122.
[57] *Case concerning the Northern Cameroons (Cameroon v. United Kingdom)*, Preliminary Objections, Judgment of 2 December 1963, ICJ Reports 1963, p. 15, at pp. 33–4.

sense, it has been suggested similarly that in particular the reasoning of the Court in the *Kosovo* Advisory Opinion, when combined with the question as it was accepted, has consequences that should have compelled it to adopt a different conclusion.[58]

On the other hand, the international legal order of the Constitutional Framework as established under Resolution 1244 (1999) remains intact. This paradox of parallel legal orders is reflected particularly, *inter alia*, on the official documents of the EU, wherein Kosovo is still being referred to as a territorial entity subject to the administration of UNMIK on the basis of the 1244 (1999) Resolution, with the explicit clarification that 'since 1999 Kosovo has been governed by the United Nations Interim Administration'.[59] What exaggerates this further is the paradoxical conclusion that both legal orders refer to the same territorial entity with mutual exclusivity.[60] Here, we might recall the crucial *dictum* of Max Huber's renowned arbitral judgment in the *Island of Palmas* case, reflecting on the necessary legal conditions of statehood viewed sovereignty in the relations between States as signifying independence, and more specifically, that 'independence in regard to a portion of the globe is the right to exercise therein, to the exclusion of any other State, the functions of a State'.[61] In this respect, it should be borne in mind once again that the declaration did not assert independence *in abstracto*, but

---

[58] D. Jacobs and Y. Radi, 'Waiting for Godot: An Analysis of the Advisory Opinion of Kosovo', (2011) 24 *Leiden Journal of International Law*, at 341–2.

[59] For instance, refer to the documents issued by the European Commission Liaison Office in Kosovo (available at eeas.europa.eu/kosovo/index_en.htm, last accessed June 2011), or to the series Support for Improvement in Governance and Management (SIGMA) reports. The SIGMA scheme is a joint initiative of the Organisation for Economic Co-operation and Development and the EU, financed principally by the latter. Assessment reports are prepared at the request of the European Commission as a contribution to its annual Progress Reports on EU Candidates and potential Candidates and to its programming of technical assistance, *q.v.*, indicatively the latest available assessment on Kosovo (under UNSCR 1244/99) ((2010) available at sigmaweb.org/, last accessed June 2011).

[60] For a manifestation of such mutual exclusive emanations, see R. Muharremi, 'The European Union Rule of Law Mission in Kosovo (EULEX) from the Perspective of Kosovo Constitutional Law', (2010) 70 *Zeitschrift für ausländisches öffentliches Recht und Völkerrecht*, 358. As Muharremi concludes at 378, '[the] failure in the UN Security Council to endorse the *Ahtisaari* Plan followed by Kosovo's declaration of independence without a formal termination of the UN's mandate in Kosovo has led to the development of two mutually exclusive legal authorities'.

[61] *Island of Palmas* case *(The Netherlands/United States of America)* Judgment of 4 April 1928, *Reports of International Arbitral Awards* 829 II, at p. 838.

assumed sovereignty and full responsibility thereon by claiming absolute rights over the territory of Kosovo.

As will be demonstrated below, the Court eschewed addressing this issue of spatial conflict between the legal orders doctrinally. Indeed, it would have been unprofitable to attempt to do so, since no theory underlying the issue of territorial acquisition can possibly resolve such an anomaly.[62] Thus, the issue of territorial sovereignty was examined literally in passing by the Court, 'disregarding the plain language of the resolution' and attaching disproportionate emphasis on its temporal facet rather than delving into its true substantive consequences, in order to 'avoid the rigidifying impact of a legalistic construction supportive of the sovereignty claim relied upon by Serbia'.[63] It merely considered, through what can be deemed an unduly broad perspective on the principle of territorial integrity,[64] that the object and purpose of the Resolution was the establishment of 'an interim régime [which] cannot be understood as putting in place a permanent institutional framework in the territory of Kosovo'.[65] In particular, the Court, in referring to the function of the Constitutional Framework, considered it as part of 'a specific legal order', reflecting its transitive nature. Furthermore, the Court concluded that its object and purpose was to establish 'a temporary, exceptional legal régime which, save to the extent that it expressly preserved it, superseded the Serbian legal order and which aimed at the stabilization of Kosovo, and that it was designed to do so on an interim basis'.[66]

---

[62] Consider, for instance, the issue of spatial coexistence of legal orders through the three main theoretical strands, namely (a) the *Object theory* in both its variations as *quoad imperium* and *quoad dominium*; (b) the *Space theory*; and (c) *Competence theory*. For the first two, see H. Lauterpacht, *Private Law Sources and Analogies of International Law* (London: Archon Books, 1970); and for the third, see A. Verdross, *Verfassung der Völkerrechtsgemeinschaft* (Vienna: Springer, 1926); and in the edited work of Verdross by B. Simma, *Universelles Völkerrecht* (Berlin: Duncker & Humblot, 1984); for a brief analysis thereof, see B. Conforti 'The Theory of Competence in Verdross', (1995) 6 *European Journal of International Law*, 70.

[63] See Falk, 'The Kosovo Advisory Opinion: Conflict Resolution and Precedent', at 57. Moreover, it was noted that the Court's reasoning was developed in such way as 'to employ this somewhat strained construction of the language in Resolution 1244 as a way of avoiding a regressive application of legality criteria'.

[64] J. Vidmar, 'The Kosovo Advisory Opinion Scrutinised', (2011) 24 *Leiden Journal of International Law*, at 375*ff*. On the argument in respect of the nature of Kosovo's Declaration of Independence, see further, Chapter 2 above.

[65] *Kosovo* Advisory Opinion, paragraph 99.   [66] *Ibid.*, paragraph 100.

The suspension of Serbian sovereignty over the territory of Kosovo was effected by the Security Council through the exercise of a quasi-fiduciary obligation,[67] creating a 'hybrid situation' by separating *de jure* sovereignty from the *de facto* exercise of public power, with the Resolution premised on the *sine qua non conditio* that the parental sovereignty of Serbia might remain dormant, though largely intact,[68] until the consummation of the final status process. In this respect, attention ought to be drawn to the fact that the initial negotiations over the Comprehensive Proposal had collapsed specifically because 'neither party was willing to cede its position on the fundamental question of sovereignty over Kosovo'.[69] It should also be noted that one of the principal responsibilities of the international administration was that of 'in the final stage, overseeing the transfer of authority from Kosovo's provisional institutions to institutions established under a political settlement'.[70] In direct relation to this, the Security Council endorsed the commencement of the final status process for a political settlement by stipulating that 'a negotiated solution should be an international priority . . . the parties [shall] engage in good faith and constructively, to refrain from unilateral steps . . .'[71] Thus, not only was the declaration proclaimed unilaterally against the international regime that acts as the *quasi*-trustee of Serbia's superseded sovereignty in the course of the ongoing transitional stage, but moreover, it may be seen as involving elements of political opportunism[72] against the spirit of the negotiations.

Not in the least shall it be disputed that the international administration of Kosovo has been constituted to function as a *pro tempore*

---

[67] As Friedrich, remarks 'the only terminology that seems to accurately describe the situation . . . is that of a trusteeship . . . Considering the fiduciary and interim character of the administration and the fact that the administration in Kosovo acts in place and in the interest of a future beneficiary without having ownership rights, UNMIK could be seen as sort of a trusteeship administration'. See J. Friedrich, 'UNMIK in Kosovo: Struggling with Uncertainty', pp. 225–93, in A. von Bogdandy and R. Wolfrum (eds.), *Max Planck Yearbook of United Nations Law – Volume 9* (Brill, 2005), at pp. 243–4.

[68] *Ibid.*, at p. 242.

[69] UN S/2007/723, 'Letter dated 10 December 2007 from the Secretary-General addressed to the President of the Security Council, enclosing the *Report of the European Union/United States/Russian Federation Troika on Kosovo*, 4 December 2007'.

[70] *Ibid.*, §11. Also noted by the Court in paragraph 59 of its Opinion.

[71] UN S/2005/709, 'Letter dated 10 November 2005 from the President of the Security Council addressed to the Secretary-General, whereto is annexed the *Guiding principles of the Contact Group for a settlement of the status of Kosovo*'.

[72] P. Šturma, 'The Case of Kosovo and International Law' (2010) 29 *Polish Yearbook of International Law*, at 51.

governmental framework. In fact, the temporariness of the administrative institutions is arguably overstressed in the phraseology of the Resolution, wherein the recurrent adjective collocation, referring to the temporal nature of the institutions, cannot be ignored. In particular, it will be recalled that its tenth operative paragraph reads as follows:

> to establish an international civil presence in Kosovo in order to provide an *interim administration* for Kosovo under which the people of Kosovo can enjoy substantial autonomy within the Federal Republic of Yugoslavia, and which will provide *transitional administration* while establishing and overseeing the development of *provisional democratic self-governing institutions* to ensure conditions for a peaceful and normal life for all inhabitants of Kosovo. (Emphasis added.)

In this context, it is not peculiar that the Court began analysing Resolution 1244 (1999) by reflecting on the particular excerpt above. Nonetheless, the issue of an affected finality, as purported in the declaration, is an altogether totally different issue to that of the Resolution's intrinsic temporality.[73] Besides, the Court itself clearly acknowledged that:

> [the] Security Council resolution 1244(1999) and the Constitutional Framework *were still in force and applicable as at 17 February 2008*. Paragraph 19 of Security Council resolution 1244(1999) expressly provides that 'the international civil and security presences are established for an initial period of 12 months, to continue thereafter unless the Security Council decides otherwise'. *No decision amending resolution 1244(1999) was taken by the Security Council at its meeting held on 18 February 2008*, when the declaration of independence was discussed for the first time, or at any subsequent meeting ... Neither Security Council resolution 1244(1999) nor the Constitutional Framework contains a clause providing for its termination and neither has been repealed; they therefore constituted the international law applicable to the situation prevailing in Kosovo on 17 February 2008.[74]

---

[73] On the termination of the effects of UNSC resolutions, see M. D. Öberg, 'The Legal Effects of United Nations Resolutions in the Kosovo Advisory Opinion' (2011) 105 *American Journal of International Law*, at p. 86ff., and 'The Legal Effects of Resolutions of the UN Security Council and General Assembly in the Jurisprudence of the ICJ', (2005) 16 *European Journal of International Law*, 879. See also, in particular, the argument advanced by R. Wilde in 'Self-Determination, Secession, and Dispute Settlement after the Kosovo Advisory Opinion', (2011) 24 *Leiden Journal of International Law* 151.

[74] *Kosovo* Advisory Opinion, paragraphs 91 and 93 (emphasis added). Moreover, the Court did not fail to notice, that 'the Special Representative of the Secretary-General continues to exercise his functions in Kosovo' and that 'the Secretary-General has continued to

V. The juridical argument of the 'different level' and the omission of the Court to consider the legal effects of the declaration

It cannot be alleged that the Court failed to notice the conflictual coexistence of legal orders, since it observed explicitly that:

> the authors of the declaration undertook to fulfil the international obligations of Kosovo, notably those created for Kosovo by UNMIK, and expressly and solemnly declared Kosovo to be bound vis-à-vis third States by the commitments made in the declaration. *By contrast,* under the régime of the Constitutional Framework, all matters relating to the management of the external relations of Kosovo were the exclusive prerogative of the Special Representative of the Secretary-General ... only consulting and co-operating with the Provisional Institutions of Self-Government in these matters.[75]

On the contrary, the Court can clearly be seen as striving to surmount the antithesis of parallel legal orders in observing that:

> Resolution 1244(1999) ... does not preclude the issuance of the declaration of independence of 17 February 2008 *because the two instruments operate on a different level:* unlike resolution 1244(1999), the declaration of independence is an attempt to determine finally the status of Kosovo.[76]

Yet, in so doing, the Court only ostensibly overcame the impasse of the antithesis generated by having recourse to a contentious consequential argument entailing a two-step syllogism, and which can be seen as forming the bedrock of the *ratio decidendi* for its Opinion. More specifically, the Court addressed the question of whether the declaration was compatible with the *lex specialis* of the international legal order by constructing its syllogistic argument upon a consideration of two sequential issues. First, it sought to determine 'the identity of the authors of the declaration'[77] and, having found that those who issued the declaration did not act in their true capacity under the Provisional

---

submit periodic reports to the Security Council, as required by paragraph 20 of Security Council resolution 1244 (1999).' See paragraph 92.

[75] *Ibid.,* paragraph 106 (emphasis added).   [76] *Ibid.,* paragraph 114 (emphasis added).

[77] *Ibid.,* paragraphs 52 and 101. *Cf.,* Vice-president, Judge Peter Tomka, in his Declaration, in paragraph 12, castigated this element of the majority's reasoning as being 'nothing more than a *post hoc* intellectual construct'.

Institutions, but rather, as persons outside it,[78] proceeded to examine the question of its conformity with the *lex specialis*.[79] In a surprisingly short analysis, it concluded *argumentum ex silentio*, that the Resolution neither 'contain[ed] any provision dealing with the final status of Kosovo or with the conditions for its achievement' nor 'reserv[ed] for itself the final determination of the situation ... [by remaining] silent on [those] conditions'.[80] Accordingly, since the Resolution had not addressed the authors *eo nomine*, it could not be construed as preventing them from issuing a Declaration of Independence from Serbia.[81] On these grounds, it was found by the Court that the declaration did not violate the Resolution.[82]

Disappointingly, however, in painting the judicial picture of the two instruments operating on that 'different level', the Court employed, not only an implausible doctrinal argument,[83] but also an imperfect logical *ratio*, which, under the same formalistic terms of deductive logic as above, cannot evade reduction into the judicial fallacy of a circular reasoning that assumes as valid a premise that essentially needs to be proved. Remarkably, it will be noted that the predecessor of the Court, the Permanent Court of International Justice, highlighting its formalistic attentiveness, had deprecated a proposed reasoning based on the fallacious argument of circular absurdity, in finding that this '[would] amount in reality to assuming as demonstrated the very thing which

---

[78] In relation to the paradox of legal orders, Mills takes a step even further to indicate that 'there is a more fundamental difficulty [in the Opinion], which the Court's analysis skates over – the fact that the authors of the declaration possess (or possessed) two independent sources of sovereign authority, one flowing down from the UN, and the other flowing up democratically from the people who elected them.' See A. Mills, 'The Kosovo Advisory Opinion: If you don't have anything constructive to say . . .?', (2011) 70 *Cambridge Law Journal*, 70 (2011) 4.

[79] *Kosovo* Advisory Opinion, paragraphs 109 and 120.

[80] *Ibid.*, paragraph 114. See C. Pippan, 'The International Court of Justice's Advisory Opinion on Kosovo's declaration of independence: An exercise in the art of silence', (2010) 3 *Europäisches Journal für Minderheitenfragen* 145.

[81] *Ibid.*, paragraphs 115 to 118. Talmon eloquently summarised this point of the Court's reasoning as: 'whatever rules of international law might have prohibited a declaration of independence were not applicable to the authors of the declaration of independence, who were acting as the "representatives of the people of Kosovo"'. See, further, S. Talmon and M. Weller, 'Kosovo: The ICJ Opinion – What next?' *Official summary of the International Law Discussion Group meeting held at Chatham House on 21 September 2010* (available at chatham-house.org.uk/, last accessed 4 October 2010).

[82] *Kosovo* Advisory Opinion, paragraph 119.   [83] See *supra*. n. 62 and accompanying text.

ha[d] to be demonstrated'.[84] On the present occasion the Court, more specifically, in order to craft the concept of the 'different level' and thereby elude the anomaly of antithetical legal orders, based its reasoning on the premise that the two instruments did not coincide in terms of their intended effects.

As has been remarked by Falk, the Court, most likely out of political considerations, 'avoid[ed] a simple textual application of the intentions of the Security Council as set forth in Resolution 1244' which contained several passages 'reaffirming the commitment . . . to the sovereignty and territorial integrity of Serbia' and therefore seemed inconsistent with the declaration.[85] However, such textual approach should not be confused in the context of the Opinion with the valid consequential type of *argumentum ab inconvenienti*, which may indeed afford teleological interpretations to the text. Otherwise, the Court should have applied uniformly the same interpretative approach to the concept of the authors of the declaration. Contradistinctively, as Öberg notes, on that occasion, which constituted an important step in its reasoning, the Court found more convenient to employ instead the rule of the plain meaning of the Resolution's language.[86] This *ad consequentiam* premise can be seen unambiguously as emanating from the Court's argument that:

> the authors of the declaration did not seek to act within the standard framework of interim self-administration of Kosovo, but aimed at establishing Kosovo '*as an independent and sovereign state*'. The declaration of independence, therefore, was not intended by those who adopted it to take effect within the legal order created for the interim phase, nor was it capable of doing so. On the contrary, the Court considers that the authors of that declaration did not act, or intend to act, in the capacity of an institution created by and empowered to act within that legal order but, rather, set out to adopt a measure the significance and effects of which would lie outside that order'.[87]

Nevertheless, the above convenient teleological view entails as an indispensable corollary the need to determine the significance and effect of the declaration upon the international legal order of Kosovo. In other words, the integrity of the Court's supposedly linear deductive syllogism

---

[84] *Free Zones of Upper Savoy and District of Gex (Second Phase)* PCIJ, Series A. No. 24, Order of 6 December 1930, at p. 11.

[85] Falk, 'The Kosovo Advisory Opinion: Conflict Resolution and Precedent', at 50.

[86] See, Öberg, 'The Legal Effects of United Nations Resolutions in the Kosovo Advisory Opinion', at 84–5.

[87] *Kosovo* Advisory Opinion, paragraph 105 (emphasis in original).

can only be secured to the extent that such significance and effects can be examined and found to be congruent with the applicable *lex specialis* on Kosovo. If not, the judicial conception of the 'different level' at best may be seen only as deriving from the realm of *fictio juris*.[88] Characteristically, Judge Koroma, in his dissenting opinion, reflected further on this legal *non sequitur* emanating from the concept of different level by observing that:

> As the Court has recognized . . ., resolution 1244 (1999) and UNMIK regulation 1999/1 constitute the legal order in force at that time in the territory of Kosovo. *Kosovo was not a legal vacuum.* Any act, such as the unilateral declaration of independence of 17 February 2008, adopted in violation of resolution 1244 (1999) and UNMIK regulation 1999/1, will therefore not be in accordance with international law.[89]

Moreover, the vice-president of the Court, Judge Tomka, stipulated in his declaration that:

> To answer the question put to the Court requires it not only to interpret Security Council resolution 1244 but also to make a determination whether an act adopted by the institutions of Kosovo, which has been put under a régime of international territorial administration, is or is not in conformity with the legal framework applicable to and governing that régime, i.e., Security Council resolution 1244 and the measures adopted thereunder, in particular the Constitutional Framework.[90]

The combined result of the Court omitting to consider the issue of the declaration's legal consequences to allow itself to conclude that the declaration was not prohibited by international law has thus engendered a widespread perception that Kosovo's statehood has been confirmed.[91] But as will be further argued, this observation is erroneous, insofar as the reasoning of the Court is flawed. More specifically, the Court deliberately eschewed the issue of legal effects, from the very beginning, by setting out a controversial argument, in claiming ostentatiously that:

---

[88] Judge André Gros had particularly stressed in the *Western Sahara* Advisory Opinion that 'it is the duty of a court to establish facts, that is to say to make findings as to their existence, and it confers a legal meaning upon them by its decision; a court may neither suppose the existence of facts nor deduce them from hypotheses unsupported by evidence.' See *infra.* at n. 107, and accompanying text.

[89] Dissenting Opinion of Judge Koroma, paragraph 7 (emphasis added).

[90] Declaration of Judge Tomka, paragraph 2.

[91] See, among others, J. Kammerhofer, 'Begging the Question? The Kosovo Opinion and the Reformulation of Advisory Requests' (2011) 58 *Netherlands International Law Review*, at 423.

> The question ... does not ask about the legal consequences of that declaration. In particular, it does not ask whether or not Kosovo has achieved statehood ... The Court notes that, in past requests for advisory opinions, the General Assembly and the Security Council, when they have wanted the Court's opinion on the legal consequences of an action, have framed the question in such a way that this aspect is expressly stated. Accordingly, the Court does not consider that it is necessary to address such issues as whether or not the declaration has led to the creation of a State ... in order to answer the question put by the General Assembly. The Court accordingly sees no reason to reformulate the scope of the question.[92]

The decision of the Court to distance itself from the issue of consequences was criticised both for deviating from previous practice in similar occasions, and on the grounds of a severe methodological error that misguided its analytical reasoning. Judge Tomka, in particular, characterised it as an 'adjustment exercise' whose importance was outcome-determinative.[93] Judge Bennouna was of the same mind,[94] but went even further in his Dissenting Opinion, noting:

> The Court responds merely by asserting that, when adopting the declaration of independence, the authors were not bound by the Constitutional framework and that the declaration was not an act intended to take effect within the legal order put in place by the United Nations (Advisory Opinion, paragraph 121). But then what legal order governed the authors and the declaration itself? It was not, in any case, the legal order of Serbia nor that of a new sovereign State. And not being part of the interim institutions does not exempt the authors from the legal order established by UNMIK regulation 1999/1, providing that '[a]ll legislative and executive authority with respect to Kosovo, including the

---

[92] *Kosovo* Advisory Opinion, paragraph 51.

[93] Declaration of Judge Tomka, paragraph 1. See also, the Declaration of Judge Simma, paragraph 1; and the Dissenting Opinion of Judge Bennouna, paragraph 7, wherein he viewed that: 'If the Court were able to employ discretion to such an extent, by replying in the end to a question which it has itself adjusted beforehand in order to make it fit a certain mould, then it would seriously prejudice the sense of judicial security that ought to prevail among the States and organs of the United Nations applying to the Court.'

[94] Similarly, Judge Skotnikov, in his own Dissenting Opinion, at paragraph 15, laconically deplored the fact that 'the majority, unfortunately, does not explain the difference between acting outside the legal order and violating it'. As Kammerhofer appositely remarks 'ironically, the *Kosovo* opinion may be a good case where *not* changing the question has negative consequences. The Court's changes were largely matters of legal logic and it was adamant in not considering the legal consequences of the declaration of independence'; q.v., Kammerhofer, 'Begging the Question? The Kosovo Opinion and the Reformulation of Advisory Requests', at 423.

administration of the judiciary, is vested in UNMIK and is exercised by the Special Representative of the Secretary-General'.[95]

Finally, of special gravity is the reaction of Judges Sepúlveda-Amor and Yusuf, who, albeit concurring with the general conclusion of the *Kosovo* Advisory Opinion, strongly objected to the Court's reasoning on this specific point. The former questioned the Court's narrow approach to the question posed, finding that the declaration was not intended to take effect within the international legal order created for the interim phase and thus, as a consequence, was outside the international legal order.[96] Similarly, the latter, in a much more intense tone, admonished the Court's reasoning on the same point in concluding that:

> the Court itself admits that 'the declaration of independence is an attempt to determine finally the status of Kosovo' (paragraph 114), but fails to examine whether such a unilateral determination of the final status of Kosovo and its separation from the parent State is in accordance with international law, as clearly implied in the question put to it by the General Assembly.[97]

V. Final Remarks

In having *proprio motu* restricted the scope of the question so as not to consider the issue of the Declaration's legal consequences, the Court should then have by formal implication of its reasoning, deemed, to have deprived itself of any opportunity for recourse to consequential argumentation, such as that of appealing to the concept of the 'different level'. Even though it is surely true that on other occasions the UN General Assembly has specified the aspect of legal consequences in its requests,[98] the Court, in deliberately omitting to consider it in the *Kosovo* Advisory Opinion, became oblivious of its own *dictum* that:

> If [the Court] is to remain faithful to the requirements of its judicial character in the exercise of its advisory jurisdiction, it must ascertain what are the legal questions really in issue in questions formulated in a

---

[95] Dissenting Opinion of Judge Bennouna, paragraph 64.

[96] Separate Opinion of Judge Sepúlveda-Amor, paragraphs 29 and 30.

[97] Separate Opinion of Judge Yusuf, paragraph 6.

[98] See, for example, *Legal Consequences for States of the Continued Presence of South Africa in Namibia (South West Africa) notwithstanding Security Council Resolution 276 (1970)*, Advisory Opinion, ICJ Reports 1971, p. 16 and *Legal Consequences of the Construction of a Wall in the Occupied Palestinian Territory*, Advisory Opinion, ICJ Reports 2004(I), p. 136.

request ... a reply to questions of the kind posed in the present request may, if incomplete, be not only ineffectual but actually misleading as to the legal rules applicable to the matter under consideration by the requesting Organization.[99]

Startlingly, the Court did not invoke the above passage in its Opinion, although extremely pertinent to the circumstances. This may be assumed as signifying two equally disturbing intentions: Either that the Court has departed *sub silentio* from its practice on this particular aspect of judicial methodology,[100] or simply because it could not adjust it conveniently to fit into its desirable reasoning.[101] In performing its advisory judicial function,[102] and conforming to its own internal practice, the Court is obliged to state those reasons whereon its ruling on the point of law is based.[103] Albeit the statement of reasons in points of law *per se* may discharge the procedural aspect of the requirement, this does not ensure *ipso facto* the fulfilment of its substantive aspect, necessary for valid reasoning. Hence, the 'statement of reasons' differs from the formalistic requisite of 'reasoning', in the sense that the latter constitutes the linear logicality of the former, thus eventually synthesising the structure of the legal *ratio*.

Scholars of comparative legal methodology have benefited greatly in terms of authoritative insight into the jurisprudential aspects of international law from an open disagreement between two distinguished figures; namely, Wilfrend Jenks and Georg Schwarzenberger. Among their divergent views is a disagreement with regard to the epistemological nature of international law and its consequences upon legal reasoning within international courts. Jenks was essentially of the view that international judicial reasoning amalgamates both deductive and inductive elements; Schwarzenberger, though conceding this proposition, favoured a more inductive form of reasoning through the doctrine of

---

[99] *Interpretation of the Agreement of 25 March 1951 between the WHO and Egypt,* Advisory Opinion, ICJ Reports 1980, p. 88, at paragraph 35.

[100] On the disruptions to the corpus of law caused by such implicit reasoning, see Shahabuddeen, *Precedent in the World Court* at pp. 130–1.

[101] Q.v., Separate Opinion of Judge Sepúlveda-Amor, paragraph 33 *et seq.*

[102] See in general, J. Crawford and M. Young (eds.), 'The International Judicial Function' in *The Function of Law in the International Community: An Anniversary Symposium,* Proceedings of the 25th Anniversary Conference of the Lauterpacht Centre for International Law, 11–12 July 2008.

[103] See Statute of the ICJ Article 56, paragraph 1, in conjunction with Article 95, paragraph 1, of the Rules of Court as adopted 14 April 1978 and entered into force 1 July 1978.

sources. However, in spite of advocating different styles of argumentation, both concurred on the inherent role of logic within judicial positivism,[104] an element that is lost in favour of practical reasoning in numerous cases with dominant political aspects.[105] It is worth noting that the Court seldom refers to the term 'reasoning' in its rulings,[106] and whenever it does, it has always been vague or indirect as to its bearing on the ascertainment of the legal question. In this respect, particularly enlightening is the general spirit of Judge André Gros's declaration in the *Western Sahara* Advisory Opinion, in viewing that 'despite the stylistic development of its reasoning' the Court had failed to identify 'the precise legal question';[107] as well as that of Judge Nagendra Singh being critical of the Court for not having explored the aspect of legal consequences in viewing that while remaining well within its judicial bounds it can be mindful of the purpose for which its opinion is sought by the UN General Assembly.[108]

Nevertheless, the Court was presented with an opportunity to reflect upon such jurisprudential issues when, on the occasion of another advisory opinion, it affirmed the above formalistic axiom of the general rule of law, noting that:

---

[104] See W.C. Jenks, *The Prospects of International Adjudication* (London: Stevens & Sons Ltd, 1964), particularly pp. 617–62, and G. Schwarzenberger, *The Inductive Approach to International Law* (London: Stevens & Sons Ltd, 1965), *passim*.

[105] An interesting view can be found in F. V. Kratochwill, *Rules, Norms and Decisions: On the Conditions of Practical and Legal Reasoning in International Relations and Domestic Affairs* (Cambridge University Press, 1989).

[106] Indicative of indirect references to the term 'reasoning' are the pronouncements in the *Judgments of the Administrative Tribunal in the ILO upon complaints made against the UNESCO* where the Court, reflecting upon the fact that its Opinion was to be accepted as binding, reassured itself that this extrinsic element to its procedural law '[would not] affect the reasoning by which the Court forms its Opinion or the content of the Opinion itself'. Advisory Opinion of 23 October 1956, ICJ Reports 1956 p. 77, at p. 84.

See also, *Certain Expenses of the United Nations (Article 17, paragraph 2, of the Charter)*, Advisory Opinion of 20 July 1962, ICJ Reports 1962, p. 151 at p. 170; *Legal Consequences for States of the Continued Presence of South Africa in Namibia (South West Africa) notwithstanding Security Council Resolution 276 (1970)*, Advisory Opinion, ICJ Reports 1971 p. 16, at p. 24 paragraph 34 and at p. 45 paragraph 89; *Applicability of Article VI, Section 22, of the Convention on the Privileges and Immunities of the United Nations*, Advisory Opinion, ICJ Reports 1989 p. 177, at p. 189 paragraph 31.

[107] Advisory Opinion of 16 October 1975, ICJ Reports 1975 p. 12, at p. 70 paragraph 1 and at p. 71 paragraph 3.

[108] *Ibid.*, Declaration of Judge Nagendra Singh, at p. 80.

> [w]hile a statement of reasons is necessary to the validity of a judgement, the question remains as to what form and degree of reasoning will satisfy this requirement ... [there are no] obligatory forms or techniques for drawing up judgments: a tribunal may employ direct or indirect reasoning, and state specific or merely implied conclusions, provided that the reasons on which the judgment is based are apparent ... In any event, the question at issue is not whether the Tribunal might have used different forms or techniques, or whether more elaborate reasoning might have been considered as preferable or more adequate. The question is whether the Judgement was sufficiently reasoned to satisfy the requirements of the rule that a judgement of the Administrative Tribunal must state the reasons on which it is based.[109]

It may be reassuring to know that it is normal for states, through their political representatives, to challenge the legal authority of advisory opinions; indeed, attitudes have varied from the extreme of complete rejection to that of unqualified acceptance, depending on how particular interests have been accommodated.[110] Similar attitudes have been precipitated by the *Kosovo* Advisory Opinion within the broader politics of recognition.[111] Illustrative of such attitudes are the official proceedings regarding the adoption of Resolution 64/298 (2010) wherewith the UN General Assembly acknowledged the content of the *Kosovo* Advisory Opinion.[112] Informative in this context is a pre-dated press release containing the summary of the UNSC 6367th meeting, which records the UN Mission Head in Kosovo's statement that the *Kosovo* Advisory Opinion 'confirms the applicability of Resolution 1244'.[113]

Even so, it is extremely disquieting to note that the Court's reasoning has not been well received within academia, with such disenchantment

---

[109] *Application for Review of Judgement No. 158 of the United Nations Administrative Tribunal*, Advisory Opinion, ICJ Reports 1973 p. 166, at pp. 210–11 paragraphs 95–6.

[110] D. Pratap, *The Advisory Jurisdiction of the International Court* (Oxford: Clarendon Press, 1972), at p. 244.

[111] See further, Chapter 6 below.

[112] For the diverse statements of the national delegations on the agenda item 77 and the adoption of the Assembly's draft Resolution A/64/L.65/Rev.1 (8 September 2010), see A/64/PV.120 (9 Sept. 2010) of the 64th Session (120th plenary meeting) of the UN General Assembly, available at un.org/en/ga/64/resolutions.shtml, last accessed December 2010.

[113] SC/10000 (3 August 2010). For a very inspired article reflecting on the interplay between the politics of recognition in Kosovo and international law, see R. J. Delahunty and A. F. Perez, 'The Kosovo Crisis: A Dostoievskian Dialogue on International Law, Statecraft and Soulcraft' (2009) 42 *Vanderbilt Journal of Transnational Law* 15.

reflecting a catholic sentiment among international lawyers.[114] The fact that its conclusions were reached through what is admittedly a very condensed and swift way of reasoning,[115] and the legal mishaps or the space left for implied inductions therefrom,[116] are amongst the many reasons for distrusting its validity. In this respect, it has been suggested that actually 'The ICJ sought for a compromise: It declared that it had jurisdiction but it shied away from addressing the substance of the question posed . . . the line of arguments presented by the ICJ is too shaky and as a consequence status and function of the ICJ end up damaged from this proceeding.'[117]

It is this strained reasoning, as exposed above, that gave birth to the paradox of parallel legal orders. In the penumbra of this paradox, and in view of the Court's unorthodox reasoning, the main *aporia* arising may thus take the following form. Shall the Opinion be read as implying that the sovereign order of the Resolution has yielded to the *earned sovereignty* of Kosovo,[118] which as a concept that, if endorsed, will entail unforeseeable metajuridical ramifications for the international order?[119] Or, on the contrary, that the Opinion shall be construed on a rather restrictive basis,

---

[114] Indicative of the general confusion is that all titles following below and which criticise the reasoning of the Court contain in their title a question mark. See, among others, R. Howse and R. Teitel, 'Delphic Dictum: How has the ICJ contributed to the Global Rule of Law by its Ruling on Kosovo?' (2010) 11 *German Law Journal* 841; H. Hannum 'The Advisory Opinion on Kosovo: An Opportunity Lost, or a Poisoned Chalice Refused?' (2011) 24 *Leiden Journal of International Law* 155; M. Bothe, 'Kosovo – So What? The Holding of the International Court of Justice is not the Last Word on Kosovo's Independence' (2010) 11 *German Law Journal*, 832; V. Röben, 'The ICJ Advisory Opinion on the Unilateral Declaration of Independence in Respect of Kosovo: Rules or Principles?' (2010) 2 *Goettingen Journal of International Law* 1063; and J. Vidmar, 'The Kosovo Opinion and General International Law: How Far-reaching and Controversial is the ICJ's Reasoning?' (The Hague justice portal (11 October 2010), available at haguejusticeportal.net/eCache/DEF/12/110.html, last accessed October 2010).

[115] M. Weller, 'Modesty Can Be a Virtue: Judicial Economy in the ICJ Kosovo Opinion' (2011) 24 *Leiden Journal of International Law*, at 127.

[116] Q.v., J. d'Aspremont, 'The Creation of States before the International Court of Justice: Which (Il)Legality?', at 3.

[117] See further, P. Hilpold, 'The ICJ Advisory Opinion on Kosovo: Different Perspectives of a Delicate Question' (SSRN (3 January 2011), available at ssrn.com/abstract=1734443, last accessed January 2010).

[118] For the political doctrine of *earned* sovereignty, see J.R. Hooper and P.R. Williams in (2002–3) 31 *Denver Journal of International Law & Policy*, at 355ff.; and for an attempt at establishing its judicial underpinnings, see in the same issue, M.P. Scharf, at 373 *et seq.*

[119] Of a kind which Weller suggests that 'would herald the beginning of a post-modern fragmentation of the state system'; q.v., Weller, *Contested Statehood*, at p. 259.

treating the Declaration of Independence purely as an inexistent act?[120] For instance, on the basis of, *inter alios*, Judge Leonid Skotnikov's emphatic conclusions that 'in no way does the advisory opinion question the fact that resolution 1244 remains in force in its entirety ...',[121] or on that of Judge Bennouna's suggestion that 'such declarations are no more than foam on the tide of time; they cannot allow the past to be forgotten nor a future to be built on fragments of the present'.[122]

It has been correctly stated that the authority of the pronouncements of all international tribunals ultimately depends upon their intrinsic merit, not on their eminence.[123] On this view, the answer may be heard reverberating in one of Sir Hersch Lauterpacht's many valuable reflections:

> However competent, however august, however final, and however authoritative a tribunal may be, it cannot, in the conditions in which its jurisdiction is in law, and compliance with its decisions is in fact essentially of a voluntary character, dispense with the powerful appeal to opinion which stems from the reason content of its pronouncements.[124]

Legal reasoning may sometimes seem to offer something of an impenetrable concept – mysterious, baroque or formless[125] – but it is to be found, explicitly or implicitly, in every judicial pronouncement. Regrettably, the reasoning in the *Kosovo* Advisory Opinion has reminded us that legal prudence might well necessitate the Court exercising its discretion to refuse requests for advisory opinions when the underlying problem can be resolved only by lengthy and difficult political negotiations,[126] rather than compromising the integrity of its legal reasoning, and ultimately its own judicial character. Alternatively, did the Court simply choose to answer the wrong question?

---

[120] A. Orakhelashvili, 'The International Court's Advisory Opinion on the UDI in Respect of Kosovo: Washing Away the Foam on the Tide of Time', pp. 65–104, in von Bogdandy and Wolfrum (eds.), *Max Planck Yearbook of United Nations Law – Volume 12*, at pp. 101–3.

[121] Dissenting Opinion Judge Skotnikov, paragraph 18.

[122] Dissenting Opinion Judge Bennouna, paragraph 69.

[123] Pratap, *The Advisory Jurisdiction of the International Court*, at p. 233.

[124] H. Lauterpacht, *The Development of International Law by the International Court* (Cambridge University Press, 1982), at p. 41.

[125] C.R. Sunstein, *Legal Reasoning and Political Conflict* (Oxford University Press, 1996), at p. vii.

[126] A. Aust, 'Advisory Opinions', (2010) 1 *Journal of International Dispute Settlement*, at 123 *et seq*.

6

The politics of recognition: The question about the final status of Kosovo

JESSICA ALMQVIST

I. Introduction

Writing in the years following the adoption of the Montevideo Convention on the Rights and Duties of States in 1933 (hereinafter the Montevideo Convention)[1] and the resolution of the *Institut de Droit International* on the recognition of new states and new governments in 1936,[2] several scholars envisioned the establishment of a standard procedure for matters of recognition. For example, Philip Jessup proposed that the United Nations (UN) General Assembly might 'by general convention or declaration' define the basic statehood criteria and pledge members to afford recognition of new states in conformity with a standard procedure.[3] Quincy Wright noted that 'there has been a tendency for states to accept collective procedures through the League of Nations and the United Nations for according general recognition',[4] adding that 'further development of this tendency would add considerably to precision in applying international law'.[5] Hersch Lauterpacht also developed proposals along the same lines.[6]

---

[1] Montevideo Convention on the Rights and Duties of States, signed at the International Conference of American States in Montevideo, 26 December 1993, entered into force 26 December 1934.

[2] *La reconnaissance des nouveaux Etats et de noveaux gouvernements* (Rapporteur: M. Philip Marshall Brown), L'Institut de Droit international, Session de Bruxelles, April 1936. An English translation of this resolution (used here) is available in (1936) 30 *American Journal of International Law*, 185–7.

[3] P. Jessup, *A Modern Law of Nations* (New York: Macmillan, 1950), pp. 44–51.

[4] Q. Wright, 'Some Thoughts about Recognition', (1950) 44 *American Journal of International Law*, 548–59, at 559.

[5] *Ibid.*

[6] See H. Lauterpacht, *Recognition in International Law* (Cambridge University Press, 1947), p. 402.

However, in spite of the passage of time since the 'advent of international organizations',[7] no such standard procedure has been set up. During the Cold War period, the issue lost significance as a certain measure of consistency in state practice was achieved following the statehood criteria set out in the Montevideo Convention.[8] Nonetheless, with the multiple declarations of independence generated by the dissolutions of the Soviet Union and Yugoslavia and the initial uncertainty among third states about how to respond, it would seem logical that the call for such a procedure surfaced again. Instead, what is observed is the reinforcement of what is referred to in this chapter as the 'politics of recognition' to settle the question of when recognition is owed or desirable and when it must be withheld.[9] Rather than fostering common ground, however, these politics have served only to bolster divisions and disagreements on this matter. The significance of the politics of recognition and the incapacity of multilateral mechanisms to prevent or curb them becomes especially evident when considering the developments in the wake of the Kosovo Declaration on Independence issued on 17 February 2008 (hereinafter Kosovo Declaration).[10] The UN-based multilateral mechanisms, which in principle could have hindered the politics of recognition from emerging in response to this Declaration, i.e. the Security Council, the General Assembly and the International Court of Justice (ICJ), have failed in this endeavour. Instead of fostering common ground, the discussions conducted within these frameworks have boosted the impression that such political considerations are the

---

[7] This notion has been borrowed from Judge Cançado Trindade. See *Accordance with International Law of the Unilateral Declaration of Independence by the Provisional Institutions of Self-Government of Kosovo* (hereinafter *Kosovo* Advisory Opinion), Advisory Opinion of 22 July 2010 (2010) ICJ Rep. Separate Opinion of Judge Cançado Trindade, para. 52.

[8] R. Rich, 'Recognition of States: The Collapse of Yugoslavia and the Soviet Union', (1993) 4 *European Journal of International Law*, 33–66, at 64.

[9] The notion of the 'politics of recognition' was originally introduced in the post-Cold War period by the Canadian political philosopher, Charles Taylor, when addressing the aspirations of nations to be recognized for their cultural worth and status. See C. Taylor, 'The Politics of Recognition', in A. Gutmann (ed.), *Multiculturalism: Examining the Politics of Recognition* (Princeton University Press, 1994), pp. 25–73. While his thesis is not incompatible with the definition of the politics of recognition advanced in this chapter (indeed, for him recognition has only symbolic and not real effects), it nevertheless fails to capture the relevance of these politics from the standpoint of international law.

[10] The Kosovo Declaration of Independence is available at www.assembly-kosova.org/? krye=news&newsid=1635&lang=en (last accessed 27 January 2012).

'only game in town' when tackling controversial cases.[11] What follows is a more detailed elaboration of this argument.

II.   The governing legal framework

According to article 1 of the resolution of the *Institut de Droit international*, adopted in 1936:

> The recognition of a new state is the free act by which one or more states acknowledge the existence on a definite territory of a human society politically organized, independent of any other existing state, and capable of observing the obligations of international law, and by which they manifest their intention to consider it a member of the international community.[12]

The resolution thus reaffirms the statehood criteria as the basis for recognition, a rule that had been laid down in the Montevideo Convention only a few years before.[13] It also endorses article 3 of the same Convention, according to which a 'recognition has a declaratory effect' and that, as a consequence, 'the existence of a new state with all the juridical effects which are attached to that existence is not affected by the refusal of recognition by one or more states'.

At the time of its inception, the declaratory thesis was fairly controversial. For example, Hans Kelsen and Hersch Lauterpacht criticized it by upholding a rival view.[14] Sharing the understanding that the recognition of new states refers to an *acknowledgement* that the statehood criteria have been met in a given case, both insisted that new states

---

[11] The Palestine proposal is another controversial case-in-point which the UN principal organs have not been able to settle. On 23 September 2011, Palestine submitted an official application to the UN Secretary-General asking for recognition by and membership in the UN. The UN Security Council began deliberating on this matter three days later. However, at the time of writing, no vote, either on recognition or on membership, has taken place. As of 12 January 2012, 129 UN member states had formally recognized Palestine. The United States continues to block a request for UN membership. Meanwhile, on 31 October 2011, the General Council of the United Nations Educational, Scientific and Cultural Oraganization (UNESCO) admitted Palestine as a member state. The UNESCO membership has been effective since 23 November 2011. See also Chapter 7 below.

[12] L'Institut de Droit international, *La reconnaissance*.

[13] Montevideo Convention. For a detailed account of the statehood criteria, see J. Crawford, *The Creation of States in International Law*, 2nd edn (Oxford University Press, 2007), pp. 37–94.

[14] H. Kelsen, 'Recognition in International Law: Theoretical Observations', (1941) 35 *American Journal of International Law*, 605–17, at 605ff.

depended on the recognition from others in order to exist as a state in a legal sense, i.e. as a subject of international law endowed with international legal rights and obligations. In this sense, recognition had *constitutive* effects. Their thesis was not well received, though. Especially problematic was that its practical application meant that new states – not yet recognized – would not be considered 'subjects' of international law, but treated as 'outlaws' without any international rights or obligations.[15] Instead, a broad agreement was built up around its counterpart, which maintained its status throughout the decolonization process.[16] However, the post-Cold War developments appeared to undermine this settlement.[17] In particular, the principle of self-determination came to function as a rhetorical device to legitimate the creation of a host of new states outside the decolonization context.[18] The EC Guidelines on the Recognition of New States in Eastern Europe and in the Soviet Union, adopted in 1991,[19] affirmed the direct relevance of the principle of self-determination when assessing the legitimacy of secessionist movements and affirmed the readiness of European Community (EC) member states to:

> Recognize, subject to the normal standards of international practice, and *the political realities in each case*, those new States which, following the historical changes in the region, have constituted themselves on a democratic basis, have accepted the appropriate international obligations and have committed themselves in good faith to a peaceful process and to negotiations.[20]

As a result of these Guidelines, the initial reluctance of Western states to react changed in favour of multiple recognitions of new states, including in the case of Bosnia and Herzegovina, where the statehood criteria

[15] H. W. Briggs, 'Recognition of States: Some Reflections on Doctrine and Practice', (1949) 43 *The American Journal of International Law*, 113–21, at 117.

[16] L'Institut de Droit international, *La reconnaissance*, at 65.

[17] D. Türk, 'Recognition of States: A Comment', (1993) 4 *European Journal of International Law*, 66–91, at 68, arguing that the policy of non-recognition (initially) pursued by the Western states with respect to the dissolution of the Soviet Union and Yugoslavia did not contribute to solving any of the historical problems in that part of the world.

[18] For an account of the revolutionary potential of the principle of self-determination as a justification for these processes, see M. Koskenniemi, 'The Future of Statehood', (1991) 32 *Harvard Journal of International Law*, 397–410.

[19] Declaration on the 'Guidelines on the Recognition of New States in Eastern Europe and in the Soviet Union', adopted by the European Community on 16 December 1991. Reproduced in (1993) 4 *European Journal of International Law*, 72–3.

[20] *Ibid.*

had most clearly not been met.[21] The new impulse to support other independence movements implied disregarding, at least in some cases, one of the established criteria for recognition: that of the effectiveness of government.[22] Third states thus came to legitimate claims for statehood which in all fairness were still premature and in this manner departing from the established legal understanding of the purpose of statements of recognitions as means of acknowledging statehood.

Against this background, Roland Rich, when reflecting on the case of Bosnia and Herzegovina, noted that 'recent events seem to point towards a trend to attempt to *constitute* states through the process of recognition'.[23] According to Christian Hillgruber, however, the act of conferring the status of a state on entities whose governments control only some parts of the national territory converts the status of statehood into a *legal fiction*.[24] The two reflections point to the real source of anxiety produced in the process of recognizing Kosovo: some states simply affirmed its status as an independent and sovereign state even if the Kosovar government was and is not in control of all its territory and remains under international supervision.[25] Other recognizing states, however, admitted that their recognitions were peculiar precisely for these reasons. In fact, their recognitions seemed to be used mainly to express their views on the plausibility and legitimacy of the aspirations to create a state out of Kosovo and their commitment to lend moral and other types of assistance, support and protection in the realization of this project.

III.   The incentives for the politics of recognition

In 1992, the EC Badinter Commission reiterated the Montevideo understanding of the effects of recognition, also recalling that recognition is a matter of discretion and choice. In the words of this Commission:

---

[21] L'Institut de Droit international, *La reconnaissance*, at 64. Bosnia and Herzegovina declared independence on 3 March 1992.

[22] Note, however, that the criteria of effectiveness had already been relaxed during the decolonization process. See A. Remiro Brotóns *et al.*, *Derecho Internacional* (Valencia: Editorial Tirant Lo Blanch, 2007), 97–101.

[23] Rich, 'Recognition of States' (emphasis added). Rich mentions that Ukraine could also fit into this class.

[24] C. Hillgruber, 'The Admission of New States to the International Community', (1998) 9 *European Journal of International Law*, 491–509, at 493.

[25] International Crisis Group, Kosovo and Serbia after the ICJ Opinion, *Europe Report* No. 206, 26 August 2010.

> While recognition is not a prerequisite for the foundation of a state and is
> purely declaratory in its impact, it is nonetheless a discretionary act that
> other states may perform when they choose and in a manner of their own
> choosing, subject only to compliance with the imperatives of general
> international law, and particularly those prohibiting the use of force in
> dealings with other states or guaranteeing the rights of ethnic, religious or
> linguistic minorities.[26]

Assuming that recognitions are endowed with only declaratory effects and
are incapable of replacing the empirical evidence that is needed for statehood, the actual incentives for communities to demand recognitions from
third states, or for third states to take part in political quarrels as to whether
or not to recognize these communities as states, are not self-evident, but call
for further reflection. A formal analysis of the rules governing this field fails
to capture the range of interests that drive the politics of recognition, the
degree of participation in these politics, and the flaring up of disagreement
on acceptable mechanisms by which new states are created.

The first thing to note in this context is that from a practical standpoint,
recognition is an essential condition for a new state actually to *exercise* in an
effective manner the international rights and obligations that are incumbent
on statehood and entering into relations with other states and thus become
a fully-fledged member of the international community.[27] In fact, without
such recognition, the rights and obligations that may well be formally
attributed to states as a matter of law can seem fairly worthless from the
standpoint of a new state unless others recognize it in the sense of *acknowledging* its 'existence' and, thus, its actual rights and obligations as a subject
of international law.[28] In this sense, recognition is a practical condition for
the effective enjoyment of the status of statehood.

Furthermore, in spite of their non-constitutive effects, recognition
acts can be used as evidence for the legal validity of the claims for
statehood. According to James Crawford:

> That an entity is recognized as a State is evidence of its status; where
> recognition is general, it may be practically conclusive. States, in the

---

[26] See Arbitration Commission of the International Conference on Yugoslavia (the
Badinter Commission), Opinion No. 10, Paris, 4 July 1992. Reproduced in (1993) 4
European Journal of International Law, 90–1.

[27] But note that in international practice, recognition from the parent state constitutes an
essential condition to becoming a member of the UN.

[28] For the relevance of the distinction between the formal protection of rights and the
worth of these rights from the standpoint of their intended beneficiaries, see J. Rawls,
Political Liberalism (New York: Columbia University Press, 1995), p. 326ff.

forum of the United Nations or elsewhere, may make declarations as to status or 'recognize' entities the status of which is doubtful: depending on the degree of unanimity and other factors this may be evidence of a compelling kind. Even individual acts of recognition may contribute towards the consolidation of status.[29]

In other words, even if not constitutive to statehood, the number of recognitions that an entity receives is of enormous practical significance when presenting evidence in support of a claim to statehood before a tribunal or when seeking to persuade hesitant or objecting third states to change their minds in the politics of recognition.

A third relevant factor that explains the emergence of the politics of recognition in the wake of claims for statehood is the openly declared and widely accepted intimate relation between international law and politics in this domain of international affairs.[30] While, formally speaking, the act of recognition is thought to be based on neutral (or objective) statehood criteria, international practice indicates that it tends to be intermeshed with a range of political considerations. Indeed, when state creations are violent or traumatic, instead of peaceful and based on agreement, it is reasonable to expect that third states will react in the light of differing political interests. There might be both national interest-driven motivations and international human rights protection stakes involved, and each state will decide how to react in line with their own understanding of the main priorities and concerns. Since the stakes will differ depending on a state's particular interests, including foreign investments, multinational make-up, etc., one cluster of states might be eager to lend considerable support to those who set forth the claims for statehood, while another such cluster will oppose the same claims in the most radical terms. The political stakes also explain the temptation of third states to grant recognition in a premature way when a new state is still only 'in its making' and is not yet a *fait accompli*.[31]

---

[29] Crawford, *The Creation of States*, p. 27.

[30] Remiro Brotóns *et al.*, *Derecho Internacional*, p. 110.

[31] See, e.g., C. Warbrick, 'Kosovo and the Declaration of Independence', (2008) *International & Comparative Law Quarterly*, 675–90, at 690: 'international lawyers know all too well that the facts can make the law – and the facts will eventually establish whether or not Serbian authority is to continue or a new State has conclusively emerged- but, at the moment, we are still waiting on the facts to be established'. See also Crawford, *The Creation of States*, pp. 415–16, when commenting on the emergence of Bangladesh: 'The indications are that the United Nations did not treat the emergence of Bangladesh as a case of self-determination despite good grounds for doing so, but rather as a *fait accompli* achieved as a result of foreign military assistance in special circumstances.'

The discretionary character of recognition acts means that states are
endowed with considerable freedom to perform or not to perform and to
motivate or not to motivate their recognitions. True, as the Badinter
Commission recalled in 1992,[32] there are some limits to recognition acts
derived from the general prohibition against the use of force and the
principle of non-intervention: recognition is not permitted if the state
has come about as a result of the use of force or other serious infringe-
ments of international law, such as in the case of illegal annexation of a
piece of territory, although even this limit can eventually be overcome if
the international community acquiesces.[33] Furthermore, even if a recognition act in principle can be unlawful in the sense of constituting an
intervention into the domestic affairs of a given state, considering the
incomplete institutionalization of international law, it is improbable that
an 'illegal' recognition will have any real repercussions. The absence of
an effective legal enforcement mechanism means that there is no clear
impediment for third states to adopt a stance of caution in relation to
especially controversial cases, or alternatively to abstain from performing a recognition act, even if the entity asking to be recognized is still not
a state in an empirical sense.

IV.   The politics of recognition in the Kosovo case

1.   The recognizing states

So far, Kosovo has been recognized by 91 states, several of which are
European Union (EU) members, together with the United States and
other so-called 'advanced democracies', including Australia, Canada,
Japan and South Korea.[34] By now, a notable number of Latin

---

[32] Badinter Commission, Opinion No. 10.
[33] The rule of non-recognition of entities that are the outcome of aggression is derived
from the principle of not accepting the acquisition of territory by the use of force.
However, acquiescence by the international community in the sense of failing to protest,
together with its recognition, are of great relevance in cases of prescription. Whereas
effective control over the territory is pivotal, with the passage of time, acquiescence and
recognition can come to constitute evidence in favour of viewing such entities as legal.
See P. Malanczuk, *Akehurst's Modern Introduction to International Law*, 7th edn
(London: Routledge, 1997), pp. 89, 154–5.
[34] A list of all of the recognizing states is available online at www.kosovothanksyou.com/
(last accessed 5 October 2012). For information on the contents of recognition texts referred
to in this section, which are no longer available online, see J. Almqvist, 'Kosovo, Politics of
Recognition and International Law', *Real Instituto Elcano Working Paper* no. 14 (March
2009), available online at www.realinstitutoelcano.org/wps/portal/rielcano_eng/Print?WCM_

American, African and Asian countries have also come to participate in an affirmative manner in the sense of performing acts of recognition.

If and when the creation of a new state is not a controversial matter, the specific reasons given in support of recognition seem to be fairly uninteresting. However, when a given case is controversial, the formulation of such texts or reasons warrants particular interest. Considering the prevailing doubts and disagreements as to whether, because of the continued international supervision of basic functions of government, Kosovo in fact, meets the statehood criteria, and whether, according to international law, is/was entitled to secede from Serbia in spite of the refusal of the latter to accept such outcome, most states that have recognized Kosovo, especially in the immediate aftermath of its unilateral decision, deemed it essential to accompany their recognition with a statement of the reasons for their position.[35]

Most recognizing states stress different political considerations in support of their act, without going into detail about the law concerning the terms and conditions of secession, including possible exceptions. A most prominent concern is the importance of guaranteeing peace and security in the Balkan region. Indeed, fourteen recognizing states, among them Afghanistan, Germany, Japan and France, assert that an independent Kosovo will strengthen these prospects.[36] In a similar spirit, Austria, Hungary and Luxembourg refer to the unsustainable nature of the status quo,[37] and Albania, the United Kingdom (UK) and Samoa are of the

GLOBAL_CONTEXT=/wps/wcm/connect/elcano/Elcano_in/Zonas_in/DT14–2009 (last accessed 30 January 2012).

[35] But note that several recognizing states have not motivated their acts. The recognition statements issued more recently are more traditional, inasmuch as they simply welcome Kosovo as a sovereign and independent state.

[36] The Statement of the Islamic Republic of Afghanistan on the Independence of Kosovo, Ministry for Foreign Affairs, Afghanistan, 18 February 2008, see *supra*. n. 34; Germany Recognises Kosovo, German Federal Government, 20 February 2008, see *supra*. n. 34; Statement by Foreign Minister Masahiko Koumura on the Recognition of the Republic of Kosovo, Ministry for Foreign Affairs, Japan, 18 March 2008, available online at www.mofa.go.jp/announce/announce/2008/3/0318.html (last accessed 30 January 2012); and Kosovo Declares Independence, Ministry for Foreign Affairs, France, 18 February 2008, see *supra*. n. 34.

[37] Plassnik, Letter on Kosovo's Recognition Signed, Austrian Foreign Ministry, 28 February 2008; Hungary Recognizes Kosovo's Independence, Ministry of Foreign Affairs of Hungary, 19 March 2008, available online at www.mfa.gov.hu/kum/en/bal/actualities/spokesman_statements/Kosovo_recognition_080319.htm (last accessed 27 January 2012); and Le Luxembourg reconnaît formellement le Kosovo, Le Gouvernement du Grande-Duché de Luxembourg, 21 February 2008, available online at www.gouvernement.lu/salle_presse/actualite/2008/02-fevrier/20-asselborn-kosovo/index.html (last accessed 27 January 2012).

view that an independent Kosovo may help close the conflict and end the disintegration process of Yugoslavia.[38]

Those recognizing states that invoke international law do so in a rather superficial manner. Few assert that Kosovo meets the statehood criteria, even if this is supposed to be the basis for performing recognition acts.[39] For example, Albania and the United Arab Emirates appeal to 'the principle of self-determination'.[40] Occasional references are also made to the consistency between their recognition acts and Security Council resolution 1244 (1999),[41] the Rambouillet Accords (1999)[42] and the conclusions of the Ahtisaari Plan (2007).[43] Though international law references are scarce, it must be noted that several states refer to 'failed negotiations' in support of their stance. Since one general condition for lawful secession is agreement between the parties, the frequent references to failed negotiations could be seen as

[38] Statement of Prime Minister of Albania, Mr. Sali Berisha, on Recognition of Independence of Kosova (Albanian Recognition), 18 February 2008, available online at www.keshilliminis-trave.al/index.php?fq=brenda&m=news&lid=7323&gj=gj2 (last accessed 27 January 2012); Samoa recognizes independent Kosovo, 15 September 2008, available online at www.new-kosovareport.com/200809151219/Politics/samoa-recognizes-independent-kosovo.html (last accessed 27 January 2012); and UK to recognise independent Kosovo, UK Prime Minister's Office, 18 February 2008, see *supra*. n. 34.

[39] But note, for instance, Burkina Faso, Declaration de Reconnaissance de l'Etat du Kosovo, 23 April 2008, referring to the principles of cooperation laid down in the UN Charter and respect for international human rights principles, as well as affirming that Kosovo meets the criteria for statehood, available online at www.kosovothanksyou.com/files/Declaration_sur_le_Kosovo_2404.pdf (last accessed 27 January 2012).

[40] See Albanian recognition, *supra*. n. 38; UAE recognizes Kosovo 14 October 2008, available online at www.wam.org.ae/servlet/Satellite?c=WamLocEnews&cid=1223546208865&p=1135099400124&pagename=WAM/WamLocEnews/W-T-LEN-FullNews (last accessed 27 January 2012).

[41] Costa Rica se pronuncia por la independencia de Kósovo, Ministerio de Asuntos Exteriores y Culto, 18 February 2008, see *supra*. n. 34.

[42] *Ibid.*

[43] Costa Rica, *ibid.*; Estonia recognizes the Republic of Kosovo, 21 February 2008, available online at www.vm.ee/?q=en/node/682 (last accessed 30 January 2012); Minister for Foreign Affairs, Dermot Ahern TD, announces Ireland's recognition of the Republic of Kosovo, 29 February 2008, available online at http://foreignaffairs.gov.ie/home/index.aspx?id=42938 (last accessed 30 January 2012); and US Recognizes Kosovo as Independent State, statement of Secretary of State Condoleeza Rice, Washington DC, 18 February 2008, *supra*. n. 34. Also cited by Christopher J. Borgen, 'Kosovo's Declaration of Independence: Self-determination, Secession, and Recognition', *ASIL Insights*, 12, fn 6, available online at: www.asil.org/insights080229.cfm (last accessed 27 January 2012). For a public restatement of the US arguments in defence of recognition, see US Department of State,'The Case for Kosovo', available online at www.state.gov/p/eur/ci/kv/c24701.htm (last accessed 27 January 2012).

affirmations that sustained efforts have been made to conform to this rule and that the basis for their stance must be found in some exception to that rule (among them, Germany, Hungary and Sweden).[44]

Several states coupled their statements about failed negotiations with the claim that Kosovo constitutes a *sui generis* case. No less than eight states assert this understanding in their formal recognition texts (e.g. Canada, Colombia, France and the United State).[45] The *sui generis* claim was explained by Condoleeza Rice, US Secretary of State at the time of the Kosovo Declaration, in the following terms: 'The unusual combination of factors found in the Kosovo situation – including the context of Yugoslavia's breakup, the history of ethnic cleansing and crimes against civilians in Kosovo, and the extended period of UN administration – are not found elsewhere and therefore make Kosovo a special case'.[46] The conclusions of the EU Council also tell of the same conviction. Although the EU Ministers for Foreign Affairs were unable to agree on how to react to the Kosovo decision, their common conclusions underline that 'Kosovo constitutes a *sui generis* case' which does not call into question the principles of sovereignty and territorial integrity as affirmed in the UN Charter and all the Security Council resolutions.[47]

The *sui generis* argument has also been combined with the claim that the final status of Kosovo touches upon a 'grey zone' in international law. In this spirit, Sweden explained that its decision had not been an easy one and that the most important factor was that Kosovo had been under international supervision for nearly ten years and that, during this period, had not been a sovereign part of Serbia.[48] Several recognizing

---

[44] Germany, *supra.* n. 36; Hungary, *supra.* n. 38; and Sweden, 'Sweden recognizes the Republic of Kosovo', press release, 4 March 2008, available online at www.sweden.gov.se/sb/d/10358/a/99714 (last accessed 30 January 2012).

[45] Canada, *supra. n.* 34; Colombia, *supra.* n. 34; France, *supra.* n. 34; and the United States, *supra.* n. 43.

[46] *Supra.* n. 43.

[47] EU Council Conclusions on Kosovo, 2851st External Relations Council Meeting, Brussels, 18 February 2008. The *sui generis* argument was also present in the conclusions of the Ahtisaari Plan of 2007 and Kosovo's Declaration of Independence. See also ICJ, *Application for Revision of the Judgment of 11 July 1996 in the case concerning the Application of the Convention on the Prevention and Punishment of the Crime of Genocide,* judgment of 3 February 2003, para. 71. According to the Court, the Former Republic of Yugoslavia (FRY) found itself in a *sui generis* position vis-à-vis the UN in the period between 1992 and 2000. See also A. Orakhelashvili, 'Statehood, Recognition and the UN System: A Unilateral Declaration of Independence in Kosovo', in Bogdandy and Wolfrum (eds), *Max Planck Yearbook of United Nations Law,* vol. XII, pp. 1–44.

[48] Sverige erkänner Kosovo, *Svenska Dagbladet,* 4 March 2008.

states seem to struggle with the fact that Kosovo, in spite of its 'new' status, will remain under international supervision. Thus, Afghanistan refers to the international trusteeship provisions in the UN Charter, and Italy recognizes the independence of Kosovo 'within a framework of international supervision'. Germany, Hungary and Sweden affirm 'continued international presence' as a sort of condition for their recognitions, and refer to the presence of the European-led European Union Rule of Law (EULEX) mission for an undefined time. According to Sweden, 'a difficult and demanding process is now being started to build a Kosovar State that meets international requirements'.[49] In a similar spirit, Australia admits that 'much remains to be done'.[50]

2. The objecting states

In contrast to the positions of recognizing states, the objections rely much more expressly upon international law, including the principle of territorial integrity as laid down in the UN Charter and the obligations of the parties to the dispute and included in Security Council Resolution 1244. The exact number of objecting states is more difficult to establish, not merely because there is no standard format for such objections, but also because the sources are not always fully reliable. Still, a reasonable estimate is that around at least forty-five states have expressed objections, some of which constitute serious accusations that the Kosovo decision amounts to a manifest abridgment of international law.[51]

One cluster of objecting states assert in bold terms that the Kosovo Declaration is at odds with international law (e.g. Algeria, Azerbaijan, Belarus, Indonesia, Libya, Russia, Slovakia, Spain, Sri Lanka and Tajikistan). Some emphasize the failure to respect the principles of territorial integrity and sovereignty of states as affirmed in the UN

---

[49] Sweden recognizes the Republic of Kosovo, press release, 4 March 2008, available online at www.sweden.gov.se/sb/d/10358/a/99714 (last accessed 27 January 2012).

[50] Australia recognises the Republic of Kosovo, Australia Foreign Department of Foreign Affairs and Trade, media release, 19 February 2008, available online at www.foreign-minister.gov.au/releases/2008/fa-s034_08.html (last accessed 27 January 2012).

[51] This study relies partly upon the collection of objections in Wikipedia (http://en.wikipedia.org/wiki/International_reaction_to_the_2008_declaration_of_independence_by_Kosovo#cite_note-132), which affirms that 102 states formally do not recognize Kosovo as independent. However, a closer examination of the statements reveals that some are in the process of recognition or are studying the situation. These states are not taken into account in this study as objecting states. It also builds upon prior research conducted by the author, which was published as a working paper, *supra.* n. 34.

Charter, while others remain more general in their statements and simply refer to 'international law'. Several express their convictions about the continued role of the Security Council in the settlement of the final status of Kosovo, including the need to support the UN system (Uzbekistan), and to respect Security Council decisions (e.g. Cyprus, Iran and Libya). Eleven states, among them Argentina, Brazil, Chile, China, India and Iran, invoke the authoritative nature of resolution 1244 and its affirmation of Serbian territorial integrity, as well as its call for mutual agreement among the parties to the dispute.

A few states, such as Kuwait, the Philippines and South Africa, request further negotiations, and in this manner indicate their disagreement with the recognizing states which assert that negotiations have failed or been exhausted. Brazil asserts that 'a peaceful solution of the issue of Kosovo must continue to be sought through dialogue and negotiation, under the auspices of the United Nations and the legal framework of Resolution 1244' and that it will 'await a UN Security Council decision before defining its official position on the matter of Kosovo's independence'.[52] In a similar vein, Cyprus holds that it 'will never recognize a unilateral decision of independence outside the UN framework, and in particular by side-stepping the role of the Security Council'.[53] The President of Iran emphatically states that international organizations have been weakened as a result of Kosovo's unilateral decision.[54]

The main arguments set forth by objecting states are summarized in a Joint Statement by the Foreign Ministers of India, Russia and China on 8 May 2008:

> We believe it must be solved solely on the basis of international law... the unilateral declaration of independence by Kosovo contradicts Resolution 1244. Russia, India and China encourage Belgrade and Pristina to resume talks within the framework of international law and hope they reach an agreement on all problems of that territory.[55]

While references to international legal principles and provisions dominate the objection statements, an in-depth analysis demonstrates

---

[52] 'Brasil não reconhece Kosovo sem acordo com Sérvia', *Diário Catarinense*, 22 February 2008.

[53] 'Cyprus will never recognize unilaterally declared independence of Kosovo', *People's Daily*, 12 February 2008.

[54] Yuri Plutenko, 'Golamreza Ansari, Iran's Ambassador to Russia: We don't have such missiles', *Moscow News*, 13 March 2008.

[55] Joint Statement of the Foreign Ministers of India, Russia and China, regarding Kosovo, Conference in Ekaterinburg, 15 May 2008.

the presence of political concerns as well. Especially evident is the fear that Kosovo will create a 'dangerous precedent'.[56] No less than twelve states, among them Argentina, Armenia, Bolivia, India, Israel and Russia, refer to the negative effects that the recognition of the unilateral decision of Kosovo will have when seeking to resolve problems in their own or neighbouring countries. China and Sri Lanka hold that the unilateral act threatens peace and stability in the region and beyond. Cuba and Venezuela depict the entire recognition process as nothing but an ideological move of the United States and/or the EU.

3.   The silent states

By no means all states have come to participate in the politics of recognition in the sense of having developed official opinions. In fact, about sixty have refrained from advancing any position whatsoever, or simply advised that they are studying the question. This group includes some Latin American countries, among them Uruguay and Guatemala, not an insignificant number of African states, including Botswana, Burundi, Cameroon, Chad, Côte d'Ivoire, Ethiopia, Eritrea, Kenya, Liberia, Lesotho, Namibia, Rwanda, Tanzania, Togo, Tunisia and Zimbabwe, and various Asian states, such as Burma, Brunei, Cambodia and Mongolia.

The factors inducing this considerable silence can only be a matter of speculation. It must be recalled that many states do not have a national stake in the outcome and settlement of the dispute regarding the terms and conditions for secession, or may not want to adopt a position because of the dominance and pressure exerted by more powerful states. Others might prioritize more urgent problems at home and leave the problems facing other (new) states at the margins. Furthermore, there might be concerns about the possible negative consequences of taking sides in what seems to be a disagreement of an especially unfortunate kind. A final explanation is a good faith preoccupation seeking clarification of the legality of the Kosovo decision from the standpoint of international law. Indeed, about thirty silent states voted in favour of the General Assembly resolution requesting the ICJ for an advisory opinion on this matter.

---

[56] C. Warbrick, 'Kosovo: The Declaration of Independence', (2008) 57 *International & Comparative Law Quarterly*, at 679, n. 29; and I. Krastev, 'Balkan Deep Freeze. What the right Kosovo precedent might look like', *The Wall Street Journal*, 2 February 2007. For a more recent analysis of this issue (also considering the Palestinian case), see R. Falk, 'The *Kosovo* Advisory Opinion: Conflict Resolution and Precedent', (2011) 105 *American Journal of International Law*, 50–60.

V. The failure of the UN Multilateral Framework

1. The UN Security Council

The Security Council had the power and competence to prevent the politics of recognition from emerging in reaction to the Kosovo Declaration. For one thing, the Declaration seemed at odds with its resolution 1244[57] establishing the international presence in Kosovo. In particular, it forestalls:

> A political process towards the establishment of an interim political framework agreement providing for a substantial self-government for Kosovo, taking full account of the Rambouillet accords and the principles of sovereignty and territorial integrity of the Federal Republic of Yugoslavia and the other countries of the region.[58]

In 2007, the UN Special Envoy, Martti Ahtisaari, who led the initial negotiations between Pristine and Belgrade, presented a comprehensive proposal on the Kosovo status settlement to the parties. However, since he proposed that Kosovo should become an independent state, and that the international community should assist its population in furthering its public institutions incumbent upon that status, it was deplored by Serbia and its allies, particularly Russia. Thus, the Council was unable to endorse the proposal, which remained as a set of recommendations. In this sense, if the authority of Resolution 1244 remained intact, as it seems to have done, the Kosovo Declaration was an apparent violation thereof, which thus called for an official condemnation or the adoption of a new resolution to replace it.[59]

Whatever importance we may (now) attach to Resolution 1244 or the Ahtisaari Plan for determining how the dispute between Kosovo and Serbia must be (or ought to have been) settled,[60] the fact that Kosovo declared independence in the way it did implied a change of situation. When a secessionist movement declares independence from its parent state, some international reaction, whether collective or unilateral, is expected, especially if such development seems to contradict a Security Council resolution. Nonetheless, because of a radical disagreement among the permanent members in the Council on how to react, they

---

[57] UNSC Res. 1244 of 10 June 1999. [58] Ibid., Annex I.

[59] But note the reasoning of the ICJ regarding the provisional authorities, International Court of Justice, *Accordance with international law of the unilateral declaration of independence in respect of Kosovo*, Advisory Opinion delivered on 22 July 2010.

[60] See Chapter 5 above on the continuing relevance of the UN Resolution.

were incapable of taking collective action. The subsequent unilateral behaviours of its permanent members reinforced the perception that each state was free to decide on its own terms whether or not to afford recognition. On 18 February 2008, the United States, the UK and France issued recognition statements declaring Kosovo to be 'a sovereign and independent state'. In contrast, the Russian Federation fervently opposed,[61] and China also expressed its deep concerns about the negative impact of the Kosovo Decision on peace and security in the Balkan region, respect for international law and the authority of the Council.[62] The open disagreement among these powerful states set the stage for the politics of recognition.

2. *The General Assembly*

The UN General Assembly session on 8 October 2008 could have represented an opportunity to discuss the final status of Kosovo in a public forum for the purpose of finding some common ground. Instead, the purpose of the session was to debate the Serbian proposal to ask the International Court for an advisory opinion on the international legality of the conduct by what it still regarded as its 'province'. In the end, the Serbian proposal found sufficient support,[63] and the General Assembly came to request the Court for its opinion whether 'the unilateral declaration of independence by the Provisional Institutions of Self-Government of Kosovo [is] in accordance with international law'.[64]

The resolution authorizing the request, which was adopted by a vote of 77 in favour to 6 against, with 74 abstentions and 28 members absent, acknowledged the 'varied reactions by the Members of the United Nations as to its compatibility with the existing international order'.[65]

---

[61] 'Russia warns US over Kosovo move', *BBC News*, 19 February 2008, available online at http://news.bbc.co.uk/2/hi/europe/7252512.stm (last accessed 27 January 2012).

[62] 'China deeply concerned over Kosovo's Declaration of Independence', *China Daily*, 18 February 2008, available online at www.chinadaily.com.cn/china/2008–02/18/content_6462222.htm (last accessed 27 January 2012).

[63] The decision was supported by a majority of states present and voting in pursuance of article 18.3 of the UN Charter.

[64] UNGA resolution 63/3: Request for an Advisory Opinion of the International Court of Justice on whether the Unilateral Declaration of Independence of Kosovo is in Accordance with International Law, adopted on the 22nd plenary meeting on 8 October 2008.

[65] UNGA, Sixty-third session, 22nd plenary meeting in New York, A/63/PV.22, 8 October 2008.

The question about the relevance of international law to settle the future status of Kosovo and, thus, for affording recognition, was the object of radical discord. States that had insisted on the political and unique nature of the solution that must be forthcoming argued that the matter was simply not apt for judicial review. Canada pointed out that the request endangered the legitimacy of the ICJ, as 'the case raises highly political matters'. Australia, Germany, Switzerland and the UK emphasized that the development prejudiced the future political stability and economic progress of the region. In addition, Albania and the United States expressed concerns about the fact that the request had not mustered unequivocal support. As the UK stressed, more members had felt the need to abstain rather than voting in favour of the resolution.[66]

Those maintaining that the Kosovo Declaration was a serious abridgement of the governing law felt that the adoption of the resolution requesting the ICJ for an opinion was a victory. The Serbian Minister for Foreign Affairs, Mr. Jeremic, concluded the 22nd session of the General Assembly by noting that 'it was a great day for the Assembly and international law ... [and that] he looked forward to working constructively on the process regarding the future status of "their province"'.[67] The Kosovar authorities, in contrast, voiced their regret over the resolution, stressing that the independence of Kosovo was irreversible and that the judicial review of the legality of its declaration would not prevent states from appreciating the constant progress in Kosovo and recognizing it as a state.[68] When the matter was working its way through the ICJ machinery, Kosovo continued to take steps that could strengthen its claims to statehood. The hope seemed to be that, by the time the ICJ had pronounced itself on the issue, statehood would be a *fait accompli*, an irreversible fact that would supersede the quarrels about the international legality of its unilateral decision.

3.   The ICJ

For governments that had assumed that an advisory opinion of the Court, if the request was accepted, would support their positions on the illegality of the Kosovo Declaration, or in any case guide them when

---

[66] *Ibid.*   [67] *Ibid.*

[68] Report of the Secretary-General on the United Nations Interim Administration Mission in Kosovo (S/2008/692) 24 November 2008, para. 3. Between 8 October 2008 and 22 July 2010, 21 states recognized Kosovo.

deciding on the Kosovo question, the contents of that opinion, when it was finally delivered on 22 July 2010, was in some way surprising and also disappointing.[69] In fact, the Advisory Opinion did not touch upon any matter related to recognition whatsoever, including the character, effects and limits of such acts, or the related questions about the meaning and scope of the principle of self-determination, the terms and conditions for secession and the statehood criteria, and if post-Cold War developments called for a revision of our understanding of the purpose and effects of recognition.[70]

Contrary to what most states that took part in the proceedings had perceived to be the most critical issues embedded in the question before the Court, a majority of ICJ judges upheld an extremely narrow and positivistic interpretation of what they had been asked to do: to respond to the query whether declarations of independence in general violate international law. Hence, it did not consider it 'necessary to address such issues as whether or not the declaration has led to the creation of a State or the status of the acts of recognition in order to answer the question put by the General Assembly'.[71] It also added that 'debates regarding the extent of the right of self-determination and the existence of any right of "remedial secession" ... concern the right to separate from a State ... and that issue is beyond the scope of the question posed by the General Assembly'.[72] In answering the question of substance – whether the Kosovo Declaration violated international law – the Court followed the logic of the *Lotus* judgment, according to which it is sufficient to demonstrate the absence of a prohibition and not the existence of a permissive rule when determining that a specific act was in accordance with international law.[73] A majority of judges (10 in favour, with 4 separate

---

[69] See, e.g., Concepción Escobar Hernández, 'The Kingdom of Spain's Stance on the Advisory Procedure: A General Approach', (2011) 23 *Revista Española de Derecho Internacional*, 1–26.

[70] For a critical assessment of the narrow approach adopted by the ICJ in response to the request in focus, see, e.g., M. G. Kohen and Katherine Del Mar, 'The Kosovo Advisory Opinion and UNSCR 1244 (1999): A Declaration of "Independence from International Law"?', (2011) 24 *Leiden Journal of International Law*, 109–26. For an early reflection on post-Cold War developments, see, e.g., T. Franck, 'Postmodern Tribalism and the Right to Secession', in C. Brölman, R. Lefeber and M. Zieck (eds), *Peoples and Minorities in International Law* (Dordrecht: Martinus Nijhoff, 1993), pp. 3–27. For a more recent account, see, e.g., K. Knop, *Diversity and Self-determination in International Law* (Cambridge University Press, 2002).

[71] *Kosovo* Advisory Opinion, para. 51.   [72] *Ibid.*, para. 83.

[73] Permanent Court of International Justice, *S.S. Lotus (France v. Turkey)*, Judgment of 7 September 1927, pp. 18–21. See also *Kosovo* Advisory Opinion, Declaration of Judge Bruno Simma, para. 2.

opinions and 1 declaration, as well as 4 against)[74] concluded that such declarations do not per se violate international law.[75] Evidently not all ICJ judges agreed, and the Advisory Opinion was officially accused by a concurring judge of being an 'exercise in mechanical jurisprudence'.[76] Judge Simma complained about the opinion's 'unnecessarily limited – and potentially misguided – analysis'; not only did it contradict the plain wording of the question that had been asked, but it also excluded any consideration of 'whether international law may specifically permit or even foresee an entitlement to declare independence when certain conditions are met'.[77] According to Judge Simma, the Court should indeed have touched upon the law regarding secession, including 'remedial secession', as well as self-determination, instead of avoiding them.[78] In the view of Judge Yusuf, 'the declaration of independence of Kosovo is the expression of a claim to separate statehood and part of a process to create a new State'. Thus, the Court was asked to 'assess whether or not the process by which the people of Kosovo were seeking to establish their own State involved a violation of international law in view of the possible existence of a positive right of the people of Kosovo in the specific circumstances which prevailed in that territory'.[79] However, it evidently failed to seize a unique opportunity to 'assess, in a specific and concrete situation, the legal conditions to be met for such a right to self-determination to materialize and give legitimacy to a claim of separation'.[80] Pronouncing himself along the same lines, Judge Sepúlveda-Amor pointed out that the 'Court, by virtue of its responsibilities in the maintenance of international peace and security under the United Nations Charter, has a duty to exercise its advisory function in respect of legal

---

[74] Looking back on previous advisory opinions of the Court in response to controversial legal questions posed to it, a split decision was to be expected. See *Legal Consequences of the Construction of a Wall in the Occupied Palestinian Territory*, Advisory Opinion, ICJ Reports 2004, p. 136; *Legality of the Threat or Use of Nuclear Weapons*, Advisory Opinion, ICJ Reports, 1996, p. 226; *Western Sahara*, Advisory Opinion, ICJ Reports, p. 12; *Legal Consequences for States of the Continued Presence of South Africa in Namibia (South West Africa) notwithstanding Security Council Resolution 276 (1970)*, Advisory Opinion, ICJ Reports 1971, p. 16.

[75] However, that the majority of judges agreed on how to respond to the request for an advisory opinion seems somewhat misleading, considering the critical contents of the separate opinions and the declaration delivered by the concurring judges.

[76] *Kosovo* Advisory Opinion, Declaration of Judge Bruno Simma, para. 10.

[77] *Ibid.*, para. 1.   [78] *Ibid.*, paras. 3 and 6.

[79] *Ibid.*, Separate Opinion of Judge Yusuf, para. 2.   [80] *Ibid.*, para. 17.

questions which, like the present one, relate to Chapter VII situations'. In
his view, many of the legal issues involved in the present case required
guidance, including 'the scope of the right to self-determination, the
question of "remedial secession", the extent of the powers of the Security
Council in relation to the principle of territorial integrity. . . and, finally,
the effect of the recognition or non-recognition of a State in the present
case'.[81] Finally, Judge Cançado Trindade, while concurring with the
majority opinion, developed a lengthy substantive argument about the
direct relevance of the human tragedy in Kosovo, the atrocities committed, and the importance of the humanitarian aspect of international law,
all of them dimensions of the question that the majority of the ICJ judges
never touched upon.[82]

While the Court's reliance upon a formalistic interpretation of international law might have helped its judges to find some common
ground,[83] it failed to give any helpful legal guidance on matters of
recognition. The fact that only one state (Oman) has explicitly referred
to the Advisory Opinion of the Court delivered on 22 July 2010 when
recognizing Kosovo is telling of how little significance it has had in
guiding states that are studying the matter, or for opposing states to
change their minds.[84] The policy of avoidance adopted by the Court
bolstered the perception that the politics of recognition is the only option
for tackling controversial cases.

V.   Conclusion

The failure of the UN multilateral framework to establish a common
position on how to react to the Kosovo Declaration is telling of the fact of
radical discord about the terms and conditions for recognition, including
what recognitions are ultimately for, as well as their effects. It is also
telling of the incapacity of existing mechanisms – whether political or
judicial – to channel and settle such discord. While the General
Assembly requested the ICJ to answer a question that was widely
assumed to touch upon several fundamental questions related to self-
determination and secession, all of them in need of legal guidance, it

---

[81] *Ibid.*, Separate Opinion of Judge Bernado Sepúlveda-Amor, para. 35.
[82] *Ibid.*, Separate Opinion of Judge Antonio Cançado Trindade.
[83] But note *ibid.*, Dissenting Opinions of Judges Bennouna, Koroma and Skotnikov.
[84] Oman: Statement of recognition, 4 February 2011. Available online at www.mfa-ks.net/?
page=2,4,629 (last accessed 27 January 2012).

refrained from plunging into any of them. The Court's posture might have its own rationale, in the sense of seeking to create an air of neutrality and impartiality in relation to rival positions among the permanent members in the Security Council. Nonetheless, its stance of avoidance has strengthened the impression that the question of how to react to declarations of independence in controversial cases will be negotiated in political settings.

The multiple declarations of independence generated by the dissolution of the Soviet Union and Yugoslavia may have called for new responses, but these responses are still extremely controversial and contradict each other. In particular, powerful states have come to use recognition acts in an attempt to constitute states in spite of the fact that recognitions have no such normative force; they never had. An alternative interpretation of such recognitions is that they are modes of affirming the plausibility and legitimacy of state-creation projects that require international assistance, support and protection to be accomplished in a successful manner. This usage of recognition is not a revival of the constitutive thesis if what is distinct about that thesis is its refusal to consider a new state as a subject of international law prior to recognition. Indeed, both the constitutive and the declaratory theses share the assumption that recognition refers to the acknowledgement of statehood in a given case. In contrast, several recognizing states in the politics surrounding Kosovo openly admitted that this entity was not, in fact, an independent and sovereign state, at least in the traditional sense, as it remained under international supervision.

So far, Kosovo has received only *partial recognition*. New talks between Belgrade and Pristine resumed in Brussels in March 2011 and are led by the EU.[85] It is the first time that the two disputing parties have attempted to negotiate since the time of the Kosovo Declaration, although Belgrade persists in its stance on refusing recognition. The democratic general elections held in Kosovo in December 2011 have been said to be successful.[86] Since June 2009, it has been a member of the World Bank and the International Monetary Fund (IMF). However, new concerns about the trafficking of organs in Kosovo have emerged

---

[85] Information about these EU-led new negotiations is available online at www.setimes. com/cocoon/setimes/xhtml/en_GB/features/setimes/features/2011/03/09/feature-02 (last accessed 27 January 2012).

[86] Report of the Secretary-General on the United Nations Interim Administration Mission in Kosovo, S/2011/43, 28 January 2011.

as a result of a recent Council of Europe report,[87] and have the potential effect of discrediting international efforts, now mainly led by the EULEX,[88] to strengthen the institutions of Kosovo. Because of Russian and Chinese opposition, however, Kosovo will not be able to become a member of the UN in the near future.

The politics of recognition do not settle the question about the final status of a community that desires to convert itself into a state. In stark contrast with the idea of a standard procedure, the corroboration of these politics implies the absence of guarantees of foreseeability or certainty about the prospects of actually gaining the status of statehood. Neither does it offer any guarantees of equal treatment and fairness across different cases and communities with similar aspirations. At the same time, these politics may be the best hope for a sort of 'second-best' in the absence of common ground. To be sure, political quarrels may eventually settle down once statehood in a given case is beyond any doubt a *fait accompli*. But there is no assurance that this will always happen. In the meantime, conflicts over recognition will be negotiated in political settings, ideally, through reason-giving and persuasive argument, but, realistically, through lobbying activities and the exertion of pressure by powerful states.[89] Though the fore-stalled voting in the General Assembly over the status of Palestine might offer new insights into the potential of this political organ to move controversial cases forward towards a final settlement with the help of an established voting procedure, it does not change the contention about the politics of recognition as the unique avenue to channel disagreements about the legitimacy and plausibility of different aspirations for statehood, to build coalitions around these matters, and eventually to accept what is often, by the time of settling on a common position, an already established fact.[90]

---

[87] Report of the Parliamentary Assembly of the Council of Europe (Rapporteur: Mr. Dick Marty), 'Inhuman treatment of people and illicit trafficking in human organs in Kosovo', 7 January 2011.

[88] Information about EULEX is available online at www.eulex-kosovo.eu/en/front/ (last accessed 27 January 2011).

[89] For an account of 'reason-giving' or 'deliberations' as a mode of resolving disagreements, see, for instance, the debate in J. Elster (ed.), *Deliberative Democracy and Its Critics* (Cambridge University Press, 1999).

[90] *Supra.* n. 11.

Revisiting lessons on the new law of statehood: Palestinian independence in a post-Kosovo world

TAMAR MEGIDDO AND ZOHAR NEVO

I. Introduction

On 23 September 2011, Mahmoud Abbas, Chairman of the Palestinian National Authority, submitted an application for the admission of the State of Palestine to membership in the United Nations (UN). While not declaring Palestinian independence anew, Abbas referred to the 1988 declaration of independence, among others, as he described himself, exceptionally, as the President of the State of Palestine.[1] The UN application was preceded by a wave of recognition of Palestine as a state, principally among Latin American countries. Starting in 2010, the State of Palestine was awarded recognition by Brazil,[2] Venezuela,[3] Argentina,[4] Bolivia,[5] Ecuador,[6]

---

[1] *Application of Palestine for Admission to Membership in the United Nations*, UN Doc. A/66/371 (23 September 2011); *Statement by H.E. Mr. Mahmoud Abbas, President of the State of Palestine before United Nations General Assembly 66th Session* (23 September 2011), http://gadebate.un.org/sites/default/files/gastatements/66/PS_en.pdf.

[2] República Federativa do Brasil, Ministério das Relações Exteriores, *Recognition of the Palestinian State along the 1967 Borders* (3 December 2010), www.itamaraty.gov.br/sala-de-imprensa/notas-a-imprensa/reconhecimento-do-estado-palestino-nas-fronteiras-de-1967.

[3] Gobierno Bolivariano de Venezuela, Ministerio del Poder Popular para la Comunicación y la Información, *Gobierno y Pueblo Venezolano Ratifican Su Solidaridad con el Estado Palestino* (27 April 2009), www.minci.gob.ve/internacionales/1/188715/gobierno_y_pue blo.html.

[4] La República Argentina, Ministerio de Relaciones Exteriores, Comercio Internacional y Cultora, *La República Argentina Ha Reconocido a Palestina Como Estado Libre e Independiente* (6 December 2010) www.mrecic.gov.ar/portal/ver_adjunto.php?id=3048.

[5] DPA, 'Bolivia Formally Recognizes Palestine as an Independent State', *Ha'aretz.com* (22 December 2010).

[6] República del Ecuador, Ministerio de Relaciones Exteriores, *Ecuador Reconoce el Estado Palestino* (24 December 2010) www.mmrree.gob.ec/2010/bol992.asp.

Chile,[7] Guyana,[8] Peru[9] and the Dominican Republic.[10] In conjunction with this trend, Russia reaffirmed its recognition of the Palestinian unilateral declaration of independence of 15 November 1988.[11] Various other states, while not (yet[12]) officially recognising an independent State of Palestine, have since upgraded the level of the Palestinian diplomatic representation in their countries to 'missions' and 'embassies', terms normally reserved for the diplomatic representatives of recognised states.[13]

Against this backdrop, this chapter will revisit conclusions outlined in a previous paper, derived from Kosovo's 2008 unilateral declaration of independence,[14] and will seek to assess whether these conclusions are consistent with developments in the Palestinian quest for independence.

II.   The international law of statehood

1.   The classical conditions for statehood

States have long acknowledged the existence of other states by means of recognition.[15] Recognition is today predominantly considered declaratory and not constitutive.[16] Nevertheless, declaration may indicate that

---

[7] Gobierno del Chile, *Declaración del Gobierno de Chile sobre el Reconocimiento del Estado de Palestina* (7 January 2011), http://informa.gob.cl/destacado/declaracion-del-gobierno-de-chile-sobre-el-reconocimiento-del-estado-de-palestina/.

[8] Republic of Guyana, *Statement by the Government of Guyana in Recognition of the State of Palestine* (13 January 2011), www.minfor.gov.gy/tsite/index.php?option=com_content&task=view&id=62&Itemid=.

[9] Ministerio de Relaciones Exteriores del Perú, *Perú Reconoce al Estado Palestino* (24 January 2011) www.rree.gob.pe/portal/boletinInf.nsf/mrealdia/5ACB6C577AC253100525782200615A34?OpenDocument.

[10] Presidencia de la República Dominicana, *RD y Palestina firman relaciones diplomáticas* (14 July 2009) www.presidencia.gob.do/app/article.aspx?id=11145.

[11] B. Ravid and A. Issacharoff, 'Medvedev Falls Short of Recognizing Palestinian State', *Ha'aretz.com* (19 January 2011).

[12] B. Ravid and A. Issacharof, 'France May Support Full UN Membership for Palestinians if Peace Talks Remain Deadlocked', *Ha'aretz.com* (5 June 2011).

[13] B. Ravid and News Agencies, 'Britain to Upgrade Palestinian Delegation to "Mission"', *Ha'aretz.com* (7 March 2011).

[14] Z. Nevo and T. Megiddo, 'Lessons From Kosovo: The Law of Statehood and Palestinian Unilateral Independence', (2009) 5(2) *Journal of International Law and International Relations* 89.

[15] R. Higgins, *Problems and Process: International Law and How We Use It* (Clarendon Press, 1994), p. 42.

[16] On the various formulations of the constitutive and declaratory approaches to recognition, *see* H. Lauterpacht, *Recognition in International Law* (Cambridge University Press, 1948), pp. 38–63.

an entity has conformed to the requirements of statehood, and may carry significant weight in borderline cases.[17]

The principle underlying the 1933 Montevideo Convention on the Rights and Duties of States' criteria of statehood – population, territory, government and capacity to enter into relations with other states[18] – is the effectiveness of the territorial unit; namely, its ability to function as an independent self-governing entity.[19]

The 'permanent population' requirement has been understood to refer to a stable community of any size, residing in a given territory. Similarly, the 'defined territory' of a state may be extremely small, fragmented, or even an enclave within another state. Furthermore, precise demarcation of the state's boundaries is not necessary.[20] The 'government' requirement refers to the effective exercise of authority with respect to persons and property within a territory, while the 'capacity to enter into relations' is the lawful right and ability to exercise that authority with respect to other states.[21] Together, these last two requirements form the central condition – *effectiveness*, which is assessed both formally and substantively.[22]

2. Additional considerations: Legality and legitimacy

A survey of international practice reveals a number of cases in which the classical requirements were not the only considerations taken into account by extant states when considering whether to recognise new states. Some entities which did not fully meet the classical criteria were nonetheless broadly recognised as independent, while, in other cases, entities which seemed to fulfil the classical criteria were denied such recognition.[23] An emerging set of additional considerations, based on

[17] 'Opinion No. 8, Conference on Yugoslavia', *International Law Reports* 92 (1992), 201; M. N. Shaw, *International Law*, 5th edn (Cambridge University Press, 2003), pp. 189, 369.

[18] Montevideo Convention on the Rights and Duties of States (26 December 1933), 165 LNTS. 19; J. Crawford, *The Creation of States in International Law*, 2nd edn (Clarendon Press, 2006), p. 46.

[19] *Ibid.*

[20] *Ibid.*, pp. 46–7, 52; I. Brownlie, *Principles of Public International Law*, 6th edn (Oxford University Press, 2003), p. 70; *North Sea Continental Shelf (Germany/Denmark)*, *International Court of Justice Reports* 3 (1969), para. 46.

[21] Crawford, *The Creation of States*, pp. 55, 62–6.

[22] R. Higgins, *The Development of International Law Through the Political Organs of the United Nations* (Oxford University Press, 1963), pp. 25–6; Crawford, *The Creation of States*, pp. 67–89.

[23] Nevo and Megiddo, 'Lessons from Kosovo', pp. 91–6.

principles of legality and legitimacy, had a decisive effect on recognition of states in these cases.[24]

Self-determination – a people's right to determine their own political status – has had the most profound impact on the willingness of states to recognise an entity's statehood. Although this principle came into being as the basis for equal rights in the context of decolonisation,[25] it has broadened over time to include certain post-colonial contexts.[26] In principle, self-determination may be exercised 'internally' within an existing state, for example, through autonomy or cultural rights granted to a certain group.[27] International law is reluctant, however, to recognise a general right to 'external' self-determination (i.e. secession from a state), as that would be at odds with the fundamental principle of the territorial integrity of states.[28] Nevertheless, self-determination has significant influence in the context of statehood. In cases where the right to self-determination of a people is recognised, it may mitigate the extent to which an entity claiming statehood is required to fulfil the classical criteria of statehood, especially in the context of decolonization.[29] The right to self-determination may also be seen as a prerequisite to the establishment of a state.[30]

In addition, it has been argued that in certain circumstances the right to self-determination generates a right to 'remedial secession'.[31] While upholding the principle of territorial integrity, the 1970 *Declaration on Friendly Relations* adopted by the UN General Assembly also implicitly acknowledges an exception to its protection, when a government denies a people the right to self-determination and

[24] Shaw, *International Law*, p. 178; Brownlie, *Public International Law*, p. 70; Crawford, *The Creation of States*, pp. 97–9.

[25] UN Charter, arts. 1(2), 55, 73(b) and 76(b); Crawford, *The Creation of States*, p. 114; Higgins, *Problems and Process*, pp. 111–14. See also *Declaration on the Granting of Independence to Colonial Countries and People*, GA Res. 1514 (XV), UN GAOR, UN Doc. A/4684 (1961) 174.

[26] International Covenant on Civil and Political Rights (16 December 1966), 999 UNTS 171, art. 1; A. Cassese, *Self-determination of Peoples: A Legal Reappraisal* (Cambridge University Press, 1995), pp. 65–6, 118–24.

[27] *Declaration on Friendly Relations*; D. Raič, *Statehood and the Law of Self Determination* (Kluwer Law International, 2002), p. 226.

[28] UN Charter, art. 2(4); Crawford, *The Creation of States*, p. 390.

[29] M. Shaw, *Title to Territory in Africa: International Legal Issues* (Clarendon Press, 1986), pp. 151–62. An example may be found in the case of Eritrea, *see* Nevo and Megiddo, 'Lessons from Kosovo', 94–5.

[30] Shaw, *International Law*, pp. 184–5.

[31] Raič, *Statehood*, pp. 324, 332; L. C. Bucheit, *Secession: The Legitimacy of Self-Determination* (Yale University Press, 1978), p. 220.

equality.[32] Further support for this position was provided by the Supreme Court of Canada, in its reference decision regarding the legality of a possible secession of Quebec.[33] Consequently, some scholars have argued that international law allows for 'remedial secession' in exceptional circumstances,[34] for example, when a minority residing in a defined territory is persistently denied the right to internal self-determination, or when grave human rights violations indicate that internal solutions are not possible.[35] Other writers have denied the existence of a right to remedial secession, pointing to a lack of international practice and *opinio juris*.[36]

Another legal principle which has gained importance with regard to the law of statehood suggests that when a state is founded through a breach of a peremptory norm of international law, other states are arguably obligated to deny it recognition.[37] Further considerations are based on notions of legitimacy, as evidenced by the guidelines on recognition of new states adopted by the then European Community in 1991, which predicate the recognition of new states on their establishment of democratic institutions and respect for human rights.[38] It is doubtful whether these suggested requirements have become peremptory norms that could invalidate an already-recognised entity's

---

[32] *Declaration on Friendly Relations*; cf. *Vienna Declaration and Programme of Action* (12 July 1993), UN Doc. A/CONF.157/23 at para. 2; *Declaration on the Occasion of the Fiftieth Anniversary of the United Nations* (24 October 1995), GA Res. 50/6 , UN GAOR, UN Doc. A/RES/50/49.

[33] 'Re Secession of Quebec' *International Law Reports* 115 (1998), para. 130 (Canada, SC); *see also, Loizidou* v. *Turkey*, no. 15318/89, [1996] VI ECHR 2216 at 2241, Wildhaber J., Concurring Opinion.

[34] C. Tomuschat, 'Secession and Self-determination' in M. G. Kohen (ed.), *Secession: International Law Perspectives* (Cambridge University Press, 2006), p. 41; J. Dugard and D. Raič, 'The Role of Recognition in the Law and Practice of Secession' in Kohen (ed.), *Secession, ibid.*, pp. 109–10.

[35] Dugard and Raič, *ibid.*, p. 109.

[36] Cassese, *Self-determination*, pp. 118–24; Crawford, *The Creation of States*, pp. 417–18; *see also* R. Higgins, 'Postmodern Tribalism and the Right to Secession, Comments' in C. Brölmann *et al.* (eds), *Peoples and Minorities in International Law* (Nijhoff, 1993); *but see* Raič, *Statehood*, pp. 362–6.

[37] International Law Commission, *Draft Articles on Responsibility of States for Internationally Wrongful Acts*, UN Doc. A/56/10 (2001), art. 41(2); UN Charter, art. 2(4); Crawford, *The Creation of States*, p. 155. The non-recognition of the Bantustan states, set up by South Africa in pursuit of its apartheid policy, is considered to be a manifestation of this principle; *see also, The Accordance With International Law of the Unilateral Declaration of Independence in Respect of Kosovo*, Advisory Opinion (unpublished, 22 July 2010), para. 81 (ICJ Kosovo Advisory Opinion).

[38] 'Opinion no. 4, Conference on Yugoslavia', *International Law Reports*, 92 (1992), 173.

statehood.[39] Nevertheless, they may have an impact on the willingness of states to recognise new entities.[40]

In our view, the classical Montevideo criteria still form the prominent requirements for assessing statehood; and yet, the complete fulfilment of these criteria is no longer the exclusive yardstick for statehood. The classical criteria remain important because they fundamentally capture the elements essential for an entity to function effectively as a state. Therefore, an entity which does not meet them must present compelling additional considerations in order to be recognised. It is at this point that the additional considerations come into play. The continued relevance of the classical criteria is evidenced by the international community's efforts to ensure that all recognised entities ultimately achieve effectiveness. Such efforts include, for example, the establishment of the United Nations Transitional Authority for East Timor (UNTAET),[41] with the objective of piloting the reconstruction of an independent East Timorese state after the Indonesian 'scorched earth' withdrawal, or the international administration installed in Kosovo.[42] We now turn to review the lessons which may be drawn from the case of Kosovo with regard to the development of the law of statehood.

III.   Lessons from Kosovo

1.   International recognition of the Republic of Kosovo

On 17 February 2008, the Republic of Kosovo declared independence.[43] This declaration was met with mixed international reactions, and raised questions regarding the international law of statehood, and Kosovo's possible precedential value for this body of international law. Some 88 states have so far formally recognised the independent Republic of Kosovo. Among them are the United States, a majority of the

---

[39] Crawford, *The Creation of States*, p. 155.
[40] For a review of relevant past cases, in which statehood was attained despite deficiencies with regard to the classical criteria, and in which the principles regarding legality and legitimacy seemed to have played a role, *see* Nevo and Megiddo, 'Lessons from Kosovo', 93–6.
[41] SC Res. 1272, UN SCOR, UN Doc. S/RES/1272 (1999).
[42] *Ibid.*, J. D'Aspremont, 'Regulating Statehood: The Kosovo Status Settlement', (2007) 20 *Leiden Journal of International Law* 654.
[43] *Kosova Declaration of Independence* (17 February 2008), www.assembly-kosova.org/common/docs/Dek_Pav_e.pdf.

European Union (EU) member states and a majority of the North Atlantic Treaty Organization (NATO) members.[44]

In a previous paper we submitted that, solely on the basis of the classical criteria, it would be difficult to find that Kosovo had attained statehood.[45] We argued, therefore, that an international recognition of Kosovo's statehood would likely draw on additional considerations. Analysing Kosovo's circumstances against the background of the development of the law of statehood in recent decades, we suggested that the following factors contributed to Kosovo's recognition so far: its right to self-determination; its history of enduring human rights violations; the dissolution of the Socialist Federal Republic of Yugoslavia; the international administration and involvement in guiding Kosovar institution building; the deadlocked negotiations and the concern that stagnation would create further regional destabilisation; the existence of a comprehensive plan for its future development; and the apparently successful establishment of democratic institutions in Kosovo. These factors signal legitimacy as an important element of the calculus of new-state recognition. While it is likely that none of these factors can independently determine an entity's statehood, they may have a cumulative impact, allowing a claim for independence to win the recognition of the international community in spite of deficiencies in the entity's fulfilment of the classical criteria of statehood.[46]

2. The International Court of Justice decision on Kosovo

In its Advisory Opinion on the *Accordance with International Law of the Unilateral Declaration of Independence in Respect of Kosovo*, the International Court of Justice (ICJ) avoided discussing the question of whether Kosovo had indeed been transformed into a state. Instead, it considered whether it is illegal unilaterally to declare independence under international law, and held that generally it was not. The Court did, however, make several interesting points on the issue of the establishment of new states. First, regarding Kosovo itself, the Court noted that UN Security Council Resolution 1244 created an interim international administration in Kosovo, which superseded the legal order in force at the time in the territory of Kosovo – that is, Serbia's rule of the

---

[44] www.rks-gov.net/sq-AL/Pages/ShtetKaneNjohurKosoven.aspx.
[45] For a more detailed review of the history of Kosovo and the circumstances of the Kosovar declaration of independence, *see* Nevo and Megiddo, 'Lessons from Kosovo', 96–9.
[46] *Ibid.*, 106.

territory and sovereignty over it – pending a future decision on Kosovo's final status. This assertion reaffirms the idea that international administration may be a key step towards statehood and one that may defeat a competing claim of sovereignty over the territory.

Another important comment made by the Court is its apparent endorsement of the assumption that declarations of independence 'connected with the unlawful use of force or other egregious violations of norms of general international law, in particular those of peremptory character [*jus cogens*], may be considered illegal'.[47] The Court further mentioned that the interim international administration of Kosovo was designed to achieve humanitarian purposes, following the crisis Kosovo had endured.[48] This point may be read to affirm that humanitarian crises or a pragmatic intent to avoid further destabilisation may also tilt the scales towards recognising the end of an incumbent regime in a territory, and perhaps the rise of a new one, under a new sovereign entity.

IV.   A State of Palestine?

Clearly, the cases of Kosovo and Palestine are not perfectly analogous, and each has its own unique characteristics. However, both Kosovo and Palestine have striven for independence and have done so within the legal framework of the international law of statehood. Thus, if the case of Kosovo has made an impact on this body of law or has highlighted existing trends, the Palestinians may benefit from such developments, notwithstanding possible differences between these cases in context or background. In light of recent developments on the Palestinian front, we submit that some of the factors that played a role in the international recognition of Kosovo are now coming into play in the Palestinian context.

In our previous paper, we concluded that the Palestinian Authority did not meet the classical criteria for statehood and that its prospects of receiving international recognition were questionable, as long as the international community had not yet lost hope of reaching a negotiated solution to the Israeli–Palestinian conflict. We suggested, however, that if future negotiations proved fruitless despite good faith engagement on the Palestinian side, and if the Palestinians achieved governance goals, undertook to respect human rights, brokered a successful reconciliation between the different Palestinian factions behind a Palestine Liberation Organization (PLO)-led government, and formally acknowledged the State of Israel, a unilateral

---

[47] ICJ Kosovo Advisory Opinion, paras. 79–81.   [48] *Ibid.*, paras. 97–100.

declaration of independence would be more likely to receive international acknowledgement and support. Reassessing Palestinian prospects for international recognition under the current circumstances, we now contend that further support for this argument has since emerged.

1. Does the Palestinian Authority meet the classical criteria of statehood?

The Palestinian population in the West Bank and Gaza Strip fulfils the requirement of a 'permanent population',[49] and is recognised as a distinct population by the international community,[50] including Israel.[51] The territory internationally regarded and accepted as a prospective territory for a Palestinian state[52] is the West Bank and the Gaza Strip, occupied by Israel since 1967. This would seem to be a sufficiently coherent territory, notwithstanding its imprecise demarcation, limited size and fragmentation.[53]

---

[49] J. Quigley, 'Palestine: the Issue of Statehood' in S. R. Silverburg, (ed.), *Palestine and International Law* (McFarland & Company, 2002), pp. 44; J. Crawford, 'Israel (1948–1949) and Palestine (1998–1999): Two Studies in the Creation of States' in G. S. Goodwin-Gill and S. Talmon (eds), *The Reality of International Law* (Clarendon Press, 1999), p. 111; F. A. Boyle, 'The Creation of the State of Palestine', (1990) 1 *European Journal of International Law*, 302; T. Becker, 'International Recognition of a Unilaterally Declared Palestinian State: Legal and Policy Dilemmas', jcpa.org/art/becker1.htm.

[50] Council of the League of Nations, *Mandate for Palestine*, arts. 2 and 3, www.mfa.gov.il/MFA/Peace+Process/Guide+to+the+Peace+Process/The+Mandate+for+Palestine.htm; GA Res. 181, UN GAOR, 2nd Sess, UN Doc. A/RES/181 (1947); GA Res. 21/43, UN GAOR, 45th 43rd Sess, UN Doc. A/RES/43/21 (1988).

[51] *Camp David Accords*, Israel and Egypt, 23 September 1978, Section A, online www.mfa.gov.il/MFA/Peace%20Process/Guide%20to%20the%20Peace%20Process/Camp%20David%20Accord and *Declaration of Principles on Interim Self-Government Arrangements*, Israel and PLO, 13 September 1993, art. 1, www.mfa.gov.il/MFA/Peace+Process/Guide+to+the+Peace+Process/Declaration+of+Principles.htm.

[52] *Ibid.*; *The Wye River Memorandum*, Israel and PLO, 23 September 1998, Sections IV and V, www.mfa.gov.il/MFA/Peace%20Process/Guide%20to%20the%20Peace%20Process/The%20Wye%20River%20Memorandum; *The Initiative of the Saudi Crown Prince Abdullah*, and *The Performance-based Roadmap to a Permanent Two-state Solution to the Israeli-Palestinian Conflict (Roadmap)* adopted by SC Res. 1397, UN SCOR, UN Doc. S/RES/1397 (2002) and SC Res. 1515, UN SCOR, UN Doc. S/RES/1515 (2003), respectively.

[53] Crawford, *The Creation of States*, pp. 46–7, 52; *but see*, G. E. Robinson, 'The Fragmentation of Palestine', (2007) 106 *Current History* 425–6; *Case Concerning Sovereignty Over Certain Frontier Land (Belgium/Netherlands), International Court of Justice Reports* (1959), 212–13, 229; *Case Concerning Right of Passage over Indian Territory (Portugal v. India), Merits, International Court of Justice Reports* (1960), 27.

On the issue of effective government, the prevailing view until recently has been that the Palestinian Authority does not fulfil this criterion.[54] Crawford supports such a conclusion by pointing out that the Palestinian Authority controls a population, not a territory.[55] Others[56] emphasise the fact that control over material issues, as well as residual control, was left in the hands of Israel by Israeli–Palestinian agreements, and that even the limited powers entrusted to Palestinian hands are derived from agreements and not from an independently constituted Palestinian mandate.[57]

While some believe the formal limitations on the Palestinian Authority's governmental capacity, set by the Israeli–Palestinian agreements, may no longer be valid,[58] these limitations are coupled with a practical dependency on Israel. Israel collects the tax revenue that comprises two-thirds of the Palestinian Authority's budget; the Palestinian economy relies heavily on the Israeli market for employment, among others; the Palestinian Authority does not have its own infrastructure, and receives its electricity and fuel from Israel; and Israel controls almost all routes in and out of the Palestinian Authority.[59] Furthermore, Israel has not refrained from using its power over the Palestinian Authority, or from applying pressure on its leaders.[60] For example, after the swearing-in of the Hamas government in 2006, the Israeli cabinet froze all of the Palestinian tax revenue it had collected, pending Palestinian approval of

---

[54] For the review of different positions on the issue, see International Criminal Court, The Office of the Prosecutor, *Situation in Palestine: Summary of Submissions on Whether the Declaration Lodged by the Palestinian National Authority Meets Statutory Requirements* (3 May 2010), www.icc-cpi.int/Menus/Go?id=d3c77fa6-9dee-45b1-acc0-b41706bb41e5&lan=en-GB.

[55] Crawford, 'Israel and Palestine', pp. 120–2.

[56] O. M. Dajani, 'Stalled Between Seasons: The International Legal Status of Palestine During the Interim Period' (1997) 26 *Denver Journal of International Law and Policy* 86; Becker, *International Recognition*; *but see* Quigley, *Palestine*, p. 51; Boyle, 'Creation', 301–3; ICC Summary of Submissions, 10–11.

[57] Declaration of Principles on Interim Self-Government, Annex II, art. 3(b); *Israeli-Palestinian Interim Agreement on the West Bank and Gaza Strip*, Israel–PLO, 28 September 1995, art. 1(1), (5), www.mfa.gov.il/MFA/Peace+Process/Guide+to+the+Peace+Process/THE+ISRAELI-PALESTINIAN+INTERIM+AGREEMENT.htm.

[58] *Cf.* G. R. Watson, 'The Wall Decisions in Legal and Political Context', (2005) 99 *American Journal of International Law*, 22–4 (arguing against this notion).

[59] N. Lochery, 'The Politics and Economics of Israeli Disengagement, 1994–2006', (2007) 43 *Middle Eastern Studies*, 14–15; Robinson, 'Fragmentation', 422; The Rafah Crossing is effectively controlled by Egypt. While, in the past, Egypt kept this crossing closed, under agreement with Israel, this has changed since the fall of the Mubarak regime, and Egypt has opened the crossing on several occasions since. See below, n. 72.

[60] Robinson, 'Fragmentation', 421.

the *Roadmap* prerequisites, such as combating terror.[61] In 2007, after declaring the Gaza Strip a 'hostile entity', the Israeli cabinet also significantly reduced the supply of electricity and fuel to Gaza.[62] The effective division of the Palestinian Authority into a Hamas-controlled Gaza Strip and a PLO-controlled West Bank[63] following the 2006 elections, further weakened the Palestinian Authority's governmental capacity.[64]

Nevertheless, positions on the issue of the effectiveness of Palestinian governance seem to be shifting. In August 2009, the Palestinian Authority declared a two-year national state-building programme,[65] the implementation of which was supported and monitored by the Ad Hoc Liaison Committee for Assistance to the Palestinians (AHLC), comprised of representatives of several donor states. The Palestinian Authority has further published a 2011–13 National Plan aimed at continued development and state-building.[66]

In a report submitted to a meeting of the AHLC in April 2011, the Special Coordinator for the Middle East Peace Process reviewed Palestinian institution-building in six different areas: governance, the rule of law and human rights; livelihoods and productive sectors; education and culture; health; social protection; and infrastructure and water provision. The Special Coordinator notes that the effective division of the Palestinian Authority and the persistence of the Israeli occupation hamper the Authority's ability to extend its institutional authority in all areas. Nevertheless, he concludes that, within the current political and physical space, Palestinian progress has paved the way for meeting the September 2011 target date of completing the institutional readiness for statehood: 'governmental functions are now sufficient for a functioning government of a state'.[67]

---

[61] Israei Cabinet Decision 4705, art. A(1) (19 February 2006) (in Hebrew) www.pmo.gov.il/PMO/Archive/Decisions/2006/02/des4705.htm; *Roadmap*, adopted by SC Res. 1551.

[62] Israel Security and Policy Cabinet Decision (19 September 2007), cited in HCJ 9132/07 *Jaber et al.* v. *Prime Minister* (unpublished, 27 January 2008), para. 2 (Israel, HC).

[63] See generally, Robinson, 'Fragmentation', 423.   [64] See below, n. 68.

[65] The Palestinian National Authority, *Palestine: Ending the Occupation, Establishing the State* (August 2009), www.mop-gov.ps/issues_details.php?pid=15.

[66] The Palestinian National Authority, *National Development Plan 2011–13: Establishing the State, Building our Future* (April 2011), www.mopad.pna.ps/web_files/publishing_file/Establishing%20the%20State%20Building%20our%20Future_%20NDP%202011-13.pdf.

[67] The Office of the United Nations Special Coordinator for the Middle East Peace Process, *Palestinian State-Building: A Decisive Period* 1 (13 April 2011), www.unsco.org/Documents/Special/UNs%20Report%20to%20the%20AHLC%2013_April_2011.pdf.

Similarly, a report published by the World Bank in 2011 cites a previous conclusion that 'if the Palestinian Authority (PA) maintains its performance in institution-building and delivery and public services, it is well-positioned for the establishment of a state at any point in the near future'. This report further comments that 'Considerable progress has been made over the years' and that 'The PA's performance to date... bodes well for the future.'[68] And indeed, according to the World Bank data, significant progress has been made by the Palestinians since 2007, when the Palestinian Authority was ranked very low in all dimensions of governance.[69] In a new Country Data Report published in 2010, while Palestinian Political Stability and Absence of Violence were still ranked at below 10%, other indicators have dramatically increased: the Government Effectiveness indicator doubled to approximately 20%; Regulatory Quality rose from below 10% in 2007 to around 50% in 2009; Rule of Law rose from a little over 20% to about 45%; and Control of Corruption quadrupled from 10% to approximately 40%.[70]

Furthermore, on 4 May 2011, Hamas and Fatah signed a reconciliation accord and agreed on an interim government supported by both factions until the general elections due the following year.[71] Shortly thereafter, Egypt's new (post-Mubarak) regime declared the opening of the Rafah passage to Gaza, which was closed until then at Israel's behest, and thus significantly diminished the impact of Israel's policy of closure of Gaza.[72]

Intra-Palestinian reconciliation is important for bringing the Gaza Strip back under the control of the Palestinian Authority, hence improving its *de facto* governing capacity in this part of the prospective Palestinian state's territory. It is also important to note that the different components of the Palestinian territory are not constituent units of any sovereign state, and not subject to any competing claims of sovereignty: with the exception of East Jerusalem, Israel does not claim sovereignty over them, and Egypt and Jordan long ago relinquished any claims over Gaza and the West Bank, respectively.[73] Moreover, following the 2005

---

[68] The World Bank, *Building the Palestinian State: Sustaining Growth, Institutions, and Service Delivery*, 5, 30 (13 April 2011).

[69] http://info.worldbank.org/governance/wgi/pdf/c238.pdf.   [70] *Ibid.*

[71] E. Bronner, 'Palestinian Factions Sign Accord to End Rift', *The New York Times* (4 May 2011).

[72] D. D. Kirkpatrick, 'Egypt to Open Border With Gaza, in the Face of Israeli Objections', *The New York Times* (25 May 2011).

[73] *Treaty of Peace between the State of Israel and the Hashemite Kingdom of Jordan*, Israel and Jordan, 26 October 1994, art. 3, www.mfa.gov.il/MFA/Peace+Process/ Guide+to+the+Peace+Process/Israel-Jordan+Peace+Treaty.htm; *Camp David Accords*,

Israeli disengagement,[74] Israel no longer views itself as an occupier of the Gaza Strip.[75] Thus, at least in the Gaza Strip, no sovereign entity now claims a foothold. Nevertheless, the reconciliation accord also creates substantial difficulties, as Hamas is classified by numerous governments as a terrorist organisation,[76] and has consistently denied the legitimacy of Israel's existence.

In sum, despite the fact that the Palestinian Authority's effective governmental control is hampered by formal restrictions and by practical obstacles, significant progress seems to have been made in recent years. The Palestinian Authority still has considerable progress to make before it can be said to have achieved fully effective governance, although perhaps not more than certain existing states.[77] It now seems to fulfil – at least by a minimal standard – the criterion of government.

With regard to the requirement of 'capacity to enter into international relations', the right and ability to independently exercise authority towards other actors on the international stage is explicitly excluded from the scope of authority granted to the Palestinian Authority pursuant to the 1993 Oslo Declaration of Principles and the 1995 Israeli–Palestinian Interim Agreement.[78] Moreover, it is the PLO,[79] not the Palestinian Authority, which has been the representative of the Palestinian people in the UN since 1974, holding observer status under the title 'Palestine', following the 1988 declaration of independence by

Section A; 'Address by His Majesty King Hussein I to the Nation', *International Legal Materials*, 27 (1988), 1638.

[74] Lochery, 'Disengagement', 7; Israeli Cabinet Decision 1996 (6 June 2004) (in Hebrew), www.pmo.gov.il/PMO/Archive/Decisions/2004/06/des1996.htm.

[75] HCJ Jaber, para. 12; Y. Shany, 'Far Away, So Close: The Legal Status of Gaza After Israel's Disengagement', *International Law Forum, The Hebrew University of Jerusalem, Research Paper No. 12–06* (2006), ssrn.com/abstract=923151.

[76] US Department of State, *Country Reports on Terrorism* (2008), Chapter VI state.gov/s/ct/rls/crt/2007; EU Council Decision 2008/583/EC, (15 July 2008), OJ L 188, eurlex. europa.eu/LexUriServ/LexUriServ.do?uri=OJ:L:2008:188:0021:0025:EN:PDF.

[77] The World Bank, *Building the Palestinian State, Sustaining Growth, Institutions, and Service Delivery*, 5 (13 April 2011) http://siteresources.worldbank.org/INTWESTBANKGAZA/Resources/AHLCReportApril2011.pdf.

[78] *Declaration of Principles on Interim Self-Government*, art. IV and Annex II, art. 3(b); *Israeli–Palestinian Interim Agreement*, art. IX(5); Crawford, 'Israel and Palestine', 120–2; Dajani, 'Stalled', 87.

[79] *National Covenant of the Palestine Liberation Organisation* (28 May 1964); *see also*, 'Palestine National Council: Charter' (1968), reprinted in W. Laqueur and B. Rubin (eds), *The Israel–Arab Reader*, 6th edn (Penguin Books, 2001), p. 117.

PLO leaders.[80] Furthermore, many states refuse to engage the Hamas government and leaders in any way.[81] This situation raises questions as to the Palestinian capacity to conduct international relations, especially following the Palestinian reconciliation accord which brought Hamas back to power at the national Palestinian level.[82]

Nevertheless, as we noted above, over the past few years, several countries have established diplomatic relations with 'the State of Palestine' or have upgraded the level of Palestinian diplomatic representation to 'missions' or 'embassies', terms regularly reserved for diplomatic delegations of states.[83] These declarations, coupled with the recent recognition of several states of an independent Palestinian State, indicate Palestinian progress towards a capacity to form international relations, especially in light of extensive diplomatic mobilisation in the run-up to the General Assembly session in September 2011, in which Palestine submitted its bid for membership with the blessing and support of the Secretary General.[84] These factors indicate a substantial strengthening of the Palestinian capacity to form international relations. Nonetheless, it is difficult to establish whether this capacity is sufficient to meet the last of the classical criteria for statehood.

As we argued above, international recognition may carry significant weight in borderline cases, and may compensate for non-decisive fulfilment of the Montevideo criteria. While supportive of future Palestinian independence, many states and international bodies do not view the Palestinian Authority as a state today.[85] This is true despite the 15 November 1988 PLO

---

[80] Quigley, 'Palestine', 41; GA Res. 3236, UN GAOR, 29th Sess. (1974); GA Res. 3237, UN GAOR, 29th Sess. (1974); *see also* SC Res. 607, UN SCOR, UN Doc. S/RES/607 (1988); GA Res. 43/177, UN GAOR, 82nd Mtg. (1988); Crawford, 'Israel and Palestine', 111.

[81] *Supra.* n. 75; *see* United States of America, President Barack Obama, *Remarks on the Middle East and North Africa at the State Department* (19 May 2011), http://whitehouse. gov/the-press-office/2011/05/19/remarks-president-middle-east-and-north-africa.

[82] *Ibid.*

[83] Notice of DR–Palestine Diplomatic Relations; Notice of Venezuela–Palestine Diplomatic Relations; B. Ravid and News Agencies, 'Britain to Upgrade Palestinian Delegation'.

[84] *Secretary-General's Message to United Nations Latin American and Caribbean Meeting in Support of Israeli-Palestinian Peace* (29 March 2011) UN Doc. SG/SM/13484, http:// un.org/apps/sg/sgstats.asp?nid=5173.

[85] *Roadmap*, adopted by SC Res. 1551; Israeli Cabinet Decision 1996; Obama, *Remarks on the Middle East*; *Legal Consequences of the Construction of a Wall in the Occupied Palestinian Territory*, Advisory Opinion, *International Court of Justice Reports* (2004), para. 139; *cf.* Higgins J., Separate Opinion, paras. 34–5, *ibid.*; M. Pomerantz, 'The ICJ's Advisory Jurisdiction and the Crumbling Wall Between the Political and the Judicial', (2005) 99 *American Journal of International Law* 26–7; *Ungar* v. *Palestinian Liberation Org.*, 402 F.3d 274 (2005), 32–34 (USA), and the authorities mentioned there; HCJ 4060/03

declaration of Palestinian independence.[86] While the General Assembly affirmed this declaration as the implementation of the 1947 Plan of Partition (General Assembly Resolution 181) and of the Palestinian 'need' to 'exercise sovereignty over their territory', the UN did not admit 'Palestine' as a member.[87] Furthermore, while some states established missions in the Palestinian territories, these were not 'embassies',[88] and other states refused to recognise Palestinian independence, in light, among other reasons, of its refusal to recognise Israel.[89] The prevailing scholarly view is that the Palestinians did not achieve statehood in the aftermath of this declaration.[90]

In the context of Kosovo, we found that the following considerations and circumstances were influential in states' decisions to recognise its independence, despite its questionable fulfilment of the classical criteria for statehood: self-determination; a history of human rights violations; federal dissolution; international involvement and administration; deadlocked negotiations; the hope to avoid further destabilisation; the existence of a comprehensive plan; and the adoption of democratic institutions. We next turn to examine whether such additional considerations and circumstances may play a role in the Palestinian context.

2. New considerations evident in recent developments

Latin American resonant support of an independent State of Palestine, the decision to upgrade the level of Palestinian diplomatic representation by the United States[91] and several EU member states,[92] and the support

Palestinian Authority v. *Dayan* (unpublished, 17 July 2007) (Israel, HC); *Written Statement Submitted by Palestine* (2009), icjcij.org/docket/files/131/1555.pdf; Watson, 'The Wall Decisions', 22–4; *see*, especially, the discussion on the recognition of Palestine by states and international organisations in ICC Summary of Submissions, 8–9.

[86] 'Palestine National Council: Declaration of Independence (November 15, 1988)', reprinted in Laqueur and Rubin, *Reader*, pp. 354–8.

[87] GA Res. 43/177; Crawford, 'Israel and Palestine', 111.

[88] Dajani, 'Stalled', 60; Quigley, 'Palestine', 47.

[89] *Ibid.*, 42; Boyle, 'Creation', 301–3; Crawford, 'Israel and Palestine', 115–16; *Country Cooperation Strategy for WHO and the Occupied Palestinian Territory 2006–2008*, UN Doc. WHO-EM/ARD/018/E/R (2005) 9.

[90] Crawford, 'Israel and Palestine', 120–2; Watson, 'The Wall Decisions', 23; *but see* Quigley, 'Palestine'; Boyle, 'Creation'.

[91] N. Mozgovaya, 'U.S. upgrades status of Palestinian mission in Washington', *Haaretz. com* (22 July 2010).

[92] K. Abu Toameh, 'Erekat: 10 EU states will upgrade their PLO missions', *The Jerusalem Post* (19 December, 2010). *See also*, 'EU recognition of a Palestinian state a "possibility": France', *EUBusiness* at www.eubusiness.com/news-eu/israel-palestinians.93s/.

of the UN Secretary-General, Ban Ki-moon[93] all seem to indicate that the international tide has turned over the two-and-a-half decades that have elapsed since Palestine's declaration of independence in 1988. We argue that this change is not only a result of progress made by the Palestinian Authority towards the fulfilment of the classical criteria of statehood, but rather, is also indicative of the growing importance of considerations other than the classical criteria. We now turn to examine whether such considerations were cited as having played a role in various states' declarations of their recognition of a Palestinian State or on the upgrading of the level of their diplomatic relations with the Palestinian Authority.

2.1   Self-determination

The Palestinian people's right to self-determination was recognised internationally as early as 1947, in General Assembly Resolution 181, which envisioned two states in the territory of Mandatory Palestine: a Jewish state and an Arab state.[94] Following the 1967 war, Security Council Resolution 242 emphasised the inadmissibility of the acquisition of territory by war, and demanded the 'Withdrawal of Israeli armed forces from territories occupied', which included the West Bank and Gaza.[95] These Resolutions indicate an international recognition of a Palestinian right to independent statehood, coupled with discontent with Israeli occupation of territories of the prospective Palestinian state. The 1978 Camp David Accords and the 1995 Israeli–Palestinian Interim Agreements later recognised the 'legitimate rights of the Palestinian people' and envisioned some degree of autonomy for the Palestinians in the West Bank and Gaza.[96] Finally, the US-sponsored *Roadmap*, adopted by the Security Council and Israel,[97] as well as the Arab Peace Initiative,[98] reflect the widely held international view that the Palestinians may eventually exercise their right to self-determination 'externally', i.e. by means of an independent state in the West Bank and Gaza.[99] As compared to pre-independence Kosovo, it seems that a Palestinian right to external self-determination enjoys broader support,

---

[93] *Secretary-General's Message to Latin American and Caribbean Meeting.*
[94] GA Res. 181, art. I.A.1.
[95] SC Res. 242 , UN SCOR, UN Doc. S/RES/242 (1967), preamble and art. 1; this was reaffirmed in SC Res. 338, UN SCOR, UN Doc. S/RES/334 (1973), art. 2.
[96] *Israeli-Palestinian Interim Agreement.*
[97] *Roadmap*, adopted by SC Res. 1551; Israeli Cabinet Decision 1996; Obama, *Remarks on the Middle East.*
[98] *Saudi Crown Prince Peace Initiative.*   [99] See also Obama, *Remarks on Middle East.*

possibly indicating that a unilateral declaration of independence would be more easily recognised, despite deficiencies in Palestinian fulfilment of the classical criteria. Possible resentment of a unilateral move may be further mitigated in light of the fact that Palestinian statehood does not require secession or the disintegration of a state, but rather, the end of a frowned-upon occupation. This hypothesis finds confirmation in the declarations of recognition recently issued by various Latin American states, most of which cited the Palestinian people's 'right to establish itself as an independent state' or its right to self-determination as one of the reasons – or as the primary reason – motivating their declarations of recognition.[100] The application for UN membership of Palestine also does not fail to cite the international recognition of the Palestinian right to self-determination since 1947.[101]

2.2 Deadlocked negotiations

It seems that a strong basis for international recognition of Kosovo was that its negotiations with Serbia had reached a dead end.[102] On this issue, contrary to our previous position,[103] we now note that international public opinion may be inching towards a conclusion that the Israeli-Palestinian negotiations are headed towards a point of irreversible stagnation. In fact, apart from the Palestinian right to self-determination, this seems to be the principal motivation behind the Latin American states' recognition of the State of Palestine. For example, Argentina specifically mentioned that it has decided to recognise the Palestinian State 'so as to promote a breakthrough in the process of negotiation'; Chile stated that it believes that recognition of Palestine 'is essential to reinvigorate the process of negotiations'; and Guyana hoped that 'increasing recognition of the State of Palestine will contribute to a resolution of the Israeli-Palestinian conflict'.[104] Secretary-General Ban also referred to this issue in a recent statement: 'The target dates for

---

[100] Brazilian Recognition of Palestine; Ecuadorean Recognition of Palestine; Chilean Recognition of Palestine; Guyanese Recognition of Palestine; Peruvian Recognition of Palestine.

[101] Abbas, *Address before General Assembly 66th Session.*

[102] *Report of the Special Envoy of the Secretary-General on Kosovo's Future Status* (26 March 2007), UN Doc. S/2007/168, para. 3.

[103] Nevo and Megiddo, *Lessons from Kosovo*, pp. 113–14.

[104] Argentinean Recognition of Palestine; Chilean Recognition of Palestine; Guyanese Recognition of Palestine, respectively (translation of Argentine and Chilean declarations is ours); *see also* Ecuadorean Recognition of Palestine, citing as base for recognition; Brazilian Recognition of Palestine, Peruvian Recognition of Palestine, and

reaching an Israeli–Palestinian agreement on permanent status issues and completing the Palestinian Authority's two year state-building programme are fast-approaching. Yet, the Israeli-Palestinian negotiations remain at a worrying standstill. We must intensity efforts to break the deadlock', he wrote. The Secretary-General also referred to Israel's continued settlement construction, house demolition and forced transfer of Palestinian residents as actions that 'erode trust' and 'prejudge the outcome of the process', and called for Israel to stop them.[105] Such statements generate the overall impression that the international community is seeking means to alter the balance of power in the Middle East peace process, in the hope that this might accelerate the resolution of the Israeli–Palestinian conflict. If this position continues to gain momentum, international endorsement of unilateral Palestinian independence, rooted in the belief that negotiations are unlikely to achieve an independent state and a solution to the conflict, is quite conceivable.[106]

This momentum may have been somewhat undercut by President Obama's emphatic rejection, in May 2011, of the Palestinian claim that negotiations have failed and, more specifically, of his denunciation of their 'walking away' from negotiations as part of a campaign to isolate Israel internationally. 'Symbolic actions to isolate Israel at the United Nations', he warned, 'won't create an independent state.'[107] The prospects of this course of action therefore remain unclear. Nevertheless, it is important to remember in this context that neither refusal by the United States to recognise a Palestinian unilateral declaration of independence nor a rejection of its bid to UN membership would be sufficient to prevent the creation of a Palestinian state. If the Palestinian Authority proves it meets the classical criteria for statehood, or if it gains the widespread recognition of the international community as a borderline case, it could make the transition from a non-state entity to an independent state notwithstanding any resistance on the part of the United States.

Mr. Abbas's address before the UN General Assembly stressed that negotiations with Israel are at a standstill. While characterising the Palestinian approach as one of 'open hearts, attentive ears and sincere

Notice of DR–Palestine Diplomatic Relations, referring to this issue, but not explicitly stating it as a basis for recognition.

[105] *Secretary-General's Message to Latin American and Caribbean Meeting.*

[106] E. Bronner, 'In Israel, Time for Peace Offer May Run Out', *The New York Times* (2 April, 2011).

[107] Obama, *Remarks on the Middle East.*

intentions', Abbas described the Israeli position as preventing any progress.[108]

2.3 Remedial secession

While the ICJ could have used the opportunity presented to it in the Kosovo Advisory Opinion to clarify the conditions and legality of remedial secession, it did not. However, this failure does not affect the Palestinian case, which does not revolve around the remedial secession framework; the Palestinian territories are not a constituent unit of a sovereign state and are not subject to competing claims of sovereignty.

Nonetheless, the remedial secession framework may be influential, as an indication that the Palestinian starting point is even more favourable than that of Kosovo, whose territory is still considered by Serbia to be an integral part of its own territory. If Kosovo represents a precedent for legitimate remedial secession, it would seem that a claim to independence made under similar circumstances by an entity whose territory is not subject to competing claims of sovereignty would be justified *a fortiori*.

2.4 International involvement and the existence of a comprehensive plan

As in the case of Kosovo, international involvement in the Palestinian future is significant. While, unlike Kosovo, no international administration has been set up to manage Palestine, the world closely monitors and supports the Palestinian Authority's independent progress. The 'Ending the Occupation, Establishing a State' programme published by the Palestinian Authority in 2009 and the Palestinian National Plan for 2011–13 lay out a comprehensive plan for institution building and for achieving governance capacity. They are monitored and supported by the UN and by the AHLC. As was the case in Kosovo, the deep involvement of the international community may add significant weight to its willingness to recognise an independent State of Palestine, even if specific programmes will not yet have achieved their ultimate goals.

2.5 Democracy and human rights and relations with Israel

Another issue which may tip the scales towards international recognition of a unilateral Palestinian declaration of independence is the character of the state established. PLO leaders, and in particular its present

---

[108] Abbas, *Address before General Assembly 66th Session*.

leaders, Mahmoud Abbas and Salam Fayyad, enjoy international sympathy, as opposed to Hamas leaders, who are viewed as extremists.[109] A Palestinian state committed to democracy and the protection of human rights will probably be acknowledged more easily than one that fails to do so, and may offset doubts as to whether Palestine meets the classical criteria for statehood.[110]

In assessing the Palestinian governance capacity, the UN Special Coordinator for the Middle East Peace Process emphasised the Palestinian institutions' progress towards achieving goals of transparency, freedom of the media, compliance with international human rights law and access to legal services. He specifically commended the Palestinian Authority's 'institutional commitment towards protecting human rights, a core function and responsibility of any state'.[111] In his address at the UN General Assembly, Mr. Abbas declared the Palestinians' aspiration for a state 'characterized by the rule of law, democratic exercise and protection of freedoms and equality of all citizens without any discrimination and the transfer of power through the ballot box'.[112] This commitment may be of importance in the world's willingness to recognise an independent Palestine.

Another point stressed by Latin American states recognising Palestine – including Brazil, Argentina, Chile, Peru and Guyana – is Israel's right to live in secure and internationally recognised borders. Secretary-General Ban and President Obama both reaffirm this position unequivocally.[113] In his address, Mr. Abbas alluded to this concern, saying that 'The PLO and the Palestinian people adhere to all renouncements of violence' and that they intend to 'adhere to all agreements' signed with Israel. Furthermore, he declared the Palestinian commitment to the building of 'cooperative relations based on parity and equality between two neighboring states – Palestine and Israel'.[114]

V.   Conclusion

Significant progress has been made in the way of Palestinian state-building over the past few years. Economic reforms and institution-building are

---

[109] Robinson, 'Fragmentation', 422; Special Coordinator Report.
[110] Brazilian Recognition of Palestine.   [111] Special Coordinator Report, 11.
[112] Abbas, *Address before General Assembly 66th Session.*
[113] *Secretary-General's Message to Latin American and Caribbean Meeting*; Obama, *Remarks on the Middle East.*
[114] Abbas, *Address before General Assembly 66th Session.*

supported and monitored by the international community. Nevertheless, the international community is likely to continue pressing for bilateral negotiations with Israel as long as these are seen as a viable course. This is likely to slow down the success of Palestinian efforts to gain international recognition of its independence, unless Palestinians succeed in convincing the world that bilateral negotiations with Israel are no longer a viable course, or one likely to lead to a peaceful resolution of the Israeli–Palestinian conflict in the foreseeable future. Such conviction appears to have been the principal motivation behind recent recognition by various states of an independent State of Palestine and has also played a central role in the Palestinian bid for UN membership. In the words of the UN Secretary General, it appears that the international community is arriving at the conclusion that 'the resolution of the Israeli-Palestinian conflict is long overdue. The status quo is untenable, particularly at a time when so many throughout the region are pursuing freedom and dignity through non-violence'.[115] As the Palestinian fulfilment of the classical criteria for statehood progresses and additional considerations lean heavily in favour of the Palestinian claim for independence, an independent State of Palestine may very well be recognised by the international community in the near future.

[115] *Secretary-General's Message to Latin American and Caribbean Meeting.*

Somaliland: scrambled by international law?

JACKSON NYAMUYA MAOGOTO

[A]lthough officially unified as a single nation at independence, the former Italian colony and trust territory in the south and the former British protectorate in the north were, from an institutional standpoint, two separate countries. Italy and Britain had left them with separate administrative, legal and education systems where affairs were conducted according to different procedures and in different languages. Police, taxes, and the exchange rates of their separate currencies were also different. The orientations of their educated elites were divergent, and economic contacts between the two regions were virtually non-existent.[1]

Perhaps debate over Africa's boundary dilemma will, increasingly, be rendered redundant. Inexorable changes are being wrought in the international legal order. The Wesphalian conception of the sovereign independent nation state – a conception that has dominated the form and content of international law throughout the period of Africa's integration into the modern world – is under siege. What Tunkin has termed the 'old' international law – premised on ideas of sovereignty and territorial integrity – is being challenged by 'new' principles of international law that, whether deliberately or incidentally, undermine those notions of sovereignty and territorial integrity.[2]

I. Introduction

Recognition of states is a complex interaction of international norms and politics stretched in differing (politically influenced) quotients across a triangle of three key norms of international law – self-determination, territorial integrity and *sovereignty*. The cradle of the three is *sovereignty* – the dominant and often viscerally self-serving concept that underpins international law and relations. Self-determination underpins sovereignty.

---

[1] H. D Nelson (ed.), *Somalia: A Country Study*, United States Government: Department of the Army (1982) 35.

[2] G. Abraham, '"Lines upon Maps": Africa and the Sanctity of African Boundaries', (2007) 15 *African Journal of International and Comparative Law*, 61–84, 83.

Theoretically it is relatively straightforward, *but* it possesses three (not often interlocking) facets. The most established is that a colonised region has a right to determine its future free from the interference of a coloniser.[3] The second is a right to internal self-determination, where dissatisfied constituents have the right to use existing political processes to gain greater participation, whether through increased representation and/or semi-autonomy.[4] Finally, there is external self-determination, through which a region of an existing state can secede to establish a new separate identity and entity.[5]

Marc Weller notes that there has been a move away from unipolar sovereignty concentrated exclusively in the central state by virtue of developments relating to democratic governance reflecting an increasing recognition that, ultimately, the authority to govern is based on the will of the people.[6] This chapter focuses on the peculiarities of Somaliland, which sit across legal, political and social quotients. It seeks to shake the corners of the extant normative recognition triangle through changing conceptualisations of sovereignty generated by the shift in the role of international human rights. The chapter's core argument is positioned on the broad premise of re-envisioned sovereignty and adjusted notions of threats to international peace and security. It grasps the legal and policy nettle by focusing on and analysing two broad questions: if we consider that the traditional Montevideo criteria[7] on statehood have implicitly been imbued with principles of human rights and democratic governance, can not statehood also acquire novel legal nuances that open avenues to accredit nascent settled *sui generis* entities? If sovereignty is

---

[3] *Declaration on Principles of International Law Concerning Friendly Relations and Cooperation Among States in Accordance with the Charter of the United Nations*, GA Res. 2625, Annex, UN GAOR, 25th Session Supp. No. 28, UN Doc A/8028 (24 October 1970) (hereinafter 'Declaration on Friendly Relations') p. 124, citing the Declaration's partial purpose '[t]o bring a speedy end to colonialism, having due regard to the freely expressed will of the peoples concerned'.

[4] A. Kreuter, 'Self-Determination, Sovereignty, and the Failure of States: Somaliland and the Case for Justified Secession', (2010) 19 *Minnesota Journal of International Law*, 363–97, 369.

[5] Ibid., 369.

[6] M. Weller, 'Settling Self-determination Conflicts: Recent Developments', (2009) 20(1) *European Journal of International Law*, 111–65, 154.

[7] The Montevideo Convention on the Rights and Duties of States, signed 26 December 1993, 135 LNTS 19 (entered into force 26 December 1934) (hereinafter 'Montevideo Convention'). Article 1 states: 'The state as a person of international law should possess the following qualifications: (a) a permanent population; (b) a defined territory; (c) government; and (d) capacity to enter into relations with the other states.'

being transformed both organically and structurally, might we not extend the project to notions of statehood?

II.   A snapshot of history and Somaliland's contemporary 'reincarnation'

Somaliland, the northern region of modern day Republic of Somalia, was once a British protectorate.[8] It attained independence on 26 June 1960.[9] It was welcomed into the international community by an overwhelming number of the then extant community of states (including the five United Nations Permanent Members). Five days later, in the quest to create 'Greater Somalia', it united with the southern half – the Trust territory of Somalia – which had just gained independence from Italy to form the United Republic of Somalia (hereinafter Republic of Somalia).[10] This fateful decision would return to haunt Somaliland decades later. Pointers to this were already evident then, with political turmoil between various clans and regions tainting the unification process that led to the formation of the United Republic of Somalia.[11]

Of great significance is the fact that when Somaliland joined Somalia in 1960 to create the Republic of Somalia, the relevant pivotal bilateral agreements – the Act of Union of Somalia and the Union of Somaliland and Somalia Law – were not signed as postulated.[12] Equally, and amplifying this further, the Somalia Act of Union was approved 'in principle', with no national referendum or popular vote on the matter.[13] The Union

---

[8] See R. W. Rahn, 'Curious Case of Somaliland', *Washington Times*, (6 January 2005) A16.

[9] Ibid.

[10] S. S. Samatar, 'Historical Setting' in H. C. Metz (ed.), *Somalia: A Country Study* (Washington DC: US Government Printing Office, 1992), pp. 14–15, 20.

[11] Ibid., (citing the north's concern over the democratic power of the south, most clearly demonstrated by a constitutional referendum in 1961 which was passed, but without a majority in the north).

[12] See generally, J. Drysdale, *Somaliland: 1991 Report and Reference* (New York: Global-Stats Ltd, 1991).

[13] It should be recalled that in the *Western Sahara Opinion* [1975] ICJ Rep 12, 60 (hereinafter *Western Sahara Case*), the freely expressed will of the people was a consistent theme in the ICJ's judgment and was described as the very *sine qua non* of all decolonisation. For example, His Excellency Judge Nagendra Singh asserted that: 'The Court has recognised the validity of the principle of self-determination, "defined as the need to pay regard to the freely expressed will of the peoples." Essentially if there was evidence that could justify the reintegration of the territory into one State, it could not be done without first determining the freely expressed will of the people. Judge Singh

was driven primarily by the desires and ambitions of the political elite, while negating two major pathways: legal formalities and the ascertainment of the will of the people.[14] Brad Poore notes drily that: '[t]he unification between Somaliland and Somalia arguably happened too fast and was poorly planned.'[15] The uncertain 'will' of the people was to be manifested post-independence and union, in sporadic clan-based flare-ups often mirroring the North–South divide.

In the late 1980s, simmering tensions finally erupted into sustained clan-based fighting after two decades of repressive and authoritarian rule by Mohamed Siad Barre (who had seized power in a *coup d'état* in 1969). The central government fell in 1991, marking the steady decline of the Republic of Somalia into ever-more widening vicious and persistent violence characterised by the Republic's loss of basic but fundamental capacities inherent in a state – political/administrative control and inability to maintain law and order.[16] The northern part briefly participated in the violent turmoil before retreating to its former colonial borders and resurrecting Somaliland through a declaration asserting its (resumption of) independence. The intent was manifest, as it went about establishing a government and administrative structure to run its affairs distinct from the chaotic south, along with adoption of a flag and currency. Despite Somaliland's declaration of independence, 'poor leadership and civil strife in the early years meant it appeared at times to be tilting dangerously towards the route the south had taken'.[17]

Keen to consolidate its fledgling peace and consolidate its declared statehood, Somaliland's leaders steadily participated in negotiations, culminating in a landmark peace conference in 1996 that reconciled clan conflicts.[18] Five years later, a referendum was held for a constitution that enshrined the reconciliation and democratic governance structures designed to focus on statehood while accommodating previously destabilising parochial chieftains. Ninety-seven per cent of votes were cast in favour of the constitution,

went on to note that the only time that this requirement could be dispensed with is when the "will" of the peoples is a foregone conclusion' (pp. 72–3).

[14] *Western Sahara Case*, pp. 72–3; see also I. M. Lewis, 'Pan-Africanism and Pan-Somalism', (1963) 1 *Journal of Modern African Studies*, 147–68, 147–51.

[15] B. Poore, 'Somaliland: Shackled To A Failed State', (2009) 45 *Stanford Journal of International Law*, 117–50, 124.

[16] Y. Osinbajo, 'Legality in a Collapsed State: The Somali Experience', *International & Comparative Law Quarterly*, (1996) 45(4) 910–23, 911.

[17] 'A Question of Recognition, UN Integrated Regional Information Network', 10 July 2001, Nairobi, available at www.hartford-hwp.com/archives/33/113.html (last accessed 12 November 2010).

[18] See, e.g., Kreuter, 'Self-Determination', 393.

with international observers finding the referendum 'largely in accordance with internationally recognized election procedures'.[19]

Over the years since its declaration of indepedence, Somaliland has morphed into a *de facto* state exhibiting all the quintessential features of a state – territory, people, a functioning government and 'independence' from the parent state.[20] It has largely avoided the political turmoil and civil strife that characterises much of the south.[21] However, tied as it is through the independence union, Somaliland finds itself in limbo – locked out of the international community by reigning norms of international law (buttressed by realpolitik). Its repeated calls for international political recognition as an autonomous state are largely ignored. As a result, it has been unable to enjoy socio-economic prosperity because it is incapacitated in forming any meaningful political relationships with other states which refuse to recognise the government of Somaliland as independent from the Republic of Somalia.[22] This denial essentially cements Somaliland's lack of a principled participation in the international arena.

The Somali Federal Transitional Government (SFTG) continues to be recognised as the official government, even though its authority does not extend much beyond Mogadishu – the Republic of Somalia's capital.[23] The status quo is that the international community consistently places the interests of the destabilising actions largely in the south of the country ahead of peace-builders in the north (i.e., Somaliland)[24] where peace and stability has been largely present for years, even as the south continues to draw the dollars and focus of attention of the international community, and now the ire of its neighbours. It is to be recalled that the Badinter Commission, established in 1991 to play the role of 'midwife' as Yugoslavia crumbled, declared the Federation dissolved because it no longer performed the functions of a state.[25] This was a view that was

---

[19] D H. Shinn, 'Somaliland: The Little Country That Could', November 2002, 9 *CSIS-Africa Note* available at http://csis.org/files/media/csis/pubs/anotes_0211.pdf (last accessed 12 April 2011).

[20] The Montevideo Convention on the Rights and Duties of States.

[21] M. B. Abdi, 'Political Economic and Social Context', available at www.harggeysa.org/Barud-politicaleconomic.htm (last accessed 16 November 2010).

[22] Kreuter, 'Self-Determination', 364.

[23] See, e.g., 'The Nation Nobody Knows', *The Economist* (London, 14 April 2001) 42, also available at www.economist.com/node/569115 (last accessed 14 January 2011).

[24] 417 Parl. Deb., H.C. (6th ser.) (2004) 273WH (statement of Tony Worthington).

[25] Conference on Yugoslavia Arbitration Commission: Opinions on Questions Arising from the Dissolution of Yugoslavia, Opinion No. 2, 4 July 1992, 31 ILM 1488, 1498 (1992) (hereinafter Badinter Commission).

resonating with major countries and blocs (The European Union (EU) the United States (US) United Kingdom and France) as they rushed to recognise entities 'spawned' by the crumbling Federation. On the back of this recollection, the next sections of the chapter reflect and analyse a further two fundamental questions: when a government loses its ability to govern and provide peace and security for its citizenry, should this not be a mark of loss of international legitimacy? Should an inability by a state to sustain its responsibilities and duties of offering functional socio-political and economic frameworks to its citizenry not diminish its claim as a member of the international community? These questions will be addressed as the chapter's analysis progresses.

III. Triangulating international law principles: sovereignty, territory, self-determination and citizenry

1. Declaratory theory

The Montevideo Convention on the Rights and Duties of States embodies the declaratory theory of statehood. It postulates the criteria for statehood thus: possessing a permanent population, defined territory, an effective government and capacity to enter into relations with other states.[26] These comprise the basic criteria for a prima facie case bolstered with acknowledgement of the factual scenario by other states.[27] On this basis, 'Somaliland has a colorable argument' that it meets the technical requirements of statehood.[28] As straightforward as this may appear, the primary stumbling block is the paradigm of territorial integrity under-pinned by the doctrine of *uti possidetis juris* ('have what you have had') and the politico-legal drama that accompanies secession claims.[29] International law postulates that: 'The right to self-determination must not involve changes to existing frontiers at the time of independence.'[30]

---

[26] See The Montevideo Convention on the Rights and Duties of States.

[27] Poore, 'Somaliland', 124, 136.

[28] Kreuter, 'Self-Determination', 380–1. It should also be observed that Somaliland's population is relatively stable, unlike in the south, which has suffered a steady exodus of refugees since the civil war began. Also in its favour is the reality that its borders from its days as a British colony, to which it retreated, serve as territorial demarcation. It also scores bonus points considering it has had several peaceful *democratic* elections.

[29] The original purpose of this doctrine was to maintain the borders of former colonies upon decolonisation. See, e.g., M. N. Shaw, 'Peoples, Territorialism and Boundaries', (1997) 8 *European Journal of International Law*, 478–507, 482.

[30] See, generally, ibid.

How do these norms impact in the dynamics of Somaliland's recognition?

1.1   Locked in borders: the curse of *uti possiditis*

The concept of *uti possidetis* had its origins in constraining foreign intervention and limiting border disputes. It was incorporated into modern international law amidst the wave of independence movements in South America in the nineteenth century, as Spanish imperialism crumbled. By declaring that *uti possidetis* applied, the new states sought to ensure that there was no *terra nullius*,[31] with the practical goal of limiting the likelihood of border wars between the newly independent states as they sought to consolidate themselves. The *uti possidetis* principle received a ringing endorsement in 1964 when members of the Organisation of African Unity (OAU, the precursor to the African Union, AU) adopted a resolution declaring that 'all the member states undertake to respect their existing boundaries at the moment they acceded to independence'.[32] No surprise here, considering that Africa had been carved up into spheres of influence by colonial powers, creating a mélange of artificial states. The utility of the concept was pragmatic in two senses. It offered a legitimate framework for the new African political elite to keep respective colonial artifices together, but also facilitated the unscrupulous to wield power over regions and peoples who otherwise would have rebelled, or sought a more definitive say in their political destiny.

Despite the OAU endorsement of the *uti possidetis* concept, Somaliland's case is not as hopeless as it may appear. It is worth recalling that five years before the OAU resolution, President Kwame Nkrumah (Ghana's leader and committed pan-Africanist) asserted at the Sanniquellic Conference that African leaders should explore methods for eradicating the artificial divisions and boundaries which balkanised the continent.[33] However, any likely rays of hope were to be swept away months later in 1960 with the attempted secession of Katanga from the Congo. Nervous newly empowered political elites retreated to a stance of

---

[31] The international law concept of territory that nobody owns so that the first nation to discover it is entitled to take it over. The more perverse use of this concept is to be seen in the conquest of the Americas by the Spanish, and Australian settlement by Europeans in disregard of the existence of indigenous communities.

[32] OAU Assembly, AHG/Res. 17(1), Cairo Ordinary Session, 17–21 July (1964).

[33] Cited in M. N. Shaw, *Title to Territory in Africa: International Legal Issues* (Oxford University Press, 1986), p. 183.

maintaining the status quo. This was evident at the Monrovia Conference the following year, which called upon African states to 'desist from such activities as the hasty recognition of breakaway regimes'.[34] Thus, by the time the OAU convened for its second annual conference in 1964, there was no sympathy for any other position, as delegates 'emphasized that whatever might be the moral and historical argument for a readjustment of national boundaries, practical attempts to reshape the map of Africa might well prove disastrous'.[35] The representative of Mali captured the mood when noting that the continent must renounce any territorial claims, as African unity demanded, through complete respect for the legacy received from the colonial system.[36] The statement was rounded off with an observation on the need to maintain frontiers of respective states.[37] Nevertheless, the two Somalias (British and Italian) in their rush to union, essentially 'breached' this exhortation and the OAU failed to respond, presumably largely on the basis that the consensual union of two states fell outside the strict remit of the *uti possidetis* rule.

In 1970, six years after the OAU resolution, the United Nations (UN) General Assembly in one of its most seminal resolutions – Resolution 2625 (XXV): Declaration on Principles of International Law Friendly Relations and Co-operation among States in Accordance with the Charter of The United Nations – while reaffirming states' territorial integrity, noted the importance of territorial integrity and political unity of sovereign and independent states conducting themselves in compliance with the principle of 'self-determination of peoples'.[38] Some two decades after this UN resolution, the most vicious war in Europe since World War II tore Yugoslavia apart. The Badinter Commission, established to find solutions for the Balkans problem, utilised the *uti possidetis* doctrine in its management of the dissolution.[39] What was significant was the Commission's conclusion that the concept of *uti possidetis*: 'had a broader meaning, implying that it also applied in instances of self-determination unrelated to decolonization'.[40] On the back of this observation, this author proffers Brad Poore's observation that: 'The principle of uti possidetis ... appears to delegitimize the original union between Somaliland and Somalia because the new borders

---

[34] Ibid., p. 184.
[35] Abraham, 'Lines upon Maps', p. 6; see also, A. C. McEwen, *International Boundaries of East Africa* (Oxford: Clarendon Press, 1971), pp. 23–4.
[36] Shaw, *Title to Territory in Africa*, p.186.　[37] Ibid.
[38] *Declaration on Friendly Relations*, p. 124 (emphasis added).
[39] Badinter Commission.　[40] Ibid., p. 1498 (emphasis added).

clashed with those delineated by Great Britain, France, Ethiopia, and Italy during the colonial period.'[41] It is not, then, an artificial stretch to opine that Somaliland, possessed of territorial rights over a definite portion of the Republic of Somalia (pre-dating the union), falls within a reasoned aspect of the framework.

In a paradoxical reflection encapsulated in the 1986 ICJ judgment in the *Frontier Dispute Case* (*Burkina Faso/Mali*),[42] the ICJ noted that maintenance of the territorial status quo in Africa was 'the wisest course', to preserve what had been achieved in the struggle for independence and avoid disruption.[43] Yet in the same breath the ICJ, in terms reminiscent of the second OAU resolution that resonated with the Mali representative, noted that stability and consolidation of independence had 'induced African states judiciously to consent to the respecting of colonial frontiers, and to take account of it in the interpretation of the principle of self-determination of peoples'.[44] A political statement in 1964, some two decades later, had meshed with a judicial pronouncement. The import is not necessarily to mesh artificially the two paradigms, but to demonstrate that between the years and stances, cases like Somaliland slid between the political and judicial mills for various reasons.

1.2   Secession: international vanity, domestic reality

Uti possidetis causes its own set of problems as identified above, but may well be ameliorated by the right to secession which sets criteria for restricting that broad-based principle. However, secession's shifting quotients are both a help and a hindrance, as will be examined in this section. The *Aaland Islands* case in 1921 articulated three grounds for justifiable secession when the parent state opposes it: those wishing to secede were 'a people'; they were subject to serious violations of human rights at the hands of the parent state; and no other remedies were available to them.[45]

On the first ground, Somaliland seemingly flounders. It does consist largely of the Issaq, but this is a large clan, and any claim to being 'a people', in the author's opinion, would not be supported by basic

---

[41] Poore, 'Somaliland', 142.
[42] *Frontier Dispute (Burkina Faso/Republic of Mali)*, ICJ Reports (1986) 554.
[43] Ibid., pp. 566–7.   [44] Ibid. (Emphasis added).
[45] Report presented by the Council of the League by the Commission of Rapporteurs, *The Aaland Islands Question*, League of Nations Council Doc. B7 (1921) (hereinafter Aaland Islands Report); *Reference re Succession of Quebec*, 2 SCR 277–78 (hereinafter Secession of Quebec).

anthropological principles.[46] However, it should be noted, despite this observation, that a survey of the international arena does reveal that a particular colonial, historical and socio-economic past can forge a distinctive national identity – a reality that maps onto the emergence of the *de facto* state of Somaliland.[47] Further affirmation is to be found in the landmark judgment by the Canadian Supreme Court in addressing the question of Quebec's secession.[48] While rejecting the idea that international law allows a component part of a state to secede unilaterally,[49] the Court was receptive to the idea that the term 'a people' was not defined by territory. This, viewed in a more nuanced manner, can be interpreted as an affirmation that 'a people' may include a portion of the entire population of a state.[50] As Marc Weller notes: 'the will of sub-state populations is being accommodated in a variety of ways from enhanced local self-governance to possible statehood demonstrating that a rigid adherence to the *uti possidetis* principle is subsumed in several settlements that allow populations in certain areas to opt into, or out of, proposed units of self-government'.[51] This offers Somaliland a principled argument that the exercise of self-determination can be undertaken by a sub-population when the state fails to provide equal rights or an environment for political participation.

The second ground, relating to human rights violations, offers greater traction on the back of empirical evidence. As Siad Barre's popularity sagged in the mid-1980s, he unleashed a reign of terror against threats to his power that targeted the three main opposing clans to his rule, which included the Isaaq.[52]

On the third ground, relating to remedial avenues, the Republic of Somalia represents the quintessential failed state.[53] This generates a host

---

[46] For evaluative criteria on what a people are, see, e.g., J. Vidmar, 'International Legal Responses to Kosovo's Declaration of Independence' (2009) 42 *Vanderbilt Journal of Transnational Law*, 779–818, 810–12.

[47] See, e.g., A. J Carroll and B. Rajagopal, 'The Case for the Independent Statehood of Somaliland', (1993) 8 *American University Journal of International Law and Policy* 653–81, 653.

[48] 'Secession of Quebec', p. 217.   [49] Ibid.

[50] For an incisive overview, see P. Radan, *The Break-up of Yugoslavia and International Law* (London: Routledge, 2002), p. 50.

[51] M. Weller, 'Settling Self-determination Conflicts: Recent Developments', (2009) 20 (1) *European Journal of International Law*, 111–65, 164–5.

[52] See, e.g., Global Security, 'Red Beret Reign of Terror', 1 July 2007, available at www.globalsecurity.org/military/world/war/somalia5.htm (last accessed 18 March 2011).

[53] See discussion in Section II below.

of dynamics regarding shifting sovereignty. Michael Schoiswohl, in his book on state collapse, develops a model of dissolving secession which contends that 'the effect of recognition is "declaratory" in undisputed cases of new statehood, "evidentiary" in borderline cases regarding the emergence of a new State and "semi-constitutional", where statehood of an entity is contentious'.[54] This leads Martina Bielawski to the 'conclusion that for entities like "Somaliland", the threshold of effectiveness required in order to conclude that a new state has emerged is lowered'.[55] This is a position that this author agrees with, buttressed by the observation that as a former (defined) British colony, Somaliland has leeway to exercise its right to self-determination because the unification process was legally and politically flawed, rendering it invalid *ipso facto*.[56]

2. Constitutive theory

Under the constitutive approach to recognition, a state becomes a legal entity once other states recognise it as such.[57] However, Somaliland's relationships with other nations are not significant enough to constitute recognition. Currently, no states or international bodies *formally* recognise Somaliland's statehood, as they are disinclined to interact with Somaliland as a *sovereign* state.[58] This doctrine hinders the exercise of the right of self-determination, because it places more importance upon the judgment of the recognising state than upon the rights of the state exercising (or claiming) self-determination.[59] It should, however, be noted that although no state

---

[54] M. Bielawski, Publication Review, 'Status and (Human Rights) Obligations of Non-Recognized De Facto Regimes in International Law: The Case of "Somaliland" – The Resurrection of Somaliland against All International "Odds": State Collapse, Secession, Non-Recognition and Human Rights', (2006) 55 (3) *International and Comparative Law Quarterly*, 778–80, 779.

[55] Ibid., 779.

[56] In the considered observation by Poore (with which the author concurs): 'If there was no union, then Somaliland still exists as an independent entity and discussions pertaining to secession are moot.' Poore, 'Somaliland', 140–2.

[57] See, e.g., W. T. Worster, 'Law, Politics and the Conception of the State in State Recognition Theory', (2009) 27 *Boston University International Law Journal*, 115–68, 118; Poore, 'Somaliland', 136.

[58] See, e.g., R. Draper, 'Shattered Somalia', *National Geographic* (London, 14 September 2009), 86; 'The Nation Nobody Knows', *The Economist* (London, 14 April 2001), 42, available at www.economist.com/node/569115 (last accessed 14 January 2011).

[59] See, e.g., Worster, 'Law, Politics'. 'It has been argued that the declaratory theory emerged because of objections to the discretion of states, as well as a principled acknowledgment of the role of self-determination.'

formally recognises Somaliland, it has had informal links with some states, regional and continental players. Engagement with other states has included Ethiopia, Kenya, Yemen, Egypt, Italy and France, which at various points in time have welcomed official delegations from the government as a responsible authority.[60] On the inter-governmental bodies front, this has encompassed the AU and the Intergovernmenal Authority on Development (IGAD).[61] Of great significance is that an AU fact-finding mission to Somaliland in 2005 expressly recommended that the country be recognised, noting that the case of Somaliland should be 'judged from an objective historical viewpoint and a moral angle vis-à-vis the aspirations of its people'.[62] Like other contested matters, the pragmatic finding of the AU remains frozen in the legitimating myth of *uti possidetis* that wraps up different variegations along the same prism.

Continued denial of recognition can lead to uncertainty across several spheres, not just political. Kosovo offers a classic example. The Kosovo 'muddle' commenced in the aftermath of the dismemberment of Yugoslavia, when several major powers and a coterie of other states granted it recognition. This was amidst vociferous objections by Serbia (the parent state) and a multitude of other states. Despite a unilateral declaration of independence in 2008 and a positive finding regarding the declaration in 2010 by the ICJ,[63] uncertainty persists. In large part this is due to a refusal of other pivotal countries, including Serbia, China

[60] In 2003, the South African Department of Foreign Affairs opined that Somaliland qualifies for statehood, and that it was 'incumbent upon the international community to recognise it'. Equally, Ethiopia (a not insignificant player in Eastern Africa) recognises Somaliland passports, with its national airline flying scheduled flights to Hargeisa (Somaliland's capital). However, because of international legal and political strictures, Ethiopia does not formally recognise Somaliland's independence since, like other states, it is 'too worried about the effect this precedent might have on its own lawless Somali clans. It is happy to keep on good terms with Somaliland, and give it enough goodies to gain access to Berbera [Somaliland's port], but that is about it.' 'The Nation Nobody Knows', *The Economist*, 42. Somaliland Centre for Peace and Development, 'A Self-Portrait of Somaliland: Rebuilding from the Ruins' (War-torn Societies Project, December 1999), 83.

[61] Intergovernmental Authority on Development. (IGAD), created to supersede the limited mandates of its predecessor, the Intergovernmental Authority on Drought and Development (IGADD), which was founded in 1986. IGAD is the Eastern Africa regional organisation that now plays a full spectrum role in promoting and establishing the regional peace, stability and development. Its members include all the minor and major economic, military and political players in the region.

[62] Somaliland News, *AU Mission to Somaliland Says Recognition Overdue*, www.radio-somaliland.com/index.php?itemid=232, last accessed 13 March 2006.

[63] GA Res. 63/3, UN Doc. A/RES/63/3 (8 October 2008), available at http://0-www.icj-cij.org.library.newcastle.edu.au/docket/index.php?p1=3&p2=4&k=21&case=141&code=

and Russia, to recognise it. Kosovo's quandary and limbo, despite some stellar supporters in its stable, is encapsulated in the following observation by Martin Waehlisch and Behar Xharra:

> Though the International Court of Justice ruled that Kosovo's declaration of independence was not illegal under international law, about two thirds of the international community is reluctant to enter into formal contacts . . . Further recognitions are crucial for Kosovo's development. Aside from the high political sensitivity of the matter, the consequences for Kosovar citizens are real . . . Afghani passport holders can cross twenty-two borders without restrictions. Kosovars can only travel to five countries visa-free: Turkey, Albania, Montenegro, Macedonia and Haiti . . . Education and job opportunities outside Kosovo are a reverie.[64]

IV.   Failed states: not even death can prise us apart?

1.   Unbundling sovereignty

There are many conceptions of 'state failure', most of which are derived from classical definitions of statehood.[65] Failed states arise when a government loses its ability to govern, signifying loss of its legitimacy.[66] Commentators emphasise loss of ability to govern which engages the crucial touchstone of inability to sustain itself as a member of the international community.[67]

> Most failed-state metrics emphasize the importance of three elements in determining the strength of a state: security, political participation, and basic civil services. These represent the basic functions of a state. Without these features, a nation would lack the ability to maintain the order necessary for a stable society. Without security, there is no check on

kos&p3=0; the initiating Advisory Opinion request, Judgment, available at www.icj-cij. org/docket/files/141/15987.pdf (last accessed 25 December 2010).

[64]   M. Waehlisch and B. Xharra, 'Three Years after Independence, Kosovo Still Struggles for Recognition', *Peace and Conflict Monitor* (San José, 17 February 2011) available at www. monitor.upeace.org/printer.cfm/id_article=77 (last accessed 27 March 2011) (emphasis added).

[65]   See generally, J. John, 'Conceptualising the Causes and Consequences of Failed States: A Critical Review of the Literature', Crisis States Research Centre, Working Paper No. 25, 2008, 3–10 available at www.crisisstates.com/download/wp/wpseries2/wp25.2 (last accessed 14 December 2010).

[66]   See R. I. Rotberg, 'Failed States, Collapsed States, Weak States: Causes and Indicators' in R. I. Rotberg (ed.), *State Failure and State Weakness in a Time of Terror* (Washington DC: Brookings Institution Press, 2003), pp. 1, 9; see I. W. Zartman, 'Introduction: Posing the Problem of State Collapse', in I. W. Zartman (ed.), *Collapsed States: The Disintegration and Restoration of Legitimate Authority* (Boulder, Colorado: Lynne Rienner, 1995) p. 1.

[67]   G. B. Helman and S. R Ratner, 'Saving Failed States', *Foreign Policy* (1992–3) 3.

violence or crime, hampering both the health and economic development of the state's citizens. Without the ability to participate in the political process, people lose the right to self-determination, calling the legitimacy of the government into question.[68]

Ira Zartman succinctly sums up the spectre of a failed state thus: 'Failed state refers to a situation where the structure, authority (legitimate power), law, and political order have fallen apart. . . For a period, the state itself, as a legitimate, functioning order, is gone.'[69] This leads to the chapter's next postulation: the international community has contributed to the elaboration and development of the declaratory theory posited by the Montevideo Convention to encompass the importance of democracy, equal rights and respect for self-determination.[70] If sovereignty is a bounded legal norm, then notions of democracy and the centrality of safeguarding human rights argument can be reframed in the context of sovereignty not being static within a state, but transferable. That, in the author's opinion, may serve to bridge the gap between the predominant concepts of state recognition – declaratory and constitutive.

In the course of the twentieth century, against a background of sovereign excesses manifest in epochal events including the two World Wars, sovereignty developed to reflect new realities, as natural law precepts surged to ameliorate the positivist tendencies that had under-pinned and often acted as an alibi for authoritarian and unprincipled government policy. Sovereignty was re-conceptualised from the classical notion of the state as the unchallenged supreme authority within a territory, free from any external interference, into the state as a political institution entrusted with fettered prerogatives by emergent distinct norms by an increasingly assertive international community. This metamorphosis pro-vided leeway for self-determination to gain traction, first as a political idea post-World War I, which morphed into a legal principle and finally a fundamental (collective) human right post-World War II. Sovereignty was re-conceptualised as a bundle of rights and correlative obligations i.e. while the state retains its traditional right to non-interference in internal affairs, human rights norms delineate that governments have to meet basic benchmarks conducive to a stable world order and dignity

---

[68] Kreuter, 'Self-Determination', 394–5; see also, John, 'Conceptualising the Causes and Consequences of Failed States', 5.

[69] Zartman, 'Posing the Problem of State Collapse', in Zartman (ed.), p. 1.

[70] For some considered reflections on this scenario in other settings, see, e.g., E. T. Huang, 'The Modern Concept of Sovereignty, Statehood and Recognition: A Case Study of Taiwan', (2003) 16 *New York International Law Review*, 99–19. 111–21; Kreuter, 'Self-Determination', 365–6.

of citizenry: these include preventing human rights violations, ensuring peace and stability domestically, regionally and internationally. It is this re-conceptualisation of sovereignty that has been the basis of novel avenues for formal and informal international intervention in the patchy landscape of fulfilling the legal principles underpinning self-determination – implicitly and covertly.

Kosovo is an exemplar. The EU, with its Conditions for Recognition of Eastern European States, encapsulated a 'standards before status' approach which conditioned 'possible independence for Kosovo on the *development of good governance* within the territory, including in partic-ular *provision for minorities*'.[71] It is of note that, despite the AU's enshrinement of the *uti possidetis* principle that militates against seces-sion and hence brutally undercuts the recognition of new entities, its Constitutive Act, which embraces a transference of state sovereignty by conferring a right of intervention in a Member State in circumstances of gross violations of human rights, contains one of the strongest provi-sions of any regional body.[72]

2.   Irresponsible 'parent' government, responsible international community: re-aligning and anchoring recognition

No state, however powerful, has been able to shield its affairs com-pletely from external influence.[73] Ronald Brand avers that: 'Although sovereignty continues to be a controlling force affecting international relations, the powers, immunities and privileges it carries have been subject to increased limitations.'[74] These limitations often result from the need to balance the recognised rights of sovereign states and duties to its citizens.[75] Among the human rights deemed fit objects of

---

[71]   Weller, 'Settling Self-Determination Conflicts', 153–4 (emphasis added).

[72]   See generally, A. Abass and M. A. Baderin, 'Towards Effective Collective Security and Human Rights Protection in Africa: An Assessment of the Constitutive Act of the New African Union', (2002) 54 *Netherlands International Law Review*, 1–38; see gen-erally, Abraham, 'Lines Upon Maps', 61–84.

[73]   See, e.g., J. L. Brierly, *The Law of Nations*, 4th edn (Oxford: Clarendon Press, 1949), pp. 48–50 for early commentary finding problems with the notion that sovereignty exempts states from being subject to international law.

[74]   See R. A. Brand, 'External Sovereignty and International Law', (1995) 18 *Fordham International Law Journal*, 1685–97, 1695.

[75]   P. A. McKeon, 'An International Criminal Court: Balancing the Principle of Sovereignty against the Demands for International Justice', (1997) 12 *Saint John's Journal of Legal Commentary*, 535–64, 542–3.

international concern is the *right of political participation*. This right is embodied in Article 21 of the Universal Declaration of Human Rights as follows:

(1) Everyone has the right to take part in the government of his country, directly or through freely chosen representatives.

(2) Everyone has the right to equal access to public service in his country.

(3) *The will of the people shall be the basis of the authority of government*; this will shall be expressed in periodic and genuine elections which shall be by universal and equal suffrage and shall be held by secret vote or by equivalent free voting procedures.[76]

This is legally enshrined through Common Article 1 of the two human rights Covenants[77] which form the backbone of the so-called International Bill of Rights:[78] the discourse, however, remains 'straitjacketed' by Article 2(7) of the UN Charter, which prohibits intervention in the 'domestic affairs' of other states. This Article remains a pillar of the UN Charter system and casts a shadow over debates relating to government legitimacy or illegitimacy. However, many states maintain fealty to resolutions and declarations proclaiming support for democracy and the right of political participation:[79] further, that each state has the 'sovereign right freely to choose and develop its political, social, economic and cultural systems, whether or not they conform to the preferences of other

---

[76] The Universal Declaration of Human Rights, GA Res. 217A (III), UN Doc. A/810 (1948) (hereinafter UDHR) (emphasis added).

[77] International Covenant on Civil and Political Rights, 16 December 1966, 999 UNTS 171, 6 ILM 368 (hereinafter ICCPR); International Covenant on Economic, Social, and Cultural Rights, 16 December 1966, 993 UNTS 3 (hereinafter ICESCR).

[78] The informal name given to the troika of international human rights instruments that form the bedrock of human rights. The UDHR and the two legally binding covenants that it spawned – ICCPR and ICESR. These covenants legally enshrine the principled assertion of Article 21 of the UDHR.

[79] As noted in Section I of this chapter, the United Nations (UN) General Assembly in one of its most seminal resolution – *Declaration on Friendly Relations*, 24 October 1970, while reaffirming states' territorial integrity, added a caveat:

Nothing in the foregoing paragraphs shall be construed as authorizing or encouraging any action which would dismember or impair, totally or in part, *the territorial integrity or political unity of sovereign and independent States conducting themselves in compliance with the principle of . . . self-determination of peoples* . . . and thus possessed of a government representing the whole people belonging to the territory without distinction as to race, creed or colour.

states'.[80] By the existence of this minimum standard, international law imposes obligations which a state must meet continuously in order to maintain legitimacy under the international system. As Kurt Mills states:

> [A state's] rights and obligations come into play when a state, or at least certain actions of a state, has been found to be illegitimate within the framework of the New Sovereignty. That is, when a state violates human rights or cannot meet its obligations vis-à-vis its citizens, those citizens have a right to ask for and receive assistance and the international community has a right and obligation to respond in a manner most befitting the particular situation, which may involve ignoring the sovereignty of the state in favour of the sovereignty of individuals and groups.[81]

As a follow-on, and of note, the 1993 Vienna Declaration of the UN World Conference on Human Rights asserts that the denial of the right of self-determination is a violation of human rights, thus underlining the importance of the effective realisation of the right.[82] The Vienna Declaration proceeds to observe that the focus should be on '[c]ooperation, development and strengthening of human rights' through a 'strengthening and building of institutions relating to human rights, strengthening of a pluralistic civil society and the protection of groups which have been rendered vulnerable'. It wraps up by noting that assistance is necessary for 'the conduct of free and fair elections ... the strengthening of the rule of law, the promotion of freedom of expression

---

[80] See, e.g., A Res. 45/150, UN GAOR 3d Comm., 45th Sess., Supp. No. 49A, UN Doc. A/45/766 (1990) 255. Though the international community, under Articles 55 and 56 of the UN Charter, may promote state observance of the right of citizens to participate in their governance, there is no clear authority to mandate a particular allocation of decision-making power within a sovereign state. Since one of the main roles of a sovereign state is to provide security and protection for its own people, the author argues that a state forfeits its sovereignty when its actions are antagonistic to guaranteeing its citizenry peace, security and governance. See generally, M. R. Fowler and J. M. Bunck, *Law Power, and the Sovereign State: The Evolution and Application of the Concept of Sovereignty* (Penn State University Press, 1995).

[81] K. Mills, *Human Rights in the Emerging Global Order: A New Sovereignty?* (London: Palgrave Macmillan, 1998), pp. 163–4.

[82] United Nations World Conference on Human Rights, *Vienna Declaration and Program of Action*, 32 ILM 1661, 1683 (1993) (hereinafter Vienna Declaration). The World Conference on Human Rights was assembled in Vienna by the UN 14–25 June 1993. Representatives of 171 states attended. The Vienna Declaration was adopted by acclamation on 25 June 1993.

and the administration of justice, and ... the real and effective participation of the people in the decision-making processes'.[83]

V. Conclusion

In 2012, a Conference on Somalia hosted in the UK and attended by some 55 countries, had the tenor of peace and stability. However, the final communiqué was rather bland in dealing with the governance issues and the contentious issue of self-declared and 'nominally' autonomous regions, considering that there were no less than four Somali presidents in attendance. Officially it was President Sheikh Sharif Ahmed of the SFTG who was the central and official focus of attention as the Head of State of the Republic of Somalia. However, the three others, representing the more stable regions in the north by a sleight of diplomacy, were there in their *formal* capacities as participants, and not merely as observers. It is of note that the British Foreign and Commonwealth Office acknowledged the attendance of Somaliland separately from that of the SFTG – the internationally and formally recognised official government.[84] Mokhtar Abshir, a Somaliland commentator and supporter, in a burst of partisan optimism, noted:

> Our success in this conference should not mean to willy-nilly participate in all future meetings regarding our brethrens to the south but we should rather choose carefully. It is only through clever political maneuvering and hard lobbying of the international community that can we assert our right to a seat at the table where it matters most, in international organisations.[85]

The sentiment above, while parochial, does reflect political reality and an inconvenient truth. Practically, the London Conference did give some prominence to the more stable northern areas – Puntland, Galmudug and Somaliland. The biggest winner was Somaliland which, unlike the other 'nominally' autonomous regions from the Republic of Somalia, was not compelled or required to sign the agreements reached at the conference.[86]

---

[83] Ibid., p. 1683.

[84] See, e.g., M. Abshir, 'Somaliland: Post the Somalia London Conference and Beyond' (25 February 2012) available at http://somalilandpress.com/somaliland-post-the-somalia-london-conference-and-beyond-26721 (last accessed 28 March 2012).

[85] Ibid.

[86] See, e.g., 'London Conference Backs Somalia Terror Fight', BBC News, www.bbc.co.uk/news/uk-politics-17131208 (23 February 2012) (last accessed 25 March 2012); M. Harper, 'Will the World Help or Hinder Somalia?' BBC News, www.bbc.co.uk/news/world-africa-17144557 (23 February 2012) (last accessed 25 March 2012) .

Somaliland offers a tricky legal problem, but also an opportunity. States should exercise their voice by recognising Somaliland. This may prove a difficult adjustment for political processes still entrenched in dual social contract relationships of yester-decades. However, developments in the twentieth century have progressively recognised emerging new trends in the understanding and location of sovereignty. This understanding of sovereignty rejects approaching relations in terms of a Lockean, second-tier social contract.[87] This two-tiered notion of sovereignty treats the relationship among states in forming the international order as parallel to the relationship among citizens in forming the order that is the state. This obscures important aspects of the relationship between the citizen and the state, and obstructs the proper functioning of that relationship vis-à-vis the government.

If international law is to be contemporary in the twenty-first century, it must acknowledge the principal social contract focus on the relationship between the citizen and the state for purposes of defining sovereignty in national (internal) and international (external) relations. In place of a social contract of states, a redefinition of sovereignty in the arena of statehood recognises the fact that international law has developed direct links between the individual and international law. Consequently, an active role on the part of the state in international relations is consistent with a sovereign's duties and responsibilities to its citizenry, and tactical recognition enhances rather than diminishes the recognition dynamic.[88]

---

[87] See, e.g., R. B. Bilder, 'Perspectives on Sovereignty in the Current Context: An American Viewpoint', (1994) 20 *Canada–United States Law Journal*, 9–17; R. Falk, 'Evasions of Sovereignty' in R. B. J. Walker and S. H. Mendlovitz (eds.), *Contending Sovereignties: Redefining Political Community* (Boulder, Colorado: Lynne Rienner, 1990); L. Henkin, 'The Mythology of Sovereignty', reprinted in 'Notes from the President', *ASIL Newsletter*, March–May 1993, 1.

[88] The basis of this assertion is synthesised from several works by the author. It is acknowledged that the scholars noted do not specifically focus on state recognition; however, their observations form part of the author's development of argument. See, e.g., M. M. Martin Martinez, *National Sovereignty and International Organizations* (The Hague, Netherlands: Kluwer Law International, 1996), p. 66; N. Arniston, 'International Law and Non-Intervention: When Do Humanitarian Concerns Supersede Sovereignty?', (1993) 17 (2) *Fletcher Forum for World Affairs*, 198–211, 207.

PART II

Self-determination

The internal and external aspects of self-determination reconsidered

JAMES SUMMERS[*]

I. Introduction

The right of peoples to self-determination is frustratingly ambiguous. Its subject, 'the people', is not defined and unlikely ever to be so. The right can be used in contradictory ways: to support or split states, to protect sovereignty or to encourage intervention. This vagueness is the perennial attraction of self-determination. It has an ability to be viewed from various perspectives and adopted for different political agendas. Nonetheless, from a legal position, this makes the principle difficult to categorise. Therefore, it might be attractive to divide self-determination into more manageable pieces which can be more readily defined.

There are various ways in which self-determination could be divided. It could be on the nature of its rights. Article 1 of the Human Rights Covenants 1966 suggests a four-fold division: political, economic, social and cultural. It could be on the basis of philosophical or political roots.[1] It could be according to subjects, such as colonial peoples, peoples under foreign occupation, states' peoples and minorities. However, the most popular subdivision of self-determination seems to be according to purported dimensions to the right: its internal and external aspects.

This distinction has not always been applied specifically to self-determination. As an explicit concept, internal and external self-determination appears to be a post-war development, which emerged

---

[*] I would like to thank Harold Johnson, Ruben Brouwer, Jure Vidmar and Marc Weller for their assistance with this chapter. All views expressed, of course, are my own.

[1] E.g., Dov Ronen divided self-determination into 'five manifestations' based to a significant degree on political ideology: Nationalism, Marxism, Wilsonian Self-determination, Decolonisation (Race), Ethnonationalism or Subnationalism (Ethnicity): D. Ronen, *The Quest for Self-determination* (Yale University Press, 1979), pp. 25–6.

in the context of Indonesian independence in 1949. Nonetheless, consideration of the right in relation to the internal and external aspects of state relations dates from the 1920s.[2] Moreover, for a long period it remained a relatively peripheral perspective in the law of self-determination which was focused on colonial independence. Nevertheless, the division is now almost standard practice in the academic literature.[3] It strongly informed the Canadian Supreme Court's judgment in *Re Secession of Quebec* (1997).[4] It was integral to the Committee on the Elimination

---

[2] The Commission of Jurists in fact made several internal and external references, none of which were explicitly connected to self-determination. '[T]he principle of self-determination of peoples may be called into play. New aspirations of certain sections of a nation, which are sometimes based on old traditions or a common language and civilisation, may come to the surface and produce effects which must be taken into account in the interests of the internal and external peace of nations.' *Report of the International Commission of Jurists*, League of Nations Official Journal, Special Supplement No. 3 (October 1920), p. 6.

The Commission of Rapporteurs described self-determination in terms that today would be referred to as internal and external: 'The idea of justice and liberty, embodied in the formula of self-determination, must be applied in a reasonable manner to the relations between States and the minorities they include ... This postulate marks one of the most noble advances of modern civilisation and, it is clear that there can be no lasting peace apart from justice, constitutes one the most powerful means of strengthening peace and combating hatred and dissentions both within the State and in international relations.' *The Aaland Islands Question: Report Submitted to the Council of the League of Nations by the Commission of Rapporteurs*, League of Nations Doc. B7 [C] 21/68/106 at p. 28.

[3] See H. Johnson, *Self-Determination within the Community of Nations* (A. W. Sijthoff, 1967), p. 28; A. Cassese, *Self-Determination of Peoples: A Legal Reappraisal* (Cambridge University Press, 1995), p. 5 ff.; D. Raič, *Statehood and the Law of Self-Determination* (Kluwer, 2002), pp. 226–307; M. Pomerance, *Self-Determination in Law and Practice: The New Doctrine of the United Nations* (Martinus Nijhoff, 1982), pp. 37–42; R. McCorquodale, 'Self-Determination: A Human Rights Approach', (1994) 43 *International and Comparative Law Quarterly*, 863–5; U. O. Umozurike, *Self-Determination in International Law* (Archon Books, 1972), p. 1; K. Henrard, *Devising an Adequate System of Minority Protection: Individual Human Rights, Minority Rights and the Right to Self-Determination* (Martinus Nijhoff, 2000), pp. 281, 299–301; H. Quane, 'A Right to Self-Determination for the Kosovo Albanians?', (2000) 13 *Leiden Journal of International Law*, 219; S. Trifunovska, 'One Theme in Two Variations – Self-Determination for Minorities and Indigenous Peoples', (1997) 5 *International Journal of Minority and Group Rights*, 182; F. L. Kirgis Jr., 'The Degrees of Self-Determination in the United Nations Era', (1994) 88 *American Journal of International Law*, 305, 307; A. Kiss, 'The Peoples' Right to Self-Determination', (1986) 7 *Human Rights Law Journal*, 170–2; P. H. Kooijmans, 'Tolerance, Sovereignty and Self-Determination', (1996) 43 *Netherlands International Law Review*, 212–15; M. Moore, 'Introduction: The Self-Determination Principle and the Ethics of Secession' in M. Moore (ed.), *National Self-Determination and Secession* (Oxford University Press, 1998), p. 10; H. Hannum, 'Self-Determination in the Post-Colonial Era' in D. Clark and R. Williamson (eds), *Self-Determination: International Perspectives* (St. Martin's Press, 1996), p. 14.

[4] *Reference re: Secession of Quebec*, DLR 161 (1998) 4th Series, para. 126.

of Racial Discrimination's General Recommendation XXI on secession.[5] Over half of states' submissions to the International Court of Justice (ICJ) in the 2010 *Kosovo* Opinion referred to it,[6] and while the Court itself did not,[7] two judges used the division in their separate opinions.[8] Nonetheless, the origins and purpose of the distinction seem surprisingly elusive. Why divide self-determination in two, and what does having such dimensions mean?

This chapter will look at the significance of an internal and external division in self-determination and its implications for the right. It is arguable that an attraction of an internal–external dichotomy is that, in itself, it says little about the content of the right. Rather, its implications depend on the unit it is focused on. The dichotomy is, in fact, an effective way of presenting self-determination from a certain perspective. However, this renders it contextual and its significance varies in different situations. Moreover, the process of self-determination involves a number of actors, typically peoples and states, but also others as well. There may be more than one perspective on the dimensions of self-determination and each approach may in itself present an incomplete and thus problematic picture of the right.

---

[5] General Recommendation XXI (48) (CERD/C/365/Rev.1 (2000) p. 16, para. 4.

[6] Written Statement of Albania, 14 April 2009, *Kosovo* (Advisory Opinion) ICJ 2010, paras. 75, 89; Written Statement of Argentina, 17 April 2009, para. 94; Written Statement of Cyprus, 17 April 2009, paras. 129, 132–6; Written Statement of Denmark, 17 April 2009, para. 2.7; Written Statement of Egypt, 16 April 2009, paras. 64, 69–71, 73; Written Statement of Estonia, 13 April 2009, para. 2.1; Written Statement of Finland, 16 April 2009, paras. 5–6; Written Statement of Germany, 15 April 2009, p. 33; Written Statement of Ireland, 17 April 2009, para. 32; Written Statement of Iran, 17 April 2009, paras. 3.6 and 4.1; Written Statement of the Netherlands, 17 April 2009, para. 3.5; Written Statement of Poland, 14 April 2009, para. 6.13; Written Statement of Romania, 14 April 2009, paras. 123, 125, 129, 145–59; Written Statement of Russia, 16 April 2009, paras. 56, 85, Written Statement of Serbia, 15 April 2009, paras. 544, 611; Written Statement of Spain, 14 April 2009, para, 24; Written Statement of Slovakia, 16 April 2009, para. 127; Written Statement of Switzerland, 15 April 2009, paras. 64–6. Written Comments of Bolivia, 17 July 2009, p. 5; Azerbaijan, 27th Public Sitting, 3 December 2009, CR 2009/27, pp. 21–3; Belarus, *ibid.* pp. 29–30, 32; Burundi, 28th Public Sitting, 4 December, CR 2009/28, pp. 38–9; Jordan, 31st Public Sitting, 9 December 2009, CR 2009/31, pp. 31, 36; Venezuela, 33rd Public Sitting, 11 December 2009, CR 2009/33, p. 12.

[7] As lamented by Judge Simma, Separate Opinion, *Kosovo* (Advisory Opinion), ICJ (2010), paras. 6–7.

[8] Judge Cançado Trindade, Separate Opinion, *Kosovo* (Advisory Opinion), ICJ (2010), para. 184; Judge Yusuf, *ibid.* paras. 9–10.

II. What could internal and external aspects relate to?

The division of self-determination into internal and external elements is not spelled out with any precision in international instruments, leaving considerable ambiguity as to what the two aspects might relate to. An illustration of the range of possibilities encompassed by the distinction is provided by Patrick Thornberry, who offered this description:

> The external dimension or aspect defines the status of a people in relation to another people, State or Empire, whereas the democratic or internal dimension should concern the relationship between a people and 'its own' State or government.[9]

Two points are evident in this description. First, self-determination involves the relationship between peoples and a number of different entities: peoples, states, empires, governments. In each of those relationships an internal and external dichotomy could take on a different significance. Second, self-determination concerns *relationships*; in other words, it is a process that always involves more than one unit. The right is considered to be held by peoples, but determining their political status and economic, social and cultural development typically involves the structure and behaviour of states and their institutions. Indeed, the history of self-determination has shown it frequently to centre on the control of established political units, which then inform the identity of peoples and the self-determination process.[10] In decolonisation, self-determination's most successful legal incarnation, both peoples and the process of self-determination were defined around the situation in colonial territories. The break-up of Yugoslavia and the Soviet Union similarly revolved around the republics of those federations. Correspondingly, the dimensions of self-determination may simultaneously relate to different units.

Self-determination encompasses a number of elements that can be seen to have internal and external dimensions. First, a people or a nation is defined by its membership, which determines its essential characteristics and who is within or outside that group. Studies of ethnic and national groups have focused on the decisive role that borders play in a group's identity, both in relation to its members, but also how that

---

[9] P. Thornberry, 'The Democratic or Internal Aspect of Self-determination with Some Remarks on Federalism,' in C. Tomuschat (ed.), *Modern Law of Self-determination* (Martinus Nijhoff, 1993) pp. 101–38 at p. 101.
[10] See J. Breuilly, *Nationalism and the State* (2nd edn) (University of Chicago Press, 1994).

people is differentiated from others.[11] What and who is internal and external is fundamental to the concept of a people or a nation. Second, self-determination usually concerns questions of self-government, which can be seen to have internal and external aspects from the scope of that governance. Self-government could be measured by the physical extent of a government's legal jurisdiction, by the population subject to its laws or by focusing on those who participate in that system of governance. Third, states, which are normally the object of claims of self-determination, have particular requirements in international law. Following the Montevideo Convention 1933, they have a defined territory, a permanent population and a government, creating scope for internal and external dimensions. The same is also true for 'other' territorially autonomous political units, as explained further below.

Thus, the self-determination process involves different units, which have their own internal and external aspects. This chapter will consider four units which provide dimensions around which self-determination could be defined: peoples, sovereign states, autonomous units within states and political units distinct from states. It will look at the implications of viewing self-determination from these particular perspectives. It will argue that a self-determination process will inevitably involve more than one of these elements and, therefore, internal and external self-determination must engage with a combination of these differing levels of perspective if it is to remain relevant.

III.   Four units for self-determination

1.   Peoples

Peoples hold the right of self-determination and are thus the most obvious entity for the measurement of the dimensions of the right.[12]

---

[11] F. Barth, 'Introduction' in F. Barth (ed.), *Ethnic Groups and Borders: The Social Organization of Cultural Difference* (Scandinavian University Books, 1969), pp. 9–38.

[12] An example of a people-centred approach can be found in oral submissions by Azerbaijan in the *Kosovo* Opinion (2010). Internal self-determination was defined as: 'all peoples have the right to pursue freely their economic, social and cultural development without outside interference'. External self-determination was: 'the right of peoples to determine freely their political status and their place in the international community based on the principle of equal rights and exemplified by the liberation of peoples from colonialism and by the prohibition to subject peoples to alien subjugation, domination and exploitation,' 27th Public Sitting, 3 December 2009, CR 2009/27, p. 21, para. 30.

And whereas internal self-determination relates to a people's own governance, the external aspect concerns its status vis-à-vis other peoples. Such a people-centred division is suggested by a literal reading of the instruments implying internal and external aspects in the right. Principle VIII(2) of the Helsinki Final Act 1979, provides that it is the dimensions of the people which determine the content of the right:

> By virtue of the principle of equal rights and self-determination of peoples, all peoples always have the right, in full freedom, to determine, when and as they wish, their internal and external political status, without external interference...

Article 4 of the 2007 Declaration on the Rights of Indigenous Peoples refers to the internal affairs of indigenous peoples:

> Indigenous peoples, in exercising their right to self-determination, have the right to autonomy or self-government in matters relating to their internal and local affairs, as well as ways and means for financing their autonomous functions.

It is important to note that if peoples are the unit for measuring the dimensions of self-determination, they may or may not match the boundaries of states. The two can coincide, in which case the internal and external aspects of a people's self-determination would correspond to the internal affairs and external relations of a state.[13] The idea of state and people matching was particularly strong in the drafting of the Helsinki Final Act, where there was a focus on the independence of Eastern European countries from the Soviet Union.[14]

This, though, was not the case with the 2007 United Nations (UN) Declaration on the Rights of Indigenous Peoples (UNDRIP), where the indigenous peoples referred to invariably fell within or crossed the boundaries of states. In the case of minority peoples within states, especially if they have autonomy, internal relations and internal self-determination could relate to the exercise of self-government within their own minority area. By extension, external self-determination could refer to the exercise of relations outside the people in respect to other peoples or institutions. If a state contained a number of peoples, from a people-centred perspective their relations with each other could be considered as the external aspect of their self-determination.

[13] See Cyprus: 'The right applies between the State and all its population, giving people the right to choose the form of government and have access to constitutional rights. This is internal self-determination.' Written Statement of Cyprus, 17 April 2009, *Kosovo* (Advisory Opinion), para. 135.
[14] See Netherlands (CSCE/I/PV.7), p. 18.

However, this interpretation is at odds with general practice in instances where peoples deviate from the boundaries of states. Article 4 supports the notion of self-determination being exercised by indigenous peoples inside their own institutions. However, commentary on the Declaration asserts that it is the relations between indigenous peoples and their states that are the factor in determining internal self-determination.[15] It does not matter how indigenous peoples are defined, internal self-determination means its exercise *within a state*.

This may reflect the state-centric nature of international law, but there are also two important problems with a people-based dichotomy, even if it appears the most natural interpretation of the distinction. First, the concept of the people is ambiguous. The existence of distinct peoples within states is often contested: some states may recognise them, others may not. Moreover, distinct peoples may coexist with the identification of the whole population of a state as people. Peoples may be tricky to apply dimensions to as a unit.[16] They may not be neatly concentrated in one particular area, but dispersed within a state, between states or worldwide as a diaspora. Attributing internal and external dimensions in such circumstances may be highly problematic.

The second problem is linguistic. If groups within states are viewed as peoples and the internal–external distinction applied from their perspective, then their internal and external relations are determined by their borders, not those of the state. The language of internal and external relations, normally used in inter-state relations, applied within a state, might sound unduly nationalistic. The idea of external relations between peoples in a state suggests a significant degree of atomisation and alienation within a multiethnic state. Consequently, the terminology may be unattractive.

2. Sovereign states

Self-determination, according to the internal and external aspects of state sovereignty, represents the most popular and established interpretation of the dichotomy. This is reflected in comments by a number of states[17] and

---

[15] E-I A. Daes, E/CN.4/Sub.2/1992/33, p. 17, para. 67; Chile, E/CN.4/1997/102 (1997), p. 61, para. 320; Finland, E/CN.4/2001/85 (2001), p. 13, para. 76; Russia, *ibid.* pp. 15–16, para. 90; New Zealand, *ibid.* p. 18, para. 109; US, E/CN.4/2003/92 (2003), p. 6, para. 22.

[16] See Judge Yusuf, Separate Opinion, *Kosovo* (Advisory Opinion), ICJ (2010), para. 9.

[17] See Poland: 'Self-determination within a "host" state'. Written Statement of Poland, *Kosovo* (Advisory Opinion) ICJ 2010, 14 April 2009, para. 6.13; Written Statement of Estonia, 13 April 2009, para. 2.1.1; Written Statement of Finland, 16 April 2009, paras.

writers,[18] as well as decisions by the Canadian Supreme Court and Committee on the Elimination of Racial Discrimination. States as self-governing units have internal and external dimensions, and their foundational principle – sovereignty – is equally divided into internal and external aspects.[19] Internal sovereignty refers to a state's internal self-government. According to Vaughan Lowe, for a state, it means 'that its courts and its government are subject to the laws of that State, but only to the laws of that State'.[20] External sovereignty is equated with independence and the external relations of states. Judge Anzilotti in the *Austro-German Customs Union* case (1931) described its significance to be, 'the State has over it no other authority than that of international law'.[21] This division is implicit in international instruments, particularly on non-intervention, which refer to the internal and external affairs of states,[22] and crudely speaking divides states' domestic law and international law as two legal systems.

Self-determination could match the internal and external aspects of state sovereignty if the whole population of a state is considered to be a people. However, if it is not, self-determination for groups within that

5–6; Written Statement of the Netherlands, 17 April 2009, para. 3.5; Belarus: 'The internal right of self-determination usually means the right of ethnic minorities for self-determination. Such right is implemented within the borders of the existing States', 27th Public Sitting, 3 December 2009, CR 2009/27, p. 29.

[18] See A. Cassese, 'Political Self-determination – Old Concepts and New Developments,' in A. Cassese (ed.), *UN Law/Fundamental Rights: Two Topics in International Law* (Sijthoff and Noordhoff, 1979), pp. 137–65 at p. 137; Thornberry, 'The Democratic and Internal Aspect', at p. 101; A. Rosas, 'Internal Self-determination' in Tomuschat (ed.), *Modern Law of Self-determination*, pp. 225–52 at p. 227.

[19] J. E. S. Fawcett, *The Law of Nations* (2nd edn) (Penguin, 1971), p. 41. Sir G. Butler and S. MacCoby, *The Development of International Law* (Longman, Green and Co., 1928), p. 8; M. Koskenniemi, *From Apology to Utopia: The Structure of International Legal Argument* (Finnish Lawyers' Publishing Company, 1989), p. 207; P. Malanczuk, *Akehurst's Modern Introduction to International Law* (7th edn) (Routledge, 1997), p. 17; H. J. Steiner, P. Alston and R. Goodman, *International Human Rights in Context: Law, Politics, Morals* (3rd edn) (Oxford University Press, 2008), pp. 689–90; T. J. Biersteker and C. Weber, 'The Social Construction of State Sovereignty' in T. J. Biersteker and C. Weber (eds), *State Sovereignty as Social Construct* (Cambridge University Press, 1996) pp. 1–21 at p. 2; T. L. Ilgen, 'Reconfigured Sovereignty in the Age of Globalization' in T. L. Ilgen (ed.), *Reconfigured Sovereignty: Multi-Layered Governance in the Global Age* (Ashgate, 2003) pp. 6–35 at p. 7: B. van Roermund, 'Sovereignty: Unpopular and Popular' in N. Walker (ed.), *Sovereignty in Transition* (Hart, 2003) pp. 33–54 at pp. 40–1.

[20] V. Lowe, *International Law* (Clarendon Press, 2007), p. 18.

[21] Judge Anzilotti, *Austro-German Customs Union* Case (1931), PCIJ, Series A/B No. 41, p. 57.

[22] See Principle IV, Helsinki Final Act 1979: Principle 3, Declaration on Friendly Relations, GA Res. 2625 (XXV) 1970.

state is defined from a state perspective by the dimensions of state sovereignty. This distinction is illustrated by Serbia's submissions to the ICJ in the *Kosovo* Opinion, in which it raised a range of arguments against Kosovo's unilateral declaration of independence. Serbia endorsed an internal–external distinction in self-determination, but considered that Kosovo exercised the right internally as part of the people of the Serbian state. The internal and external aspects of both state and people coincided. However, Serbia had another line of argument in the alternative that Kosovo was considered to be a people in its own right: its self-determination could only be internal, exercised within the Serbian state.[23] Therefore, where the dimensions of a people deviated from a state, the borders of self-determination were determined by those of the state.

The internal aspect of the right in this context was described by the Canadian Supreme Court in *Re Secession of Quebec* as: 'a people's pursuit of its political, economic, social and cultural development within the framework of an existing state'.[24] Judge Yusuf, in his Separate Opinion to the *Kosovo* Opinion, described it in these terms: 'inside the boundaries of existing States in various forms and guises'.[25] The exercise of self-determination from this perspective corresponds with internal aspects of state sovereignty and takes place following the state's laws and within its institutions. There is a strong correlation between internal self-determination and common constitutional principles.[26] The right is held by peoples, just as various constitutions assert that sovereignty or authority derives from the people or nation.[27] It is commonly seen to be exercised by enjoyment of individual human rights, which are frequently constitutionally guaranteed,[28] and by democratic governance, the process of which is again spelled out in constitutions.[29]

It is not clear whether internal self-determination in a state context has developed into something more definite than an expression of a state's constitutional provisions or its international human rights

---

[23] Written Comments of Serbia, *Kosovo* (Advisory Opinion) ICJ 2010, 15 July 2009, p. 131, para. 311 and p. 138, para. 330.

[24] 161 DLR (1998) 4th Series, para. 126.

[25] Judge Yusuf, Separate Opinion, *Kosovo* (Advisory Opinion), ICJ (2010), paras. 9–10.

[26] On various interpretations of sovereignty, see D. Sarooshi, *International Organizations and their Exercise of Sovereign Powers* (Oxford University Press, 2005), pp. 3–17.

[27] E.g., Article 3, Constitution of France 1958; Article 1, Constitution of Ireland 1937.

[28] E.g., Chapter 2, Sections 6–23, Constitution of Finland 1999.

[29] E.g., Articles 66–70, Constitution of Spain 1978.

obligations.[30] The aspect has often been treated by states as simply a reflection of their own constitutional standards. The Soviet Union argued in its submissions to the Human Rights Committee, that its peoples enjoyed internal self-determination following its constitution.[31] More recently, the right was raised in submissions to the ICJ by authoritarian states such as Belarus, Iran, Egypt, Russia, Venezuela, Jordan and Azerbaijan.[32] Guatemala's military dictatorship in the drafting of the Friendly Relations Declaration, offered a definition as open to political oppression as liberal democracy: 'a State's right to choose the type of political, economic and social organization best suited to it'.[33] Alternatively, internal self-determination has been used to simply reflect established human rights. This can be seen, in particular, in the recommendation of the Committee on the Elimination of Racial Discrimination which connected internal self-determination to existing rights: participation in public affairs, non-discrimination and minority rights.[34] There is no clearly identifiable independent content to a right of self-determination exercised internally within a state.

External self-determination relates to external aspects of sovereignty and the relations between states. If a people seceded from a state or a state changed its borders, that would change the point where the state's external relations and external sovereignty began.[35] The Committee on the Elimination of Racial Discrimination's description placed it in the sphere of international relations as a people's 'right to freely determine their political status and their place in the international community'.[36]

---

[30] Mr. Mavrommatis, Human Rights Committee member: 'He was not certain that everyone meant the same thing by the internal aspect of self-determination' 43–45 HRCOR (1991–2) I, SR.1092, para. 47.

[31] USSR, 23–28 YHRC (1985–6) I, SR565, para. 2.

[32] Written Statement of Egypt, Kosovo (Advisory Opinion), 16 April 2009, para. 64; Written Statement of Iran, 17 April 2009, paras. 3.6 and 4.1: Written Statement of Russia, 16 April 2009, p. 22, para. 56 and p. 30, para. 85; Oral Submission of Azerbaijan, 27th Public Sitting, 3 December 2009, CR 2009/27, pp. 21, 23, paras. 30, 38; Oral Submission of Belarus, ibid. p. 29; Oral Submission of Jordan, 31st Public Sitting, 9 December 2009, CR 2009/31, p. 31, para. 17; Venezuela, 33rd Public Sitting, 11 December 2009, CR 2009/33, p. 12.

[33] Guatemala, A/C.6/SR.1086 (1968), para. 52.

[34] CERD/C/365/Rev.1 (2000) pp. 16–17, paras. 3–5.

[35] See, e.g., Netherlands: 'whether the right to self-determination has been exercised in a manner that preserves international boundaries, that is, internal self-determination, or in a manner that involves a change of international boundaries, that is, external self-determination,' Kosovo (Advisory Opinion) ICJ 2010, 32nd Public Sitting, 10 December 2009, CR 2009/32, p. 9, para. 5.

[36] CERD/C/365/Rev.1 (2000) p. 16, para. 4.

This interpretation is also supported by Article 1(4) of Moldova's Organic Law on the Special Legal Status of Gagauzia 1994. This provided for external self-determination for the Gagauz people in the event of a change of the status of Moldova (by union with Romania), which was understood as a right to secede from the Moldovan state.[37]

The focus on the state creates a significant legal distinction between internal and external aspects of self-determination. An essential corollary of state sovereignty is the principle of the territorial integrity of states. International instruments which proclaim the right of self-determination also require respect for the territorial integrity of states, which is seen to limit the principle.[38] The Canadian Supreme Court spelled out the restrictive consequences of this: 'self-determination of a people is normally fulfilled through *internal* self-determination ... A right to *external* self-determination ... arises only in the most extreme of cases'.[39]

This leads to the question of the relationship between the internal and external aspects. Can internal self-determination become an external right, and if so, under what circumstances? The usual reference point on this relationship is a controversial provision, Principle 5, Paragraph 7 of the Declaration on Friendly Relations, GA Res. 2625 (XXV) 1970. This upheld the territorial integrity of sovereign and independent states conducting themselves in compliance with the principle of equal rights and self-determination of peoples and thus possessed of a government representing the whole people belonging to the territory without distinctions. It also suggested an idea similar to the internal–external dichotomy in a state context: that self-determination could be enjoyed by non-discriminatory representative government within a state. The Canadian Court developed the distinction from the formula in the Declaration and a similar provision in the Vienna Declaration 1993. However, comments by states on this paragraph suggest widely differing interpretations of the provision and its potential for a

---

[37] See P. Järve, 'Gagauzia and Moldova: Experiences in Power-Sharing' in M. Weller and B. Metzger (eds), *Settling Self-determination Disputes: Complex Power-Sharing in Theory and Practice* (Martinus Nijhoff, 2008), pp. 307–43, at pp. 319–20, 323.

[38] Principle 6, Declaration on Granting Independence to Colonial Countries and Peoples, GA Res. 1514(XV), 1960; Principle 5, Paragraphs 7 and 8, Declaration on Friendly Relations, GA Res. 2625(XXV), 1970; Principle VIII(1), Helsinki Final Act 1975; Article 2, Vienna Declaration 1993; Article 46(1), Declaration on the Rights of Indigenous Peoples 2007, GA Res. 61/295, 2007.

[39] 161 DLR (1998) 4th Series, para. 126 (emphasis in original).

corresponding relationship between internal and external aspects of the right.[40]

Most significantly, if an internal and external distinction in a state context does not create new rights, what is it its significance? The main function of the internal–external dichotomy is to highlight two strands in self-determination, preventing a monopoly of any one interpretation. In the state context, self-determination is commonly understood to involve secession, especially following its close association with independence from the decolonisation process. The dichotomy identifies an alternative. Secession is external self-determination, but there is also an internal aspect to the right. The use of the distinction to weaken a right of secession can be seen in *Re Secession of Quebec* where the Court, proceeding from the distinction, emphasised the representative nature of the Canadian political system and Quebec's participation in it.[41] The strong implication was that Quebec enjoyed internal self-determination within Canada and had no entitlement to an external right.

The dichotomy thus weakens the position of any one outcome from self-determination and supports a broader range of possibilities from the right. In particular, the dichotomy to an extent, can be seen to separate the nationalist and liberal elements in self-determination. Self-determination can easily be reduced to a nationalist argument for independence and the formation of nation-states, which has been expressed in the assertion that the right is the prerequisite for human rights. In other words, in the order of

[40] Support for the possibility was expressed by Written Statement of Albania, *Kosovo* (Advisory Opinion), 14 April 2009, paras. 78–84; Written Statement of Estonia, 13 April 2009, para. 2.1; Statement of Finland, 16 April 2009, paras. 11–12; Statement of Germany, 15 April 2009, 33–4; Statement of Ireland, 17 April 2009, paras. 28–32; Written Statement of Netherlands, 17 April 2009, paras. 3.1–3.20; Written Statement of Norway, 16 April 2009, para. 5; Written Statement of Poland, 14 April 2009, paras. 6.4–6.13, 7.7; Written Statement of Slovenia, 17 April 2009, p. 2; Written Statement of Switzerland, 15 April 2009, paras. 60–8; Jordan, 31st Public Sitting, 9 December 2009, CR 2009/31, p. 36. Nonetheless, exercise of remedial secession was presented as a last resort after the failure of a political process.

Restrictive views were expressed by Written Statement of Argentina, 17 April 2009, paras. 85, 94–7; Written Statement of Azerbaijan, 17 April 2009, para. 24; Written Statement of Brazil, 17 April 2009, 2; Written Statement of China, 16 April 2009, pp. 2–7; Written Statement of Cyprus, 17 April 2009, paras. 132–49; Written Statement of Egypt, 16 April 2009, paras. 57–74; Written Statement of Iran, 17 April 2009, para. 4.1; Written Statement of Japan, 17 April 2009, p. 4; Written Statement of Libya, 17 April 2009; Written Statement of Romania, 14 April 2009, paras. 119–59; Written Statement of Serbia, 15 April 2009, para. 589; Written Statement of Spain, 14 April 2009, paras. 20–7; Written Statement of Slovakia, 16 April 2009, paras. 6–17. See also Judge Koroma, Dissenting Opinion, paras. 21–2.

[41] 161 DLR (1998) 4th Series, paras. 126, 134–5.

human rights, self-determination comes first. The dichotomy, however, allows internal self-determination to ensure liberal arguments are raised – i.e. that self-determination can be exercised through individual rights and representative government – without always, or even usually, through recourse to statehood.[42]

A state-based approach to the internal–external dichotomy, however, suffers from two problems. The first is legitimacy. Dividing self-determination into two halves, and then limiting one half according to principles of sovereignty and territorial integrity, make the distinction appear merely a useful instrument for states' interests. This can be seen in the position of indigenous non-governmental organisations (NGOs), in the drafting of the Declaration on Indigenous Peoples. These groups, whom one would have thought would benefit from greater internal self-determination, nonetheless condemned the distinction as 'artificial', 'unhelpful' and 'discriminatory'.[43]

The second problem is the accuracy of a distinction based around a sovereign state. The distinction between internal and external sovereignty has been progressively eroded. Domestic laws and the behaviour of national bodies are subject to obligations in international law, particularly international human rights. Indeed, the right of self-determination has been integral to breaking down this distinction. Obligations under Article 1 of the twin Human Rights Covenants have enabled the Human Rights Committee and the Committee on Economic, Social and Cultural Rights to pose questions to states on various aspects of their domestic, constitutional and electoral laws. The Declaration on the Rights of Indigenous Peoples *potentially* opens a state's constitutional structure to international obligations still further. This erosion was also not lost in the drafting of that instrument. Indigenous peoples' representatives argued that their participation in the UN working group at an international level was, in fact, an exercise of self-determination for those peoples externally.[44]

---

[42] Australia: 'Articles 6, 7, 8, 9, 16, 17 and 20 [of the Civil and Political Covenant]... seemed to provide a more logical standard for measuring the extent of "internal" self-determination than the simple claim that the exercise of the right of self-determination was a prerequisite for the enjoyment of other rights,' A/C.3/SR.674 (1955), para. 26.

[43] E/CN.4/2001/85 (2001), p. 13, para. 78. See also 'Report on the 6th Session of the Commission on Human Rights Working Group on the Declaration on the Rights of Indigenous Peoples' in A. Molbech (ed.), *The Indigenous World* (IWGIA, 2001) pp. 414–47, at p. 423; Saami Council, E/CN.4/2001/85 (2001), p. 14, para. 79; Indian Council of South America, *ibid.* para. 84.

[44] *Ibid.*, p. 13, para. 78.

Nonetheless, the state-based approach has an advantage over the people-based interpretation. As normally well-developed political units, the dimensions of states are easier to identify than peoples. The Canadian Supreme Court in *Re Quebec* could define self-determination according to the dimensions of the Canadian state, while noting uncertainty over whether Quebec actually constituted a people.[45]

3.   Distinct political units within a sovereign state

A third possibility is that self-determination could be defined by the dimensions of a political unit exercising some form of self-government within a state. Examples could include autonomous regions or federal units representing particular peoples. In this context, local self-government within an autonomous region would constitute the internal aspect of that people's self-determination. The external affairs of that unit, in relation to the central government or other autonomous units, might be characterised as the external dimension. However, self-determination in this context can be seen to operate at different levels: local and national. While autonomous political units within a state may be legitimated as representative of particular peoples or ethnic groups, their legal status would normally be derived from the state's constitution or national law. This would connect them to the internal aspects of the state's sovereignty and provide a reasonable interpretation of self-determination exercised in that context. In such an understanding, internal self-determination within autonomous units is quite plausible, though external self-determination in relation to other units within the state or against the state *in toto* is much more problematic. Alternatively, when viewed collectively those units could be the expression of the self-determination of the whole population of a state as a people determining its form of political organisation.

This dimension can be readily implied from Article 4 of UNDRIP, which refers to indigenous peoples' self-determination involving self-government in matters relating to their internal affairs. However, as has been seen, this might not represent an altogether robust interpretation of the internal/external distinction for such peoples, which remains based on the state. Nonetheless, there may be circumstances where self-governing units within a state also provide the contours for more far-reaching approaches to self-determination. In the break-up of

---

[45]   161 DLR (1998) 4th Series, paras. 123, 125, 138.

Yugoslavia, the principle of *uti possidetis* was applied, not only to uphold the existing borders of Yugoslavia's self-governing federal units, the republics, but to create the framework for their self-determination.[46] Within their borders, the republics exercised self-determination both internally (passing new laws and constitutions) and externally (asserting their independence) to establish new states. Moreover, their borders not only defined how external self-determination could be exercised, but also limited the options for groups that existed within those frontiers.[47]

4. Political units distinct from a sovereign state

A fourth context for self-determination encompasses territorial or political units that a state may exercise either title or control over, but which have a distinct status under international law. There are four examples. First, there are non-self-governing territories, where there may be specific obligations to develop self-government under the principles of trusteeship, as well as self-determination. The Declaration on Friendly Relations asserts that such territories have a distinct status from the administering state.[48] Second, freely associated territories, which are internally self-governing, but have an association with a state based on an agreement. Third, occupied territories, such as the Palestinian territories, in which the occupying state is legally prohibited from annexing and thus extending the internal aspects of its sovereignty.[49] Fourth, there may be territories under international territorial administration, though there are significant differences in their status. In East Timor international administration took place in a recognised non-self-governing territory with an established right to independence. Eastern

---

[46] Badinter Commission: 'It is well established that, whatever the circumstances, the right to self-determination must not involve changes to existing frontiers at the time of independence (*uti possidetis juris*) except where the States concerned agree otherwise.' Opinion No. 2, 31 *ILM* (1992) p. 1498, para. 1.

[47] See Argentina: 'the Arbitration Commission of the Conference on Yugoslavia did not accept that the Serbian populations of Croatia and Bosnia-Herzegovina were entitled to external self-determination,' Written Statement of Argentina, *Kosovo* (Advisory Opinion), 17 April 2009, para. 96.

[48] 'The territory of a colony or other Non-Self-Governing Territory has, under the Charter, a status separate and distinct from the territory of the State administering it; and such separate and distinct status under the Charter shall exist until the people of the colony or Non-Self-Governing Territory have exercised their right of self-determination in accordance with the Charter, and particularly its purposes and principles,' GA Res. 2625 (XXV) 1970.

[49] *Wall in Occupied Palestinian Territory (Advisory Opinion)* ICJ (2004) paras. 75, 120–122; SC Res. 298 (1971); SC Res. 478 (1980).

Slavonia's administration was in the context of developing autonomy within Croatia, while Kosovo's self-government took place against an ambiguous final status.

Unlike internal self-governing units, the distinctive legal status of these entities means that self-government is focused within those territories rather than within the *demos* of a state, though it is possible that they may also have representation there. An example of this can be seen in comments by Israel before the Human Rights Committee at the time of the Oslo Peace Accords. On self-determination for the Palestinians, Israel stated that:

> Internal self-determination was already being practiced: Palestinians in the West Bank and Gaza Strip, as well as those living in Jerusalem, have taken part in democratic elections under international supervision. As a result, they had their own freely-elected administration, governing all spheres of civil life, with no interference by Israel.[50]

Internal self-determination thus took place in a territory under Israeli control but separately from the Israeli state and *demos*.

In this context, external self-determination could mean the populations of those units determining relations with the administering state and other states, which they could do through asserting their statehood. The right to statehood is generally established for non-self-governing territories, remains an option for freely associated territories and is widely recognised for Palestine. Whether it exists for territories under international territorial administration depends on the nature of their regime. Political units distinct from a sovereign state may, therefore, have different rights from ones within states in having a right to external self-determination, which may include a recognised right to establish an independent state.

The effects of an internal–external division in this context are the same as that of states: identifying two strands in the right with the potential to prevent the monopoly of any single interpretation. However, the implications may be somewhat different. An example is colonial self-determination. The right in this context developed strongly as a right of colonial peoples to independence. It also developed as a challenge to the principle of trusteeship by which colonial rule could be legitimate if it advanced a population economically, socially and educationally and developed their capacity for self-government.[51] This

---

[50] CCPR/C/SR.1675, para. 19.
[51] See *Namibia (Advisory Opinion)* ICJ 1971, paras. 52–53.

principle, though obviously paternalistic, has parallels to internal self-determination. Self-government through trusteeship was originally presented as a mechanism for peoples to exercise self-determination and attain internal self-government within different levels of colonial administration.[52] Thus, an internal–external dichotomy in this context had the potential to weaken colonial self-determination as a right to independence and it was argued as such by colonial powers.

The internal–external distinction appears to have been first used by the Netherlands in the context of post-war Indonesia. Dutch power had collapsed following the Japanese occupation of the territory and the Netherlands was engaged in a protracted struggle with the Indonesian independence movement. A series of conferences were organised, some involving the UN, to negotiate a political solution. In 1949 a roundtable conference under UN auspices brought together the Dutch, the Indonesian Republicans (who favoured a unitary Indonesia) and Federalists (traditional rulers, who were more inclined towards the Dutch). Negotiations at the time centred on a federal Indonesian state (the United States of Indonesia) in a very loose union with the Netherlands. In the course of these negotiations, the Dutch argued that self-determination had internal and external aspects and that both applied. Internal self-determination, they asserted, was a right of different populations in Indonesia to determine their position within the federation.[53] External self-determination involved, 'the right of populations to disassociate their respective territories from . . . the United States of Indonesia',[54] and thus perhaps form separate associations with the Dutch. In essence, identifying internal and external aspects in self-determination was a Dutch attempt to divide Indonesian politicians and maintain their influence.

Similarly, in the development of colonial self-determination at the UN, internal and external aspects were raised by colonial powers rather than supporters of the right.[55] The Netherlands was prominent in asserting

---

[52] J. C. Smuts, 'The League of Nations: A Practical Suggestion' in D. H. Miller (ed.), *The Drafting of the Covenant* (G. P. Putnam's Son, 1928) vol. II, pp. 23–60, at pp. 28–31.

[53] 'The right of populations to determine, by democratic procedure, the status which their respective territories shall occupy within the federal structure of the Republic of the United States of Indonesia.' United Nations Commission for Indonesia, *Special Report to the Security Council on the Round Table Conference*, S/1417/Rev.1 (1949), p. 19, para. 52.

[54] *Ibid.*

[55] A notable exception was a reference to 'domestic' and 'international' aspects of self-determination by Syria: A/C.3/SR.397 (1951), para. 5.

such a distinction in debates on GA Resolution 637 (VII) of 1952[56] and the draft Human Rights Covenants, where it was joined by Denmark and Australia.[57] The internal–external distinction was used to undermine the notion of alien domination as synonymous with colonialism, and the Netherlands argued that the denial of self-determination was far wider than colonial situations.[58] Similar arguments were raised by colonial powers at the time, notably the 'Belgian Thesis' that non-self-governing territories effectively existed within states.[59] The Dutch use of internal and external self-determination was essentially their version of this. The Netherlands also argued that internal and external dimensions meant that self-determination was too complex to include in the Human Rights Covenants, and ultimately voted against Article 1.[60] Greece, on the other hand, an advocate of self-determination in Article 1, dismissed the distinction as 'hair-splitting'.[61]

The effect of the internal–external distinction in colonial self-determination was to weaken the right as one of independence and was used in this context mostly by colonial powers. It is interesting that the Canadian Supreme Court in 1997 considered that in the colonial context: 'the people in question are entitled to a right to external self-determination because they have been denied the ability to exert internally their right to self-determination'.[62] However, by that stage the Court could find that the right of colonial peoples to break away from an imperial power was 'now undisputed'.[63] It could apply the distinction to a state context without implications for a colonial right which had already been established as one of independence.

---

[56] Netherlands: '[T]he idea of self-determination was a complex of ideas rather than a single concept. Thus the principle of internal self-determination, or self-determination on the national level, should be distinguished from that of external self-determination, or self-determination on the international level. The former was the right of a nation, already constituted as a State, to choose its form of government and to determine the policy it meant to pursue. The latter was the right of a group which considered itself a nation to form a State of its own,' A/C.3/SR.447 (1952), para. 4.

[57] Denmark, A/C.3/SR.644 (1955), paras. 2, 6; Australia, A/C.3/SR.669 (1955), para. 22.

[58] Netherlands, A/C.3/SR.642 (1955), para. 25.

[59] Belgium, A/C.4/SR.419 (1954), para. 20.

[60] Australia also voted against, while Denmark abstained: A/C.3/SR.311 (1955), para. 24.

[61] Greece: 'The Greek delegation would therefore not take part in arguments on technicalities which had aptly been described as "hair-splitting." For his part, he could not accept subtle distinctions drawn by some representatives between individual and collective human rights and between "internal" and "external" self-determination,' A/C.3/SR.454 (1952), para. 25.

[62] 161 DLR (1998) 4th Series, para. 138.   [63] Ibid., para. 132.

IV.   A synthesis

Fundamentally, the internal–external division relates to emphasis and perspective. Self-determination is a process which involves different actors and institutions. The distinction finds differing levels of support depending upon the perspective of the particular actor. It creates various options based around that actor's political expectations. The separation is unsurprisingly divisive. While self-determination movements, political units and 'host' states may each seek to promote their preferred interpretation of the right, the distinction helps to suggest a range of equally valid alternatives. This appears to be the case regardless of the context in which self-determination is considered; peoples, states or other political units. In the case of the state, an alternative to secession may be self-determination within state institutions. In the colonial context, an alternative to independence might be a looser union with the administering state. In each instance the division into internal and external self-determination has the potential to blunt the force of any one particular interpretation.

This chapter has looked at how the perspective on self-determination can differ depending on the units to which the division is applied. Four units were considered: peoples, sovereign states, political units within states and political units outside states, and in each case internal and external aspects took on a different significance. Self-determination could be exercised internally in relation to one unit and externally towards another. Moreover, these perspectives can operate simultaneously across different elements of a self-determination process. As a result, it is argued that there is no single understanding of internal and external self-determination, rather, a range of perspectives. To focus on one actor may be to overlook the role of others in the process. Nonetheless, it may be possible to draw together these perspectives and consider their relationship.

Two perspectives are most significant in relation to the fundamental tensions within the law of self-determination: the state-based and people-based perspectives. The state-based approach is undoubtedly the most popular interpretation of the division. This reflects the dominant role of states in international law and their essential interest in territorial integrity and domesticating self-determination. Nonetheless, it is more than states' self-interest. It also reflects the prominent role that the state and its institutions can play in the exercise of self-determination, either as medium for the right (through elections, participation in the legislature or government, etc.) or as a goal for the right (statehood). However, the division will often neatly correspond to the application of sovereignty and territorial integrity in self-determination, appearing to create an arbitrary division in the right, which undermines its legitimacy. From the rationale of self-determination, it appears that the 'tail' (the state) is 'wagging the dog' (the people).

A people-based perspective is more in keeping with the liberal-nationalist ideas behind self-determination and more reflective of the language used to describe such a distinction in the right. Moreover, it does not create a sharp distinction between the legal status of internal and external aspects. However, it does introduce nationalistic language normally used in inter-state relations into the national context of a state. Thus, neither approach is entirely satisfactory. They represent contrasting poles in self-determination. Nonetheless, there may be a middle ground which is less arbitrary than the state-based approach and more moderate in its language than the people-based approach. The key feature of a more balanced model of internal and external self-determination is recognition of the multiple and simultaneous perspectives that may be taken on the distinction. The perspective that is more prominent will then depend on the circumstances.

It is possible to conceive of a situation in which self-determination, held by a people, is exercised *predominantly* in an internal fashion within a state. This depends on two considerations. First, if self-determination is understood as determining political status and social, economic and cultural development, state institutions provide an extensive framework for its exercise. This can be achieved through elections, participation in the legislature and government, as well as other institutions such as the civil service, legal system, army and police, as well as health and education. Second, identity can exist on multiple levels, and there may be an overlap between a state's national identity and other identities within a state. A people-based approach may, in this context, complement a state-based approach. To assert that relations between peoples within a state and the state are purely 'external' is to deny any sense of cohesion of fellow-feeling within the population of a state.

Within this model there are areas where people-based and state-based perspectives do not conflict. If peoples have relations with NGOs, states or international organisations outside the state, this could be considered external self-determination from both perspectives. This could also encompass the perspective of autonomous units and could be conducted consistently with a state's constitution or international agreements. Acts of secession would also constitute external self-determination, but the aspect as a whole would be notably broader than independence.

An alternative scenario is a state without those two elements. State institutions do not provide a mechanism for exercising self-determination, and the population is so polarised that there is no national state identity. A state may lack functioning national institutions, or they may be exclusionary and discriminatory. There is also a significant polarisation between the peoples of the state, so that they act as distinct entities. In such a case, the people-based perspective becomes more significant and the relations of peoples may be considered to *predominantly* reflect the external self-determination of those peoples. This would resemble the situation described by the African Commission on Human and Peoples' Rights in *COHRE* v. *Sudan* (2009), where the Commission referred to the domination of one people by another within the same state.[64] If the situation further deteriorated, and the state broke up, the state-based perspective would align with the people-based approach, as peoples or autonomous units replaced the failed state with their own states, exercising self-determination from a state-based perspective.

Under this model, no perspective has an exclusive role, rather, it is one of emphasis and context. The degree to which the focus of self-determination changes from exercise within a state to exercise between peoples is open to subjective interpretation. Ethnic nationalists within a state may seize on the idea that their relations with the central government are external. State authorities might be reluctant to consider relations within the state as anything other than internal. Nonetheless, this approach arguably has advantages over a single perspective on internal and external self-determination. It is more reflective of the different actors in self-determination rather than focusing on just one of them. It also works to defuse the internal–external distinction as a sharply loaded dichotomy. Moreover, it provides an explanation for state-based internal self-determination that is more than just the exercise of the right within a state, and lastly, it creates a framework for the shift from internal to external self-determination in the case of the failure of a state.

---

[64] *Sudan Human Rights Organisation and the Sudan Centre on Housing Rights and Evictions* v. *Sudan*, Communication Nos. 279/03 and 296/05, para. 223.

Trading fish or human rights in Western Sahara? Self-determination, non-recognition and the EC–Morocco Fisheries Agreement

MARTIN DAWIDOWICZ

I. Introduction

It is notoriously difficult to cross a desert. This is still so when the final destination is clear. Biblical figures famously experienced many difficulties in the desert during their exodus, even as the vision of the final destination was divinely revealed to them. Likewise, it appears that the international community (albeit absent any divine intervention) has spent almost forty years in the 'frontierless sea of sand'[1] of Western Sahara without finding its way. And yet the direction of travel has always been clear. International law may not provide for a promised land of milk and honey in any biblical sense, but it does provide for the basic right of peoples to self-determination – a point emphatically reaffirmed by the International Court of Justice (ICJ) in its 1975 Advisory Opinion in *Western Sahara*.[2]

In *Western Sahara*, the Court denied that Morocco and Mauritania had any ties of territorial sovereignty to Western Sahara and affirmed the right of the people of Western Sahara to self-determination. But this cardinal right has seemingly only manifested itself as a forlorn mirage in the desert. Morocco is still denying this right and purports to exercise territorial sovereignty over Western Sahara. Almost forty years later, the international community is yet to assure the people of Western Sahara of the realization of their own promised land in accordance with the right of self-determination under international law. Worse still, it appears that

---

[1] *Western Sahara*, ICJ Rep (1975), Dec. Judge Gros, p. 71
[2] *Western Sahara*, ICJ Rep (1975), p. 12.

important actors in the international community may effectively be forestalling the effective exercise of this basic right.

A recent example in point concerns the controversy surrounding the temporary renewal in February 2011 of the 2006 EC–Morocco Fisheries Partnership Agreement (the FPA). The FPA grants European Community (EC) vessels certain fishing rights off Morocco's Atlantic coast – one of the richest fishing grounds in the world. The FPA has remained controversial, since its reference to 'Moroccan waters' does not explicitly exclude the waters off the coast of Western Sahara. The controversy stems from the concern that the FPA might in practice allow for the exploitation of the natural resources of Western Sahara in a manner contrary to the fundamental right of the people of Western Sahara to self-determination, and as such might serve as an implicit recognition of Morocco's irredentist claim to territorial sovereignty over Western Sahara. However, in December 2011, the Council of the European Union (EU) with immediate effect terminated the temporary extension of the FPA. While this is a positive development, as we shall see below, it remains uncertain whether a renewed FPA, which the EU remains committed to conclude with Morocco, will fully comply with international law.

The analysis in this chapter will proceed as follows. Section II outlines the content and scope of the right of the people of Western Sahara to self-determination. Section III examines whether Morocco's actions in relation to Western Sahara are tantamount to denying that basic right; an affirmative answer is provided to this question. Section IV makes some general observations about the obligation of non-recognition and its putative application in relation to the denial of the right of the people of Western Sahara to self-determination. Section V evaluates whether the FPA is consistent with the obligation of EU Member States not to recognize Morocco's claim to sovereignty over Western Sahara. Finally, section VI offers some concluding observations.

II. The right of the people of Western Sahara to self-determination

On 26 December 1884, during its participation in the Berlin Conference, Spain, by royal decree, proclaimed a protectorate over present-day Western Sahara.[3] Although the golden age of so-called 'salt-water

---

[3] Ibid., p. 38, para. 77; ibid., *Written Pleadings*, vol. I, p. 288 (Spain), available at http://www.icj-cij.org/docket/files/61/9468.pdf.

colonialism'[4] may have reached its apex with the 1885 General Act of the Berlin Conference, 'the setting of the sun on the age of colonial imperium'[5] soon appeared on the horizon. Nevertheless, it was not until 1960 that the United Nations (UN) General Assembly famously adopted the Declaration on the Granting of Independence to Colonial Countries and Peoples, by which it declared the right of self-determination applicable to all trust and non-self governing territories (NSGT).[6] In the same year, the General Assembly also adopted Resolution 1541 (XV) by which it provided additional guidance on the decolonization process within the meaning of the UN Charter.

In this resolution, the General Assembly provided a definition of an NSGT as enshrined in Article 73 of the UN Charter; in short, an NSGT was described as a colonial territory whose people had not yet attained a 'full measure of self-government'.[7] In principle, such self-government would be reached by means of a process which respected the 'freely expressed wishes of the people' in a free and fair referendum providing for three broad modes of implementation: namely, (1) emergence as a sovereign independent State; (2) free association with an independent State; or (3) integration with an independent State.[8]

At least in a traditional sense, the core right of peoples to self-determination can thus be described as a process right aimed at safeguarding the expression of the free and autonomous will of a people to dispose of their destiny as they wish. In short, as Judge Dillard observed in *Western Sahara*, 'self-determination is satisfied by a free choice not by a particular consequence of that choice or a particular method of exercising it'.[9] Under Article 73 of the UN Charter, the responsibility to ensure the successful completion of this process – a 'sacred trust' no less – falls on the administing power of the NSGT.

[4] See GA Res. 1541 (XV) of 15 December 1960 (Principle IV).
[5] *Sovereignty over Pulau Ligitan and Pulau Sipadan, Indonesia/Malaysia (Philippines Intervening)*, ICJ Rep (2001), p. 575, Sep. Op. Judge *ad-hoc* Franck, para. 15.
[6] GA Res. 1514 (XV) of 14 December 1960. See previously GA Res. 637(A) (VII) of 16 December 1952.
[7] GA Res. 1541 (XV) of 15 December 1960 (Principle I).
[8] Ibid. (Principles VI–IX). See previously GA Res. 742 (XIII) of 27 November 1953; GA Res. 648 (VII) of 10 December 1952; GA Res. 567 (VI) of 18 January 1952 (all emphasizing the element of free choice – and the corresponding option of independence – as a factor in determining whether an NSGT has attained a 'full measure of self-government' in accordance with Chapter XI of the UN Charter).
[9] *Western Sahara*, ICJ Rep (1975), Sep. Op. Judge Dillard, p. 123.

In 1965, after some years of Spanish intransigence,[10] the UN General Assembly called on Spain, identified as 'administrating Power' under Chapter XI of the UN Charter, to take immediate steps towards the decolonization of Western Sahara in accordance with the right of self-determination.[11] In 1966, the General Assembly made more specific demands and requested Spain, in consultation with other parties (Morocco, Mauritania and Algeria), to organize a referendum in Western Sahara under UN auspices in order to enable the people of Western Sahara to exercise freely their right to self-determination.[12] But in the waning years of the Franco regime, notwithstanding repeated calls from the General Assembly,[13] little progress was made towards the realization of this right. An apparent breakthrough came in August 1974 when Spain finally committed itself to the holding of a referendum in the first half of 1975, and even successfully completed a census to that effect.[14]

In theory, Morocco assented to a referendum on the future status of Western Sahara, but subject to a strong caveat. On repeated occasions since at least November 1958, when Spain had reaffirmed its sovereignty over Western Sahara, Morocco vigorously protested that Western Sahara formed an integral part of Moroccan territory.[15] In practice, Morocco therefore felt compelled to publicly express its strong opposition to a free vote in the planned referendum – entailing the *option* of outright independence for Western Sahara – on the grounds that it had historic ties to the territory.[16] In Morocco's view, the option of full independence was excluded under the UN decolonization law in *statu nascendi* since the right of self-determination was circumscribed by the overriding principle of territorial integrity.[17]

---

[10] In November 1958, less than three years after becoming a UN member, Spain declared that Western Sahara was a Spanish province and that therefore it did not qualify as an NSGT under Chapter XI of the UN Charter. Morocco promptly protested, on the basis that Western Sahara formed an integral part of Moroccan national territory. See *Western Sahara*, ICJ Rep (1975), p. 25, para. 34.

[11] GA Res. 2072 (XX) of 16 December 1965.

[12] GA Res. 2229 (XXI) of 20 December 1966.

[13] See GA Res. 2354 (XXII) of 19 December 1967; 2428 (XXIII) of 27 December 1968; 2591 (XXIV) of 16 December 1969; 2711 (XXV) of 14 December 1970; 2983 (XXVII) of 14 December 1972; and 3162 (XXVIII) of 14 December 1973.

[14] See Letter dated 20 August 1974 from the Permanent Representative of Spain addressed to the Secretary-General, UN Doc. A/9714.

[15] *Western Sahara*, ICJ Rep (1975), pp. 25, 35, paras. 34, 65.

[16] Ibid., p. 35, para. 65; T. Franck, 'The Stealing of the Sahara', (1976) 70 *AJIL*, 702, 705.

[17] GA Res. 1514 (XV) of 15 December 1960 (op. para. 6); GA Res. 2625 (XXV) of 24 October 1970, (principle 5, para. 7). See also *Western Sahara*, ICJ Rep (1975), Sep. Op. Judge Petrén, p. 110 (for recognition of the intricate interplay between the two principles

In essence, Morocco's position was that its historical ties to Western Sahara justified 'the reintegration or retrocession of the territory without consulting the [Western Saharan] people'.[18] Put bluntly, Morocco presented the issue as essentially one of 'colonial amputation'.[19]

With full independence for Western Sahara now a real possibility, Morocco (later assisted by Mauritania) sought, as a minimum, to postpone the planned referendum. It successfully did so by proposing that the General Assembly request an advisory opinion from the ICJ on the status of Western Sahara. On 13 December 1974, the General Assembly adopted Resolution 3292 (XXIX), by which it sought advice from the Court on a rather limited question; namely, Morocco's putative historical claim to Western Sahara at the time of Spain's colonization in 1884.[20] However, the General Assembly took special care to ensure that the language of the resolution was without prejudice to the application of the decolonization principles embodied in Resolution 1514 (XV).

In light of this request, Resolution 3292 (XXIX) urged Spain to postpone the planned referendum until the General Assembly was in a position to decide on the policy to be adopted following receipt of the Advisory Opinion from the ICJ. Moreover, in line with established UN practice on decolonization,[21] the General Assembly requested its Fourth (Decolonization) Committee to send a visiting mission to Western Sahara in order to evaluate the opinion of the population as to the possible change of status they might desire and report back to the Assembly on its findings at its next session. Two parallel UN processes were thus set in motion.

As it happened, while the ICJ in *Western Sahara* recognized that there might be an exception to the general principle of self-determination based on territorial integrity,[22] it rejected in categorical terms 'any tie of

---

enshrined in GA Res. 1514 (XV) forming part of the 'veritable law of decolonization in the course of taking shape').

[18] See *Western Sahara*, ICJ Rep (1975), Dec. Judge Nagendra Singh, p. 79; ibid., Sep. Op. Judge Dillard, p. 120 (i.e. a case of 'automatic retrocession' based on the principle of territorial integrity embodied in op. para. 6 of Resolution 1514 (XV)).

[19] To use the stark terms of Judge Dillard (Sep. Op.) in *Western Sahara*, ICJ Rep (1975), p. 120.

[20] GA Res. 3292 (XXIX) of 13 December 1974 (83–0–43). For the debate in the plenary, see UN Doc. A/PV.2318.

[21] GA Res. 850 (IX) of 22 November 1954 (op. para. 2). For a brief discussion, see R. Jennings and A. Watts (eds.), *Oppenheim's International Law*, vol. I (9th edn, 1992), p. 713.

[22] This is clear from the Court's detailed treatment of Morocco's claim that would have been futile in the event that no exception could ever prevail over the right to self-

territorial sovereignty between ... Western Sahara and ... Morocco'.[23] Having unmistakably rejected any Moroccan claims to territorial sovereignty over Western Sahara, the Court turned to the putative right of self-determination and the modes for its implementation.

The ICJ first reiterated its position – espoused four years earlier in *Namibia* – that the principle of self-determination applied to all NSGTs, including Western Sahara.[24] The Court went on to refer to General Assembly Resolution 1514 (XV) which 'provided the basis for the process of decolonization' as 'complemented' by General Assembly Resolution 1541 (XV). It noted that the right of self-determination provides the General Assembly with 'a measure of discretion' regarding the manner in which the right is to be realized.[25] At the same time, however, the Court recognized the three main different modes of implementation of the right of self-determination embodied in Resolution 1541 (XV) and emphasized that this resolution gave effect to the 'essential feature' of the right of self-determination, namely, 'the basic need to take account of the freely expressed wishes of the territory's people'. The General Assembly's procedural discretion was accordingly circumscribed by the principle of free choice. Thus defined, the Court recognized the right of peoples to self-determination as forming part of customary international law.

In sum, while it is true that the modes of implementation of the right of self-determination may not always be clear, the 'essential feature' of the right nonetheless resides in the principle of free choice, entailing the *option* of a 'right to independence' – a point most recently reaffirmed (though not *per se* endorsed) by the Court in the *Kosovo* opinion.[26] It remained for the General Assembly to determine the wishes of the indigenous population. On 7 November 1975, the Fourth Committee of the General Assembly adopted the anticipated report of the UN visiting mission. The report concluded in categorical terms that 'the majority of the population within the Spanish Sahara was manifestly in favour of independence'.[27] The guidance provided by UN organs on the

---

determination. See further, e.g., *Western Sahara*, ICJ Rep (1975), Dec. Judge Gros, pp. 70, 73; ibid., Sep. Op. Judge Dillard, p. 120.

[23] *Western Sahara*, ICJ Rep (1975), pp. 67–8, paras. 161–2.   [24] Ibid., p. 31, para. 54.

[25] Ibid., p. 36, para. 71.

[26] *Accordance with international law of the unilateral declaration of independence in respect of Kosovo*, Advisory Opinion of 22 July 2010, para. 79. See also *East Timor*, ICJ Rep (1995), Sep. Op. Judge Vereschetin, p. 135.

[27] See Report of the Special Committee on the Situation with Regard to the Implementation of the Declaration on the Granting of Independence to Colonial

procedure to be followed by the General Assembly in the decolonization of Western Sahara seemed clear.

As is well known, in spite of this unambiguous advice, the implementation of the right of self-determination in Western Sahara has been fraught with difficulty. In fact, despite the clear opinion provided by the ICJ in *Western Sahara*, Morocco promptly proceeded to take a number of unilateral steps that resulted in the denial of the right of the people of Western Sahara to self-determination – a situation that endures to this day.

III.   The denial of the right of self-determination

On 17 October 1975, purportedly basing itself on the legal ties affirmed by the ICJ a day before, Morocco announced its plan for the so-called 'Green March' of 350,000 unarmed civilians into Western Sahara 'in order to gain recognition of its right to national unity and territorial integrity'.[28] Morocco declared that its action should be understood as 'a manifestation of the unanimous will of the Moroccan people to assert its legitimate right over its Sahara'.[29] It even boldly proclaimed that 'a referendum was not necessary [since] the populations of the territory had already exercised *de facto* self-determination and declared themselves in favour of the return of the territory to Morocco'.[30] These wishes had allegedly been expressed on 4 November 1975 in a ceremony held in the city of Agadir by means of an 'oath of allegiance' to King Hassan II of Morocco taken by the servile President of the Yema'a (an indigenous local assembly established by Spain in 1967) on behalf of the Saharan tribes.[31]

In effect, Morocco appeared determined to create a situation in which the carefully elaborated UN position on the decolonization of Western Sahara would simply be 'overtaken by events'.[32] Spain decried an imminent Moroccan 'invasion' and called for an emergency session of the

Countries and Peoples, UN Doc. A/10023/Add.5, p. 55. See further, *UNYB* (1975), pp. 798–801; Franck, 'The Stealing of the Sahara', 707–9.

[28] Letter dated 18 October 1975 from the Permanent Representative of Morocco to the UN addressed to the President of the Security Council, UN Doc. S/11852.

[29] Report by the Secretary-General in Pursuance of Security Council Resolution 379 (1975) Relating to the Situation Concerning Western Sahara, UN Doc. S/11874, para. 16.

[30] Ibid., para. 17 (emphasis in original).

[31] Ibid. See also Letter dated 10 December 1975 from the representative of Algeria to the Secretary-General on behalf of the Saharan Provisional National Council, UN Doc. S/11903 (denouncing the spurious petition).

[32] Ibid., para. 17.

Security Council.[33] In the next few weeks, the Security Council adopted three resolutions on the matter, *inter alia*, requesting the UN Secretary-General to enter into immediate consultations with the parties.[34] But to no avail.

On 6 November 1975, the day before the official adoption of the report of the UN visiting mission, Morocco initiated the Green March. The Security Council deplored the action on the same day and called for Morocco's immediate withdrawal.[35] Spain informed the Council that Morocco would not halt the march unless urgent bilateral negotiations 'dealing with the transfer of sovereignty over the Sahara to Morocco' were initiated. It was said that unless Spain acceded to such negotiations, 'a state of belligerency' between the two countries might ensue.[36] Morocco categorically denied the existence of such a bellicose ultimatum.[37] In fact, two weeks earlier Spain had already expressed publicly that it was confronted with a *fait accompli* and declared that 'in practice the two aspects of the question [i.e. the situation created by the Green March and the decolonization policy concerning Western Sahara] could not be separated'.[38]

On 14 November 1975, as Morocco had withdrawn the marchers a few days earlier,[39] Spain, Morocco and Mauritania signed the so-called Madrid Declaration.[40] For Western Sahara, to whom Spain owed a sacred duty of trust under international law, this was perhaps the unkindest cut of all. The Madrid Declaration provided that Spain would terminate its presence in Western Sahara by 28 February 1976

---

[33] Letter dated 18 October 1975 from the Permanent Representative of Spain to the UN addressed to the President of the Security Council, UN Doc. S/11851.

[34] SC Res. 377 (22 October 1975); SC Res. 379 (2 November 1975); SC Res. 380 (6 November 1975).

[35] Ibid.; Letter dated 6 November 1975 from the Permanent Representative of Spain to the UN addressed to the President of the Security Council, UN Doc. S/11867.

[36] Letter dated 6 November 1975 from the Permanent Representative of Spain to the UN addressed to the President of the Security Council, UN Doc. S/11871; *UNYB* (1975), p. 182.

[37] Letter dated 7 November 1975 from the Permanent Representative of Morocco to the UN addressed to the President of the Security Council, UN Doc. S/11873; *UNYB* (1975), p. 183.

[38] Report by the Secretary-General in Pursuance of Security Council Resolution 377 (1975) Relating to the Situation Concerning Western Sahara, UN Doc. S/11863, para. 16(b).

[39] Report by the Secretary-General in Pursuance of Security Council Resolution 379 (1975) Relating to the Situation Concerning Western Sahara, UN Doc. S/11880, para. 2.

[40] Declaration of Principles on Western Sahara by Spain, Morocco and Mauritania (entered into force 19 November 1975), 988 UNTS 259.

and, in the interim, it would transfer its responsibilities as administrating power to a temporary tripartite administration composed of the Spanish Governor-General and a Moroccan and Mauritanian Deputy Governor, respectively. The Yema'a, which expressed the views of the Saharan population, would collaborate in this interim administration and its views would be respected. Morocco's interpretation of the Madrid Declaration was clear. It informed the Secretary-General's Special Envoy that:

> the main provision of such an agreement had already been determined and stipulated a transfer of sovereignty from the administrating Power to Morocco and Mauritania. However, Morocco was prepared to submit such an agreement to the competent organs of the United Nations for approval.[41]

As it happened, this incredulous interpretation was not without merit.

A secret pact between the three states reportedly accompanied the Madrid Declaration and was said to provide for the ultimate partition of Western Sahara between Morocco and Mauritania in exchange for Spanish access to important phosphates and fishing resources in the territory.[42] Some two weeks later, the Yema'a responded to these events by declaring that no further legitimacy would be bestowed on this 'puppet institution . . . of Spanish colonialism' and unanimously decided upon its own final dissolution.[43] It was not long before Moroccan and Mauritanian armed forces invaded Western Sahara.

Whatever the actual terms of the secret pact, the Madrid Declaration required, as a minimum, the approval of the General Assembly, since an administrating power cannot unilaterally dispose of an NSGT at will; it does not exercise full powers akin to a territorial sovereign under Chapter XI of the UN Charter (*nemo dat quod non habet*).[44] Without

---

[41] Report by the Secretary-General in Pursuance of Security Council Resolution 379 (1975) Relating to the Situation Concerning Western Sahara, UN Doc. S/11874, para. 18.

[42] For a brief discussion (with further references to press reports) see, e.g., Franck, 'The Stealing of the Sahara', 715; T. Hodges, *Western Sahara: The Roots of a Desert War* (1983), p. 224. See also, Letters dated 9 and 10 December 1975 from the representative of Algeria to the Secretary-General on behalf of the Saharan National Council, UN Docs. S/11902, S/11903.

[43] Letter dated 9 December 1975 from the representative of Algeria to the Secretary-General on behalf of the Saharan National Council, UN Doc. S/11902.

[44] See, e.g., *Western Sahara*, ICJ Rep (1975), Dec. Judge Gros, p. 71; ibid., Sep. Op. Judge de Castro, p. 145; Letter dated 29 January 2002 from the Under-Secretary-General for Legal Affairs addressed to the President of the Security Council, UN Doc. S/2002/161, para. 6; *East Timor*, ICJ Rep (1995), Diss. Op. Judge Skubiszewski, p. 273.

more, it is therefore difficult to disagree with Brownlie's conclusion that the Madrid Declaration 'lacks a legal basis'.[45] The absence of a legal basis could, however, be cured by an explicit decision of the UN. In fact, no such explicit decision was adopted.[46] The UN process was soon overtaken by events.

On 27 February 1976, King Hassan II of Morocco reconvened some former members of the defunct Yema'a in Moroccan-occupied Laayoune for a 'special session'[47] and presented a spurious petition that ended up endorsing the partition and transfer of territorial sovereignty to the joint occupiers of Western Sahara.[48] For its part, Spain officially announced its withdrawal from Western Sahara in accordance with the Madrid Declaration, and henceforth considered itself 'exempt from any responsibility of an international nature in connection with the administration of the Territory'.[49] The Frente Polisario (the national liberation movement of the Western Saharans), engaged in heavy fighting against the invading forces from Morocco and Mauritania, responded to these events by proclaiming independence and the establishment of the Sahrawi Arab Democratic Republic.[50] The invading forces were gradually gaining control of major parts of the territory.

On 14 April 1976, Morocco and Mauritania purported to formalize their annexation of Western Sahara by signing a boundary treaty that partitioned the territory between them.[51] However, Mauritania soon proved unable to defend its part of the territory and, on 10 August 1979, it signed a peace agreement with the Frente Polisario in which it agreed to withdraw totally its armed forces, and renounced any territorial claim to Western

---

[45] I. Brownlie, *African Boundaries: A Legal and Diplomatic Encyclopedia* (1979), p. 149.

[46] For the plainly contradictory UN position, see GA Res. 3458 A (XXX) of 10 December 1975; GA Res. 3458 B (XXX) of 10 December 1975.

[47] See the preamble to the Convention concerning the State frontier established between the Islamic Republic of Mauritania and the Kingdom of Morocco (signed at Rabat 14 April 1976), 1035 UNTS 120.

[48] See, e.g., Franck, 'The Stealing of the Sahara', 718; Hodges, *Western Sahara: The Roots of a Desert War*, p. 237.

[49] Letter dated 26 February 1976 from the Permanent Representative of Spain to the UN Addressed to the Secretary-General, UN Docs. A/31/56–S/11997. For a brief discussion, see *UNYB* (1976), p. 738.

[50] The text of the proclamation is reproduced at www.arso.org/03–1.htm (last accessed 19 February 2012). The SADR proclamation has not been considered a valid exercise of the Sahrawi people's right to self-determination. See further, GA Res. 33/31 (A); 34/37; 35/19; 36/46.

[51] See Convention concerning the State frontier established between the Islamic Republic of Mauritania and the Kingdom of Morocco.

Sahara.[52] Moroccan armed forces soon moved to occupy the southern part of Western Sahara vacated by Mauritania. As a final measure, Morocco consolidated its *de facto* annexation and legal claim to territorial sovereignty over Western Sahara by incorporating it under Moroccan domestic law as forming part of four of its sixteen administrative regions.[53] The old Moroccan nationalist aspiration of the 'reconstitution of Greater Morocco'[54] seemed partly fulfilled, but no formal recognition has ever been given to Morocco's territorial claim.

Since the late 1980s, several UN-sponsored solutions have been advanced to address the future status of Western Sahara, but without any tangible results. An important obstacle has been Morocco's categorical insistence over time that Western Sahara forms an integral part of its territory. In 1990–1, the Security Council approved the so-called 'Settlement Plan', which proposed a free and democratic referendum in Western Sahara – supervised by a UN mission (MINURSO) – entailing a choice between independence and integration with Morocco based on the 1974 Spanish census.[55] This plan did not ultimately meet with Moroccan approval.

In 2001, the Secretary-General's Personal Envoy, former US Secretary of State Mr. James A. Baker III, introduced an ill-conceived plan that envisaged 'the preservation of the territorial integrity against secessionist attempts whether from within or without the territory' and proposed integration of Western Sahara into Morocco with a degree of autonomy.[56] In 2003, a revised Baker plan was introduced, which contemplated a free choice for Western Saharans between independence, integration and autonomy subject to certain modalities.[57] The Security Council expressed its support for the plan as the 'optimal political solution'.[58] The Frente

---

[52] The Mauritano–Sahraoui Agreement (signed at Algiers 10 August 1979) is annexed to Letter dated 18 August 1979 from the Permanent Representative of Mauritania to the UN addressed to the Secretary-General, UN Doc. A/34/427–S/13503.

[53] See further, the website of the Moroccan government at www.maroc.ma/NR/exeres/ 7D7EAEC9-FEC7–4B33–806E-9059FE2C749D.htm (last accessed 19 February 2012).

[54] *Western Sahara*, ICJ Rep (1975), Sep. Op. Judge de Castro, p. 127.

[55] See SC Res. 690 (1991); SC Res. 658 (1990); SC Res. 621 (1988). See further, Reports of the Secretary-General on the situation concerning Western Sahara, UN Docs. S/21360 (18 June 1990) and S/22464 (19 April 1991).

[56] Report of the Secretary-General concerning the situation in Western Sahara, UN Doc. S/2001/613 (Baker Plan I), art. 2.

[57] Report of the Secretary-General concerning the situation in Western Sahara, UN Doc. S/2003/565 ('Baker Plan II').

[58] SC Res. 1495 (2003). See also Report of the Secretary-General concerning the situation in Western Sahara, UN Doc. S/2003/1016.

Polisario cautiously supported the plan, but Morocco rejected it. It explained in categorical terms yet again that it could only accept a solution that recognized the 'colonial hiatus' and 'preserve[d] its sovereignty and territorial integrity'.[59] It would soon introduce such a proposal.

In April 2007, emphasizing its 'commitment to a final political solution', Morocco formally introduced to the Security Council 'an autonomy proposal for the Sahara, within the [constitutional] framework of the Kingdom's sovereignty and national unity'.[60] The proposal would be subject to a referendum by the local population.[61] The Frente Polisario rejected the proposal and maintained its commitment to the second Baker plan, subject to a number of guarantees.[62] The Security Council took note of both proposals and called on the parties 'to enter into negotiations without preconditions'.[63] These negotiations are still continuing.

This overview prompts a number of brief observations. Morocco's official position since at least the 1950s (and repeated on numerous occasions since) is clear: Western Sahara forms an integral part of Morocco. Indeed, it has legislated to incorporate Western Sahara, which today forms part of four of its sixteen administrative regions. In short, Morocco is *de jure* claiming the status of territorial sovereign in Western Sahara. It follows that Morocco has categorically ruled out the option of independence in any future status negotiations. While it may be true that the precise modalities of implementation of the right of self-determination remain somewhat unclear, what Judge Petrèn in *Western Sahara* termed its 'guiding principles'[64] (at least in the traditional decolonization context with which we are concerned here) are nevertheless well established in ICJ jurisprudence and State practice.

The traditional law of self-determination does not guarantee a particular outcome or method of reaching that outcome, but it does ensure the free choice of a people to determine its future territorial status. This is what the ICJ in *Western Sahara* referred to as the 'essential feature' of the right of self-determination. It constitutes the irreducible core of the right.

---

[59] See Letter dated 24 September 2004 from the Permanent Representative of Morocco to the UN addressed to the Secretary-General, UN Doc. S/2004/760, paras. 9 and 28.

[60] See Letter dated 11 April 2007 from the Permanent Representative of Morocco to the UN addressed to the President of the Security Council, UN Doc. S/2004/760 (Annex).

[61] Ibid.

[62] Letter dated 16 April 2007 from the Permanent Representative of South Africa to the UN addressed to the President of the Security Council on behalf of the Frente Polisario, UN Doc. S/2007/210.

[63] SC Res. 1754 (2007).

[64] *Western Sahara*, ICJ Rep (1975), Sep. Op. Judge Petrèn, p. 110.

It therefore seems clear that Morocco's seemingly irreversible position, as a minimum, 'severely impedes'[65] the exercise of the right of the people of Western Sahara to self-determination as affirmed by the ICJ in *Western Sahara* and is a breach of Morocco's obligation to respect that *erga omnes* right. There is a real risk that the status quo will consolidate and ultimately prevail, through international acquiescence with the inexorable passage of time.

It is in order to prevent such possible erosion – or even complete disintegration – of the right of the people of Western Sahara to self-determination that states are under an obligation not to recognize Morocco's claim to sovereignty over Western Sahara. Nevertheless, the FPA provides a recent illustration of state practice that might potentially confer a degree of recognition on Morocco's irredentist claim to status. Before we turn to an assessment of the FPA, however, a few general observations about the obligation of non-recognition are warranted.

IV.   The obligation of non-recognition

The obligation of non-recognition of an unlawful situation is in large part based on the well-established general principle that legal rights cannot derive from an illegal situation (*ex injuria jus non oritur*).[66] In an 'essentially bilateral minded'[67] international legal order, however, with relatively weak enforcement mechanisms, this principle is subject to 'considerable strain and to wide exceptions'.[68] This important qualification delineates the contours of the principle of non-recognition in significant ways. Considerable strain is caused by an apparent antinomy of legality (*ex injuria jus non oritur*) and effectiveness (*ex factis jus oritur*). This is especially relevant where unlawful situations are maintained for extended periods of time, for example, in the case of forcible annexation of territory.[69] As John Adams once observed, facts are stubborn things. Even Portugal in *East Timor* appears to have partly accepted

---

[65] *Legal Consequences of the Construction of a Wall in the Occupied Palestinian Territory*, ICJ Rep (2004), p. 184, para. 122.

[66] See, e.g., M. Dawidowicz, 'The Obligation of Non-Recognition of an Unlawful Situation', in J. Crawford, A. Pellet and S. Olleson (eds), *The Law of International Responsibility* (Oxford University Press, 2010), p. 677 (with further references).

[67] W. Riphagen, 'Third Report on State Responsibility', (1982) *YbILC*, vol. II/1, p. 38, para. 91.

[68] H. Lauterpacht, *Recognition in International Law* (1947), pp. 420–30.

[69] Ibid., pp. 420–7; T. C. Chen, *The International Law of Recognition* (1951), pp. 420–2.

that 'it is what happens over time and the legal qualification of facts-through-time that is legally relevant'.[70] An unlawful situation may thus be 'cured' or validated over time through a gradual process of waiver, acquiescence and prescription.[71] The Moroccan annexation of Western Sahara is no exception.

In 2006, after four decades of a normative dead-end, the UN Secretary-General finally accepted 'the political reality that no one was going to force Morocco to give up its claim of sovereignty over Western Sahara'; accordingly, 'obliging Morocco to accept a referendum with independence as one of the options was ... unrealistic'.[72] The Secretary-General specifically pointed to the recently concluded 2006 FPA as evidence that as 'the impasse continues, the international community unavoidably grows more accustomed to Moroccan control over Western Sahara'.[73] It was equally clear to the Secretary-General, however, that the UN could not endorse a plan that excluded a referendum with independence as an option while claiming to provide for the self-determination of the people of Western Sahara. A new approach was evidently required.

As a way out of the impasse, the Secretary-General proposed that the UN should be 'taking a step back' and hand over 'responsibility' to Morocco and the Frente Polisario, who should have recourse to direct negotiations without preconditions.[74] He explained that:

> Their objective should be to accomplish what no 'plan' could, namely to work out a *compromise between international legality and political reality* that would produce a just, lasting and mutually acceptable political solution, which would provide for the self-determination of the people of Western Sahara.[75]

More specifically, he observed that:

> The Security Council would not be able to invite parties to negotiate about Western Saharan autonomy under Moroccan sovereignty, for such

---

[70] *East Timor*, ICJ Rep (1995), p. 90, Verbatim Record, 2 February 1995, CR 95/5, p. 8, para. 3 (Mrs. Higgins on behalf of Portugal).

[71] In practice, such a process may be illustrated by the examples of the Indonesian province of West Irian (now West Papua) and the Indian state of Goa.

[72] Reports of the Secretary-General on the situation concerning Western Sahara, UN Docs. S/2006/249 and S/2006/817, paras. 32 and 13, respectively.

[73] Report of the Secretary-General on the situation concerning Western Sahara, UN Doc. S/2006/817, para. 20.

[74] Report of the Secretary-General on the situation concerning Western Sahara, UN Doc. S/2006/249, para. 34.

[75] Ibid. (emphasis added).

> wording would *imply recognition* of Moroccan sovereignty over Western
> Sahara, which was out of the question as long as no States Member of the
> United Nations had recognized that sovereignty.[76]

In 2007, the newly appointed Secretary-General came to the same conclusion.[77] In the same year, the Security Council endorsed this approach and
called on the parties to enter into negotiations without preconditions.[78]

In December 2010, the Security Council adopted Resolution 1920, by
which it took note of Morocco's 2007 autonomy proposal and welcomed
its 'serious and credible efforts to move the process forward towards
resolution'. At the same time, the Security Council also endorsed the
Secretary-General's recommendation that 'realism and a spirit of compromise' should guide the status negotiations.[79] In plain terms, as France
stated in the Security Council debate before the adoption of Resolution
1920, this realist formula effectively meant treating the Moroccan
autonomy proposal as 'the basis for credible, open and constructive
negotiations that respect the principle of self-determination'.[80] In effect,
a position not far removed from implicit recognition. The UN thus
appears to have concluded that the answer to the decolonization of
Western Sahara should be found in a compromise between international
legality and political reality – a position that not only seems to contradict
the essential right of the people of Western Sahara to freely determine
their own future status, but also constitutes an implicit recognition of
Morocco's claim to title.

As a minimum, the rationale of the obligation of non-recognition in so
far as possible, is to prevent the validation of an unlawful situation, by
seeking to ensure that a *fait accompli* resulting from serious illegalities
does not consolidate and crystallize over time into situations recognized
by the international legal order – a concern recently expressed by the ICJ
in the *Wall* Advisory Opinion.[81] As Lauterpacht has observed, the

---

[76] Ibid., para. 37 (emphasis added).

[77] Report of the Secretary-General on the situation concerning Western Sahara, UN Doc.
S/2007/202, para. 47.

[78] SC Res. 1754 (2007).

[79] SC Res. 1920 (2010). For more recent support, see SC Res. 1979 (2011) and SC Res. 2044
(2012). See also GA Res. 65/112 of 10 December 2010 and GA Res. 66/86 of 9 December
2011.

[80] UN Doc. S/PV.6305, p. 5 (statement by France).

[81] *Legal Consequences of the Construction of a Wall in the Occupied Palestinian Territory*,
ICJ Rep (2004), p. 184, para. 121.

function of non-recognition is to vindicate the 'legal character of international law against the 'law-creating effect of facts'.[82]

The obligation of non-recognition of an unlawful situation is set out in Article 41(2) of the International Law Commission (ILC) Articles on State Responsibility in the following terms:

> No State shall recognize as lawful a situation created by a serious breach
> [by a State of an obligation arising under a peremptory norm of general
> international law] . . .

The ILC's definition of the principle is based on three interrelated elements. First, all peremptory norms may in principle give rise to an obligation of non-recognition. Second, only a serious breach of a peremptory norm is subject to the obligation of non-recognition. Third, the principle of non-recognition is only applicable where a serious breach of a peremptory norm specifically results in the assertion of a legal claim to status or rights by the wrongdoing state – 'a situation' all states are obligated not to recognize 'as lawful'.[83] It finds support in international practice and in decisions of the ICJ and reflects 'a well-established practice' which forms part of customary international law.[84] In contrast, Article 41(2) does not elaborate the content of the obligation of non-recognition. Let us briefly consider these three elements in the light of Morocco's purported annexation of Western Sahara.

The right to self-determination is 'clearly accepted and recognized' as a peremptory norm under general international law.[85] It is also well established that states are under an obligation to refrain from any forcible action which deprives peoples of their right to self-determination.[86] International courts and tribunals have confirmed that forcible territorial acquisitions, including the forcible denial of self-determination, constitute

---

[82] Lauterpacht, *Recognition in International Law*, p. 430.

[83] See Commentary to article 53 [1996], ILC Report (1996), UN Doc. A/51/10, p. 72, para. 2; compare para. 6 of Commentary to article 41 ARSIWA, ILC Report (2001), UN Doc. A/56/10, p. 114.

[84] See Commentary to draft article 53, (1996) *YbILC*, vol. II/2, p. 114, para. 2. For a recent assessment, see Dawidowicz, 'The Obligation of Non-Recognition of an Unlawful Situation', in Crawford, Pellet and Olleson (eds), *The Law of International Responsibility*, p. 677.

[85] See para. 3 of the commentary to what became article 53 VCLT, (1966) *YbILC*, vol. II, p. 248; paras. 4 and 5 of the commentaries to articles 26 and 40 ARSIWA, respectively, ILC Report (2001), UN Doc. A/56/10, pp. 85, 112–13.

[86] For a recent reaffirmation, see *Legal Consequences of the Construction of a Wall in the Occupied Palestinian Territory*, ICJ Rep (2004), pp. 171–172, para. 88 (citing GA Res. 2625 (XXV)).

the unlawful situation *par excellence* proscribed by the obligation of non-recognition under customary international law.[87] Almost by definition, the forcible denial of self-determination, especially where maintained over an extended period of time, constitutes a serious and systematic breach of a peremptory norm.[88] However, as Judge Kooijmans rightly observed in the *Wall* Advisory Opinion, the purpose of the obligation of non-recognition is not to deny the existence of facts.[89] It is not a quixotic principle aimed at fighting windmills. Rather, the principle applies to the extent that an unlawful 'situation' flowing from the breach of a peremptory norm results in a *legal* claim to status or rights by the wrongdoing State. It is this 'situation' that states are under an obligation not to recognize 'as legal'. The conduct proscribed for third states by the obligation of non-recognition is a separate question.

Article 41(2) of the ILC Articles on State Responsibility does not elaborate the content of the obligation of non-recognition, and international courts and tribunals, as well as the political organs of the UN, have been reluctant to develop relevant criteria beyond concrete cases. Hence Spain's observation that the content of the obligation of non-recognition 'remains largely undefined'.[90] As Spain suggested, it is true that it is difficult to determine with confidence precisely what conduct is proscribed. A few basic points nevertheless seem clear. The ILC commentary notes that the obligation of non-recognition 'not only refers to the formal recognition of [situations created by the relevant breaches], but also prohibits acts which would *imply* such recognition'.[91] This position is explicitly based on the ICJ's advisory opinion in *Namibia*, and was reaffirmed by the Court in the *Wall* Advisory Opinion.[92] This clarification of the content of the principle is significant, since to date there has been no formal recognition of Morocco's *de jure* claim to sovereignty over Western Sahara.

As is well known, the ICJ in *Namibia* provided several examples of acts which may imply recognition of a state's purported annexation of an

---

[87] See, e.g., *Legal Consequences of the Construction of a Wall in the Occupied Palestinian Territory*, p. 171, para. 87.

[88] See, e.g., para. 8 of Commentary to article 40 ARSIWA, p. 113.

[89] *Legal Consequences of the Construction of a Wall in the Occupied Palestinian Territory*, Sep. Op., Judge Kooijmans, p. 232, para. 44.

[90] See Comments and Observations from States on State Responsibility (19 March 2001), UN Doc. A/CN.4/515, p. 54 (Spain).

[91] See para. 5 of Commentary to article 41 ARSIWA, p. 114 (emphasis added).

[92] *Legal Consequences of the Construction of a Wall in the Occupied Palestinian Territory*, p. 200, para. 159.

NSGT.[93] In short, such recognition may result from any act by which a state purports to exercise territorial sovereignty over an NSGT. In *Island of Palmas*, Judge Huber famously emphasized the inextricable link between sovereignty and territory.[94] In a well-known passage, he observed that:

> Sovereignty in the relations between States signifies independence. Independence in regard to a portion of the globe is the right to exercise therein, to the exclusion of any other State, the functions of a State. The development of the national organisation of States during the last few centuries and, as a corollary, the development of international law, have established this principle of the exclusive competence of the State in regard to its own territory.[95]

A prime example of such a function of a state is its capacity to enter into treaties. In relation to that portion of the surface of the globe where the state lawfully exercises territorial sovereignty, its treaty-making competence will normally be exclusive. In *Wimbledon*, the Permanent Court of International Justice (PCIJ) stated that 'the right of entering into international engagements is an attribute of State sovereignty'.[96] This classic conception of the relationship between territory and sovereignty remains the basis for two basic principles of treaty law. Indeed, the capacity to enter into treaties remains one of the most emblematic attributes of state sovereignty and finds expression in Article 6 of the Vienna Convention on the Law of Treaties (VCLT).[97] It is complemented by Article 29 VCLT on the territorial scope of treaties, which contains a presumption in favour of territorial sovereignty. In sum, there is an intimate link between treaty-making capacity and territorial sovereignty.

By parity of reasoning, it follows from the absence of any formal recognition by third states of Morocco's legal claim to sovereignty over Western Sahara – that is, a claim to status incompatible with the basic right of the people of Western Sahara to self-determination – that Morocco cannot *a priori* claim a *general* treaty-making capacity akin to

---

[93] *Legal Consequences for States of the Continued Presence of South Africa in Namibia (South West Africa) Notwithstanding Security Council Resolution 276 (1970)*, ICJ Rep (1971), pp. 55–6, paras. 122–4.
[94] *Island of Palmas (Netherlands/United States)*, Award of 4 April 1928, 2 RIIA, p. 829.
[95] Ibid. at p. 838.   [96] PCIJ, Ser. A, No. 1 (1923), p. 25.
[97] See, e.g., para. 3 of Commentary to what became article 6 VCLT, (1966) *YbILC*, vol. II, p. 192; H. Waldock, (1965) *YbILC*, vol. I, p. 252, para. 44; A. D. McNair, *The Law of Treaties* 2nd edn. (1961), p. 35; Jennings and Watts (eds), *Oppenheim's International Law*, vol. I, p. 1217.

a territorial sovereign in matters relating to Western Sahara. This position is reinforced by the observation that an NSGT is a separate legal
entity under international law with attendant (albeit limited) legal personality.[98] Any putative Moroccan claim to general treaty-making
capacity should therefore be construed as an implicit *legal* claim to
territorial sovereignty over Western Sahara – which third states are
obligated not to recognize – unless it can be determined that a specific
provision of international law recognizes the existence of some limited
Moroccan treaty-making capacity over Western Sahara. As Norway
recently observed:

> Norway's consistent view is that Morocco does not exercise internation-
> ally recognised sovereignty with regard to Western Sahara. As a point of
> departure, therefore, Morocco does not have the right to exploit the area's
> resources as if they were its own.[99]

Therefore, let us finally consider in turn (1) whether the 2006/2011 FPA
purports to apply to Western Sahara, (2) whether, if in the affirmative,
Morocco can exceptionally claim some limited treaty-making capacity
for the FPA, or (3) whether the FPA constitutes an implicit legal claim to
sovereignty over Western Sahara and the obligation of non-recognition
applies.

V.   The FPA: Recognition of Morocco's claim to sovereignty over Western Sahara?

On 28 February 2011, the EC and Morocco agreed on a one-year temporary renewal of the protocol to an FPA originally concluded in May 2006
for a period of four years, which entered into force on 28 February 2007.[100]
In turn, the 2006 FPA replaced three earlier fisheries agreements between
the parties that were similar in geographical scope.[101] Under the FPA,

---

[98] See GA Res. 2625 (XXV) of 24 October 1970.

[99] See statement dated 3 March 2011 by Norwegian Minister of Foreign Affairs Gahr
    Støre, reproduced at www.wsrw.org/index.php?parse_news=single&cat=105&art=
    1884 (unofficial translation) (last accessed 19 February 2012).

[100] See http://ec.europa.eu/fisheries/news_and_events/press_releases/2011/20110228/index_en.
    htm; http://register.consilium.europa.eu/pdf/en/11/st11/st11225.en11.pdf (last accessed 19
    February 2012); FPA between the European Communities and the Kingdom of Morocco,
    Council Regulation (EC) No. 764/2006 of 22 May 2006, OJ L141/1 (29 May 2006).

[101] See 1988 Agreement on relations in the sea fisheries sector between the European
    Community and the Kingdom of Morocco, OJ L/181 (23 June 1988); 1992 Agreement

Morocco has received EUR 144.4 million in financial compensation in exchange for certain fishing rights granted to EC vessels in 'Moroccan waters'. The geographical scope of the FPA is circumscribed by Article 2(a), which defines the Moroccan fishing zone as 'the waters falling within the sovereignty or jurisdiction of the Kingdom of Morocco'. The FPA provides only limited guidance on what this means.

In light of Morocco's formal annexation of Western Sahara, the adoption of the 2006/2011 FPA has been controversial, since – unlike the 2004 United States–Morocco Free Trade Agreement and the 1997 European Free Trade Association (EFTA)–Morocco Free Trade Agreement[102] – it does not explicitly exclude waters off the coast of Western Sahara from its territorial scope. On 21 February 2011, the European Council of Ministers therefore only approved the temporary renewal of the agreement by a qualified majority, with Germany and Finland abstaining and Denmark, Sweden and the United Kingdom voting against it.[103]

The FPA provides complete geographical coordinates of all Moroccan fishing zones off its Atlantic coast, with one notable exception. The southernmost geographical limit of the FPA (which delineates the area of exploitation of demersal and industrial pelagic fishing of up to 60,000 tonnes per year)[104] is defined merely as 'South of 29° 00' N'.[105] This

on relations in the sea fisheries sector between the European Community and the Kingdom of Morocco, OJ L/407 (31 December 1996); 1995 Agreement in the sea fisheries sector between the European Community and the Kingdom of Morocco, OJ L/30 (31 January 1997). See also Legal Service of the European Parliament, 'Proposal for a Council Regulation on the Conclusion of the Fisheries Partnership Agreement between the European Community and the Kingdom of Morocco: Compatibility with the Principles of International Law', European Parliament, SJ-0085/06, D(2006)7352, 20 February 2006, p. 8, para. 41 (footnote 19).

[102] See Letter dated 20 July 2004 from the US Trade Representative, Mr. Zoellick, to US Congressman Pitts, available at www.vest-sahara.no/files/pdf/Zoellick_FTA_2004.pdf (last accessed 19 February 2012). For statements by Norway and Switzerland, see *Afrol News*, 'Western Sahara "not part of EFTA-Morocco free trade"', 13 May 2010, available at www.afrol.com/articles/36091 (last accessed 19 February 2012); *Western Sahara Resource Watch*, 'Western Sahara not part of EFTA–Morocco free trade agreement', 12 May 2010, www.wsrw.org/index.php?parse_news=single&cat=105&art=1410 (last accessed 19 February 2012).

[103] Press release, 3070th meeting, European Council of Ministers, Agriculture and Fisheries, Brussels, 21 February 2011, p. 12, available at www.consilium.europa.eu/uedocs/cms_data/docs/pressdata/en/agricult/119436.pdf (last accessed 19 February 2012).

[104] FPA between the European Communities and the Kingdom of Morocco, Appendix 2, Council Regulation (EC) No. 764/2006 of 22 May 2006, OJ L141/29 (29 May 2006).

[105] FPA between the European Communities and the Kingdom of Morocco, Appendix 4, Council Regulation (EC) No. 764/2006 of 22 May 2006, OJ L141/33 (29 May 2006).

coordinate is located two degrees north of the internationally recognized maritime boundary between Morocco and Western Sahara fixed at 27° 40' N.[106] This geographical indication could mean either that certain fishing rights of EC vessels under the FPA are limited to a rather narrow strip of water north of Western Sahara – that is, in uncontested Moroccan waters – or that the southernmost geographical limit of the FPA extends to the commencement of Mauritanian waters at around 21° N. The matter has been settled by the subsequent practice of the parties to the 2006 FPA in favour of the latter interpretation. On several occasions the European Commission has recognized that demersal and industrial pelagic fishing by EC vessels is, in fact, taking place in the waters off the coast of Western Sahara.[107] Under the 2006 FPA, such fishing rights have been allocated to vessels from Spain, Portugal, Italy, France, Germany, Lithuania, Latvia, Poland, the Netherlands, Ireland and the United Kingdom.[108]

The Commission, purportedly basing itself on a legal opinion by the UN Legal Counsel,[109] has essentially argued that the FPA is consistent with international law, since Morocco must be considered the *de facto* administrating power in Western Sahara, and the agreement takes into account the needs and interests of the people of Western Sahara.[110] In essence, the Commission is suggesting that Morocco has acted within its limited treaty-making capacity in relation to Western Sahara. The application of the FPA to Western Saharan waters is permissible, and accordingly it does not entail an implicit recognition of Moroccan sovereignty over Western Sahara otherwise proscribed under international law. In

---

[106] See, e.g., Brownlie, *African Boundaries*, pp. 155–7; Legal Opinion of Legal Service of the European Parliament, 20 February 2006, SJ-0085/06, para. 31. This coordinate is also recognized in recent Food and Agriculture Organization statistics.

[107] See, e.g., Reply from European Commissioner Ferrero-Waldner to Written Question E-4425/08 (12 September 2008), available at www.europarl.europa.eu/sides/getDoc.do?type=WQ&reference=E-2008-4425&language=PL (last accessed 19 February 2012); Reply from the European Commission to Oral Question H-0079/09 (12 March 2009), available at www.europarl.europa.eu/sides/getDoc.do?type=QT&reference=H-2009-0079&language=MT (last accessed 19 February 2012).

[108] See Article 2 of Council Regulation (EC) No. 764/2006 of 22 May 2006 on the conclusion of the FPA between the European Community and the Kingdom of Morocco, OJ L141/2 (29 May 2006).

[109] Letter dated 29 January 2002 from the Under-Secretary-General for Legal Affairs addressed to the President of the Security Council, UN Doc. S/2002/161.

[110] Reply from the European Commission to Written Question MARE-B-3/AMF D(2010), 23 June 2010, available at www.wsrw.org/files/dated/2010-06-24/letter_commission-wsrw_23.06.2010.pdf (last accessed 19 February 2012).

theory, it is possible to conceive of at least three possible sources of limited treaty-making capacity that would not imply such recognition.

First, Morocco would have limited treaty-making capacity in relation to Western Sahara in a putative capacity as administrating power under Chapter XI of the UN Charter. It is true that Morocco occasionally refers to the Madrid Declaration as the basis for its presence in Western Sahara as the 'sole competent administrative authority' in the territory.[111] It is equally true that the UN and the EU treat Morocco as *de facto* administrating power and that Spain's official position since 2005 has even been to treat Morocco as *de jure* administrating power.[112] In reality, leaving aside Spain's position that as such is incapable of producing any objective legal effect, this is nothing more than a statement of fact. Morocco has not formally claimed any status as administrating power under Chapter XI of the UN Charter; indeed, such a position would plainly contradict its categorical legal claim to sovereignty over Western Sahara. As of March 2011, the UN still recognized Spain as the sole administrating power in Western Sahara.[113] The fact that Spain does not perform its obligations under Chapter XI of the UN Charter, including its reporting obligations under Article 73(e), is not decisive.

Second, Morocco could enter into treaties or other international agreements concerning the exploitation of natural resources with third states on behalf of Western Sahara if it did so on the basis of a valid expression of consent by the Frente Polisario, the legitimate representatives of the people of Western Sahara.[114] No such consent has been given. In fact, the Frente Polisario on several occasions has vigorously protested that no exploitation of Western Saharan natural resources may take place without its express authorization.[115]

---

[111] See, e.g., Letter dated 26 January 2006 from the Permanent Representative of Morocco to the UN addressed to the Secretary-General, UN Doc. S/2006/52.

[112] See, e.g., Letter dated 29 January 2002 from the Under-Secretary-General for Legal Affairs addressed to the President of the Security Council, UN Doc. S/2002/161; Legal Opinion from the Legal Service of the European Parliament, 20 February 2006, SJ-0086/06, para. 37; C. Ruiz Miguel, 'Spain's legal obligations as administrating power of Western Sahara', in N. Botha *et. al.* (eds), *Multilateralism and International Law with Western Sahara as a Case-Study* (2010), p. 208 (with further references to Spanish press reports).

[113] See Report of the Secretary-General, Information from Non-Self-Governing Territories transmitted under Article 73(e) of the Charter of the United Nations (8 March 2011), UN Doc. A/66/65.

[114] This status was first granted to the Frente Polisario by the UN in 1979. See GA Res. 34/37 of 21 November 1979, op. para. 7.

[115] See, e.g., Report of the Secretary-General on the situation concerning Western Sahara, UN Doc. S/2011/249, p. 4, para. 20; Letter dated 9 April 2009 from the Permanent Representative of Namibia to the UN on behalf of the Frente Polisario addressed to the

Third, Morocco could potentially enjoy limited treaty-making capacity in relation to Western Sahara under the law of belligerent occupation. Morocco does not accept the application of the law of belligerent occupation to Western Sahara, since that status would be *prima facie* incompatible with its claim to sovereignty over the territory. For example, in its fifth periodic report submitted to the Human Rights Committee in 2004, Morocco reaffirmed its compliance with the right to self-determination under Article 1 International Covenant on Civil and Political Rights (ICCPR) by stating that it continued to cooperate closely with the United Nations in seeking a solution to the conflict in Moroccan Sahara while guaranteeing national sovereignty over the whole of Moroccan territory.[116]

But this claim to territorial sovereignty has not been recognized as a matter of international law. In the 1970s, the UN General Assembly twice characterized Morocco's presence in Western Sahara as belligerent occupation.[117] The fact that this term has not been repeated in subsequent resolutions from the General Assembly or the Security Council is not decisive. The application of the law of belligerent occupation is largely a matter of fact dependent upon a demonstration of effective authority and control over a territory to which the occupying state holds no sovereign title. This understanding of occupation finds support in Article 42 of the 1907 Hague Regulations Respecting the Laws and Customs of War, which is widely accepted as forming part of general international law.

In the present case, Morocco's effective authority and control over Western Sahara – poignantly expressed by its *de jure* incorporation into Morocco – would appear to be sufficient to trigger the application of the general international law of occupation. As a recent example, Norway explicitly stated that the law of belligerent occupation applies in Western Sahara.[118] It is true that this legal regime may provide the occupying state with limited treaty-making capacity in relation to the natural resources

---

Secretary-General, UN Doc. A/63/871–S/2009/198 (making reference to a 2009 law on maritime spaces adopted by the Sahrawi Arab Democratic Republic).

[116] See UN Doc. CCPR/C/MAR/2004/5, p. 8, para. 39.

[117] GA Res. 34/37 of 21 November 1979; 35/19 of 11 November 1980; Letter from the President of the Sahrawi Arab Democratic Republic (and Secretary-General of the Frente Polisario) to the editor of *European Voice*, 10 March 2011, 'The (fishy) value that the EU places on democracy', available at www.fishelsewhere.eu/files/dated/2011–03–10/european_voice_10.03.2011.pdf (last accessed 19 February 2012).

[118] See statement dated 3 March 2011 by Norwegian Minister of Foreign Affairs Gahr Støre.

of the occupied territory.[119] But in the case of Morocco's occupation of Western Sahara this putative treaty-making capacity is more apparent than real.

In the *Wall* Advisory Opinion, the ICJ considered the relationship between international humanitarian law and human rights law. The Court observed that some rights could be exclusively matters of either body of law, or they might concurrently be subject to both.[120] The Court took into account both bodies of law in that case. In the present case, a similar situation obtains. The *lex specialis* expressed in the limited rights of the occupying state to exploit the natural resources of the occupied territory of an NSGT under international humanitarian law must be interpreted in accordance with peremptory human rights law, that is to say, the right of peoples to self-determination.

In 1962, at the height of the era of decolonization, the General Assembly adopted Resolution 1803 (XVII), by which it affirmed the principle of permanent sovereignty over natural resources as a 'basic constituent of the right to self-determination'.[121] In the *Armed Activities* case, the ICJ recognized that this resolution forms part of general international law.[122] It follows that under both international human-itarian law and human rights law, Moroccan exploitation of Western Saharan natural resources can only take place in accordance with the peremptory norm of self-determination. It may be recalled that the essential feature of that right is the autonomous will of the indigenous population. In the absence of consent from the people of Western Sahara, Morocco does not have treaty-making capacity and cannot exploit the natural resources of the territory.

Any Moroccan attempt to exploit these resources by international agreement therefore gives rise to an unlawful situation – that is to say, a Moroccan legal claim to sovereignty in denial of the right of the Western Saharans to self-determination – which third states are under an obligation not to recognize as legal. Switzerland's succinct position on

---

[119] See, e.g., Articles 43 and 55 of the 1907 Hague Regulations.

[120] *Legal Consequences of the Construction of a Wall in the Occupied Palestinian Territory*, p. 178, para. 106.

[121] GA Res. 1803 (XVII) of 14 December 1962. For a recent reaffirmation, see GA Res. 65/109 of 10 December 2010.

[122] *Armed Activities on the Territory of the Congo* (*Democratic Republic of the Congo v. Uganda*), ICJ Rep (2005), p. 168, at p. 251, para. 244. See also ibid., Dec. Judge Koroma, para. 11; *East Timor*, ICJ Rep (1995), Diss. Op. Judge Weeramantry, p. 197ff.

the territorial scope of application of the 1997 EFTA–Morocco Free
Trade Agreement is instructive:

> Since Switzerland does not recognise the Moroccan annexation, the free
> trade agreement between EFTA and Morocco is not applicable for
> Western Sahara.[123]

Put differently, Switzerland evidently considers that an extension of the
agreement to include Western Sahara would imply recognition of
Morocco's legal claim to sovereignty over the territory. This might
explain Morocco's account of the less-obvious benefits of the FPA:

> The financial aspect [of the Fisheries Agreement] is not necessarily the
> most important aspect of this agreement. The political aspect is just as
> important.[124]

In sum, the FPA should be understood as an implicit recognition of
Morocco's claim to sovereignty over Western Sahara by at least twenty-
two EU Member States, for which they bear several responsibility under
international law as expressed in Article 47 of the ILC Articles on State
Responsibility. However, it appears that any such wrongful conduct
recently ceased.

On 14 December 2011, the European Parliament adopted a resolution
by which it decided not to give its consent to the temporary extension of
the 2006/2011 FPA. By the same resolution, the European Parliament
instead called on the European Commission to negotiate a new FPA with
Morocco and to ensure that the new agreement 'fully respects international law and benefits all the local population groups affected'.[125] On 19

---

[123] Statement dated 6 April 2007 from the Swiss State Secretariat for Economic Affairs,
reproduced at www.wsrw.org/index.php?parse_news=single&cat=105&art=1410 (unofficial translation; last accessed 19 February 2012). The EFTA–Morocco Free Trade
Agreement is available at www.efta.int/`/media/Documents/legal-texts/free-trade-
relations/morocco/EFTA-Morocco%20Free%20Trade%20Agreement%20EN.pdf (last
accessed 19 February 2012).

[124] See statement of Morocco's Minister of Agriculture (Mr. Laenser), *Aujourd'hui Le
Maroc*, 24 May 2006, 'Accord de pêche: naufrage polisarien', available at www.aujourd-
hui.ma/nation-details46545.html; *Western Sahara Resource Watch*, 28 February 2011,
'EU Commission and Morocco sign extension of controversial fish pact', available at
www.wsrw.org/index.php?parse_news=single&cat=105&art=1880 (unofficial translation; last accessed 19 February 2012).

[125] See European Parliament resolution of 14 December 2011 on the future Protocol setting
out the fishing opportunities and financial compensation provided for in the FPA
between the European Community and the Kingdom of Morocco, available at: www.
europarl.europa.eu/sides/getDoc.do?type=TA&language=EN&reference=P7-TA-2011-0573
(last accessed 19 February 2012).

December 2011, the Council of the EU accordingly informed Morocco of its termination of the provisional application of the 2006/2011 FPA pursuant to Article 25(2) VCLT with immediate effect.[126]

In January 2012, EU Fisheries Commissioner Damanaki stated that the European Commission had tabled a new negotiating mandate for a renewed FPA with Morocco 'in line with the position expressed by the EU Council and the vote in the European Parliament' and that 'the Commission [is] committed to conclude a new protocol on that basis'.[127] Although this is a positive development, it is noteworthy that the negotiating mandate in the relevant resolution adopted by the European Parliament – i.e. to ensure that the new agreement 'fully respects international law and benefits all the local population groups affected' – is conspicuously silent on the wishes of the Western Saharans, an integral component of the principle of self-determination under international law. In any event, notwithstanding recent positive developments, the compatibility of any future EC–Morocco fisheries agreement with international law remains uncertain at this stage.

VI. Concluding observations

With the efflux of time, even the hardest of rocks will eventually wither and disintegrate into grains of sand. A similar process can be observed in international law. Even the hard-core of fundamental rules in the international legal landscape is capable of disintegration as a result of the inevitable force that ultimately shapes its configuration: state practice. Like the steady stream of water slowly eroding the stone, the efflux of time is having a similar effect on the right of the people of Western Sahara to self-determination – at least, as originally envisaged by the principal UN organs. On the other hand, the purpose of the obligation of non-recognition is to prevent, in so far as possible, the occurrence of

---

[126] See http://register.consilium.europa.eu/pdf/en/11/st18/st18687.en11.pdf (last accessed 19 February 2012). See also statement dated 14 December 2011 by EU Fisheries Commissioner Damanaki, available at http://ec.europa.eu/commission_2010–2014/ damanaki/headlines/press-releases/2011/12/20111214-2_en.htm (last accessed 19 February 2012).

[127] Statement by EU Fisheries Commissioner Damanaki (10 January 2012), available at: http://ec.europa.eu/commission_2010–2014/damanaki/headlines/press-releases/2012/ 01/20120110_en.htm (last accessed 19 February 2012). Sweden voted against the new negotiating mandate, while Finland, the United Kingdom and the Netherlands abstained (www.consilium.europa.eu/uedocs/cms_data/docs/pressdata/en/trans/127982.pdf).

such a gradual process of erosion through waiver, acquiescence and prescription.

Almost forty years after the ICJ rendered its Advisory Opinion in *Western Sahara*, the international community is seeking the answer to the enduring question of the process of decolonization of Western Sahara in a compromise between international legality and political reality. The apparent assumption is that anything must be better than the impasse of the current *status quo*. Whatever the appeal of the siren-song of expediency, the current laissez-faire policy adopted by the UN appears to severely impede – and therefore contradict – the right of the people of Western Sahara to self-determination under international law. The UN policy is, in effect, not far removed from an implicit recognition of Morocco's irredentist claim to sovereignty over Western Sahara.

It is against this background of creeping recognition of Morocco's claim to Western Sahara that the EU position on the FPA should be understood. As we have seen above, the UN Secretary-General made this link in 2006. In his own words, the international community has unavoidably grown more accustomed to Moroccan control over Western Sahara. The recent EU position on the FPA is a welcome exception to this state of affairs, but it remains to be seen to what extent (if any) a future EC–Morocco fisheries agreement will respect international law and affect the gradual process of creeping recognition of Morocco's claim to Western Sahara. It can only be hoped that the future decolonization process will be more firmly guided by the salutary words of Judge Dillard in *Western Sahara*:'It is for the people to determine the destiny of the territory and not the territory the destiny of the people.'[128]

---

[128] *Western Sahara*, Sep. Op. Judge Dillard, p. 122.

Self-determination, peacemaking and peace-building: recent trends in African intrastate peace agreements

KELLY STATHOPOULOU[*]

I. Introduction

The chapter will examine the application of self-determination in the context of peacemaking and peace-building processes in Africa, in order to assess some preliminary trends and their impact on the traditional understanding of self-determination. In other words, self-determination will be discussed by reference to a particular context and within a specifically chosen geographic and normative area. The analysis relies heavily upon the study of post-Cold War African intrastate peace agreements. This focus has been selected, as African intrastate peace agreements are on the 'borderline' between peacemaking and peace-building, being both products of peace processes and also initiating processes of peacebuilding. The inquiry is limited to three 'self-determination issues': the principle/right and its significance in this particular context, the issue of content/beneficiaries and the issue of self-determination as both a process and a right of substance. Thus, the analysis will deal with self-determination both as a principle and a right under international law and also as primarily relevant in the phase of transitioning from conflict/ crisis to peace. The exposed issues will be presented as follows: section II will introduce the context within which self-determination issues and relevant findings and trends are studied, by making a few preliminary remarks about intrastate peace agreements in Africa; section III, by conceiving self-determination as part of international human rights

[*] The research conducted for this chapter is part of the author's Ph.D. research; special thanks to Prof. Nigel White for his suggestions and comments on an earlier draft of the chapter.

law, will present the use of self-determination standards (internal self-determination language) in the substantive components of peace agreements and assess such trends in terms of self-determination entitlements and in terms of beneficiaries. Then the chapter will turn to self-determination as a general principle of international law and the emerging duties for the international community when involved in peacemaking and peace-building processes, in particular through the brokering and implementation of peace agreements; finally, some initial conclusions will be drawn for further consideration.

II.   The context

1.   On the borderline between peacemaking and peace-building: intrastate peace agreements

Peace agreements intersect between peacemaking and peace-building processes, concepts that this chapter refers to in terms of the definitions provided for in the 'Agenda for Peace'.[1] The analysis of peace agreements usually focuses on one of the above, with legal analysis mostly looking at peace agreements as end-products of a peace process.[2] For traditional peace treaties, peace would be conceived as the return to the *status quo ante*, the situation before the war. This is not the case for current intra-state agreements, where the return to the *status quo ante* is rarely desirable. In order to address conflict and its root causes and to establish sustainable peace, there is an attempt to reshape the form of the state and the relationship between the state and its people. This is why 'peace agreements not only signify the formal cessation of armed conflict *but also provide the framework for the reconstruction of political, legal, economic and social structures*. As such, peace agreements are the basis for the ensuing institutional arrangements of a State or Community.'[3] Thus, current intrastate peace agreements are portrayed as the 'maps' for subsequent peacebuilding, as they set the agenda and introduce the tasks with which locals and international actors will be engaging and/or

---

[1]   'An Agenda for Peace, Preventive Diplomacy, peacemaking and peacekeeping', Report of the Secretary-General, A/47/277-S/24111, 17 June 1992, paras 20 and 21, respectively

[2]   C. Bell, *Peace Agreements and Human Rights* (Oxford University Press, 2001), pp. 15–37; for the notion of peace process, cf. with B. G. Ramcharan, 'Peace Process' in V. Chetail (ed.), *Post-conflict Peacebuilding: A Lexicon* (Oxford University Press, 2009), pp. 228–42.

[3]   'Peace agreements as a means for promoting gender equality and ensuring participation of women – A framework of model provisions', Expert Group Meeting, 10–13 November 2003, www.un.org/womenwatch/daw/egm/peace2003 (emphasis added).

articulate the applicable principles and processes, which are then elaborated by subsequent agreements.[4]

Unlike interstate peace agreements, which are concluded between states, intrastate agreements are concluded amongst a variety of actors within a single state.[5] Their legal status remains highly contested and unclear, seemingly falling outside the scope of the Vienna Convention on the Law of Treaties.[6] The most controversial issues are their nature, being in the grey area where international law meets (pre)national law, the level of international involvement and its impact on the applicable law, and their content, including consistencies and inconsistencies in reflecting general principles of international law. The word 'intrastate', in particular, emphasises that the agreements and the preceding conflicts, or crises that fall short of an 'armed conflict', occur within the territory of a pre-defined state and thus by their very nature possess a 'domestic element'.

The documents inspected have been concluded between 1989 and 2011 in 30 African countries. The estimated number of African peace agreements in the post-Cold War era is 191.[7] The research has attempted to be as comprehensive as possible, by looking at the United Nations

---

[4] For an overview of peace agreements and subsequent peacebuilding as of 2007, see A. K. Jarstad and T. D. Sisk (eds), *From War to Democracy: Dilemmas of Peacebuilding* (Cambridge University Press, 2008), pp. 33–4.

[5] As will be shown later, there are also 'external'/'outside' actors involved, such as international organisations, and/or other states, but these have the role of 'outsiders' to the agreement, and the matter will be returned to in section IV.

[6] Vienna Convention on the Law of Treaties entered into force 27 January 1980, *UNTS* vol. 1155, p. 331, in particular arts. 1, 2(a) and 3; for recent works on the nature of peace agreements, see C. Bell, *On the Law of Peace: Peace Agreements and the Lex Pacificatoria* (Oxford University Press, 2008), chapter 3; O. Corten and P. Klein, 'Are Agreements between States and Non-State Entities Rooted in the International Legal Order?' in E. Canizzaro (ed.), *The Law of Treaties: Beyond the Vienna Convention* (Oxford University Press, 2011), pp. 1–23; S. Sheeran, 'International Law, Peace Agreements and Self-Determination: the Case of the Sudan', (2011) 46 *International & Comparative Law Quarterly*, 423–58. As regards the inquiry into the legal nature of intrastate peace agreements in general, and African peace agreements in particular, that is beyond the reach of this chapter, and the author considers it necessary to assess each agreement on a case-by-case basis.

[7] The 30 African countries and the exact numbers of peace agreements are: Angola (Republic of Angola) (7), Burundi (Republic of Burundi) (9), CAR (Central African Republic) (7), Chad (The Republic of Chad) (20), Comoros (Union of the Comoros) (5), Congo (Republic of the Congo) (2), Côte D'Ivoire (Republic of Côte D'Ivoire) (16), Djibouti (Republic of Djibouti) (3), DRC (Democratic Republic of the Congo) (9), Eritrea (State of Eritrea) (1), Ethiopia (Federal Democratic Republic of Ethiopia) (1), Gabon (Gabonese Republic) (1), Guinea-Bissau (Republic of Guinea-Bissau) (3), Kenya (Republic of Kenya) (5), Lesotho (Kingdom of Lesotho) (1), Liberia (Republic of Liberia) (9), Libya (Great Socialist Peoples' Libyan Arab

(UN) peacemaker database, launched by the UN Department of Political Affairs and providing 130 of these agreements, but also other research institutes, with the INCORE database,[8] providing the most comprehensive list of peace agreements; others include the lists by Conciliation Resources,[9] the Uppsala Peace and Conflict Database,[10] and Marshall.[11] The texts, apart from the UN peacemaker,[12] have been found from other research databases, such as the USIP digital collection,[13] the collection of the International Association of Francophonie,[14] governmental sites and official journals,[15] and specialised non-govermental organization (NGO) websites.[16] Some of these agreements come in their official form;[17] others come from the African Union (AU) or the Economic Community of West African States (ECOWAS), when involved in the peacemaking processes, with the texts having the logos of the respective organisations, but not numbered according to the organisations' own internal documentation system.[18] A great amount comes from the UN itself; almost 20 per cent – 41 agreements – are listed as official UN Security Council

Jamahiriya) (1), Mali (Republic of Mali) (2), Mozambique (Republic of Mozambique) (1), Niger (Republic of Niger) (5), Rwanda (Republic of Rwanda) (7), Senegal (Republic of Senegal) (3), Sierra-Leone (Republic of Sierra Leone) (5), Somalia (Somali Republic) (14), South Africa (Republic of South Africa) (8), Sudan (Republic of the Sudan) (29), Togo (Togolese Republic) (2), Uganda (Republic of Uganda) (13) and Zimbabwe (Republic of Zimbabwe) (2).

[8] The database provided by the Transitional Justice Institute of Ulster University, www.peaceagreements.ulster.ac.uk.

[9] Conciliation Resources Database provided by ACCORD, www.c-r.org/resources/peace-agreements.php.

[10] www.ucdp.uu.se/gpdatabase/search.php.

[11] Monty Marshall's online list of African peace agreements, www.systemicpeace.org/africa/ACPPAnnex5.pdf.

[12] The UN peacemaker provides 130 intrastate peace agreements in the following countries: Angola, Burundi, CAR, Côte d'Ivoire, DRC, Guinea-Bissau, Kenya, Liberia, Morocco, Mozambique, Republic of Congo, Rwanda, Sierra-Leone, Somalia, Sudan, Uganda and Zimbabwe, http://peacemaker.unlb.org/index1.php.

[13] See www.usip.org/publications-tools/digital-collections; countries include Angola, Burundi, Congo, DRC, Guinea-Bissau, Liberia, Sierra-Leone, Somalia and Sudan.

[14] See http://democratie.francophonie.org/rubrique.php3?id_rubrique=184; countries include Burundi, CAR, Comoros, Côte d'Ivoire, DRC, Mali, Niger and Togo.

[15] For instance, the peace agreements in Djibouti are all available in the online version of the official journal of the government.

[16] See, for instance, BeyondJumba.org, focusing on Uganda and providing all texts concluded during the Jumba peace process, as well as previous peace agreements in Uganda, such as the Yumbe peace agreement (2002), not available elsewhere.

[17] Countries include CAR, Djibouti and DRC.

[18] For instance, the Declaration of Principles for the Resolution of the Sudanese Conflict in Darfur of 2005 is provided by the AU.

Documents, after having been annexed to letters sent to the UN and circulated through the UN Security Council;[19] for this reason, some of the research focuses on these agreements only, and the implications of Security Council circulation or endorsement under chapter VII for the legal nature of these agreements. A considerable number of peace agreements are unverified and have been provided to these interactive websites by 'informal negotiators' or researchers. A small number, like private contracts, are not available to the public, just listed in the other databases.[20]

Africa has been selected for a number of reasons. First, the majority of current intrastate conflicts and large-scale atrocities have in fact taken place there; for this, Africa has infamously been labelled the 'blooded continent'.[21] Second, Africa has been of particular interest to the international community, conceived in the widest possible sense, raising issues of its obligations under general international law. UN involvement is prominent, but it is not the only form of assistance. The UN is involved in Africa providing its auspices for peacemaking,[22] in peace-keeping missions and in peace-building missions;[23] recently, the newly

[19] Countries include Angola, Burundi, CAR, Côte D'Ivoire, DRC, Guinea-Bissau, Liberia, Mozambique, Rwanda, Sierra Leone, and Somalia; see UN Documents S/1999/268, S/22609/1992, S/2001/466, S/1994/1441, S/2003/1105, S/2003/971, S/1998/219, S/1997/561, S/1997/561, S/2005/270, S/2003/704, S/2003/99, S/2003/99, SC Resolutions 1721 and 1633 of 2006, S/1999/815, S/2001/466, S/1998/825. S/1998/1025, S/24815 (1992), S/26272 (1993). S/1994/1174, S/995/7, S/1995/742, S/2003/657, S/2003/850, S/24636 (1992), S/1996/1034, S/1997/824, S/1999/585, S/2002/1359, S/2006/442 and S/26915.

[20] The best example would be Chad, having 16 of its 19 peace agreements listed by everyone and accessible by no one; that fact in itself is telling about the great diversity in the African practice of brokering and concluding peace agreements and the impossibility of grouping all of these under a single category of legal document.

[21] J.-M. Guéhenno, 'Africa: A Fragile Peace on a Bloodied Continent', *International Herald Tribune*, 29 January 2004, www.un.org/en/peacekeeping/articles/article290104.htm.

[22] Ramcharan defines a peace process under 'UN auspices' when negotiations are held 'with the mediation or good offices of a representative of the Secretary-General'. See B G. Ramcharan, *The Security Council and the Protection of Human Rights* (London, The Hague: Martinus Nijhoff Publishers, 2002), p. 103.

[23] For instance, 7 out of 16 peacekeeping missions are currently operating in Africa: UNMIS in Sudan, UNAMID in Darfur, UNOCI in Côte d'Ivoire, UNMIL in Liberia, MINURSO in Western Sahara, MINUSRHAT in Chad and CAR, MONUSCO in DRC, according to the UN background note on peacekeeping missions, www.un.org/en/peacekeeping/bnote.htm; 6 out of 11 field operations of the Department of Political Affairs (DPA) of the UN are operating in Africa, 4 of them being peace-building missions: BINUB in Burundi, BINUCA in CAR, UNIOGBIS in Guinea-Bissau and UNIPSIL in Sierra Leone, www.un.org/wcm/content/site/undpa/main/about/field_operations.

established Peacebuilding Commission (PBC) has taken up 5 cases on its agenda, all of them being African.[24]

In addition, the inspected peace agreements have been concluded within states that are members of the AU. The AU is a peace, security and development organisation consisting of 54 member states, all African states except Morocco.[25] It is hugely involved in the mediation of African conflicts and has also articulated its own policy on post-conflict reconstruction and development.[26] The AU also has its own Charter on Human and People's Rights, with a particular emphasis on group rights, including the right to self-determination.[27] Judging from a rule-based comparison between the UN system and the AU system, the self-determination provisions might read the same, or not necessarily reveal any tensions. Looking at the wider underlying policy interests and values embedded in these documents, more can be said: the AU in the same line with its predecessor organisation, the Organisation of African Unity (OAU), is highly influenced by the idea of pan-Africanism.[28] This can be witnessed simply from a reading of the logo of the AU, for instance: 'Africa must unite';[29] however, the idea of pan-Africanism is not only forward-looking, but also brings the past of the African continent into the discussion; the idea of pan-Africanism was prominent in

---

[24] Burundi, Sierra Leone, Guinea-Bissau, Liberia and CAR, www.un.org/peace/peace building/pbcagenda.shtml; this is of particular importance, as the mandate of the Peacebuilding Commission (PBC) is to coordinate all actors involved in immediate post-conflict peace-building and to marshal the resources and expertise to this end; thus, it is one of the bodies being competent in the implementation of peace agreements and actively doing so.

[25] Morocco withdrew from the AU predecessor, the Organisation of African Unity, in protest for the recognition of the Saharawi Arab Democratic Republic (SADR) government-in-exile of the Frente Popular para la Liberacion de Saguia El-Hamra y Rio de Oro (Polisario) as the legitimate government in Western Sahara; see http://news.bbc.co.uk/1/hi/world/africa/1428796.stm.

[26] Report on the Elaboration of a Framework Document on post-conflict reconstruction and development (PCRD) EX.CL/274 (IX), www.africa-union.org/root/au/AUC/Departments/PSC/PSC.htm.

[27] African (Banjul) Charter on Human and Peoples' Rights, adopted 27 June 1981, OAU Doc. CAB/LEG/67/3 rev. 5, 21 ILM 58 (1982), entered into force 21 Oct. 1986, especially Arts. 20–1 (Chapter I, Part I).

[28] For an overview of what he calls the invented idea of pan-Africanism, as an idea of unity, solidarity and cooperation of African peoples and its institutionalisation through the Pan-African Congress, the OAU and the AU, see T. Murithi, *The AU, Pan-Africanism, Peacebuilding and Development* (Aldershot: Ashgate, 2005), pp. 35–6.

[29] www.africa-union.org, when accessed in 17 October 2010, subsequently rephrased as 'a United and Strong Africa'.

the anti-colonial struggles of the African states-to-be and their attempt
to be admitted in the international community in the first place. So pan-
Africanism is endorsed by the AU system and its institutions, as some
writers have observed when presenting the AU peace and security
architecture,[30] this is also of importance in the context of peacemaking
and peace-building, where the African state meets the involvement of
'others' in its internal affairs. Thus, it can be said that the term 'African
Region' is used in the current chapter not in mere geographical terms,
but also as a separate normative system with its own specificities and
values that need to be researched, and also a system where some of the
most interesting findings can be traced.

It is within this context and in this region-system that the relevance of
self-determination is to be discussed; these situations, though occurring
within the confines of predefined states, as shown in the following
sections, often appear to be akin to the creation of states, as the power
structures within the state are hugely altered and it is through those
peace agreements that the actors and the conditions upon which this
takes place are more or less determined. The relevance of self-determination will be discussed by reference to three main issues: the articulation of self-determination as a (legal) principle in the UN Charter and as
a right in both Covenants; issues of content and beneficiaries; and issues
of process and substance.[31] By doing this, the research will not deal with
external self-determination (secession), its relationship with the creation
of states and *uti possidetis*, and self-determination within the colonial
context, as current intrastate peace agreements are concluded after the
'era of decolonisation'. In doing so, the study engages with issues that
might highlight what was been said about the vagueness of self-determination, poignantly termed '*lex obscurra*' by Crawford, not least outside

---

[30] Murithi, *The AU, Pan-Africanism, Peacebuilding and Development*, pp. 35–6.
[31] See, for instance, Klabbers's evaluation of ICJ jurisprudence and the understanding of
self-determination as a procedural principle in the *Western Sahara* advisory opinion, in
J. Klabbers, 'The Right to be Taken Seriously: Self-Determination in International Law'
(2006) 28 *Human Rights Quarterly* 186–206, 197; for a critique of the content for self-
determination, see C. Drew, 'The East Timor Story: International Law on Trial' (2001)
12 *European Journal of International Law* 651–84. Some works also categorise previous
scholarly work under different criteria. Most recent examples include Xanthaki's 'minimalist' and 'maximalist' and Knop's 'categories' and 'coherence' approach; see
A. Xanthaki, 'The Right to Self-determination: Meaning and Scope' in N. Ghanea and
A. Xanthaki (eds), *Minorities, Peoples and Self-Determination* (Leiden, Boston: Martinus
Nijhoff Publishers, 2005), pp. 15–33; K. Knop, *Diversity and Self-Determination in
International Law* (Cambridge University Press, 2002), pp. 50–4.

the colonial context,[32] and raise issues for which we might not have answers, not least from looking at the jurisprudence of the International Court of Justice (ICJ). The Court has settled the issue of the normative value of self-determination in the *Namibia* Advisory Opinion,[33] and has affirmed that self-determination is 'one of the essential principles of contemporary international law',[34] but as Cassese observes, 'historical and political circumstances led the court to deal with only the most "classical" or "traditional" dimension of self-determination'.[35] In observing the divides in the court's self-determination jurisprudence, Crawford identifies a thematic divide between a 'strong affirmative approach to self-determination within the colonial context [...] and a comparative silence on general problems of self-determination'.[36]

In addition, the chapter assumes that the distinction between internal and external self-determination,[37] as well as between legal principle[38] and legal right (or rules) are valid, not least for the issues the chapter is emphasising. Self-determination is discussed as both a general principle of international law enshrined in the UN Charter,[39] and also a collective right of peoples found in the two International Covenants,[40] and

[32] J. Crawford, 'Self-Determination in International Law: Its Development and Future' in P. Alston (ed.), *People's Rights* (Oxford University Press, 2001), pp. 1–16.

[33] *Legal Consequences for States of the Continued Presence of South Africa in Namibia (South West Africa) notwithstanding Security Council Resolution 276 (1970)*, Advisory Opinion, ICJ Reports 1971, 16, paras 52–3.

[34] *Case Concerning East Timor (Portugal v. Australia)*, Judgment, 30 June 1995, ICJ Reports 1995, 102, para. 29.

[35] A. Cassese, 'The International Court of Justice and the Right of Peoples to Self-determination' in V. Lowe and M. Fitzmaurice (eds), *Fifty Years of the International Court of Justice: Essays in Honour of Sir Robert Jennings* (Cambridge University Press, 1996), pp. 351–64, 352.

[36] J. Crawford, 'General Assembly, the International Court and Self-determination', in ibid., pp. 585–606, 586.

[37] For good examples, see M. Pomerance, *Self-determination in Law and Practice* (Martinus Nijhoff, 1982), pp. 37–42; A. Cassese, *Self-Determination of Peoples: A Legal Reappraisal* (Cambridge University Press, 1995), pp. 53–60, 101–2, and 159–62; R. Emerson, 'Self-determination' (1971) 65(3) *American Journal of International Law* 459–75, 465–6.

[38] See J. Crawford, *The Creation of States in International Law* (Oxford: Clarendon Press, 1979), pp. 84–118; see also Cassese, *Self-Determination of Peoples*, pp. 126–33.

[39] See Arts. 1 and 55 of the UN Charter; also, Declaration of the General Assembly on Principles of International Law concerning Friendly Relations and Co-operation among States in accordance with the Charter of the United Nations, adopted by the General Assembly on 24 October 1970 (General Assembly Resolution 2625 (XXV)).

[40] See Art. 1 of the International Covenant on Civil and Political Rights (ICCPR) and Art. 1 of the International Covenant on Economic, Cultural and Social Rights (ICECSR).

elaborated by the relevant commentaries.[41] The ICJ in its jurisprudence usually refers to self-determination as both a right and a principle of international law,[42] but as observed elsewhere, the reference to right and principle is made interchangeably.[43] Still, the interplay between principle and right can be found in the original documents (UN Charter art. 1 (principle) and art. 55 and art. 1 of the International Covenant on Civil and Political Rights (ICCPR) and the International Covenant on Economic, Social and Cultural (ICESCR)), and although, in recent works, the emphasis has been on the 'right' dimension of self-determination either as a solution to the limitation of 'peoples' or within a 'territorial' approach,[44] or as an element in progressive development/transformation,[45] the chapter looks at them separately. This is done because the emphasis on self-determination as a legal right might be pertinent when looking at the exercise of self-determination, but the chapter is interested in the role of self-determination in influencing policy-making and rule-drafting in interim periods of transition from conflict/crisis to peace, rather than the secondary issue of enforcement of these 'primary rule-type provisions'. It is submitted that for the purpose of this analysis it is still valid to look at self-determination as both a legal principle and a right. The generating principle of legal character remains relevant for the inquiry,[46] as the study examines how peace agreements make use of self-determination when engaging in this rule-drafting and policy-making exercise, as well as the

---

[41] General Comment No. 12 of the Human Rights Committee on 'The right to self-determination of peoples (Art. 1) and CCPR General Comment No. 12', (General Comments) (Twenty-first session, 1984).

[42] For the jurisprudence of the ICJ, see *Legal Consequences of the Construction of a Wall in the Occupied Palestinian Territory*, Advisory Opinion, ICJ Reports 2004, 136; *East Timor (Portugal v. Australia)*, Judgment, ICJ Reports 1995, 90; *Frontier Dispute*, Judgment, ICJ Reports 1986, 554; *Western Sahara*, Advisory Opinion, ICJ Reports 1975, 12; *Legal Consequences for States of the Continued Presence of South Africa in Namibia (South West Africa) notwithstanding Security Council Resolution 276 (1970)*, Advisory Opinion 16, and *South-West Africa–Voting Procedure*, Advisory Opinion 1955, ICJ Reports 1955, 67.

[43] J. Summers, *Peoples and International Law: How the Right of Self-Determination and Nationalism Shape a Contemporary Law of Nations* (Leiden, Boston: Martinus Nijhoff Publishers, 2007), pp. 380–1.

[44] R. McCorquodale, 'Self-Determination: A Human Rights Approach' (1994) 43 *International and Comparative Law Quarterly* 857.

[45] See the discussion by Summers, *Peoples and International Law*, pp. 379–87.

[46] See *Namibia Advisory Opinion*, paras 52–3; J. Crawford, 'General Assembly, the International Court and Self-determination', in Lowe and Fitzmaurice (eds), *Fifty Years of the International Court of Justice*, pp. 585–606, 590.

potential role self-determination might play where peace agreements have gaps or unclear provisions.

The chapter also departs from the literature focusing on the 'exceptional role or character of self-determination',[47] in the sense that the inquiry is thematically and timely limited to a particular context, which in itself is exceptional. As such, there is, of course, the assumption of the writer that self-determination is a relevant principle for the contexts of peacemaking and peace-building, within which peace agreements are drafted and implemented. In acknowledging the importance of self-determination when transitioning from conflict to peace, the study seems to share a similar assumption with some of the literature on post-conflict reconstruction, as shown in section III of the chapter. But not to overlook what was been said about the vagueness of self-determination, the aim is to highlight how these texts are using, or drawing upon, rules on self-determination, or in other matters having gaps and silences, for which the principle of self-determination could come into play by providing aid in interpretation.[48]

III. The right to self-determination: reading its 'terms and conditions' in African peace agreements

1. The substantive components

The tasks a typical peace agreement has to address are the cessation of hostilities and the provision of military security, including demobilisation, disarmament and dispersal of combatants, and tasks that will lead to the establishment of a positive peace, including justice and reconciliation; these tasks include return and repatriation of refugees, the establishment of provisional governments and mechanisms until the holding of elections/referenda/constitution promulgation, and relevant reforms (including institution and capacity-building, and economy reforms) in the interim period.[49] The corresponding provisions of intrastate peace agreements can thus be grouped under two broad categories: provisions

---

[47] N. Berman, 'Sovereignty in Abeyance: Self-Determination and International Law' (1988) *Wisconsin International Law Journal* 51, reprinted in M. Koskenniemi (ed.), *International Law* (Aldershot: Ashgate, 1992) and in R. McCorquodale (ed.), *Self-Determination in International Law* (Aldershot: Ashgate, 2000); W. G. Werner, 'Self-Determination and Civil War' (2001) 6 *Journal of Conflict and Security Law* 171–90.

[48] For the use of principle in cases not covered by specific rules, and a standard of interpretation, see Cassese, *Self-Determination of Peoples*, pp. 132–3.

[49] See the UN peacemaker and the INCORE websites.

relating to ceasefire/cessation of hostilities ('peace and security provisions'), and provisions relating to positive peace and/or peace-building ('peace-building provisions').

In the African context, most agreements are designated as 'the framework for peace in the country', some good examples being Liberia (1994),[50] and Guinea-Bissau (1998).[51] These almost-lookalike opening sentences can be said to have some normative value: the conclusion of intrastate peace agreements is in itself an exceptional event, going beyond the domestic rules of constitutional normality; this does not mean that domestic law of the state is set aside in its entirety, though some peace agreements explicitly set aside constitutional provisions and/ or entire constitutions;[52] but, in most cases peace agreements introduce significant departures and modifications that can be grouped under the following categories: the establishment of an interim period until the holding of elections[53]/referenda, or constitution promulgation,[54] or constitutional amendments,[55] and the establishment of a transitional government[56] with law-making powers, varying from the introduction

[50] Akosombo Agreement (1994) (Liberia), S/1994/1174, art. 1 describes the agreement as the 'framework for peace'.

[51] Abuja Protocol (1998) (Guinea-Bissau) S/1998/1178, para. II describes the original Abuja Agreement as the 'framework for lasting peace and normal political life'.

[52] The Accord Cadre pour La Reconciliation aux Comores (Fomboni Agreement) (2001) (Comoros) declares null and void every contrary existing provision of the constitution; the Bangui Accords (1997) (CAR) S/1997/561, affirm the constitution stays in force, but still introduce amendments; the Cotonou Agreement (1993) (Liberia) S/26272, though not setting it aside, leaving room for amendment as the relevant provision says: 'The Parties further agree that the transitional Government shall operate *as closely as practicable* under the Constitution and laws of Liberia.' (emphasis added)

[53] Countries include Angola (Bicesse Accords (1991) S/22609, Lusaka Protocol (1994) S/ 1994/1441); Côte D'Ivoire (Linas-Markousis Accords (2003) S/2003/99, Pretoria I Agreement (2005) S/2005/270, Pretoria II Declaration (2005)); Liberia (Cotonou Agreement (1993) S/26272, Akosombo Agreement (1994) S/1994/1174, Abuja Agreement (1995)); Guinea-Bissau (Abuja Accord (1998) Abuja Additional Protocol (1998)); Sierra Leone (Conakry Peace Plan (1997) S/1997/824, Togo (Lomé Framework Agreement (1999)); and Zimbabwe (Comprehensive Peace Agreement (2008)).

[54] Countries include Burundi (Arusha Agreement (2000)); DRC (Pretoria Agreement (2002)); Madagascar (Maputo Political Agreement (2009)); Kenya (Principles–Longer Term Issues Agreement (2008)); Somalia (Cairo Declaration (1997), Djibouti Agreement (2008)); and Zimbabwe (Comprehensive Peace Agreement (2008)).

[55] Countries include Djibouti, Lesotho.

[56] Countries include Burundi, Comoros, Djibouti, Guinea-Bissau, Liberia, Sierra-Leone, Zimbabwe, CAR, Kenya, Uganda, Somalia, Sudan, Côte d'Ivoire, Togo; see Arusha Agreement (2000) (Burundi), Accord Cadre pour La Reconciliation aux Comores (Fomboni Agreement) (2001), Moroni Accord (2003) (Comoros), Linas-Markousis

of electoral reforms, wider institutional reforms, and the restructuring of the national army and police. In this sense, the peace agreements in Africa constitute, or at least modify, for an interim period, the legal regime whose duration cannot be anticipated at the outset. It is this fluid period of transitioning to peace, stability and order, that the provisions of these peace agreements govern, at least, partially, and effectively determine the actors that will have a say in the processes that will alter the power structures within a given state.

It is with regard to these provisions that the use of self-determination language comes into play, and where the research has tried to identify 'self-determination factors' in these peace agreements. Thus, while the term 'self-determination' may not be used as such in peace agreement provisions except in cases like Sudan,[57] and Burundi,[58] still the influence of self-determination language can be found in provisions relating the themes mentioned in the previous paragraph; some of these themes have already been grouped by research institutes in a thematic fashion; these include the themes of security, constitution and political system structure/institutions, Rule of Law and the administration of justice, Electoral Framework, Human Rights, minorities/Indigenous Peoples/Other Groups, Transitional Security, Governance and Institutional Arrangements, Traditional and Local Actors, Statehood and Identity.[59] According to the UN peacemaker database,[60] 61 African intrastate peace agreements deal with human

---

Accords (2002) (Côte D'Ivoire S/2003/99, Tripartite Peace Agreement (2003) (Liberia) S/2003/850, Lomé Framework Agreement (Togo) (1999).

[57] Term used in the Machakos Protocol (2002), art. 1.3.

[58] The Arusha Agreement (2000) as a basic requirement specifies the government to be representative of the will of the Burundian people; see section II, art. 1.

[59] Two institutions using key themes are the UN peacemaker and INCORE: the UN uses the themes Security: Military, police DDR etc., Constitution and political system structure/institutions, Rule of Law and the administration of justice, Electoral Framework, Human Rights, Women, Children, minorities/Indigenous Peoples/Other Groups, Humanitarian and Refugee Issues, Socio-Economic and Development, Media and Information, Transitional Security, Governance and Institutional Arrangements, Transitional Justice, Traditional and Local Actors, Statehood and Identity; INCORE uses women, children, statehood and identity, and development and socio-economic issues are identical, the theme of transitional justice is split into 3 sub-themes of amnesty, victims and past-mechanism, the theme of Human Rights is split into the 2 sub-themes of Human Rights Framework and National Human Rights Institutions, the Rule of Law and the administration of justice is split into the sub-themes of governance and democratic institutions, criminal justice reform and judicial reform, the Security theme is split into the sub-themes of policing and prisoner release, and the theme of refugees is grouped with land issues. See UN peacemaker and INCORE, *supra.* nn. 12 and 8, respectively.

[60] http://peacemaker.unlb.org/index1.php.

rights;[61] 80 with issues relating to the theme of constitution and political system/structure/institutions;[62] 60 with the theme of statehood and identity;[63] and 11 with the key theme of traditional and local actors.[64]

In secondary literature, Ramcharan observes that 'the practice of the Security Council in dealing with internal conflicts shows a strong emphasis on human rights in processes of peacemaking. The Council has placed its authority behind negotiated solutions, national dialogue, democracy, the rule of law, respect for human rights, and justice for the victims of gross violations.'[65] Interestingly, Ramcharan refers to international human rights law in the widest sense possible, including the rule of law and general principles of international law, pinpointing at self-determination, when talking about negotiated solutions.

In terms of the agreements analysed, the most important findings relate to the requirement of free and fair elections found in various agreements,[66] and the substantive components establishing processes and principles for the accommodation of former hostile parties and their access to power. This is done either by injecting a general principle of 'political participation' in the key agreement[67] or a principle of inclusive political dialogue, or by more detailed provisions of 'power-sharing'. Power-sharing is a term that appears in some agreements, but not in others.[68] It is often used for the accommodation of former warring

---

[61] Countries include Sudan, Angola, Sierra Leone, Côte d'Ivoire, Kenya, Zimbabwe, Liberia, Burundi, Rwanda, Somalia and CAR.

[62] Countries include Zimbabwe, CAR, Kenya, Uganda, Somalia, Sudan, Côte d'Ivoire and DRC.

[63] Countries include Angola, Liberia, Rwanda, Somalia, Ivory Coast, Sudan and Burundi.

[64] Countries include Sudan, Uganda, Liberia, Burundi and Sierra Leone.

[65] B. G. Ramcharan, *The Security Council and the Protection of Human Rights* (London, The Hague: Martinus Nijhoff Publishers, 2002), pp. 103–4.

[66] See, for instance, the Moroni Accord (2003) (Comoros), Principle II, 'the parties pledge to work towards the organisation of free, fair and democratic elections'; also the Bicesse Accords (1991) S/22609 and Lusaka Protocol (1994) S/1994/1441 in Angola; the General Peace Agreement in Mozambique (1991) S/24635/1992 and the Lomé Framework Agreement (1999) in Togo.

[67] See, for instance, the Global Peace Agreement (CAR) (2006), Art. 6, affirming the principle of political participation.

[68] For examples of power-sharing forming part of the agreements' name, see Pretoria I Protocol (2003) (Burundi) (2003) and Pretoria II Protocol (2003) (Burundi), Power-sharing Protocol (1992) (Rwanda) A/48/824 and S/26915 and Power-sharing Protocol (2004) (Sudan); for explicit reference to power-sharing, see Abuja Protocol (Guinea-Bissau) (1998).

parties during the transitional periods. As regards theories/types of power-sharing, the standard literature divides them into the 'consociational approach',[69] and 'integrative'.[70] From the perspective of international law, however, what is perhaps more interesting is examining how these power-sharing provisions are 'crafted', what matters they cover, whether the language deployed makes use of 'internal self-determination' standards, and also the parties that benefit from these provisions.

Exemplary cases include Rwanda,[71] Sudan,[72] Burundi,[73] Côte D'Ivoire,[74] Guinea-Bissau,[75] Liberia,[76] DRC,[77] the Congo[78] and Sierra-Leone.[79] Usually, power-sharing is deployed for the establishment of transitional governments, with Guinea-Bissau being an illustrative example.[80] Still, the provisions in peace agreements might relate to political, as well as defence and security matters, or wealth and resources. Political matters can vary from the executive, judiciary and legislature, to public enterprises, local government/authorities, and public

---

[69] This is influenced by Lipjard, consisting of techniques that include granting groups territorial autonomy, employing proportional representation in administrative appointments and parliamentary elections, and recognizing group rights; see T. Sisk, *Power-sharing and International Mediation in Ethnic Conflicts* (Washington DC: US Institute of Peace, 1996), chapter 3.

[70] This type contains techniques that focus on creating a unitary, inclusive central state; see ibid.

[71] Arusha Agreement (1993), and its five related protocols, namely, the Power-sharing Protocol (1992) A/48/824 and S/26915.

[72] Machakos Protocol (2002).

[73] Arusha Agreement (2000), Pretoria I Protocol (2003).

[74] Linas-Markousis Accords (2003), S/2003/99.

[75] Additional Protocol to the Abuja Accord (1998), S/1998/1178, Annex II, arts: 1–2 (power-sharing in the government of national unity – division of 16 ministries between the two signatory parties – military junta and president of Guinea Bissau).

[76] Cotonou Agreement (1993), S/26272, Part II, section B, Art. 14, paras. 7–9 (power-sharing in the three branches (executive, judiciary, legislature) of the transitional government); subsequently amended by Akosombo Agreement (1994), S/1994/1174, Part II, Section A, Art. 13(i), Section B, Art. 14(i).

[77] Pretoria Agreement (2002).

[78] D. Rothchild, 'Africa's Power Sharing Institutions as a Response to Insecurity: Assurance without Deterrence' in S. Saiderman and M.-J. Zahar (eds), *Intrastate Conflict Governments and Security* (London: Routledge, 2009), pp. 138–60, pp. 142–8.

[79] Lomé Accords (1999) (Sierra-Leone) power-sharing arrangements between the elected government and the Revolutionary United Front (RUF).

[80] See Abuja Protocol (1998) (Guinea-Bissau)), Annex II on the Formation of the Government of National Unity, arts. 1–2, Cotonou Agreement (1993) (Liberia), Section B, art. 14 on the structure of government, Abuja Accord (1993) (Liberia) Part. II, Section A, on the formation of transitional government and the participation of former warring parties to the ministries and the public entities.

administration.[81] These provisions are sometimes designed in general terms, sometimes in more detail. More specifically, provisions might generally require that 'in assigning ministries a balance will be struck among the parties throughout the term of office of the government';[82] similarly, in Comoros, the Government of National Unity is to be formed/composed on an equal basis.[83] More detailed provisions can be found in the peace agreements in Liberia where, for instance, the 16 ministries of the transitional government are divided by half, or in Burundi. There the division of posts between the transitional government and the National Council for the Defence of Democracy-Forces for the Defence of Democracy has been provided in detail for all of these political matters (executive–legislature–local government–public enterprises) and defence and security matters, including the police force.[84] Thus, the peace agreements have been regulating the amount of ethnic representation regarding all of these issues.

1.1   Of parties and beneficiaries

The previous section presented some examples of the substantive components of intrastate peace agreements that adopt, or seem to have been influenced by, self-determination language or standards, detail of which is discussed further below. Moving from the substantive provisions to the parties to these agreements, the issue of beneficiaries comes into play. In the case of African peace agreements, the variety of actors is striking. The typical African peace agreement is not necessarily concluded between a government and an organised armed group under the notion of Common article 3 of the Geneva Conventions, or a group exercising a right to self-determination, under Additional Protocol I. This is because, as noted above, peace agreements are concluded not only in order to establish peace after a conflict, but also after situations of internal disturbance, such as incidents of escalated electoral violence, or coups.[85] It is evident that the signatories to intrastate peace agreements can be

---

[81] Accord de paix définitive (Ouagadougou Accord) (1995) (Niger), art. 22, D (3).

[82] Linas-Markousis Accords (2003) (Ivory Coast), S/2003/99, Art. 3(d).

[83] Accord Cadre pour La Réconciliation aux Comores (Fomboni Agreement) (2001) (Comoros), section II, art. 15.

[84] See Pretoria I Protocol (2003) (Burundi) S/2003/971, sections on political power issues, defence and security issues (I) and (II), 1.3 and 2.2; and Pretoria II Protocol (2003) (Burundi), art. 5.

[85] In Zimbabwe, ZANU-MDC Memorandum (2008) and Comprehensive Peace Agreement (2008), or in Kenya, Public Statement (2008), Acting Together for Kenya (2008), Kenyan Dialogue/Reconciliation –TRC (2008), Kenyan Dialogue/Reconciliation – Review (2008),

of a different nature, both in terms of their general treaty capacity-making attributes under international law (possessing or lacking this capacity), and also in terms of qualifying as traditionally understood self-determination beneficiaries. Some agreements have been concluded between governments and armed groups, some good examples being the Angolan peace agreements;[86] in Burundi, the Dar-Es-Salaam cease-fire;[87] in Rwanda, the Arusha agreement and its five related protocols;[88] in Sierra Leone, the Lomé Agreement;[89] also, the peace agreements in Liberia, in response to a multi-party conflict, have been concluded between the government and two armed movements, amongst others.[90] At the other end of the spectrum, there are parties to these agreements that are not traditional armed groups. In the recent two cases of post-electoral violence, the agreements have been concluded between the government and the opposition: the two agreements in Zimbabwe have been concluded between the Zimbabwe African National Union-Patriotic Front (ZANU) (government) and the two formations of the Movement for Democratice Change (MDC);[91] the five agreements in Kenya have been concluded between the Party of National Unity (PNU) (government) and the Orange Democratic Movement (ODM);[92] the

Kenyan Dialogue/Reconciliation – Principles (2008); also, in Madagascar the Maputo Accords (2009) and the Addis Ababa Additional Act (2010). These are the cases grouped as 'crises' under this research, and vary in their intensity, but they all have the issue of mass abuse and lack of security as common features.

[86] See the Bicesse Accords (1991) S/22609 and the Lusaka Protocol (1994) S/1994/1441 (signed between the Government of the Republic of Angola and UNITA) and the Luanda Protocol (1999) and Luena Agreement (2002) (signed between the Government of Angola and UNITA Renovada).

[87] See Dar-Es-Salaam Ceasefire (2006) signed between the transitional Government of Burundi and the FNL/Palipehutu.

[88] See Arusha Agreement (1993), Power-sharing Protocol (1993), Rule of Law Protocol (1992), the Armed Forces Protocol (1993), IDPs Protocol (1993) and Miscellaneous Issues Protocol (1993) A/48/824 and S/26915 (signed between the Government of the Republic of Rwanda and the Rwandese Patriotic Front (RPF)).

[89] See Lomé Peace Agreement (1999) (Sierra Leone) (signed between the Government and the Revolutionary United Front (RUF)).

[90] See the tripartite ceasefire (2003) and the tripartite peace agreement (2003) S/2003/850 concluded between the Government of the Republic of Liberia, Liberians United for Reconciliation and Democracy (LURD), the Movement of Democracy in Liberia (MODEL), as well as the political parties.

[91] See the ZANU-MDC memorandum (2008) and the Comprehensive Peace Agreement (2008) concluded between the Zimbabwe African National Union-Patriotic Front (ZANU) and the two-Movement for Democratic Change (MDC) Formations on Resolving the Challenges Facing Zimbabwe.

[92] See the Public Statement (2008), Acting together for Kenya (2008), Kenyan Dialogue/ Reconciliation – TRC (2008), Kenyan Dialogue/Reconciliation – Review (2008), Kenyan

same applies to the earlier peace agreements in Lesotho and Djibouti; the final examples, highlighting the diversity of the parties to these agreements, would be from peace agreements concluded in Côte d'Ivoire, Burundi and the Democratic Republic of Congo (DRC): the agreements in these countries have been signed by a mixture of actors, including political forces and political parties, in addition to traditional armed groups.[93]

What needs to be observed is what exactly the parties are signing up to: the parties are signing these agreements, identified as parties to the agreements in their entirety; however, they are not always straightforwardly identified as beneficiaries in relation to general or specific entitlements in peace agreement provisions; in some of the cases there is a general clause on guiding principles (Central African Republic, CAR), but in other cases (Angola, Burundi, DRC) there are detailed provisions on the right to participate in the forthcoming elections, for instance, or in the reconfiguration of power. However, this ambiguity cannot overrule the importance of the general trend.

While the relevance of self-determination in the drafting of peace agreements is observed nowadays, the ways of drawing upon self-determination seem to be diverse: from a specific entitlement identifying the beneficiaries, or the bearers, as in the case of former warring parties participating in elections, or the case of former warring parties sharing powers in government and other matters, as discussed above, to a more general provision on political participation, which might make it more difficult to understand what exactly the parties have signed up to; however, a preliminary conclusion that can be drawn is that those standards are used in both conflicts and crises, and also irrespective of whether the preceding conflict has or has not been perceived/recognized as a self-determination struggle. In this sense, Cassese's remark about African states being 'engaged in the

Dialogue/Reconciliation – Principles (2008) concluded between the Party of National Unity (PNU) and the Orange Democratic Movement (ODM).

[93] See the Arusha Agreement (2000) (Burundi) (2000) signed by Parti Socialiste et Panafricaniste (INKINZO), Parti pour le Redressement National (PARENA), Parti Indépendant des Travailleurs (PIT), Parti Libéral (PL), Parti du Peuple (PP), Parti pour la Economique et Social (RADDES), Rassemblement du Peuple Burundais (RPB) and Union pour le Progrès National (UPRONA) in addition to the government and the armed forces; see also the Linas-Markoussis Accords (2003) (Côte d'Ivoire) S/2003/99 signed by Ivorian 'political forces', namely, FPI, MFA, MJP, MPCI, MPIGO, PDCI-RDA, PIT, RDR, UDCY and UDPCI; see also Pretoria Agreement (2002) (DRC), Sun-City Agreement (2001) (DRC), North and South Kivu Agreements (2008) (DRC), signed not only by armed forces, but also by a group of parties listed under the heading 'unarmed opposition'.

wholesale destruction of any semblance of either internal or external commitment to that concept [self-determination]' might have been overstated, not least in the context of transitioning from conflict/crisis to peace.[94] In a pragmatic fashion, in most cases, the emphasis is on the entitlements rather than the beneficiaries; still, when making the logical connection between the provisions and who benefits from those provisions, it can be seen that the purpose of these entitlements, which govern the interim period of transitioning from conflict/crisis to peace, is to ensure that former hostile parties are included in the reformed/restructured state; thus, the benefits of inclusion are intended for all parties to these agreements, be they governments, armed opposition groups, politico-military movements and/or political factions and political parties.

IV. The principle of self-determination: the line of demarcation between 'locals' and 'outsiders'

1. The strange case of intrastate peace agreements: immediate parties and internationals (international actors)

This section looks at the relevance of self-determination as a principle of international law in the context of peacemaking and peacebuilding in Africa. It moves from the substantive components and their entitlements for former hostile parties, which are the immediate parties to these agreements, and shifts to provisions relating to international involvement in peacemaking and peacebuilding, in particular the implementation of peace agreements. By conceiving of self-determination as a general principle of international law, the chapter focuses on the obligations of the international community when involved in the drafting and the implementation of these peace agreements, not least for the involvement that is evidenced in the texts of these agreements. Thus, when discussing the relevance of self-determination in transitioning from conflict/crisis to peace, in addition to drawing upon standards for including former warring parties in the restructured state, as discussed in the previous section, the applicability of self-determination should be inquired in relation to issues arising from the encounter between the various groups within a given state vis-à-vis the members of the international community, when involved in these processes.

---

[94] Cassese, *Self-Determination of Peoples*, p. 6.

The issues of self-determination in the context of transitioning from conflict to peace have been raised in relation to peace-building, in particular post-conflict reconstruction and direct administration of territory. Critique in literature has observed how international involvement in the various peacebuilding projects has been seen as a positive engagement of the international community. Outside Africa, in the cases of international administration, for instance (East Timor, Bosnia-Herzegovina, Kosovo), the presence and the role of the international community has not been questioned, but presumed as legitimate. As Orford notes,

> The idea that the international community has a legitimate role as administrator of post-conflict territories has gained increasing acceptance at the international level. These developments in international relations flow from a new faith in the international community as a benign, even civilising administrator.[95]

Indeed, this kind of critique points out that the international engagement could be in tension with a state's independence, and brings the principle of self-determination into the discussion.[96] Though the chapter discusses self-determination in to the same post-conflict/transition context, the issues here are slightly different, as the focus is not on the process of peacebuilding itself, but the texts of peace agreements to the extent they govern this process. In the case of peace agreements, one could argue that the ability of a people within a given state to decide the terms of receiving the assistance of the international community is not at all compromised; on the contrary, peacebuilding seems to have a consensual basis, in accordance with self-determination; it is the peace agreement providing for basic principles, procedures and oversight mechanisms of peace-building that constitutes the act of providing consent to international involvement; and that consent is given by all former warring parties, not just the government of the state in question, signing up to the agreement.

[95] A. Orford, *Reading Humanitarian Intervention: Human Rights and the Use of Force in International Law* (Cambridge University Press, 2003), p. 128.
[96] For a good discussion of self-determination in relation to post-conflict reconstruction, see M.W. Saul, 'International Law and the Will of the People in Post-Conflict Rebuilding' in *The Future of Statebuilding: Ethics, Power and Responsibility in International Relations*, www.westminster.ac.uk/__data/assets/pdf_file/0009/81594/Saul.pdf; M.W. Saul, 'Local Ownership of Post-Conflict Reconstruction in International Law: The Initiation of International Involvement' (2011) 16(1) *Journal of Conflict and Security Law* 165–206.

However, the inquiry into self-determination would be far from exhausted: as the following paragraphs will show, peace agreements provide for various forms and degrees of involvement, often making it difficult to understand what is the international involvement. This is why self-determination, conceived as a general principle of international law, could be of significance: not to preclude the international involvement, but instead, to assist in identifying, interpreting and evaluating the various forms and the amount of this involvement.

In the previous sections, it has been indicated that intrastate peace agreements do contain a domestic element by their very nature; at the same time, these documents are usually neither produced nor implemented without international involvement. In the case of Africa, outside involvement seems to be the rule rather than the exception: the typical African agreement is concluded among the parties to the conflict – and sometimes only some of these parties – but not between those parties alone. As a product of a peace process, it is ordinarily facilitated by negotiators or mediators, or held under the 'auspices' of another state or an international organisation. These non-parties to the conflict, states, as well as international organisations – such as the UN, the AU, five out of the six Regional Economic Communities of Africa, the Community of Sahel-Saharan States (CEN-SAD),[97] the Southern African Development Community (SADC),[98] the Economic Community of Central African States (CEMAC),[99] the Intergovernmental Authority on Development (IGAD),[100] and the Economic Community of Western African States (ECOWAS),[101] the EU,[102] the Organisation of the Islamic Cooperation,[103] the League of Arab States,[104] the International Organisation of Francophonie,[105] and the

---

[97] Countries of involvement include Chad (Syrte Accord) (Tripoli III Accord) (2009).

[98] Countries of involvement include DRC (Lusaka Ceasefire) (1999), Madagascar (Maputo Political Agreement) (2009) and Zimbabwe (Global Agreement) (2008).

[99] Countries of involvement include CAR (APRD Ceasefire).

[100] Countries of involvement include Sudan (Chapeau CPA).

[101] Countries of involvement include Côte D'Ivoire, Guinea-Bissau, Liberia, Sierra Leone (Conakry Peace Plan (1997) S/1997/824 (Ceasefire Agreement).

[102] Countries of involvement include CAR (Global Ceasefire), Comoros (Fomboni Agreement) (2001) and (Moroni Accord) (2003), Chad (N'Djamena Accord) (2007), Somalia (Djibouti Agreement) (2008) Sudan (Darfur Peace Agreement) (2005), Togo (Lomé Political Agreement) (2006), Uganda.

[103] Countries of involvement include Somalia (Djibouti Agreement) (2008).

[104] Countries include Comoros, Somalia, Sudan (Chapeau CPA) (2004), (DPA) (2005).

[105] Countries of involvement include Burundi, CAR, Comoros, Côte D'Ivoire, DRC, Mali, Niger and Togo.

Commonwealth Organisation[106] – are present in the negotiations, as well as the texts of these agreements: they sign as witnesses, observers or guarantors and according to provisions in the agreements, they are competent to oversee the performance of ceasefire/security provisions contained therein, as part of a joint verification mechanism or committee of implementation, and also to engage in support/assistance with implementation.

In an article on Africa, the Under-Secretary-General for Peacekeeping, Jean-Marie Guéhenno, stated that 'the peace processes are mostly home-grown'.[107] This seems to be at odds with the inspected materials: of 30 African countries and their respective 184 agreements, only three peace agreements in Djibouti,[108] one in Côte D'Ivoire,[109] one Ethiopia,[110] one in Eritrea,[111] and two in Uganda[112] have been concluded without any outside involvement whatsoever.[113] Yet the primary purpose of a peace agreement is to establish peace between the municipal (and occasionally neighbouring) parties to the conflict; it is those parties' behaviour that, in principle, is agreed upon and regulated by the agreement.

From a review of the UN peacemaker database, 'third party involve-ment' (termed as such by the database) is found in all types of agreements, be they ceasefires, framework/comprehensive or implementation agree-ments. The UN database uses the theme 'implementing/supporting actors' for third party involvement. In total, outsiders have been involved as 'implementing or supporting actors' in 104 peace agreements. Based on the UN peacemaker listings, external actors have been involved in 33 ceasefire agreements, concluded in 14 countries.[114] Regarding the frame-work and comprehensive agreements, third party involvement can be found in a total of 36 agreements (8 framework and 18 comprehensive,

---

[106] Sierra-Leone (Abidjan Peace Agreement) (1996) S/2002/1359.

[107] J.-M. Guéhenno, 'Africa: A Fragile Peace on a Bloodied Continent', *International Herald Tribune*, 29 January 2004, www.un.org/en/peacekeeping/articles/article290104.htm.

[108] See Peace and Reconciliation Agreement (1994), Framework Reform and Reconciliation Agreement (2000) and Reform and Reconciliation Agreement (2001).

[109] See Abidjan Ceasefire (2003).   [110] Reform Agreement (1991) listed by INCORE.

[111] Constitutional Commission of Eritrea Draft Constitution (1996).

[112] Yumbe Ceasefire (2002) and Yumbe Peace Agreement (2002).

[113] The chapter primarily uses the term external/international actors, in contrast to the term 'third parties' or 'third-party signatories' used by research databases such as INCORE and UN peacemaker.

[114] Somalia, CAR, Congo, Uganda, Burundi, Sudan, DRC, Liberia, Angola, Sierra Leone, Mozambique, Rwanda, Côte d'Ivoire and Guinea-Bissau.

respectively).[115] And it is also found in 34 implementation agreements; these agreements have been concluded in 8 countries.[116] This first quantitative overview gives an idea of the size of international involvement.

In qualitative terms, the degree of international involvement is particularly high in the peace and security provisions of peace agreements, with external actors being signatories and having supervisory and oversight competences, but this can also be found in various degrees in the peacebuilding part of intrastate peace agreements, which can be distinguished as high, intermediate and low. The highest level of intensity (enforcement) concerns mostly the peace and security part of the agreement, namely, the implementation of ceasefire provisions and sometimes demobilisation and demilitarisation; the others (intermediate and low) usually concern the peace-building part of peace agreements, supervision of the agreement and the economic and/or general support.

The high degree of international involvement can be found in the supervisory and enforcement powers delegated to the international community (the UN, or other international organisations), forming part of joint verification monitoring mechanisms, or UN, joint UN/AU, UN/ECOWAS missions with specific oversight powers regarding the military aspects of these agreements; in a similar fashion of high degree involvement, outsiders are exceptionally labelled co-signatories,[117] and signing a specific provision/protocol of 'guarantees'.[118]

---

[115] These agreements have been concluded in countries like Kenya, Somalia, Guinea-Bissau, Sudan, Liberia, CAR, Zimbabwe, Burundi and Sierra Leone.

[116] Uganda, Kenya, Côte d'Ivoire, Somalia, Sudan, DRC, Guinea-Bissau and Angola.

[117] See Arusha Agreement (2000) (Burundi) and Dar-Es-Salaam Principles Agreement (2004) (Burundi) (2004).

[118] Good examples can be found in the Bangui Guarantee Agreement part of the Bangui Accords (1997) (CAR), S/1997/561 and the Comprehensive Agreement (2008) (Zimbabwe), art. 22.6 ('The implementation of this agreement shall be guaranteed and underwritten by the Facilitator, SADC and the AU'), where the AU and SADC are mentioned as guarantors; see also the Maputo Political Agreement (Madagascar) (2009), art. 21 ('L'Equipe Conjointe de Médiation pour Madagascar composée par l'UA, la SADC, l'OIF et l'ONU est garante de la mise en oeuvre du présent accord), the Syrte Accord (Chad) (2007), art. 10 ('Les médiateurs sont garants de l'application de cet accord'), cases where the mediator/mediation team are also mentioned as guarantors of the implementation of the peace agreement in its entirety; these cases in contrast with cases where the term guarantee appears in a different fashion; cf. Arusha Agreement (2000) (Burundi), containing a separate protocol (Protocol V) on Guarantees on the implementation of the Agreement (2000), though the facilitator is mentioned as 'moral guarantor' (art. 4, Protocol V) and the international community (UN, AU, Regional Peace Initiative for Burundi) participates in the implementation and monitoring

The intermediate degree of involvement (interpretation/implementation) relates to powers delegated to, or shared with international actors regarding the general implementation of the peacebuilding part of a peace agreement, or a peace agreement in general. The language used varies from the international actors being part of a joint committee, which either has the power to authoritatively interpret or arbitrate differences arising out of the peace agreement.[119] It could be argued that the signature of international actors could be tantamount to express acceptance/consent to be bound by the relevant provisions of peace agreements relating to their role as supporters, or enforcers, and thus, sign up to these commitments, in a similar fashion to article 35 of the Vienna Convention on the Law of Treaties,[120] or the Vienna Convention on the Law of Treaties between States and International Organisations or between International Organisations,[121] providing for rights of third parties. On the other side, regarding the third category, in terms of economic or other support, some of the peace agreements', provisions contain a general legal-political appeal to the 'international community' as a whole, or on international organisations and/or friendly states (in the actual text appearing as '*pays amis*') for economic support,[122] and not specific actors; sometimes this is framed rather as the undertaking of the immediate parties to seek support in the future, and thus a commitment between the parties to obtain consent of international actors in the subsequent stages.[123]

committee (arts. 2–3, Protocol V) alongside local representatives; cf. Casamance General Peace Agreement (2004) (Senegal), art. 2, where the words 'guarantee of the accord' appear in art. 2, but the oversight being up to the Surveillance Council, consisting of parties and domestic civil society, not outsiders.

[119] For a good example of a mixture of parties and outsiders, see Global Peace Agreement (2006) (CAR), arts 6 and 9, establishing a mixed oversight commission consisting of both locals and international actors equipped with the power to authoritatively interpret the agreement.

[120] Vienna Convention on the Law of Treaties entered into force 27 January 1980, *UNTS* vol. 1155, p. 331.

[121] Vienna Convention on the Law of Treaties between States and International Organizations or between International Organizations, 21 March 1986, not yet in force, A/CONF.129/15.

[122] See Moroni Accord (2003) (Comoros), Arts. I(4) and VII, Lomé Agreement (1999) (Sierra Leone) arts XXXIII and XXX, Djibouti Agreement (2008) (Somalia), art. 11 and Accord de paix définitive (Ouagadougou II Accord) (1995) (Niger), art. 23.

[123] See Comprehensive Agreement (2008) (Zimbabwe), where the parties shall 'seek the support and assistance of the SADC and the AU in mobilizing the international community to support the new Government's economic recovery plans and programmes together with the lifting of sanctions taken against Zimbabwe and some of its leaders'; see also Global Political Agreement (2006) (Togo), art. 5.4 ('Elles (Les Parties prenantes au Dialogue) demandent en outre à l'Union Européenne et à toute la Communauté Internationale

Whether it is a high (supervision), intermediate (interpretation/implementation), or low (legal-political support) level of engagement, the variety of roles played by international involvement highlights why formal distinctions between parties and third parties to an agreement under treaty law is less applicable in the case of peace agreements. It also shows why self-determination as a general principle has a general relevance in identifying, analysing and interpreting the duties and obligations of international actors.

V. Conclusion

This chapter has attempted to discuss the relevance and the most problematic aspects of self-determination in the transitioning from conflict/crisis to peace. By looking at recent trends in peacemaking and peacebuilding processes in Africa, trends primarily drawn through the study of African intrastate peace agreements, two preliminary remarks can be drawn: first, that self-determination (or its precepts) are increasingly drawn upon in the drafting of African intrastate peace agreements, even if only as a background fact, by providing the standards to be observed during the interim period when a state reconfigures its internal power structures. Internal self-determination standards are used in a subtle manner, in order to enable former hostile groups to be accommodated within existing states, thus, not towards the withering of the state, but towards reconfiguring its power structures and institutions; to this end, 'inclusiveness', 'participation' or the 'will of the people' are used as standards to be benefited and observed by the former warring parties, not only the governments.

Second, however, when it comes to the issue of international involvement in the drafting (peacemaking) and the implementation (peacebuilding) of these agreements, self-determination, though relevant, seems to be articulated in rather general terms. This is to be borne in mind, as self-determination could be of significance when looking at the weakly articulated or sometimes unclear roles of outsiders. The chapter is neither presupposing nor making a claim about the applicability of international law to the entire text of a peace agreement, or all peace agreements, due to the diversity of the inspected materials, and the various forms and levels of engagement (presented here as high,

---

d'apporter un soutien financier et technique au processus engage'); see also Ouagadougou Ceasefire (Ouagadougou I Accord) (1994) (Niger), art. 17.

intermediate, low). Still, self-determination as a general principle of international law can be used to affirm relevant duties for external actors; and, by conceiving of self-determination as a principle, in addition to a right, it can equally assist to identify gaps in obligations/duties. Thus, self-determination has three normative functions: as affirming duties in the case of gaps and silences in the agreements, as interpretive in the case of unclear undertakings, and as evaluative, by being a general standard for appraising international involvement. Thus, even where the precise contours of the rule of self-determination remain uncertain, the principle can nevertheless assist even in the most difficult peace-building processes.

Can religious norms influence self-determination struggles, and with what implications for international law?

KATJA SAMUEL[*]

I. Introduction

Even in the post-decolonization era, unresolved issues and controversies linger regarding the principle of self-determination, not least in terms of its interpretation and reach. This is equally true of those self-determination struggles which the late Cassese termed as being 'external' in nature, which is the focus of the current chapter, in which certain people(s) seek the creation of their own state, often in response to repressive behaviour by the state's governing authorities.[1] Generally, though not necessarily, such struggles involve the use of armed force. This may take the form of activities which are regarded as being 'terrorist' by some, but 'liberating' by others, as is reflected within continuing debates and disagreements concerning the ongoing struggle by the Palestinian people for the creation of a Palestinian state; or it may escalate into an internal and/or international armed conflict in pursuit of secession, as was the case in the former Yugoslavia and Kosovo.

In the context of such struggles, religious norms are sometimes referred to and discussed, normally in an attempt to explain under-pinning motivations for, or to seek to justify, such struggles. However,

---

[*] The issues considered in this chapter were examined in the course of the author's doctoral thesis at Sheffield University, soon to be published as a monograph: K. L. H. Samuel, *The OIC, the UN, and Counter-Terrorism Law-Making: Conflicting or Cooperative Legal Orders?* (Hart, Oxford, 2013).

[1] See, for example, A. Cassese, 'The Self-Determination of Peoples' in L. Henkin (ed.), *The International Bill of Rights: The Covenant on Civil and Political Rights* (Columbia University Press, New York, 1981), p. 111; A. Cassese, *Self-Determination of Peoples: A Legal Reappraisal* (Cambridge University Press, 1995), pp. 90–9, especially pp. 90–1, who first introduced the concepts of 'internal' and 'external' self-determination.

there is far less discussion as to whether, and if so how, such religious norms may in fact be influencing the normative development, interpretation, or application of general self-determination and related principles, at least within the context of some specific struggles. Such relative silence may, at least in part, be attributable to a political unwillingness to openly acknowledge such influences – for example, to refer to the often controversial, and sometimes misunderstood, Islamic principle of *jihad* – especially in the context of multinational relationships.

Nevertheless, the potential influence of certain religious norms on self-determination struggles may be far more than merely aspirational or rhetorical, as this chapter seeks to demonstrate by examining the relationship between comparable international and Islamic principles.[2] Islamic principles have been selected for the purpose of the current discussion because they are currently the most commonly referred to religious norms in the context of external self-determination debates. The primary focus here is on those grounds for external self-determination which are lawful (or at least legitimate) under international and Islamic principles, which are most illustrative of these issues. More specifically, this chapter considers three aspects: the grounds associated with the right to external self-determination in international law; comparable grounds within Islamic *Shari'ah*, especially those provided for by an Islamic conception of justice and the principle of *jihad*; and whether or how identified normative differences existing between them may be reconciled, with what implications for international law principles on self-determination.

II. Grounds for the exercise of the right of self-determination in international law

As was noted at the outset, many aspects of the international law principle of self-determination remain unresolved, or at least disputed.[3] This is equally true of the grounds which may justify the exercise of this

---

[2] It is acknowledged from the outset, however, that there are certain inherent differences between international law and Islamic *Shari'ah*, including with respect to the principles examined here, which mean that an exact comparison is not possible.

[3] For example, the exact status of self-determination movements as the legitimate representatives of any peoples seeking self-determination, and legal consequences of any such legitimating. On such issues, see Cassese, *A Legal Reappraisal*, pp. 166–7, 238–9; H. A. Wilson, *International Law and the Use of Force by National Liberation Movements* (Clarendon Press, Oxford, 1988), pp. 71–5, 104–5; N. Higgins, *Regulating the Use of Force in Wars of National Liberation – The Need for a New Regime: A Study of the South Moluccas and Aceh* (Martinus Nijhoff, Leiden, 2010), pp. 80–3.

right. The current position appears to be as follows. First, as the right was conceived originally in the context of decolonization, it may be exercised when 'peoples' within any state experience alien or colonial subjugation, typically political or economic, which is prohibited under international law.[4] Inherent within this prohibition is the right of colonial peoples to self-determination.[5]

Similarly, because historically alien or colonial subjugation usually involved some form of physical occupation, the right to self-determination includes a ground in response to foreign or alien occupation, especially following unlawful invasion and subsequent occupation.[6] These grounds are the most commonly relied upon in the context of ongoing external self-determination struggles, not least with respect to the continuing struggle of the Palestinian people against the state of Israel for the creation of a Palestinian state. Significantly, the currency of these grounds[7] was reaffirmed by the International Court of Justice (ICJ) in its Advisory Opinion on the *Legal Consequences of the Construction of a Wall*, in which it found that the right of the Palestinian people to exercise the right to self-determination is sourced now in the fact of occupation, of which foreign domination or subjugation is a direct consequence, rather than in historic colonialism.[8]

---

[4] Cassese, 'The Self-Determination of Peoples', p. 111; R. Higgins, *Problems and Process: International Law and How We Use It* (Oxford University Press, 1994), p. 115; Separate Opinion of Judge Higgins, *Legal Consequences of the Construction of a Wall in the Occupied Palestinian Territory* (*Legal Consequences of the Wall* Advisory Opinion) [2004] ICJ Rep. 136, 214.

[5] *Legal Consequences for States of the Continued Presence of South Africa in Namibia (South West Africa) notwithstanding Security Council Resolution 276 (1970)* (Advisory Opinion) [1971] ICJ Rep. 16, 119 (*Namibia* Advisory Opinion); *Western Sahara* (Advisory Opinion) [1975] ICJ Rep. 12, 31–2.

[6] Higgins, *Problems and Process*, pp. 113–15; V. Lowe, 'The Principle of Non-Intervention: Use of Force' in V. Lowe and C. Warbrick (eds), *The United Nations and the Principles of International Law: Essays in Memory of Michael Akehurst* (Routledge, London, 1994), p. 114; R. Pails, 'Self-Determination, the Use of Force and International Law: An Analytical Framework' (2002) 20 *University of Tasmania LR* 70, 73, 79; Cassese, *A Legal Reappraisal*, pp. 90–9, especially pp. 90–1.

[7] See, too, for example, Preamble to the UN Global Counter-Terrorism Strategy, UNGA Res. 60/288 (8 September 2008) UN Doc. A/RES/60/288, which reaffirms 'the right to self-determination of peoples which remain under colonial domination or foreign occupation'.

[8] J.-F. Gareau, 'Shouting at the Wall: Self-Determination and the Legal Consequences of the Construction of a Wall in the Occupied Palestinian Territory' (2005) 18 *Leiden JIL* 489, 504–5.

It is also possible that additional grounds may be developing which are triggered by different forms of oppressive, discriminatory, humiliating and/or tyrannical treatment. Most notably here, in the *Kosovo* Advisory Opinion,[9] Judge Trindade delivered a Separate Opinion in which he suggested that:

> In the current evolution of international law, international practice (of States and of international organizations) provides support for the exercise of self-determination by peoples under permanent adversity or systematic repression, beyond the traditional confines of the historical process of decolonization. Contemporary international law is no longer insensitive to patterns of systematic oppression and subjugation.[10]

Therefore, he suggested that '[t]he principle of self-determination applies in new situations of systematic oppression, subjugation and tyranny',[11] as well as to discrimination and humiliation, which are contrary to human rights principles, including those of the Universal Declaration on Human Rights 1948.[12] Although these are not believed to be established grounds for the exercise of external self-determination at this time, if they are on such a normative course, they may become significant in the future in mitigating some of the issues of conflict between comparable international and Islamic principles identified below.

1. External self-determination struggles involving the use of force

Despite the existence of the right to external self-determination in certain circumstances, it does not necessarily follow that forcible measures may be employed in the exercise of that right. Indeed, any use of force by non-state actors, which includes by those engaged in self-determination struggles, remains contentious within international law and politics, evident in the context of terrorism law-making and the continued inability of the international community to agree a universal definition of terrorism.[13]

---

[9] *Accordance with International Law of the Unilateral Declaration of Independence in Respect of Kosovo* (Advisory Opinion) [2010] ICJ Rep. 1 (*Kosovo* Advisory Opinion). For a critique of this opinion see, for example, R. Falk, 'The *Kosovo* Advisory Opinion: Conflict Resolution and Precedent' (2011) 105 *AJIL* 50.
[10] *Kosovo* Advisory Opinion, para. 184.   [11] Ibid., para. 175.   [12] Ibid., para. 208.
[13] Cassese, *A Legal Reappraisal*, including at pp. 153–4, 160, 194–5, 198; M. Halberstam, 'The Evolution of the United Nations Position on Terrorism: From Exempting National Liberation Movements to Criminalizing Terrorism Wherever and by Whomever Committed' (2003) 41 *Columbia JTL* 573.

Two principal, and opposing camps, persist: those states which distinguish between non-state actors engaged in legitimate forcible self-determination struggles and unlawful terrorist actors (this camp is comprised largely of former colonized African and Asian nations, many of which are Member States of the Organisation of Islamic Cooperation (OIC, formerly the Organisation of the Islamic Conference)), and (former) socialist countries; and those which oppose any such legitimation or distinction. Cassese suggested that the current legal position is that self-determination movements:

> ... although they do not possess a *legal right* to enforce their substantive right to self-determination by resort to war, nevertheless have a *legal licence* to do so ... wars for self-determination are not ignored by international law, or left in a legal vacuum as being outside the realm of law *qua* mere factual occurrences. Rather, legal rules take these wars into account, without however upgrading them to the status of manifestations of *jus ad bellum* proper.[14]

In particular, he argued that recourse to forcible measures is invoked when the right to self-determination is denied by forcible means.[15] While all may not support this contention, and despite ongoing broader disagreement on these matters, importantly for the current purposes the UN General Assembly has affirmed the possibility of using forcible measures in the context of self-determination when the grounds of alien or foreign subjugation, domination and exploitation;[16] colonialism;[17] racist regimes;[18] and/or foreign occupation[19] are present.

---

[14] Cassese, *A Legal Reappraisal*, pp. 153–4; similarly pp. 160, 198.

[15] Ibid.; B. Saul, *Defining Terrorism in International Law* (Oxford University Press, 2006), p. 37. For a contrary view see, for example, Halberstam, 'The Evolution of the United Nation's Position on Terrorism', 573.

[16] 'Declaration on the Granting of Independence to Colonial Countries and Peoples', UNGA Res. 1514 (XV) (14 December 1960), para. 1, similarly paras 2 and 4.

[17] UNGA Res 2105 (XX) (20 December 1965) UN Doc. A/RES/20/2105. See, too, 'Declaration on Principles of International Law concerning Friendly Relations and Co-operation among States in accordance with the Charter of the United Nations', UNGA Res. 2625 (XXV) (24 October 1970), para. 1, section on principle of self-determination, which reaffirmed the legitimacy of self-determination struggles by both colonial peoples and peoples under alien domination.

[18] See, for example, UNGA Res. 2787 (XXVI) (6 December 1971) UN Doc. A/RES/26/2787, para. 4.

[19] See especially, UNGA Res. 42/159 (7 December 1987) UN Doc. A/RES/42/159, para. 14; UNGA Res. 44/29 (9 December 1989) UN Doc. A/RES/44/29, para. 17; UNGA Res. 46/51 (9 December 1991) UN Doc. A/RES/46/51, para. 6 (which endorsed colonialism, racism, alien occupation or domination, and foreign occupation as legitimate grounds);

III. The potential relevance of religious norms on external self-determination struggles

Within Islamic *Shari'ah*, there are two principles which are of particular significance to determining the grounds which may legitimate external self-determination struggles, namely, *jihad* and justice. Each will be considered in turn, before illustrating these grounds in practice through a brief survey of related OIC practice.

1. Islamic principle of jihad

Any detailed examination of the complex and often controversial principle of *jihad* is beyond the scope of the current chapter. Briefly stated, much disagreement exists, including within Islamic scholarship, regarding its exact nature, scope and accompanying obligations, especially between classical and more contemporary, liberal approaches.[20] The focus here is on the 'lesser *jihad*' prescribed under Islamic *Shari'ah*,[21] which is concerned with the individual or collective struggle by Muslims to defend their religion, community,[22] or territory, and is generally (although not necessarily) synonymous with war.[23] In particular, the collective duty (*fard kifāyah*) to respond when certain grounds exist is of significance to the current discussion. Mahmoudi summarizes these obligations in the following terms:

> One important issue with particular bearing on the contemporary application of the term *jihâd* is that when *jihâd* is in pure self-defence, every Muslim man or woman has an individual obligation to participate: it is an eternal, undisputable and predominant obligation for all Muslims to

and para. 15. However, the exact meaning and scope of these grounds remain ambiguous, e.g. 'racist regimes' and 'alien occupation' – Wilson, *International Law*, pp. 167–8.

[20] D. Feirahi, 'Norms of War in Shia Islam' in V. Popovski, G. M. Reichberg and N. Turner (eds), *World Religions and Norms of War* (United Nations University Press, Tokyo, 2009), p. 256; S. Mahmoudi, 'The Islamic Perception of the Use of Force in the Contemporary World' (2005) 7 *Journal of the History* of IL 55, 56.

[21] The 'greater *jihad*' is concerned with the personal, constant and eternal struggle of individual Muslim believers with the evil and immoral aspects of self – Feirahi, 'Norms of War', 256.

[22] This duty includes helping the weak and the oppressed, even if this means going to war on their behalf – M. A. Haleem, 'Human Rights in Islam and the United Nations Instruments' in E. Cotran and A. O. Sherif (eds), *Democracy, the Rule of Law and Islam* (Kluwer Law International, The Hague, 1999), p. 435.

[23] Feirahi, 'Norms of War', 256. Similarly, see A. Sonbol, 'Norms of War in Sunni Islam' in Popovski, Reichberg and Turner (eds), *World Religions and Norms of War*, p. 282.

participate in a defensive *jihâd*.[24] For other uses of force, *i.e.*, liberating wars, Muslims have a collective obligation: everyone should be ready to join the war when the commanders deem it necessary.[25]

More specifically, this chapter focuses on those grounds associated with defensive *jihad*,[26] which is concerned with protecting Muslim believers.[27] Although this may take different non-forcible forms, including political, social, economic and religious measures, it also includes the possibility of forcible responses.[28] With respect to the military aspect of *jihad*, the approach of much of contemporary scholarship is to adopt interpretative approaches to this principle which effectively equate it with international law rules governing the use of force and self-defence under Articles 2(4) and 51 United Nations (UN) Charter,[29] often arguing in the process that no (significant) conflict or incompatibility exists between corresponding UN and Islamic norms. Furthermore, and of especial relevance here, such commentators argue that any references to *jihad* by Islamic states are largely *motivational* in religious rather than military or legal terms.[30] However, as an examination of those grounds triggering the right to *jihad* reveal, important

---

[24] Mahmoudi, 'The Islamic Perception', 59. [25] Ibid., 60.

[26] Depending on the interpretative approaches adopted, *jihad* may also be defensive and/or offensive in nature – see, for example, ibid., 57, 60.

[27] N. A. Shah, *Self-defense in Islamic and International Law: Assessing Al-Qaeda and the Invasion of Iraq* (Palgrave Macmillan, New York, 2008), p. 24, referring to S. Abu al-A'la al-Mawdudi, *Al-Jihad Fil-Islam* (Urdu) (Islamic Publications, Lahore, 1996), pp. 53–82, who argued in favour of both defensive and offensive *jihad*.

[28] See, for example, R. Ridā, 'Patriotism, Nationalism, and Group Spirit in Islam' in J. J. Donohue and J. L. Esposito (eds), *Islam in Transition: Muslim Perspectives* (2nd edn, Oxford University Press, New York, 2007), p. 42.

[29] See, for example, A. Abou-el-Wafa, 'Contributions of Islam to the Development of a Global Community Based on Rules of International Law' in R. St. J. Macdonald and D. M. Johnston (eds), *Towards World Constitutionalism: Issues in the Legal Ordering of the World Community* (Martinus Nijhoff, Leiden, 2005), pp. 340–1; S. Sardar Ali, 'Resurrecting *Siyar* through *Fatwas*? (Re) Constructing "Islamic International Law" in Post-(Iraq) Invasion World' (2009) 14 *JCSL* 115, 127; more generally on such approaches, see Mahmoudi, 'The Islamic Perception'. Some develop this further to reject any notion of offensive *jihad*: Shah, *Self Defense*, p. 31; S. Mahmassani, 'The Principles of International Law in the Light of Islamic Doctrine' (1966) 117 *Recueil des Cours* 201, 280; Sheikh Wahbeh al-Zuhili, 'Islam and International Law' (2005) 87 *IRRC* 269, 271.

[30] Mahmoudi, 'The Islamic Perception', 60, 63. Others have suggested that such references are sometimes used secularly to simply refer to the use of force in international law, for example, H. M. Zawati, *Is Jihād a Just War? War, Peace and Human Rights under Islamic and Public International Law* (The Edwin Mellen Press, Lewiston, 2001), p. 13; R. Peters, *Islam and Colonialism: The Doctrine of Jihad in Modern History* (Mouton Publishers, The Hague, 1979), p. 4.

and not easily reconcilable differences exist between those international and Islamic grounds which may trigger the legitimate exercise of the right to external self-determination. Indeed, as one commentator has observed, prominent Sunni and Shi'a scholars often define their conception of 'legitimate use of war' in far wider terms than a formal interpretation of international law.[31]

1.1.   Grounds existing within the principle of *jihad*

A number of grounds exist within the principle of *jihad* which may evoke the collective duty to respond to assist other members of the Islamic *ummah*[32] in an external self-determination context.

As a starting point, it would appear that each of the international law grounds identified previously – alien or foreign subjugation, domination and exploitation, colonialism, racist regimes and foreign occupation – are incorporated within the wide-ranging concept of 'liberating' *jihad* referred to in Mahmoudi's quotation just cited. This concept requires a collective response to the suffering of Muslims under any form of oppressive political regimes. Not only would this incorporate such grounds as alien or foreign subjugation, domination and exploitation, but it has been explicitly invoked in the context of colonial oppression (especially political, economic, cultural and social[33]) also.[34] Similarly, any regimes which are racist or even discriminatory towards Muslims – for example, in a context of foreign occupation, or non-Muslim governments towards Muslim minorities – could fall within this principle's scope.

The concept of 'liberating' *jihad* has been referred to also in the context of alien or foreign occupation by non-Muslims of any territories considered to be Muslim,[35] which has been described as 'the most unequivocal example of *jihad*' by both classical and modern Islamic scholars.[36] The measures taken may be pacific or forcible in nature depending upon the particular circumstances, and are considered to be

---

[31] Mahmoudi, 'The Islamic Perception', 60.

[32] Haleem,'Human Rights in Islam', p. 435.

[33] Mahmoudi, 'The Islamic Perception', 58.

[34] See, for example, H. Moinuddin, *The Charter of the Islamic Conference and Legal Framework of Economic Cooperation among its Member States* (Clarendon Press, Oxford, 1987), p. 32; Peters, *Islam and Colonialism* (this is the theme of the whole book); S. H. Hashmi, 'Is There an Islamic Ethic of Humanitarian Intervention?' in A. F. Lang, Jr (ed.), *Just Intervention* (Georgetown University Press, Washington DC, 2003), pp. 69–70.

[35] Abou-El-Wafa, 'Contributions of Islam', p. 342.

[36] Hashmi, 'Is There an Islamic Ethic?', p. 69.

defensive *jihad* to liberate the oppressed.[37] Furthermore, each of these grounds would most probably be included within the general religious duty to protect and defend those who are helpless and unable to protect themselves in the face of any aggression.[38] Related responses may take the form of the Muslim *ummah* responding collectively to assist them, or the physical removal of those people being oppressed from the territory (*hijra*).[39]

So far, the grounds existing within both international and Islamic law appear to be largely comparable and compatible. Hereinafter, however, there are important differences. In particular, the extended grounds which exist within *jihad* reflect those additional grounds referred to by Judge Trindade in the ICJ's *Kosovo* Advisory Opinion of oppressive, discriminatory, humiliating and/or tyrannical behaviour, upon which international consensus does not yet exist. For example, while the concept of aggression exists as a ground for *jihad*,[40] it has a much wider scope here than the corresponding concept in international law, especially under Article 51 UN Charter. Significantly, the existence or imminence of an armed attack is not a prerequisite for its invocation,[41] nor is any distinction made between internal or external sources of aggression.[42] Instead, the commission of non-forcible acts of injustice and oppression against Muslim believers and property, or where the Islamic religion is being threatened,[43] may be sufficient to cross the aggression threshold for the purpose of *jihad*. Nor is the actual occupation of any territory considered to be Muslim required before forcible measures may be used; rather, circumstances falling short of this, such as the expulsion of Muslim or other helpless people from their homes, may suffice.[44]

There are other grounds which go beyond those of international law also, namely, the duty upon the Islamic *ummah*: to protect the Muslim community, which extends to any breakdown of public order;[44] to defend

---

[37] Mahmoudi, 'The Islamic Perception', 58.

[38] Sonbol, 'Norms of War', p. 289, referring to the *Qur'an* 4:75.

[39] Hashmi, 'Is There an Islamic Ethic', p. 69.

[40] See, for example, Shah, *Self-defense*, pp. 15–16.

[41] See, for example, Mahmoudi, 'The Islamic Perception', 56–7; Mahmassani, 'The Principles of International Law', 280, 282, 286; Zawati, *Is Jihād a Just War?*, pp. 20–1; Shah, *Self-defense*, pp. 15–16; A. A. Kurdi, *The Islamic State: A Study based on the Islamic Holy Constitution* (Mansell Publishing Ltd, London, 1984), p. 100; Abou-El-Wafa, 'Contributions of Islam', pp. 341–2; Sonbol, 'Norms of War', p. 289.

[42] Ibid., p. 288.   [43] Ibid.; Shah, *Self-defense*, pp. 15–16.

[44] Mahmoudi, 'The Islamic Perception', 56; Mahmassani, 'The Principles of International Law', 279–80, 282.

freedom of religious belief for all humanity,[45] especially the preservation of the Islamic faith and community;[46] to respond where Muslims are persecuted because of their Islamic beliefs and are unable to defend themselves;[47] and to defend Muslim places of worship where these are being destroyed, for example, during foreign occupation or expulsion.[48] It is not difficult to see how many, if not all, of these grounds may be considered to exist, at least by some members of the Islamic *ummah*, in relation to ongoing external self-determination situations like the Palestinian struggle, and the continued presence and operations of non-Muslim military forces and political entities within, inter alia, Afghanistan.[49]

2. Islamic principle of justice

Brief mention must be made here also of the Islamic principle of justice (*adl*)[50] and its reinforcing relationship with the principle of *jihad*. The notion of justice underpins both international and Islamic law, and the development of their respective norms. That said, an international conception of justice does not compare with the depth, breadth, scope or significance of Islamic justice. As Zemanek has observed, a concept such as justice may only be understood in a meaningful way within the specific legal order in which it operates.[51]

Islamic justice is an absolute right at the heart of the Qur'an[52] and a primary objective of its revelation.[53] Consequently, it has been described as 'the supreme and overarching value of Islam, integrating all spheres of

---

[45] Mahmoudi, 'The Islamic Perception', 56; Mahmassani, 'The Principles of International Law', 280, 282–4; al-Zuhili, 'Islam and International Law', 281; Sonbol, 'Norms of War', p. 289.

[46] Abou-El-Wafa, 'Contributions of Islam', pp. 340–1; Zawati, *Is Jihād a Just War?*, pp. 20–1; Mahmassani, 'The Principles of International Law', 283–4.

[47] Shah, *Self-defense*, pp. 15–16; Moinuddin, *The Charter of the Islamic Conference*, p. 32. See, too, Mahmassani, The Principles of Islamic Laws', 279–80, 285; al-Zuhili, 'Islamic and International Law', 281; Sonbol, 'Norms of War', pp. 288–9.

[48] Sonbol, 'Norms of War', p. 289.

[49] Formerly, too, in Iraq, between the military intervention by US-led troops in 2003, until the withdrawal of US troops in December 2011.

[50] The Islamic word '*adl*' means justice in the sense of being fair, balanced and neutral (*Qur'an* 6:152). On the characteristics of justice, see, too, Z. Iqbal, *Justice: Islamic and Western Perspectives* (The Islamic Foundation, Leicester, 2007), p. 31.

[51] K. Zemanek, 'Basic Principles of UN Chapter Law' in Macdonald and Johnston(eds), *Towards World Constitutionalism*. See, too, Higgins, Separate Opinion, 221 on the importance of context.

[52] See, for example, the *Qur'an* 4:58, 5:8.

[53] Haleem, 'Human Rights in Islam', 436, who refers to the *Qur'an* 57:25.

life within one coherent moral and legal framework, or system',[54] attributable to the fact that 'God says in the Quran that He has created the
whole universe, its creatures and everything in it in conformity with the
principles of justice'.[55] As such, it possesses constitutional qualities
which have been described as 'an inviolable aspect of law beyond
human intervention within the Islamic legal system'.[56]

There are two characteristics of Islamic justice which are especially
important to the current discussion. The first concerns the normative
relationship existing between differing international and Islamic grounds
for self-determination, as identified in the previous section. In particular,
Islamic justice is believed to be superior to any other kind of justice, not
least in terms of the substantive content of law norms:[57] 'Islamic justice is
something higher than the formal justice of Roman law or any other
human law. . ... It searches out the innermost motives, because we are to
act as in the presence of Allah, to whom all things, acts, and motives are
known.'[58] Consequently, in the event of any normative incompatibilities
or conflicts existing between Islamic and other norms, an Islamic conception of justice suggests that the former must prevail over the latter.
Certainly, Article IV(e) Universal Islamic Declaration of Human Rights
1981 (UIDHR) states that '[i]t is the right and duty of every Muslim to
refuse to obey any command which is contrary to the [Shari'ah] Law, no
matter by whom it may be issued.'[59]

The other key characteristic of Islamic justice relates to its accompanying religious obligations upon the Islamic *ummah*[60] to ensure

[54] G. Krämer, 'Justice in Modern Islamic Thought' in A. Amanat and F. Griffel (eds),
Shari'a: Islamic Law in the Contemporary Context (Stanford University Press, 2007),
pp. 27–9.
[55] S. Dayf, 'Introduction' in Islamic Educational, Scientific and Cultural Organization
('ISESCO'), *The Universality of Islam* (ISESCO, Rabat 1997) www.isesco.org.
ma/english/publications/The%20University%20of%20Islam/p2.php, last accessed 8
April 2012.
[56] Krämer, 'Justice in Modern Islamic Thought', p. 28, referring to the views of the
Egyptian scholar, Farīd 'Abd al-Khāliq.
[57] Ibid., p. 30.
[58] A. R. I. Doi, *Shari'ah: The Islamic Law* (A S Noordeen, Kuala Lumpur, 2007), pp. 3, 5.
[59] Available at www.alhewar.com/ISLAMDECL.html, last accessed 8 April 2012. Although
the UIDHR was an initiative of the Islamic Council rather than OIC, it received support
and input from a number of influential OIC Member States.
[60] This concept refers to the universal community of Muslim believers. See further,
S. S. Khan, *Reasserting International Islam: A Focus on the Organisation of Islamic
Conference and Other Islamic Institutions* (Oxford University Press, 2001), pp. 2–4;

and safeguard such rights also.[61] In particular, a primary requirement of Islamic justice is for Muslims to respond to any oppression, injustice or humiliation being experienced by Muslim individuals and society, such as perceived domination or subordination, and to release them from it.[62] This is a divine and unequivocal religious command, because the *Qur'an* prohibits tolerating injustice,[63] requiring the response of believers as an expression of their faith,[64] for which they will receive eternal judgment (rewards or punishment) for their actions or failures.[65] In order to fully comprehend the gravity of this duty, any acceptance of, or failure to respond to, the mistreatment of Muslims by other members of the Islamic *ummah* is considered in the *Qur'an* to be more serious than the physical slaughter of fellow believers.[66]

Such religious obligations to oppose any form of oppression, injustice or humiliation of Muslim believers makes the relationship between Islamic justice and the principles of *jihad* self-evident,[67] not least in terms of the collective duty which exists upon the Islamic *ummah* to respond. Indeed, the influential Islamic classical scholar, al-Mawdudi, explicitly linked Islamic justice with *jihad* when arguing that the requirements of justice authorized the use of force in relation to, inter alia, defensive *jihad*.[68]

A. al-Ahsan, *Ummah or Nation? Identity Crisis in Contemporary Muslim Society* (The Islamic Foundation, Leicester, 1992).

[61] See Iqbal, *Justice*, pp. 37, 49.

[62] Kurdi, *The Islamic State*, pp. 48–9; A.U. Jan, 'The Limits of Tolerance' in J. Cohen and I. Lague (eds), *The Place of Tolerance in Islam: Khaled Abou El Fadl* (Beacon Press, Boston, 2002), p. 45.

[63] See, for example, ibid., pp. 48–9; M. Rizvi, 'Intolerable Injustices' in Cohen and Lague (eds), ibid., p. 70.

[64] *Qur'an* 4:75.   [65] Kurdi, *The Islamic State*, pp. 48–9, referring to the *Qur'an* 16:90.

[66] See, for example, Jan, 'The Limits of Tolerence', pp. 48–9; Rizvi, 'Intolerable Injustices', p. 70.

[67] For such a link see, for example, O. A. A. Abouzeid, 'The Policy of the Organization of the Islamic Conference Towards International Issues that Concern the Islamic World' in M. El S. Selim (ed.), *The Organisation of the Islamic Conference in a Changing World* (Center for Political Research and Studies, Cairo University, 1994), pp. 63–4; A. ibn Naqib al-Misri, *Reliance of the Traveller: A Classic Manual of Islamic Sacred Law*, trans. and ed. N. H. M. Keller (Amana, Beltsville, MA, 1991, 1994 rev.), pp. 578–9, 594–605, which locates issues of *jihad* under the overall heading of 'justice'.

[68] S. Abu al-A'la al-Mawdudi, *The Islamic Movement: Dynamics of Values, Power and Change*, trans. and ed. K. Murad (Islamic Foundation, Leicester, 1984), pp. 38–9, 41.

3. OIC practice

The grounds which exist under the principles of *jihad* and Islamic justice are not confined to theory or history, which is illustrated by recent and current OIC[69] practice in external self-determination contexts.

More generally, the OIC has regularly referred to, and affirmed the legitimacy of, self-determination struggles in terms of colonial or alien domination,[70] racism[71] and oppression by foreign occupation,[72] together with exhorting the collective responsibility of the Islamic *ummah* to respond to such situations.[73] Significantly, it has also explicitly and implicitly affirmed the application of the principle of *jihad*, and its related grounds, to such situations, not least in terms of considering related struggles by the Islamic *ummah* to be 'sanctioned by all divine laws, human values and international conventions'.[74]

The relevance and influence of *jihad* and Islamic justice have been most pronounced in the context of the ongoing Palestinian struggle against Israel for the creation of a Palestinian state, with Jerusalem as its capital.[75] This was especially evident in the OIC's related practice

---

[69] Created in 1969, the OIC is the largest Islamic inter-governmental organization with a membership of 56 internationally recognised states, in addition to treating Palestine as a sovereign state. It is a useful starting point for analysis of state or institutional practice on Islamic norms, upon which much of its OIC Charter 2008 is premised, due to its heterogeneous nature which is uniquely representative of the diversity within the Islamic *ummah*. See, further, Khan, *Reasserting International Islam*, C. Mallat, *Introduction to Middle Eastern Law* (Oxford University Press, 2007), pp. 129, 131, 135–8; and the OIC's official website, www.oic-oci.org, last accessed 8 April 2012.

[70] The OIC has also sought to equate all forms of colonialism with acts of aggression. See, for example, 7th Islamic Summit (1994), Final Communiqué, para. 101; 8th Islamic Summit (1997), para. 80; 9th Islamic Summit (2000) Res. 39/9-P(IS), para. 1; Article 11 (b) Cairo Declaration on Human Rights 1990.

[71] During the 1980s, the OIC not only affirmed the legitimacy of the struggles by South Africans and Namibians, but also of the use of 'every means at their disposal, including armed struggle, to free themselves from colonial, domination, racist, oppression and apartheid', 4th Islamic Summit (1984), Res. 11/4-P(IS), Preamble, para. 4. Similarly, 5th Islamic Summit (1987), Res. 12/5-P(IS), paras. 1, 18.

[72] Article 1(4) OIC Charter 2008 affirms the OIC's 'support [of] the restoration of complete sovereignty and territorial integrity of any Member State under occupation, as a result of aggression'.

[73] For example, Article 1(2) OIC Charter 2008.

[74] 'International Terrorism of all Types and Forms', 5th Islamic Summit (1987), Res. 19/5-P (IS), Preamble. Similarly, see, 'Declaration of Holy Jihad', 3rd Islamic Summit (1981), Res. 5/3-P(IS), Preamble.

[75] Such support has always been a specific OIC objective, as reflected within Article 1(8) OIC Charter.

between the 1980s and early 1990s when the UN General Assembly's Membership was at its most supportive of armed self-determination struggles.[76] For example, in 1987, the OIC linked the 'Jihad for the liberation of Al-Quds [Jerusalem]', with the accompanying 'individual religious obligation on all Muslims . . . . . and a duty imposed by Islamic Fraternity, for the vindication of right and the removal of evil'.[77] Similarly, it endorsed the right of the Palestine Liberation Organization (PLO) to 'struggle militarily, politically and, by any other means, [in order] to liberate their occupied territories, secure the inalienable national rights of the Palestinian people . . . . . ',[78] exhorting its Membership to support the PLO's activities, including through the provision of military expertise and equipment.[79]

Although such explicit references were largely discontinued after the OIC's 6th Islamic Summit in 1991 – reflecting the changing approach of the UN General Assembly towards the increased criminalization of such struggles[80] – the substantive content of OIC resolutions regarding the Palestinian struggle and liberation of Jerusalem have continued to reflect the grounds and collective duty inherent within *jihad* as previously described. For example, during the 1st Intifada (1987–93) involving violent resistance by the Palestinian people against continued Israeli repressive measures and its occupation of the Gaza Strip and the West Bank: 'The Conference affirmed its active solidarity and total support for the just struggle of the valiant Palestinian people, under the leadership of the Palestine Liberation Organisation, their sole legitimate representative and saluted with great pride the blessed Intifada of the Palestinian people against Israeli occupation.'[81] Similarly, the OIC endorsed what it considered to be the 'heroic and valiant' 2nd Al-Aqsa Intifada (since 2000),[82] despite the

---

[76] On such themes, see, for example, Higgins, referring to UNGA Res. 36/103 (9 December 1981) UN Doc. A/RES/36/103, Part III(b).

[77] For example, 5th Islamic Summit (1987), Res. 2/5-P(IS), para. 2.

[78] 3rd Islamic Summit (1981), Res. 2/3-P(IS), para. 2. Similarly, see 5th Islamic Summit (1987), Res. 1/5-P(IS), para. 16.

[79] For example, 4th ICFM (1973), Res. 1/4, para. 5. See, too, Abouzeid, 'The Policy of the Organization of the Islamic Conference', p. 70; Al-Ahsan, 'Ummah or Nation?', p. 118.

[80] Since 1994, the UN General Assembly has adopted a stance of silence on the issue of the use of force by self-determination movements. See further Higgins, *Regulating the Use of Force*, pp. 70–1; Saul, *Defining Terrorism*, pp. 201–3.

[81] 6th Islamic Summit (1991), Final Communiqué, para. 26.

[82] 9th Islamic Summit (2000), Final Communiqué, para. 17; 9th Islamic Summit (2000), Declaration on the Al Aqsa Intifada, which refers also to the 'legitimate Intifada of the Palestinian people'.

utilization of terrorist methods which have included the deliberate targeting of Israeli civilians.[83]

Those wider aspects of 'liberating' *jihad* described in the previous section have been evident within OIC practice also. In particular, the OIC considers that the 'cause of Palestine and Al-Quds Al-Sharif [Jerusalem] takes priority over all other questions for all Muslims', which includes the protection and liberation of its holy sites,[84] not least in terms of the collective duty of the *ummah* to respond.[85] Jerusalem is of particular religious significance to the Islamic *ummah*, who consider it to be its third most holy city.[86] Consequently, its 'liberation' has been and remains a fundamental objective, especially to the OIC and its Membership, whether through military means (as referred to earlier),[87] or by other non-military means, for example, exhorting an Islamic boycott against Israel in response to its declaration in 1980 to make Jerusalem its capital.[88]

Similarly, the OIC has been supportive of various secession claims by Muslims, for example those of Muslim-dominated Bosnia, following its referendum on 29 February 1992 during which 75 per cent of the population voted in favour of independence; and of Kosovo when it declared its independence on 17 February 2008.[89] Whilst the exact basis for this political and diplomatic support (which may constitute an expression of defensive *jihad*) is not explicit,[90] it is quite probable (and also implicit within its rhetoric) that the OIC regarded the threshold of several Islamic grounds governing the exercise of self-determination (especially 'liberating' *jihad*) to have been crossed, particularly following Serbian aggression (with external support) towards Bosnian-Muslims

---

[83] C. Herzog (updated by S. Gazit), *The Arab-Israeli Wars* (Greenhill Books/Lionel Leventhal, London, 2005), pp. 427–35.

[84] For example, 5th Islamic Summit (1987), Res. 2/5-P(IS), para. 2. Similarly, 11th Islamic Summit (2008), Res. 1/11-PAL(IS), para. 1.

[85] 6th Islamic Summit (1990), Final Communiqué, para. 26; 9th Islamic Summit (2000), Res. 1/9-P(IS), para. 4.

[86] N. A. Baba, *OIC: Theory and Practice in Pan-Islamic Cooperation* (Oxford University Press, Karachi, 1994), p. 54.

[87] For example, in 1972 the OIC decided to create a 'Palestine Fund' to assist in the liberation of Jerusalem (Al-Quds) (3rd ICFM (1972), Res. 2/3, para. 5), which is now the 'Al-Quds Fund'.

[88] 3rd Islamic Summit (1981), Res. 2/3-P(IS), para. 1. Similarly, for example, 10th Islamic Summit (2003), Res. 1/10-PAL(IS), para. 23.

[89] 11th Islamic Summit (2008), Final Communiqué, para. 63.

[90] See, for example, Khan, *Reasserting International Islam*, pp. 127–34 who suggests that OIC motivations for such interventions included its concern for the security of the Islamic *ummah*.

subsequent to the 1992 referendum,[91] and the mistreatment of the Muslim Kosovar people prior to the declaration of independence.[92] Additionally, there were other forms of oppression of believers, accompanied by various attacks (physical or otherwise) against the Islamic religion, its holy places, cultural heritage and identity.

IV.   Conflicting international and Islamic self-determination principles

It is apparent that while many similarities exist between comparable international and Islamic principles governing self-determination, significant and not easily reconcilable differences exist too, specifically in relation to those grounds which may trigger external self-determination struggles.

Two issues are believed to be of particular importance here: whether, and if so how, such identified differences may be reconciled as essentially conflicting norms; and the implications upon international law norms/ practices if they cannot be.

1.   The concept and existence of conflicting norms

Inherent within any conflict between two sets of norms is the notion of actual or potential breach, violation, incompatibility, or inconsistency existing between them.[93] As Pauwelyn notes, such conflicts are an inevitable and inherent aspect of any system of law.[94] Two possible outcomes of any such conflict, which are of potential relevance to the current examination, are that one norm (or one legal order) prevails over the other (if it is not found to be illegal), or both norms

---

[91] 7th Islamic Summit, Final Communiqué, para. 179, and Declaration on Bosnia and Herzegovina, Preamble (which affirmed the OIC's solidarity with the 'just Bosnian cause'); 8th Islamic Summit, Final Communiqué, para. 66, which 'strongly condemned the large-scale repression, discrimination and violation of human rights against the defenseless Albanian population committed by the authorities of the Federal Republic of Yugoslavia (Serbia and Montenegro)'.

[92] For example, the OIC 'called on the United Nations to defend the right of Kosovars to self-determination and to protect their cultural heritage and Islamic identity' (9th Islamic Summit (2000), Final Communiqué, para. 45).

[93] J. Pauwelyn, *Conflict of Norms in Public International Law: How WTO Law Relates to other Rules of International Law* (Cambridge University Press, 2003), pp. 175–6.

[94] Ibid., p. 12. See, too, D. Shelton, 'Normative Hierarchy in International Law' (2006) 100 *AJIL* 291, 322.

are found to be of equal validity.[95] With the exception of peremptory norms, no discernible hierarchy currently exists between the plethora of law-making activities and outputted international law norms generated by states and international organizations,[96] in the absence of any centralized body, with general and compulsory jurisdiction, to adjudicate on the issues of conflicting norms.[97] Therefore, the focus here is on identifying the existence of, and normative relationship between, any peremptory norms inherent within international and Islamic self-determination principles.

1.1   Self-determination as a principle of *jus cogens*

Any principle of *jus cogens* (or peremptory) character is binding upon all political entities, whether states[98] or international organizations[99] and, as such, 'sets out the highest law to which all other norms of international law must conform'.[100] While the exact nature, sources and criteria of these norms are not agreed,[101] a useful starting point is Article 53 Vienna Convention on the Law of Treaties 1969, which states that a peremptory norm is 'a norm accepted and recognised by the international community of States as a whole as a norm from which no derogation is permitted and which can be modified only by a subsequent norm of general international law having the same character'.[102] Therefore, as Orakhelashvili has noted, '[p]eremptory norms prevail not because the States involved have so decided but because they are intrinsically superior and cannot be dispensed with through standard inter-State transactions'.[103] This hierarchy over any other incompatible norms is believed to be premised upon their substance rather than source.[104]

There is general consensus that certain international law principles are peremptory in nature, which include the prohibition against the use of force, subject to the exception of self-defence permitted under Article 51 UN Charter or customary international law; and the right of peoples to

---

[95] Pauwelyn, *Conflict of Norms*, p. 278.   [96] Ibid., p. 13.   [97] Ibid., p. 16.

[98] Ibid., p. 148.   [99] Ibid., p. 324.   [100] Ibid., p. 149.

[101] See, for example, Shelton, 'Normative Hierarchy', 292, 299.

[102] See further, D. Shelton, 'International Law and "Relative Normativity"' in M. D. Evans, *International Law* (3rd edn, Oxford University Press, 2010), pp. 146–7; Pauwelyn, *Conflict of Norms*, p. 98; ILC, 'Documents of the second part of the seventeenth session and of the eighteenth session including the reports of the Commission to the General Assembly' (1966) 2 Yearbook of the ILC, UN Doc. A/CN.4/SER.A/1966/Add.1, 248.

[103] A. Orakhelashvili, *Peremptory Norms in International Law* (Oxford University Press, 2006), p. 8.

[104] Pauwelyn, *Conflict of Norms*, pp. 98, 148.

self-determination as a general principle of international law which, together with some of its accompanying rules of customary international law, has acquired *jus cogens* status[105] with *erga omnes* character.[106] Nevertheless, some interpretative uncertainties remain, not least in terms of the exact content and scope of these principles, for example, as previously mentioned with respect to any use of force by non-state actors in exercise of their right to external self-determination.[107]

1.2 Islamic peremptory norms

While most scholars of international law will be familiar with the notion of *jus cogens*, they may be less familiar with a comparable concept which also exists within Islamic law norms, which is referred to here as 'Islamic peremptory norms'.[108]

Not all Islamic norms are of equal normative force, rather, '*Shari'ah* can take the form of positive law or prescriptive norms and moral exhortations'.[109] Of the five categories of norms which exist, the one of particular significance here is what is obligatory and cannot be ignored (*fard* or *wajib*).[110] Generally, these norms are of an unequivocal and legal[111] nature, with the threat of potential divine sanctions, illustrated

[105] See, for example, Orakhelashvili, *Petemptory Norms*, pp. 50–66; Cassese, *A Legal Reappraisal*, pp. 126–7, 136–40; Wilson, *International Law*, p. 79; *Namibia* Advisory Opinion, 31; *Western Sahara* Advisory Opinion, 31–3.

[106] *Case Concerning East Timor (Portugal v Australia)* (Judgment) [1995] ICJ Rep. 4, 102; *Legal Consequences of the Wall* Advisory Opinion 172, 199. On the *erga omnes* character of the principle and rules on self-determination, see Cassese, *A Legal Reappraisal*, p. 134; Pails, 'Self-determination', 74.

[107] Wilson, *International Law*, pp. 68–9; Pails, 'Self-determination', 74, 83.

[108] Khan uses the term 'peremptory norms' in relation to 'the norms of Islamic divine texts' – L. A. Khan, 'The Immutability of Divine Texts' [2008] *Brigham Young ULR* 807, 872–3. See, too, as one of few explicit examples of state practice, Libya's reservation to Article 2 UN Convention for Elimination of Discrimination against Women 1979, which was made expressly on the grounds of 'peremptory norms of the Islamic Shariah' – CEDAW, 'Other Matters: Declarations, Reservations, Objections and Notifications of Withdrawal of Reservations relating to the Convention on the Elimination of All Forms of Discrimination against Women' (8 February 1996) UN Doc. CEDAW/SP/1996/2, 24, Libyan Arab Jamahiriya reservation, para. 1.

[109] N. Abiad, *Sharia, Muslim States and International Human Rights Treaty Obligations: A Comparative Study* (BIICL, London, 2008), p. xviii.

[110] The other four categories are: what is absolutely prohibited (*haram*); ethical (*mustahab* or *mandūb*); permissive (*mubah*); and abominable (a moral rather than legal wrong) (*makruh*). See M. K. Kamali, *Principles of Islamic Jurisprudence* (3rd edn, The Islamic Texts Society, Cambridge, 2003), pp. 45–6, 413–31.

[111] Ibid., p. 46; International Law Association, 'Draft Report of the Islamic Law and International Law Committee, presented to the Hague Conference' 9 (2010)

by the belief that:[112] '[c]ommitting the *harām* [i.e. what is absolutely prohibited] is punishable and omitting it is rewarded'.[113]

Furthermore, such obligatory norms are believed to be 'peremptory' in character, namely, non-negotiable and prevailing over any incompatible norms as the term is understood within international law, largely attributable to their (quasi-)divine sources (rather than their substantive content as under international law). Briefly stated, any legal principles articulated within the *Qur'an*,[114] as the primary legal source of *Shari'ah*,[115] are 'the highest in the hierarchy of legal norms. They are immutable and cannot be contradicted or modified by rules derived from any of the other sources of the Shari'ah.'[116] Consequently, in contrast to norms of *jus cogens* which may evolve and be replaced by comparable norms of a peremptory nature,[117] many believe that Islamic peremptory norms are of an eternally immutable nature,[118] are non-derogable,[119] and that '[n]o universal text, even if it is derived from the consensus of all non-Muslim states, may revoke or even modify the peremptory norms of the Qur'an and the Prophet's Sunna'.[120]

Of especial relevance to the current examination, the principle of *jihad*, as underpinned by the Islamic principle of justice, is considered to be such an Islamic peremptory norm, reflected within its accompanying collective and individual duties to act in particular circumstances as

(ILA Report), www.ila-hq.org/en/committees/draft-committee-reports-the-hague-2010.cfm, last accessed 8 April 2012, on these categories of norms.

[112] Naqib al-Misri, *Reliance of the Traveller*, pp. 30–1.

[113] Kamali, *Principles of Islamic Jurisprudence*, p. 421.

[114] See J. Rehman, *Islamic State Practices, International Law and the Threat from Terrorism: A Critique of the 'Clash of Civilisations' in the New World Order* (Hart, Oxford, 2005), p. 17; and S. Zubaida, *Law and Power in the Islamic World* (IB Tauris, London, 2003), p. 12, on the legal content of the *Qur'an* and related disputes regarding the exact number of verses with legal content.

[115] For an explanation of the primary and secondary sources of *Shari'ah*, and their religious and normative qualities see, for example, M. C. Bassiouni and G. M. Badr, 'The Shari'ah: Sources, Interpretation, and Rule-Making' (2002) 1 *UCLA J Islamic and Near EL* 135, 152.

[116] Ibid., 149. See, too, generally Khan, 'The Immutability of Divine Texts'.

[117] Article 64 Vienna Convention on the Law of Treaties 1969 states: 'If a new peremptory norm of general international law emerges, any existing treaty which is in conflict with that norm becomes void and terminates.'

[118] C. A. Ford, 'Siyar-ization and Its Discontents: International Law and Islam's Constitutional Crisis' (1995) 30 *Texas ILJ* 499, 525.

[119] Ibid., 523–5.

[120] Khan, 'The Immutability of Divine Texts', 872–3, commenting on Libya's reservation (see n. 108). Presumably, this would include by implication the UN Charter, and its principles governing the use of self-determination and self-defence.

previously described.[121] Indeed, a recent International Law Association Report of the Islamic Law and International Law Committee not only acknowledged the existence of Islamic peremptory norms, but specifically included the principle of *jihad* within its scope.[122]

2. The dilemma of conflicting international and Islamic self-determination principles

From the current analysis, it is evident that some grounds for external self-determination struggles (whether forcible or non-forcible, depending upon the particular prevailing circumstances) exist under Islamic principles which extend beyond those permissible under international law. Amongst them are those triggered by such factors as oppressive, discriminatory, humiliating, persecuting and/or tyrannical behaviour directed against Muslim believers, the Islamic religion and/or places of worship. In turn, this means that there is a lower threshold for responding in self-defence under defensive *jihad* to any acts of aggression, which do not require the imminence or existence of an armed attack, as is the case under Article 51 UN Charter.

The potential resolution of such normative conflicts is further complicated by the fact that both international and Islamic principles underpinning self-determination struggles are considered to be peremptory, and therefore will prevail over any conflicting norms, within their respective legal orders or contexts.[123] This is not generally problematic where their respective norms are the same or comparable; it is, however, normatively significant where marked divergences exist, as is the case here. Indeed, at least some of the extended grounds which exist under Islamic principles – for example, the lower threshold constituting aggression and legitimation of any use of force – are not only in conflict with, but potentially unlawful under, international law.[124]

---

[121] Naqib al-Misri, *Reliance of the Traveller*, p. 600, paras. 9.1 and 9.2 refers to *jihad* being a communal and individual obligation, respectively. See, too, Kamali, *Principles of Islamic Jurisprudence*, p. 415, who identifies the duty to participate in *jihad* as a collective obligation (*wājib kafā'ī*) residing on the Muslim community.

[122] Khan, 'The Immutability of Divine Texts', 872–3; ILA Report, pp. 11–12, which acknowledges that some Islamic principles, specifically *jihad*, are of a peremptory legal character, and describes the law governing *jihad* (*qanun al-qital*) as 'forming part of the *jus cogens* of Islamic international law' (16).

[123] Bassiouni and Badr, 'The Shari'ah', 150 on prevalence of Islamic norms over any conflicting ones. See generally, Ford, 'Siyar-ization'.

[124] For example, some forms of assistance (financial support, training, supply of weapons, intelligence and logistic support) are contrary to the established international law principle of non-intervention in the domestic affairs of another state. See *Case*

3. *Resolving conflict: is it possible?*

At present, there are no clear or definitive guidelines or rules in international law as to how such conflicts – whether between specific norms or legal orders – should be resolved, whether they are norms of a more general or peremptory nature. Therefore, to some extent, their normative status and how any conflicts are resolved are likely to depend, at least to some degree, upon which prism those grounds authorizing self-determination struggles are considered through and operate in: that of international law, in which case norms of *jus cogens* will prevail; or that of Islamic law, where Islamic *Shari'ah* advocates its own primacy[125] and would be offended by the introduction of any man-made law with priority over *Shari'ah*,[126] which presumably would include even any conflicting elements of norms of *jus cogens* (including the principles governing self-defence and self-determination).

One way in which such conflicting norms may be mitigated, or even disappear altogether, is if those additional grounds articulated by Judge Trindade in his Separate Opinion in the *Kosovo* Advisory Opinion, as outlined earlier in this chapter, develop to the point that they achieve international consensus and become additional established grounds in international law for external self-determination struggles. Certainly, any extension of the established grounds to include systematic oppression, subjugation, tyranny, discrimination and/or humiliation would absorb many of the factors currently encompassed within the concept of 'liberating' *jihad* which do not yet justify self-determination struggles under existing international law principles. Such normative developments would not, however, fully reconcile all sources of potential conflict currently existing between divergent grounds for self-determination under international and Islamic principles, especially where forcible rather than non-forcible measures are employed.

V. Conclusion

In conclusion, returning to the overarching questions this chapter posed at the outset – whether religious norms may influence self-determination

---

Concerning Military and Paramilitary Activities in and against Nicaragua (Nicaragua v USA) (Merits) [1986] ICJ Rep. 14, para. 228 especially.

125 ILA Report, (n. 111) 5.

126 A. E. Mayer, 'War and Peace in the Islamic Tradition and International Law' in J. Kelsay and J. T. Johnson (eds), *Just War and Jihad* (Greenwood, New York, 1991), p. 199. Secular general principles may only be introduced to the extent that they are not contrary to divine law – Ford, 'Siyar-ization', 527.

struggles, and with what implications for international law – it is apparent that the impact of religious norms (in this case illustrated by Islamic norms) on the substance and application of self-determination principles may not be merely inspirational or otherwise normatively insignificant; rather, they may lie at the very core of the substance, interpretation and application of such principles by certain actors. This is clearly demonstrated by the individual and collective obligations upon Muslim believers to respond under the Islamic principles of *jihad* and justice to certain injustices, which are clearly intended to be much more than justificatory or motivational within the context of the Islamic *ummah*. Indeed, as with the lower threshold of responses to aggression, such norms may ultimately include grounds which conflict with and are unlawful under international law, and will not be resolved even by those extended grounds for self-determination envisaged by Judge Trindade in the *Kosovo* Advisory Opinion.

It is not suggested that religious norms – such as *jihad* and an Islamic conception of justice – will always operate in practice to their full theoretical reach as outlined here. At the end of the day, if, how and when they are applied in practice is dependent upon the policy decisions of Islamic political entities at the state or intergovernmental levels, together with the national, regional and international legal orders in which they function. Nevertheless, what this chapter has sought to demonstrate is that religious norms are potentially relevant and influential to the normative development of and practice relating to self-determination principles: to categorize or attempt to confine them as being merely inspirational or motivational influences risks (significantly) underestimating their true potential law and policy-making importance.

13

Self-determination, oil and Islam in the face of the League of Nations: the Mosul Dispute and the 'non-European' legal terrain

MAI TAHA*

I. Introduction

If international law is just an empty language, which embodies within itself its own antithesis, and which can be used not only to emancipate but also to oppress, then its practical utility becomes a function of the sophistication of the international lawyer's arguments. The international lawyer can use this language to make one argument and simultaneously argue its opposite. In the context of the right to self-determination, the ancestral prerequisite of a claim to nationhood establishes a necessary link between the realization of self-determination and the ethnic 'people' to be self-determined. Self-determination, instead of being an open-ended language that can enable and stifle, becomes a very specific one. While understanding law as an indeterminate language that can be manipulated in different contexts to realize particular political goals,[1] it is imperative to engage with, and contest, the history that normalized

---

* I would like to thank Nehal Bhuta, Duncan French, Karen Knop and Kerry Rittich for their insightful comments and feedback. I would also like to thank participants of the International Law Association Conference: British Branch, the London School of Economics Conference 'Towards Radical International Law' and the Institute of Global Law and Policy (IGLP) Workshop at Harvard Law School.

[1] Michel Foucault argues that rules are 'empty' and can be manipulated to serve any purpose. The triumphs of history belong to those who can seize those rules, 'replace those who had used them, ... disguise themselves so as to pervert them, invert their meaning, and redirect them against those who had initially imposed them'. M. Foucault, 'Nietzsche, Genealogy, History' in E. D. F. Bouchard (ed.), *Language, Counter-memory, Practice: Selected Essays and Interviews* (Cornell University Press, 1977), p. 151. In the legal academy, Martti Koskenniemi finds that indeterminacy should not be thought of as 'a scandal or (even less) a structural "deficiency" but that indeterminacy is an absolutely central aspect of international law's acceptability'. M. Koskenniemi, *From Apology to*

the marriage between emancipation and national self-determination and thus to understand the defiance, as opposed to only the flexibility of the language contained within international law.[2]

To demonstrate such blind spots in legal scholarship, I bring in an untold story of self-determination – specifically, the national experience of the Arabic-speaking provinces of the former Ottoman Empire. The story is not only about the contribution of a specific geographical location in the structuring of self-determination in international law, but also the very nature and character of that region which makes it distinguishable. In other words, the project tells this story, not only because the 'Arab' story has rarely been told, but also because of its specific character as a 'semi-periphery', stranded between a powerful North and an alienated South, and not belonging to either. While the project of nation building in the region started towards the end of the nineteenth century, it only took an institutionalized form in the interwar period through the creation of the League of Nations and the Mandate System.[3] Only in the inter-war period did the right to self-determination become a site of contestation in the international legal terrain.[4]

In the inter-war period, a number of cases raised the question of self-determination, and not only, as is traditionally depicted, in the debacle for

---

Utopia: The Structure of International Legal Argument (Cambridge University Press, 2005), p. 591.

[2] See S. Marks, The *Riddle of All Constitutions: International Law, Democracy and the Critique of Ideology* (Oxford University Press, 2000). Marks argues that the language of international law 'can serve to stabilize oppression but also to unsettle it, to obstruct emancipation, but also to enable it'. Therefore, indeterminacy of international legal rules is not only international law's weakness, but also its strength.

[3] See C. Schmitt, *The Nomos of the Earth: In the International Law of the Jus Publicum European* (Telos Press, 2003), p. 185; H. Lauterpacht, 'The Legal Aspect' in C. A. W. Manning (ed.), *Peaceful Change: An International Problem* (Macmillan and Co. Limited, 1937); J. F. Williams, *Some Aspects of the Covenants of the League of Nations* (Oxford University Press, 1934).

[4] For a discussion on how the inter-war period was a landmark moment for the national self-determination movement in the Arab world, see M. C. Wilson, 'The Hashemites, the Arab Revolt, and Arab Nationalism' in R. Khalidi, L. Anderson, M. Muslih and R. S. Simon (eds), *The Origins of Arab Nationalism* (Columbia University Press, 1991). Nationalist leaders in the Egyptian legislature, for example, welcomed President Wilson upon his arrival in Europe with a grand message: 'To the chief of the great American democracy, who left his country in order to bring about a durable peace based on equal justice for all and guaranteed by the Society of Nations, we submit the cause of Egypt, which is subjugated to a foreign domination that Egypt unanimously rejects. Long live the United States! Long live President Wilson!' See E. Manela, *The Wilsonian Momement: Self-Determination and the International Origins of Anticolonial Nationalism* (Oxford University Press, 2007), pp. 71–2.

the postwar European settlement, but also in the post-Ottoman region. The nineteenth-century mystery of the 'Eastern Question' turned more specifically into the narrower 'Question of Palestine', the 'Mosul Dispute', and the 'Alexandretta Dispute', among others. In this chapter, I inquire into the Mosul Dispute between the new Republic of Turkey and the British Mandate of Iraq, to investigate the nature of the right to self-determination in the formative moments of the international legal imagination of the region. A dispute arose between the Republic of Turkey and the British Mandate of Iraq over the predominantly Kurdish *wilayet*[5] of Mosul in Northern Iraq. The issue was brought before the Council of the League of Nations, which eventually awarded Mosul to the British Mandate of Iraq. Through this case, I investigate the limits and possibilities of the legal *form* of national self-determination as a counter-hegemonic tool for emancipation. This provides an opportunity to contest the marriage between nationhood – as embodied in the principle of self-determination – and emancipation.[6] And more importantly, it provides an opportunity to open the space for law as an emancipatory device beyond the confines of nationhood, and perhaps to redirect attention to other matters arising out of the anti-colonial fervour, such as labour movements and class struggle, whilst being mindful of the law's limited radical reach.

The case of Mosul further demonstrates that the simple North–South binary cannot be the only universal unit of analysis, as portrayed by different streams of critical scholarship. The post-Ottoman region cannot be positioned in the international lawyer's memory as belonging either to the '*barbaric*' South or to the '*civilized*' North. While recognizing the significance of the colonial encounter, the use of the North–South binary as the primary (and perhaps the only) unit of analysis within the anti-imperial argument accentuates and homogenizes the portrayed passivity of the non-European subject and its submission to the civilizing mission.

---

[5] *Wilayet* means a small province.

[6] The ancestral prerequisite of a claim to nationhood establishes a necessary link between the realization of self-determination and the ethnic 'people' to be self-determined. In the words of renowned international legal scholar, James Crawford, 'the legal consequence of being a "people" is that you have a right of self-determination.' J. Crawford, 'States, Peoples, and Minorities: whither the nation in international law?', Keynote Address, International Law Association British Branch, University of Sheffield (April, 2011). The ideological form of nationalism that is based on an ideal of self-determination is only sensible if nations are presumed to be specific and distinct from other groups, where common ancestry is their defining characteristic. See O. Dahbour, *The Illusion of the Peoples: A Critique of National Self-Determination* (Lexington Books, 2003), at p. x.

My motivation is to study abandoned history of the relational tension, and even violence, that lies at the margins of many historical studies of nationalism, colonialism, and post-modernism. I am interested in what lies outside the 'ethnic', namely, the material realities of the subjects, which was arguably considered as subsidiary by the form of self-determination. This also sheds light on questions of historical agency, which tend to take the shape of strict dichotomies of domination and subjugation.

II. The dispute

The protagonists of the Mosul Dispute were empires, states, communities and individuals. The history of the competing tensions within the relationship between those actors demonstrates the material existence of agency on each front. On the local level, a constant positioning was quickly adaptable to developments on the regional and international level. On the state level, King Faisal of Iraq and Mustafa Kemal of Turkey had their own aspirations. On the level of empire, the Western powers were all competing to control as much as possible. This is not necessarily expressed by just territorial acquisitions, but also in terms of their virtual presence in the overall economic and political structure that provided the foundation of an international law, which sustained that structure. The seemingly competing ideologies, embedded within juridical arguments about statehood and emancipation, are actually *not* competing, but reinforcing each other on an abstract level. In other words, opposable actors used the same language towards some claim of emancipation, albeit manipulating the factual 'evidence'. This manipulation is merely a façade for an essentially identical argument.

The outbreak of World War I signalled a significant shift in British policy in the Near East. When the Ottoman Empire declared its support to the Central Powers in the War, Britain became ready to satisfy Russian interests in Constantinople, French aspirations in Syria and, more importantly, foster Arab nationalism and the ambitions of Sharif Husain of Mecca. The latter policy was seen as an easy target that would calm down the Arab nationalists whilst disturbing the Turkish armies by subverting its Arab officers.[7] The outbreak of the 1908 Young

---

[7] H. Atarodi, *Great Powers, Oil and the Kurds in Mosul (Southern Kurdistan/Northern Iraq 1910–1925)* (University Press of America, 2003), pp. 16, 22–3. Before the 1917 Bolshevik Revolution, Russia had aspirations in the Ottoman Empire, particularly in

Turk Revolution marked the start of a new regime of more centralization, Ottomanization and Turkification of the non-Turkish provinces
of the Ottoman Empire.[8] These policies were instrumental in raising
Arab national consciousness, which was initially ignited towards the end
of the nineteenth century, leading to the 1909 Arab counter-coup and
later, with British support, the 1916 Arab Revolt led by Sharif Husain.[9]

The shift in British policy prompted a series of secret agreements,
most significantly, the Sykes–Picot Agreement of May 1916, which,
subject to later modifications, formed the basis of the post-war settlement between Britain and France with regard to the territories of the
Former Ottoman Empire.[10] During the negotiations before signing the
agreement, France and Russia agreed that in the case of a potential
partition of Turkey, Russia could have Constantinople and a strip of
territory on either side of the Bosphorus, the Armenian and Kurdish
portions of eastern Anatolia. The rest of the Near East was to be divided
between Britain, France and an international zone in Palestine. Britain
was to annex Basrah and Baghdad in Mesopotamia,[11] and France was to
annex Syria, Southern Anatolia and Mosul.[12] Britain and France also
agreed that an independent Arab state or federation was to be created

Constantinople and the Dardanelles. After the revolution, Russia was no longer interested in the region. However, during 1915, Britain and France had informed Russia that
they accepted its proposals for the Ottoman Empire. At that time France had indicated
its willingness to annex Syria, Alexandretta and Cilicia. As for Britain, Winston
Churchill, then the First Lord of the Admiralty, advocated the annexation of
Mesopotamia, with or without Alexandretta.

[8] A. Cobban, *The Nation State and National Self-Determination* (Thomas Y. Crowell
Company, New York, 1970), p. 46.

[9] P. Khoury, *Urban Notables and the Politics of Damascus: 1860–1920* (Cambridge
University Press, 2003), pp. 60, 76.

[10] E. Kedourie, *In the Anglo-Arab Labyrinth: The MacMahon-Husayn Correspondence and
its Interpretations (1914–1939)* (Cambridge University Press, 2010), p. 159.

[11] H. H. Asquith, Prime Minister of Britain, set up an inter-departmental committee
headed by Maurice de Bunsen. The de Bunsen Committee proposed the annexation of
the *wilayet* of Mosul arguing that 'oil . . . makes it commercially desirable' for Britain to
control Mosul, and this area could become a granary for an unhampered supply of corn.
It also recommended that Turkey should be preserved as a federal state and be required
to recognize the independence of the newly crafted states in the Arabian Peninsula.
Atarodi, *Great Powers, Oil and the Kurds*, pp. 24–7.

[12] The reason behind assigning Mosul to France was give by Mark Sykes, claiming that
'nowhere must Britain run the risk of sharing an Asian frontier with Russia'. French-
ruled Mosul was to act as a buffer between the British zone and the Russian Caucasus.
This allotment was only agreed upon after France had pledged to respect the existing
economic rights of British nationals in all ex-Ottoman territories that fell under the
French spheres of influence. Ibid., p. 44.

within the British and French spheres of influence.[13] These allocations became the basis of the new treaty that was to reimagine the borders of the Levant, Anatolia and Mesopotamia in a post-Ottoman world. The disclosure of the Sykes–Picot agreement fuelled resentment among the Arabs, since it was in direct contradiction with the Husain–MacMahon correspondence.[14] Knowing that this agreement would also create tension with President Woodrow Wilson, the British had the perfect excuse to appease the president. They argued that it was necessary for Britain to acquire Mesopotamia, since no one would wish for the successor of the Ottoman Empire – Turkey – to rule over vast regions of Mesopotamia, 'incidentally this would give us [(the British)] most of the oil-bearing regions'.[15] When the British eventually reached Mesopotamia in October 1918, the forces were ordered to proceed to the *wilayet* of Mosul. Earlier in the same year, Lloyd George had declared: 'I am in favour of going up as far as Mosul before the war is over ... [I do not care if Britain was accused of being] capitalistic, monopolistic, or imperialistic.'[16]

France was promised Mosul in the Sykes–Picot Agreement, but with Russia out of the way after the Bolshevik Revolution, Britain had a renewed interest in Mosul. Proposals went back and forth between the two countries; eventually in December 1918, Lloyd George and Georges Clemenceau, in an undocumented car ride in London, reached a secret agreement, which indicated that Mosul was to belong to Mesopotamia under British rule.[17] The secrecy was to be maintained to avoid any conflict with President Wilson.[18] In the meantime, Lord Curzon, advocating what was called the 'the Western school of British doctrine', which supported an indirect rule over the colonies, instructed A. T. Wilson, the chief political officer to the British force in Mesopotamia, to undertake a plebiscite in Iraq. The following three questions were asked of the local population: '(1) Do they favour a single Arab state including the three *wilayats* of Basrah, Baghdad, and Mosul under British tutelage? (2) If so, do they desire this Arab state be put under an Arab Emir? (3) In that case,

---

[13] Ibid., p. 24.   [14] Kedourie, *In the Anglo-Arab Labyrinth*, p. 76.

[15] Atarodi, *Great Powers, Oil and the Kurds*, p. 50.   [16] Ibid. at p. 51.

[17] Ten years later, Clemenceau explained the concession he made to British demands over Mosul. He said, 'I should like to speak to you of another of my crimes – yes – Mosul.... Well, yes, I gave up Mosul [and the oil fields]; but what they forget is that I used it as a bait in order to get Cilicia, which several of our good allies wanted us not to have. Cilicia was ... a very pleasant country.... I therefore said to the English, 'which would you rather have, Mosul or Cilicia...?' Ibid., p. 65.

[18] J. Nevakivi, *Britain, France and the Arab Middle East: 1914–1920* (Athlone Press, 1969), p. 91.

whom would they prefer as head?'[19] As one observer notes, only 'satisfactory' answers were considered. The meetings held for the inquiry
were not seen as representative. The holy cities of Karbala and Najaf gave
a partially negative response. In Mosul, the Kurds (including the non-
Muslim Yazidis) clearly indicated that they did not wish to be included
under an Arab state. Those interviewed in Basrah were mostly landowners, who had a significant interest in maintaining the British occupation over the whole of Mesopotamia, including Mosul.[20]

What was the purpose behind this plebiscite? One argument could be
a simple appeasement of the growing resentment to the British occupation in Iraq. However, this only fully intensified after the term 'mandate'
was officially adopted, a term that was despised by the Arabs. The
purpose of the plebiscite was evidently not to inquire into the will of
the people. It might have been an attempt to foster an idea of civic
participation and a conception of citizenship. The plebiscite, a policy
that was to be followed throughout the inter-war territorial claims, was
adopted in Iraq before the institutionalization of the Mandate System in
the Covenant of the League. Evidently, the questions gave little room for
decision-making by the people. Regardless of the language of the questions and procedural fairness, it was an important showcase for the inter-
war settlement. Without reaping any substantive gains for the people,
still, it was a move to formalize national consciousness through a procedure of democratic inclusion and participation, basic rights that are
the entitlement of citizens in any liberal democracy.

On the international front, the settlement of the Mosul question became
deeply entangled with French control over Syria. As a result, President
Wilson decided to send a US commission (King–Crane Commission) to
carry out an investigation during the months of June and July 1919. The
commission never actually went to Mesopotamia, but an Arab delegation
from Iraq led by Ja'far Pasha presented the Iraqi position before it. The
commission reported that there was a desire for complete independence in
Iraq, including Mosul, Baghdad, Basrah and Mohemmera (now an Arabic-
speaking province in Iran). If supervision was needed, the United States was
to assume that role; however, no other Western power was accepted as a
second choice (later the British-orchestrated League of Nations
Commission reached the same results, except that the tutelary preference
was for Britain). The commission finally recommended that the unity of
Iraq should be maintained to include at least Basrah, Baghdad and Mosul

[19] Atarodi, *Great Powers, Oil and the Kurds*, p. 134.   [20] Ibid. at pp. 134, 135.

and that its mandate should be assigned to Britain. However, with strong US domestic opposition to the Covenant of the League of Nations, President Wilson had to leave Paris for the United States, and consequently, the King–Crane Commission produced no practical outcome.[21]

On the one hand, Britain and France were competing over influence in the Near East; on the other, the United States was starting its project of oversees 'nation-building' in the region (at least verbally), be it through internationalist means and Wilsonian diplomacy, or bargaining for oil concessions behind closed doors. Inter-imperial rivalry was visibly surrounding the Mosul question. Relations between Western powers were further intensified with the disclosure of the San Remo Agreement in July 1920, through which Britain had gained full control of Iraq, including Mosul.[22] The United States protested against the agreement, claiming that it gave exclusive rights[23] to the mandatory power to exploit the oil in the region. Lord Curzon, then British Foreign Minister, explained to the Americans that the agreement did not aim to create monopolies; it was consistent with the 'most-favoured nation' (MFN) clause that was followed by the United States.[24] It quickly became evident that the official absence of the United States from the negotiations was, however, supplemented by a material existence. The United States' 'official absence and effective presence' was embedded within a larger idea that separated politics from economics, which was expressed by the 'typical maxim: as much trade as possible, as little politics as possible'.[25] The free market was the basic constitutional standard of international law, which created devices such as the open door policy and the MFN principle to sustain itself.[26] Later, after the signature of the Treaty of Alliance between Britain and King Faisal of Iraq in 1922 (as an appeasement to Iraqi resentment of the term 'mandate'), there remained a few obstacles to the conclusion of the mandates' treaties in the region. One of them was a direct consequence of the US *effective presence*. With direction from the British government, the Anglo-Persian Oil Company offered

---

[21] Ibid., pp. 75, 76.

[22] C. Hunt, *The History of Iraq* (Greenwood Publishing Group, 2005), p. 61.

[23] Article 7 of the San Remo Agreement stated the following: 'The British Government undertake to grant to the French Government or its nominee 25 percent of the net output of crude oil at current market rates...It is also understood that the said petroleum company shall be under permanent British control.' For full text, see J. C. Hurewitz, *Diplomacy in the Near and Middle East: A Documentary Record (1914–1956)* (New York: Octagon Books, 1956) (1972), pp. 75-7.

[24] Ibid., p. 97.   [25] Schmitt, *Nomos of the Earth*, p. 255.   [26] Ibid.

the Standard Oil Company and other US interests a concession of fifty per cent of the its share in the Turkish Petroleum Company's rights to the exploitation of oil in Iraq.[27]

In the same year (1920), the stillborn Treaty of Sèvres was signed between the Allies and the defeated Ottoman Empire (excluding the United States and Russia). Most significantly, articles 62–4 of the treaty provided for the creation of an independent Kurdish state, including southern Kurdistan (Mosul):

> **Article 62:** A Commission . . . shall draft a scheme of local autonomy for the predominantly Kurdish areas . . . [with] full safeguards for . . . Assyro-Chaldeans and other racial or religious minorities within these areas. . .

> **Article 64:** If within one year . . . the Kurdish peoples within [these] areas . . . shall address themselves to the Council of the League of Nations. . .[28]

The Treaty of Sèvres was described by Philip Marshall Brown to be 'as fragile as the porcelain of that name, though lacking its charm'.[29] Despite its fragility, it was a great victory for the Kurdish nationalists. The treaty was renounced by the Turkish government and never ratified. With other issues out of the way during the years leading up to the Lausanne Conference (1922–3),[30] the question of sovereignty over Mosul remained a stumbling block in finalizing a peace treaty between the Allies and Turkey.[31] In fact, it has been argued that US agents (including

[27] A. Toynbee, *Survey of International Affairs* (Oxford University Press, 1927), p. 466.

[28] The Treaty of Peace Between the Allied and Associated Powers and Turkey, signed at Sèvres (10 Aug. 1920). Available at http://wwi.lib.byu.edu/index.php/Section_I, _Articles_1_-_260.

[29] P. M. Brown, 'From Sèvres to Lausanne' (1924)1 *American Journal of International Law*, 113. In addition to providing for a Kurdish state, the Treaty of Sèvres had other significant challenges to the Turkish government, including most notably the reinstitution of the Capitulations after being abrogated by the Ottoman government in 1914. See P. M. Brown, 'The Capitulations', (1922–3)1 *Foreign Affairs*, 71.

[30] After the signature of the treaty, particularly after the San Remo Agreement, which confirmed the British mandate over Iraq, Arab nationalism sparked massive protests in Iraq leading to the denunciation of the resented term 'Mandate' to be replaced by a Treaty of Alliance between Britain and King Faisal (1922). The change was merely a change of name; it had very limited substantive implications. Iraq was to become an independent but *protected* state. H. Mejcher, 'Iraq's External Relations: 1921–26', (1977) 13 *Middle Eastern Studies*, 340.

[31] T. Dodge, *Inventing Iraq: the Failure of Nation-Building and a History Denied* (Columbia University Press, 2003), p. 31.

public officials and corporate leaders) were providing discreet moral support to the Turks to prevent a settlement of the Mosul boundary at Lausanne. The United States Special Mission to Lausanne even supported Turkey's representative, Ismet Pasha, in remaining firm on the matter before British demands to settle the question of Mosul and to incorporate a provision that would confirm Britain's pre-war claim to the oil fields in Mosul through the Turkish Petroleum Company.[32] At Lausanne, the British position regarding the creation of an independent Kurdish state had changed. The creation of a Kurdish nation-state was no longer a viable option; it posed a direct threat to the process of nation-building that had started before the war in the Arab provinces of the Ottoman Empire. The different levels of imperial dynamics (as opposed to clear binary relationships) directed the negotiations at Lausanne. Here, the post-colonial lens becomes quite useful in understanding the imperial logic that utilized nationalism for opposing purposes. However, essentially it becomes an argument about realpolitik as opposed to a structural critique of the dynamics of inter- and intra-imperial relationships. Therefore, it misses the complexity of agency present in such negotiations. This stream of scholarship glosses over the dialectical nature of such negotiations. While national consciousness certainly played an important role in the struggle against imperialism, it has, at the same time, hampered an emancipated conception of 'independence' that is not only concerned with national autonomy, but also with the underlying socio-economic basis of imperialism.

Discussions at Lausanne bring back Nathaniel Berman's categorization of nationalism – 'good and bad';[33] one is promoted and fostered because it sustains the entire system; the other is rebellious and should be deprecated. Good nationalism (Arab nationalism) was preferred. Bad nationalism (Kurdish nationalism) would subvert the proceedings at Lausanne and prevent the finalization of the peace treaty with Turkey.[34] Furthermore, supporting bad nationalism would create a

[32] Before the war, Britain had secured its share of oil exploitation in Mosul. However, the outbreak of the war brought the project to a halt before being ratified by the Ottoman Empire. As for the United States, its support for Turkey was rewarded by granting Chester and his Ottoman-American Company concessions for the building of railways and exploitation of mines, etc. Atarodi, *Great Powers, Oil and the Kurds*, pp. 118–19.
[33] This term is borrowed from N. Berman's article, 'Nationalism "Good" and "Bad": The Vicissitudes of an Obsession' (1996) 90 *American Society of International Law Proceedings*.
[34] Lord Curzon indicated that Britain 'shall not go to war for the sake of Mosul ... if the French ... will not join us, we shall by ourselves try to enforce what is left of the Treaty of

break in the still vulnerable shells that surrounded the new regional order comprised of individual, self-interested nation-states. While hampering one nationalism, the Lausanne Treaty fostered the other.

Turkey made an esteemed presentation at Lausanne[35] on its entitlement to the entire *wilayet* of Mosul to Jabal Hamrin in northern Iraq. Turkey based its claim on the following arguments: (1) 'Race'; Arabs are a separate race and are only a small minority, while the Turks and the Kurds are not racially distinguishable (as defined in the Turkish National Pact of 1920); (2) 'Economy'; most of the Mosul area conducted the majority of its trade with Anatolia, not with Iraq; (3) 'Illegal Occupation'; Britain occupied Mosul after the conclusion of the Mudros Armistice, which meant a maintenance of the status quo until an agreement was reached; (4) 'Self-determination'; the will of the people of Mosul was to join with Turkey. Lord Curzon defeated all these arguments as follows: (1) the majority of the inhabitants were Kurds of Indo-European origin, who were essentially different from Ural-Atlantic Turks; (2) most of the trade of the *wilayet* was with the remainder of Mesopotamia, not with Anatolia; (3) the British government had legal tutelage over Iraq per the mandate treaties; (4) the self-determination of the Kurds lie in their union with Iraq and not with Turkey, as demonstrated by the nineteenth century, the immediate pre-war and post-Kurdish revolts against Turkey.[36] As was argued, the language of self-determination has been repeatedly used by opposing parties. However, it never moved beyond the national question. The language's flexibility then becomes 'rhetorical flexibility', which seemingly provides an empty and yielding device, but is actually restating the same argument based on different empirical assertions. It is not surprising, therefore, that such a device only led to a deadlock at the negotiations table. This prompted the parties temporarily to exclude the question of Mosul from the peace negotiations. The result was the following provision:

> The frontier ... shall be laid down in friendly arrangement ... within nine months. In the event of no agreement ... the dispute shall be referred to the Council of the League of Nations.[37]

Sèvres'. O. Ali, 'The Kurds and the Lausanne Peace Negotiations, 1922–23' (1997) 33 *Middle Eastern Studies*, 522.

[35] Ismet Pasha Inunu was the Turkish delegate representing the new national government after the Grand National Assembly at Ankara had abolished the Sultanate on 1 November, 1922, and the Ottoman government was no longer in existence. See preamble to the Treaty of Lausanne.

[36] Ali, 'The Kurds', at 521, 522.

[37] The Official Journal of the League of Nations, 'The Question of the Frontier Between Turkey and Iraq, Article 3 (2) of the Treaty of Lausanne', *League of Nations Official Journal*, 5 (Oct. 1924), 1318.

The start of the negotiations at Lausanne coincided with a landmark event in the history of the region; after more than 600 years of Ottoman rule, the Islamic Caliphate was abolished in November 1922 (officially ratified in 1924).[38] This marked an important ideological turn (though not necessarily only caused by it) in the domestic politics of the provinces, specifically the intensification of *wataniyya* in the post-Ottoman Arab provinces. *Wataniyya* is essentially a territorial conception of the nation, which should not be conflated with *qawmiyya* (nationalism) that is generally associated with Arab nationalism (*Al-Qawmiyya Al-Arabiyya*). It has been an invasive feature of provincial politics since the second half of the nineteenth century.[39] The disintegration of the House of Osman signalled the consolidation of a regional order composed of self-interested and territorially defined states with a different conception of nationhood – *wataniyya*. This shift meant that the call for an Arab nation was to be gradually replaced by the call for an Iraqi (as well as Syrian, Lebanese, etc.) nation-state. This puts the Lausanne discussions on Mosul into perspective. By revoking any commitment to an independent Kurdish state, the parties were implicitly supporting the development of this regional order of self-interested participants that had already been set in motion. There was perhaps a fear of subverting this order by crumbling the rising national consciousness of the stronger nation-states. This larger strategy had arguably informed the smaller tactical approaches used in addressing the question of Mosul. Despite the holding of a plebiscite in Upper Silesia, during the Lausanne negotiations, Lord Curzon argued that a different course should be taken in Mosul. Referral to the Council of the League of Nations was deemed the wiser course of action, threatening that Britain would exercise its rights under Article 11 of the Covenant of the League to bring the matter before the Council. As stipulated in the Turkish National Pact of 1920, Mosul was seen as an integral part of Turkey. The pact had asserted that the destiny of the areas occupied by enemy forces should be determined by 'the votes which shall be freely given by the inhabitants ... united in religion, in race and in aim ... [and] form a whole which does not admit

---

[38] M. Khadduri, 'Islam and the Modern Law of Nations' (1956) 50 *American Journal of International Law*, 369. Khadduri argues that 'the triumph of nationalism on the basis of Muslim polity resulted in the destruction of the Ottoman Empire ... and the abolition of the Caliphate (1924)', which provided the space for new Muslim sovereign states to exist independently of the Caliphate and the Empire.

[39] F. H. Lawson, *Constructing International Relations in the Arab World* (Stanford University Press, 2006), p. 9.

of division for any reason in truth or in ordinance'.[40] This argument was later used by Turkey before the Council of the League of Nations in support of holding a plebiscite in Mosul, which was categorically rejected by the British government, not because of the substantive aim of the plebiscite – national self-determination – but for the procedure of the plebiscite itself.[41] The above provision (Article 3(2) of the treaty) was the compromise reached,[42] which then became the origin of the Mosul Dispute before the Council of the League of Nations.

The nationalist underpinning of the whole dispute takes a more concrete form, exhibiting the different aims and responsibilities of the parties. While the consolidation of a strong Iraq was an important British (and Iraqi) aim, finalizing peace with Turkey was of equal importance. Britain was therefore constantly engaging in a balancing act of its political and economic priorities in the region. This was threatened by strong internal pressure to withdraw from Iraq, a sentiment that had to be appeased to continue the project in the post-Ottoman territories. Sir Bernard Henry Bourdillon, the Political Secretary to the High Commissioner of the civil administration in Iraq, speaking at a 1924 conference in Britain, said the following:

> Those of us who have been working out there for the past few years have often felt that the British public, even the more intelligent sections of it, regard Iraq in the light of a rather unattractive war baby of highly suspicious parentage whom they have been compelled from a sense of duty to adopt, but for whom they have no feeling of parental affection. Consequently, they take very little interest in the child, and are constantly expecting it to be naughty. When it fulfils these expectations, they take a rather unseemly delight in spanking it. We have had a good many spankings in the last five or six years, and we have honestly felt that some of them have been rather undeserved.[43]

[40] J. De v. Loder, *The Truth About Mesopotamia, Palestine & Syria* (London: George Allen & Unwin Ltd., 1923), p. 146. Loder was working for the League of Nations Union and as per the preface of the book, he wrote it to apply the ideas of the League of Nations to the territories of the former Ottoman Empire. He saw no strategic advantage to the presence of Britain in Iraq. However, he noted that it would be a mistake for Britain suddenly to leave Iraq, since this would leave it vulnerable to Turkish aspirations in the region.

[41] As will be argued, Britain essentially made the same argument, but claimed that the correct procedure was an International Commission of Enquiry as opposed to a plebiscite.

[42] B. Keith, 'The League of Nations and Mosul' (1926) 8 *Journal of Comparative Legislation and International Law*, 38.

[43] B. H. Bourdillon, 'The Political Situation in Iraq' (1924) 3 *Journal of the British Institute of International Affairs*, 273.

Other than the linguistically obscure tone, Bourdillon was attempting to justify the British presence in Iraq, resorting again to the nationalist paradigm. He argued that Arab nationalism 'pre-existed' the British occupation of Iraq, and this was instrumental in gaining British support against the Turkish threat. The defining characteristics of this nationalism were 'community of language and dislike of the Turk'.[44] He argued that the British used the Arab national consciousness in its struggle against Turkey, and that it had made certain promises to strengthen that feeling. Most significantly, these promises included the inclusion of Mosul within the borders of Iraq. He further stated: 'quite apart from certain broad principles of self-determination which have won recognition as the result of the war, our policy in Iraq is in direct pursuance of certain definite pledges which we entered into in order to gain certain definite ends'.[45]

The British position did not deter Kurdish nationalism; one year after Bourdillon's speech, a Kurdish rebellion broke out in Turkey, under the leadership of the Naqshabandi dervish and tribal leader, Shiekh Sait. The rebellion soon turned into a fully-fledged uprising across all the areas inhabited by the Kurds in Turkey. Mustafa Kemal had maintained that this rebellion was infused by the British to subvert Turkey's position in relation to Mosul.[46] Notably, the Kurdish leaders in Turkey had initially supported the Kemal regime in the war of independence aspiring to be an indispensaible wing in the new Ankara government.[47] Earlier, the Kurdish leader, Sharif Pasha, had interestingly instigated Percy Cox, then British colonial administrator and army officer (and High Commissioner of Iraq 1922-3), to occupy all of southern Kurdistan,

---

[44] Ibid., 275.

[45] Ibid., 276. The question of 'good and bad nationalism' is again manifested by 'good and bad self-determination'. Self-determination of the Arab state of Iraq was instrumental in creating the new post-war regional order of independent self-interested states, while Kurdish self-determination would have disrupted the build-up of Iraqi nationalism (and Arab nationalism before) that was being fostered since the nineteenth century, not only by the British, but by different local elites as a tool for mass mobilization against Constantinople. Self-determination's flexibility is only rhetorical flexibility, which precludes any other representations of emancipation, other than the ethnic nation.

[46] R. W. Olson and W. F. Tucker, 'The Sheikh Sait Rebellion in Turkey (1925): A Study in the Consolidation of a Developed Uninstitutionalized Nationalism and the Rise of Incipient (Kurdish) Nationalism' (1978)18 Die Welt des Islams, New Series, 195.

[47] Ibid., 199. Some scholars have argued that this rebellion was also caused by religious resentment of the reforms undertaken by the Kemalist regime.

which constitutes the *wilayet* of Mosul, aspiring to assume the role of Iraq as Britain's new child[48] nation-state in the region.[49]

The nine-month period required by the Lausanne Treaty had expired and no friendly settlement was reached between the parties by the time Britain requested the advice of the Council of the League of Nations in August 1924.[50] Two months earlier, Fethi Bey, the Turkish representative before the League of Nations, presented a memorandum claiming that Mosul was juridically constituted as part of Turkey, despite the fact that it was under provisional British administration: therefore, Britain was in no position to bring a claim before the League on behalf of Iraq. Sir Percy Cox refuted this argument, maintaining that the British proposal was consistent with the terms of the Treaty of Lausanne.[51] The British government proceeded with its claim before the Council of the League. Throughout the proceedings, the question of self-determination appeared in the form of a murky discussion between Lord Parmoor (the British representative) and Fethi Bey on the holding of a plebiscite near the boundary. The British government had maintained its original position during the Lausanne negotiations, listing three reasons why a plebiscite should not be held. First, the definition of the frontier was not seen as a matter 'that lends itself to a decision by plebiscite'. Second, the population inhabiting the vicinity of the frontier consisted mainly of 'uneducated tribesmen who can hardly be regarded as competent to deal with the complicated issue involved so often in boundary settlement'. Finally, holding a plebiscite around the frontier would cause a disturbance to peace. Therefore, it was felt that the Council should appoint a

---

[48] Sir Henry Dobbs, the High Commissioner for Iraq, speaking before the League of Nations, analogized the new Iraqi state to a child. 'There are two theories in regard to the proper upbringing of children. One, that a child should be guarded from all possibility of harm, that it should be ... surrounded by nurses, petted ... when it falls or hurts itself ... prevented by ever-present parental restraint from exercising infantile initiative. The other theory, the modern one, ... is that a superfluity of nurses, of clothing and of parental protection not only retards the development of the faculties of initiative ... but not infrequently has a deleterious effect upon the constitution of the child. ... when the British Government accepted mandatory responsibility for Iraq in 1920 ... it attempted to put in practice the first of these two theories.' Commission Seventh Meeting, 'Iraq: Examination of the Annual Reports for 1923–24 and 1925: General Statement by the Accredited Representative' *The League of Nations* (8 November 1926), 45.

[49] Atarodi, *Great Powers, Oil and the Kurds*, p. 148 n. 3.

[50] Q. Wright, 'The Mosul Dispute' (1926) 20 *American Journal of International Law*, 453.

[51] Keith, 'The League of Nations and Mosul', 39.

Commission to study the documents that had already been prepared and any additional evidence that it collected from the investigation.[52] Fethi Bey also maintained the same Turkish position adopted at Lausanne. With plebiscites used as an inter-European tool to manage the post-war settlement, Fethi Bey argued that the territories of the former Ottoman Empire should have the option of using the same mechanism as its European counterparts. There was no reason why the Turkish–Iraqi dispute should be handled any differently from other European nations and that a plebiscite should be held to determine the exact wishes of the population inhabiting the region. He further submitted that a commission of enquiry would never adequately capture an accurate and representative position of the will of the people of Mosul.[53] Essentially, both parties were making the same argument – that the key concern was determining the will of the people to realize national self-determination – but the procedural aspect acted as an obstacle, accompanied by pseudo-accusations of eurocentrism.

After agreement by both parties – Fethi Bey and Lord Parmoor – the Council passed a resolution to set up an international Commission of Enquiry to investigate the *status quo* at the borders, especially after allegations of military activities on both sides. From the outset, a dispute arose as to the definition of the *status quo* – the British claimed it was the one of 24 July 1923, marking the conclusion of the Treaty of Lausanne; the Turks claimed that it was 30 September 1924, when the Council of the League of Nations approved a document on Iraq that accepted the Anglo-Iraqi treaty and other British guarantees as the defining documents of what practically was the mandate's obligations. To answer this question, among other issues, an extraordinary session of the Council convened in Brussels; the Council proposed a line that was initially drawn by Dr. Hjalmar Banting, the Swedish Premier, which later became known as the 'Brussels Line'.[54] The Brussels line was to be the provisional frontier between Turkey and Iraq.[55]

---

[52] 'The Question of the Frontier Between Turkey and Iraq, Article 3 (2) of the Treaty of Lausanne', 5 (1924), *League of Nations Official Journal*, 1321.

[53] 'The Question of the Frontier Between Turkey and Iraq, Article 3 (3) of the Treaty of Lausanne' *League of Nations Official Journal*, 5 (Oct. 1924), 1318.

[54] Council of the League of Nations, 'Question of the Frontier between Turkey and Iraq; Report Submitted to the Council by the Commission Instituted by the Council Resolution of September 30th, 1924', *LN doc. C. 400 M. 147* (1925); Atarodi, *Great Powers, Oil and the Kurds*, p. 191.

[55] Ibid.

The next step was the creation of the commission of enquiry; it consisted of three members: Af Wirsen, the Swedish Minister to Romania, as chairman, Paul Teleki,[56] the former Hungarian premier and A. Paulis, a Belgian colonial and renowned expert in Congo affairs. The committee conducted a series of meetings with the officials from the Turkish and British governments, during their visits to London and Constantinople. The commission eventually reached Iraq, first Baghdad, then Mosul. It conducted a series of interviews from late January to March 1925, despite the state of unrest inspired by Shaikh Mahmoud, the Kurdish leader. Under close British oversight,[57] members of the commission had an extensive 'tour' of the *wilayet* of Mosul, roaming the bazaars, interviewing some of the inhabitants, and visiting principal localities. The result of this investigation produced neither a consensus nor a revelation on nationalist tendencies. The commission found that the political future of Mosul was related to '*non-identity issues*'. Furthermore, in some of the areas within the *wilayet* there was a precise preference, while in others, there was a mix of ambivalence and diversity of opinions regarding the destiny of Mosul. However, the political and socio-economic issues were mostly the primary concerns and '[e]thnicity was clearly *not* the determining factor'.[58] With the idea of a Kurdish nation out of the way, the Arab nation took over. The commission argued that the economic viability of Baghdad and Basra were mostly dependent on the grain from the north (Mosul).[59] Therefore, the survival of the child nation state, Iraq, was the determining factor.

> The Commission eventually stated the following:
> The fact seems to be established that ... the desires expressed by the population are more in favour of Iraq than of Turkey ... the attitude of most of the people was influenced by the desire for effective support

[56] It was alleged that Teleki earlier acted as a mediator between the Turkish Petroleum Company (TPC) and the Iraqi government. Shortly after, the oil concessions were granted to the TPC. Ibid. at p. 193.

[57] It was argued by Cecil J. Edmonds, the political officer in Iraqi Kurdistan, that the British remained in full control. The British had taken a number of initiatives to suppress nationalist expression, such as popular demonstrations and riots. They had also co-opted the feudal chiefs, most notably the *Mutasarrif* of Arbil instructed the people to be as agreeable as possible. Edmonds wrote, 'through the bazaars ... we encountered a quite uncanny silence'. See C. J. Edmonds, *Kurds, Turks, and Arabs: Politics, Travel, Research in North-eastern Iraq, 1919–1925* (Oxford University Press, 1957), p. 411.

[58] S. Shields, 'Mosul Questions: Economy, Identity and Annexations' in R. Spector Simon and E. H. Tejirian (eds.), *The Creation of Iraq: 1914–1922* (Columbia University Press, 2004), p. 55 (emphasis added).

[59] Ibid., p. 57.

under the mandate, and by economic considerations, rather than by any feeling of solidarity with the Arab kingdom; if these two factors had carried no weight ... it is probable that the majority of them would have preferred to return to Turkey rather than ... Iraq.[60]

Eventually, the commission recommended that Mosul should be part of Iraq, but only if the British mandate was extended for twenty-five years, and that Kurds had official representation in the administration, education and judicial institutions in the region, with Kurdish language as the designated language for these services. The commission noted that if the British mandate was to expire in four years (as was initially envisioned), and certain guarantees were not provided for the Kurds, the majority of the people would have preferred Turkish to Arab sovereignty.[61]

As was exemplified, the League of Nations had to devise a number of semi-institutional procedures to reach its final decision. Within the time span of only one year, the Council created four bodies to deal with the Mosul Dispute (in addition to its later referral to the Permanent Court of International Justice (PCIJ) on procedural matters). This cosmetic approach to national disputes was symptomatic of the League's choice of procedure during the inter-war period.[62] In the case of Mosul, after deliberations in Geneva, the Council decided to appoint another sub-committee in September 1925 to reach a just and peaceful resolution to the conflict. During its proceedings, an old dispute between Turkey and Britain resurfaced over the binding force of the decision to be reached by the Council under Article 3(2) of the Treaty of Lausanne. The British government argued that the article empowered the Council to assume the role of arbitrator in the event of a dispute and that its decision was to be binding on both parties. The Turkish government argued that the Council could merely provide a recommendation as stipulated in the Covenant. The parties decided to take that issue to the PCIJ, which eventually found that the Council had the capacity to make a decision on the matter and that the unanimity rule should apply, excluding the parties concerned.[63]

---

[60] A. D'Amato, *International Law and Political Reality* (Martinus Nijhoff Publishers, 1995), p. 348.

[61] Ibid.

[62] See, for example, the details of the Saar Plebiscite. A four-member commission was appointed, which then appointed a special committee, which provided another procedure for the plebiscite itself to be conducted after fifteen years of the League's administration of the territory by another five-member commission. See, generally, S. Wambaugh, *The Saar Plebiscite* (Harvard University Press, 1971), pp. 42–58.

[63] See *Interpretation of Article 3, Paragraph 2, of the Treaty of Lausanne (Frontier Between Iraq and Turkey) Permanent Court of International Justice (PCIJ) Reports,*

In the meantime, Turkish regulars had been engaging in military activities at the Mosul frontier, creating thousands of Chaldean Catholic refugees, fleeing southward towards the British sphere of influence. Britain, on its part, carried out a number of naval manoeuvres on the north-eastern maritime borders. Sectarianism added further complexity to the conflict; in addition to the Sunni–Shi'a question in Iraq, the Muslim–Christian divide was presented as an additional reason for awarding Mosul to the British Mandate, since the safety of the Christians was at stake. Britain asked the League of Nations to consider the massive deportations of Christians from Turkey and the violation of the status quo determined by the Brussels Line.[64] In the predominantly Sunni Muslim Kurdish area of Mosul, Turkey allegedly was spreading anti-Christian, and by association, anti-British sentiments in the region. One leaflet read, '[b]efore long your ears will be deafened by the sound of the bell – the voice of the mu'ezzin will no longer be heard. Christian officials will treat you as did the Russians, and you will have to kiss the feet of the Arabs and Chaldeans.'[65] With all such allegations, the Council of the League of Nations adopted a resolution creating yet another five-member Commission to investigate the situation at the frontier, led by General F. Laidoner, on 30 October 1925.[66] The Laidoner Commission, while condemning the attacks directed against the Christians, eventually found that the events that took place at the vicinity of the frontier were merely 'ordinary' incidents that were inevitable, given the indeterminate situation at the border.[67]

Advisory Opinion No. 12 (21 November 1925). The questions raised before the Court were: 'I) What is the character of the decision to be taken by the Council in virtue of Article 3, paragraph 2, of the Treaty of Lausanne – is it an arbitral award, a recommendation or a simple mediation? II) Must the decision be unanimous or may it be taken by a majority? May the representatives of the interested Parties take part in the vote?' For a legal analysis of the procedure and the decision of the Court on the question of Mosul, see generally, G. Schwarzenberger, 'The Nemo Judex in Sua Causa Maxim in International Judicial Practice' (1927) 1 *Anglo-American Law Review*, 487–92; O. Spiermann, *International Legal Argument in the Permanent Court of International Justice: The Rise of the International Judiciary* (Cambridge University Press, 2005), pp. 230–41.

[64] Wright, 'The Mosul Dispute', 115.

[65] Atarodi, *Great Powers, Oil and the Kurds*, p. 155 n. 3.

[66] F. Laidoner, *Report to the Council of the League of Nations on the Situation in the Locality of the Provisional Line of the Frontier between Turkey and Irak Fixed at Brussels on October 29, 1924* (London: H. M. Stationery Office, 1925).

[67] Ibid.

In Geneva, at the Council of the League, L.S. Amery, the British Colonial Secretary, and Munir Bey, the Turkish jurist and minister in Bern, in a final confrontation, each presented their positions. The British government, confident of a favourable outcome, declared its willingness to accept the decision by the Council. Turkey rejected the Council's legitimacy as a norm-creating body. After the League's dismissal of the Turkish rejection, Turkey withdrew and the Council awarded most of the Mosul *wilayet*[68] to the British Mandate of Iraq, adopting the Brussels Line as the official frontier between Turkey and protected Iraq.

The award was contingent upon three conditions: (1) A treaty to be drafted between the Mandatory Power and Iraq, *prolonging the mandate for twenty-five years* starting in December 1925; (2) the British Government required to present before the Council the administrative measures to be taken with the purpose of ensuring all the guarantees for the Kurdish populations, regarding local administration as recommended by the Commission of Enquiry; (3) the Mandatory Power asked to act in accordance with all other suggestions made by the Commission, regarding measures taken to ensure equal protection of the population, and regarding commercial matters.[69] The text of the treaty does not make any mention of self-determination or the will of the people. It merely refers to the question of independence in the context of the membership of the League of Nations.[70] Significantly, and without direct reference, the League's decision was essentially one of the first applications of the principle of *uti possidetis juris* in the region, adopted initially during the decolonization of the Americas. The ex-Ottoman territories (notably for this case, Iraq) were passed from the victorious allies to their respective mandatories within the same boundaries drawn towards the creation of a post-imperial regional order of discrete nation-states. The attached proviso to the Lausanne Treaty, which stipulated that the future

---

[68] Notably, Amery expressed discontent regarding the Council's decision to exclude the southern portion of the *wilayet* of Hakari with its Christian population in the boundaries of Iraq. Nevertheless, he accepted the decision. Atarodi, *Great Powers, Oil and the Kurds*, p. 203.

[69] *Decision of the Council of the League of Nations* (16 December 1925).

[70] 'Treaty Between His Britannic Majesty and His Majesty the King of Iraq', *League of Nations Official Journal*, 7 (January 1926), 550. Later, the Anglo-Iraqi Treaty was ratified by Britain and Iraq in their local assemblies. The official transfer of the *wilayet* of Mosul took place on 11 March 1926. Turkey, recognizing the *de facto* situation, decided to settle the issue, which resulted in a tripartite agreement between Britain, Iraq and Turkey (June 1926).

of the territories be settled by 'the parties concerned', was merely recognition of that fact.[71]

With the outcome of the Mosul Commission of Enquiry in the background, emancipation was not necessarily linked only to identity, but also tribal relations and nationhood. Both the British and the Turkish governments underscored national identity and self-determination in their arguments before the Council. What is more significant than the empirical outcome of the Council is the deconstruction of binaries presumed by the League. Simplistic questions asked by the commissioners such as, 'are you a Turk or an Iraqi?', were evidently inadequate in capturing the different dynamics at play, including strategy.[72] The Council may successfully have 'resolved' the conflict, but it essentially laid the groundwork in the region for an international legal system that sees emancipation as an exercise of national self-determination.[73]

In the process of crafting national consciousness and identity, a certain level of mystification exaggerates subtle differences between the nation and its other (or its another), while the most obtrusive distinctions within the designated nation are almost always abstracted.[74] Such distinctions are most glaringly apparent in the politics of economic inequality among members of the same nation. The legal vehicle of national self-determination precisely precludes such distinctions as outside the scope of juridical emancipation. Arguments to that effect have rightly traced the use of nationalism as an emancipatory device to be directly linked to foreign colonial and local elite patronages. In the words of Eric Hobsbawm, '[n]othing like nationalism is discoverable elsewhere . . . the forces which were later to produce nationalism were [earlier] opposed to the alliance of tradition, religion and mass poverty which produced the most

---

[71] See M. F. Lindley, *The Acquisition and Government of Backward Territory in International Law: Being a Treatise on the Law and Practice Relating to Colonial Expansion* (New York: Negro Universities Press, 1926 [1969]); O. Okafor, 'After Martyrdom: International Law, Sub-State Groups, and the Construction of Legitimate Statehood in Africa' (2000) 41 *Harvard International Law Journal*, 518. *Uti possidetis* stamped the child nation-state with inviolable boundaries, formally consolidating it as part of the 'system'. A number of TWAIL scholars argue that the process of nation-building in Africa sought to homogenize the state's socio-cultural differences in an attempt to 'exorcise the "demon" of ethnicity.' The purpose of such nation-building was to sustain the inherited territorial state by 'killing the tribe to build the nation'. This is a compelling argument but also, like the colonial argument, it elides other non-hereditary factors that are often at the margins of any engagement with the legal right of self-determination.

[72] Shields, 'Mosul Questions', 58.   [73] Ibid.

[74] Lawson, *Constructing International Relations*, p. 7.

powerful resistance to the encroachment of western conquerors and exploiters'.[75] In the nineteenth century, the Ottoman Empire was not only subjugated by colonialism, it was also legitimated by it. From the re-ordering of the empire to the Ottomanization reforms, the Ottoman Porte sustained its position by these very dynamics of colonialism. In the post-Ottoman world, the fragments of the Empire have presumed a similar role. Iraq was not only an aspiring nation-state, its very existence (with other states) as a self-determined nation-state is the basis of the rising regional order, and ultimately the international legal system.

III. Conclusion

The tautological conception of the legal rule of national self-determina-tion as a formal façade with a malleable heart is precisely what creates the anachronism of self-determination. National self-determination becomes international law's foundation and its salvage at the same time. It serves to legitimate the current global order whilst claiming to emancipate this order's fatalities. This implores a desire to understand the principle's tension and internal contradiction. As was argued, the language of national self-determination was used by competing and opposable entities across the political and ideological spectrums. Still, the language of a legal right to self-determination was able to conceal the discussion from any 'non-national' concerns.

The intellectual strength of the indeterminacy thesis provides the space for alternative approaches to contemporary international law in a post-colonial era. Most significantly, Third World Approaches to International Law (TWAIL) sees international law to be essentially about the history of domination and exclusion of third world people.[76] It is also concerned with the stories and lived experiences of third world peoples, and not merely with

---

[75] E. Hobsbawm, *The Age of Revolution: 1789–1848* (Vintage Books, 1962), p. 143. Notably, with regard to nationalism in the Ottoman Empire, Hobsbawm argues that '[n]ational-ism in the East was thus the eventual product of Western influence and Western conquest', which, as he argued, meant that Arab nationalism was only a product of the twentieth century, referencing Egypt as the first oriental state to adopt that, under the reign of Mehmed Ali. See Ibid., p. 144. This essentially means that the rise of an Arab consciousness, particularly from the second half of the nineteenth century, was a discontinuous project that ended at the close of the century.

[76] See, generally, B.S. Chimni, 'Third World Approaches to International Law: A Manifesto' (2005) 8 *International Community Law Review*, and J. Gathii, 'International Law and Eurocentricity' (1998) 9 *European Journal of International Law* 184.

foreign policies of states represented in international institutions. Only by understanding that the foundation of international law lies in the colonial encounter can international legal rules be interpreted and evaluated.[77] Such recognition also illuminates the larger normative framework of international law, which reproduces 'oppressive and patriarchal international law rules'. In their critique of the New Haven School, TWAIL scholars highlight the fact that the content of international legal rules is written by power.[78] They aspire to determinate legal rules, whilst acknowledging the inevitability of indeterminacy. The key is to manipulate the power-based content of international legal rules in favour of those disadvantaged by the international legal regime. While recognizing the colonial encounter as a central and a constitutive feature of international law and its language as a strategic tool for enlightenment, as this chapter has also revealed, it is essential to evaluate the North–South binary as not the only unit of analysis and to confront the challenges posed by the semi-periphery.[79]

The purpose of this chapter was to entertain the space that lies outside an ethnic or national conception of self-determination that is often discounted as being inessential to the mutually-constitutive projects of nation-building and global governance. My aim was simply to reimagine what lies at the margins of self-determination in an attempt to refute the conviction that marries emancipation with national self-determination by looking at history. During the end of the nineteenth century and into the twentieth century, the self-determination euphoria in the Arab provinces of the former Ottoman Empire underscored the nationalist struggle as the vanguard of anti-colonial resistance, whilst suppressing other forms of political organization.[80] Towards the end of the nineteenth and well into the beginning of the twentieth century, the question of nationalism had certainly been central to anti-oppression claims in the Arab Ottoman region, which – more often than not – were entangled with the anti-imperialist rhetoric that focused largely on the language of national self-determination. According to Ilham Makdisi, historical

---

[77] A. Anghie and B.S. Chimni, 'Third World Approaches to International Law and Individual Responsibility in Internal Conflicts' (2003) 21 *Chinese Journal of International Law* 78.

[78] Ibid., at 99.

[79] For a discussion of the characterization of the former Ottoman Empire as the 'semi-periphery' in the context of the inter-war Greek-Turkish population transfer, see U. Özsu, 'Fabricating Fidelity: Nation-Building, International Law, and the Greek-Turkish Population Exchange', unpublished SJD thesis, University of Toronto (2011).

[80] I. Makdisi, The *Eastern Mediterranean and the Making of Global Radicalism, 1860–1914* (University of California Press, 2010).

writing was almost exclusively concerned with nationalist struggles, glossing over other sites of resistance during this period. In the region, ideas ranging from social justice, workers' rights, mass secular education and anticlericalism were among many non-ethnic-centric struggles that challenged the prevailing social and economic order locally, and globally. Such struggles 'in these global, yet "semi-peripheral cities" were . . . full participants in the making of . . . an alternative vision . . . or subverting the version created . . . by European imperialism'.[81] Be it in the industrial or agrarian sectors, other forms of social movements were often in the backdrop of an overt centrality on the nationalist movement (notwithstanding the important role played by such movements in resistance against empire in the region). In international law, the language of nationalism created a convenience, whereby sites of social resistance were based on a conceptualization of 'peoplehood' translated into a formalized right to self-determination of peoples.

In the backyard of Ankara's new nationalist government, the Arab territories of the Former Ottoman Empire were building their *wataniyya*, rising as independent self-interested entities. Within those territories, a combination of factors contributed to the consolidation of this new regional order; it was the mixture between the roles of actors, norms, institutions and ideology that sustained this order. From European racism and international capitalism to 'Ottoman Orientalism'[82] and dignified nationalism, such semiotics represented the relationship that underpinned the modern structure of the region. On the one hand, the Ottoman Empire positioned their own Arab periphery as an integral component of its relationship with, and acceptance of, the West. On the

[81] Ibid. at 16. Makdisi attempts to reclaim the term 'radicalism', which has been strongly correlated with leftist ideas in the Western world, nationalist ideas in the Third World, and political Islam in the Muslim world. There was a wave of globalization that started in the 1870s, which integrated the semi-peripheral labour into the global market and established a dependency on foreign investments and loans. The creation of non-nationalist social resistance was a consequence of a variety of factors, defined largely by the incorporation of the region into the world capitalist system. Outside the urban centres the *fellah* (peasant) rebellions were fuelled by the commercialization of agriculture and the intensification of private property (creating a strong landholding elite) in the second half of the nineteenth century. E. Burke, III, 'Changing Patterns of Peasants' Protests in the Middle East (1750–1950)' in F. Kazemi and J. Waterbury, *Peasants and Politics in the Modern Middle East* (Florida International University Press, 1991), pp. 24, 28.

[82] This term is Ussama Makdisi's, who analogizes to Edward Said's orientalism. Makdisi argues, 'every nation creates its own orient'. U. Makdisi, 'Ottoman Orientalism' (2002) 3 *The American Historical Review* 768.

other hand, it used the Arab periphery as an explicit form of resistance to the Western representations of 'the indolent Ottoman East'.[83]

In the twentieth century, the Arab provinces used the same strategy to situate themselves as discrete self-interested nation-states within the newly crafted regional order. European colonialism was still present, but the relationship was characterized by more sophistication than simply imperial imposition in the near East. The contest over Mosul was a symbolic reflection of this dynamic. Iraq, as one of the post-Ottoman successor states, on the one hand was engaging in dignified nationalism as a form of resistance to the British Mandate, while sustaining itself as an egotistical state as imagined by the system of international law after the war. The League of Nations on its own part was the institutionalized symbol of that structure and was to manage the inter-war disputes accordingly. The web of ideological affiliations and the triumph of the nationalist paradigm in a 'semi-peripheral' region where there was a certain level of agency or participation shows, at least partially, that calls for cultural inclusion and participation in contemporary international legal rhetoric (whether in the legal academy or in international institutions) can be scrutinized as partaking in a language that is associated with a very specific conception of emancipation. Ultimately, historical agency and participation were not able to buffer the larger structure that sought to defy agency at its most intrinsic and popular level.

[83] Ibid.

The question of indigenous peoples' rights: a time for reappraisal?

MALGOSIA FITZMAURICE

I. Introduction

In the view of many scholars and practitioners, the rights of indigenous peoples have been clarified and strengthened by the adoption of the 2007 United Nations Declaration on the Rights of Indigenous Peoples (the UNDRIP).[1] Of course, it is an inconvertible fact that the UNDRIP is indeed a ground-breaking instrument, crystallising the right of indigenous peoples, adopted after a long period of complex negotiations. However, a more sceptical view can equally be expressed, in particular that several fundamental issues have not been resolved by the Declaration, either due to the lack of the agreement of States, or because new developments regarding the right of indigenous peoples in certain areas (mostly at the national level) have not been captured by the UNDRIP. For example, in relation to the former, the definition of the notion of 'peoples' remains unresolved. Moreover, the generality of the UNDRIP prevents it from adopting a more nuanced approach to particular developments regarding the legal position of indigenous peoples in various States. National regulations are so diversified that such a general instrument as the UNDRIP is not capable of capturing all the legal variety contained in domestic law. The case study of Greenland presented in this chapter clearly indicates that new developments concerning indigenous peoples do not fit easily into the provisions of the UNDRIP on self-determination, nor do they conform to frequently expressed views on self-determination, which have traditionally been presented as regards the division between external and internal self-determination. It may be

---

[1] United Nations Declaration on the Rights of Indigenous Peoples, GAOR 61st Session, Supp. 49, Vol. 3, 15. The United Nations Declaration on the Rights of Indigenous Peoples has been approved after 143 Member States voted in favour, 11 abstained and four – Australia, Canada, New Zealand and the United States – voted against the text.

noted that Greenland is not the only example of such new developments outside of traditional legal notions; also as regards Norway, the situation of the Saami peoples is unique, as regulated by the 2005 Finnmark Act, though discussion of this legislation is not covered in this chapter.

Of particular concern is that the mainstream theories underlying the right of self-determination of indigenous peoples, as well as the practice of international and national courts and that of the Human Rights Committee on the issue, continues not to clarify many of the pertinent issues and controversies surrounding this right. Indeed, the extent of the right and its characterisation in respect of indigenous peoples (even, as noted above, who these indigenous peoples are) are still largely unresolved questions. Therefore, the present author's hypothesis is that new developments in domestic laws concerning indigenous peoples invariably changes the focus of the debate from a traditional – increasingly sterile and staid – international discourse onto national regulations, which are characterised by a variety of legal arrangements too diversified to be grouped under one *chapeau*. Though not without its conceptual problems, analysing national laws is arguably by far a better way of understanding the contemporary legal *positions* of indigenous peoples. They may not be uniform, but at least they reflect current practice, which cannot necessarily be said about what might be found in the traditional (classical) debates on the international legal nature of the right to self-determination. Though such theoretical discourses have undoubtedly been very useful in order to crystallise and define the general parameters and legal terms of the right of self-determination and its elements for indigenous peoples; in practical terms, however, they have their short-comings and limitations, as they cannot capture the diversity contained within national systems. Therefore in order to do so, recourse to national practice appears to be absolutely necessary. The case study of Greenland, set out below, will illustrate how the notion of self-determination has thus evolved.

II. The UNDRIP, self-determination and indigenous peoples: general considerations

The notion of self-determination in general is one of the most analysed[2] (or even over-analysed) and researched areas in international law, but

---

[2] See, e.g., on general issues of self-determination, J. Crawford, *The Creation of States in International Law*, 2nd edn (Oxford University Press, 2006), pp. 107–48 and 333–421. For a review of various scholarly positions, see M. Fitzmaurice, 'The New Developments

still remains a very complex issue, including the specific question of self-determination of indigenous peoples. As any survey of theoretical approaches and the relevant case law would indicate, and as stated above, numerous questions are still open and it is unlikely that they will be resolved at the international level due to the political nature of the issues involved. In particular, the right of self-determination in a post-colonial context is one of the most discussed and daunting issues of international law. In this section only an outline of the relevant issues will be presented. However, many aspects of the right to self-determination have still not been fully clarified[3] and it remains a 'conceptual morass' of international law,[4] lacking consistent application.[5] As Crawford has said, "'[t]he right of self-determination of peoples" is perhaps the most controversial and contested of the many controversial and contested terms in the vocabulary of international law'.[6] This was evident during the proceedings before the International Court in the matter of the Advisory Opinion on *Accordance with International Law of the Unilateral Declaration in Respect of Kosovo*, where statements by various States were evidence to the fact of the continuing complex nature of the right to self-determination.[7] Specifically, the question of so-called remedial secession was the subject of many contrasting views.[8]

Regarding the Saami Peoples of the North', (2009) 16 *International Journal on Minorities and Group Rights*, in particular pp. 128–56.

[3] For a good overview of various issues relating to self-determination, see S. Wheatley, *Democracy, Minorities and International Law* (Cambridge University Press, 2005), pp. 64–124.

[4] J. Castellino, 'Conceptual Difficulties and the Rights of Indigenous Peoples', in N. Ghanea and A. Xanthaki (eds.), *Minorities, Peoples and Self-Determination* (Leiden/Boston: Martinus Nijhoff Publishers, 2005), p. 64.

[5] K. Hossain, 'Status of Indigenous Peoples in International Law', (2008) 5 *Miskolc Journal of International Law*, 25.

[6] J. Crawford, 'The Right of Self-Determination in International Law: In Development and Future', in P. Alston (ed.), *Peoples' Rights* (Oxford University Press, 2001), p. 7.

[7] www.icj-cij.org/docket/files/141/15987.pdf (last accessed 26 January 2012). The analysis of this Opinion exceeds the framework of this chapter.

[8] The Court held as follows: '[s]imilar differences existed regarding whether international law provides for a right of "remedial secession" and, if so, in what circumstances. There was also a sharp difference of views as to whether the circumstances which some participants maintained would give rise to a right of "remedial secession" were actually present in Kosovo...The Court considers that it is not necessary to resolve these questions in the present case' (paras. 82–3). *Accordance with International Law of the Unilateral Declaration in Respect of Kosovo*, Advisory Opinion of 22 July 2010, ICJ, available at www.icj-cij.org/docket/files/141/15987.pdf (last accessed 26 January 2012).

However, despite such controversies, there is no doubt that the notion of self-determination continues to be a very attractive one in international law and relations and

> [w]ith great popular appeal, demands for self-determination are being made by a growing number of groups; it has become like a large umbrella giving shelter to everybody's claims. The claims are fuelled by imprecise and incomplete language used in the international instruments and consequently the underdevelopment of the standards, by inconsistent international and national practices which are based on political and selective criteria, and be the variety and confusion of scholarly theories.[9]

It is a truism, but nevertheless worth saying, that the right of self-determination of indigenous peoples is even more ambiguous than the general discourse concerning this right.[10] Indeed, the very issue of the relationship between the right of indigenous people and minorities is far from clear-cut.[11] As Thornberry has observed, the notions of autonomy and collective rights as they relate to indigenous peoples present a different set of parameters than those applied to minorities.[12] Moreover, the issue of the right of self-determination of indigenous peoples is further complicated by the question of how indigenous peoples relate to the State.[13]

Certain national regulations of the rights of indigenous peoples will be presented to evidence that generalisations and reliance on classical and traditional constructs of the concepts do not reflect fundamental changes in the position of indigenous peoples worldwide. Developments in domestic legislation have resulted in permutations of these concepts exhibiting many divergent features; thus grouping them under one *chapeau* would appear to simplify the issues at hand. It may also be suggested that the ongoing

---

[9] G. Alfredsson, 'Indigenous Peoples and Autonomy', in M. Suksi (ed.), *Autonomy: Applications and Implications* (The Hague: Kluwer Law International, 1998), p. 136.

[10] Kingsbury writes that '[t]he construction and affirmation of distinct programme of the "rights of indigenous peoples," going beyond universal human rights and existing regimes of minority rights, has been one of the objectives of the international indigenous peoples' movement'. B. Kingsbury, 'Reconciling Five Competing Conceptual Structures of Indigenous Peoples' Claims in International and Comparative Law',(2001) 34 *New York University Journal of International Law and Politics*, 235.

[11] G. Alfredsson, 'Minorities, Indigenous and Tribal Peoples and Peoples: Definitions of Terms as a Matter of International Law', in Ghanea and Xanthaki (eds.), *Minorities, Peoples and Self-Determination*, pp. 163–72.

[12] P. Thornberry, 'Images of Autonomy and Individual and Collective Rights in International Instruments on the Rights of Minorities', in Suksi (ed.), *Autonomy: Applications and Implications*, pp. 97–124.

[13] Kingsbury, 'Reconciling Five Competing Conceptual Structures', 226.

analysis of the traditional understanding of the right to self-determination of peoples (forever linking it back to the colonial context) does not appear to depict the multifaceted reality of the situation of indigenous peoples, which has developed its own distinguishing characteristics, and therefore on this particular issue it should be viewed *outside* the paradigm of the traditional institutions of international law. Thus, in the view of the present author, the discourse concerning the right to self-determination of indigenous peoples should now be refocused onto the national level and the overriding importance of municipal law.

1. The scope of indigenous peoples' rights, including the right to self-determination

The long-standing theoretical debate on the legal character of indigenous peoples' rights has no doubt been of great importance at the initial stages of the discourse on such rights. There is no question that the rights granted in national laws to certain indigenous groups of peoples (i.e. Saami, or inhabitants of Greenland generally) are undoubtedly collective rights. Therefore, in the view of this author, a debate on a legal character of such rights is of only a historical importance at the present stage. It may be noted that at the international level, the rights granted by the 1989 International Labour Oraganization (ILO) 169 Convention on Rights of Indigenous and Tribal Peoples in Independent Countries grants collective rights.

The debate on the legal character of indigenous rights evolved around the interpretation of Article 27 of the 1960 International Covenant of Political and Civil Rights (ICCPR). Historically, it related to the rights of minorities; however, the Human Rights Committee (HRC) confirmed that this Article also defines the rights of indigenous peoples. It reads as follows:

> In those States in which ethnic, religious or linguistic minorities exist, persons belonging to such minorities shall not be denied right, in community with other members of the group, to enjoy their own culture and practice their own religion, to use their own language.

Although Article 27 can be criticised as providing 'little more than the rights, which the rest of the International Covenant says that everyone has, are not to be denied to members of certain minorities',[14] it has been

---

[14] Crawford, 'The Right of Self-determination', p. 24.

developed and interpreted by General Comments of the HRC, and its decisions and General Comments.

The 1994 HRC's General Comment stated that the rights guaranteed by Article 27 are individual rights. The Committee acknowledged territorial sovereignty and integrity of States, on the one hand but, nonetheless, described the rights flowing from Article 27 as being closely associated with territory and natural resources, in particular in respect to indigenous communities, constituting a minority, on the other. The Committee stressed that the community plays a fundamental role in the enjoyment of traditional life by indigenous peoples and announced that for that reason the rights granted by Article 27 should be exercised in a community, although they are individual rights.[15]

Moreover, according to Koivurova, regarding the HRC's practice with respect to indigenous peoples' rights, a new era was then commenced with the adoption of the concluding observations on the periodic report of Canada in 1999, which requested the Canadian government to report on the situation of its aboriginal peoples in the next period report under Article 1 of the ICCPR on self-determination. Koivurova observes that '[t]his was a significant departure from the earlier focus of the HRC; previously it had regarded indigenous peoples as covered by Article 27; now it also viewed them as peoples under the Covenant's Article 1'.[16] These new developments also manifested themselves in the *Aspirana Mahuika* case, in which the HRC first confirmed that the Optional Protocol established the procedure of individual communication regarding the alleged violation of the rights contained in Articles 6–27 of the Covenant submitted by individuals. However, the Committee added that 'the provisions of Article 1 may be be relevant to the interpretation of other rights protected by the Covenant, in particular

---

[15] UN CCPR/C/2Rev.1/Add.5. This Comment was consistent with the decision taken in the *Lubicon Band* case *(Bernard Ominayak et al. v. Canada)* where it was held that the rights protected by Article 27 include rights of persons, in community with others, to engage in economic and social activities which are part of the culture of the community to which they belong. Historical inequities and certain more recent developments threaten the way of life and culture of the Lubicon Lake Band, and constitute a violation of Article 27 so long as they continue: *Lubicon Lake Band* case *(Bernard Ominayak et al. v. Canada)*, Communication No. 167/1984, (1990) 11 *Human Rights Law Journal*, 305–11.

[16] T. Koivurova, 'From High Hopes to Disillusionment: Indigenous Peoples' Struggle to (re)Gain Their Right to Self-Determination', (2008) 15 *International Journal of Minority and Group Rights*, 1–26.

article 27'.[17] Koivurova notes that after an initial period of a rather cautious attitude by the HRC regarding indigenous peoples in light of Article 1 of the ICCPR (in conjunction with Article 27), it developed a more forceful policy. Koivurova gives the example of the report of Finland on Article 27 and indigenous people, which was criticised by the Committee as not addressing the rights of indigenous peoples in the light of Article 1 of the Covenant.[18]

The catalogue of human rights which are guaranteed to protect minorities may be summarised as follows: the right to non-discrimination; the right to preservation of identity; the right to protection of identity by the governments of States they live in, by means of measures taken by these governments; the right to establish and maintain institutions; and the right to effective participation in public affairs.[19] The fundamental question in relation to the protection of minorities is the type of rights accorded to them: individual rights, group rights or collective rights (distinctions considered further below). In some cases, the differences between rights are blurred; for example, the right to equality is an individual and a group right. For example, Eide argues that there is no doubt that the rights belonging to minorities are individual rights, even if they are enjoyed in community with others,[20] and the ILO 169 Convention accords collective rights to indigenous peoples.[21] A view was expressed that collective rights 'are not reducible to but consistent with individual rights and the basic justification of which

---

[17] *Aspirana Mahuika et al. v. New Zealand*, HRC, Communication No. 547/1993: New Zealand, para. 9.2. McGoldrick comments negatively on the lack of reference by the HRC to the margin of appreciation in relation to Article 27: D. McGoldrick, *The Human Rights Committee: Its Role in the Development of the International Covenant on Political and Civil Rights* (Oxford University Press, 1991), p. lxiii.

[18] Koivurova, 'From High Hopes to Disillusionment', 7.

[19] A. Eide, 'Commentary to the Declaration on the Rights Belonging to National or Ethnic, Religious and Linguistic Minorities', 6th Session of the Sub-Commission on the Promotion and Protection of Human Rights, UN Doc. E/CN.4/Sub.2/AC.5/2000/WP.1 (2000), 249; M. Freeman, *Human Rights: An Interdisciplinary Approach (Key Concepts)* (Cambridge: Polity Press, 2002), p. 125.

[20] Eide, 'Commentary'.

[21] However, Cassese for example, was of the view that only the entire population of an existing State constitutes 'people' with the right to self-determination: A. Cassese, *Self-Determination of Peoples: A Legal Reappraisal* (Cambridge University Press, 1999), pp. 5, and 2–62. See also the 1970 Declaration on the Principles of International Law concerning Friendly Relations and Co-operation among States, which extended the right of self-determination to peoples under colonial or racist regimes, or other forms of alien domination.

is the same as the basic justification of individual human rights and that the practical recognition of such rights is problematic'.[22] The quest for defining the legal character of collective rights led Peter Jones to the distinction between collective rights as a pooling of individual human rights, and collective rights attributed to groups through their status as groups, therefore held only by a group (i.e. 'corporate rights'). In such a division only collective rights, reducible to individual human rights, can truly be human rights.[23] Nevertheless, there seems to be a general agreement in law that a significant part of rights that indigenous peoples enjoy are corporate rights.[24] Article 27 of the ICCPR protects the minority rights of an individual. These rights are, nevertheless, enjoyed in a community. Some of the international conventions which have a bearing upon the legal position of indigenous people do, in fact, recognise collective rights, for example, the 1965 International Convention on the Elimination of All Forms of Racial Discrimination. According to this Convention, not only individuals, but groups, have the right to adequate advancement (e.g. Article 1(4)).

It is explained that the main difference between the rights of minorities and indigenous peoples are the collective rights accorded to the latter group. The purpose of minority rights is to enable minority individuals to maintain and develop their specific identity as a part of the majority community, whilst the collective rights of indigenous peoples stress their right to maintain and develop their specific society and social structures differently (or, if relevant, in parallel) with the majority community. Further, minorities aim at efficient political participation in the community of which they form a part; whilst the aim of the collective rights of indigenous peoples is to provide for them the opportunity to make their own decisions (the aim of participation in a larger political system of the society is of lesser importance).[25] Nonetheless, despite the efforts to elucidate the legal nature of all type of rights, distinctions and the relationship between them, there is still a significant lack of clarity, which is a stumbling block in any attempt to formulate clear and firm

---

[22] Freeman, *Human Rights*.

[23] P. Jones, 'Human Rights, "Group Rights and Peoples' Rights"', (1999) 21 *Human Rights Quarterly*, 80–127. On a broader issue of collective human rights and solidarity rights within the third generation of human rights, see J. Donnelly, *Universal Human Rights in Theory and Practice*, 2nd edn (Ithaca, NY: Cornell University Press, 2003).

[24] Henriksen *et al.*, 'The Saami Peoples' Right to Self-Determination', (2007) 3 *Journal of Indigenous Peoples Rights*.

[25] Ibid.

classifications. For example, both group and collective rights in fact, have a collective dimension, i.e. they both exist for the benefit of a particular organised group or collective entity, be it minorities, groups or governments. Henriksen, Åhrén and Scheinin, referenced above, consider that the most central of collective rights is the right to self-determination. Such a right (or, for that matter, other collective rights) may be the result of discrimination against peoples, rather than individuals belonging to an ethnic group.

The right to self-determination is a collective right. Peoples represent communities, consisting more of 'social creatures' than of autonomous individuals, involved in the constitution and functioning of communities. Therefore, a narrowly defined notion of self-determination does not fully reflect its true and diversified nature. The challenges facing governments in relation to the right to self-determination as pursued by indigenous peoples are many. First of all, governments have to accommodate and justify granting of special cultural and environmental requirements for indigenous people without compromising the general principle of non-discrimination in relation to their non-indigenous population; second, the claims to self-determination of indigenous peoples may be seen as threatening the territorial integrity (unity) of States, and 'such claims may potentially entail a risk of segmentation into ethnically based subdivisions of society, loss of political control and ultimately national dissolution'.[26]

It must be said that neither the ICCPR nor the International Covenant on Economic, Social and Cultural Rights (ICESCR) define what is understood by the term 'peoples' for the purposes of self-determination. Henriksen, Åhrén and Scheinin presented an extensive survey of the views of various States on 'peoples' and the right to self-determination. In the 1960s, they say, it was possible that the predominant view was that the term 'peoples' in Article 1 was understood as all inhabitants of a State or a colony. Nonetheless, the authors observe that as early as the time of the ratification of both Covenants, several States opined that the right to self-determination is not applicable exclusively within the colonial context, but constitutes a right for all peoples without any limitations. They support this view by use of the statement of the United Nations (UN) General Assembly's Third Committee, which proclaimed the right to self-determination 'as a universal right and for all time' (Article 73).

---

[26] F. Harhoff, 'The Status of Indigenous Peoples under International Law: Greenland and the Right to Self-Determination', (1994) 32 *Canadian Yearbook of International Law*, 243.

In 1999, the HRC, 'inspired' by the judgment of the Supreme Court of Canada in *the Reference re Secession of Quebec* case,[27] for the first time applied Article 1 of the ICCPR to indigenous peoples of Canada, a stand which was followed in many other cases: 'The Committee emphasizes that the right to self-determination requires, *inter alia*, that all peoples must be able to freely dispose of their natural wealth and resources and that they may not be deprived of their own means of subsistence ...The Committee also recommends that the practice of extinguishing inherent aboriginal rights be abandoned as incompatible with article 1 of the Covenant.'[28] Scheinin observes that Article 1 of the ICCPR (and the ICESCR) relates to various dimensions of self-determination: 'right to freely determine their [indigenous peoples'] status' – political dimension; and to pursue their 'economic, social and cultural development' – resource dimension. The same author clarifies that '[t]he political dimension, in turn includes an external aspect of sovereignty and an internal democratic governance which in turn can be linked to Article 25 that requires democratic governance', as often stressed by the Committee in its concluding observations.[29] Henriksen, Åhrén and Scheinin stress the paramount question of the inclusion into the scope of the right to self-determination of land rights and free disposal of natural resources.[30] The ILO 169 Convention is silent on the peoples' right to self-determination. However, some guidance can be found in the ILO Guide to the Convention, which indicates that in the Convention the term 'indigenous peoples' is used as 'peoples'.

The aim of ILO 169 Convention Indigenous and Tribal Peoples in Independent Countries is to facilitate indigenous peoples' preservation of their own social and distinct structures, within the majority society. It is argued that the 169 ILO Convention has to be viewed within the context of the right to self-determination. This is evident from the fact that this Convention, in contrast to the 107 ILO Convention Concerning the Protection and Integration of Indigenous and Other Tribal and Semi-Tribal Populations in Independent Countries, uses the term 'indigenous peoples'. The 107 ILO Convention uses the term

---

[27] *Secession of Quebec* [1998] 2 SCR 217 (Supreme Court of Canada), 37 *ILM* 1340, 1373
[28] Concluding observations on Canada, Section 8, UN Doc. CC PR/C/79/Add.105 (1999), cited in Henriksen *et al.*, 'The Saami Peoples' Right to Self-Determination'.
[29] Ibid.; M. Scheinin, 'Indigenous Peoples' Land Rights under the International Covenant on Civil and Political Rights', 9, available at: www.galdu.org/govat/doc/ind_peoples_land_rights.pdf (last accessed 26 January 2012).
[30] Henriksen *et al.*, 'The Saami Peoples' Right to Self-Determination', Section 5-1 and 5-2

'indigenous populations', which indicates the recognition of the existence of organised societies with an identity of their own, rather than groupings sharing some racial or cultural characteristics. The main purpose of the 107 ILO Convention was to provide protection to indigenous peoples; however, it was also based on a more limited premise as to the nature of integration between indigenous and tribal populations and the non-indigenous society. The 169 Convention has changed the approach to one of respect for the cultures, ways of life, traditions and customary laws of the indigenous and tribal peoples. It is based on the presumption of their existence, forming a part of their national societies with their own identity, their own structures and their own traditions. The Convention is based on a principle that these indigenous structures and ways of life have an intrinsic value requiring protection. The 169 ILO Convention takes the approach that in most cases indigenous peoples are able to voice their own concerns and ideas and also to participate in the decision-making process in matters which affect them.[31]

The practice of the HRC in acknowledging the link between Articles 1 and 27 of the ICPPR has not been consistent, however. In its General Comment No. 23 on Article 27, the HRC observed that the ICPPR clearly distinguishes between the right to self-determination and the rights protected under Article 27.[32] However, analysis of the HRC General Comment No. 12 indicates that it linked individual human rights and self-determination:

> The right of self-determination is of particular importance because its realization is an essential condition for the effective guarantee and observance of individual human rights and for the promotion and strengthening of those rights. It is for that reason that States set forth the right of self-determination in a provision of positive law in both

---

[31] The 169 Convention of the International Labour Organisation on Indigenous and Tribal Peoples in Independent Countries 1989 (entered into force 5 September 1991). Number of ratifications 22, 72 *ILO Official Bull.*, 59, *UNTS* 1650, No. 28383; 107 ILO Convention Concerning the Protection and Integration of Indigenous and Other Tribal and Semi-Tribal Populations in Independent Countries, entered in force 2 June 1959 17 ratifications; 328 UNTS 247, M. Tomei and L. Swepston, *Indigenous and Tribal People: A Guide to ILO Convention No 169* (Geneva: ILO, 1996), available at: www.indigenousrights watch.org/librarydocuments/Guide%20to%20ILO%20169.doc (last accessed 26 January 2012).

[32] Human Rights Committee, *General Comment 23 on Article 27* (50th session, 1994), Compilation of General Comments and General Recommendations Adopted by the Human Rights Treaty Bodies, UN Doc. HRI/GEN/1/Rev.1 (1994).

Covenants and placed this provision as article 1 apart from and before all
of the other rights in the two Covenants.[33]

The HRC has observed several times that in the case of indigenous
peoples, the preservation and use of their land resources constitutes an
essential right of persons belonging to such a group. The HRC has made
several statements in relation to Article 1. For example, in its concluding
remarks on Canada, it has stressed that the right to self-determination
includes, *inter alia*, 'free disposal by peoples of their natural resources
and the prohibition of their deprivation of natural means of subsistence'.[34] The HRC took a stand based on indivisibility and interdependence of human rights law, and stated that Article 1 should be used as a
tool in interpreting other individual rights under the Covenant including, *inter alia*, those stemming from Article 27. The relationship between
Articles 1 and 27 was analysed by Scheinin, who was of the view that
indigenous peoples should use it as a tool for making their case for the
recognition of their right of self-determination, as he argued that for
indigenous peoples the right of self-determination is in fact the right of
freedom of the disposal of their natural resources and the negative
guarantee not to be deprived of their own means of subsistence.[35]
Therefore, as Castellino and Gilbert argue, the right to self-determination
is not a static right.[36] They are also of the view that the applicability of
Article 1(1) should be considered as deriving from the acceptance of Article
1(2), 'as the article as a whole was in place to deal with the situation of
subjugated peoples'.[37]

Traditional theories, which aimed at the reconciliation of these conflicting views, were based on the premise of so-called 'external' and 'internal'
self-determination, a division which was also endorsed by States. However,
these concepts again suffer from vagueness, and there are no general or
widely accepted definitions of both types of self-determination, as James

---

[33] Human Rights Committee, *General Comment No. 12, Article 1*, para. 1 (21st session,
1984), in ibid., 12.

[34] M. Scheinin, 'The Right to Enjoy a Distinct Culture', in T. Orlin *et al.* (eds.), *The
Jurisprudence of Human Rights Law: A Comparative Interpretative Approach* (Turku:
Abo Akademi University, 2000), p.159

[35] M. Scheinin, 'The Right to Self-Determination under the Covenant of Civil and Political
Rights', in P. Aikio and M. Scheinin (eds.), *Operationalizing the Right of Indigenous
Peoples to Self-Determination* (Turku: Abo Academy University, 2000), pp. 179–99.

[36] J. Castellino and J. Gilbert, 'Self-Determination, Indigenous Peoples and Minorities',
(2003) 3 *Maquarie Law Journal*, 172.

[37] Ibid., 176.

Summers considers in Chapter 9 above. External self-determination is not only secession from a State, but also considered to be the right to participate in international organisations and conferences; thus a treaty-making power.[38] Henriksen, Åhrén and Scheinin submit that the internal aspect of the right to self-determination of indigenous peoples includes a right to determine their own cultural, social and economic development. Therefore, internal aspects of the right to self-determination should cover all issues fundamental for maintaining and developing the cultural, social and economic aspects of the indigenous peoples' communities. Such a right should also include the right to land and natural resources.[39] The special relationship of indigenous peoples with the environment 'should not be interpreted, however, as a freedom to engage in unsustainable uses of the environment. The right to self-determination must be understood in the context of common responsibilities for maintaining the health of our ecological systems, which know no jurisdictional boundaries.'[40] The issue of the right to external self-determination is further complicated by the recent views that the participation by indigenous peoples in the political process which transcends States boundaries should itself be assessed as the dimension of external self-determination without secession.[41]

In Article 3 of the UNDRIP the formulation of the right to self-determination is an outcome of long-term struggle. In 1994, Russel Barsh wrote that:

> [a]rguing that they were 'peoples' under United Nations Charter, indigenous peoples have been struggling for the explicit recognition of their unqualified right to self determination. Such recognition would establish that indigenous peoples are members of the international community who have legal personality under international law – 'subjects' of international legal rights and duties rather than mere 'objects' of international concern. Although most United Nations Member States shrink fearfully

---

[38] G. Alfredsson, 'The Right of Self-Determination and Indigenous Peoples', in C. Tomuschat (ed.), *Modern Law of Self-Determination* (The Hague/Boston: Martinus Nijhoff Publishers, 1983), pp. 41–54. The author presents arguments for and against the right of external self-determination of indigenous peoples.

[39] Henriksen *et al.*, The Saami Peoples' Right to Self-Determination' at Section 6–2.

[40] B. J. Richardson, 'Indigenous Peoples, International Law and Sustainability', (2001) 10 *Review of European Community and International Environmental Law*, 11.

[41] J. B. Henriksen, 'Implementation of the Right of Self-Determination of Indigenous Peoples', (2001) 3 *Indigenous Affairs*, 6–21; T. Koivurova and L. Heinämäki, 'The Participation of Indigenous Peoples in International Norm-Making in the Arctic', (2006) 42 *Polar Record*, 101–9. This concerned the Draft 2005 Saami Convention, Art. 19, that Saami representation in international institutions and their participation in international meetings, is an expression of the external right of self-determination.

from explicit references to 'peoples' and 'self-determination' in the
United Nations documents relating to indigenous peoples in deed if
not always in word.[42]

However, as will be shown in the next section, the adoption of the
UNDRIP did not satisfactorily solve all problems relating to indigenous
peoples, as many of them are still outstanding and perhaps will never be
resolved. The formulation of Article 3 of the UNDRIP gave rise to many
interpretations, and the quest for its exact meaning continues. The most
adhered-to interpretation is based on the assumption of the right of
indigenous peoples to freely negotiate their political status, and their
access to political institutions of a State – thus accommodating their
aspirations in a democratic manner – embodies the right to self-
determination in Article 3 of the UNDRIP. Indigenous peoples have
the correlative duty to share power with the existing State.[43] Indeed, it is
also emphasised that the right to land plays a crucial role in the self-
determination of indigenous peoples. The right to land can be seen as an
element of self-determination which contributes to indigenous peoples'
well-being and living as human being according to their choices,
which some authors perceive as an element of the expression of self-
determination more important than having its own institutions, judges,
etc.[44] According to Weissner, self-determination and self-governance
also obliges States to embrace cultural rights of indigenous peoples, as
incorporated in Article 3 of the UNDRIP.[45]

The Report of the International Law Association (ILA) Committee on
the Rights of Indigenous Peoples, commenting on Article 46 UNDRIP –
which references the importance of territorial integrity and political
unity of States – supports the view that it does not grant indigenous
peoples a wider right to self-determination, i.e. secession. However, it
also adds that 'indigenous peoples continue to have the same right that
all other peoples have to move toward the secession in appropriate

---

[42] R. Barsh, 'Indigenous Peoples in the 1990s: From Object to Subject of International Law',
(1994) 7 *Harvard Human Rights Journal*, 35.

[43] E.-I. Daes, 'An Overview of the History of Indigenous Peoples: Self-Determination and
the United Nations', (2008) 21 *Cambridge Review of International Affairs*, 23.

[44] E.-I. Daes, 'The Concept of Self-Determination and Autonomy of Indigenous Peoples in
the Draft United Nations Declaration of Indigenous Peoples', (2001)14 *Thomas Law
Review*, 263 *et seq*.

[45] S. Weissner, 'Indigenous Sovereignty: A Reassessment in Light of the UN Declaration on
the Rights of Indigenous Peoples', (2008) 41 *Vanderbilt Journal of Transnational Law*,
1176.

cases'.[46] Support for this statement is found in the case of the Supreme Court of Canada regarding the secession of Quebec.[47]

In the view of the present author, the ongoing debate on indigenous peoples' rights and the content of their right to self-determination has not resulted in a satisfactory outcome. The present author is of the (perhaps controversial) view that despite the long-standing discussion, even the fundamental issue of the differentiation between indigenous peoples and minorities has not been fully explored and explained. That state of affairs is perhaps due to the sheer impossibility of a precise and all-encompassing definition of certain rights, despite the efforts invested in the solving of this question. The variety of contemporary regulations escapes one single strict definition, and strengthens the argument that a further debate should be focused on the variety of national approaches, instead of a quest for general and elusive definitions.

IV.   The UNDRIP, autonomy and indigenous peoples

1   General considerations

Autonomy (self-government) is a complex area of international law and exceeds the framework of this chapter. Generally there are different types of autonomy: territorial (e.g. Greenland), non-territorial (personal) and cultural (functional).[48] There are also differences between autonomy in national and international legal orders. In a domestic legal order, autonomy constitutes a part of the self-government of certain public corporation and institutions, including the power to regulate their own affairs by enacting legal rules. In the international legal order autonomy means that certain portions of the State's territory have the power to govern themselves in some matters by way of promulgating laws and statutes, without, however, being an independent State.[49] The most important feature of autonomy, it may be said, is that under its regime an internal self-government is granted

---

[46] International Law Association, *Rights of Indigenous Peoples: Interim Report of the Hague Conference* (2010), available at: www.ila-hq.org/en/committees/draft-committee-reports-the-hague-2010.cfm (last accessed 26 January 2012).

[47] *Secession of Quebec*, para. 138. The Court said that all peoples have 'the right to external self-determination [. . .] where a definable group is denied meaningful access to government to pursue their political, economic, social and cultural development'.

[48] See in general, H.-J. Heintze, 'On the Legal Understanding of Autonomy', in Suksi (ed.), *Autonomy: Applications and Implications*, pp. 7–42.

[49] Ibid., p. 7.

to a region or group of persons in recognition of a partial independence from the national or a central government.[50]

What is also of importance is that practice shows that autonomy is always based on the specific circumstances of the case, and therefore it defies general definitions.[51] For that reason, in legal theory 'autonomy is a general legal term to be given concrete content'.[52] Autonomy means bestowing certain rights on certain specific groups of population, such as linguistic, cultural and ethnic minorities.[53] Autonomy is regarded as the only legal institution which can effectively protect minorities of a State – a 'queen' of human rights protection mechanisms.[54] This institution, however, has raised some concerns. For example, it was said that it may lead to ethnic conflicts between the groups, in the event of one of them being granted differentiated treatment. The subject of autonomy is always a group (not an individual), such as minority or indigenous peoples. Therefore, a necessary condition for autonomy is the recognition as a group, on the one hand, and the acceptance of collective rights, on the other. The concept of collective rights, however, is one of the areas of international law, still lacking proper understanding, which may lead to further problems with autonomy.[55] Finally, it may be said that content of autonomous arrangements between States differs very considerably; the 'models of accommodation' may be expressly recognised in constitutions of States or 'through ethnic calculation in legislative, executive and judicial organs to decentralisation, regionalisation and federalism'.[56]

It is a widely accepted view that the key concept within the paradigm of internal self-determination appears to be autonomy. As Loukacheva explains, whatever its form, '[i]t should allow direct indigenous participation in international affairs when it concerns their homelands, and include indigenous people involvement in security issues relevant to the development of their lands'.[57] Loukacheva is of the view that there is no one rigid definition of autonomy that is accepted in international law. In that author's view, the lack of clarity makes it attractive to many groups

---

[50] Ibid.   [51] Ibid., p. 8   [52] Ibid.   [53] Ibid., p. 9   [54] Ibid., p. 10   [55] Ibid., p. 13.
[56] Ibid., p. 18.
[57] N. Loukacheva, 'On Autonomy and Law', Working Paper (2005), available at www.socialsciences.mcmaster.ca/institute-on-globalization-and-the-human-condition/documents/IGHC-WPS_05-3_Loukacheva.pdf (last accessed 26 January 2012); N. Loukacheva, *The Arctic Promise. Legal and Political Autonomy of Greenland and Nunavut* (Toronto University Press, 2007); see also, S. Roach, 'Minority Rights and Emergent International Rights to Autonomy: A Historical and Normative Assessment', (2004)11 *International Journal on Minority and Group Rights*, 411–32.

and allows for flexibility in institutional arrangements. In the view of the present author, however, it may also lead to conflicts, as ultimately it is up to a State how to frame the specifics of autonomy and thus give it meaningful effect. Therefore, aspirations of indigenous peoples regarding a broad application of this concept may be dashed, depending on national regulation. Loukacheva further argues that notwithstanding the system of the autonomy within the ambit of internal self-determination, it should have the following characteristics:

> a strong voluntary will of the population to achieve autonomy existence of particular geographical, demographic, or historical factors, cultural, linguistic, and ethnic distinctiveness; creation of a legislative body elected by local residents in a democratic way and capable to enact its own legislation, as well as the establishment of an executive body; provisions of conditions for economic sustainability and a financial base versus fiscal dependency on central/federal authorities and pragmatic expectations of future financial independence and liability for managing its own affairs; the desire and ability of all residents of the autonomous entity to be a part of existing or to be building structures and institutions, making them more amenable to peoples' aspirations and needs.[58]

Autonomy means the cultural, political and legislative inclusion of indigenous peoples into the national system, and is sufficiently broad to impact upon the policies of a State. Therefore, 'inclusion' raises many questions as to its extent in the political system of a State, in order to represent autonomy. As Wheatley observes, 'modern justification for territorial self-government, that is, autonomy, concern the idea of cultural identity and integrity, which allows certain groups (such as ethnic, linguistic, cultural, etc.) to pursue their own competing nation-building, including spreading their societal culture through their traditional territory'.[59] Xanthaki argues, however, that autonomy, while possessing many advantages, 'is not a panacea for indigenous problems around the world'.[60] It can be disadvantageous, as it may promote segregation and separation; may fail to encourage dialogue; may adversely affect the evolution of the group, prompting a stagnated image; and may promote a narrow view of stability.[61]

---

[58] Loukacheva, *Arctic Promise*, p. 21.
[59] S. Wheatley, *Democracy, Minorities and International Law*, pp. 64–124, and p. 125.
[60] A. Xanthaki, *Indigenous Rights and United Nations Standard: Self-Determination, Culture and Lands* (Cambridge University Press, 2007), pp. 165–6.
[61] ILA Report, 166.

Article 5 of the UNDRIP is particularly relevant here, as it includes two fundamental aspects: the right of indigenous peoples to maintain and strengthen their distinct political, legal, economic, social and cultural institutions, and the right to participate fully, if they so choose, in the political, economic, social and cultural life of the State. The 2010 ILA Report interpreted this Article as including the right of indigenous peoples to 'determine their political status' that is a key element of their right to self-determination. Moreover, since the concept of 'institution' is not defined by the provision, the Report assumes that an open-ended meaning can be accorded to it, to include the regulation of social, economic and political life through the laws, traditions and customs adopted or recognised by the political and legal institutions of indigenous peoples. Further, States have a general duty of non-interference in the workings of these institutions, on the condition that they respect basic human rights standards.[62] The Report explains that the second aspect of Article 5, i.e. the participatory right of indigenous peoples to take part in the political, economic, social and cultural life of the State, is in accordance with the general rule of international human rights law, that all citizens enjoy rights of political participation on the basis of equality. This right also includes negative and positive aspects. The first is non-interference in the enjoyment of the right, and the second requires the State to introduce the necessary measures to guarantee the effective enjoyment of the rights of political participation. The expression 'so they choose', affirms the prohibition imposed on a State not to force the participation of indigenous peoples in the political and other spheres of the life of the State, thus confirming the absolute prohibition of forced assimilation under international law.[63]

Connected to this are Articles 18 and 19, which need to be read jointly. Article 18 recognises the right to collective participation and establishes that indigenous peoples 'have the right to participate in decision-making in matters which would affect their rights, through representatives chosen by themselves in accordance with their own procedures, as well as to maintain and develop their own indigenous decision-making institutions'. The modalities of this participation are not specified, but must be effective. In order to achieve this aim, two conditions must be fulfilled: procedural and substantive. The first is one that grants indigenous peoples the possibility of participating in decision-making processes. This may require a multitude of arrangements, such as the

---

[62] Ibid., 14.   [63] Ibid.

provision of relevant information in indigenous languages, as well as that mechanisms and institutions are available for participation and indigenous peoples are made aware of their existence. The second element demonstrates the idea of effective political participation through the capacity to influence the outcomes of decision-making processes.[64]

Article 19 is equally important and establishes a collective right which requires States to 'consult and cooperate in good faith with the indigenous peoples concerned through their own representative institutions in order to obtain their free, prior and informed consent before adopting and implementing legislative or administrative measures that may affect them'. The ILA Report stresses that indigenous communities must be aware of the possible effects of any measure adopted by a State before their consent is granted.[65] Other Articles which bear on the right to autonomy or self-government are Articles 27,[66] 34,[67] 35[68] and 36.[69]

Autonomy, similar to the right to self-determination, is defined in broad brushstrokes and cannot depict its divergent forms in various

---

[64] Ibid.

[65] Ibid. The Report also raises the question of the right to a *veto* 'in relation to the adoption of the measures concerned or, rather, simply presupposes that States have only a duty to consult in good faith with indigenous peoples with the objective of reaching a consensus. In this respect, while the ideas of democracy and political equality of citizens would suggest that no individual or group within the society should be provided with a veto over legislation with majority support, this conclusion is inconsistent with the recognition of collective rights of indigenous peoples favour of indigenous peoples seems to be confirmed by the object and purpose of UNDRIP, as shown by other provisions included in its text, as well as by pertinent international practice' (pp. 14–15).

[66] 'States shall establish and implement, in conjunction with indigenous peoples concerned, a fair, independent, impartial, open and transparent process, giving due recognition to indigenous peoples' laws, traditions, customs and land tenure systems, to recognize and adjudicate the rights of indigenous peoples pertaining to their lands, territories and resources, including those which were traditionally owned or otherwise occupied or used.'

[67] 'Indigenous peoples have the right to promote, develop and maintain their institutional structures and their distinctive customs, spirituality, traditions, procedures, practices and, in the cases where they exist, juridical systems or customs, in accordance with international human rights standards.'

[68] 'Indigenous peoples have the right to determine the responsibilities of individuals to their communities.'

[69] '1. Indigenous peoples, in particular those divided by international borders, have the right to maintain and develop contacts, relations and cooperation, including activities for spiritual, cultural, political, economic and social purposes, with their own members as well as other peoples across borders. 2. States, in consultation and cooperation with indigenous peoples, shall take effective measures to facilitate the exercise and ensure the implementation of this right.'

national jurisdictions. In practice, there is a multitude of variations, in particular concerning institutional arrangements and substantive rights, a variety which again has not been captured by general provisions of the UNDRIP. The substantive rights granted to indigenous peoples by different States are so diverse that they are mostly incomparable. The procedural rights are more uniform and the right of the prior, informed consent is accepted in almost all jurisdictions. Nevertheless, the primary characteristic remains the differences between States, as the case study below on Greenland will indicate.

V.   Greenland

The legal situation of Greenland is very complicated, as it has undergone a development from a Danish colony, through being a part of the territory of Denmark, then home rule, to self-government (the Act in force since 2009). Prior to 1953, Greenland constituted a colonial territory of Denmark within the scope of Article 73 of the UN Charter. On the basis of Resolution 849 (IX), from 1954[70] Greenland became part of Denmark. In 1978 a new Act was promulgated establishing Greenland home rule.[71] Its constitutional status was the subject of many controversies. Mostly it referred to the possible necessity of constitutional amendment in order to accommodate the Greenlanders' rights. Such rights included, *inter alia*, the right to nullify laws and orders promulgated by the Parliament of Denmark (the *Folketing*) and the Government.[72]

From the point of view of the substantive provisions, the Home Rule Act provided that Greenland is a distinct community within the Kingdom of Denmark. The Greenland Home Rule authorities consisted of the Assembly elected in Greenland (the *Landsting*) and the administration headed by an Executive (the *Landsstyre*) (Section 1). According to Section 4 of the Act, the home rule authorities determined the jurisdiction in any field or part of such field listed in the Schedule to the Act, which can be transferred to the home rule authorities. One of the most important provisions of the law was Section 8, which stated that the resident population of Greenland has the fundamental right to its natural resources. In order

---

[70] Cessation of the Transmission of the Information under Article 73e of the Charter in Respect of Greenland, Resolutions adopted on the reports of the Fourth Committee http://daccess-dds-ny.un.org/doc/RESOLUTION/GEN/NR0/095/84/IMG/NR009584.pdf?OpenElement (last accessed 19 March 2012).

[71] Appendix 1.6, The Greenland Home Rule Act, Act No. 577 of 29 November 1978.

[72] Harhoff, 'The Status of Indigenous Peoples', 28.

to safeguard the rights of the resident population regarding non-living resources and to protect the unity of the Kingdom of Denmark, it was enacted that preliminary study, prospecting and the exploitation of these resources were to be regulated by agreement by the Government and *Landsstyre*. In particular, the home rule authorities were bound by the obligations arising from international agreements concluded by Denmark. Conduct of foreign relations remained within the jurisdiction of central authorities (Section 11). In matters of particular interest for Greenland, the central authorities, on the request of home rule authorities, might authorise them to negotiate directly, with the cooperation of the Foreign Service of Denmark, provided such negotiations were not incompatible with the unity of the Kingdom of Denmark (Section 16). For instance, the Home Rule Government concluded bilateral treaties on fisheries with Norway. It may also be mentioned that Greenland is party to the 1992 North Atlantic Marine Mammal Commission, together with the Faroe Islands, Iceland and Norway.[73] A vast range of responsibilities was transferred to the Home Rule Government, such as the management of municipalities, taxes, schools, management of fishing, both commercial and non-commercial hunting, the training of teachers, conservation, labour market regulations, traffic management, financial support industry, air traffic, competition regulation and its health service.[74] From the above-discussed legal structure, it can be said that Home Rule bestowed on Greenland a certain degree of autonomy.

In 2009, Greenland's legal structure developed further and at present is regulated by the Act on Self-Government. Section 21(1) thereof states as follows: 'Decisions regarding Greenland's independence shall be adopted by the people of Greenland.' The wish of Greenland's people to be independent will create a complex process involving several stages, completion of which will take a considerable period of time. As it stands at present, they have rights to the following areas (without exercising the right of independence): to determine their political status; autonomy (self-government) obtainable within all areas of competence (with the exception of five areas); Danish Government bills and draft administrative orders will be submitted for comments (Sections 17–18); Greenland can conclude certain treaties (Section 13); it can pursue its economic, social and cultural development; and the Greenlandic language will

---

[73] Text of the NAMMCO Agreement, available at: www.nammco.no/webcronize/images/Nammco/659.pdf (last accessed 26 January 2012).
[74] See Harhoff, 'The Status of Indigenous Peoples', 28.

be the official language (Section 20). The Government of Greenland (the *Naalakkersuisut*) cooperates in international affairs with a view to safeguarding the interests of the country, as well as in general interests of the Kingdom of Denmark (Section 11). The provisions concerning the conclusion of international agreements are extensive. The principal rule is that the Government of Greenland may, on behalf of the Kingdom of Denmark, negotiate and conclude agreements (including administrative agreements) under international law with foreign States and international organisations which exclusively concern Greenland and relate entirely to fields of responsibility that have been taken over (Section 12).

Under the Act there are only five areas of competence which cannot be bestowed on Greenland: the constitution; nationality; the Supreme Court; foreign defence and security policy; and currency and monetary policy. In so far as the rights to mineral resources are concerned, Greenland enjoys the property rights of disposal over and exploitation of the mineral resources in its subsoil. Nevertheless, the Kingdom of Denmark will formally continue to have sovereignty over Greenland. The Act also provides that the government will grant the Greenland self-government authorities an annual subsidy of Danish kronor 4,439.6 million (this subsidy will be adjusted annually, Art. 5). However, if the revenue from mineral resource activities in Greenland accrues to its self-government authorities, the subsidy shall be reduced by the amount corresponding to half of the revenue if it exceeds seventy-five million kronor in a given year (Art. 8). During the first five years of self-governance, the Government of Denmark and the Self-Government of Greenland authorities will cooperate on matters concerning mineral resources. After the expiry of the five-year period, the Government of Greenland will decide whether to renew the agreement. Should the block grants be reduced to zero, both governments will commence negotiations regarding their future economic relations.

There are several differences between home rule and self-government. Under home rule, the Danish Parliament and administration retained control over some areas of governance, such as the judicial system and mineral resources, defence and foreign policy. The Home Rule Act did not mention the right of Greenland to future sovereignty. It may be said that home rule established regional governance but combined it with national characteristics, however, maintaining Danish influence through block grants and foreign policy. It may also be said that home rule secured, to a certain extent, continuity of the Kingdom of Denmark, but at the same time was a necessary measure to constitute a step forward to gradual independence of the population of Greenland.[75]

Increased self-government in Greenland is not, of course, a declaration of independence, as it is still part of the Danish Commonwealth. Interestingly, the legal character of self-governance is ruled both by national law (the Constitution of Denmark) and international law (in so far as it concerns the right to self-determination of peoples of Greenland). It may be said that the implementation of self-government is a gradual and progressive takeover of new areas of governance, subject to administrative and economic conditions.

It was observed that self-governance is an institution between home rule and full independence.[76] The main issue concerning the future gaining of independence by Greenland is not a political, but an economic one, i.e. it depends on Greenland becoming self-sufficient (sustainable) in financial and economic terms. However, this may prove to be a very lengthy process, as gaining such economic independence relies on minerals, including oil reserves, the existence of which have not yet been confirmed. The movement within Greenland to attract foreign capital, in order to gain independence from Denmark, was met with some criticism that it would bring a new type of dependency.[77]

As stated above, though Greenland remains part of the Commonwealth of Denmark, the Self-Government Act does not exclude the legal possibility of Greenland declaring its full independence, granted by the Constitution of Denmark based on a treaty between the Danish Government and Greenland. However, there are several questions which should be raised. First, whether independence granted on the basis of a constitutional right can qualify as an external self-determination (secession). Secondly, who are the beneficiaries (or units) of this right: the 'people of Greenland' as a whole (indigenous and non-indigenous), or perhaps indigenous peoples have a further and separate right?[78] In the case of Greenland, the right to independence belongs to the territory of

---

[75] N. D. Graugaard, 'National Identity in Greenland in the Age of Self-Government', Centre for the Critical Study of Global Power and Politics, Working Paper, CSGP 09/5 (Ontario, Canada: Trent University, 2009), 46, available at www.trentu.ca/globalpolitics (last accessed 26 January 2012) (citing Dahl, *Arktisk Selvystre* (*Arctic Self-Governance*) (Viborg: Akademisk Forlag, 1986), p. 128.

[76] Graugaard, 'National Identity in Greenland', 47–8.   [77] Ibid., 50–4.

[78] See situation in Fiji (the question of self-determination and conflict between indigenous peoples and the Indian population in Fiji). Crawford, *The Creation of states*, pp. 333–4; C. H. Grant and M. Kirton (eds.), *Governance, Conflict Analysis and Conflict Resolution* (Kingston: Ian Randle Publishers, 2007).

Greenland (including both the indigenous and non-indigenous population). Further, as the independence of Greenland is granted by an Act of
the Danish Parliament, it is thus a matter of internal law of Denmark, not
of general international law.

Greenland is also an example of problems concerning the definition of
indigenous peoples. In 1999, a case was brought to the ILO alleging that
Denmark had failed to comply with Article 14(2) of Convention No. 169
ILO Convention.[79] The complaint related to the relocation in May 1953 of
the population living in the settlement of Uummannaq (Thule District) in
north-western Greenland. The reason was the extension of the Thule air
base. Subsequently, the Uummannaq population claimed specific land
rights within the Greenlandic territory. In the context of this case, the
question arose whether the Uummannaq population was distinct from
the Inuit population of Greenland, which merited distinct land rights. The
ILO Tripartite Committee noted that the Parties agreed that at the time of
relocation other Inuit communities lived there, that the Uummannaq spoke
the same language and engaged in the same activities (hunting, trapping
and fishing) and that they identified themselves as Greenlanders. The
Committee also found that this community shared the same social, cultural
and political conditions as the rest of Greenland. Therefore the
Uummannaq were considered no different or separate from other peoples
of Greenland.[80] According to Article 1(1) of the 169 ILO Convention, self-
identification is one of the most fundamental criteria for defining the
peoples to which the Convention is applicable. However, in this case, the
criterion of self-identification may be said to have acquired an 'objective'
dimension. The Committee was of the view that there was no basis for
considering the inhabitants of the Uummannaq community to be separate
'peoples' from other Greenlanders. The Committee noted that 'the land
traditionally occupied by the Inuit people has been identified and consists of
the entire territory of Greenland' and therefore 'under the particular circumstances of this case, the Committee considers that to call for a demarcation of lands within Greenland for the benefit of a specific group of
Greenlanders would run counter to the well-established system of collective

---

[79] This Article stipulates that governments shall take steps to identify the lands that
indigenous peoples traditionally occupy, and to guarantee effective protection of their
rights of ownership and possession.

[80] B. Feiring, *Indigenous & Tribal People's Rights in Practice – A Guide to ILO Convention
No. 169*, 10–11, available at: www.ilo.org/wcmsp5/groups/public/—ed_norm/—normes/
documents/publication/wcms_106474.pdf (last accessed 26 January 2012).

land rights based on Greenlandic tradition and maintained by the Greenland Home Rule Authorities'.[81]

It must also be added that an expert on the rights of indigenous peoples, Professor Alfredsson, was of the view that the colonial past of Greenland is the core of their claims for independence, thus giving them a different legal basis to external self-determination from other indigenous peoples, since colonisation itself constitutes a legal ground for external self-determination.[82] From the historical point of view, Greenland was a colony of Norway until 1814, when, under the Treaty of Kiel, Sweden and Norway ceded the Atlantic possessions of Norway to Denmark. Denmark confirmed the colonial status of Greenland when it had Greenland listed an a non-governing territory under Chapter XI of the UN Charter. Denmark was submitting annual reports to the UN on conditions of the territory, under Article 73 of the UN Charter, until 1954, when it announced that Greenland was integrated with the metropolitan territory.[83] This was effected by the 1953 constitutional amendment, on the basis of which the peoples of Greenland obtained the right to send two representatives to the national Parliament. As Professor Alfredsson argues, Denmark attempted to internationalise this internal act by promoting the Resolution through the UN General Assembly, which removed Greenland from the list of non-self-governing territories, and this Resolution stated that the peoples of Greenland had exercised their free right to self-determination.[84] Regarding the integration process, it was noted that Greenlanders did not actively participate in the promulgation of the Act of 1953, and several irregularities were committed concerning the General Assembly's substantive and procedural requirements regarding the exercise of colonial peoples' rights to self-determination.[85] Therefore it was argued that the validity of Greenland's integration with Denmark cannot be considered binding.[86] However, a view was expressed that these irregularities were not significant enough to render the integration process

---

[81] Ibid., 11.

[82] G. Alfredsson, 'Greenland and the Law of Political Decolonisation', (1992) 25 *German Yearbook of International Law*, 290–308.

[83] Ibid., 300.

[84] K. Göcke, 'The 2008 Referendum of Greenland's Autonomy and What It Means for Greenland's Future', (2009) 69 *Zeitschrift für ausländisches öffentliches Recht und Völkerrecht*, 105.

[85] Alfredsson, 'Greenland', 308.   [86] Ibid.

invalid.[87] Moreover, Göcke argues, contrary to Professor Alfredsson's views, that when the Greenlanders decided to integrate with Denmark on an equal basis in 1953, they were fully informed of the alternative of becoming an independent State, but at that time independence was not considered a desirable option. The Provincial Council of Greenland unanimously accepted the proposal of integration.[88] However, Alfredsson contends that it was not fully informed about the content of constitutional amendment integrating Greenland with the mother country, and that the composition of the Council was regulated by a statute adopted when Greenlanders had no representatives in the Danish Parliament.[89] Göcke puts forward a further argument that at no time had Greenlanders complained about the integration process or challenged its validity.[90] She also observes that the criticism of the integration of Greenland is based on the assumption of the colonial peoples' right to self-determination which had already been recognised under international law in 1953–4. However, she argues, that in this period such a right had not yet emerged as a norm of customary international law.[91]

VI.   Conclusions

The right to self-determination of indigenous peoples (one of the most complicated issues in international law), is also very different in practice, as arrangements in various States would grant divergent rights to indigenous peoples.

The classical discussion on the external and internal right to self-determination, in the view of this author, is not as meaningful as it was in the past. There are authors who had always found such a division very unhelpful.[92] The issues of self-government and autonomy have developed and must be approached as a process, not a static institution in which legal characteristics are permanently set. The best example is the legal status of Greenland, which has evolved from a colony into self-government, granting Greenland the right to claim independence. There

---

[87] J.E. Rytter, 'Self-Determination of Colonial Peoples – The Case of Greenland Revisited', (2008) 77 *Nordic Journal of International Law*, 388; Göcke, 'The 2008 Referendum', 115.

[88] Rytter, 'Sef-Determination', 388.   [89] Alfredsson, 'Greenland', 303–4.

[90] Göcke,'The 2008 Referendum', 116.   [91] Ibid.

[92] See, Alfredsson, 'The Right of Self-Determination', pp. 50–4.

also many other forms; each and every State with indigenous peoples, such as Norway, has very diverse institutions. As Loukacheva stated:

> [t]his analysis of the extensive international involvement of the Inuit in trans-national, global, and indigenous politics reveals the necessity of a new dimension in international law and domestic legal regimes regarding the legal capacity of indigenous peoples as international actors. These activities do not challenge the sovereignty of former colonisers but they call for a new partnership with national states for the protection and promotion of indigenous cultures, traditions, and knowledge.[93]

Therefore, the discussion on the right of self-determination of peoples has to be more practical, changing focus from well-rehearsed debate, and taking into account new developments.

The extremely long period of the negotiation of the UNDRIP and contentious debates surrounding its drafting process and adoption, impacted on its content, though possibly never fully reflecting the evolution in indigenous rights. If the rights of indigenous peoples are approached as an ongoing process which, especially in recent periods, has been developing very robustly, then the provisions contained in the UNDRIP can be assessed as outlining only in a *very general manner* the rights of indigenous peoples, and certainly not reflecting their dynamic character.

The UNDRIP is also in part aspirational, in so far as it relates to the rights to land and natural resources by indigenous peoples. Therefore the focal point of the debate on the question of self-determination of indigenous peoples has been changed from international into national law, which is usually more robust and offers new solutions in contrast to international law, which for a very long period of time has been centred on discussion of the right to secession, and internal and external self-determination, without reaching firm conclusions.

As was suggested, the right to self-determination regarding indigenous peoples as defined in the UNDRIP did not really bring anything new to the debate. For instance, the question of the definition of who are indigenous peoples was left open, it sometimes being argued that there is no need for such a definition as it would be unduly stifling and restrictive. The author is of the view that autonomy (which is mentioned in Art. 4 of the UNDRIP) is probably the most important development regarding the rights of indigenous peoples. However, as has been explained,

---

[93] N. Loukacheva, 'Arctic Indigenous Peoples' Internationalism: In Search of a Legal Justification', (2009) 45 *Polar Record*, 54.

autonomy has different forms (from self-government in Greenland to certain procedural rights in Norwegian Finnmark). However, the taxing question of the rights of indigenous peoples, and indeed non-indigenous population in certain areas (such as Finnmark or Greenland), frequently result in conflicts and dissatisfaction for all parties, as the matter is left unresolved by the UNDRIP. Domestic law, on the other hand, is rich with possibility.

The Kanak indigenous peoples of New Caledonia: decolonization and self-determination in practice

JACQUI ZALCBERG

I. Introduction

The Kanak indigenous people of New Caledonia find themselves in the common situation of disadvantage that many indigenous peoples around the world experience.[1] Yet beyond the social and economic difficulties and ingrained attitudes of discrimination they face in their daily lives, New Caledonia's unique political history offers an interesting perspective on the ever-important question of self-determination as a fundamental right of indigenous peoples.

A well-established principle of international law,[2] self-determination has been traditionally understood to encompass the right of colonial peoples to be emancipated from a colonial oppressor, and is often connected to independence or secession.[3] In recent decades, however, thanks to the persistent advocacy of indigenous peoples and activists, the concept of self-determination has expanded to represent a distinct right in international law specific to indigenous peoples. As one of the key principles underlying the 2007 United Nations (UN) Declaration on the Rights of Indigenous Peoples,[4] self-determination in an indigenous rights context is

---

[1] J. Anaya, 'Report of the UN Special Rapporteur on the Rights of Indigenous Peoples on the Situation of Kanak people in New Caledonia, France', A/HRC/18/35/Add.6, paras. 18–63.

[2] Charter of the United Nations, preamble; ICCPR, Art. 1, ICESCR, Art. 1; supporters of the view that the right of self-determination is part of *jus cogens* include: J Crawford, *The Rights Of Peoples* (Oxford University Press, 1988); I. Brownlie, *Principles of Public International Law* (6th edn, Oxford University Press, 2003); A. Cassese, *International Law* (Oxford University Press, 2005).

[3] See generally M. Moore, *National Self Determination and Succession* (Oxford University Press, 1998).

[4] United Nations Declaration on the Rights of Indigenous Peoples, GA Res. 61/295, Annex, UN Doc. A/Res/61/295 (Sept. 13, 2007) (hereinafter UN Declaration).

no longer connected to the right of secession,[5] but rather, conceived as a general principle comprised of 'a universe of human rights precepts extending from core values of freedom and equality'[6] which encompasses indigenous peoples' right to 'make meaningful choices in matters touching upon all spheres of life on a continuous basis'.[7]

The unique status of New Caledonia as a Special Collectivity of France, and the possibility of a pending referendum on whether New Caledonia will remain within the French Republic or become a fully independent State, however, pose particular questions regarding the self-determination right of the Kanak, who are the indigenous Melanesian inhabitants of the country, and make up almost half its total population. Whilst the independence of New Caledonia may have significant implications for the self-determination of the territory from France, a positive vote in the referendum will not automatically guarantee the right of self-determination for the Kanak. Rather, self-determination for the Kanak is an ongoing right that, though it may be bolstered by independence, will also require other specific rights to be granted to the Kanak, including the guarantee of the Kanak people's ability to maintain personal spheres of autonomy, and simultaneously their rights to interact within the larger societal structures in New Caledonia.[8]

In light of the danger in associating Kanak self-determination exclusively with New Caledonian independence from France, and also given the uncertain character of both the nature and outcome of the referendum, this chapter will therefore consider the 1998 Noumea Accords – the key agreement signed between the French Government and New Caledonia which set out a gradual transfer of power and provide for a final vote on full independence from France – as one potentially influential, but not necessarily decisive, aspect regarding the realization of self-determination for the Kanak. The chapter will focus on one of the key challenges of self-determination for the Kanak: their right to maintain control over their traditional lands, territories and natural resources, and to make real choices about development of those lands in line with their own priorities, as provided for by the Declaration,[9] in light of the impact of corporate activities on their lands.

---

[5] Ibid., Art. 46(1) (explaining that self-determination in the Declaration is deemed compatible with the principle of territorial integrity and political unity of sovereign and independent States).

[6] J. Anaya, *Indigenous Peoples in International Law* (Oxford University Press, 2004), p. 104.

[7] Ibid., p. 106.   [8] Ibid.

[9] UN Declaration, Art. 32, which requires the free and informed consent of indigenous peoples prior to the approval of any project affecting their lands or territories and other

In New Caledonia, the Goro-Nickel mine, one of the largest nickel deposits in the world, is located on Kanak lands and territories. The mine was initially the object of fierce opposition by the Kanak and the subject of a number of legal disputes and injunctions. Ultimately, however, a mediated settlement was reached between the mine developers, Vale Inco, and the Kanak impacted tribes. By examining the resulting agreement in light of the political context of New Caledonia's decolonization process, this chapter will consider how the agreement, which afforded the Kanak certain co-management rights over of aspects of the mine, may demonstrate a positive example of indigenous self-determination over traditional lands and resources. Given the increasing encroachment of multinational corporations and extractive industries on indigenous lands,[10] this case study will be considered as an example of aspects of self-determination in practice.

Section II will provide an outline of the colonial history of New Caledonia, focusing on the treatment of the Kanak by the French. Section III will then present the case study, giving a brief history of nickel mining in New Caledonia and some details about the history and development of the Goro-Nickel project. Section IV will analyse the agreement reached between the Kanak and the company, identifying ways in which the agreement advances aspects of the right of self-determination of the Kanak.

II. Historical overview: New Caledonia

1. The Kanak indigenous peoples of New Caledonia

Situated in the Pacific Ocean, New Caledonia is a Melanesian archipelago that consists of one main island, 'La Grande Terre', the Loyalty Islands and several smaller islands. The Kanak indigenous peoples are believed to have arrived in the territory around 3,300 years ago, during what is referred to as the Lapita period. During the following Neolithic period, known as the *Naia Oundjo*, the Kanak mastered the art of toolmaking and developed their civilization and culture based on the cultivation of yams, taro and fishing. The cultivation of these crops was

---

resources, particularly in connection with the development, utilization or exploitation of mineral, water or other resources. Article 32 further affirms that 'indigenous peoples have the right to determine and develop priorities and strategies for the development or use of their lands or territories and other resources'.

[10] Expert Mechanism on the Rights of Indigenous Peoples (EMRIP), 'Progress report on the study on indigenous peoples and the right to participate in decision-making', A/HRC/15/37, para. 26.

closely linked to spiritual and cultural belief systems. Kanak identity was closely based on a relationship with a specific area of land, described as 'a geographical identity that flows from . . . places'.[11]

Kanak society was based on a complex system of multilayered clans and chiefdoms. Clan size varied from 200 to 500 members, and consisted of individuals from different families who shared common ancestry and had a specific attachment to a territorial area. The clan led a communal existence and shared the land, which was closely linked to customary ties to ancestral spirits. Membership in the clan also served as the principal basis for identifying and distinguishing social groups.

2. Colonization

New Caledonia was first 'discovered' by Captain James Cook, on his second voyage to the Pacific, while he was en route to New Zealand after exploring the New Hebrides archipelago.[12] By the early 1800s, European ships were sailing through the archipelago regularly, and the first Europeans began settling the islands in the 1840s. French fear of a growing British presence on the islands, coupled with French interest in countering British dominance in the South Pacific region, led New Caledonia to be annexed by France on 24 September 1853. To entrench French control of the islands, European occupation was encouraged, and large waves of both free settlers and political and criminal prisoners were sent to the territory. By the late 1870s, over 7,000 free Europeans had settled on the islands, and by 1897 there were more than 8,000 convicts in the territory.[13]

The presence of French and European citizens in the territory had a significant impact on the Kanak peoples, their ways of life and traditions. From the outset, European settlers began cattle-rearing on the Noumea peninsula, using land-extensive techniques and pushing their herds up the coast, letting them graze freely, destroying Kanak yam and taro plots.[14] New settlement brought not only new farming technologies,

---

[11] R. G Ward and E. Kingdon, 'Land Tenure in the Pacific Islands' in R. G Ward and E. Kingdon (eds.), *Land, Custom and Practice in the South Pacific* (Cambridge University Press, 1995), p. 46.

[12] Now known as Vanuatu.

[13] David Robie, *Blood on Their Banner: Nationalist Struggles in the South Pacific* (London: Zed Books, 1989), p. 85; Alan Berman, 'Future Kanak Independence in New Caledonia: Reality or Illusion?', (1998) 34 *Stanford Journal of International Law*, 287 and 294.

[14] Jean Guiart, 'One of the Last Colonies: New Caledonia', (1982) 36, *Journal of International Affairs*, 105, 107.

but also diseases[15] and missionaries,[16] all of which had a significant impact on the physical well-being and cultural lives of the Kanak.

However, it was the decisive and strategic use of legal means that legitimated French control over the territory and enabled the widespread dispossession of the Kanak from their ancestral lands and territories. Two years after French annexation, the first Governor of New Caledonia proclaimed all vacant lands the domain of the state and available for alienation and settlement.[17] Although vibrant forms of land use, possession and tenure existed within Kanak society, and indeed, nearly all land in New Caledonia was claimed by at least one clan,[18] the French 'elastic notion of what constituted vacant land'[19] resulted in the wide-scale dispossession of Kanak from their traditional lands and territories. Moreover, the French government issued a number of decrees in 1868, 1876 and 1897, which provided the legal authority for Kanak land dispossession. From this basis, the French instituted a policy of forcibly confining Kanaks to government-created reserves.[20] Kanak activities within and outside the reservations were also strictly regulated by the 1887 Indigenat, an oppressive code of conduct promulgated by the French Government.[21]

Kanak rights to lands were further compromised by the undermining of Kanak cultural institutions. By refusing to acknowledge the clan as the legal owner of land, and by recognizing only the artificial construct of the tribe, which was invented by the colonial administration, Kanak political and social structures were also attacked.[22] The invention of the tribe disregarded traditional land tenure systems based on customary lineage. Land rights of the clans were subordinated to the formal authority of tribal chiefs, who nonetheless were never given full title over the land and could therefore

[15] Ingrid A. Kircher, 'The Kanaks of New Caledonia', (1986), 71(5), Minority Rights Group Report 6.
[16] Jean Marie Kohler, 'The Churches in New Caledonia and the Colonial Order' in Michael Spencer et al. (eds.), New Caledonia: Essays in Nationalism and Dependency (University of Queensland Press, 1988), pp. 231, 245–6.
[17] Alan Ward, Land and Politics in New Caledonia (Sydney University Press, 1984), p. 2.
[18] Berman, 'Future Kanak Independence', 295.
[19] M. Lyons, The Totem and the Tricolor: A Short History of New Caledonia Since 1774 (New South Wales University Press, 1986), p. 16.
[20] See Kircher, 'The Kanaks of New Caledonia', 5.
[21] Berman, 'Future Kanak Independence', at 296. See also Michael Ntumy, 'New Caledonia' in Michael Ntumy (ed.), South Pacific Islands and Legal Systems, (University of Hawaii Press, 1993), p. 597.
[22] Patrick Pillon and Francis Sodter, 'The Impact of Colonial Administrative Policies on Indigenous Social Customs in Tahiti and New Caledonia', Journal of Pacific History, 26 (1991), 165–6.

never unilaterally dispose of clan land.[23] Moreover, the colonial administration appointed puppet tribal chiefs sympathetic to French administration, who could be dismissed by the colonial administrations.[24] Chiefs who promoted the interests of their own people were often removed and replaced by those more favourable to the administration.[25] Furthermore, Kanak customary traditions were consistently eroded through the application of French law.[26]

With the establishment of these colonial legal regimes, by the first decades of the twentieth century the reserve system was entrenched and land confiscation continued. This was later justified by the decrease in Kanak population due to the impact of disease,[27] and to the emerging nickel industry.[28] This clear attack on Kanak land rights 'undermined [their] ability to maintain their traditional ways of life, severed their spiritual links with their ancestral ways, changed their traditional system of land rights and ... the political and social relationships reflected in that system'.[29]

3.   Post-world war: a shift in French–Kanak relations?

The end of World War II marked a turning point in French–Kanak relations. France's key role in the establishment of the UN system, the emergence of the discourse of human rights, and the recognition of the right of States to decolonization, meant that France could not completely disregard these principles in relation to its own territories. In 1946, France abolished the repressive *Indigenat* and listed New Caledonia with the UN Decolonization Committee.[30] However, this approach to New Caledonian affairs was short-lived. Just one year later, in 1947, France withdrew New Caledonia from the UN list of non-self-governing territories, declared it a French Overseas Territory, and

---

[23]   See Kircher, 'The Kanaks of New Caledonia', at 5.

[24]   Pillon and Sodter, 'The Impact of Colonial Administrative Policies' at 163.

[25]   Berman, 'Future Kanak Independance' at 297.   [26]   Ibid., at 301.

[27]   Due to susceptibility to European diseases, the Kanak population dropped from 42,500 to just 22,000 in less than ten years. Dwindling Kanak population due to European diseases was given as a justification for the contraction of the reserves. See Kircher, 'The Kanaks of New Caledonia', 6.

[28]   Alain Saussol, 'New Caledonia: Colonization and Reaction' in R. Crocombe (ed.), *Land Tenure in the Pacific* (Oxford University Press, 1988), p. 242.

[29]   Berman, 'Future Kanak Independence', 299.

[30]   M. Rafiqul Islam, 'The Recent Self-Determination Referendum in New Caledonia: Terms Militating Against Its Validity', (1987) 15 *Melanesian Law Journals*, pp. 136–7.

refused to submit information to the UN Secretary-General as required under Article 73(e) of the UN Charter.[31] These acts were a reassertion of French control over the territory and were a clear denial of any obligation to quickly and unconditionally end colonialism, as provided for by international law.[32]

Commentators have speculated as to why the French were so interested in keeping a stronghold on New Caledonia. Some point to the French desire to use Polynesia 'as a testing ground for the French independent nuclear deterrent'.[33] Others argue that France's hold on its territories in the Pacific region was deemed to reflect their view on their position as a global power.[34] Whatever the reason, over the next decades the French retained a firm grip on New Caledonia, and 'resisted all UN attempts to analyze the situation in New Caledonia or supervise the process by which the right of self-determination should be exercised'.[35]

Despite France's reluctance to release New Caledonia, it also realized that it could no longer continue to rule it with such a strong colonial presence. In order to maintain international credibility, defuse mounting local pressure in New Caledonia, and thereby mitigate Kanak demands for self-government, a number of concessions were granted to the Kanak. In the post-war era, voting rights were granted to the Kanak in 1951, and in 1953 the first Kanak political party was permitted – the *Union Caledonie* (UC). The UC enjoyed the support of most Kanaks and many settlers, and endorsed moderate policies, including a gradual move towards self-government (not independence), and the maintenance of close ties with France, even supporting the 1958 vote for New Caledonia to remain an overseas territory. Moreover, France granted some political rights to New Caledonia through the establishment of the *loi cadre* (framework law) under which it was granted greater internal autonomy.[36]

[31] See 'Self-Determination: The Cases of Fiji, New Caledonia, Namibia, and the Western Sahara', (1998) 82 *American Society of International Law Proceedings*, 434. However, on 2 December 1986, the General Assembly determined that New Caledonia was a Non-Self-Governing Territory, and put it back on the list. See GA Res. 41/41A, UN GAOR, 41st Sess., Supp. No 53 at 49, UN Doc. A/RES/41/41A (1986).

[32] Berman, 'Future Kanak Independence' at 340.

[33] Jean Chesneaux, 'The Function of the Pacific in the French Fifth Republic's "Grand Design": Theory and Practice of the "Puissance Mondiale Moyenne", (1991) 26 *Journal of Pacific History* 256.

[34] Ibid.   [35] Berman, 'Future Kanak Independence', 302.

[36] The framework law decentralized power to all French overseas territories. See Lyons, *The Totem and the Tricolor*, 107; Kircher, 'The Kanaks of New Caledonia', 7.

In 1958, however, spurred by domestic French political interests and an increasing fear amongst the conservative settler society (*les caldoches*) of growing UC influence, the French government withdrew important powers which had earlier been conferred on New Caledonia, thereby completely stifling emerging UC political influence. Furthermore, waves of migration to the territory, which had 'the avowed purposes of swamping the electoral roll',[37] had relegated the Kanak to a minority in their own country, thereby minimizing their political influence. France explicitly encouraged loyalist migration to New Caledonia, and between 1969 and 1971, of the 25,000 new settlers, about 2,000 of 'the new immigrants were influential anti-independence *pieds noirs* from Algeria'.[38] Unsurprisingly, the same year the UC lost its first Territorial Assembly election to loyalist parties.[39] The loss of political rights was coupled with the ongoing experience of disadvantage and economic marginalization. Therefore it had become blatantly apparent that despite certain changes in French policies following the end of World War II, any meaningful improvement for the Kanak in their economic or political situation remained lacking.

As tensions mounted, Kanak demands radicalized to include full independence. By the late 1970s, these demands had become widespread, and were often accompanied by violent confrontations. In an attempt to defuse the situation, the French government responded in varying ways to these demands, introducing piecemeal reforms that addressed some Kanak concerns.[40] However, the failure of these approaches to address the fundamental Kanak goal of independence led to the rejection of the initiatives by the Kanak, and the consolidation of the Kanak independence movement as the *Front de Liberation Nationale Kanak et Socialist* (FLNKS).

In the 1980s, the more open policy of the French Mitterrand government led to improvements in French–Kanak relations. However, these 'nominal overtures'[41] were thwarted by Chirac's majority in the 1985 French legislative elections. The Chirac years saw the adoption of

---

[37] Guiart, 'One of the Last Colonies', at 106.
[38] David Chappell, 'The Black and the Red: Radicalising Anti-colonialism in 1970s New Caledonia', (2004) 27 *Journal of Pacific Studies*, 49–62.
[39] Ibid.
[40] See Berman, 'Future Kanak Independence', 311–13 (summarizing the ten-year plan of Paul Dijourd, French Secretary for the Colonies in 1979, and François Mitterand's approach in 1981).
[41] Berman, 'Future Kanak Independence', 320.

aggressive anti-independence policies that included redistributing power to remove all political influence of the FLNKS,[42] a regressive land distribution policy that favoured settlers,[43] and a sham referendum in 1987 that was politically designed to ensure a vote against independence.[44]

The particularly aggressive approach of the Chirac government towards the Kanak backfired, in that it aided in 'foster[ing] regional and international recognition of Kanak demands'.[45] In 1986, the Pacific Forum agreed to support the re-listing of New Caledonia with the UN Decolonization Committee[46] and the UN General Assembly voted to reinscribe New Caledonia on the list of non-self-governing territories.[47] The South Pacific Forum denounced the results of the 1987 referendum.[48]

Despite international pressure, France pursued aggressive anti-independence policies in New Caledonia. A high point in tension was reached in 1998 after Kanak militants raided French army barracks in which two policemen and nineteen Kanak ultimately were killed.[49] Although the territory appeared to be on the brink of civil war, Chirac's mismanagement of the crisis, and his subsequent defeat by Mitterrand in the French presidential election, created a space for renewed dialogue between the French Government and the Kanak.

4.   The Matignon Accords

One month into Mitterrand's second term of office as president in May 1988, the Matignon Accords were agreed upon by the French government, the FLNKS and the conservative settler party, *Rassemblement Pour la Caledonie dans la Republique* (RCPR) (which, after 2002, became the *Rassemblement-UMP* (R-UMP)). Essentially a 'political compromise designed principally to restore stability to the territory',[50] the Accords

---

[42] John Connell, *New Caledonia, The Matignon Accord and the Colonial Future* (Research Institute for Asia and the Pacific, 1988), p. 2.

[43] 'The Adraf Scandal', *Pacific Islands Monthly*, Dec. 1989, at 18.

[44] Kircher, 'The Kanaks of New Caledonia at 17.

[45] Berman, 'Future Kanak Independence', at 322.

[46] Helen Fraser, 'New Caledonia: Anti-Colonialism in a Pacific Territory', *Parliament of Australia Legislative Services*, 7 (1987–88), 29.

[47] GA Res. 41/41a, UN GAOR, 41st Sess., Supp. No. 53 at 49, UN Doc. A/RES/41/41A (1986).

[48] See generally, Fraser,'New Caledonia', 37.

[49] Jean Guiart, 'A Drama of Ambiguity: Ouvea 1988–89', (1997) 85 *Journal of Pacific History*, 102; Mark Fineman, 'French Storm Cave, Free 23 Hostages in New Caledonia,' *Los Angeles Times*, 5 May 1988.

[50] Berman, 'Future Kanak Independence', at 327

made some important structural changes to the political landscape of New Caledonia and addressed some key concerns of the Kanak.

Under the agreement, the territory was divided into three administrative divisions – the North, the South and the Loyalty Islands. Each province was granted its own executive and the power to administer its own affairs through an assembly. Since the first election in 1989,[51] up to the most recent in June 2011, the Kanak have ruled both the Northern Province and the Loyalty Island Province, while the majority European population controls the Southern Province.[52] The Matignon Accords also established a Territorial Customary Assembly, comprised of representatives from eight customary areas, each of which maintained its own customary council. The Territorial Customary Assembly was given the power to examine all resolutions of each provincial assembly relating to customary law, including land law.

Yet, perhaps the most significant aspect of the Accords was that they established a ten-year transition with a vote on the future of New Caledonia scheduled before the end of 1998. Many Kanaks accepted the transition period with 'the expectation that the 1998 referendum would lead to political independence for New Caledonia'.[53]

5. The Noumea Accords

By the mid-1990s, however, it had become apparent that in all likelihood the scheduled 1998 referendum would have resulted in a 'No Vote' for independence, due to demographic and political realities.[54] For this reason, the Kanak leadership entered into a complex series of protracted negotiations with the French government, which resulted in a negotiated agreement that would lead to a gradual transition to independence in lieu of the referendum.[55]

---

[51] See below, Section II.6.

[52] Berman, 'Future Kanak Independence', 328; Nic Maclellan, 'The New Government in New Caledonia: The May 2009 Elections in a French Pacific Territory', *State Society and Governance in Melanesia*, Briefing Note No. 3/2009, available at: http://ips.cap.anu.edu.au/ssgm/publications/briefing_notes/BriefingNote_NewGovtinNewCaledonia.pdf

[53] Nic Maclellan, 'The Noumea Accord and Decolonization in New Caledonia', (1999) 34 (3) *Journal of Pacific History*, 245.

[54] Alan Berman, 'The Noumea Accords: Emancipation or Colonial Harness?' (2001) 36 *Texas International Law Journal*, 281 see also Berman, 'Future Kanak Independence', 332–3.

[55] John Connell, 'New Caledonia: A Crisis of De-Colonisation in the South Pacific,' (1988) 305, *Round Table*, 53, 60–1.

THE KANAK INDIGENOUS PEOPLES OF NEW CALEDONIA 387

On 21 April 1998, the day that the scheduled referendum provided for under the Matignon Accords should have taken place, the French government entered into the Noumea Accords with the FLNKS and the RPCR.[56] While the Noumea Accords were 'largely an extension of the measures previously undertaken by the Matignon Accords',[57] they included some significant additions. First, the preamble provided the first formal recognition of the Kanak as the indigenous peoples of New Caledonia, and an acknowledgement that 'the territory [was] not empty',[58] when the European settlers arrived. It further recognized that Kanak identity is based on a particular connection to the land, and formally acknowledged the 'traumatic consequence of colonization for Kanak social organization, economic livelihood, dignity and identity'.[59]

The preamble falls short in that it inaccurately suggests the legality of French colonization of the territory, claiming that France's possession of New Caledonia 'was taken in accordance with the conditions of international law at the time'.[60] This is an incorrect proposition of law, as the French did not formalize any legal relationship with the Kanak when they settled the territory. This would have been required by the international doctrine of conquest, which was the prevailing international legal theory of the time and applicable to New Caledonia, given the presence of the Kanak on the territory.[61] Notwithstanding this inaccurate portrayal of 'the legality of French colonization and . . . attempt to justify the colonial past',[62] the preamble does represent an important symbolic step by acknowledging 'the legacy of French colonial involvement in the territory and the devastating impact of such actions on Kanak customs, political organizations, socio-economic structures and identity'.[63]

Moreover, the Noumea Accords created a number of key political concessions for the Kanak. First, the agreement established the importance of Kanak identity for New Caledonia – including reinstating Kanak names, identification of Kanak sacred sites, the return of Kanak cultural material from French museums to New Caledonia, and encouraged the development of Kanak languages.[64] The agreement also redefined the

---

[56] *Accord de Nouméa*, 5 May 1998, FR. New Caledonia [hereinafter Noumea Accords], available at www.legifrance.gouv.fr/affichTexte.do?cidTexte=JORFTEXT000000555817& dateTexte (last accessed 20 April 2011). The Subsequent Legislation in the French National Assembly and Senate, *Loi Organique*, 12 Mar. 1999.

[57] Berman, 'The Noumea Accords', at 281.   [58] Noumea Accords, preamble.

[59] Berman, 'The Noumea Accords', 280.   [60] Noumea Accords, preamble.

[61] Berman, 'The Noumea Accords', 282–4.   [62] Ibid., 284.   [63] Ibid.

[64] Noumea Accords, §§1.3.1, 1.3.2.

relationship between customary law and ordinary civil law, allowing persons who had lost the ability to be governed by customary law in certain areas, due to the earlier legal regime, to reclaim their customary status.[65] Customary authorities were also granted consultative status in criminal procedures, and were empowered to provide information, but not binding advice, to the courts on issues regarding the adjudication of criminal matters.[66]

Administratively, the Accords left the political structure of New Caledonia largely the same as under the Matignon Accords, with three provincial assemblies, a national congress made up of proportional representation from those assemblies, and a multi-power executive,[67] which is chosen by the Congress. Significantly, under the Noumea Accords, the Kanak Customary Council, established under the Matignon Accords, was transformed into a Customary Senate. The Senate is a consultative body with the power to advise the Territorial Congress on all subjects relating to Kanak identity. However, the Customary Senate has no veto power, and if it requests review of a law, it is simply sent back to the Territorial Congress, who must re-examine it, but whose vote is final.[68]

On the issue of land rights, the Noumea Accords recognized the need to reassess the controversial Rural Development Land Management Board.[69] It also provided for the survey and registration of all customary land,[70] and established a fund to assist in financing development projects on that land.[71]

However, the cornerstone of the Noumea Accords is twofold: first, there is the staged, yet irreversible, transfer of administrative powers from Paris to local authorities.[72] Until that point, France had retained control over a number of important reserve powers including justice, law and order, defence and currency, until the referendum.[73] Different powers have since been irrevocably transferred in phases. Importantly, France and New Caledonia now share control over matters related to external affairs, with New Caledonia able to represent itself in international organizations such as the the International Labour Organization (ILO), the United Nations Educational, Scientific and Cultural Organization (UNESCO), and Pacific international organizations.[74] Since 1986, New

---

[65] Ibid., §1.1   [66] Ibid., §1.2.4
[67] Ibid., §§2.1.1, 2.1.2, 2.3. Since the Noumea Accords, elections for the Assemblies and the Territorial Congress have been held every five years, in 1999, 2004 and 2009.
[68] Ibid., §1.25; Berman, 'The Noumea Accords', at 287.
[69] Noumea Accords, §1.4; see also Berman, 'The Noumea Accords', at 321.
[70] Noumea Accords, §1.4.   [71] Ibid., §4.2.4.   [72] Ibid., §§3.1.1, 3.1.2.   [73] Ibid., §3.3.
[74] Ibid., §3.2.1.

Caledonia has also been reinstated on the list of non-self-governing terriorties, for the purposes of its representation at the UN.[75]

Second, and certainly the most anticipated aspect of the Accords, is the possibility of achieving full emancipation from France at the end of a twenty-year period if a majority of the eligible electorate in New Caledonia so decides.[76] Unlike a UN referendum on independence or a guaranteed transfer of statehood, going to the polls will require three-fifths of the members of the Territorial Congress to agree to holding the referendum.[77] Only then, if an overall majority votes in favour of the proposal, will New Caledonia enjoy the full transfer of the reserved powers and access to full international personality.

It is significant that the Accords use the term 'emancipation' and do not include the words self-determination or independence. Emancipation is somewhat ambiguous in its meaning, and may 'mean different things to different people in New Caledonia'.[78] For example, the then RPCR suggested that emancipation may simply mean that territory politicians control those matters belonging to New Caledonia and deregulation of the economy,[79] whereas the FLNKS equates it with full independence.[80]

These political questions aside, it is clear that the outcome of any referendum would be pivotal in French–New Caledonian relations. Therefore, a major consequence of the Noumea Accords related to voter eligibility. The Accords required the passing of the *Loi Organique* (Organic Law)[81] which established New Caledonian 'citizenship' and conferred voting rights only on those citizens resident for 10 years after 1998, and their descendants of voting age.[82] However, New Caledonian citizens retained their French nationality, and New Caledonia continued to be represented in the French Parliament in Paris, with two seats in the National Assembly and one in the Senate.[83]

These voting limitations have been the subject of much political and legal dispute.[84] In March 1999, the restrictions were challenged by a

---

[75] www.un.org/en/decolonization/nonselfgovterritories.shtml#foot5.
[76] Noumea Accords, §5.   [77] Ibid.,   [78] Berman, 'The Noumea Accords', at 292.
[79] 'Lafleur Rejects Associated Statehood as an Option for New Caledonia' 11 *Pacific Report*, 28 Mar. 1998, p.1.
[80] 'French Premier Urges Greater Understanding on Pacific Isle', AFP, 4 May 1998.
[81] Noumea Accords, §2.2.1
[82] *Organic Law of New Caledonia* (No. 99–209) of 19 March 1999, Article 281 (reflecting article 2.2 of the Noumea Accords §(2)).
[83] Maclellan, 'The Noumea Accords', 246.
[84] See generally, David Chappell, 'Melanesia in Review: Issues and Events, 2006: New Caledonia', (2007) 19(2) *The Contemporary Pacific*, 583.

number of disenfranchised French citizens as unconstitutional. The provisions were subsequently amended by the Constitutional Court of Paris, which ruled that all French citizens residing in New Caledonia for at least 10 years, whatever their date of arrival, could participate in the elections.[85] Further appeals were made against the French decision, arguing that any time limit is an infringement of universal rights to participate in political processes. These claims reached a number of international bodies; however, both the Human Rights Committee[86] and the European Court of Human Rights[87] rejected the arguments, finding the length of residence criterion not to be discriminatory or excessive, but rather reflective of a political reality of a self-determination process 'involving the participation of persons able to prove sufficiently strong ties to the territory whose future is being decided'.[88]

Whilst the 10-year restriction was thus deemed by international bodies not to be too onerous a requirement, the rejection of the 1998 year limit by the French courts had serious implications on the eligible voting constituency, and therefore on the potential outcome of the referendum on independence. The FLNKS lobbied Paris to reimplement the original terms of the Noumea Accords, and to restrict the electorate to a 'frozen' pool of long-term residents, namely, people who were eligible to vote in the 1998 referendum on the Accords, and their descendants. On 19 February 2007, the French Congress of Parliament finally adopted amendments to the French Constitution allowing New Caledonia to reinstate the original terms of the Accords, thus ensuring strong representation of the Kanak population in the future referendum.

6.   Post-2009 election: where to from here?

For many years New Caledonia was a bipartisan country, with the FLNKS demanding independence, and the settler-dominated R-UMP 'control[ling] developments in the Territory, through both its dominance in the Territorial Congress and its ability to gain majority control of the executive'.[89] However, by 2004 this approach no longer rang true.

---

[85] Maclellan, 'The Noumea Accords', at 249.
[86] *Ms. Marie-Hélène Gillot* v. *France*, Communication No. 932/2000, Human Rights Committee, UN Doc. A/57/40 at 270 (2002).
[87] *Py* v. *France*, Communication No. 66289/01, European Court of Human Rights, 11 January 2005.
[88] *Gillot* v. *France*, para. 14.7; *Py* v. *France*, para. 63.
[89] Berman, 'The Noumea Accords', 290.

The *l'Avenir Ensemble* emerged as a new voice in the anti-independence movement, which for the first time linked both Caucasian and Polynesian New Caledonians opposed to independence but tired of the hegemonic and allegedly corrupt anti-independence R-UMP. In 2008, another centrist anti-independence party – *Caledonie Ensemble* – emerged, led by Philippe Gomès. On the pro-independence side, there has been a sharp political contest between *Union Calédonienne* (UC) and the *Parti de Liberation Kanak* (Palika), the largest members of the FLNKS coalition. Furthermore, the rise of the new *Parti Travailliste* (PT, Labour Party), backed by the Trade Union of Kanak Workers and the Exploited (*Union syndicale des travailleurs kanaks et des exploités*, USTKE) and other disenchanted FLNKS supporters, has strengthened, but also further complicated the pro-independence movement.[90]

The outcome of the 2009 elections was indicative of some of these political shifts.[91] The conservative R-UMP won 13 seats, and remained the largest political party in the Congress. Interestingly, pro-independence parties increased their presence in the Congress by five seats. Thus, the 54-seat Congress was made up of 31 members of anti-independence parties and 23 independence supporters. Importantly, while anti-independence parties dominated the Southern Province Assembly, they were largely irrelevant outside the capital, Noumea.[92]

According to the terms of the Noumea Accords, the referendum on emancipation is to be called after three terms, and before the end of the fourth term of the Territorial Congress. Following the provincial elections of May 2009, there was therefore a Congress empowered to call the referendum, and to transfer the final tranche of powers from Paris to Noumea. The 2009 elected congress also had the responsibility of adopting new national symbols for the country, as prescribed by the Noumea Accords. The outcome of the 2009 elections was thus very significant for the future political landscape of New Caledonia.

Within this complex and dynamic political climate, heated debate over the decision about the new flag led to a political crisis in the island in 2011. Although the Noumea Accords provided that the 2009 government should choose a new flag to express the territory's identity,[93] for

---

[90] Maclellan, 'The New Government in New Caledonia', 1.   [91] Ibid.

[92] Nic Maclellan, 'Under a New Flag: New Caledonia debates citizenship, development and new ties to the region' *Overseas Territories Review*, 8 March 2011, available at: http://overseasreview.blogspot.com/2011/03/challenges-to-new-caledonia-political.html (last accessed 27 April 2012).

[93] Noumea Accords, §1.5

years political parties have been divided about the issue. A coalition of anti-independence parties, including the influential R-UMP, lobbied for the joint use of both Kanak and French flags, which was deemed to be suitable for some pro-independence parties, including the FLNKS. On 17 February 2011, the Gomes government was brought down by the resignation of the FLNKS over the flag issue. This was possible due to a provision of the Noumea Accords promoting a multi-party executive which deemed that one party resigning meant the whole government was considered to have resigned.[94]

On 3 March 2011 a newly elected government, headed by *Avenir Ensemble*'s Harold Martin, was elected. This government in turn was brought down by the immediate resignation of members of *Calédonie Ensemble*. The third (elected 17 March) and fourth (elected 1 April) Martin governments were also brought down following resignations of *Calédonie Ensemble* members. The fifth Martin government was elected on 10 June 2011. In July, the constitutional law was amended to remove the mechanism which had led to successive governments being brought down by the resignation of government members.[95] The current government comprises members drawn from the pro-France R-UMP, *Avenir Ensemble* and *Calédonie Ensemble* parties (7 in total); and the pro-independence FLNKS (4 members). On 1 April 2011, Rock Wamytan was elected President of Congress, the first pro-independent candidate to hold this position. His election was overturned in July 2011 by the French Supreme Court, on the grounds of procedural irregularity,[96] but Wamytan was re-elected Congress President on 19 August 2011.

Notwithstanding the political turmoil, the key issue remains whether a referendum will actually be called by the present government, as it requires a majority vote by the current Congress.[97] Whilst the traditionalist limbs of the FLNKS and the anti-independence movement have indicated their willingness to hold the referendum, the latter believing they still have the votes to quash the initiative, there are also indicators of a compromise being sought. The importance of French economic support to the territory has led some to suggest that another transitional

[94] Ibid.
[95] Patrick Antoine Decloître, 'France Tidies up Politics in New Caledonia, Polynesia in a bid to Stem Instability', *Pacific Scoop*, 4 July 2011, available at: http://pacific.scoop.co.nz/2011/07/france-tightens-loose-ends-in-new-caledonia-french-polynesia-in-bid-to-stem-instability/ (last accessed 13 February 2012).
[96] www.rnzi.com/pages/news.php?op=read&id=61907 (last accessed 6 May 2012).
[97] Noumea Accords, §5.

agreement will be negotiated, leaving the Territory in 'a form of free association with France'.[98] Indeed, France has increased its aid programmes in the region, engaging in what critics have called a 'charm offensive' to promote France's reputation in New Caledonia. Sceptics indicate this may be linked to France's awareness of the mineral wealth of New Caledonia, not only in nickel, but also the potential undersea resources it might harvest from its 200-mile Exclusive Economic Zone.[99] Moreover, the once hegemonic blocs of the FLNKS and the RCPR in the 1980s and 1990s, have fractured into competing political parties, with increased representation from smaller parties, including an important role for new parties such as the PT, which creates further instability regarding the outcome of the vote.[100] The outcome is therefore still unclear, but sceptics warn that failure to hold the referendum will allow the 'colonial dynamics of subjugation and domination' to continue, and that the Noumea Agreement is 'simply a convenient guise for maintaining more than a century old colonial harness'.[101]

III.   The nickel industry in New Caledonia

1.   Nickel mining in New Caledonia and the Kanak

Nickel laterite deposits were discovered in 1864 in New Caledonia and commercial production began as early as 1875.[102] The early discovery of these nickel deposits, coupled with the emergence of the global industry in the late nineteenth century, had serious implications for France's treatment of its colony from the outset, and a direct impact on the Kanak.

From the first exploration and exploitation of the metal in New Caledonia, nickel mining was used to justify land confiscation from Kanak clans and as an excuse later in the century for the contraction of reservation areas.[103] Furthermore, as nickel mining activities in New Caledonia have largely taken place in the north and centre of the island, both areas heavily populated by Kanaks, it has been the Kanak that have been impacted most by extraction processes. Pollution from nickel

---

[98]   Maclellan 'The New Government in New Caledonia', 11.
[99]   David Chappell, 'The Noumea Accord: Decolonization without Independence in New Caledonia', (1999) 72(3) *Pacific Affairs*, 390.
[100]   Chappell, 'Melanesia in Review', 434.   [101]   Berman, 'The Neumea Accord', 297.
[102]   Eric C.F. Bird, Jean-Paul Dubois and Jacques A. Iltis, *The Impacts of Opencast Mining on the Rivers and Coasts of New Caledonia* (The United Nations University, 1984) available at: http://archive.unu.edu/unupress/unupbooks/80505e/80505E00.htm#Contents
[103]   Sussol, 'New Caledonia', p. 234.

mining has continually affected Kanak communities, and has been a precipitating factor in many conflict situations between Kanak tribes and the authorities.[104]

Moreover, the fast developing industry played a key role in shifting the demographics of the territory. Nickel mining required more labour, and as segregationist policies precluded the Kanak working in the mines,[105] by 1930, approximately 14,000 indentured labourers had come to New Caledonia from Indonesia, Vietnam, Tahiti, and the Wallis and Futuna Islands,[106] contributing to the growth of the non-Kanak population. Many of these labourers were loyal to the French, as it was due to French support that they were able work in New Caledonia and benefit from the economic opportunities made available by the expansion of the nickel industry.[107] The nickel boom and the associated immigration therefore enabled the French to 'tip the demographic balance and thus the voting electorate increasingly in favour of loyalists to Paris'.[108]

The importance of nickel also played a key role in the policies of the French government towards its overseas territory. Following the Second World War, New Caledonia's nickel mining industry was the key factor in the territory's rapid economic growth, due to the global nickel boom. Demand escalated even further during the Vietnam War, where nickel remained in high demand. Nickel was therefore considered to be 'a strategic industry that Paris regarded as a key national resource'.[109] Thus, a key aspect of France's interest in retaining a presence in New Caledonia revolved around the archipelago's mineral resources.

The severe downturn experienced by the nickel industry following the end of the Vietnam War in the mid-1970s, however, had further negative consequences for the Kanak. While they never benefited economically from the boom of the New Caledonian nickel industry, the slump in nickel exporting led policy-makers to start developing other avenues for revenue, which further marginalized the Kanak. In particular, the development of Noumea as a tourist destination, and the emphasis on tourist-specific infrastructure needs, highlighted for the Kanak the total

---

[104] Lyons, The Totem and the Tricolor, at pp. 116–17.
[105] A. Thompson, 'The Uses and Missuses of Capital: New Caledonia's Mining Industry, 1870–1901', (1984) 19 Journal of Pacific History, 91.
[106] These migrant groups often suffered from very poor labour and social conditions. See Dorothy Shineberg, 'The New Hebridean Is Everywhere: The Oceanian Labour Trade to New Caledonia 1865–1930', (1995) 18(1) Pacific Studies, 6.
[107] Chappell, 'The Noumea Accord', 379.
[108] Chappell, 'The Black and the Red', at 51.   [109] Ibid.

disregard of their own rights, and strengthened thier resolve for independence. As Lyons noted:

> While the white-controlled municipalities spent money on installing parking meters and swimming pools in urban centres like Noumea, more remote villages lacked even basic amenities like running water and sealed roads.[110]

Yet despite this fluctuation in the market over the past decades, nickel has remained an important global commodity, and has continued to be mined in New Caledonia. Although in 2010 the price per ton suffered an almost 50 per cent drop because of the global economic crisis, nickel ore and derived metallurgical products still represent about 90 per cent of the total value of exports from New Caledonia.[111]

2.   The Goro nickel mine: a brief corporate history

Though nickel has long been New Caledonia's most important export commodity, for a long time there was only one nickel refinery in the country, located near Noumea. Yet the discovery of the Goro site in the South Province of the Grand Terre generated much interest and speculation as it is believed to be the world's largest nickel deposit, with an expected annual capacity of 60,000t of nickel and 4,300 to 5,000t of cobalt, representing approximately 20 per cent of global production.[112]

In 1992, the Canadian corporation Inco acquired the mining rights for the deposit at Goro, in collaboration with *Bureau de Recherches Géologiques et Minières*, France's public mining agency, which held a 15 per cent share in the project. In 1992, Inco began developing a new hydrometallurgical process specific to nickel, and by 1999 construction of the pilot plant at Goro began. In 2001, Inco announced that it would be commencing commercial operations at the site, and projected production to begin by 2004, with a budget of US$1.9 billion. Construction of the factory began in 2002; however, it was soon halted for almost two years due to budget blowout, a downturn in global nickel prices, permit delays and opposition from Kanak communities and environmentalists. Nevertheless, in late 2004 the project announced it would recommence operations, and in 2005 site construction resumed.

---

[110]   Lyons, *The Totem and the Tricolor*, at p. 123.
[111]   See: www.isee.nc/anglais/keyfigures/keyfigures.html;   see   also: www.mfat.govt.nz/ Countries/Pacific/New-Caledonia.php.
[112]   See: http://nickel.vale.com/countries/new_caledonia/default.aspx.

In October 2006, the Brazilian entity *Companhia Vale do Rio Doce* (Vale) acquired Canada's second-largest mining company, Inco, for $18.9 billion. Inco's share in the Goro nickel mine was thus transferred to Vale, and Vale gained a controlling a 69 per cent interest in what will be referred to henceforth as the Goro Nickel Project. Three provinces of New Caledonia gained a 10 per cent equity interest in the project, through their holding company *Société de Participation Minière du Sud Calédonien*. The remaining 21 per cent interest in the project is held by Sumic Nickel Netherlands (owned by Japan's Sumitomo Metal Mining Co. Ltd and Mitsui Co. Ltd).[113]

Apart from the mineral extraction site, the project also includes a hydrometallurgical factory for the treatment of the minerals extracted, a waste treatment plant, a coal-fired thermal power plant, an accommodation compound for workers and a port.[114] In 2008 the construction of the factory was completed, and in 2009 extraction began in phases. The new consortium expects that production of nickel and cobalt will be at full capacity by 2013.[115]

3. The Goro Nickel Project and the Kanak

The Goro Nickel open pit mine is located in the South Province of the Grande Terre, a region notable for its important marine and land biodiversity and of importance to a number of Kanak communities. The Kanak tribes of *Goro, Unia, Touaourou, Waho, Yaté, Saint-Louis, Conception, Ile Ouen* and *Ile des Pines* and *Paita* all reside in the region around the Goro nickel mine. The tribes depend on the environment for their subsistence needs, and their ways of life revolve around agriculture and fishing. The area also has important spiritual significance, and according to Kanak tradition, the territories of the Grand Sud are inhabited both physically and spiritually according to cycles related to different aspects of their tradition and foundational myths. Their traditional guardians visit these sites according to different cycles. The forests and scrublands of the region also contain medicinal and mythical plants.[116]

---

[113] See Ibid.   [114] See: www.vale.nc/.   [115] Ibid.

[116] *Protocole D'accord Portant Pacte Pour un Developpement Durable du Grand Sud*, Preamble: The perception of the Tribes of the history of the indigenous Kanak of the Grand Sud, signed 11 September 2008. p. 4. (hereinafter *Protocole D'accord*) Original on file with author – all translations are the author's own.

The project is also in an area of environmental significance, located in the heart of a multitude of natural marine and land reserves, including mountains, lakes, wetlands, forests and underground mineral basins which are the native habitat of numerous species. The marine environment of the region is equally rich, and Prony Bay, which borders the project site, is an internationally renowned location recognized for its natural beauty and visited by humpback whales. The environmental importance of this area has been recognized internationally, and the New Caledonian lagoon was recently declared as natural heritage by UNESCO.[117]

As with any mining project, the Goro Nickel Project was forecast to significantly affect the physical environment on which the Kanak depend for daily life. Impacts of the project included large losses of land, the deposit of waste heavy metals in the lagoon, erosion created by the exploitation of nickel, forest fires and atmospheric pollution and mudslides, all too often effects of nickel extraction. The pollution of lands and waters would also affect the biodiversity of marine life and fauna and flora, thereby seriously impacting the Kanak communities of the region's ability to maintain their subsistence way of life, including their ability to continue traditional hunting and subsistence agriculture and fishing, wood collecting and the cultivation of medicinal plants.

Affected Kanak communities were initially heavily opposed to the project. Foremost, they complained that as the traditional owners of the lands, they were never consulted regarding the project, and that their free, prior and informed consent was never sought regarding this massive project on their territories that would affect almost every aspect of their lives. Authorization permits for exploitation were granted by the Province to Inco under the framework of the general law, without any consultation with the affected Kanak communities. This was also true regarding the construction permit for the site and other mining permits. Even construction works on the factory began without the publication of any prior impact assessment.[118]

---

[117] On 8 July 2008 the New Caledonian Lagoons were inscribed on the UNESCO World Cultural Heritage List. See http://whc.unesco.org/en/list/1115/.

[118] Jérôme Bouquet-Elkaïm, *Etude de Case: le Projet Minier Goro Nickel et l'accord du 27 septembre 2008 Nouvelle Caledonie pour le Seminaire International sur les companies extractives, les peuples autochtones et les droits de l'homme: Etablir un cadre pour la consultation, le partage des benefices et la resolution des conflits*, UN OHCHR International Workshop on natural resource companies, indigenous peoples and human rights: setting a framework for consultation, benefit-sharing and dispute

This was compounded by a lack of legal recognition of the rights of the Kanak over their lands. Despite the mine being located on traditional Kanak territories, the lands remain officially controlled by the South Province. The Kanak, with no official title to their traditional lands, were therefore unable to stop development of these lands as landowners. Moreover, their exclusion from participating in the development of the project also meant that the Kanak were marginalized from sharing in any potential benefits that the project might bring to the region.

The lack of consultation of the Kanak, coupled with a complete disregard of their traditional land rights, led to various blockades of the project in 2004, 2005 and 2006.[119] Kanak groups were particularly concerned about specific aspects of the project which would affect them directly, including environmental, cultural and social impacts on their lands and communities. Kanak opposition to the project also took on a legal dimension. Kanak groups filed a number of proceedings against the company using administrative laws to challenge the validity of exploitation authorizations granted to the project. At one point, up to 15 civil suits were filed by various Kanak groups and individuals against the project. By 2006, the conflict had degenerated into an armed confrontation, and various criminal charges were laid against Kanak militants and protestors, and certain Kanak were imprisoned.[120]

III.   *Le Protocol d'accord*: a workable solution for the Kanak?

Following years of blockades, protest and protracted legal battles, the parties entered into protracted negotiations with a view to resolving the conflict and finding a compromise that would satisfy their demands. In 2008, an agreement was reached between the Goro Nickel Project and the Customary Council (*Conseil Coutoumier*) of Djubea-Kapone, an institution which represents the chiefs of the traditional area of Djubea

resolution (hereinafter OHCHR Workshop), Moscow, 3–4 December 2008, at 4. Available at www2.ohchr.org/english/issues/indigenous/docs/workshops/Bouquet_ Moscow_Workshop.pdf. (All translations are the author's.) (Hereinafter Bouquet-Elkaïm, *Etude de Case.*)

[119] See www.miningwatch.ca/en/indigenous-kanaks-blockade-inco-s-goro-site-demand-hearing-inco-government-authorities.

[120] Ibid., at 5. See also, Rafael Tiago Juk Benke, *Etude De Cas: Le Projet Minier Et Mé tallurgique De Vale-Inco En Nouvelle-Calédonie Et Le « Pacte Pour Un Développement Durable » Signé Le 27 Septembre 2008*, OHCHR Workshop, Moscow 3–4 December 2008, at 7. Available at www2.ohchr.org/english/issues/indigenous/docs/workshops/ Vale_Inco_New_Caledonia_Case_Moscow_Workshop.doc.

Kapone (*Le Gran Sur*), the Customary Senators of the region of Djubea-Kapone and the Kanak Environmental nongovermental organization *Comité Rheebu Nuu*.

The negotiated agreement (*Protocole D'accord Portant Pacte Pour un Developpement Durable du Grand Sud*[121] – 'the Agreement') established a clear framework which has as its aim promotion of a 'sustainable and shared approach to development' that will 'reinforce the role of indigenous populations, contribute to the improvement of their lives and allow them to become key actors in their own development in the long term'.[122] Beyond recognizing the role of the Kanak, the Agreement notes that the scheme will be established around three key pillars associated with sustainable development: first, the social and cultural development of the communities; second, the protection of the environment; and third, an economically balanced approach to development. Lastly, the Agreement's overarching aim is to stop the conflict between the parties.

1.   Recognition of the Kanak as development partners

A key aspect of the Agreement is its recognition of the Kanak as equal partners in development. It explicitly recognizes the special rights of the Kanak as the indigenous peoples of New Caledonia. The preamble to the Agreement incorporates direct sections of the Noumea Accords, in particular taking note of the unilateral colonization of New Caledonia by the French of an inhabited territory, and the failure of the French to establish any legal relationship with the Kanak at the time of colonization. The Agreement further incorporates a section of the Noumea Accords relating to Kanak culture and civilization, noting the distinct identity of the Kanak, and in particular how that identity is connected to traditional lands and territories. The Agreement recognizes the Kanak people of the project area in the Grand Sud, acknowledging the importance of the region for those tribes both physically and spiritually. It also makes note of the UN Declaration on the Rights of Indigenous Peoples[123] in connection with the recognition of the unique position of the Kanak as the traditional owners of the lands.

Furthermore, the Agreement explicitly commits itself to upholding the principle of sustainable development as defined by the international

---

[121] *Protocole D'accord.*   [122] Ibid., Article 1: Aim of the Agreement.
[123] UN Declaration on the Rights of Indigenous Peoples.

community at the 1992 Rio Conference on Environment and Development.[124] Sustainable development is therefore defined in the Agreement as a new approach to development that recognizes the important contribution of indigenous peoples, particularly regarding respect of the environment and the well-being of humankind.

2. Benefit sharing

Perhaps most notable in the Agreement is that there is no profit-sharing mechanism or royalty payments from the mining operations that go directly to the Kanak. This has been attributed to the political constraints imposed by the legal framework of New Caledonia. New Caledonian law does not automatically recognize the Kanak as the owners of their traditional lands. Whilst a mechanism has been put in place for Kanak land claims, this is a slow and arduous process, with limited efficiency.[125] Given that the tribes party to the negotiation process did not hold formal title to their traditional lands, they were in a difficult position to be able to negotiate successfully for a share in the profits. However, Article 23 of the Agreement leaves open the possibility of future negotiations on this point, which also makes clear that if the rights of the Kanak over their lands and territories are fully recognized in the future, new negotiations could be conducted on the issue.[126]

Notwithstanding this shortcoming, the preamble to the Agreement acknowledges that the Goro Nickel sustainable development project must ensure that local populations benefit from the economic aspects of the project. Thus, the Agreement establishes two key mechanisms that will enable the Kanak to benefit from the project.

First, it provides for the establishment of a compensation mechanism that will provide financial reparation to the Kanak for socio-cultural impacts of the project.[127] A foundation will be established for this purpose and will be controlled by a board composed of eight indigenous representatives, two representatives from the Goro Nickel board and an employee of Goro Nickel. The foundation will finance projects in indigenous communities impacted by the project in the fields of social and cultural development, protection of the environment, training and education, development of sustainable economic activities and any other

[124] 1992 United Nations Conference on Environment and Development (UNCED).
[125] Bouquet-Elkaïm, *Etude de Case*, at 5.   [126] *Protocole D'accord*, Article 23.
[127] Ibid., Title 1: Foundation for Sustainable Development: Arts 4–8.

initiative that contributes to the participatory and sustainable development of the communities of the Grand Sud. A budget of US$6.8 million from the company for the first five years will establish the foundation, and this will be supplemented by an additional US$1.4 million per year for thirty years. The involvement of the customary authorities in the foundation will ensure that the projects financed by the company are responsive to the needs and interests of the tribes.

Second, the Agreement establishes a revegetation programme for areas impacted by the project.[128] This programme will be financed by the company, with a budget of US$25.5 million over thirty years, and is aimed at revegetating areas affected by activities or incidents connected with the project.[129] Local peoples will lead the reforestation programme via a reforestation committee made up of a majority of indigenous representatives. The association will identify areas for reforestation, develop a plan and manage the project.[130] The reforestation committee will guarantee the balanced development of communities alongside the project that will be relevant to social and cultural interests.

The Agreement also provides for the creation of satellite nurseries developed by the tribes on their traditional lands. The goal of production on these nurseries is 250,000–500,000 plants per year. Specific funds are allocated for this purpose.[131]

3. Improved consultation

The Agreement also establishes a number of mechanisms for participatory involvement and consultation, which will provide not only material benefits for the Kanak, but will also enable them to make decisions about the operation of the project.

Chapter Two creates a participatory indigenous-run council that will allow Kanak communities to be consulted regarding environmental impacts of the project. The body, the *Conseil Consultatif Coutumier Environnemental* (the Consultative Customary Environmental Council, CCCE), will provide advice regarding proposed exploitation and places susceptible to impact, on environmental surveillance programmes and on monitoring programmes of the projects, taking into account Kanak customary authorities and traditional knowledge. The CCCE will also

[128] Ibid., Title 2: Chapter 2: Reforestation in non-impacted Zones, Arts 16–20.
[129] Ibid., Article 16: Aim of the Revegetation Programme.
[130] Ibid., Article 18: Management of the Revegetation Programme.
[131] Ibid., Article 19: Satellite Nurseries.

develop a strategy to prioritize the traditional knowledge of the Kanak in its operations. A budget of approximately US$270,000[132] will be set aside by Goro Nickel for the CCCE.[133]

The CCCE is made up of 15 members from representative indigenous institutions, thereby taking into account Kanak customary authorities. Two observers from Goro Nickel will also participate in the CCCE. The latter will not have decision-making authority, however, they will be able to participate in discussions and inform Goro Nickel about the contents of the meetings.[134]

Moreover, the Kanak will also be involved in environmental monitoring of the project. The CCCE has the power to decide and undertake environmental impact studies of its own. The Agreement further provides that the CCCE is to be informed by the corporation of the content and progress of all requests for environmental permits, regarding which it can equally give its opinion or recommendations, and also provide recommendations for corrective measures to be taken in cases of non-conformity of the environmental permit or authorization.[135]

4. Resolution of the conflict

The final, but equally important, aspect of the Agreement, is the resolution of conflict between the parties. Indeed, the process of negotiation and consultation about the Agreement was itself an important part of this process. In bringing the opposing parties to the negotiating table, negotiations allowed for the development of an open dialogue between the parties, enabling a frank exchange of views in order to reach an agreement acceptable to all concerned. This process of dialogue, and ultimately reconciliation, was essential to ensure not only the success of reaching a final agreement, but also that it was based on a mutually acceptable platform of values in order to ensure its successful implementation and sustainability moving forward.

Moreover, the Agreement expressly notes as its aim the goal of ending the perpetuation of conflict between the parties, and finding a workable solution to ensure a sustainable approach to development that takes into account not only economic, but also social and human aspects.[136] In

---

[132] 24 million New Caledonian francs.
[133] *Protocole D'accord*, Article 13: Budget of the CCCE.
[134] Ibid., Article 14: Functioning of the CCCE.
[135] Ibid., Article 12: Mission of the CCCE   [136] Ibid., Preamble, p. 6.

order to settle past grievances and proceed amicably and in good faith, the Agreement itself expressly provides for the termination of all court-related procedures.[137] It also requires all parties to renounce all illegal or violent acts, and imposes the principles of dialogue and good faith as a new basis for relations between the parties.[138] Finally, in order to prevent future conflicts born out of the accord, recourse to an arbitration mechanism is established.[139]

III.   Analysis and conclusions

There is a widespread misconception that recognition of the rights of indigenous peoples will result in automatic opposition by them to all development projects on their lands. Yet the rights prescribed by international law, including the Declaration on the Rights of Indigenous Peoples, simply envisage including indigenous people in the planning, development and execution of such projects, in light of their unique position as peoples with specific connections to those lands and territories.[140] As the Special Rapporteur on the Rights of Indigenous Peoples has aptly noted:

> The majority of indigenous peoples and communities are not opposed to corporate activity per se or to the potential benefits of such activity for their own economic and social development. Indeed, experience has shown that corporate activity may become a key factor in indigenous peoples' development when they themselves can control such activity in the exercise of their rights to autonomy and self-government. What indigenous people are opposed to, understandably, is development which is carried out without respect for their basic rights, which brings with it only adverse impacts and which does not result in any visible benefits for their communities.[141]

Indeed, in New Caledonia, as early as 2001, the chiefs of *Yaté* were aware of this dichotomy, observing that the Goro Nickel Project could bring 'a new era of economic development to the Grand Sud', yet equally aware that the project, by proceeding without consulting them, may also signal the 'beginning of a rupture for the indigenous peoples of the region'.[142]

---

[137] Ibid., Article 28: Current Conflicts.   [138] Ibid., Article 2(iii) and (iv).

[139] Ibid., Article 29: Conflicts as a Result of the Present Agreement.

[140] UN Declaration, on the Rights of Indigenous Peoples, Article 8.

[141] Anaya, 'Report of the UN Special Rapporteur on the rights of indigenous peoples on the Situation of Kanak people in New Caledonia, France', para. 31.

[142] *Protocol D'accord*, Preamble, p. 4.

Whilst for many years the project was the root of conflict between the Kanak and investors, the resulting Goro Nickel–Kanak Agreement provides an interesting and recent example of how this tension was mitigated. Although the Agreement does not specifically reference the term 'self-determination' or 'free prior and informed consent', it illustrates a number of creative and unique solutions, including a range of participatory mechanisms for the Kanak[143] as development partners, and can be seen as an example of the implementation of some aspects of self-determination. As the Special Rapporteur has noted, for indigenous peoples meaningfully to benefit from projects on their land, mechanisms must be established that 'genuinely strengthen the capacity of indigenous peoples to establish and follow up their development priorities and which help to make their own decision-making mechanisms and institutions more effective'.[144] Indeed, the Agreement appears to do just that, by creating novel participatory structures that give the Kanak a key role in the promotion and development of their own rights and empowering them to make important development choices about their own lives.

First, the Agreement explicitly recognizes the special rights of the Kanak as indigenous peoples, making reference to a number of international instruments, including the Noumea Accords, the UN Declaration on Indigenous Peoples and the 1992 Rio Declaration on Environment and Development. This symbolic recognition is significant. By recognising the Kanak not only as individuals affected by the project, but as an indigenous people with *sui generis* rights that are affected in particular ways by development on their lands, the Agreement provides a strong grounding for the building of mutual understanding and respect among the parties.

Second, although the Kanak are not included as direct economic partners, the agreement proposes unique and tailored benefit-sharing arrangements to ensure they profit from the project. As the Special Rapporteur has argued, 'benefit sharing must go beyond restrictive approaches based solely

---

[143] As the Expert Mechanism on the Rights of Indigenous Peoples has clarified: 'Self-determination is an ongoing process which ensures that indigenous peoples continue to participate in decision-making and control over their own destinies. It means that the institutions of decision-making should be devised to enable indigenous peoples to make decisions related to their internal and local affairs, and to participate collectively in external decision-making processes in accordance with relevant human rights standards.' See EMRIP, Progress Report, para. 31.

[144] Ibid., para 80.

on financial payments'[145] and create positive mechanisms which strengthen the rights of indigenous peoples. The mechanisms created do just that: the compensation mechanism, revegetation programme and the creation of satellite nurseries are all innovative and productive mechanisms that will allow the Kanak to participate directly in activities that have the potential to generate revenue and benefit them, as a result of the project. This is not to say that specific profit-sharing arrangements would not be welcomed, if such a scheme could be developed in consultation with the Kanak. However, the mechanisms envisaged by the Agreement do establish a solid grounding for the sharing of tangible benefits relating to the project for the impacted communities.

The improved consultation mechanisms envisaged by the Agreement are also significant, and are positive examples of the implementation of international law. Article 7.3 of ILO Convention No. 169 requires States to conduct 'studies ... in co-operation with the peoples concerned, to assess the social, spiritual, cultural and environmental impact on them of planned development activities'.[146] By empowering the CCCE to independently investigate situations of concern and make recommendations to Goro Nickel, the Kanak clearly will play an important role in assessing environmental impacts. It is significant that the Agreement envisages the training of eight Kanak to become environmental experts, who will then be put at the disposal of the CCCE, thus enabling them to carry out their independent investigations as envisaged by the Agreement.[147] These mechanisms therefore envisage a large degree of influence and control by the Kanak over the environmental monitoring process. Importantly, the outcome of those studies and recommendations will be used as 'fundamental criteria' for the implementation of those activities by Goro Nickel, as required by international law.

It would be naïve to believe that the Agreement is a fix-all solution that will automatically resolve all issues for the Kanak peoples affected by the mine. The benefits of the Agreement will require the ongoing good faith efforts of all parties for its proper implementation. Moreover, the possibility of the pending referendum on independence will surely be cause

---

[145] Ibid.

[146] ILO Convention 169 Concerning Independent and Tribal Peoples in Independent Countries, entered into force 05/09/1991.

[147] *Protocole D'accord*, Article 15: Training and Recruitment of Environmental Technicians.

for much political instability, and could contribute to internal frictions between Kanak tribes, and in relations with the company.

It must also be remembered that these types of large-scale development projects, notwithstanding good intentions, collaboration with impacted communities and comprehensive environmental impact assessments, do come with major environmental risks. And it is the Kanak traditional owners who depend on these lands for their subsistence needs and cultural practices, who will be most directly impacted. Indeed, this has already been experienced: on 1 April 2009, a leak in a container of treated minerals caused the release of 18,000 litres of sulphuric acid in the river, and subsequently the lagoon.[148]

Tension between development priorities and indigenous rights is a widespread phenomenon, and a source of ongoing conflict for indigenous peoples, governments and private development partners. However, this 'innovative, participatory and consensual'[149] agreement may provide one example of how working together, in line with human rights standards, may achieve results. Nevertheless, the creation of new political structures, in part through the demands of self-determination, presents both challenges and threats to the indigenous peoples of New Caledonia.

[148] See: www.ibtimes.com/articles/20090408/acid-spill-at-vale-incos-giant2-bn.htm.
[149] *Protocole D'accord*, Preamble, p. 6.

The ethnic dichotomy of 'self' and 'other' within Europe: inter-war minority protection in perspective

MOHAMMAD SHAHABUDDIN*

I. Introduction

The concept of 'ethnicity' emanating from the Greek root *ethnos* has always been used to refer to the 'other' in a derogatory sense.[1] However, from about the mid-nineteenth century, in the German Romantic literature the notion of 'otherness' in *ethnos* shifted to the image of the 'self', expressed through the dominant political vocabulary of the nineteenth century – 'nation'.[2] Such a romantic image of the nation having its foundation in ethnicity was destined to exclude the remaining 'other' in the process of constructing the 'self'.[3] Conversely, if the liberal nation

* I am indebted to Professor Antony Anghie, Professor Matthew Craven and Professor David Kennedy for their insightful comments on the draft chapter.

[1] E. Tonkin, M. McDonald and M. Chapman, *History and Ethnicity* (Routledge, 1989), pp. 11–20.

[2] As the etymology of the term demonstrates, 'nation' used to refer to shared biological characteristics. Deriving from the past participle of the verb *nasci*, meaning to be born, the Latin noun *nationem* connotes breed or race. See W. Connor, 'A Nation Is a Nation, Is a State, Is an Ethnic Group, Is a ?' in J. Hutchinson and A. D. Smith (eds.), *Nationalism* (Oxford University Press, 1994), p. 38. Although at some medieval universities, a student's *nationem* designated the sector of the country from which he came, when introduced into the English language in the late thirteenth century, nation was with its primary connotation of a blood-related group (ibid.). In this sequence, it is also argued that in the nineteenth century, as in the Middle Ages, nations were conceived of as units of common biological descent as well as of common culture. See S. Raynolds, 'Regional Sentiments and Medieval Communities' in Hutchinson and Smith (eds.), *Nationalism*, p. 139.

[3] J. G. von Herder, 'Reflections on the Philosophy of the History of Mankind (1791)' in O. Dahbour and M. R. Ishay (eds.), *The Nationalism Reader* (Humanities Press, 1995), pp. 48–57; J. G. Fichte, 'An Outline of International and Cosmopolitan Law (1796–97)' in H. S. Reiss and P. Brown (eds.), *The Political Thought of the German Romantics* (Basil

is conceived as the reflection of universal spirit in the temporal form, ethnicity must remain at the sidelines in the liberal construction of the nation.[4] Thus, the liberal discourse on whether the ethnic 'other' should be assimilated or allowed to maintain cultural distinctiveness is informed by an instrumental understanding of ethnicity.

Against this nineteenth-century backdrop, this chapter demonstrates how 'ethnicity' expressed through this dichotomy of 'self' and 'other' along the line of the liberal and conservative traditions informed the inter-war international law of minority protection at three different levels. First, the inter-war minority protection system came into being as a compromise between the liberal and conservative traditions vis-à-vis ethnicity and its role in the political organisation of nation-States. The idea of minority rights appeared as a fall-back position whenever Wilson's proposition of the right to self-determination in conservative terms could not be realised. In such a case, liberal individualism as well as the assimilationist agenda always coexisted with the conservative ethnic notion of the 'minority'. Secondly, a dichotomy of the liberal Western 'self' and the conservative Eastern 'other' was evident in the imposition of special minority protection obligations on Eastern and Central European (ECE) States, whereas minorities within Western Europe remained outside any international protection. And finally, the inherent drawbacks of the system (that became evident in its actual operation) demonstrated another layer of the self–other discourse in which bypassing the international system, the agenda of mutual exclusion of the ethnic 'other' was brutally pursued in the process of constructing the ethnic self-image along the conservative line.

II.   Minority rights as the halfway between the liberal and conservative traditions

The Peace Conference following the Great War aggravated the minority issue by drastically redrawing the frontiers in Eastern and Central

---

Blackwell, 1955), pp. 73–84; J. G. Fichte, 'Addresses to the German Nation – Thirteenth Address (1808)' in Reiss and Brown (eds.), *The Political Thought of the German Romantics*, pp. 102–8; L. von Ranke, 'The Great Powers (1833)' in Dahbour and Ishay (eds.), *The Nationalism Reader*, pp. 158–9.

[4] See, G. W. F. Hegel, *Lectures on the Philosophy of World History (1837)*, D. Forbes and H. B. Nisbet (eds.) (Cambridge University Press, 1975), pp. 76–97, 147–51; J. S. Mill, 'Considerations on Representative Government (1861)' in *Three Essays* (Oxford University Press, 1975), pp. 380–8; J. E. E. Dalberg-Acton (Lord Acton), *The History of Freedom and Other Essays*, J. N. Figgis and V. L. Reginald (eds.) (Macmillan & Co. Ltd., 1907), pp. 289–93.

Europe that followed the collapse of the old empires. In the aftermath of the war, international law had to respond to this minority 'problem' against the backdrop of the most influential notion of the time – self-determination. In his famous Fourteen Points, Wilson enshrined the notion of self-determination, without actually using the term, as one of the key guiding principles of the post-war international order.[5] In the aftermath of the war, his first draft of the Covenant categorically mentioned in Article III the principle of self-determination along with the provision of certain territorial adjustments which was to qualify the mutual guarantee of political independence and territorial integrity among the contracting powers.[6]

However, the Wilsonian proposition of self-determination, being premised on the centrality of ethnicity in the political organisation of nation-States, faced criticism even from other American delegates, as it transpired that the territorial adjustments made at the Paris Peace Conference were unlikely to satisfy all nationalist claims, and therefore, would not prevent ethnic tensions erupting. David Miller – an American jurist and also one of the draftsmen of the Covenant – in his comment on Wilson's draft, asserted that such a general provision of self-determination 'will make that dissatisfaction permanent, will compel every Power to engage in propaganda and will legalise irredentist agitation in at least all of Eastern Europe'.[7]

Miller was not alone in criticising Wilson's proposition. It is evident from the US Secretary of State, Robert Lansing's personal narrative of the peace negotiations in Paris, that he was extremely critical of the idea of self-determination as a general principle, let alone as a *right*.[8] Faced with vehement opposition from other statesmen, Wilson dropped the idea of self-determination in his fourth draft and also in the Covenant, nevertheless Lansing found it regrettable that such opposition did not obtain from Wilson an open disavowal of the principle as the standard for the determination of sovereign authority; hence, the phrase remained one of the general bases for peace negotiation.[9]

---

[5] For the full text of Wilson's address to the Congress, see, G. R. Suriano (ed.), *Great American Speeches* (Gramercy Books, 1993), pp. 143–6.

[6] See, D. H. Miller, *The Drafting of the Covenant*, vol. II (G P Putnam's Sons, 1928), p. 70.

[7] Ibid., p. 71.

[8] R. Lansing, *The Peace Negotiations: A Personal Narrative* (Houghton Mifflin Company, 1921), p. 95.

[9] Ibid.

Perhaps Wilson himself was aware of the limitations of his policy of self-determination expressed along the conservative line, and therefore, he had to deviate from this principle on a number of occasions. In a note written on 30 December 1918, Lansing claims that in the actual application of the principle Wilson, rather, relied on a number of exceptions to his own creation: millions of ethnic Germans were denied the right to self-determination and transferred to the new States of Poland and Czecho-Slovakia under the Treaty of Versailles; Austrian Tyrol was ceded to the Kingdom of Italy against the will of substantially the entire population of that region under the Treaty of Saint-Germain; Austria was denied the right to form a political union with Germany; the peoples of Estonia, Latvia, Lithuania, the Ukraine, Georgia and Azerbaijan were left to the mercy of Great Russia despite their distinct identities and aspirations to become independent States.[10]

However, during the peace negotiations, efforts were made to reconcile the classical notion of sovereignty and the conservative notion of self-determination. As Miller asserted, since the principle of self-determination could not be generally applied, '[i]t is submitted that the contrary principle should prevail; as the drawing of boundaries according to racial or social conditions is in many cases an impossibility, protection of the rights of minorities and *acceptance of such protection by the minorities* constitute the only basis of enduring peace'.[11]

Thus, on the one hand, instead of Wilson's initial proposal of incorporating self-determination as a general principle, an unqualified guarantee of political independence and territorial integrity of all State members of the League was stipulated, and on the other, the nationalities within the new States, which were not granted the right to self-determination due to pragmatic or strategic reasons, were put under an international mechanism of minority protection. In other words, the notion of the protection of minorities appeared as a fall-back position where the principle of self-determination in the conservative sense could not be applied.

Yet, it was not easy for the liberal West to design a mechanism for the protection of Eastern minorities, who not only were depicted as the product of the conservative Eastern tradition of relying on ethnicity for the political organisation of nation-States, but also allegedly desired to

---

[10] Ibid., pp. 98–100. See also, M. Mazower, *Hitler's Empire – Nazi Rule in Occupied Europe* (Penguin Books, 2009 [2008]), pp. 33–4.

[11] Miller, *The Drafting of the Covenant*, vol. II, p. 71, emphasis in original.

maintain their ethnic features.[12] This resulted in an attempt to reconcile both traditions. It is, therefore, a significant characteristic of the inter-war minority protection mechanism that while producing a number of legal experimentations to 'manage' nationalist passions,[13] it actually avoided any general recognition of minority rights. Instead of inserting any provision on minority protection in the League Covenant, as Wilson initially proposed, a series of minority treaties were concluded to put certain ECE States under the treaty obligation of protecting minorities within their territories, with the guarantee mechanism being entrusted to the League.[14]

However, the fact remains that Wilson himself had something else in mind. During the session of the Supreme Council on 23 June 1919, in a brief exchange with Headlam-Morley – a member of the British delegation – about the use of minority language as a medium of instruction in schools in Poland, Wilson is reported to have expressed the view that the American model of cultural assimilation should also be applicable to Eastern and Central Europe. When he was reminded that the German population was long established in the territories to be ceded and in some Polish towns even constituted the majority, he replied: 'Yes, but their properties will become part of Poland and it is not our wish that they remain German forever.'[15]

Nevertheless, it needs to be noted that throughout the Peace Conference, Wilson had to advance his pro-minority ideas under immense pressure from his counterparts in Europe, and even his deputies. Regarding the Jewish population in ECE States, at a session of the Council of Four on 1 May 1919, the US President indeed drew the attention of the Supreme Council to the anti-Semitic pogroms in Poland and Romania and read out

---

[12] This aspect of the inter-war minority protection mechanism will be detailed in the following section.

[13] See generally, N. Berman, 'A Perilous Ambivalence: Nationalist desire, Legal Autonomy, and the Limits of Interwar Framework', (1992) 33(2) *Harvard International Law Journal*, 353–80; also, N. Berman, 'But the Alternative is Despair: European Nationalism and the Modernist Renewal of International Law', (1993) 106 *Harvard Law Review*, 1792–904.

[14] In Article 12 of the Polish Minority Treaty, which served as a model minority treaty, Poland agreed that 'the stipulation in the Foregoing Articles, so far as they affect persons belonging to racial, religious or linguistic minorities, constitute obligations of international concern and shall be placed under the guarantee of the League of Nations'.

[15] P. Mantoux, *Deliberations du Conseil des Quatres. Notes de L'Officier Interprete*, vol. II (1955), p. 489, cited in C. R. von Frenz, *A Lesson Forgotten – Minority Protection under the League of Nations: The Case of the German Minority in Poland, 1920–1934* (St. Martin's Press, 1999), p. 66.

the Jewish draft treaty of 29 April, but he had to agree with the other members in their unanimous rejection of any demands for a 'group autonomy'.[16] Lloyd George adopted the same assimilationist approach towards the Jewish minorities in Poland: 'every effort ought to be made for the Jews of Poland to merge in Polish nationality, just as the Jews in Great Britain or France became merged in British and French nationality'.[17] He was particularly concerned about the risk of 'the creation of a state within a state' associated with the claim of autonomy for the minorities.[18]

Ultimately, while defining the protected minorities in the Polish Minority Treaty, the phrase 'persons belonging to linguistic, racial and religious minorities' rather than 'national minorities' was used in order to avoid their recognition as a separate legal corporation within the State.[19] Given the liberal underpinning of the French understanding of nationalism, France even initially refused to endorse any objective criteria such as ethnicity, language or religion as the basis of the application of the right to self-determination; instead, it proposed the principle of plebiscite that would guarantee the primacy of individual choice in conformity with the French liberal ideology.[20] Although the provision of plebiscite was not extended to most of the transferred territories, there was essentially a right for the transferred population to decide on their political allegiance, which again demonstrated the tendency of reducing the collectivism in the notion of minority to individualism.[21]

Thus, to what extent the *raison d'être* of the minority protection regime was the 'protection' of minorities at all (in line with the conservative tradition) remains an open question. The Report of de Mello-Franco[22] revealed that the architects of the minority protection system in no way envisioned the minorities as groups of inhabitants who would regard themselves as permanently foreign to the general organisation of

---

[16] Mantoux, *Deliberations*, vol. I, p. 440, cited in Frenz, *A Lesson Forgotten*, p. 59.

[17] Papers relating to the Foreign Relations of the United States (FRUS) 1913–21, *The Paris Peace Conference 1919*, vol. VI (Government Printing Press, 1942), p. 626.

[18] Mantoux, *Deliberations*, p. 440, cited in Frenz, *A Lesson Forgotten*, p. 59.

[19] See Article 12 of the Polish Minority Treaty.

[20] French government note of 15 November 1918 sent to the US Government. See FRUS, *The Paris Peace Conference 1919*, vol. I, p. 349.

[21] See Article 91(3) of the Versailles Treaty of 28 June 1919 which stipulated: 'Within a period of two years after the coming into force of the present Treaty, German nationals over 18 years of age habitually resident in any of the territories recognised as forming part of Poland will be entitled to opt for German nationality.'

[22] Report of A. de Mello-Franco, Council Meeting of 9 December 1925 in *League of Nations Official Journal*, 7(2) (February, 1926), 142.

the country; instead, they intended for the minorities certain legal protection which might gradually prepare the way for conditions necessary
for the establishment of a complete 'national unity' within an environment
of mutual respect. Joseph Roucek noted that the minority treaties never
intended to mitigate the differences of groups within a State; in contrast,
the treaties had a desire to promote the consolidation of the States who
would then give to the minorities certain rights, and thereby protect them
from ultra nationalism, and in this way, contain ethnic tensions leading to
international conflict.[23] Legal adviser to the American Peace Commission
to Paris, Manley Hudson, wrote in 1921 that in that troubled situation of
world affairs, the first and foremost responsibility of the Peace Conference
was to establish a stable peace, and in this connection, it was mandatory to
anticipate new irredentisms, which might call for future vindication.[24] In
that sense, the idea of minority protection, as a safety valve, came on board
when it was more or less ascertained that the conservative right to self-
determination could not be applied to all nationalities, a fact that had the
necessary potential for destabilising the peace that the Paris Conference
was expected to bring forth.

However, it would be less than fair to portray the interwar minority
protection regime as a purely assimilationist mission. Instead, efforts
were made to reconcile the victors' liberal ideology with the conservative
ethnic-nationalism of the East, which ultimately provided the minority
treaties with a hybrid character and the whole regime with a transitory
nature. The Polish Minority Treaty that served as a model for other
similar minority treaties is an archetypical example of such an effort of
reconciliation. On the one hand, Poland guaranteed equality before law
and undertook to assure full and complete protection of life and liberty
as well as the free exercise of religion and language to *all inhabitants* of
Poland without any distinction of birth, nationality, language, race or
religion;[25] on the other hand, Poland had to guarantee that the minorities within its territory would enjoy the same treatment and security as
the other Polish nationals, and also an 'equal right to establish, manage
and control at their expense charitable, religious and social institutions,
schools and other educational establishments, with the right to use their

[23] J. S. Roucek, *The Working of the Minorities System under the League of Nations* (Orbis
Publishing Co., 1929), p. 74.
[24] M. O. Hudson, 'The Protection of Minorities and Natives in the Transferred Territories'
in E. M. House (ed.), *What Really Happened at Paris? The Story of the Peace Conference,
1918–1919 by American Delegates* (Charles Scribner's Sons, 1921), p. 208.
[25] Articles 2 and 7 of the Polish Minority Treaty.

own language and to exercise their religion freely therein'.[26] Therefore, the Polish Minority Treaty adopted a hybrid character incorporating both liberal individualism and the conservative ethnic group phenomenon. As Thornberry notes, '[t]he first two classes of rights above, dealing with the rights of all inhabitants and nationals, reflect the preoccupations of Western statesmen, who were convinced that whatever rights minorities should have would be served best in a liberal setting'.[27]

The hybridity of the minority rights regime under the League appeared precisely in the Advisory Opinion of the Permanent Court in the *Minority Schools in Albania* case, wherein the Court declared:

> The idea underlying the treaties for the protection of minorities is to secure for certain elements incorporated in a State, the population of which differs from them in race, language or religion, the possibility of living peacefully alongside that population and co-operating amicably with it, while at the same time preserving the characteristics which distinguish them from the majority, and satisfying the ensuing special needs.[28]

Thus, to attain this object, the Court continued, it was necessary to ensure that not only were minorities treated equally to the other nationals of the State, but also that suitable means for the preservation of their racial peculiarities, their traditions and their national characteristics were made available.[29]

Although Berman argues that in this case the Court, by relying on the minorities' view of their 'essential' requirement, attempted to deviate from the assimilationist approach of the peacemakers,[30] the Dissenting Opinion reveals that a simultaneous counter effort was made to underscore the assimilationist goal of the minority rights regime with the argument that the interpretation of the Albanian Declaration of 2 October 1921 concerning the protection of minorities must not deviate from the actual will of the State parties.[31] In the *German Settlers* case, while underscoring the primacy of the private rights of individual settlers, and thereby extending protection to the members of the ethnic German community under Polish repression, the Court bypassed the political aspects of the whole issue of

---

[26] Article 8 of the Polish Minority Treaty. Also Article 9 thereof relating to the use of minority language in schools located in minority-populated areas.

[27] P. Thornberry, *International Law and the Rights of Minorities* (Clarendon Press, 1991), p. 43.

[28] PCIJ Report (1935), Ser. A/B, No. 64, p. 17.   [29] Ibid.

[30] Berman, 'A Perilous Ambivalence', pp. 370–2.

[31] PCIJ Report (1935), Ser. A/B, No. 64, p. 27.

Germanisation – a product of conservative German nationalist thrust – declaring that the political purpose behind the colonisation scheme could not affect the private rights acquired under the German Civil Code.[32] On the other hand, the Court refuted the Polish claim of constructing and consolidating their national 'self' through the process of de-Germanisation in this particular context.[33] The Permanent Court's attitude towards ethnicity located against the backdrop of liberalism – the ideology that had been juxtaposed with conservative Romanticism throughout the nineteenth century and now emerged victorious – symbolised the inter-war minority protection mechanism in the most significant way.

A similar compromising attitude was also demonstrated in the fact that although minority groups as separate entities were recognised in practice, formally the League repeatedly denied any international standing for minority groups. The League was rather comfortable with the understanding that the arrangements were between the treaty States and the League, the latter being the guarantor of the promises made by the former.[34] And in this way, the 'minority' itself was denied direct access to the mechanism supposedly designed for its protection, and thereby, pushed to the periphery in the discourse on the protection of their rights. As Roucek approvingly wrote in a publication of 1929, the minority treaties did not constitute the minorities as new special subjects of international law; the protection of minorities was, thus, given internationally, but *within* the State.[35]

Thus, the inter-war minority protection regime demonstrated an inherent tension between the conservative ethnic notion of minority protection and the liberal assimilationist agenda of the victors of the war. Efforts were made to mitigate this tension by various actors, the Permanent Court being the most prominent in this context. However, such efforts were marked with a clear message of undesirability of ethnic 'primitiveness' – a fact that characterised the whole minority protection regime in a number of ways.

---

[32] *Questions Relating to Settlers of German Origin in Poland Case*, PCIJ Report (1925), Ser. B, No. 6, p. 33.

[33] Ibid., p. 37. See also, *Case Concerning Certain German Interests in Polish Upper Silesia*, PCIJ Report (1926), Ser. A, No. 7; and *Case Concerning the Factory at Chorzow*, PCIJ Report (1925), Ser. B, No. 3; PCIJ Report (1928), Ser. A, No. 17.

[34] FRUS, *The Paris Peace Conference 1919*, vol. VI, p. 514.

[35] Roucek, *The Working of the Minorities System*, p. 75.

III.   The liberal West and its conservative 'other' within Europe

Subjecting some States of Eastern and Central Europe to an international scrutiny of minority protection under the League, instead of creating a universal system of minority protection, naturally engendered protest and anger among the representatives of these States during the Paris Peace Conference.[36] While responding to such oppositions, the Western Great Powers attempted to locate the special obligations for the ECE States in a historical continuum – obligations that new entrants of the international society must commit to. This appeared clearly in Clemenceau's letter to Paderewski in response to Poland's position against any special obligation of minority protection for her under the Polish Minority Treaty.[37] Referring to the Congress of Berlin (the Protocol of 28 June 1878), Clemenceau asserted that the Principal Allied and Associated Powers would be false to the responsibility which rested upon them if they departed from this established tradition of stipulating additional responsibility for new States.[38]

Clemenceau's effort to historicise the imposition of special obligations on new States was later substantiated by a number of publicists. For example, Hudson shared the view that there were sufficient precedents before the peacemakers in Paris for imposing additional obligations on the new States, and on States to which large accessions of territory were to be made.[39] In a publication of 1928, Mair recorded the earliest

---

[36] See League of Nations, *The League of Nations and the Protection of Minorities*, p. 17. See also, FRUS, *The Paris Peace Conference 1919*, vol. VI, p. 88; ibid., vol. III, p. 400; H. W. V. Temperley (ed.), *A History of the Peace Conference of Paris*, vol. V (Henry Frowde and Hodder and Stoughton, 1921), p. 129. The meeting took place in an environment of confidentiality; the press were excluded and the proceedings were regarded as confidential.

[37] Letter addressed to the Polish President, M. Paderewski, by the President of the Conference and the French Premier, Clemenceau, transmitting to him the treaty to be signed by Poland under Article 93 of the Treaty of Peace with Germany (Paris, 24 June 1919). See FRUS, *The Paris Peace Conference 1919*, vol. VI, pp. 629–34; Temperley, *A History of the Peace Conference*, vol. V (Appendix IV), p. 433.

[38] Ibid.

[39] Hudson noted that the Conference of London in 1832 prescribed the form of government to Greece on the occasion of her admission to the family of nations; the recognition of the acquisition of the Ionian Islands by Greece in 1864 was made subject to the guarantee of religious freedom. The Congress of Berlin in 1878 that Clemenceau specifically mentioned was another example he had in mind. He thus concluded that for almost a century, it had been an established practice, if not a principle of the public law of Europe, that guarantees to religious minorities should be included among

precedent in which the Congress of Vienna of 1814 stipulated clear provisions of minority protection while creating the United Netherlands.[40] The most detailed account of such precedents is found in Temperley's edited volume, *A History of the Peace Conference of Paris*, published in 1921. However, his conclusion, which followed an apparently linear narrative of imposing special minority protection obligations on new States, threw light on rather a different aspect of the issue – that underlying the general claim of continuity of a tradition of imposing special minority protection obligations on new States or States to which territories had been ceded, there was a dichotomy of 'West' and 'East'. Throughout the nineteenth century, it was generally the non-Western States in Europe who had to consent to such obligations.[41]

Berman argues that the very idea of nationalism was at the heart of this East–West dichotomy. According to him, although the term 'national' was not ultimately used in the definition of protected minorities in the final version of the Treaty, the dichotomy between Eastern and Western Europe often centred on the implications of the word 'national' to describe the 'minority group', and '[t]he 1919 debate about the "nationalness" of minorities was understood not only as opposing states to minorities generally but also as opposing two different cultural conceptions of group identity – those of Western and Eastern Europe'.[42]

Berman's reference to 'nationalness' here needs to be understood in the nineteenth century's conservative Romantic sense of ethnicity as the foundation of the nation in contrast to the liberal version that characterises the Western 'self'. The liberal construction of Eastern Europe for the purpose of a special minority rights regime was premised upon the notion that Eastern Europe was the 'home' of conservative tradition of understanding the 'self' in ethnic terms. And it is in this process that the East becomes the 'ethnic other' of the liberal West, for which ethnicity has no real relevance. In other words, the minority problem was seen as the result of the conservative Eastern tradition of relying on the centrality of ethnicity in nation-building. As the instrumentalist intuition of this liberal construction

provisions dealing with the transfer of territory inhabited by heterogeneous peoples. See Hudson, 'The Protection of Minorities', p. 209.

[40] L. P. Mair, *The Protection of Minorities – The Workings and Scope of the Minorities Treaties under the League of Nations* (Christophers, 1928), p. 30.

[41] Temperley, *A History of the Peace Conference*, pp. 116–17. Emphasis added.

[42] N. Berman, 'International Law of Nationalism: Group Identity and Legal History' in D. Wippman (ed.), *International Law and Ethnic Conflict* (Cornell University Press, 1998), pp. 40–2.

informs that the ethnic character of the East is a source of conflict it thus needs to be managed through the minority protection mechanism.

Therefore, it is no surprise that in its Advisory Opinion in *the Greco-Bulgarian Communities* case, the Permanent Court found the ethnic elements, such as 'sentiment of solidarity' and the salience of collective identity, as the attributes of 'Eastern Countries'. With reference to the mutual emigration of the Greco-Bulgarian communities, the Court held the view that the objective features of the community that unites it – same race, religion, language and traditions of their own – and the subjective factor, i.e. the willingness to maintain these characteristics, formed the core of a 'community'.[43] Having so defined the notion of 'community', the Court then attributed the ethnic character of the 'community' specifically to Eastern countries, by asserting that the very structure of the Greco-Bulgarian Convention (1919) that provided for the population transfer was designed to ensure that the individuals forming the communities could respectively make their homes permanently among their own race, 'the very mentality of the population concerned'.[44] Such an arrangement had its justification in the century-old (conservative) tradition of the Eastern countries, which the Court thought necessary to take into account in dealing with the case before them.

As a matter of fact, the protection of the League was not extended to any minorities within the Western States. Although German minorities suffered in a number of States both under and outside the League jurisdiction, Germany itself adopted increasingly brutal policies towards the minorities within its borders, and the League had no means to stop that.[45] Yet, while refuting the criticism that the Paris Conference did not bring defeated Germany under the minority protection obligation, Temperley relied on the scope of the provisions that these obligations were meant for completely new States, or States to which very extensive territories were assigned.[46] He thus argued that it would have been inappropriate to bring Germany under such a minority protection mechanism, in that she was neither newly emerged, nor gained any territory following the war.[47] Temperley then warned that the inclusion of Germany could have jeopardised the interests of other Great Powers,

---

[43] Advisory Opinion, PCIJ Report (1930), Ser. B, No. 17, p. 33.   [44] Ibid., p. 21.

[45] J. J. Preece, 'Minority Rights in Europe: from Westphalia to Helsinki', (1997) 23(1) *Review of International Studies*, 75–92. Also, J. Preece, 'National Minorities and International System', (1998) 18(1) *Politics*, 17–23.

[46] Temperley, *A History of the Peace Conference*, p. 141.   [47] Ibid.

who also had significant minorities within their territories, by engendering a universal system of minority protection and thereby bringing them under international scrutiny.[48] It is implied that only the non-Western States could be under such international supervision.

Thus, France and Italy, despite receiving extensive territories populated by minorities, similarly remained conspicuous exceptions to the League's scope of minority protection. France was not even asked to guarantee the protection of German minorities in Alsace-Lorraine; it was generally regarded as a case of annexation, hence no question of special obligation was raised.[49] Similarly, despite receiving South Tyrol with a quarter of a million ethnic Germans and 480,000 Yugoslavs, Italy was also exempted from any minority protection obligation. Although unlike Alsace-Lorraine, in the case of Trentito, a suggestion was made that Italy provide guarantees for the protection of German minorities, the Italian delegation held to the view that it was entirely inconsistent with its position as a principal Power to have any such suggestion made.[50] Therefore, Italy remained outside the scope of the minority protection mechanism.

Thus, the dichotomy of West and East within Europe is demonstrated in two ways: first, the problem of minorities is articulated as a concern for Eastern Europe alone by attributing 'special needs' for these States due to the different characters of these people, to use Temperley's words, as well as the conservative tradition of emphasising the centrality of ethnicity in the nation-building process. Second, to deal with these minorities, the political independence of East European States was restricted by international minority protection treaties and thereby, 'internationalising' the minority issue, to use Berman's term.[51] While the sovereign prerogatives of these countries were made subject to the protection of their minorities, the Allies continued the deference to Western European sovereignty in refusing to extend international scrutiny to all League members.[52] Even in the case of the restoration of Belgium, no such restriction to her sovereignty was imposed; instead, she enjoyed an unqualified right to self-determination, despite her heterogeneous demographic composition.[53]

---

[48] Ibid., p. 142.   [49] Hudson, 'The Protection of Minorities', p. 212.

[50] Comments made by Hudson in an interview. See ibid., p. 474.

[51] Berman, 'But the Alternative is Despair', pp. 1858–9.

[52] Hudson, 'The Protection of Minorities', p. 49.

[53] Number seven of Wilson's fourteen points states that: 'Belgium, the whole world will agree, must be evacuated and restored, without any attempt to limit the sovereignty which she enjoys in common with all other free nations. No other single act will serve as

However, this ethnic discourse on the 'self' and the 'other' was not confined to the dichotomy of liberalism and conservatism alone. As the following discussion reveals, the tripartite interactions among minorities, their host-States, and kin-States – all in the process of defining the 'self' in the ethnic term, within the conservative Romantic framework – exposed the practical drawbacks of the inter-war minority protection mechanism.

IV.   The ethnic 'other' within the ethnic 'self': a case of reciprocal exclusion

While re-creating Poland as a sovereign State, the Versailles Treaty unmistakably envisaged the Polish State along the conservative ethnic line. Article 91(2) of the treaty allowed Poland to deny citizenship to certain ethnic German residents in Poland.[54] Simultaneously, clauses 4 and 9 of the same Article provided for the inclusion within the Polish State of certain Poles who usually resided outside the territory of the new State.[55] Poland was then evidently determined to undo the Germanisation project advanced under Prussian rule. Nevertheless, in the actual implementation of this conservative nationalist project, the matter became much more complicated, given that as a precondition to the reacquisition of her sovereignty, Poland had to extend Polish citizenship to certain ethnic Germans who were born in Poland of 'parents habitually resident there, even if at the date of the coming into force of the present Treaty, they were not themselves habitually resident there'.[56]

this will serve to restore confidence among the nations in the laws which they have themselves set and determined for the government of their relations with one another. Without this healing act the whole structure and validity of international law is forever impaired.'

[54] Article 92(2) reads: 'German nationals, however, or their descendants who became resident in these territories after 1 January 1908, will not acquire Polish nationality without a special authorisation from the Polish State.'

[55] Clause 4 of Article 91 of the Versailles Treaty stipulates that: 'Poles who are German nationals over 18 years of age and habitually resident in Germany will have a similar right to opt for Polish nationality.' Again Clause 9 of the article mentions that '[...] Poles who are German nationals and are in a foreign country will be entitled, in the absence of any provisions to the contrary in the foreign law, and if they have not acquired the foreign nationality, to obtain Polish nationality and to lose their German nationality by complying with the requirements laid down by the Polish State.'

[56] See Article 4 of the Polish Minority Treaty. According to Article 91(1), 'German nationals habitually resident in territories recognised as forming part of Poland will acquire Polish nationality *ipso facto and* will lose their German nationality.' Article 91(3) stipulated that within a period of two years after the coming into force of the present

When the Polish government refused to extend Polish nationality to former German nationals if their parents were not habitually resident in Poland both on the date of birth of the persons concerned and on the date of the enforcement of the Treaty, the Permanent Court in an Advisory Opinion held that such an interpretation by Poland amounted to breach of her international treaty obligations.[57]

In contrast, with the drastic defeat in the war and with no immediate hope of altering the Versailles settlement, German officials learned, at least officially, how to keep its nineteenth-century notion of ethnic nationalism at distance for an interim period that lasted only a little more than a decade. Although there existed an ultra-nationalist urge for confrontational policies towards Poland and the other Eastern European States, where a significant number of ethnic Germans faced discriminatory treatment, the official position in the 1920s held that a 'correct relation' had to be maintained with these countries.[58] The German Foreign Minister, Gustav Stresemann, was the proponent of such a policy with the strategic argument that if there were no Germans in the Eastern European countries, it would be difficult for Germany to advance its revisionist agenda. Thus, Stresemann took the policy of internationalising the plight of German minorities by joining the League and positioning Germany as the 'Protector of Minorities' for the continent.[59] As a part of the same project, Stresemann advocated for liberal minority schools within Germany with a view to rationalising the claim of more extensive rights for the overseas German minorities.[60] In the meantime, generous support was extended to a number of organisations, such as the European Nationalities Congress, to voice the rights of minorities, especially, German minorities. Protecting the *Kultur* of the ethnic Germans in the ceded territories was also a great concern, which demanded government aid to German newspapers as well as to boarding schools and club houses.[61] Yet, in another strategic move, Germany avoided any direct official involvement with minority organisations in the ceded territories; instead, it adopted a policy of supporting German minorities through a number of covert organisations.[62]

Treaty, German nationals over 18 years of age habitually resident in any of the territories recognised as forming part of Poland will be entitled to opt for German nationality.

[57] *The Question Concerning the Acquisition of Polish Nationality Case*, PCIJ Report (1923), Ser. B, No. 7.

[58] Mazower, *Hitler's Empire*, p. 35.   [59] Ibid., p. 38.

[60] Frenz, *A Lesson Forgotten*, p. 160.   [61] Ibid., p. 143.

[62] A. Komjathy and R. Stockwell, *German Minorities and The Third Reich* (Holmes and Meier Publishers, Inc., 1980), pp. 1–3.

However, the German politics on the minority issue drastically changed with the seizure of power by the Nazis in 1933. Being premised on the nineteenth-century concepts of Romanticism and cultural specificity as well as polygenic social Darwinism, the racial theory of law proposed that each of the various races and peoples had its own law which was inseparably bound up with that specific race or people; law was so specific to the cultural understanding that it could be neither replaced by the law of another people nor transferred to another race.[63]

Under such a construction of law, the obvious question was whether any idea of international law could be compatible with the Nazi ideology. In fact, shortly after the seizure of power by Hitler, Nazi international lawyer Schecher in a publication of 1933 reduced the whole idea of international law to 'an *emblem* of rules belonging exclusively to the German order of law'.[64] Nevertheless, such an approach to international law was pragmatically and strategically difficult to advance, given Germany's then weak military and economic position. What followed was a series of reconciliatory approaches to international law. Carl Schmitt, for example, in an article published by the National Socialist Party in 1934, explicitly presented the subjective dimension of international law, which for him had the foundation in the *volkische* character of States.[65] For him, the idea of law, *Nomos*, supposed a concrete order and a concrete community that stood above individuals in contrast to what the liberals proposed.[66] This idea of specificity premised upon the interplay of land and race found expression in his famous (or infamous) theory of *Grossraum* (Grand Space), developed in line with the American Monroe doctrine.[67]

---

[63] Ibid.

[64] See J. H. Herz, 'The National Socialist Doctrine of International Law and the Problems of International Organisation', (1939) 54(4) *Political Science Quarterly*, 539.

[65] A. Carty, 'Carl Schmitt's Critique of Liberal International Legal Order Between 1933 and 1945', (2001) 14 *Leiden Journal of International Law*, 31 (emphasis in original).

[66] A detailed criticism of individualism and liberal imperialism through the use of international law as a tool by the Anglo-American liberals appeared in his work, *The Nomos of the Earth*. See, C. Schmitt, *The Nomos of the Earth in the International Law of the Jus Publicum Europaeum* (Telos Press, Ltd., 2003 [1950]). Although published in 1950, this volume was completed just before World War II ended. Given that by that time the fate of Germany was more or less decided, much of his racial ideas did not appear directly in *The Nomos of the Earth*; rather, the book warns about the dominance of the Anglo-American ideologies and their potential disastrous consequences for the post-World War II world order.

[67] D. F. Vagts, 'International Law in the Third Reich', (1990) 84 *American Journal of International Law*, pp. 687–90; Carty, 'Carl Schmitt's Critique', pp. 34–47; A. Gattinni, 'Sense and Quasisense of Schmitt's Grossraum Theory in International Law – A Rejoinder to

However, within the top Nazi official circle, Schmitt's theory of *Grossraum* got translated, much to the denial of his intellectual contribution, into the theory of *Lebensraum* (Living Space) that entitled Germany as a racially superior State to expand spatially as far as its biological needs carried it and in whatever manner it was deemed necessary for this purpose.[68]

Against this politico-legal backdrop, the Nazi lawyers thus claimed that treaties were binding as long as they did not jeopardise the racial health of a people; war, not law, was the ultimate arbiter of international order.[69] With such a perception of international order, Nazi Germany decided on a more explicit and direct involvement in the minority affairs. Given the racial foundation of the regime, such claims for involvement were often propgated along the lines of ethnic affiliation with the minorities.[70] Juxtaposing the ethnic phenomenon of minorities with the individualist framework of the minority protection mechanism under the League, Schmitt similarly argued that Germany must be assigned a special rôle in the minority protection system to protect the 'Eastern space' from the ideological hegemony of liberalism; there had to be a defence of the national peculiarity of each ethnic group against Western assimilation, and it had to be by Germany.[71]

Nazi Germany, under Hitler and his aides such as Himmler, was committed to its long-standing agenda of Germanising of Eastern Europe. However, such a vision of Germanisation was different in character to previous efforts, in that it was set to advance the nineteenth-century German philosophy of historicism and race on a previously unforeseen scale. Their invasion policy was marked by the conviction that the Eastern territories were what the Teutonic knights occupied many centuries ago.[72] But to match the racial underpinnings of the regime, such re-occupation of the 'ancient territories' had to be conducted to the exclusion of everything else. Such an idea was also rationalised by the social Darwinist notion of the 'survival of the fittest'. In his classic work, *Behemoth*, Neumann explains how the Nazi idealists had recourse to the works of the nineteenth-century

Carty's "Carl Schmitt's Critique of Liberal International Legal Order Between 1933 and 1945'", (2002) 15 *Leiden Journal of International Law*, 57–62.

[68] Carty, 'Carl Schmitt's Critique', p. 74; Vagts, 'International Law in the Third Reich', pp. 687–90.

[69] For details, see, Vagts, 'International Law in the Third Reich', pp. 692–3; also, Mazower, *Hitler's Empire*, pp. 44–5.

[70] For example, in a debate in the League Assembly in 1933, the German delegate defended interventions by the kin-States along the line of ethnic affiliations. See *League of Nations Official Journal*, spec. supp. 120 (1933), 23.

[71] See Carty, 'Carl Schmitt's Critique', p. 40.   [72] Mazower, *Hitler's Empire*, p. 181.

polygenist Gobineau, which were later reworked by Houston Stewart Chamberlain and Richard Wagner. They, along with conservative nationalist Friedrich List, offered the Nazis necessary ideological foundation for advancing imperialism on the basis of race.[73]

Himmler is reported to have said with reference to his predecessors' mild approach to Germanisation: 'Our mission is not to Germanise the East in the old sense – bringing the German language and laws to those living there, but rather to ensure that in the East dwell only men with truly German, Germanic blood.'[74] That was an open agenda for complete expulsion of the 'other', which of course was later to materialise into something much more sinister. Again, for Himmler such measures to reflect the diverse but increasingly serious nature of the policies employed, were part of the 'necessary ethnic separation of races and peoples in the European New Order as well as in the interest of the security and purity of the German Reich'.[75]

However, before such an exclusionist mission could be realised, the Nazi regime directed its minority policy towards transforming the international mechanism of minority protection under the supervision of the League into a bilateral issue, thereby, facilitating its involvement as a kin-State. Sidelining the British and the French, Germany started negotiating with the States hosting German minorities in bilateral terms. In this context, Schmitt argued that since the *Reich* had concluded a series of bilateral treaties for the protection of German minorities, the Versailles Treaty for minority protection was firmly rejected.[76] While Schmitt perceived such a disavowal of the Versailles system as an essential step towards the creation of *Grossraum*, other Nazi jurists, too, generally conceived bilateralism as a necessary attempt to minimise international law to contractual relations among individual States.[77]

Given that Poland was also unhappy about the Versailles arrangements (their special obligations regarding minority protection), by concluding a ten-year non-aggression pact on 26 January 1934, the Nazi regime offered Poland an incentive to violate her international treaty obligations. The pact allowed Germany considerable time for

---

[73] F. Neumann, *Behemoth* (Ivan R. Dee, 2009 [1942]), pp. 98–111.
[74] Quoted in Mazower, *Hitler's Empire*, p. 181.
[75] Quoted in ibid., p. 247. See also, M. Burleigh, *The Third Reich: A New Story* (Pan Books, 2001 [2000]).
[76] See, Carty, 'Carl Schmitt's Critique', p. 43.
[77] For the details of this argument, see Herz, 'The National Socialist Doctrine of International Law', p. 547.

rearmament, but simultaneously offered Poland an opportunity to re-Polonise the Prussianised Poles, as well as to clear up the border regions by displacing the disloyal German elements.[78] So, induced by the German politics on the minority issue, Poland increasingly deviated from the treaty obligations, and later, in November 1937, jointly signed the Minority Declaration with Germany, formally declaring the question of minority protection as a bilateral issue between them, and thereby accepting Germany as an advocate for German minorities.[79] As a principle it was clearly contrary to the Versailles understanding that kin-States would be kept out of minority affairs.

Having gained a recognised position in minority affairs inside Poland, Germany was now better equipped to manoeuvre the minority issue internally and internationally, and set a premise for her revisionist claims. At the same time, Poland relied on de-Germanisation in the process of constructing her own ethnic self-image, which the Great Powers moderately authenticated at Versailles. Even after the Declaration, 'untrustworthy' German families were relocated or expelled from strategically important areas under the Frontier Zone Decree of 22 January 1927.[80] The overall number of German minority schools and the percentage of German pupils declined, despite high demand for such schools.[81] Although 'land reform' had been a key policy of de-Germanisation since the beginning, the situation of the German minorities deteriorated significantly during this time. The area of German land redistributed, almost exclusively to Poles, under the land reforms, increased from 8,444 hectares in 1936 to 20,325 hectares in 1937; 22,254 hectares in 1938; and 22,732 hectares in 1939.[82] These land 'reforms' caused severe unemployment among the Germans, who were then compelled to emigrate to Germany.[83]

Thus, the foregoing account of the treatment of minorities in pre-World War II Germany and Poland demonstrates how the task of mutual exclusion of the ethnic 'other' was advanced in the process of constructing their ethnic self-image along the line of the conservative

---

[78] Komjathy and Stockwell, *German Minorities and The Third Reich*, pp. 71, 73.

[79] Ibid., p. 85. Behind the Declaration, the Polish motive was to gain commitment from Germany regarding the non-violation of Polish rights in Danzig. Poland also had the hope that such a declaration would ameliorate the condition of 1,300,000 Poles inside Germany who were outside any special minority protection mechanism. Hitler, on the other hand, had the purpose of neutralising Poland before taking over Austria and invading Czechoslovakia.

[80] Ibid., pp. 86–7.   [81] Frenz, *A Lesson Forgotten*, p. 226.

[82] Komjathy and Stockwell, *German Minorities and The Third Reich*, p. 87.

[83] Frenz, *A Lesson Forgotten*, p. 248.

tradition of the nineteenth century. Although the extent of the measures employed in the process are in no way comparable, the ethnic dichotomy of 'self' and 'other' continued to inform the whole structure of the campaign that took final shape in the midst of the war.

V.   Concluding remarks

The inter-war international law of minority protection relates to the nineteenth century's ethnic dichotomy of the European 'self' and the non-European 'other' as expressed in colonialism, in that the same ethnic discourse on 'self' and 'other' was translated through the liberal and conservative traditions into the dichotomy of the liberal Western 'self' and the conservative non-Western 'other' within Europe. The regime also witnessed the exclusionist response to the ethnic 'other' – minorities – in the process of constructing the ethnic self-image. At the same time, the inter-war minority protection mechanism demonstrated a tension that resulted from the efforts to reconcile the liberal assimilationism of the West with the ethnic underpinning of conservative minorities and their host-States in East Europe.

Nazism collapsed, as did the minority protection mechanism with its guarantor, the League. But the liberal–conservative dichotomy within Europe, as well as the tension emanated from the response of liberal individualism towards the ethnic phenomenon attributed to the concept of 'minority', survived much beyond the inter-war international law. International protection of minorities in the aftermath of the World War II, especially in the post-Cold War context, continued to demonstrate such a phenomenon. In this sense, the inter-war minority protection mechanism could be understood as an important link between the nineteenth-century ideas of colonialism and the post-World War II regime of minority protection, in each of which the ethnic dichotomy of 'self' and 'other' expressed through the liberal and conservative streams provides the necessary analytical framework for a better understanding of international law as was applied to these systems and also constructed in the process.

PART III

Tradition, opportunities and challenges: the changing nature of the state

A monument, identity and nationhood: the case of the Old Bridge of Mostar

JADRANKA PETROVIC[*]

I. Introduction

Despite the importance of its protection, cultural property is always at risk. Armed conflict makes such property particularly vulnerable. Although they are precious to all humanity, objects of cultural property are often among the first wilful targets in armed conflicts. The wilful destruction of the Old Bridge, a landmark of the city of Mostar and national monument of Bosnia and Herzegovina, is emblematic of tragedies wrought on price-less cultural objects internationally. Using the incident of the Old Bridge's destruction, this chapter considers the relationship between cultural prop-erty and nationhood. It argues that cultural property is both 'national' and 'international' at the same time. A dual nature of cultural property is analogous to a constant interplay between the primacy of a nation and its withering in international law. The chapter first considers the role of a nation in determining the nature of cultural property and the importance of its preservation. It then looks at the factual background of the incident of the destruction of the Old Bridge and its effects at both the national and international level. Finally, the chapter reflects on international adju-dication as a means of increasing respect for cultural property and con-currently as an indicator of the decline of the nation.

II. The State-centred regulation of cultural property

States play a significant role in the international legal protection of cultural property. It is a State itself rather than some supra-national

[*] The author is grateful to Professor Duncan French, Professor Christopher Arup, Dr Petra Mahy and Nicola Charwat for their invaluable comments on earlier drafts. Special thanks to Peter Mellor for his comments and outstanding editing assistance. This chapter was completed prior to the destruction of tombs in Timbuktu (June 2012) and the ensuing international outrage.

entity that determines the scope of application of international legal
instruments. This means that international law protects those objects
that States deem 'cultural' and deserving of protection under their
national laws concerning cultural property. Consequently, international
law in this field is heavily reliant on the domestic context.[1] States' central
role in the protection of cultural property is not *per se* in conflict with
international law.[2] It is a State's sovereign right to designate its own
cultural treasures. By assigning States this crucial role in the protection
of cultural property, international law recognizes the unique contribution of each State, and ultimately of each people existing within a State, to
the cultural heritage of humankind.[3]

Although cultural property belonging to any people also belongs, in
the end, to the cultural heritage of all humankind, under existing international law no State or international organization is authorized to
intervene in domestic matters in order to guarantee the protection of
cultural property, without the consent of the host State.[4] As a result, a
State can do whatever it pleases with cultural property to which it is
territorially linked. Even if cultural property of exceptional value to
humanity is deliberately destroyed, no one outside a given State can
ultimately prevent this. The deliberate destruction of the world's two
largest Buddha statues in Bamiyan, Afghanistan, by the Taliban in
March 2001, is a clear example of this problem.[5] International law
could not force Afghanistan either to protect these two particular objects
of cultural property or to consider them cultural objects any longer.
Under international law, in times of armed conflict, as well as in times of
peace, cultural property can be guarded by the United Nations forces on

[1] See, e.g., M. Müller, 'Cultural Heritage Protection: Legitimacy, Property and Functionalism',
    (1998) 7 *International Journal of Cultural Property*, 400; R. O'Keefe, 'The Meaning of "Cultural
    Property" under the 1954 Hague Convention', (1999) 46 *Netherlands International Law
    Review*, 26, 51; C. Vernon, 'Common Cultural Property: The Search for Rights of Protective
    Intervention', (1994) 26 *Case Western Reserve Journal of International Law*, 435.
[2] Müller, 'Cultural Heritage Protection'.
[3] See Convention for the Protection of Cultural Property in the Event of Armed Conflict,
    opened for signature 14 May 1954, 249 UNTS 215 (entered into force 7 August 1956),
    Preamble, para. 2 (*1954 Convention*).
[4] S. Williams, *The International and National Protection of Movable Cultural Property: A
    Comparative Study* (New York: Oceana Publications, 1978), p. 55.
[5] See 'UN seeks laws to halt cultural vandalism', 13 March 2001 (quoting Koïchiro
    Matsuura, Director-General of UNESCO: 'We did everything possible to prevent this
    happening but we have failed miserably'), www.cnn.com/2001/WORLD/asiapcf/03/13/
    afghanistan.buddhas/.

behalf of the international community, but even then, a State's authorization is required. The only possible exception to the prohibition of
intervention in internal matters of any State is the application of enforcement measures under Chapter VII of the Charter of the United Nations.[6]
Although it can be argued that destruction of cultural property under
extreme circumstances may pose a threat to international peace and
security, the enforcement measures under Chapter VII have never
been applied for the exclusive purpose of cultural property protection.[7]
Yet, the duty of States to protect cultural property already exists in
international law. This duty is premised on the idea of common heritage,
which is enshrined in a number of international legal instruments.[8]

It has been contended that because of the power of the nation-State,
international legal regimes, including those concerned with cultural property, are largely powerless 'paper tigers'.[9] Some scholars believe that unless
the current status of cultural property law is 'eliminated',[10] the concept of
common heritage is meaningless.[11] A proposal has been put forward to
allow a right of protective intervention in the territorial sovereignty of
individual States by other States or international organizations to protect
cultural property situated in a host-State.[12] In view of the dual appeal of
cultural property – as the cultural heritage of both a particular State and
of humankind – there is a corresponding 'dual accountability'[13] of a State.
Given that cultural property belonging to any people ultimately belongs to
all humankind, it should follow that in situations where a State is unwilling
or unable to protect cultural property situated within its borders, either in

---

[6] Charter of the United Nations, adopted by the Conference on international organisations, San Francisco, 26 June 1945, 59 Stat. 1031, TS 993, 3 Bevans 1153 (entered into
force 24 October 1945), art. 2(7).

[7] For the *de lege ferenda* nature of the obligation to intervene see, e.g., United Nations
General Assembly, *Implementing the Responsibility to Protect: Report of the Secretary-
General*, 12 January 2009, A/63/677; United Nations General Assembly Resolution on
the responsibility to protect of 7 October 2009, A/RES/63/308; United Nations Security
Council Resolution 1973 on no fly zone over Libya of 17 March 2011, SC/RES/1973. See
also T. Chataway, 'Towards Normative Consensus on Responsibility to Protect', (2007)
16 *Griffith Law Review*, 193–224.

[8] See sources referred to at nn. 3 above and 23, 61 and 62 below. Similar to international
protection of the environment, there are three approaches to, or stages in, international
legal protection of cultural property: the present generation's self-interest, future generations' interests and the intrinsic value of cultural property.

[9] Müller, 'Cultural Heritage Protection', 404.   [10] Ibid.

[11] Ibid., 437. See also, J. Yarwood, 'Cultural Warfare', (2003) 8 *Art Antiquity and Law*,
191–200, 198.

[12] Vernon, 'Common Cultural Property', 437–9.   [13] Ibid. 453.

times of peace or armed conflict, the international community should be entitled to step in. Indeed, this is the only way to prevent or halt the impoverishment of humanity's cultural heritage. Intervention for cultural protection purposes should not be optional but, in fact, should be the responsibility of the international community. This is especially the case in situations involving massive destruction of irreplaceable cultural treasures and those where the survival of cultural property of exceptional importance to humanity's cultural heritage is threatened. If this had been permissible under international law during the 1990s armed conflicts in the Balkans, the Old Bridge might have been guarded and spared. The issue of intervention in the territorial sovereignty of a State has been the subject of the *Report of the International Commission on Intervention and State Sovereignty*.[14] The *Report* focused on intervention for human protection purposes. However, the espoused principle that the international community has a responsibility to protect could, and might even, extend to cultural property as well. An attack on cultural treasures is also an attack on people. Cultural property is inseparable from human dignity. Its destruction represents a violation of the human right to culture.[15] While the means of intervention for cultural property purposes should differ to some extent from those applicable to intervention for human protection purposes, the necessity of re-characterizing State sovereignty is relevant to both contexts.

III.   Cultural significance of an object

The terminology makes it apparent that 'cultural property' is property of *cultural* significance. The cultural significance of the property distinguishes it from other property and thus makes it property of a unique

---

[14]   *The Responsibility to Protect*, Report of the International Commission on Intervention and State Sovereignty, December 2001(ICISS) (Ottawa: IDRC, 2001), www.dfait-maeci. gc.ca/iciss/report2-en.asp.

[15]   See, e.g., The Universal Declaration of Human Rights, GA Res. 217A (III), UN doc. A/810 (1948), art. 27 (UDHR); International Covenant on Civil and Political Rights, 16 December 1966, 999 UNTS 171, 6 ILM 368, art. 27 (ICCPR); International Covenant on Economic, Social and Cultural Rights, 16 December 1966, 993 UNTS 3, art. 15 (ICESR). See also, ICJ Request for interpretation of the judgment of 15 June 1962 in the case concerning the *Temple of Preah Vihear* (*Cambodia* v. *Thailand*), Request for the indication of provisional measures of 18 July 2011; G. Mose, 'The Destruction of Churches and Mosques in Bosnia-Herzegovina: Seeking a Rights-based Approach to the Protection of Religious Cultural Property', (1996) 3 *Buffalo Journal of International Law*, 180; K. J. Patel, 'Culture Wars: Protection of Cultural Monuments in a Human Rights Context', (2001) 14 *Harvard Human Rights Journal*, 1; H. Silverman and D. Fairchild Ruggles (eds.), *Cultural Heritage and Human Rights* (New York: Springer, 2007).

kind. If stripped of cultural significance, cultural objects would be merely commodities or consumer goods.[16] The cultural significance is therefore based on particular understandings of the importance of culture. It is precisely this concept that raises a series of questions: how are tangible movable and immovable objects related to culture? With whose culture do such objects enter into the relationship? Is culture specific to an individual, group, community or nation? What is culture after all?

The primary problem here lies with the indeterminacy of the notion of culture. This is not surprising, because culture is not a static concept, but is evolving all the time.[17] Because it is a forward-looking phenomenon, culture is constantly elusive.[18] Since culture is an ever-changing concept, it might be difficult, if not impossible, to determine with precision which objects should qualify for legal protection under the rubric of cultural property. As Prott observes, 'the variety of objects regarded as important cultural property is intriguing'.[19] Nevertheless, 'every culture should be able to protect what is essential cultural heritage for them'.[20]

The debate about the cultural significance of the object is recognizable in the so-called 'cultural internationalism v cultural nationalism' debate over the question of who is the legitimate guardian of cultural property.[21] Here, the debate revolves around the question of disposition of movable cultural property. However, the arguments put forward are also relevant to an overall understanding of the cultural significance of the object in international law, thereby including immovable cultural property as well. The 'cultural internationalists'[22] argue that cultural property

---

[16] R. Mastalir, 'A Proposal for Protecting the "Cultural" and "Property" Aspects of Cultural Property under International Law', (1993) 16 *Fordham International Law Journal*, 1033, 1039.

[17] L. Prott, 'Understanding One Another on Cultural Rights', in UNESCO, *Cultural Rights and Wrongs* (Paris and London: UNESCO Publishing and Institute of Art and Law, 1998), pp. 161, 164–5 ('Understanding').

[18] S. Harding, 'Value, Obligation and Cultural Heritage', (1999) 31 *Arizona State Law Journal*, 291, 334.

[19] L. Prott, 'The International Movement of Cultural Objects', (2005) 12 *International Journal of Cultural Property*, 225, 227 ('International movement').

[20] Ibid.   [21] See discussion accompanying nn. 22–30 below.

[22] The *1954 Convention* is widely considered to take an 'internationalist' approach to cultural property. See generally, J. Merryman, 'International Art Law: From Cultural Nationalism to a Common Cultural Heritage', (1983) 15 *New York University Journal of International Law and Politics*, 757 ('International Art Law'). See also, F. Fechner, 'The Fundamental Aims of Cultural Property Law', (1998) 7 *International Journal of Cultural Property*, 376.

belongs to all humankind whereas the 'cultural nationalists'[23] contend
that cultural property is exclusively the property of nations of origin.[24]
While the preservation of cultural property is the principal concern for
both schools, they differ in their approach as to whether the cultural
object is a value in itself or whether the object's meaning in a nation-state
should take precedence. The cultural internationalists give preference to
the cultural object as a value in itself.[25] The cultural nationalists, on the
other hand, focus on the meaning of cultural property and put
the culturally affiliated – an identifiable group, people, or nation – into
the centre. This school of thought emphasizes the role of cultural property in identity-generation.[26]

The meaning of a cultural object in society is undoubtedly an important factor in defining cultural property. Cultural objects are made by
humans, either individually or collectively, and their meaning in society
is also constructed by humans. However, cultural objects are also important markers of humanity's development and they ultimately have an
'identificatory' function in the context of *all* humanity. In this sense,

[23] Convention on the Means of Prohibiting and Preventing the Illicit Import, Export and
Transfer of Ownership of Cultural Property, adopted by the 16th Session of the
UNESCO General Conference, Paris, 14 November 1970, opened for signature 14
November 1970, 832 UNTS 231 (entered into force 24 April 1972) (*1970 Convention*).
The *1970 Convention* is considered to take a 'nationalist' approach to cultural property.
For discussion on this approach to cultural property, see generally, R. Handler, 'Who
Owns the Past?: History, Cultural Property, and the Logic of Possessive Individualism',
in B. Williams (ed.), *The Politics of Culture* (New York: Arcade Publishers, 1991), pp.
63–74. See also, J. Moustakas, 'Group Rights in Cultural Property: Justifying Strict
Inalienability', (1989) 74 *Cornell Law Review*, 1179. The dichotomy between 'cultural
internationalism' and 'cultural nationalism' has been challenged. See, e.g, Prott,
'International Movement', 225–48.
[24] For a review of the competing claims that works of art belong either to a particular
people and place, or, from a cosmopolitan perspective, to all humankind, see, e.g.,
D. Gillman, *The Idea of Cultural Heritage* (London: Institute of Art and Law, 2006).
[25] J. Merryman, *Thinking about the Elgin Marbles: Critical Essays on Cultural Property, Art
and Law* (The Hague, London and Boston: Kluwer Law International, 2000), pp. 43–5
(*Elgin Marbles*).
[26] Moustakas, 'Group rights', 1199. For discussion on the role of cultural property in
generating identity, see also A. Elsen, 'Introduction: Why do we Care about Art?',
(1976) 27 *Hastings Law Journal*, 951, 952. The International Council of Museums is of
the view that the 'community of nations now considers as an element of *jus cogens* the
right of all people to recover property which forms an integral part of their cultural
identity'. Quoted in J. Merryman and A. Elsen, *Law, Ethics and the Visual Arts* (The
Hague, London and Boston: Kluwer Law International, 4th edn, 2003), p. 267, quoting
'Study of the principles, conditions, and means for the restitution or return of cultural
property in view of restitution of dispersed heritage', (1979) 31 *Museum*, 62.

cultural property may have an identity-generation function for the group or nation most immediately concerned. At the same time, cultural property may also be a value in its own right through its significance for a wider audience as a source of information, or because of its aesthetic contents or its age.[27] Accordingly, cultural property is both 'national' and 'international'.

This dual nature of cultural property is expressly recognized in the 1954 Hague Convention for the Protection of Cultural Property in the Event of Armed Conflict. The Convention makes clear that the loss of or damage to any cultural object, irrespective of its origin, ultimately impoverishes the heritage of the entire international community:

> Being convinced that *damage to cultural property belonging to any people* whatsoever *means damage to the cultural heritage of all [hu]mankind,* since each people makes its contribution to the culture of the world.[28]

Because of its internationalist character, pursuant to which cultural property belonging to any people forms part of the cultural heritage of all humankind, including the generations that are yet to come, all people are only the custodians of cultural property and, thus, such property 'belongs' to everyone and indeed to no one in particular. Irrespective of peoples' divergent cultures, which should remain diverse to some extent,[29] there are shared values with respect to cultural property that transcend national and cultural boundaries. As both the internationalist and nationalist approaches to cultural property demonstrate, everyone depends on cultural property and has a corresponding sense of duty and responsibility to protect it.[30]

IV. Importance of cultural property

1. Why do people care about cultural property?

When one considers deaths, loss of homes and jobs and other hardships emanating from armed conflict, thinking of cultural objects in this context might seem to be inappropriate. However, it would be wrong to assume that people affected by armed conflict care only about their physical survival and need only material help. Boylan explains that those people are hungry, cold and frightened, but that 'their heart, their soul

---

[27] Fechner, 'The Fundamental Aims of Cultural Property Law', 381.
[28] *1954 Convention*, Preamble, para. 2 (emphasis added).
[29] Harding, 'Value, Obligation and Cultural Heritage', 304.   [30] Ibid.

and their memory have also been wounded'.[31] Cultural property plays an important role in human life. In fact, the two are so interconnected that they form part of one inseparable whole.[32] Through the safeguarding of cultural property, people protect the human spirit as it manifests itself in the tangible, artistic products of culture. As one conservator of cultural property puts it:

> To the Devil's advocate who would mischievously repeat with Oscar Wilde that art is useless, I would reply that useless it is indeed – if we were to judge the matter from a purely utilitarian perspective. Art is in fact as useless to society as the spirit is to body. The human species as a biological organism *can* survive without art and culture. But the definition of what it is to be human cannot. Culture is to human civilization as trees are to the environment. That is the justification for our preoccupation with its survival.[33]

People care about cultural property for a variety of reasons. Cultural property links the present to the past.[34] Although it is sometimes contested, the past provides a sense of security as it is permanent and completed. People also appreciate cultural property because cultural objects are unique objects.[35] Once destroyed, they are gone forever and cannot be replaced.[36] An argument might be raised that an object of cultural property, as with any other material object, can be restored or rebuilt. However, a rebuilt object is not an adequate substitute for the original. When the original is gone, the old building techniques, authentic material and generally the old age patina – factors that contribute to the cultural value of an object – are also gone. A rebuilt object may strikingly resemble the original, but even a perfect replica remains exactly that – a replica, or as Merryman puts it, 'a poor second best'.[37] Where works of art are concerned, people 'want to look at the real thing'[38] and not a reproduction. A reproduction inadequately represents the culture.[39] The same can be argued with respect to architectural structures. The problem was addressed by the Trial Chamber in the *Prosecutor* v. *Jokić* case:

> [r]estoration of buildings of this kind when possible, can never return the buildings to their state prior to the attack because a certain amount of

[31] P. Boylan, 'Come hell or high water' *Sources* (UNESCO) no. 117, November 1999, 10.
[32] Ibid. 11 (quoting Herb Stovel, the President of ICOMOS Canada).
[33] M. Corzo, 'The Hague Convention of 1954: History, Significance and Compliance', in P. Vandiver *et al.* (eds.), *Material Issues in Art and Archaeology III* (Pittsburgh: Materials Research Society, 1992), pp. 5, 6 (emphasis in original).
[34] Moustakas, 'Group Rights', 1195.   [35] Ibid. 1223.
[36] See Merryman and Elsen, *Law, Ethics and the Visual Arts*, p. xvi.
[37] Merryman, 'International Art Law', 757.   [38] Ibid.   [39] Ibid.

original, historically authentic, material will have been destroyed, thus affecting the inherent value of the buildings.[40]

History and memory are stored in the old age patina and not in a rebuilt object irrespective of the degree of resemblance between the replica and the original. That is why, as one commentator succinctly puts it, 'modern replicas, however exact, or over-restored monuments, however meticulously carried out, seem so flat, trivial, and unrevealing. Time and humanity have been scrubbed out of them'.[41] Thus, the loss of the original cultural object remains a tragedy, even if such an object has been rebuilt. Nothing can remove this tragedy.

Another reason why people care about cultural property is because cultural objects embody memory. Humanity yearns for the preservation of cultural property because of its desire to remember and to be remembered, and to prevent 'the eternal silence created by the destruction of culture'.[42] As Humphreys explains, memory is essential to a human life.[43] If people do not have authentic memories of their own, they cannot know who they are, where they came from and to whom they are connected. Without memory, they are only what others tell them they are. In Humphreys' words, '[m]emory floats in the mind, but it is fixed and secured by objects'.[44] Collective memory is deposited in cultural objects. Cultural objects visibly set a people or society apart from others. In the case of immovable cultural objects, they also noticeably indicate a certain people's or society's existence in a given geographical area. When such objects are gone, the affected people's or society's distinctiveness and boundaries disappear along with them. As a consequence, others can arbitrarily implant their own versions of the lost memory. The destruction of cultural property in armed conflict is often a part of ethnic cleansing. When people are expelled and their memory is erased through the destruction of their relics, it makes it easier for the ethnic cleansers to espouse their claim to a given territory, as there is no physical evidence that the expelled people lived there.

---

[40] *Prosecutor v. Miodrag Jokić*, Sentencing Judgment, Trial Chamber I, 18 March 2004, Case no. IT-01-42/1-S, para. 52.

[41] S. Humphreys, 'The Destruction of Cultural Memory' (2001 presidential address), *Middle East Studies Association Bulletin*, Summer 2002, para. 5, http://fp.arizona.edu/mesassoc/Bulletin/Pres%20Address/humphreys.htm.

[42] M. Lachs, 'The defences of culture', *Museum*, 37 (1985), 167, 168.

[43] Humphreys, 'The Destruction of Cultural Memory', para. 1.   [44] Ibid. para. 2.

Cultural objects are powerful symbols.[45] They bind people together, nourishing communities,[46] giving them a sense of identity,[47] and bridging the gap between cultures.[48] Their destruction or removal causes an insurmountable amount of pain[49] and is perceived as psychologically intolerable.[50] Some cultural objects, as was the case with the Old Bridge of Mostar, are so loved and treasured that they are regarded as living things[51] and their loss is mourned by some almost as deeply as the loss of human life. Destruction of a cultural object can make communities drift apart and prompt serious violence. The 1992 destruction of the Babri Mosque in Ayodhya in northern India is one such example.[52]

2. What are the underlying principles for the international protection of cultural property?

While each of the reasons people care about cultural property could justify its protection at some level, an explanation as to what motivates legal protection of this property derives at the same time from a group's or nation's attachment to cultural objects and from the universal and cross-generational value of such property.

2.1   National value and concern

As discussed, cultural property originates at the national level. Consequently, cultural property is seen as representative of the cultural specificity of a people or a nation. The emergence of cultural property laws reflects the importance of cultural property in the development of national self-determination and nationalist movements, which began in the eighteenth century in Europe and soon spread to other parts of the world.[53] The modern idea of self-determination emerged at the time of the French and

---

[45] Moustakas, 'Group Rights', 1195.

[46] See, e.g., Merryman, *Elgin Marbles*, p. 105; Moustakas, 'Group Rights', 1184.

[47] Merryman, *Elgin Marbles*; Moustakas, 'Group rights', 1195.

[48] Ibid. 1223–4 and n. 186.

[49] A. Schwartz, 'Is it wrong to weep for buildings?' *Washington Post*, 19 May 1994, 17.

[50] Moustakas, 'Group Rights', 1196.

[51] Yarwood, 'Cultural Warfare', 197 and n. 13, quoting Edith Durham who, in 1909, called Kosovo 'the land of the living past': E. Durham, *High Albania* (London: Arnold, 1909), p. 296.

[52] See, e.g., D. Mandal, *Ayodhya: Archaeology after Demolition* (Hyderabad: Orient Longman, 1993).

[53] H. Nieć, 'Legislative Models of Protection of Cultural Property', (1976) 27 *Hastings Law Journal*, 1089.

American Revolutions, which in turn coincided with the arrival of liberalism and the heritage of humankind doctrine. Unlike liberalism, which focused on the individual, the concept of self-determination and the accompanying cultural patrimony doctrine put 'people' and group identity centre stage. A group calling for self-determination would also often call for the preservation of its cultural property because such property, *inter alia*, gave a group a sense of distinctiveness. Cultural property provided groups claiming self-determination with evidence of historical presence – a 'historical identity card',[54] in Nahlik's words. To put it another way, cultural property helped groups and nations 'determine' their existence.

2.2   Universal value and concern

As with the interplay between the primacy of a nation and its decline in international law generally, the 'national' aspect of cultural property is inseparable from its 'international' counterpart. International law concerning cultural property is premised on the idea that it is valuable to all humankind. As noted, the law asserts unambiguously that cultural property is part of the joint heritage of all inhabitants of the planet and that the concern for cultural objects extends beyond national borders and ethnicity:

> damage to cultural property belonging to any people whatsoever means damage to the cultural heritage of all [hu]mankind, since each people makes its contribution to the culture of the world.[55]

Today, all peoples have the right to, and a share in, cultural property.[56] The right to enjoy cultural property corresponds with the responsibility to respect it and to transmit it to future generations.[57] International law points to 'the moral obligations [of every State] to respect its own cultural heritage and that of all nations'[58] and to 'protect the cultural property existing within its territory'[59] against the dangers that threaten its survival. The law obligates States to 'take all possible steps to protect cultural property'.[60] The responsibility to respect and protect cultural

---

[54] S. Nahlik, *Pillage of Works of Art* (Cracow: Wroclaw, 1958), p. 155.

[55] *1954 Convention*, Preamble, para. 2.

[56] See, e.g., Prott, 'Understanding', 163 *et seq.*; Mose, 'The Destruction of Churches', 200–2.

[57] See, e.g., UNESCO Culture Sector, 'Message from the Director-General of UNESCO, Koïchiro Matsuura', http://portal.unesco.org/culture/ev.php.

[58] *1970 Convention*, Preamble, para. 5.   [59] Ibid. para. 4.

[60] *1954 Convention*, Preamble, para. 6.

property is accounted for by 'the duty [of each State] of ensuring the ...
transmission [of the cultural heritage] to future generations'.[61] The law
emphasizes that cultural heritage serves as the wellspring of creativity:

> Creation draws on the roots of cultural tradition, but flourishes in contact
> with other cultures. For this reason, *heritage in all its forms must be*
> preserved, enhanced and *handed on to future generations* as a record of
> human experience and aspirations, so as to foster creativity in all its
> diversity and to inspire genuine dialogue among cultures.[62]

V.   The case of the Old Bridge of Mostar

Despite the imperative of its preservation, cultural property is deliberately
targeted in armed conflicts. Cultural objects are targeted because they are
precious.[63] When targeting these objects, the perpetrators' ultimate aim is
to annihilate the enemy and to degrade the people on the 'other' side – to
crush them psychologically. Yarwood contends that 'cultural warfare'[64] is
associated with nationalism and that '[a]n enemy will seek to weaken the
will to fight or even to exist, by undermining identity'.[65] Attackers know
that by striking at cultural property they are striking at the social fabric of
the community to which the cultural object is most immediately linked.[66]

Cultural devastation in the former Yugoslavia during the 1990s is sad
testimony to the fate of cultural treasures in times of armed conflict.[67]
Immovable cultural property embodied in objects of both cultural
specificity and cultural unity was deliberately targeted, *inter alia*, to
cause people to flee and to deter them from ever returning, to destroy
evidence of coexistence and to rewrite history. Cultural property was
destroyed to such an extent that the terms 'cultural genocide' and
'cultural cleansing' were coined.[68] While cultural heritage in all parts of

---

[61] Convention Concerning the Protection of the World Cultural and Natural Heritage,
opened for signature 16 November 1972, UN doc. A/CONF.48/PC/11Add. 3.15 (1972)
1037 UNTS 151 (entered into force 17 December 1975), art. 4.

[62] *Universal Declaration on Cultural Diversity*, adopted by 31st UNESCO General
Conference, Paris, 2 November 2001, UNESCO Press no. 2001–120–5, art. 7 (emphasis
added).

[63] Yarwood, 'Cultural Warfare', 197.   [64] Ibid. 192.   [65] Ibid. 194.

[66] R. Bevan, *The Destruction of Memory: Architecture at War* (London: Reaktion Books,
2006).

[67] For documents on cultural devastation in the Balkans during the 1990s, see nn. 79 and 91
below.

[68] C. Kaiser, 'Crimes against culture' *UNESCO Courier*, Sept. 2000, 41, http://web1.
infotrac.galegroup.com/itw/infomark/109/511/.

the former Yugoslavia suffered significant losses, the cultural heritage of Bosnia and Herzegovina was particularly affected.[69] The case that has attracted the greatest publicity[70] was the deliberate destruction of the Old Bridge of Mostar on 9 November 1993.

1. Construction of the Old Bridge

1.1 The geography, demography and history of Mostar

The Old Bridge was the landmark of the city of Mostar, which is the largest city of Herzegovina, the southern part of Bosnia and Herzegovina. Before the conflict, just over 30 per cent of Mostar's citizens were of Muslim ethnicity, approximately the same percentage Croat, around 17 per cent Serb and the rest of other ethnicities.[71] The city was said to have the highest percentage of ethnically mixed marriages in the former Yugoslavia.[72] Before the conflict, Mostar was renowned for its cosmopolitanism, harmony and urban spirit.

Mostar was the city of bridges.[73] While all of its bridges were considered beautiful, the Old Bridge was of exceptional beauty.[74] The historic precinct called the Old City (Stari Grad) of Mostar, with the Old Bridge as a focal point, was under the special care of the citizens of Mostar because it marked the place from which their city arose.[75] The precinct was the recipient of one of the world's most prestigious architectural awards, the Aga Khan Award, for outstanding historic restoration.[76] The award is a confirmation of the importance of buildings, spaces, settlements and cities in the process of human development. According to the United Nations Educational, Scientific and Cultural Organisation

---

[69] J. Tunbridge and G. Ashworth, *Dissonant Heritage: The Management of the Past as a Resource in Conflict* (New York: John Wiley & Sons, 1996).

[70] A. Pašić, *The Old Bridge (Stari most) in Mostar* (Istanbul: Research Centre for Islamic History, Art and Culture, 1995).

[71] *Prosecutor v. Jadranko Prlić, Bruno Stojić, Slobodan Praljak, Milivoj Petković, Valentin Ćorić and Berislav Pušić*, Amended Indictment, 16 November 2005, Case no. IT-04-74-PT, para. 88 (*Prlić*).

[72] C. Woodard, 'Stillborn', (2000) 56 *Bulletin of the Atomic Scientists*, 1719 2000 WL 10491163, http://web2.westlaw.com.

[73] The Old Bridge was one of several bridges over the Neretva river. All of the bridges of Mostar were destroyed during the 1990s conflicts, but they have all now been rebuilt. See, e.g., 'Visit Mostar/Bridges', www.visitmostar.net/Bridges.htm.

[74] See, Pašić, *The Old Bridge*.   [75] Ibid., pp. 32–6.

[76] N. Adams, 'Architecture as the Target', (1993) 52 *Journal of the Society of Architectural Historians*, 389.

(UNESCO), the Old Bridge 'was in a perfect state of conservation before the outbreak of military hostilities in the region'.[77] The Bridge was designated as a monument of invaluable significance for the city of Mostar, and later was added to a list of national monuments of Bosnia and Herzegovina.[78] This bridge was also deemed to be one of the most important monuments of the whole of the former Yugoslavia. Before it was destroyed, together with the rest of the Old City precinct, the Old Bridge was recommended for inscription on the World Heritage List,[79] which was realized, but only after the Bridge was rebuilt, on 15 July 2005.

1.2   Building the Old Bridge

The Old Bridge was the work of Mimar Hayreddin, a disciple of Mimar Sinan, believed to be the greatest Ottoman architect. The length of time taken in building the Old Bridge is disputed. While some argue that the Bridge was built over the period 1557 to 1566,[80] others believe that the building works took only two years.[81] In any event, it was a patient and delicate process, the outcome of which was a gentle, but very solid, beautiful single stone arch. For its time, with a span of 28.70 metres, it was 'a very "brave" arch'.[82] The Bridge was 3.97 metres wide, and stood 20.34 metres above the river level measured during summer.[83] With a supporting vault of only 77 cm, it was described as 'an incredibly elegant vaulted structure'.[84] The two grand symmetric, half-cylindrical towers, one at each end of the Bridge, were built later.[85] They were keepers of the Bridge's stability. Supported in this way, the Old Bridge was said to look like an old man resting in his luxurious armchair with massive armrests.[86] In this regard, the Bridge also symbolized a replica of the city

---

[77] UNESCO's activities, 'Mostar and its historical monuments', www.unesco.org/culture/ heritage/tangible/mostar/html_eng/monument.shtml.

[78] UNESCO, 'Rebuilding of Stari Most (Old Bridge) and the rehabilitation of the old town of Mostar', www.unesco.org/opi2/starimost.htm.

[79] See Council of Europe, Parliamentary Assembly, *Committee on Culture and Education Reports* (*COE Reports*) (available at http://assembly.coe.int) *Information reports on the destruction by war of the cultural heritage in Croatia and Bosnia and Herzegovina.* See especially, *Second information report*, doc. 6869, 17 July 1993 and *Fourth information report*, doc. 6999, 19 January 1994.

[80] S. Özkan, 'The destruction of Stari most', *Development Network*, 14 (1994), 5. Other research shows that the bridge was built in two years at a cost of 300,000 silver coins. See Pašić, *The Old Bridge*, p. 12.

[81] Ibid.   [82] Ibid.   [83] Ibid., p. 14.   [84] Ibid., p. 21.

[85] Pašić notes that one tower was built in 1676 and the other in 1736-7. Ibid.

[86] B. Bogdanović, 'Može li grad bez svog mosta, može li most bez svog grada?' ('Can the city exist without its bridge; can the bridge exist without its city?'), *Most* (2001), 139.

of Mostar itself – the Bridge, squeezed between the giant towers, resembled the urban landscape of the city of Mostar, developed around the Bridge on both sides and squeezed between mountains and hills.[87] The perfection of engineering logic coupled with the elegance of a splendid stone structure made the Old Bridge a monument of exceptional value from both an artistic and scientific point of view.[88] Over time the Bridge developed into a great symbol of tolerance for diversity – a bridge which bridged cultures – a symbol of Mostar and the whole of Bosnia and Herzegovina, as it marked an important episode in the cultural history of this nation.

2. Destruction of the Old Bridge

'A thin, soaring structure [which] seemed impossibly delicate, too thin to take the weight of a . . . man',[89] the Old Bridge was incredibly solid. It endured centuries of earthquakes, harsh weather conditions and the wear of millions of locals' and tourists' feet. It also survived centuries of wars fought in that region, including both world wars. It did not survive the 1990s conflicts, however. From 1992 to 1994, Mostar was the site of two armed conflicts fought in the territory of Bosnia and Herzegovina, first between Serb and Croat–Muslim forces, and then between Croat and Muslim forces. The Bridge was destroyed during the latter conflict. Tanks that belonged to Croat forces shelled the Bridge 'at point-blank range'.[90] At 10:16 a.m. on Tuesday, 9 November 1993, one of the great cultural treasures of the world and one of the greatest cultural monuments of Bosnia and Herzegovina was reduced to limestone blocks and fragments.[91]

3. Motives behind the destruction

As Riedlmayer notes, people are often told that the destruction of immovable cultural property in Bosnia and Herzegovina during the

---

[87] Ibid.

[88] UNESCO's activities, 'Mostar and its historic monuments', www.unesco.org.

[89] M. Ignatieff, 'When a bridge is not a bridge', *The New York Times*, 27 October 2002, www.nytimes.com/2002/10/27/magazine/27MOSTAR.html.

[90] *COE Reports.*

[91] *Final report of the United Nations Commission of experts established pursuant to Security Council resolution 780 (1992), Annex XI: Destruction of cultural property report, S/1994/674/Add.2 (vol. V) 28 December 1994.*

1990s conflicts occurred because of 'ancient hatreds', comprising ethnic and religious animosity.[92] On this view, the Old Bridge was targeted as an object of cultural specificity. In other words, since the Old Bridge was built by the Ottoman Empire, with which the Mostar Muslims are linked through shared religious beliefs, the Croats considered it a Muslim monument. Kaiser correctly observes that the Old Bridge became 'ethnicized' in war.[93] Before the war, no one in Mostar regarded the Old Bridge as a 'Muslim' monument. As the conflict progressed, however, this approach changed. An increasing number of Muslim soldiers saw the Old Bridge not as a symbol of bridging cultures, but as an Islamic symbol. In turn, Croat soldiers increasingly saw the Bridge as a 'Muslim' relic, which needed to be eliminated.[94]

While hatreds flared up during the conflict and nationalistic exclusiveness as opposed to urban multiculturalism played a significant role in the destruction of the Old Bridge, the underlying motive behind the destruction was what was considered to be the ultimate aim of the entire Croat–Muslim armed conflict: the division of Bosnia and Herzegovina.[95] Nationalism and ethnic and cultural cleansing were only instruments used to achieve this aim. Pašić reasons that since the Old Bridge 'contained the meaning and the spirit of all Bosnia and Herzegovina: the essence of the bridge was meeting and joining together; the country, like the bridge, could be divided only by destroying it'.[96]

4.   Effects of the destruction

4.1   Municipal level

Celebrating the elimination of the last physical span and the most symbolic monument of Mostar, and indeed of the whole of Bosnia and Herzegovina, Croat forces cheered and fired their guns into the air.[97] At the same time, the 'true' Mostarians cried on both sides of the city.[98]

---

[92] A. Riedlmayer, 'Killing memory: the targeting of Bosnia's cultural heritage', testimony presented at a hearing of the Commission on Security and Cooperation in Europe, US Congress, 4 April 1995.

[93] Kaiser, 'Crimes against culture'.

[94] J. Pomfret, 'A bridge becomes a wedge as span crumbles, unity dreams die', *The Seattle Times*, 30 August 1993, A3 1993 WL 6014999, http://web2westlaw.com.

[95] G. Malić, 'Herceg camp' *Feral Tribune* (Split, Croatia) 29 April 1996, para. 4 (referring to Roy Gutman).

[96] Pašić, *The Old Bridge*, p. 39.

[97] J. Dodds, 'Bridge over the Neretva', (1998) 51 *Archaeology*, 1.   [98] Ibid.

Reportedly, after months of hiding from the constant shelling, people on the left bank of the Neretva, without any longer fearing whether they would be shot, left their cellars and other shelters and headed towards the beloved Bridge:

> People were walking slowly, the way people do when passing-by a coffin of a deceased human being. Some were crying, some were passing by [the fallen Bridge] silently. . . . It was heartbreaking to watch them.[99]

Then a 'day of mourning' was proclaimed in the municipality of Mostar.[100]

The destruction of the Old Bridge was felt deeply not only in Mostar, but also in the rest of Bosnia and Herzegovina and throughout the former Yugoslavia. All spoke with a single voice in denouncing the tank artillery shelling of the Bridge.[101] 'I felt sick when I saw the pictures. No one has the right to destroy our history',[102] lamented a Belgrade student. 'It is a tragic loss for everyone, not just the Muslims but for the Croats who live there as well', said one Zagreb citizen.[103]

4.2   International level

Throughout the world, the media coverage of the tragic loss of the Old Bridge was extensive. International organizations dealing with cultural property also spoke out. '[T]he perpetrators of this disgraceful act are trying to eradicate the history of a country and its people',[104] declared Federico Mayor, then Director-General of UNESCO, the organization that had worked to add the Old Bridge to the World Heritage in Danger List. 'They are thereby also destroying the bridges of mutual understanding built by people of different origins and religious beliefs who had learnt to live in harmony',[105] said the UNESCO Director-General. 'It is an attack against the values cherished by the international community and dear to the lovers of freedom. The destruction of the Stari Most Bridge has robbed all the communities of Bosnia and Herzegovina of a

---

[99] S. Broz, *Dobri ljudi u vremenu zla: sudionici i svjedoci (Good People in an Evil Time: Participants and Witnesses)* (Banja Luka: Prelom, 1999), p. 247.

[100] See Republic of Bosnia and Herzegovina, Wartime Presidency of the Mostar municipality, *Decision about proclaiming 10 November 1993 a day of mourning in the Mostar municipality*, 9 November 1993, published in *Most*, no. 108–109 November–December 1998, www.most.ba/01920/006.htm.

[101] C. Williams, 'Destruction of landmark Mostar span felt deeply – warring foes united in grief', *The Seattle Times*, Sunday, 14 November 1993, http://web2.westlaw.com.

[102] Ibid.   [103] Ibid.   [104] *Fourth COE Report.*   [105] Ibid.

symbol of hope, ruptured their links with a time of peace and struck at the very roots of their cultural heritage'.[106]

VI. Reconstruction of the Bridge and rebuilding a nation

Almost immediately after the destruction of the Old Bridge, while the fighting was still ongoing, local architects and heritage experts began to plan its reconstruction to keep its memory alive and to show that history and the people's spirit were unbreakable.[107] A date was set for the grand opening of a new bridge.[108] Citizens of Mostar anticipated this event, hoping that the resurrection of their city's emblem would bring them closer to each other.[109] Once a symbol of coexistence, and then through its destruction, a symbol of conflict and partition, the Bridge became a new metaphor, symbolizing the hope for peace and reconciliation and rebuilding of the nation.

The Bridge was rebuilt in 2004. The grand re-inauguration ceremony, attended by a number of heads of State and other State officials at the highest level, was held on 23 July that year. The rebuilding of the Old Bridge was an impressive international project,[110] involving the World Bank, UNESCO and a number of donors. It was also an extremely expensive project, costing millions of dollars. The international community deemed the rebuilding of the Bridge 'a basic prerequisite to the national healing process across the whole region of former Yugoslavia'.[111] It was believed that 'the rebuilding of the fallen Old Bridge w[ould] heal the wounds of the past by reuniting former antagonists and stitching together a divided city – Christian Croatians on the western side and Muslim Bosnians on the eastern side'.[112] Charlesworth criticizes the project as a 'misguided priority' in the light of more pressing needs in this war-ravaged region, such as environmental issues and the high level of unemployment.[113] Besides, in Charlesworth's view,

---

[106] Ibid.
[107] See Carnegie Endowment for International Peace, 'A symposium on destruction and rebuilding of architectural treasures in Bosnia and Herzegovina', Monday, 2 May 1994, www.kakarigi.net/many/carnegie.htm.
[108] Ibid.   [109] See Ignatieff, 'When a Bridge is not a Bridge'.
[110] Detailed information on the rebuilding of the Old Bridge can be accessed at http://portal.unesco.org/culture/en/ev.php.
[111] E. Charlesworth, *Architects without Frontiers: War, Reconstruction and Design Responsibility* (Oxford: Elsevier, 2006), p. 100.
[112] J. Calame, 'Commentary on cities on the edge conference', *Architecture Review*, Summer issue (2002).
[113] Charlesworth, *Architects without Frontiers*, pp. 100–11.

this particular reconstruction project has not achieved its goal of reconciliation. She argues that the reconstruction of a national symbol of
unity – the Old Bridge – and the adjoining historic precinct of the Old
City of Mostar has neither resulted in a full cessation of the conflict itself
nor has it healed the wartime wounds. Charlesworth correctly observes
that the building and rebuilding of religious structures on both sides of
the river, which in some cases are 'ridiculously tall . . . in fact represent[s]
a continuation of the war by other means'.[114]

Nevertheless, the rebuilding of the Old Bridge has brought about some,
albeit modest, steps towards reconciliation. As was the case before the
conflict, the Old City offers its visitors a range of entertainment programmes. In summer, it is once again crowded with young people coming
from both banks of the river. At first glance, this resembles the old
pre-conflict times. However, despite the construction of a replica, the
destruction of the original Old Bridge has irreversible consequences. It
has been predicted that this particular incident of cultural destruction 'will
leave the strongest impression on the memory of . . . tragic war in Bosnia-
Herzegovina'.[115] While people from both sides of the city do cross the
Bridge, no true social unification between the city's east and west has as yet
taken place. Many Croats in the city's west carry the burden of 'collective
guilt' for the destruction of the original Old Bridge.[116] They often emphasize the other side's 'right to pain' and their own 'obligation to silence and
shame'. This is a heavy burden, which cannot be eased until the individuals
who are responsible for the destruction of the Bridge are identified and
brought to justice.[117] Thus, whether the past embodied in other cultural
objects will have a future greatly depends on how the present treats the past.

VII.   Justice for the destruction of the Bridge

Wilful destruction of cultural property may constitute a war crime and
give rise to individual criminal responsibility. In March 2004, six persons

---

[114] Ibid., p. 109.

[115] M. Dinnes and F. Ćatović, *Hommage to Mostar* (Mostar: Slovo Printing and Publishing
Company, 1997), p. 7.

[116] Author's observation based on research over many years on the subject of the destruction of the Old Bridge.

[117] See, e.g., V. Pusic, 'Mostar – in the Croat name', *Erasimus*, no. 16, Zagreb, April 1996,
available at www.barnsdle.demon.co.uk/bosnia.vesna.html (stressing that there is no
such concept as 'collective guilt' in international law and urging Croats to denounce
war criminals who committed crimes in their name).

were indicted by the International Criminal Tribunal for the Former
Yugoslavia (ICTY) for war crimes committed during the Croat–Muslim
conflict, including the destruction of the Old Bridge. Given the significance of the cultural contribution of every people to the cultural heritage
of all humankind, it is important that the case *Prosecutor* v. *Jadranko
Prlić et al.* (*Prlić*),[118] which *inter alia* concerns the Old Bridge, is heard at
the international rather than national level. To this extent, such an
international tribunal represents the entire international community.
Its decisions send a stronger message than those of a national tribunal.
Such a message resonates worldwide, warning potential wrongdoers and,
simultaneously, reinforcing the international aspect of cultural property.

There are several major problems with the *Prlić* case, however. One is
the size. *Prlić* is one of the largest International Criminal Tribunal for the
former Yugoslavia (ICTY) cases, as noted, involving six accused in a
joint trial on charges for various war crimes, specified under twenty-six
counts of the indictment, geographically stretching across eight municipalities. The Old Bridge-related charges are only a drop in the ocean of
other charges, which makes it unlikely that the destruction of the Bridge
will receive the attention it deserves in the awaited trial judgment.
Another problem is the timing of the indictment and the trial. More
than ten years passed between the date of the destruction of the Bridge
and the *Prlić* indictment. The Bridge was destroyed on 9 November 1993,
but it was not until 4 March 2004 that the initial indictment was
confirmed. The indictment was kept confidential until its unsealing
on 2 April 2004.[119] The following year, on 16 November 2005, the
indictment was amended and the trial commenced on 26 April 2006,
concluding in March 2011.[120] It should be noted that the ICTY prosecution was obliged to complete all investigations and issue its last indict-
ments by the end of 2004, in accordance with the deadline accepted
under the Tribunal's completion strategy required by the UN Security
Council. Thus, the *Prlić* indictment was among the last filed by the
prosecution. An investigation into the destruction of the Old Bridge
was completed in 1994,[121] a decade prior to the indictment. This timeline
highlights the slow pace of justice for the destruction of the Old Bridge.

---

[118] *Prlić*.
[119] See, e.g., A. Uzelac, 'Hague prosecutors rest their case', IWPR's Tribunal update no.
387, 27 December 2004, www.iwpr.net.
[120] Judgment was expected to be delivered in July 2012, but is still awaited.
[121] See, e.g., J. Rosenberger, 'UN to prosecute culture crimes', (1994) 82 *Art in America*,
para. 4 www.members.tripod.com/`UnconqueredBosnia/Cultur2.html.

Justice delayed may be seen as justice denied, as the passage of time may alter perspectives. Although the destruction of the Bridge stirred passions on both sides of the city of Mostar, it should not be forgotten that the crime was committed almost two decades ago. The truth remains somewhat elusive so many years after the destruction of the Bridge.[122] Still, as Teitel argues, 'interest in the pursuit of justice does not necessarily wane with the passage of time'.[123] Interest in justice is perpetual.

> Here, I return again to the importance of sanctions against those who destroy cultural heritage. We must recognize that such attacks do not arise simply from 'the heat of the moment' but are calculated, pre-meditated and deliberate; in fact, they often form part of a strategy of hostility, especially in inter-ethnic conflicts. We must get to grips with these sobering realities. In facing them, we must not tire, we must not doubt the importance of our work, and we must not allow setbacks and disappointments to deter us [from protecting] the world's cultural heritage in all its rich diversity.[124]

VIII.   Conclusion

To sum up, the dual nature of cultural property – national and international – amplifies the importance of its preservation. As part of cultural patrimony, cultural property is indispensable in identity generation. The post-war reconstruction of the Old Bridge, aimed at reconciliation, emphasized the role of cultural property in nation building. At the same time, cultural property forms part of a larger whole and is invaluable to all humankind. While the Bridge was primarily rebuilt to re-establish broken interethnic links within a particular nation, the reconstruction project was 'international' in character. This reveals a wider significance of the Bridge. That the importance of the Bridge transcends national borders is further demonstrated by its inscription on the World Heritage List. The 'international' aspect of the Bridge limits the power of a nation-state. The universal value of the Bridge was reinforced, and concomitantly national sovereignty was diminished, by the fact that the case was brought before an international tribunal.

---

[122] Testimony of Larry Forbes in *Prlić*, Transcript, 21372.

[123] R. Teitel, 'Transitional Justice Genealogy', (2003) 16 *Harvard Human Rights Journal*, 69, 86.

[124] UNESCO, Address by Koïchiro Matsuura, Director-General of UNESCO at the Opening of the Fifth Meeting of the States Parties to the 1954 Hague Convention for the Protection of Cultural Property in the Event of Armed Conflict, DG/2001/115, UNESCO, 5 November 2001.

The impact of supranationalism on state sovereignty from the perspective of the legitimacy of international organisations

ERIC DE BRABANDERE

I. Introduction

In view of the proliferation of international organisations in the past century, it has become trite to claim that, especially through the creation of regional and supranational organisations aimed at integration rather than cooperation, state sovereignty is close to becoming an empty box.[1] The rise of international organisations during the last century is without doubt one of the most important developments international law has witnessed. However, it is doubtful that this evolution in and of itself has any bearing on the current traditional concept of state sovereignty.

This chapter argues that instead of viewing regionalism and supranationalism as implying *ipso facto* a threat to state sovereignty, the form of the legitimacy of international organisations is a determinant for the impact of international organisation on the sovereignty of states. The question of the legitimacy of international organisations and the alleged threat that supranationalism and regionalism poses to the current conception of state sovereignty is, of course, closely intertwined with the type of international organisation and the activity exercised by that organisation. Both questions are confined to those forms of supranationalism and regionalism which include the takeover of certain functions traditionally exercised by states, and thus go well beyond mere cooperation at the international legal level. It is not the purpose here to enter into a detailed analysis of certain specific organisations or types of organisations and their influence on the

---

[1] See generally, for a discussion of the notion and concept of sovereignty in the current international legal order: Martti Koskenniemi, 'What Use for Sovereignty Today?', (2011) 1 *Asian Journal of International Law*, 61–70.

sovereignty of states. Although we will, of course, refer on many occasions to certain specific international organisations, the purpose here is to reflect more broadly on the concept of state sovereignty in its relation to the concept and functioning of international organisations.

I will first argue that the transmission of competences by a state to another entity is essentially a form of exercise of the rights of a sovereign state, and thus not a transfer or restraint of sovereignty. Second, the creation of international organisations at the regional or supranational level is not necessarily threatening to the current conception of statehood. The type of legitimacy used to assess the authority of international organisations is a determinant in assessing the alleged weakening of state sovereignty. As long as international organisations are viewed as deriving their legitimacy from the powers that have been conferred on them by the member states of that organisation (legitimacy of origin), and the exercise of their powers in conformity with these powers (legitimacy of exercise), this reinforces rather than weakens the position of states.[2] However, if one takes into account the recent inclination of certain international organisations to establish a form of legitimacy through several forms of direct or popular legitimacy, supra-nationalism can – but not automatically effectively does – amount to a weakening of the current conception of state sovereignty.

II.   International organisations, supranationalism and state sovereignty

The question whether the state-centred model of international law is still valid today, in view of the changing social and societal needs, is an ongoing but relatively old debate in international law.[3] The current international legal system, often qualified as 'state-centric', is generally considered to be based on the Peace Treaties of Westphalia in 1648, which have established the modern notion of sovereign nation-states as the main – if not exclusive – actors in international law and relations.[4]

---

[2] See generally, on the legitimacy of states and international organisations, from this dual perspective: Jean d'Aspremont and Eric De Brabandere, 'Legitimacy of Origin v. Legitimacy of Exercise: The Complementary Faces of Legitimacy in International Law', (2011) 43 *Fordham International Law Journal*, 102–45.

[3] See the symposium 'Nationalism and Internationalism: Shifting World Spheres', published by *Harvard International Law Journal* in 1992 ((1992) 33 *Harvard International Law Journal*, 339–570).

[4] See Leo Gross, 'The Peace of Westphalia, 1648–1948', (1948) 42 *American Journal of International Law*, 20 *et seq.*

The Peace, therefore, is generally considered as one of the foundational events of the current international legal system. States from that moment onwards are seen as detached from imperial and religious rule, and their sovereign authority is now established within the territorial boundaries of the state, coupled with the principle of non-intervention in the internal affairs of other states.[5] Although some have challenged the influence of the Peace of Westphalia on the current conception of the international legal system,[6] the result is nevertheless that today, international law essentially relies on the consent of states, and the concepts of state sovereignty and sovereign equality remain the corner-stones of the international legal system. Although this reality will be further developed in the discussion on the legitimacy of international organisations in the next section, I shall start by analysing the relation and link between states and international organisations.

Several meanings are often attributed to the notion of sovereignty and it is subject of much confusion in international scholarship. Moreover, the relation between sovereignty and the exercise of competences – or the transfer thereof – by states is frequently misconceived. Sovereignty is closely related to the notion of 'international legal personality', and can be described as the right to exercise, to the exclusion of any other, the functions of a state.[7] Although the notion of sovereignty has in fact been held to have different meanings,[8] here we will use the definition mentioned above. Sovereignty is thus an intrinsic aspect of a state, distinct from the competences of the state which are both territorial and personal.[9]

Some clarification is also necessary as to the use of 'supranationalism' in this chapter. Supranational organisations are often seen as a specific

---

[5] See generally, R. Joyce, 'Westphalia: Event, Memory, Myth', in F. Johns, R. Joyce and S. Pahuja (eds.), *Events: The Force of International Law* (London: Routledge, 2011), pp. 55 *et seq.*

[6] See, for example, Andreas Osiander, 'Sovereignty, International Relations and the Westphalian Myth', (2001) 55 *International Organisation*, 251–87; S.D. Krasner, *Sovereignty: Organised Hypocrisy* (Princeton University Press, 1999), pp. 20 *et seq.* and S. D. Krasner, 'Westphalia and All That', in J. Goldstein and R. O. Keohane (eds.), *Ideas and Foreign Policy: Beliefs, Institutions and Political Change* (Ithaca: Cornell University Press, 1993), pp. 235–64.

[7] Cf. 'Island of Palmas Case' (*The Netherlands* v. *United States of America*), Arbitral Award, 4 April 1928, (1928) 22 *American Journal of International Law*, 875.

[8] See Krasner, *Sovereignty*, pp. 8 *et seq.*, distinguishing between 'domestic sovereignty', 'interdependence sovereignty', 'international legal sovereignty', and 'Westphalian sovereignty'.

[9] I. Brownlie, *Principles of Public International Law* (Oxford University Press, 2003), p. 107 and James Crawford, *The Creation of States in International Law*, 2nd edn (Oxford: Clarendon Press, 2006), p. 33.

category of international organisations, as opposed to 'intergovernmental' organisations.[10] The main characteristic of supranational organisations is 'the direct statutory effects of their laws on the national laws of their members'.[11] However, at the same time, such a categorisation has no real added value[12] since today, according to some scholars, there is only one true supranational organisation – the European Union (EU)[13] – and according to other scholars, and another definition of supranationalism, no international organisation today fulfils the criteria of a 'supranational' organisation.[14] I will thus use here the notion of supranationalism in the sense of an international organisation which contains *some elements of supranationalism*, i.e. those international organisations which – in certain areas at least – function in an integrated way that goes beyond mere interstate cooperation.

One of the main reasons behind states' need to create international organisations is the growing interdependence of states,[15] and the need to manage 'common problems'.[16] In many instances, states have an interest in cooperating with other states in order to regulate transnational activities, such as post and (tele-)communication, navigational rights on rivers, use of transboundary water resources, international peace and security, trade and foreign direct investment. This need for and interest in cooperation in the last century has resulted in the creation of numerous and diverse international organisations – the so-called 'proliferation of international organisations' – in order to administer and manage interstate cooperation. The first series of international organisations were created essentially in technical areas, such as the Central Commission for Navigation on the Rhine (1815–16), the International Telegraph Union, created in 1865 and later renamed International Telecommunications Union, and the Universal

---

[10] H. G. Schermers and N. Blokker, *International Institutional Law* (Leiden/Boston: Martinus Nijhoff Publishers, 2003), p. 45 and J. Klabbers, *An Introduction to International Institutional Law* (Cambridge University Press, 2009), p. 24.

[11] Kirsten Schmalenbach, 'International Organisations or Institutions, General Aspects', in R. Wolfrum (ed.), *Max Planck Encyclopedia of Public International Law* (Oxford University Press), online edition, para. 15, available at www.mpil.com (last accessed 1 December 2011).

[12] Klabbers, *An Introduction*, p. 24.

[13] For a discussion see *ibid.* See also Schmalenbach, 'International Organisations', para. 15 and Jost Delbruck, 'Exercising Public Authority Beyond the State: Transnational Democracy and/or Alternative Legitimation Strategies?', (2003) 10 *Indiana Journal of Global Legal Studies*, 34 *et seq.*

[14] Schermers and Blokker, *International Institutional Law*, p. 47.   [15] Ibid., p. 1.

[16] Jan Klabbers, 'Two Concepts of International Organisation', (2005) 2 *International Organisations Law Review*, 278.

Postal Union created in 1874.[17] A radical shift occurred with the creation of both the League of Nations in 1920 and the United Nations in 1945, two international organisations which, especially compared to the previous 'technical' organisations, were created to address a vast array of essentially political issues. In the same vein, the creation of the International Monetary Fund (IMF), the World Bank Group, including the International Bank for Reconstruction and Development (IBRD), and the attempt to create an International Trade Organisation in the 1940s – which finally succeeded with the creation of the World Trade Organisation (WTO) in 1995 after the Uruguay Round – resulted in important new participants with potentially far-reaching powers in areas traditionally reserved to state action only. At the same time, and since then, many regional (economic) organisations were also created, aimed more at integration than mere cooperation, such as the Organisation of American States (1948), the Council of Europe (1949), the European Communities (European Coal and Steel Community (1951), the European Economic Community (1957) and the European Atomic Energy Community (1957) now integrated in the EU), the Organisation of African Unity (1963) replaced by the African Union in 2002), the Association of Southeast Asian Nations (ASEAN) in 1967 and many of the regional development banks.[18]

The rise of international organisations during the last century is without doubt one of the most important developments international law has witnessed. It is doubtful, however, that this evolution in itself has any bearing on the current traditional concept of state sovereignty. However, it is often claimed in literature that the avenue of supranational organisations has resulted in the decline of the sovereign nation state.[19] This is especially advocated, considering that several international organisations, such as the United Nations, the WTO, the IBRD or the IMF have the capacity to (relatively) independently impose certain measures or sanctions on their member states.[20] However, it is not as if international organisations

---

[17] See Klabbers, *An Introduction*, pp. 16 *et seq.*   [18] See for an overview ibid.

[19] See, for example, Neil McCormick, 'Beyond the Sovereign State', (1993) 56 *Modern L. Rev.*, 1 *et seq.*; Neil McCormick, 'Sovereignty, Democracy and Subsidiarity', in R. Bellamy *et al.* (eds.), *Democracy and Constitutional Culture in the Union of Europe* (London: Lothian Foundation Press, 1995), p. 95 and Paul B. Stephan, 'Accountability and International Lawmaking: Rules, Rents and Legitimacy', (1996–7) 17 *Nw. J. Int'l L. & Bus.*, 681.

[20] See for a discussion, Joyce, 'Westphalia', p. 61. See also, generally, John W. Head, 'Supranational Law: How the Move toward Multilateral Solutions Is Changing the

and their power were imposed on states. States *voluntarily* consent to create and participate in international organisations. At the same time, it would be wrong to claim that by doing so, states have relinquished their sovereignty by transferring competences to these separate legal persons.[21] Despite the fact that states are still the primary actors in international law and relations, the mere creation of international organisations is often mistakenly viewed as an important restriction on state sovereignty.

The creation of international organisations, in particular intrusive organisations such as the IMF, did not involve any 'transfer of sovereignty', as often claimed.[22] Certain situations clearly can *moderate* a state's exclusive competence, one of them being the transfer of administrative powers or other competences. However, the transfer of state competences to an international organisation does not imply the transfer of the state's *sovereignty* to the international organisation. As noted by the Permanent Court of International Justice in the well-known *Wimbledon* case, 'the right of entering into international engagements is an attribute of State sovereignty'.[23] The transmission by a state of competences to another entity essentially is a form of exercise of the rights of a sovereign state, and thus not a transfer or restraint of sovereignty. By doing so, states can voluntarily deviate from the principles of sovereign equality, even in the adoption of certain rules by the organisation.[24] As put by the arbitrators in the *Lac Lanoux* award: 'territorial sovereignty plays the part of a presumption. It must bend before all international obligations, whatever their origin, but only before such obligations.'[25] It can therefore be concluded that if states are bound by the treaties they have signed, this is not a *derogation* of their sovereignty, but rather, an *effect* of it.[26]

It is clear that the degree of integration sought by the international organisation – i.e. the extent to which the organisation contains

Character of "International Law"', (1993–4) 42 *University of Kansas Law Review*, 605–66. See also, Patrick Tangney, 'The New Internationalism: The Cession of Sovereign Competences to Supranational Organisations and Constitutional Change in the United States and Germany', (1996) 21 *Yale J. Int'l L.* 395 *et seq*

[21] See, however, Neil McCormick, arguing that today, in particular in Europe, no state is a 'sovereign' state, essentially because all the power exercised by states no longer derives solely from purely internal sources (McCormick, 'Beyond the Sovereign State', p. 16).

[22] See, for example, Head, 'Supranational Law', pp. 627–8.

[23] Permanent Court of International Justice, *Case of the S.S. 'Wimbledon'*, Judgment, 17 August 1923, 1923 PCIJ Rep, Ser. A., No. 1, 25.

[24] See Juliane Kokott, 'States, Sovereign Equality', in Wolfrum (ed.), *Max Planck Encyclopedia of Public International Law* online edition.

[25] 'Lac Lanoux' (*France* v. *Spain*), ILR, 24 (1959), 101.

[26] Koskenniemi, 'What Use for Sovereignty Today?', 62.

supranational elements – will influence the degree of transfer of competences by states to the organisation. This is particularly blatant when one
looks at the EU, with a decision-making process based on majority voting
and a Court of Justice with compulsory jurisdiction over EU matters, and
competences in various areas traditionally solely within the sovereign
competences of states, such as commercial policy, fisheries, currency and
financial policy. However, the level of integration of the organisation does
not necessarily imply that the 'supranational' organisation should be seen
more as a threat to state sovereignty than an organisation aimed at mere
cooperation – a so-called 'intergovernmental organisation'.

It is important to point out why the notion of legitimacy of international
organisations is relevant, in particular, in view of the question whether
supranationalism has eroded the sovereignty of states. It is beyond doubt
that many international organisations, in particular those that we will
discuss in the next section, exercise powers which have a considerable
impact, not only on the member states, but also, either directly or indirectly,
on the population in the territories of member states.[27] It is in view of this
development that international organisations have sought to obtain some
form of legitimacy outside the context of state consent alone. As we will
point out in the next section, the type of legitimacy sought by the organisation to justify its action will prove to be a more adequate standard to
measure the alleged weakening of state sovereignty than the mere existence
of 'supranationalism' or 'regionalism'. Indeed, from a formal legality and
legitimacy perspective, the existence of international organisations
strengthens rather than weakens state sovereignty. This is so not only
because states are legally necessary in order to create international organisations, but because, from the perspective of the legitimacy of international
organisations, one sees that traditionally this legitimacy is tested, either by
the valid consent given by states through the signature of the constitutional
treaty (legitimacy of origin), or the way in which functions are exercised
(legitimacy of exercise).

III.   International organisations: between state-centred and popular legitimacy

As I have argued elsewhere with Jean d'Aspremont, a distinction needs
to be made between the legitimacy of exercise and the legitimacy of
origin, which points to the distinction between the legitimacy pertaining

[27] See Delbruck, 'Exercising Public Authority', 34–6.

to the source of power and the legitimacy related to the exercise of power.[28] It is not the purpose here to reiterate the theoretical foundations of that argument. I will instead focus on the application of these two forms of legitimacy to international organisations.

From a conventional perspective, as mentioned earlier, international organisations derive their legitimacy from the powers that have been conferred on them by the member states of that organisation. The *source* of their powers is thus only very briefly tested through the consent of states when signing the constitutional treaty of the organisation. In this sense, the legitimacy of origin of international organisations is not necessarily a controversial issue, but has important consequences. Because of the limited original legitimacy test, international organisations have developed the need to ensure that they exercise their powers in conformity with the functions assigned to them by the states. Therefore, international organisations traditionally sustain their legitimacy by ensuring that decision-making in respect of the exercise of their specific functions is in conformity with the institutional law of the organisation and international law in general. This is a manifestation of the legitimacy of exercise. We see in recent practice that the way in which authority is exercised by international organisations is increasingly subjected to the growing importance of how authority to exercise certain activity is granted to international organisations, i.e. the legitimacy they can derive from the origin of their power. Recent developments in the role and functions of international organisations, such as the increasing involvement of international organisations in the exercise of governmental functions, have indeed caused a cross-fertilization of both forms of legitimacy, with a clear move from the legitimacy of exercise to various forms of legitimacy of origin, including legitimacy of origin derived from the people.

1. International organisations and the legitimate exercise of powers

Decision-making at the international level by international organisations lacks any direct electoral foundation, since intergovernmental organisations have no direct popular legitimacy of origin. Since an international organisation is created by states, the source of and the

---

[28] d'Aspremont and De Brabandere, 'Legitimacy of Origin'. This section draws on research conducted in the context of that article, in particular part III, B thereof.

legitimacy for the exercise of their powers by international organisations is derived from the consent validly expressed by the different states party to the constitutional treaty of the organisation. Since states and their governments are to be considered as the legitimate representatives of the population in their territory, the lawful delegation of certain powers to international organisations by these representatives is *indirectly* based on a form of popular consent. Consequently, the exercise of powers by international organisations cannot be considered as *illegitimate* by definition, although its legitimacy will often not be 'democratic', as traditionally understood.[29]

In view of this lack of *direct* legitimacy of origin, in the sense that the organisation does not directly hold powers granted to it by the population of the states parties to the organisation, and the absence of a periodical legitimacy test through direct elections, for example, or any other mechanism, the legitimacy of international organisations has been classically addressed through the way in which the functions were exercised, i.e. the legitimacy of exercise.[30] The exercise of powers by international organisations is then subjected to a legitimacy assessment, principally through the procedures followed in the decision-making process within the organisation,[31] often referred to as in-put legitimacy.[32] From a legal perspective, the most obvious method to ensure the legitimate exercise of powers by international organisation through a focus on the procedural aspects of decision-making is to ensure that the decisions taken are in conformity with the legal obligations of the international organisation,[33] both in terms of the legal restraints stemming from the application of general international law and the legal restraints stemming from the organisation's constitutional treaty.

---

[29] See P. L. Lindseth, 'Democratic Legitimacy and the Administrative Character of Supranationalism: The Example of the European Community', (1999) 99 *Colum. L. Rev.*, 646 *et seq.*

[30] d'Aspremont and De Brabandere, 'Legitimacy of Origin'.

[31] See, in particular, on the issue of procedural legitimacy and fairness, Thomas M. Franck, *The Power of Legitimacy Among Nations* (New York: Oxford University Press, 1990), pp. 204–7 and Thomas M. Franck, *Legitimacy in the International System*, (1988) 82 *Am. J. Int'l L.* 705 *et seq.*

[32] See generally, M. Krajewski, 'International Organisations or Institutions, Democratic Legitimacy', in Wolfrum (ed.), *Max Planck Encyclopedia of Public International Law*, online edition. The substantive outcome of the decisions of international organisations is then referred to as out-put legitimacy.

[33] See in respect of Security Council action, Erika de Wet, *The Chapter VII Powers of the United Nations Security Council* (Oxford: Hart Publishers, 2004).

Especially when international organisations take action which has potential impact on human rights and the daily lives of individuals, such as in the case of certain decisions of the United Nations (UN) Security Council, there is a tendency to subject this exercise of power to some form of *ex post facto* legitimacy or legality check.[34] A decision which is taken within the limits of the constitutional treaty and international law will traditionally be seen as a legitimate decision.[35]

Against this backdrop, and taking into account the legitimacy of international organisations derived from the consent expressed by the member states, the debates on the legitimacy of *origin* of international organisations and the question whether international organisations are a threat to state sovereignty are, in theory, superfluous. Of course, the question of the legitimacy of origin of international organisations, and by implication the question whether the proliferation of supranational and regional international organisations has become a threat to state sovereignty, has particular relevance for those organisations which have activities that go beyond a mere technical interstate cooperation, but rather, aim at integration.[36] This is why the question of the legitimacy of origin of international institutions and their impact on state sovereignty is a relatively recent phenomenon. A few decades ago, the activities of international organisations generally were relatively weak in respect of effectively exercised authority and integration, with the exception, perhaps, of the European Community, and these questions were therefore of little global relevance.[37]

2. International organisations and the legitimacy of origin

When the organisation's activity has a relatively strong impact on the state and the individuals, international organisations, in the exercise of their functions, have traditionally relied on the general or *ad hoc* consent of states.[38] This, for instance, has been the case in intrusive missions authorised by the UN Security Council, such as the UN Interim Administration Mission in Kosovo (UNMIK), which, although established under Chapter VII of the UN Charter, also relied on the consent of

---

[34] Klabbers, *An Introduction*, p. 250.

[35] See also Franck, *The Power of Legitimacy*, pp. 219–21.

[36] Krajewski, 'International Organisations', para. 11.

[37] Daniel Bodansky, 'The Legitimacy of International Governance: A Coming Challenge for International Environmental Law?', (1999) 93 *Am. J. Int'l L.*, 597.

[38] Ibid.

the host state, the then Federal Republic of Yugoslavia.[39] Again, when viewed from this perspective, the creation of such far-reaching missions, in which the UN has taken over the entire administration of a portion of a state's territory, does not *ipso facto* imply a weakening of state sovereignty. The mere fact that the Security Council relies on the consent of the host state in authorising such missions, although this was not legally required, since the mission was established under Chapter VII of the UN Charter, shows that the state remains the central building block of international organisations and thus of the international legal system.

Nevertheless, several developments confirm that international organisations more and more are seeking to establish a form of legitimacy of origin beyond the mere consent of the member states, and beyond the legitimacy in the exercise of their functions. As a consequence, the legitimacy of certain international institutions no longer solely rest upon the consent of states expressed at the time of the creation of the organisation and on the control exercised by states on the legitimate exercise by the established international organisations of their assigned functions.

It should also be remembered here that, as noted, these developments towards the legitimacy of origin are both a consequence of, and proportional to, the impact of the activity of the organisation on the population. The debate on the legitimacy of origin of international organisations, and by necessary implication, the debate on supranationalism as a threat to state sovereignty, has little or no relevance for those organisations of which the direct impact on the population is limited. However, it is precisely in the shift towards the establishment of a form of legitimacy of origin emanating from the population that one can assess whether the existence and activities of international organisations might pose a threat to the sovereignty of states.

The first development towards the establishment of a form of legitimacy of origin relates to the EU. The functioning and legitimacy of the EU now lies at the intersection between states and international organisations in terms of democratic legitimacy. Evidence of this is the direct election by the citizens of the Members of the European Parliament. As

---

[39] On the legal basis and legitimacy of this and related missions, see d'Aspremont and De Brabandere, 'Legitimacy of Origin' and Eric De Brabandere, *Post-conflict Administrations in International Law: International Territorial Administration, Transitional Authority and Foreign Occupation in Theory and Practice* (Boston/Leiden: Martinus Nijhoff Publishers, 2009).

SOVEREIGNTY AND ORGANIZATIONAL LEGITIMACY   461

such, the legitimacy of the EU in the exercise of its function is very well established, since the decisions of its various institutions, under certain conditions, are subjected to direct judicial scrutiny by the General Court of the EU (formerly the European Court of First Instance) and/or the European Court of Justice. However, the direct election of the Members of the European Parliament is important for the EU, because it adds a popular legitimacy of origin to the exercise of the functions of states exercised by the organisation. This has particular relevance, taking into consideration the undeniably strong impact of the EU's decisions on the daily lives of the European citizens. It is also for the same reason that several member states had decided to organise referenda in order to add a certain popular legitimacy to proposed institutional changes.[40] On the other hand, one has to keep in mind that EU member states retain many competences, for example, in the area of national defence policy.

A second example which evidences an apparent shift from the legitimacy of exercise to the legitimacy of origin in assessing institutional legitimacy is the recent discussions on the reform of the Security Council and the need to expand (permanent) membership of it. The question of whether a decision is taken in conformity with the UN Charter and other principles of general international law, (i.e. whether a decision is legitimate from the perspective of the exercise of functions), is increasingly being complemented by the question whether the Security Council as an institution has the necessary legitimacy in terms of its composition to take certain decisions.[41] The High-Level Panel on Threats, Challenges and Change which, besides suggesting a set of guidelines to be used by the Security Council in its decision-making process (legitimacy of exercise), proposed a reform of the Council in order to 'increase the democratic and accountable nature of the body' (legitimacy of origin).[42] Former Secretary-General Kofi Annan, in his report 'In Larger Freedom', also criticised the lack of legitimacy of origin

---

[40] See for a discussion of the constitutional treaty, and the legitimacy question in the EU, J. H. H. Weiler, 'A Constitution for Europe? Some Hard Choices', (2002) 40 *Journal of Common Market Studies*, 563. See on the question of the referenda, J. Zemánek, 'Consent of parliament or people's referendum?', in I. Pernice and J. Zemánek (eds.), *A Constitution for Europe: The IGC, the Ratification Process and Beyond* (Baden-Baden: Nomos, 2005), pp. 141–8.

[41] See for a discussion, J. Taubman, 'Towards a Theory of Democratic Compliance: Security Council Legitimacy and Effectiveness after Iraq', (2004) 37 *N.Y.U Journal of International Law and Politics*, 192 *et seq.*

[42] Report of the High-level Panel on Threats, Challenges and Change, 'A more secure world: our shared responsibility', UN Doc. A/59/565 (2004), para. 73.

of the Security Council, by stating: 'the Security Council has increasingly asserted its authority and, especially since the end of the cold war, has enjoyed greater unity of purpose among its permanent members but has seen that authority questioned on the grounds that its composition is anachronistic or insufficiently representative'.[43] The Secretary-General therefore suggested making it more broadly representative of the international community as a whole.[44] The idea here is that since states represent the population on their territory, an expansion of the Security Council would at the same time expand the 'popular' legitimacy of the decision. Of course, this presupposes that states themselves have democratic legitimacy[45] and are effectively representing the population within their territory. The justification of the authority of the Security Council is thus no longer seen as a consequence of state consent to the constitutional treaty of the organisation which grants certain functions and powers to it, but, rather, the 'universal' and popular acceptance or endorsement of certain decisions. The origin of the functions exercised by the Security Council thus needs to be 'democratic', or at least representative of the international community. The idea, as has been suggested, is that 'the more powerful an international organisation is, the greater its effect on the life of individuals. This supports fair representation of peoples in the international organisation, thus more voting power for States with more population.'[46]

To date, the debate on the composition of the Security Council has not (yet) yielded any concrete results, but this development clearly shows the tendency to create a form of popular legitimacy for the UN beyond the mere consent of states. However, it is also clear that every effort to expand the Security Council's configuration still essentially relies on the willingness and consent of states. In other words, the addition of certain states as (permanent) members to the Security Council at the same time reinforces the roles of states within that organ, although the final objective is to render the Council more representative of the international community. Nonetheless, one sees that here again this exercise is necessary in view of the increased impact of Security Council activity on the daily lives of individuals.

[43] Report of the Secretary-General, 'In larger freedom: towards development, security and human rights for all', UN Doc. A/59/2005 (21 March 2005), para. 165.
[44] Ibid.   [45] See d'Aspremont and De Brabandere, 'Legitimacy of Origin'.
[46] Kokott, 'States, Sovereign Equality'.

A third development is the increased influence of international economic and financial institutions on public policy decisions of states, and
the coinciding renewed attention paid to the legitimacy of these institutions. In particular, on the one, the involvement of the World Bank and
the IMF in the financial development of states, and the strengthened
impact of the WTO and its dispute settlement mechanism on various
non-trade policies on the other, has been subjected to increased scrutiny
in terms of legitimacy. As noted in the previous paragraphs, the legitimacy of many international organisations and their potential threat to
the state-centric international legal system in the past has attracted little
attention, principally because their activity was limited in terms of
impact on the state or its individuals. The growing impact of international institutions on the domestic affairs of the state, and thus on the
nationals of the state, has brought about an increased attention to the
legitimacy of institutions in taking or imposing far-reaching measures
on the state. International financial and trade institutions especially have
seen a considerable intensification of the impact of their rules, regulations and policies, not only on states, but also and mainly, as a consequence, on individuals.

The impact of the Bretton Woods institutions on the human rights
situations in states, for example, has seriously expanded in the past
decades. Traditionally, international financial institutions did not have a
competence even to address human rights issues under their respective
constitutions.[47] For instance, the World Bank at its inception was
prohibited from conditioning loans on political or non-economic considerations.[48] The IMF also traditionally paid little attention to human
rights considerations, since, as stated by the Fund's General Counsel,
Mr. Gianviti, it is a monetary agency, not a development agency.[49] These
traditional perspectives stand in contrast with an undeniable amplification

---

[47] Andrew Clapham, *Human Rights Obligations of Non-State Actors* (Oxford University
Press, 2006), p. 142.

[48] See Marc Cogen, 'Human Rights, Prohibition of Political Activities and the Lending-
policies of the World Bank and International Monetary Fund', in R. S. Chowdhury, E. G.
Denters and P. J. I. M. de Waart, *The Right to Development in International Law*
(Dordrecht/Boston/London: Martinus Nijhoff Publishers, 1992), p. 379.

[49] Economic and Social Council, Committee on Economic, Social and Cultural Rights,
'Report on the Twenty-Fifth, Twenty-Sixth and Twenty-Seventh Sessions (23 April–11
May 2001, 13–31 August 2001, 12–30 November 2001)', UN Doc. E/C.12/2001/17, para.
988. See also, F. Gianviti, 'Economic, Social, and Cultural Rights and the International
Monetary Fund' in P. Alston, *Non-State Actors and Human Rights* (Oxford University
Press, 2005), p. 132.

of international financial institutions' policies on states and individuals, which in its turn has prompted a debate on the legitimacy in general of international financial institutions. Discussions on the legitimacy of international financial and trade institutions have resulted in a renewed attention to the legitimacy of the origin of these institutions. As will be pointed out, the perceived lack of legitimacy has principally been remedied by attempts either to re-think the distribution of voting powers or to accept some form of public participation in order to ensure a 'popular' acceptance of institutional policies. As far as the latter is concerned, a clear parallel can be drawn with what we mentioned earlier in respect of the legitimacy of the EU, and the attempts there to establish some form of popular legitimacy.

When viewed from the traditional perspective, international financial institutions, like any other international organisation, derive their legitimacy from the powers that have been conferred on them by the member states of that organisation. The source of their powers is thus principally derived from the consent of states.[50] Besides the question of how power is bestowed upon these institutions, enhancing *public participation* in both decision-making and dispute settlement processes is an important part of the debate.[51] To a large extent, public participation is a form of legitimacy of origin, since it aims at ensuring that the 'general public'

[50] However, a specificity of international financial institutions such as the IMF, is that the unequal financial contribution of donor states to the institutions as a whole and to projects in other states has resulted in a departure from the 'traditional' equality in voting rights in favour of a weighted vote. See generally, S. A. Voitovich, *International Economic Organisations in the International Legal Process* (Dordrecht: Martinus Nijhoff Publishers, 1995), p. 78. Although the principle of 'weighted voting' can easily be defended taking into account the financial character of these institutions, this peculiarity has raised the important question of the legitimacy of the organisation, especially when dealing with projects in developing countries which have little or no representation in the institution. See I. Seidl-Hohenveldern, 'International economic law: general course on public international law', (1986–III) 198 *Recueil des cours*, 118. See, for a critique of the 'weighted voting': M. Bedjaoui, *Towards a New International Economic Order* (Paris: UNESCO, 1979), p. 210. The recent exercise at the level of the IMF to review the distribution of voting power is clear evidence of the attempt to enhance and reinforce the legitimacy of origin of the IMF because of the changed factual realities. See generally, J. M Griesgraber, 'Reforms for Major New Roles of the International Monetary Fund – The IMF Post-G-20 Summit', (2009) 15 *Global Governance*, 180. See also A. Buira, 'The Bretton Woods Institutions: Governance without Legitimacy?', in A. Buira, *The Bretton Woods Institutions: Governance without Legitimacy* (London: Anthem Press, 2005), pp. 7–43 and D. P. Rapkin and J. R. Strand, 'Reforming the IMF's Weighted Voting System', (2006) 29(3) *The World Economy* 305–24.

[51] See N. Matz, 'Financial Institutions between Effectiveness and Legitimacy – A Legal Analysis of the World Bank, Global Environment Facility and Prototype Carbon Fund', (2005) 5 *Int'l Envtl. Agreements*, 271–2.

supports the exercise of power. Individuals are often seen as the final recipients of the adopted rules and regulations, and are thus given a sense of ownership in the process.[52] This form of legitimacy of origin thus *complements* rather that *replaces* the consent of states as the original legitimacy of international institutions. An example of this development at the level of the World Bank is the establishment of the World Bank Inspection Panel. The Inspection Panel can receive requests for inspection from any party which is a community of persons 'such as an organisation, association, society or other grouping of individuals', which needs to show that their 'rights or interests have been or are likely to be directly affected by an action or omission of the Bank'.[53] Although the Inspection Panel will review whether the Bank is complying with its own policies and procedures – essentially a question of *legitimacy of exercise* – the reason behind the establishment of the panel is to increase public participation of non-state actors in the activities carried out by the World Bank, and thus to add legitimacy of origin to it.[54]

A similar development has taken place at the WTO, albeit at a different level.[55] In fact, the 'legitimacy gap' at the WTO has been the result of two different discourses. On the one hand, representatives from developing member states have had the impression of being excluded from mainly informal decision-making processes. On the other, representatives of 'civil society' criticise the organisation for its lack of consideration of non-state and non-corporate interests in decision-making and dispute settlement procedures, thus lacking a genuine legitimacy of origin.[56] The first issue essentially relates to a critique of the legitimacy in the functioning of the organisation and thus to the *legitimacy of exercise* of the organisation, while the latter fundamentally concerns

---

[52] Bodansky, *The Legitimacy of International Governance*, p. 617. See also, generally, L. Boisson de Chazournes, 'Changing Roles of International Organisations: Global Administrative Law and the Interplay of Legitimacies', (2009) 6 *Int'l Org. L. Rev.* 655.

[53] International Bank for Reconstruction and Development, 'The World Bank Inspection Panel', Resolution No. IBRD 93–10, para. 12.

[54] See L. Boisson de Chazournes, 'Compliance with Operational Standards: The Contribution of the World Bank Inspection Panel', in G. Afredsson and R. Ring (eds.), *The World Bank Inspection Panel* (The Hague: Kluwer Law International, 2001), pp. 67–85.

[55] See on the impact of globalisation on the sovereignty of states, in relation to the WTO, G. Wang, 'The Impact of Globalization on State Sovereignty', (2004) 3 *Chinese Journal of International Law*, 473–83.

[56] M. Krajewski, 'Democratic Legitimacy and Constitutional Perspectives of WTO Law', (2001) 35 *Journal of World Trade*, 167 and D. C. Esty, 'Non-Governmental Organisations at the World Trade Organisation: Cooperation, Competition, or Exclusion', (1998) 1 *J. Int'l Econ. L.*, 131.

the need to broaden the *legitimacy of origin* of the WTO. The legitimacy problem of the WTO is thus essentially linked to the difficult societal acceptance of the institution and its policies, despite the indisputable existence of a legitimacy of origin because of the consent of member states expressed through their signature and ratification of the WTO Constitution. However, since international economic law is traditionally open only to states, only state – and perhaps, indirectly, corporate – interests are represented at the WTO level, thus effectively disregarding broader 'public' or 'transnational interests', including human rights issues and environmental policies. However, trade disputes increasingly involve other policy areas such as human rights issues and environmental policies.[57] Since the WTO is ill-equipped to take into consideration such non-state concerns, because of its traditional interstate character, it has habitually been regarded as closed, lacking both transparency and legitimacy.[58] Here again, one can clearly see that institutional legitimacy is closely interconnected with the impact of international organisations on individuals directly or through policy decisions taken at the level of the organisation.

The legitimacy gap at the WTO has resulted in many scholarly discussions and proposals to enhance and restore its legitimacy.[59] Proposals include, *inter alia*, an increased role for national parliaments, and even the establishment of a WTO Parliamentary Assembly.[60] However, these suggestions, although theoretically sound, do not seem to be realistically practicable in the short term. A more realistic suggestion is to rely on increased public participation and in general enhancing transparency of the WTO.[61] Public participation, using the representative function of non-governmental organisations (NGOs), at various stages in the WTO system, has been suggested in legal literature. NGO participation as *amici curiae* in dispute settlement procedures,[62] but also,

---

[57] J. L. Dunoff, 'Institutional Misfits: The GATT, the ICJ and Trade-Environment Disputes', (1994) 15 *Mich. J. Int'l L.*, 1043.

[58] Esty, 'Non-Governmental Organisations', 123. See for a discussion, S. Cho, 'A Quest for WTO's Legitimacy', (2005) 4 *World Trade Review*, 391–9.

[59] See on the different forms of 'remedies' to legitimacy problems in international institutions, Boisson de Chazournes, Changing Roles, p. 655 and Krajewski, 'International Organisations', paras. 13 *et seq.*

[60] Krajewski, 'Democratic Legitimacy', 183.

[61] See S. Charnovitz, 'Transparency and Participation in the World Trade Organisation', (2003–4) 56 *Rutgers L. Rev.*, 927.

[62] See more generally on NGO participation in international dispute settlement, Eric De Brabandere, 'Pragmatism in International Law: Non-State Actor Participation in

for example, participation through consultation at the decision-making level and access to documents, has been suggested and also partly implemented.[63] In the same line, the 'Sutherland Report', a high-level panel report on the future of the WTO issued at the tenth anniversary of the organisation, indirectly tackled the legitimacy problem of the WTO. Without explicitly mentioning the 'legitimacy' of the WTO, the report contains a Chapter V entitled 'Transparency and Dialogue with Civil Society', aimed at remedying and countering the often alleged lack of legitimacy and transparency of the institution.[64] However, NGO and civil society participation cannot solve every legitimacy problem, and, as already noted, is insufficient in replacing the legitimacy of origin conferred on the organisation through state consent. For example, it has often been pointed out that such participation does not necessarily enhance 'democratic legitimacy', since NGOs *of themselves* are non-democratic, in the sense that they are generally not elected, nor accountable to their members or the general public.[65] These procedures do, however, show the tendency to ensure that international decision-making is generally 'supported' by the people subject to such decisions.

IV.   The legitimacy of international organisations and state sovereignty

As long as institutional legitimacy is seen as essentially derived from the consent of states, through the signature and ratification of the constitutional treaty of the organisation, the existence and functioning of

International Dispute Settlement', in Jean d'Aspremont (ed.), *Participants in the International Legal System: Theoretical Perspectives* (Routledge: London 2011), p. 342.

[63] See for an overview of NGO involvement in the WTO, P Van den Bossche, 'NGO Involvement in the WTO: A Comparative Perspective', (2008) 11 *Journal of International Economic Law*, 717; Y. Bonzon, 'Institutionalizing Public Participation in WTO Decision Making: Some Conceptual Hurdles and Avenues', (2008) 11 *Journal of International Economic Law*, 751–77; F. Loy, 'Public Participation in the World Trade Organisation', in G. P. Sampson (ed.), *The Role of the WTO in Global Governance* (Tokyo: United Nations University Press, 2001).

[64] Report by the Consultative Board to the Director-General Supachai Panitchapkdi, 'The Future of the WTO: Addressing Institutional Challenges in the New Millennium', (2004), para. 261, www.wto.org/english/thewto_e/10anniv_e/future_wto_e.htm (last accessed 7 April 2010). See also Cho, 'A Quest for WTO's Legitimacy', 391–9.

[65] See generally, K. Anderson, 'What NGO Accountability Means – and Does Not Mean', *American Journal of International Law*, 103 (2009), 170–8. See on the legitimacy of NGOs as participants in international investment arbitration, C. H. Brower II, 'Structure, Legitimacy, and NAFTA's Investment Chapter', (2003) 36 *Vanderbilt Journal of Transnational Law*, 73.

international organisations is far from constituting a threat to state sovereignty, even in cases of strongly integrated regional international organisation. As noted earlier, the reliance on states strengthens the central position that states take in the creation, but also in the functioning of the organisation. It has therefore been argued that international organisations, besides 'limiting' sovereignty, can also enhance state sovereignty.[66]

However, in view of the developments described in the previous section, one can easily detect a trend which tends to remove the legitimacy of the existence of the international organisation, and the exercise of the assigned functions by that organisation, from the sole prerogative of states. To the extent that international organisations tend to derive their legitimacy – at least partially – directly from the population, the state seems to become less relevant. The question remains, however, whether this phenomenon implies either a threat to the sovereignty of states, or an evaporation of the central role of states in international law and international relations.

It should first be remembered that here we are witnessing an evolution in the legitimacy of international organisations, which by definition implies that the impact of that evolution on the current conception of state sovereignty in the international legal system is difficult to assess at this stage. On the other hand, one clearly sees that in those cases where the evolution towards a legitimacy resting on the consent or 'approval' of the population, either in granting powers to the organisation or in checking the exercise by that organisation of its powers, the central role of the state is indeed 'weaker'. Moreover it is important to point out that questions such as the impact of regionalism and supranationalism on the concept and content of state sovereignty cannot be answered by reference to absolute standards. Every organisation discussed earlier responds to its own dynamics and it is by no means possible to draw from the evolution described above unconditional conclusions which are applicable generally to all international organisations.

It is clear that from a traditional perspective, the usual means to assess the legitimacy of international organisations, i.e. the legitimacy of origin derived from state consent and the legitimacy of exercise, are still very much linked to the state and the exercise of sovereign powers. Moreover,

---

[66] Michael R. Lucas, 'Nationalism, Sovereignty, and Supranational Organisations', Institute for Peace Research and Security Policy (IFSH), IFSH Hamburger Beiträge 114, p. 9.

if one views states as representatives of their population, this implies that decision-making at the international level indirectly rests on the consent of the population as well. The tendency to rely more on a form of legitimacy which depends on the consent or indirect approval of the population, however, clearly shows that in certain institutions, the consent of states as the primary legitimating factor is being complemented by the consent and/or control by the population directly affected by measures taken by that organisation. To that extent, it is clear that the state, although in a limited way, is losing part of its exclusive control over the legitimacy process. However, again, such an evolution is not as dramatic as it might seem on first sight. Practice – and the cases discussed above – show that states remain the primary actors in the functioning of the institution. Moreover, it should be highlighted that in many international organisations, states still retain many sovereign prerogatives in relation to the area for which the organisation has been granted certain competences. In the case of the EU, for example, despite the mentioned tendency to rely on the consent of the population for the exercise of competences by EU institutions, states retain a large number of competences on the one hand, and on the other, several aspects of the functioning of the EU still bear many 'traditional' intergovernmental characteristics.[67]

V. Concluding remarks

This chapter has contended that although it has become common to argue that through the creation of regional and supranational organisations aimed at integration rather than cooperation the concept and content of State sovereignty is weakening, this claim is largely overstated. It argued that instead of viewing regionalism and supranationalism as *ipso facto* implying a threat to state sovereignty, the form of legitimacy used to assess the international organisation is a more efficient determinant for the organisation's relation with the sovereignty of states.

The transmission of competences by a state to another entity is essentially a form of exercise of the rights of a sovereign state, and thus not a transfer or restraint of sovereignty. Moreover, the alleged threat that supranationalism poses to the current conception of state sovereignty is confined to those forms of supranationalism which include the

---

[67] See for a discussion, Dora Kostakopoulou, 'Floating Sovereignty: A Pathology or a Necessary Means of State Evolution', (2002) 22 *Oxford Journal of Legal Studies*, 135–56.

takeover of certain functions traditionally exercised by states. The creation of international organisations at the regional or supranational level is not necessarily threatening to the current conception of statehood. The type of legitimacy used to assess the authority of international organisations determines assessment of the alleged weakening of state sovereignty.

As long as international organisations are viewed as deriving their legitimacy from the powers that have been conferred to them by the member states of that organisation, and the exercise there of in conformity with these powers, this reinforces rather than weakens the position of states. However, if one takes into account the recent inclination of certain international organisations to establish a form of legitimacy through several forms of direct or popular legitimacy, supranationalism can amount to a theoretical weakening of the current conception of state sovereignty. In the view of the developments described, one can easily see a trend which tends to remove the legitimacy of the existence of the international organisation, and the exercise of the assigned functions by that organisation, from the sole prerogative of states.

However, I have questioned whether this phenomenon implies either a threat to the sovereignty of states, or a weakening of the central role of states in international law and international relations. The tendency to rely more on a form of legitimacy which depends on the consent of the population clearly shows that in certain institutions, the consent of states as the primary legitimating factor is being complemented by the consent and/or control by the population directly affected by measures taken by that organisation. To that extent, it is clear that the state, although in a limited way, is losing part of its exclusive control over the legitimacy process. Such an evolution is not as dramatic as it might seem on first sight, especially considering that states not only remain the primary actors in the creation and functioning of international organisations, but also in ensuring the legitimacy of the organisation. The legitimacy of international organisations resting on the direct consent or approval of the population is still in its infancy, and it is doubtful whether this form of legitimacy will ever be able fully to replace state-centred legitimacy.

Democracy out of instrumental reason? Global institutions and the promotion of liberal governance

CHARLOTTE STEINORTH

I. Introduction

The recent wave of popular uprisings in the Middle East suggests that the value of democracy has universal appeal across cultures and religions. These events once again raise the question whether the international community should support internal democracy, and if so, in what manner it should do so. For its part, international law had historically little interest in domestic politics and took an agnostic attitude towards the political organization of power within states. Only in the 1990s did the political form of government become an issue of concern to international legal scholarship.[1] In the wake of third wave democratization,[2] the thesis of an emerging democratic entitlement argued for international law's embrace of multi-party democracy, elevating a Western ideal to a global legal standard. For a number of commentators, the altered geopolitical context of the post-Cold War, characterized by an 'almost-complete triumph of the democratic notions of Hume, Locke, Jefferson

---

[1] See G. H. Fox and B. R. Roth 'Introduction: The Spread of Liberal Democracy and its Implications for International Law' in G. H. Fox and B. R. Roth (eds.), *Democratic Governance and International Law* (Cambridge University Press, 2000), pp. 1–22; and other contributions in the volume.

[2] Describing the spread of modern democracy, Samuel P. Huntington distinguished between three waves of democratization. The first had its root in the American and French revolutions of the late eighteenth century; the second followed allied occupation after World War II; the third wave began with the overthrow of dictatorships in Southern Europe, then spread to Latin America and parts of Asia, before reaching the Soviet Union and the Baltic Republics. See S. P. Huntington, *The Third Wave: Democratization in the Late Twentieth Century* (University of Oklahoma Press, 1991).

and Madison'[3] in many parts of the world, raised the prospects for the crystallization of liberal democracy into a global norm.

The ensuing years, however, demonstrated that the end of the Cold War had not led to the anticipated 'political unification of the world'.[4] Although the number of formal democracies had increased considerably by the end of the twentieth century, the rise of powerful non-democratic states precluded the emergence of a unipolar world order based on one political system adopted by all states. Democracy, though often invoked in international fora, never attained a determinate content in international law. Rather than viewing democracy as a legal requirement, states preferred to invoke it as a political ideal with vague contours. No global consensus that ascribes to one form of domestic order exclusive legal legitimacy has emerged within the international community to date.

Yet, in spite of this lack of agreement, international institutions have increasingly engaged in the replication of the liberal model of the state. Moral, security and economic concerns have placed increased focus on domestic governance, widening the remit of outside intervention. Within the context of state-building operations and good governance programmes, global actors have shaped the form of domestic institutions to an unprecedented level. Acting on the assumption that liberal governance is instrumental for the achievement of sustainable peace and development, international organizations have come to view this particular form of political organization within a state as the basic governance template for strife-ridden under-developed countries.

The chapter aims to highlight this institutional practice which has promoted liberal governance in an instrumental manner and to reflect on its consequences for international law. To better appreciate the nature of this practice, section II reviews the lack of post-Cold War consensus within the international community on any one form of domestic order. Despite the high expectations for a liberal democratic world order following the end of the Cold War, discussions on democracy within international fora have pointed to the lack of a global consensus on democratic government as a legal requirement for all states. Against this background, section III describes the replication of liberal institutions at the domestic level within the context of post-conflict peace-building operations and

---

[3] T. M. Franck, 'The Emerging Right to Democratic Governance' (1992) 86 *American Journal of International Law*, 49.

[4] C. Mouffe 'Democracy in a Multipolar World', (2009) 37 *Millenium: Journal of International Studies*, 553.

development assistance. The chapter focuses on the contribution of the United Nations (UN) and the World Bank. Both organizations are global actors that are not mandated by their constitutive agreement to promote a particular political system within states. Notwithstanding their global character, both actors have taken on a leading role in the promotion of democracy and good governance. In doing so, they have adopted an instrumental approach given the perceived factual benefits that liberal democracy has for the achievement of peace and development. The chapter concludes by providing an assessment of the consequences of this development on international law. It will be argued that current practices constitute a profound challenge to international law's traditional principle of regime neutrality and its underlying conception of a pluralistic world order.

II.   The lack of post-Cold War consensus on one form of domestic order

Prior to the end of the Cold War, the form of a state's government did not receive much attention in international law. Although the right to free elections had been part of the international bill of human rights that developed in the UN era,[5] Cold War tensions precluded any substantive engagement with the scope of this right – let alone its implications for the form of government a state had to choose. With the exception of the condemnation of the system of apartheid,[6] the form of domestic political organization within states was generally regarded as a matter beyond the reach of international law.[7]

The end of the bipolar political order in 1989, however, seemed to afford an opportunity to radically break with international law's regime

---

[5] Art. 21 Universal Declaration of Human Rights, UNGA Res. 217 A (III) (10 December 1948) GAOR 3rd Session Part I Resolutions 71; Art. 25 International Covenant on Civil and Political Rights (adopted 19 December 1966, entered into force 23 March 1976) 999 UNTS 171.

[6] See, e.g., UNGA Res. 1761 (XVII) (6 November 1962) and A/RES/36/162 (16 December 1981).

[7] In this sense, see ICJ judgment, *Military and Paramilitary Activities in and Against Nicaragua (Nicaragua v. United States of America)* ICJ Rep. 1986, 14. As late as 1986, the World Court declined to find Nicaragua internationally accountable in the conduct of elections. Commenting on the Court's attitude, James Crawford observed that '[t]he holding of free elections was treated still as essentially a matter of "domestic policy"'. See J. Crawford, 'Democracy and the body of international law' in Fox and Roth (eds.), *Democratic Governance and International Law*, p. 100.

neutrality. In the 1990s a number of international legal scholars argued
for the emergence of a democratic norm in international law. What
became known as the democratic entitlement school was a group of
scholars who claimed that the trend towards democratization in international relations had altered international law. In his influential article,
'The Emerging Right to Democratic Governance', Thomas M. Franck
argued that liberal democracy was on the way to becoming a global
entitlement which required 'democracy to validate governance'.[8] He
predicted the emergence of a new world in which 'citizens of each State
[would] look to international law and organization to guarantee them
fair access to political power and participation in societal decisions'.[9]
Proponents of the democratic entitlement asserted that the political
participatory norms enshrined in international human rights instruments in the post-Cold War era had finally achieved a 'determinate
content grounded in liberal-democratic institutional practices'.[10] Since
the right to political participation pertains to the 'fundamental question
of who holds sovereign authority within a State', it impacts on the
freedom of states to choose a political system. The question of regime
legitimacy would thus be conditioned upon the 'fulfilment of liberal-
democratic participatory standards', making the traditional understanding of state sovereignty 'outmoded'.[11]

These propositions appeared to be largely informed by the commentators' empirical observations about the increasing acceptance of liberal
democracy beyond the confines of Western states. In Franck's account,
the formation of the democratic entitlement in international law 'is due
in part to the very recent political reality of a burgeoning pro-democracy
movement within States that constitutes the world community'. As a
consequence of the continuing spread of democracy movements he
viewed the 'entitlement now aborning' as 'widely enough understood
to be almost universally celebrated'.[12] Similarly, Cerna asserted that
'Western ideas have gained the legitimacy and currency of universal
values'.[13] She characterized 'the right to live under a democratic form
of government' as having achieved 'universal recognition', pointing to

[8] Franck, 'The Emerging Right to Democratic Governance', 47.   [9] Ibid. at 50.
[10] As formulated by Fox and Roth (eds.), 'Introduction', p. 11.
[11] G. H. Fox 'The Right to Political Participation in International Law', (1992) 17 *Yale
Journal of International Law*, 592, 595.
[12] Franck, 'The Emerging Right to Democratic Governance', 90.
[13] C. Cerna, 'Universal Democracy: An International Legal Right or the Pipe Dream of the
West?', (1995) 27 *New York University Journal of International Law and Politics*, 290.

the proliferation of regional instruments and mechanisms in support of democracy.[14]

Yet, arguments in favour of the democratic norm thesis seemed not only driven by the continuing expansion of liberal democracy.[15] Rather than merely describing a legal development occurring, most commentators also took the view that international law *should* embrace democracy. For some, international law's perceived turn to democracy followed a long overdue moral imperative. Not only was international law's regime blindness an 'anachronism' – it was also morally indefensible. While Tesón expressed sympathy for the reluctance of international lawyers to 'forsake the statist assumptions of classical international legal discourse', he saw the time ripe for a re-conceptualization of that discourse as 'a more liberal world needs a more liberal theory of international law'.[16] According to his 'Kantian' theory of international law, it was only through a society of liberal democratic states that a just international order could be achieved. That order also brought the promise of peace among nations, as democratic governments that were accountable to their peoples were less likely to engage in war than autocratic ones whose contempt for human rights at home made an aggressive foreign policy more likely.

In addition to the furtherance of human rights, justice and peace, the democratic entitlement was also seen to promote greater prosperity, 'open[ing] the stagnant political economies of states to economic, social and cultural, as well as political development'.[17] Finally, the democratic norm thesis also appealed to international lawyers for structural reasons, promising to remedy the legitimacy-deficit of international decision-making.[18] As Eric Stein observed, 'a tension prevails between the currently expanding acceptance of the idea of democracy and the growth of diverse international organizations and regimes'.[19] The prospect for a norm requiring democratic governance at the domestic level provided at least a fig leaf of popular legitimation.

---

[14] Ibid. 291.

[15] For a critical account of the underlying assumption of the democratic entitlement thesis, see S. Marks, *The Riddle of All Constitutions: International Law, Democracy and the Critique of Ideology* (Oxford University Press, 2000).

[16] F. R. Tesón, *A Philosophy of International Law* (Boulder, CO: Westview Press, 1998), p. 1.

[17] Franck, 'The Emerging Right to Democratic Governance', 90.

[18] See contributions in R. Wofrum and V. Röben (eds.), *Legitimacy in International Law* (Heidelberg, Berlin: Springer, 2008).

[19] E. Stein, 'International Integration and Democracy: No Love at First Sight', (2001) 95 *American Journal of International Law*, 489.

The post-Cold War expectations concerning democracy's normative value in international law can be rather sharply contrasted with the continuing diversity of views on democracy expressed by states. Although the number of (formal) democracies within the UN did increase following third-wave democratization, the world organization continued to include ideologically diverse states. In contrast to regional organizations in Europe,[20] the Americas[21] and Africa,[22] which had all expressed a commitment to democracy as a legal standard after the end of the Cold War, no comparable development had taken place within the United Nations. Given the substantial number of states which remained non-democratic at the end of the twentieth century,[23] it may not be surprising that a cross-cultural consensus on liberal democracy as a legal requirement for all states was never articulated within UN bodies – even though resolutions and declarations invoking democracy proliferated with the end of the bipolar order.

Since the end of the 1980s the General Assembly has adopted a series of resolutions on the principle of genuine periodic elections. While the first of these resolutions, entitled 'Enhancing the effectiveness of the principle of periodic elections', attempted to define democratic processes, specifying the need for an electoral process which 'accommodates distinct alternatives',[24] subsequent resolutions adopted under the same

[20] The Council of Europe, the first regional organization which was founded in Europe after World War II, envisioned the construction of a new Europe founded on the principle of democracy; see Statute of the Council of Europe (signed 5 May 1949, entered into force 3 August 1949) CETS No 1. The EU, although initially focused on integration through economic cooperation, also developed into a value community, making democracy a condition of ongoing membership in Art. 7 TEU. Europe's most inclusive organization, the Organization for Security and Co-operation in Europe, has similarly made democracy the only system acceptable within it; see, e.g., Charter of Paris for a New Europe (done and entered into force 21 November 1990) (1991) 30 ILM 190.

[21] While the 1948 Charter of the Organization of American States (entered into force 13 December 1951, 119 UNTS 3) made reference to the principle of 'representative democracy', it was only in the post-Cold War era that democracy effectively became a regional standard of governance. See, e.g., OAS Resolution 1080 'Representative Democracy', adopted 5 June 1991, OEA Ser. P, AG/RES.1080; Protocol of Washington, adopted 14 December 1992, OEA/Ser. A/2 Add. 3; Inter-American Democratic Charter, adopted 11 September 2001, www.oas.org.

[22] In contrast to the Organization of African Unity, the African Union commits its members to promote and defend democracy. See Art. 3(g) and Art. 30 Constitutive Act of the African Union (done 11 July 2000, entered into force 26 May 2001) 2158 UNTS 3.

[23] According to the 1999 survey of Freedom House, over one-third of all states could not be classified as democracies. See www.freedomhouse.org.

[24] A/RES/43/157 (18 December 1988).

title could not sustain this commitment to multi-party pluralism and used more evasive language.[25] This series of resolutions was, moreover, accompanied by counter-resolutions, entitled 'Respect for the principle of national sovereignty and non-interference in the internal affairs of states in electoral processes'.[26] A frequent inclusion in both types of resolutions was the statement that there was 'no single political or electoral method that is suited to all nations and their people'. Rather than affirming a legal requirement for all states to hold multi-party elections, these resolutions expressed a more ambiguous attitude towards democratic standards of governance.[27]

Discussions on democracy within the now defunct Human Rights Commission did not fare much better in establishing the parameters of democracy's legal content. The debate within the Commission concerning the Resolution 'Promotion of the Right to Democracy 1999/57' is particularly illustrative of the misgivings many states had in defining democracy as a right. The Representative of the United States, the main sponsor of the resolution, had noted at the outset that 'it was time that all members of the Commission supported the notion that the right to democratic governance was not just a privilege...but a fundamental human right'.[28] Yet, it was precisely the legal characterization of democracy as 'right' that caused most controversy within the Commission. India's representative stated that his delegation would have preferred omitting any reference to the concept of a right, as the proposed title 'raised questions and legal issues that found little support in international human rights instruments'. Pakistan's delegate also voiced doubts about the title of the resolution, expressing hope that it 'was used in a political and ethical sense rather than in a legal one'. Similarly, the Russian Federation, though supportive of the 'ideas contained in the resolution', argued that 'the concept [of a right to democracy] required further discussion by experts in intergovernmental forums'. Cuba considered the resolution 'a dangerous precedent', proposed that the title be changed to 'Promotion of Democracy', and asked that a separate vote

---

[25] E.g., A/RES/44/146 (15 December 1989); A/RES/45/150 (18 December 1990; A /RES/46/137 (17 December 1991).

[26] E.g., A/RES/44/147 (15 December 1989); A/RES/58/189 (22 March 2004).

[27] In this sense, see observation by S. Laghmani, 'Vers une légitimité démocratique?' in R. Ben Achour and S. Laghmani (eds.), *Les nouveaux aspects du droit international* (Paris: Pedone, 1994), p. 273.

[28] E/CN.4/1999/SR.57.

should be taken. While the Cuban proposal was narrowly defeated,[29] the vote and the preceding discussion demonstrate the lack of agreement among states on a legal requirement of democratic governance.

The above cited resolutions provide an indication that neither the content of democratic processes nor their legal status has been clearly defined by states. Rather than pointing to a common conviction regarding liberal democracy's normative value, these resolutions demonstrate the lack of agreement on a general norm requiring states to have a democratically legitimated government. What has changed, however, is the fact that 'the language of democracy is now widely accepted by international institutions'.[30] Hence, states did not shy away from expressing their commitment in the 2000 Millennium Declaration to 'promote democracy'.[31] In the 2005 World Summit Outcome Document, UN member states even went so far as to describe democracy as a 'universal value', but reiterated at the same time that 'there is no single model of democracy' and the 'necessity of due respect for sovereignty and the right of self-determination'.[32] While statements on democracy have thus become more frequent within the international community, they 'lack clear indications of whether the statements are *lex lata, de lege ferenda* or mere political aspirations'.[33]

III.   The replication of the liberal model of the State by global institutions

Despite this lack of consensus on one form of domestic organization as a normative requirement, since the end of the Cold War global actors have become engaged in the promotion of liberal institutions at the domestic level. Within the framework of post-conflict peace operations and good governance programmes, the UN Security Council and the World Bank have come to support one substantive model of societal organization.

---

[29] Twelve Members voted in favour of the Cuban amendment (Bhutan, Chile, Congo, Cuba, India, Indonesia, Madagascar, Mexico, Pakistan, Russian Federation, Sudan), while 28 states rejected it and 13 abstained. The resolution was finally adopted by 51 votes to none, with two abstentions.

[30] B. Bowden and H. Charlesworth, 'Defining Democracy in International Institutions' in B. Bowden, H. Charlesworth and J. Farrall (eds.), *The Role of International Law in Rebuilding Societies after Conflict* (Cambridge University Press, 2008), p. 100.

[31] A/RES/55/2 (8 September 2000).   [32] A/RES/60/1 (16 September 2005).

[33] G. H. Fox, 'Democracy, Right to International Protection' in R. Wolfrum (ed.), *Max Planck Encyclopedia of Public International Law* (Oxford University Press, 2012).

Both actors have justified the shaping of domestic governance by adopting an instrumental logic.

1. The UN Security Council, state-building and the creation of democratic institutions

The UN has not traditionally been an agent for democratization. Since its inception, the organization has comprised states with diverse political regimes – from dictatorships to liberal democracies. Although it had been debated at the San Francisco conference whether membership should be restricted to states that are democratically constituted, the principle of universality prevailed in the end.[34] The UN Charter espoused in Article 2(1) the principle of sovereign equality, according to which states enjoy the same rights under international law, regardless of their internal political institutions. While the right to political participation, included in the canon of international human rights law that was adopted under the aegis of the United Nations, could have provided a challenge to the non-judgmental attitude of the organization towards political regimes, Cold War tensions precluded any consensus on what kind of political organization they prescribed. Writing in the 1980s, Louis Henkin observed with regard to the Universal Declaration of Human Rights that in so far as it expressed a commitment to democracy, it was 'consistent with different brands of democracy'.[35]

Only in the aftermath of third-wave democratization did democracy become an issue on the agenda of the UN. Support for democratization became an objective of many activities carried out by the Organization. In 1989 Nicaragua requested the UN to observe its national elections – which marked a new phase of electoral assistance following the period of decolonization. Since the beginning of the 1990s, more than 100 independent countries have received various forms of UN assistance for the holding of multi-party elections.[36] Democratic processes have been

---

[34] See R. B. Russel and J. E. Muther, *A History of the United Nations Charter* (Washington DC: Brookings Institution, 1958). See also, G. Simpson, *Great Powers and Outlaw States* (Cambridge University Press, 2004), p. 263.

[35] L. Henkin, 'Introduction' in L. Henkin (ed.), *The International Bill of Rights* (New York: Columbia University Press, 1981), p. 28. Similarly, Karl Josef Partsch remarked with regard to the political participation clause of the 1966 International Covenant on Civil and Political Rights, that it 'does not establish clear standards for democratic and representative government'. K. J. Partsch, 'Freedom of Conscience and Expression and Political Freedoms', in ibid. at p. 238.

[36] www.un.org/wcm/content/site/undpa/main/issues/elections.

further promoted through the UN Development Programme, which directs a significant portion of its funding to activities which aim to consolidate and deepen democratic practices.[37] In addition, in 2005 the UN established the Democracy Fund, which supports democratization efforts through project funding that strengthens civil society, promotes human rights, and encourages inclusive democratic processes.[38]

This move by the world organization to promote democratic processes within member states coincided with a more general preoccupation within the international community concerning the quality of domestic governance. Since the 1990s, the UN has increasingly become involved in matters that were formerly considered to be purely internal ones.[39] The Security Council demonstrated a greater willingness to use its Chapter VII powers, characterizing internal matters as a threat to peace and security.[40] It made use of its enforcement powers under Chapter VII not only to secure humanitarian relief and protect civilians, but also to restore democratic rule following military coups.[41] From a moral or humanitarian perspective, the scope of domestic jurisdiction has come under attack from a heightened concern among member states for human rights abuses committed by governments against their own people. This development has found expression in the doctrines of humanitarian intervention and the responsibility to protect.[42] In addition, security concerns militated in favour of regulating domestic

---

[37] See contribution by UNDP administrator M. M. Brown, 'Democratic Governance: Toward a Framework for Sustainable Peace', (2003) 9 *Global Governance*, 141–6. See also, analysis of UNDP's work in promoting democracy, in S. Marks, 'What has Become of the Emerging Right to Democratic Governance?', (2011) 22 *European Journal of International Law*, 515–17.

[38] www.un.org/democracyfund.

[39] In this sense, see Grewe's comment that 'developments seem to indicate that the traditional loophole of the Charter's domestic jurisdiction clause (Art. 2(7)) might narrow to a needle's eye'. W. Grewe, 'History' in B. Simma (ed.), *The Charter of the United Nations: A Commentary* (Munich: Beck, 1995), p. 21.

[40] As evidenced by the statement of the President of the Security Council at the conclusion of the 3046th meeting held at the level of Heads of State and Government on 31 January 1992 in connection with the item entitled 'The responsibility of the Security Council in the maintenance of international peace and security' (S/23500).

[41] E.g., S/RES/794 (3 December 1992) concerning the establishment of 'a secure environment for humanitarian relief operations' in Somalia; S/RES/929 (22 June 1994) authorizing the use of force to protect civilians in Rwanda; S/RES/940 (31 July 1994) authorizing the formation of a multinational force to 'facilitate the departure from Haiti of the military leadership'; S/RES/1132 (8 October 1997) imposing a mandatory arms embargo against Sierra Leone's military junta.

[42] A/RES/63/308 (7 October 2009).

governance structures, as so-called 'failed states' were perceived as breeding grounds for violence, extremism and terrorism. In the words of Orford, '[t]he collective security system...has come to represent a means for the liberal alliance of democratic states to bring human rights, democracy, and humanitarian principles to those in undemocratic or failed states'.[43]

In the field of peacekeeping the Security Council since the 1990s has authorized complex missions that not only include the classical tasks of monitoring ceasefires, creating buffer zones and rebuilding a war-torn country's infrastructure, but also aimed at building democratic institutions. An early example of a 'multidimensional' mandate was that of the ONUMOZ mission in Mozambique, established under SC Resolution 797 (1992), which combined political, military and humanitarian elements. In accordance with the General Peace Agreement signed by the President of the Republic of Mozambique and the President of the Resistência Nacional Moçambicana (RENAMO), the UN mission was to verify the ceasefire, to monitor the disbanding of irregular armed groups and the collection of weapons, to provide security for UN activities, to monitor humanitarian assistance operations, and to assist with the organization and holding of elections. In Resolution 957 (1994), the Security Council gave particular weight to the political aspect of the mission. Welcoming the October 1994 elections held in Mozambique, the Council called upon 'all Mozambican parties to complete the process of national reconciliation based...on a system of multi-party democracy and the observance of democratic principles which will ensure lasting peace and political stability'.[44]

In subsequent UN practice, the establishment of democratic institutions through the holding of multi-party elections has remained an essential aspect of peacekeeping. As conceptualized by the 'Capstone Doctrine', rule of law activities (reform of military, armed forces and judiciary), the promotion of human rights, the strengthening of state institutions and the provision of electoral assistance, constitute key elements of complex missions.[45] In this 2008 Capstone document, which sets out the guiding principles and core objectives of contemporary peacekeeping operations, the successful holding of elections is

---

[43] A. Orford, 'Locating the International: Military and Monetary Interventions after the Cold War', (1997) 38 *Harvard International Law Journal*, 443.

[44] S/RES/957 (15 November 1994), para. 3.

[45] United Nations Peacekeeping Operations, *Principles and Guidelines* (Capstone, 2008).

assigned a two-fold function: it is viewed as an integral part of UN post-conflict operations and serves as an indicator for the success of a mission, often providing the exit strategy and end point of a mission.

The involvement of the UN in building democratic regimes has been even more extensive in the case of international territorial administration.[46] In the face of severe internal crises, the Security Council in some instances has authorized missions temporarily to administer a territory in place of the national government. The mandates of such missions have consistently aimed at the creation of democratic institutions viewed as a precondition for self-government. Thus SC Resolution 1272 (1999) which established the UNTAET mission in East Timor, emphasized 'the need for UNTAET to consult and cooperate closely with the East Timorese people in order to carry out its mandate effectively with a view to the development of local democratic institutions'.[47] The objective to build democratic institutions has also been formulated as a primary aim of the UNMIK mission in Kosovo. SC Resolution 1244 (1999) characterizes as objectives of the civil presence in Kosovo to establish and oversee 'the development of provisional democratic self-governing institutions to ensure conditions for a peaceful and normal life for all inhabitants of Kosovo'.[48] The aim of ensuring a democratic future for Kosovo has been further reaffirmed in the course of the UNMIK mission by the Security Council's approval for the 'standards before status' policy which made the question of Kosovo's status dependent on the fulfilment of democratic standards of governance.[49]

In comparison to peace-building missions, the UN, when taking the role of interim-administrator, has even greater influence over the shaping of new governance structures, accompanying the constitution-drafting process and the adoption of electoral laws. In doing so, the Organization exercises decisive influence and can promote policy objectives, e.g. the inclusion of women into political processes despite local resistance. As Tansey notes:

> through their extensive authority at the domestic level and their explicit aims to promote democracy, international administrations can ensure

---

[46] O. Tansey, *Regime-Building: Democratization and International Administration* (Oxford University Press, 2009) and J. d'Asprémont, 'Post-Conflict Administrations as Democracy-Building Instruments', (2008) 9 *Chicago Journal of International Law*, 1–16; M. Cogen and E. De Brabandere, 'Democratic Governance and Post Conflict Reconstruction', (2007) *Leiden Journal of International Law*, 669–93.

[47] S/RES/1272 (25 October 1999), para. 8.   [48] S/RES/1244 (10 June 1999), para. 10.

[49] Statement by the President of the Security Council of 12 December 2003 (S/PRST/2003/26).

that some avenues are closed off for those who would seek to undermine democratic development, and thus create opportunities for successful democratization.[50]

While the promotion of democracy has constituted but one aspect of a broad post-conflict agenda of UN peace operations, the creation of democratic institutions has become an indispensable component of such missions, which have all followed a 'democratic reconstruction model'.[51]

2.   The World Bank and the promotion of good governance

In the last few decades, concern for domestic governance has also permeated the World Bank's agenda.[52] The institution's mandate as 'financier of investment for productive purposes in reconstruction or development efforts, and as facilitator of international investment and trade'[53] does not ascribe to the Bank a role in promoting a particular model of domestic politics. In fact, the Articles of Agreement, the Bank's constitutive treaty, specifically provide that 'the Bank and its officers shall not interfere in the political affairs of any member; nor shall they be influenced in their decision by the political character of the member or members concerned. Only economic consideration shall be relevant to their decisions, and these considerations shall be weighed impartially'.[54] During the drafting process, Harry D. White and Lord Keynes, the authors of the provisions, placed strong emphasis on the political and ideological neutrality of the institution which was designed as an organization of universal membership.[55] As explained in a World Bank legal memorandum of 1967, the rationale of the political prohibition was twofold: First, in an organization comprising governments with 'different political characters and aims or interests' it was thought necessary 'to prevent the use of the leverage that would be provided by granting or

---

[50] Tansey, *Regime-Building*, p. 31.
[51] Term ascribed to M. Ottaway in C. T. Call and S. E. Cook, 'On Democratization and Peacebuilding', (2003) 9 *Global Governance*, 233.
[52] The 'World Bank', or 'Bank' for the purposes of this contribution, refers to the International Bank for Reconstruction and Development and the International Development Authority.
[53] I. F. I. Shihata, *The World Bank in a Changing World*, Vol. I (Dordrecht: Martinus Nijhoff, 1992), p. 5.
[54] Art. 4 Section 10, Articles of Agreement.
[55] Ibid. Vol. III at 164–5. For a detailed account of the drafting history of Art. IV Section 10 of the Bank's Articles of Agreement, see S. Killinger, *The World Bank's Non-Political Mandate* (Köln, Berlin, München: Heymanns, 2003), pp. 91–6.

withholding financial assistance. . .for the furtherance of the political aims of any member'. Second, strict political neutrality was regarded as 'essential for the ability of the Bank to raise large amounts of capital from the savings of the investing public'.[56] In light of the prohibition to take political considerations into account, the World Bank has traditionally been concerned with the quality of government only in a narrow sense, relating to issues of economic management.

Coinciding with the end of the Cold War, however, the World Bank has widened its focus on governance. The experience of structural adjustment lending in the 1980s had revealed that economic liberalization without far-reaching institutional reform was insufficient for achieving economic development.[57] In 1989 the Bank published the report, 'Sub-Saharan Africa: from Crisis to Sustainable Growth – A Long-Term Perspective Study', which described a 'crisis of governance' as one of the root causes of the continent's development problems.[58] The report noted that the countries with the best economic performance in Africa had 'effective parliamentary democracies'.[59] To achieve better outcomes, the report called for a 'political renewal' in Africa, comprising the creation of a 'pluralistic institutional structure'.[60] The report marked a shift in World Bank thinking which has since placed increased emphasis on the state as the framework for development.[61]

Defining governance as 'the manner in which power is exercised in the management of a country's economic and social resources for development',[62] the World Bank has paid attention to governance issues in three main areas: (i) legal reform, (ii) public sector management, and (iii) civil society involvement.[63] Legal reform and rule of law programmes are viewed as essential for creating an enabling environment for economic

---

[56] Memorandum transmitted to the UN on 5 May 1976, UN Doc. A/6825 (1976). For the background of events leading to the 1965 memorandum, see V. E. Marmorstein, 'World Bank Power to consider Human Rights Factors in Loan Decision', (1978–9) 13 *Journal of International Law and Economics*, 113–36.

[57] World Bank, *World Bank Development Report 1990*, p. 115.

[58] World Bank, *Sub-Saharan Africa: From Crisis to Sustainable Growth 1989*, p. 60.

[59] Ibid. at p. 61.   [60] Ibid.

[61] On the role of the state in World Bank thinking, see A. Orford and J. Beard, 'Making the State Safe for the Market: The World Bank's World Development Report 1997', (1998) 22 *Melbourne University Law Review*, 195–216. See also, A. Anghie, 'Time Present and Time Past: Globalization, International Financial Institutions, and the World Bank', (1999–2000) *New York University Journal of International Law and Politics*, 257.

[62] World Bank, *Governance and Development*, 1992.

[63] For an analysis of the content of the governance agenda, see Killinger, *The World Bank's Non-Political Mandate*, pp. 121–31 and S. Seppänen, *Good Governance in International*

growth. According to the Bank, only where laws are applied without arbitrary interference and fair processes are established through functioning government and judicial institutions can market-led growth occur.[64] Legal and judicial reform as components of the Bank's governance agenda thus focus mainly on ensuring the predictability of legal frameworks necessary for the protection of property rights and the enforcement of contracts. Good governance, according to the Bank, further requires a civil service that is free from corruption and operates in an accountable and transparent manner.[65] The role of the Bank in improving public sector management has involved reducing public sector personnel, strengthening administrative capacity and bureaucratic procedures and promoting accountability of public funds. In particular, the fight against corruption has become a central theme of World Bank policies. In addition, the Bank's governance agenda seeks the advancement of civil society. Recognizing the link between participation and development, the World Bank has included non-governmental organizations in development projects, aiming to strengthen a public sphere in an effort to develop institutionally plural environments.[66] In its 1999/2000 World Development Report, 'Entering the 21st Century: The Changing Development Landscape', the Bank described 'greater participation in public life' as a 'pre-condition for sustainable development', adding that 'authoritarian regimes. . .except in rare cases have not succeeded in creating efficient, technocratic bureaucracies or in single-mindedly pursuing development'.[67]

While the World Bank's governance agenda has traditionally not included civil and political rights, the notion of 'empowerment', introduced in the World Development Report 2000/2001, 'Attacking Poverty', has widened the conception of governance, characterising the absence of 'voice' and 'participation' as 'key dimensions of poverty'.[68] The Bank's concern for accountability has thus come to include overt

Law (Helsinki: Erik Castrén Institute of International Law and Human Rights, 2003), pp. 86–8.

[64] Shihata expresses this view when stating 'reforms aimed at ensuring the rule of law. . .are of obvious importance in achieving the order essential for economic growth. . .'. Shihata, *The World Bank in a Changing World*, vol. II, p. 58.

[65] For an early articulation of this component of the Bank's governance agenda, see The World Bank, *Development in Practice: Governance* (Washington DC: IBRD, 1994).

[66] World Bank, *The World Bank and Participation*, 1994.

[67] World Bank, *World Development Report 1999/2000*, p. 2.

[68] World Bank, *World Development Report 2000/2001*, p. 112. In this sense, see also contribution by World Bank legal counsel R. Danino, 'The Legal Aspects of the World Bank's Work on Human Rights: Some Preliminary Thoughts' in P. Alston and

political dimensions – as reflected by the 2006 statement by then World
Bank President Wolfowitz – who defined as important components of
good governance 'an independent judiciary, a free press, and a vibrant
civil society' as '[t]hey balance the power of governments, and 'hold
them accountable for delivering better services, creating jobs, and
improving living standards'.[69] The World Development Report 2007,
'Development and the Next Generation', also underlined the value of
political participation, observing that: 'citizen participation is greater in
democracies than in non-democracies, almost by definition, and some
evidence indicates that democracies, on balance, have better development outcomes than authoritarian government.'[70]

Although it would be an overstatement to equate the Bank's governance
approach with a prescription for liberal democracy, the World Bank policy
invariably implies that the liberal democratic state is the gold standard of
societal organization. As William and Young note, the Bank's 'so-called
"technical reforms" are necessarily guided by a prior conception of the
good'.[71] They view the Bank's 'construction of governance' as based 'upon
three levels of transformation: at the institutional level the creation of a
"neutral" State; at the social level the creation of a liberal public sphere of
civil society; and at the personal level the corresponding creation of a liberal
"self" and "modern" patterns of behaviours'.[72]

IV.   The instrumental turn to democracy

Common to both the UN and the World Bank is that their respective
mandates do not embrace the promotion of a particular model of politics
that would give preference to the system of governance of some of their
members to the exclusion of others.[73] Yet, as the preceding sections have

M. Robinson (eds.), *Human Rights and Development: Towards Mutual Reinforcement*
(Oxford University Press, 2005), p. 522.
[69] Address by P. Wolfowitz, 'Good Governance and Development – A Time For Action',
Jakarta, Indonesia (11 April 2006).
[70] World Bank, *World Development Report 2007*, p. 165.
[71] D. Williams and T. Young, 'Governance, The World Bank and Liberal Theory', (1994)
42 *Political Studies*, 94.
[72] Ibid. at 99.
[73] The conditions under which the UN and the World Bank promote a democracy and
good governance agenda are thus entirely different from those under which regional
bodies operate. Whereas regional organizations such as the Organization of American
States, the EU, or the African Union have all embraced democracy as a constitutive
community value in the post-Cold War era, if not before, no comparable agreement has
been reached within the UN. The difference between the regional and the global level is

sketched out, both the UN and the World Bank have become engaged in promoting democracy within the context of post-conflict reconstruction and development assistance. Constrained by their duty of political impartiality, both institutions have justified the shaping of domestic governance – privileging a liberal model of the state – by adopting a functional approach. Achieving sustainable peace and development necessitates, in the view of these organizations, the creation of liberal domestic institutions.

The instrumental justification for the UN's involvement in democracy promotion in the 1990s has been most clearly expressed by UN Secretary-General Boutros Boutros-Ghali in his triple agenda on peace, development and democracy. In the first of the three agendas, Boutros-Ghali noted the global phenomenon of democratization within formerly authoritarian regimes and advocated support for democratic institution-building which was, in his view, conducive to peace within states as well as to peace among states.[74] He further expanded on the link between democracy and peace in his Agenda for Democratization. Regarding peace among states, he noted that 'the accountability and transparency of democratic Government...may help to restrain recourse to military conflict with other States'.[75] With respect to internal peace, the Secretary-General underlined that freely chosen governments are 'more likely to promote and respect the rule of law' and 'cope effectively with social conflict'.[76] In addition to establishing a correlation between peace and democracy, Boutros-Ghali in his Agenda for Development outlined the importance of democratic institutions in achieving development, noting that in 'the absence of democracy...development will remain fragile and be perpetually at risk'.[77] This approach to democracy has been shared by Secretary-General Kofi Annan, who emphasized that 'efforts to promote democracy and good governance are fundamental to the consolidation of peace and development'.[78]

---

also evident if one compares the Agreement establishing the European Bank for Reconstruction and Development, which explicitly expresses in its Preamble a commitment to 'the fundamental principles of multiparty democracy, the rule of law, respect for human rights and market economics' with the World Bank's Articles of Agreement. See I. F. I. Shihata, *The European Bank for Reconstruction and Development: A Comparative Analysis of the Constituent Agreement* (Leiden: Brill, 1991).

[74] Boutros Boutros-Ghali emphasized the 'obvious connection between democratic practices...and the achievement of true peace and security in any new and stable order', A/47/277-S/24111 (17 June 1992), para. 59.

[75] A/51/761 (20 December 1996), para. 18.   [76] Ibid. para. 17.

[77] A/48/935 (6 May 1994), para. 122.   [78] A/52/513 (21 October 1997), para.26.

More than a decade later, Secretary-General Ban Ki-moon, noting the debate surrounding democracy assistance through the UN, issued his 'Guidance Note on Democracy'. In this document, he conceptualized the UN approach to supporting democracy along the same lines as his predecessors, characterizing democracy as an 'instrument' for achieving the main purposes of the organization: peace, respect for human rights and development.[79] '[D]emocracy', the Secertary-General observed, 'is indeed inextricably linked with the three pillars of the United Nations, in that genuinely democratic institutions and practices are essential for fostering long-term security and stability by allowing peaceful political dialogue and contestation. . .'.[80] While the assumption of a positive correlation between democracy and peace, including internal peace, has received much criticism in the political science literature,[81] from both an empirical and a theoretical perspective, suffice it to note that it has provided the legitimation for UN democracy promotion and has formed the rationale for the Security Council's post-conflict agenda.

The promotion of liberal governance for functional purposes is perhaps even more apparent in the World Bank's good governance agenda. In light of the political prohibition contained in its Articles of Agreement, the Bank has consistently linked its concern for governance to economic consequences, making the consideration of political factors dependent on their 'effects on a country's economy or on the feasibility of project implementation of monitoring'.[82] The very appeal of the term 'good governance' for the Bank lies arguably in its technocratic apolitical character.[83] The term does not name what or whose concept of 'good' it purports to promote, but presents 'good' simply as a 'self-evident' qualification of governance. In Bhuta's view, the concept of good governance 'takes institutions that are the *products* of a

---

[79] Guidance Note on Democracy www.un.org/en/globalissues/democracy.

[80] Ibid. Section III 'Guiding Principles for Effective Assistance'. See also, comment by R. Rich in *Journal of Democracy*, 21 (2010), 182.

[81] See, e.g., A. Chua, *World on Fire: How exporting Free Market Democracy breeds Ethnic Hatred and Global Instability* (New York: Doubleday, 2003); R. Paris, 'Peacebuilding and the Limits of Liberal Internationalism', *International Security*, 22 (1997), 54–89; and R. Schweller, 'US Democracy Promotion: Realist Reflections' in M. Cox, G. J. Ikenberry *et al.* (eds.), *American Democracy Promotion: Impulses, Strategies, and Impacts* (Oxford University Press, 2000), pp. 41–62.

[82] M. Cogen, 'Human rights, prohibition of political activities and the lending-policies of World Bank and International Monetary Fund' in S. R. Chowdhury, E. M. G. Denters *et al.* (eds.), *The Right to Development in International Law* (Dordrecht: Martinus Nijhoff, 1992), pp. 379–96.

[83] J. Demmers, A. E. F. Jilberto and B. Hogenboom (eds.), *Good Governance in the Era of Global Neoliberalism: Conflict and Depolitisation in Latin America, Eastern Europe, Asia and Africa* (London: Routledge, 2004).

particular history and trajectory of political development and posits them as the principal *solutions* to undesirable political dynamics and outcomes'.[84] Indeed, the World Bank's preference for democracy seems largely guided by empirical observations of how (idealised) liberal states function.

The concept of good governance itself has undergone an evolution. While starting from a predominantly technical conception which avoided direct references to democracy, in recent years it has more forcefully articulated a political dimension. The basic premise of the Bank's policy, that is, subjugating demands for governance to their consequences for development has, however, remained unchanged.

V.   Conclusion

The institutional practice reviewed above profoundly challenges the traditional principle of international law's regime-neutrality. Notwithstanding the lack of a global consensus on one form of domestic order within the international community, democracy, and more specifically liberal democracy, has emerged as the dominant model of domestic political organization for fragile states. In the fields of post-conflict reconstruction and development assistance, global actors such as the UN and the World Bank have consistently promoted the creation of domestic institutions that are accountable through periodic elections, respect the rule of law, and embrace market freedoms. In the context of UN peace operations, the establishment of 'democratic institutions' through multi-party elections has become a key component of the organization's post-conflict missions, offering recipient states no alternative to the liberal model of the state. Whereas democracy is not prescribed as such by the World Bank's good governance agenda, its emphasis on an efficient civil service, the rule of law and a vibrant civil society is clearly modelled on the organization of political power in 'modern' liberal societies. As former legal counsel Shihata of the World Bank acknowledged, the Bank plays a significant role in 'paving the way to more democratic forms of governance',[85] even though it has not completely adopted the language of democracy promotion.

A defining feature of the work of the UN and the World Bank in promoting liberal governance is the adoption of an instrumental logic in privileging one substantive model of domestic order over others. In light

---

[84] N. Bhuta, 'Democratization, State-building and Politics as Technology' in B. Bowden, H. Charlesworth and J. Farrall (eds.), *The Role of International Law in Rebuilding Societies after Conflict* (Cambridge University Press, 2009), p. 52 (emphasis in original).

[85] Shihata, *The World Bank in a Changing World*, vol. III, p. 151.

of their universal mandate, both actors have justified their support for liberal institutions by reference to the supposed factual outcomes they produce. Rather than invoking democracy as a normative requirement,[86] global institutions have thus supported liberal governance as an instrument for peace and prosperity, de-politicizing the shaping of domestic governance along liberal parameters.[87] Their support for democracy is thus not based on the global acceptance of a standard of governmental legitimacy, but is the result of a widespread assumption of a positive correlation between democracy, peace and development.[88]

Notwithstanding the functional approach these institutions have adopted, their considerable practice of promoting a particular form of domestic order sits uneasily with international law's tolerance of diversity, signalling the turning away from a pluralistic conception of world community.

[86] In this sense, see T. J. Farer, 'Promoting Democracy: International Law and Norms' in E. Newman and R. Rich (eds.), *The UN Role in Promoting Democracy: Between Ideals and Reality* (Tokyo: UN Press, 2004), pp. 32–61. Commenting on UN practice, he contemplates: 'Must we construe this practice as implying UN recognition of democracy as a legally privileged political arrangement? Not necessarily. While it is susceptible to that construction, UN practice also could be construed more modestly as imputing to democracy the character of a very useful, perhaps even indispensable, tool in the context of intrastate conflict for the reshaping of violent competition for power into less destructive forms' (p. 52).

[87] On the subject of de-politization, see D. Chandler, *Empire in Denial: The Politics of State-building* (London: Pluto Press, 2006); Demmers, Jilberto and Hogenboom (eds.), *Good Governance in the Era of Global Neoliberalism.*

[88] Susan Marks comments in relation to development: 'the democratic norm [Thomas M. Franck] had in mind has mutated into something else. Whereas his vision was of a universal entitlement backed up by an institutionalized and ideally world-wide system of election-monitoring, today democracy promotion is a dimension of development work'. In 'What has Become of the Emerging Right to Democratic Governance?', (2011) 22 *European Journal of International Law*, 515.

Federated entities in international law: disaggregating the federal State?

GLEIDER I. HERNÁNDEZ

The dominant role of the sovereign State in international relations, it hardly needs recalling, remains the basis for our conception of international law; it is generally accepted that this has been so since the Peace of Westphalia imposed a horizontal inter-State model of international relations.[1] However, such a paradigm does not easily reconcile itself to the long-standing practices of certain subnational components of a federation to assert themselves and act on the international plane, forging links with each other or with foreign States. This is a practice which has amplified in recent years due to the growing interdependence between States and economies. The interface between international and domestic legal orders is reciprocal: the expansion of international law to touch upon issues heretofore considered as within the reserved domain of domestic constitutional law, and even to the activities of the federated entities of States, has led to a search for alternative paradigms through which better to understand how international law accommodates such entities.

In this respect, the orthodoxy that a central executive acts exclusively on behalf of a State in matters of foreign policy[2] has come to be challenged, and in many respects has a marked impact on the internal legal order of a federal State.[3] Yet, international legal scholarship has yet

---

[1] R. Falk, 'The Interplay of Westphalia and Charter Conceptions of International Legal Order', in R. Falk and C. Black (eds.), *The Future of the International Legal Order* (Princeton University Press, 1969), vol. I, pp. 32, 43.

[2] The classic expression of this rule may be found in Article II of the Montevideo Convention on the Rights and Duties of States, Montevideo, 26 December 1933, in force 26 December 1934, 165 LNTS 19.

[3] See, e.g., B. Hocking (ed.), *Foreign Relations and Federal States* (Leicester University Press, 1993), p. 6, suggesting that it would be misleading to dismiss non-central governments as second-order players: '[t]he global web of world politics ensures that non-central governments have interests and responsibilities which can often, quite unexpectedly and sometimes against their wishes, project them into the international limelight'.

to erect a conceptual framework suitable for incorporating the practice of federated, sub-State entities into international law in a manner which would allow for their practice to be extricated from the State level and accommodated on the international plane.

   This chapter will review the constitutional structures of a few federal States[4] and the manner in which these allocate the competence to enter into treaties, and will present some thoughts as to how these might be reconciled with contemporary international law. Although a thorough exploration of how international law accommodates these constitutional arrangements is beyond the scope of this chapter, the research presented here aims to be a springboard for analysing how international law accommodates these constitutional realities.

I.   The orthodox position

Defined pragmatically for the purposes of this chapter, a 'federal State'[5] is a State that, according to its constitutional arrangements, distributes the competences which normally fall to a State between two or more orders of government.[6] Usually, one of these orders will have jurisdiction over the whole of the State's territory, and the other will have territorially

---

[4]   A notable exclusion from this chapter is Spain, one of the most decentralised States in the world, but one which formally remains a unitary State (Art. 2 of the Spanish Constitution). It is true that under Art. 149 of the constitution, the autonomous communities may conclude agreements with the constituent units of other federations, or even with foreign States; however, these have no formal treaty-making power, and ultimately the central State has a preponderant role in foreign policy and the conclusion of binding international legal agreements. Consequently, they cannot be qualified as treaties in the sense of public international law. For further discussion, see, generally, S. Beltrán Garcia, *Los acuerdos exteriores de las comunidades autónomas españolas: marco jurídico actual y perspectivas de futuro* (Barcelona: Institut d'Estudis Autònomics Generalitat de Catalunya, 2001).

[5]   A colourful definition of a federal State is that it is a 'pluralistic democracy in which two sets of governments, neither being fully at the mercy of the other, legislate and administer within their separate and yet interlocked jurisdictions': I. Duchacek, 'Perforated Sovereignties: Towards a Typology of New Actors in International Relations', in H. J. Michelmann and P. Soldatos (eds.), *Federalism and International Relations: The Role of Subnational Units* (Oxford: Clarendon Press, 1990), pp. 1, 3.

[6]   According to W. Rudolf, 'Federal States', in R. Wolfrum (ed.), *Max Planck Encyclopaedia of Public International Law* (Oxford: Oxford University Press, 2012), vol. II, p. 1136, para. 4, only 18 States are properly constituted as federal States: Argentina, Australia, Austria, Bosnia-Herzegovina, Brazil, Canada, Germany, India, Malaysia, Mexico, Micronesia, Nigeria, Russia, South Africa, Switzerland, Tanzania, the United Arab Emirates, the United States and Venezuela. Serbia and Montenegro has since formally dissolved. To this one can add Belgium, a federal State in all but name.

limited jurisdiction over a portion of the whole. A federation is often likened to a 'composite "nation", . . . able to assert its sovereign unity *vis-à-vis* other nation-states while cultivating jurisdictional diversity inside'.[7] Normally, such a constitutional arrangement can only be amended through a new agreement which requires the consent of the different levels of government which comprise a State.[8]

The traditional position in international legal discourse on federal States regards them as opaque, monolithic international legal subjects, as neatly encapsulated by Malanczuk and Akehurst:

> [i]nternational law is concerned only with states capable of carrying on international relations; consequently the federal state is regarded as a state for the purposes of international law, but the member states of the federation are not. If a member state of the federation acts in a manner which is incompatible with the international obligations of the federal state, it is the federal state which is regarded as responsible in international law.[9]

This classic approach suggests that, in so far as federated entities are empowered or authorised under the constitution of a federal State to negotiate or enter into treaties with foreign States, even if it is in their own name, they do so as agents for the federal State which, 'as alone possessing international personality, is necessarily the entity that becomes bound by the treaty and responsible for carrying it out'.[10]

---

[7] Duchacek, 'Perforated Sovereignties', p. 4. Duchacek characterises as 'dialectic' the encounter between unifying and fragmenting tendencies that is embodied by the federal structure.

[8] The consent of the various levels of government conventionally distinguishes a federal State from a 'decentralised State' such as the United Kingdom, where the power granted to the lower levels emanates from a unilateral decision of the central government, and where it can unilaterally decide to reclaim powers so devolved.

[9] P. Malanczuk, *Akehurst's Modern Introduction to International Law*, 7th edn (New York: Routledge, 1997), p. 81, citing J. B. Moore, *A Digest of International Law* (Washington DC: Government Printing Office, 1906), vol. 6, pp. 837–41, who cites a quintessential early example. A mob lynched some Italian nationals in New Orleans in 1891, and the United States admitted liability and paid compensation to Italy, even though the prevention and punishment of the crime fell exclusively within the powers of the State of Louisiana, and not within the powers of the federal authorities.

[10] G. G. Fitzmaurice, 'Third Report on the Law of Treaties', *Yearbook of the International Law Commission*, 1958, vol. II, UN Doc. A/CN.4/54, p. 24; see also his proposal, *ibid.*, 32, Art. 8(3). Another classic restatement of the principle can be found in H. Waldock, 'First Report on the Law of Treaties', *Yearbook of the International Law Commission*, 1962, vol. II, UN Doc. A/CN.4/144Add.1, pp. 36–37, Art. 2.

Under this view, such entities are merely agents or designees of the State.[11]

It is certainly true that 'the federal system of government is particularly ill-adapted to international cooperation',[12] and the orthodox position has an attractive simplicity in an international system that is complex enough. However, does it correspond to contemporary social reality? Does ignoring the letter and spirit of domestic constitutions that painstakingly establish federal structures further remove international legal practice from domestic developments of international significance?[13] It is with these questions in mind that the next sections will delve into the constitutional arrangements of a few federal States whose component entities have engaged in affairs of relevance for international law.

II.   Federal States with no express conferral of treaty-making power on its constituent entities

1.   United States

Perhaps the archetypal federal State projecting itself as a unitary actor in foreign policy is the United States, whose constitution provides at Article I(1) that 'no state shall, without the consent of Congress . . . enter into any agreement or compact with . . . a foreign power'.[14] Article II(2) allows the president to make treaties 'with advice and consent of the

---

[11] See H. Kelsen, *General Principles of International Law*, 2nd edn (New York: Holt Reinhart & Winston, 1966), pp. 260–1: 'since the component states have their competence in accordance with the federal constitution, the organs of the component states, in concluding treaties with the competence conferred upon them by the federal constitution, may also be considered as indirect organs of the federal state; hence the international person concluding the treaty may be considered to be the federal state acting, in certain regards, through a component state'. His reasoning was recalled in R. Ago, 'Third Report on State Responsibility', *Yearbook of the International Law Commission*, 1971, vol. II, UN Doc. A/CN.4/217, p. 272, to suggest that the acts and omissions of the officials of the component units could be imputable to the federal government, as if they had acted as its organs. Ago had included a draft article 6 to this effect, *ibid.*, p. 262.

[12] M. Sørensen, 'Federal States and the International Protection of Human Rights' (1952) 46 *American Journal of International Law* 195, 218.

[13] As L. Van den Brande, 'The International Legal Position of Flanders: Some Considerations' in K. Wellens (ed.), *International Law: Theory and Practice. Essays in Honour of Eric Suy* (The Hague: Kluwer Law International, 1998), pp. 145, 150 suggests, the attribution of international competences by domestic constitutions was far more than merely technical, entailing an important political and psychological added value of autonomy and institutional independence.

[14] Constitution of the United States of America, Art. 1, s. 10, cl. 3.

Senate' and Article VI(2), the so-called 'supremacy clause', states that treaties '. . . shall be the supreme law of the land'. The exceptions allowed by Congress are relatively few, and emphatically exclude the exchange of ambassadors or generally to engage in relations with a foreign government.[15] A series of early judgments by the United States Supreme Court confirmed that the federal government alone has the capacity to conclude treaties.[16] Thus, at least since the *Missouri* v. *Holland* judgment of 1920, the distribution of powers in the constitution has not restricted entry into treaties by the federal government.[17] However, in practice, US states have occasionally concluded unauthorised agreements with foreign powers,[18] a recent example being Missouri in 2000.[19]

---

[15] *Restatement (Third) of the Foreign Relations Law of the United States* (Washington DC: American Law Institute, 1987), vol. 1, para. 201, Reporters' Notes, p. 76. See generally, E.H. Fry, 'The United States of America', in Michelmann and Soldatos (eds.), *Federalism and International Relations* at pp. 279–81. For a review of recent American jurisprudence on the federal issue and the treaty-making power, see C. A. Bradley, 'Treaty Power and American Federalism Part II' (2000–01) 99 *Michigan Law Review* 98, 111–18.

[16] See, e.g., *United States* v. *Arjona* (1887) 120 US 479 (United States); *Chae Chan Ping* v. *United States* (1889) 130 US 581 (United States) ('*Chinese Exclusion* case'), p. 606; *Holmes* v. *Jennison* (1940) 39 US 540 (United States), p. 573.

[17] *Missouri* v. *Holland*, 252 US 416 (1920) (United States): this judgment by the US Supreme Court upheld federal legislation implementing a treaty obligation dealing with the protection of migratory birds, a subject over which the federal government possessed no explicit legislative power. After an unsuccessful attempt in the 1950s to overrule *Missouri* v. *Holland* with a constitutional amendment (the 'Bricker Amendment', Senate Judiciary Resolution 1, 83rd Cong., 1st Sess. (1953)) failed in the Senate, the question of States' rights with respect to the treaty-implementation power has not resurfaced. For further discussion on the impact of that judgment, see J. L. Friesen, 'The Distribution of Treaty-Implementing Powers in Constitutional Federations: Thoughts on the American and Canadian Models' (1994) 94 *Columbia Law Review* 1415, 1423–8; L. Henkin, *Foreign Affairs and the Constitution*, 2nd edn (Oxford University Press, 1996), p. 190; H. C. Dillard, 'Should the Constitution be Amended to Limit the Treaty-Making Power?' (1953) 26 *Southern California Law Review* 373; and Q. Wright, 'Should the Constitution be Amended to Limit the Treaty-Making Power?' (1953) 26 *Southern California Law Review* 385. *Cf.* L. Wildhaber, *Treaty-Making Power and Constitution* (Basel and Stuttgart: Helbing & Lichtenhan, 1971), p. 330, who argues that *Missouri* v. *Holland* 'is nothing but an eloquent assertion of the principle well established by earlier cases'; at *ibid.*, pp. 324–8, he recalls that early jurisprudence from 1797 onwards.

[18] The US Supreme Court stated in *Virginia* v. *Tennessee*, 148 US 503 (1893), p. 518, that the prohibition against the conclusion of 'treaties' found in Art. I, s. 10 of the US Constitution did not apply to agreements concerning such minor matters as the adjustment of boundaries, which have no 'tendency to increase and to build up the political influence of the contracting states, so as to encroach upon or impair the supremacy of the United States'.

[19] The earliest example being North Dakota's administrative interstate agreements with Canadian municipalities, upheld by the Supreme Court of North Dakota in *McHendry County et al.* v. *Brady*, 37 North Dakota 59, 163 N.W. 540 (1917) (United States). In

2. Canada

In Canada, the allocation of competences between the federated provinces and the federal government was settled under the British North America Act of 1867.[20] Thus, in the original settlement, under Section 91 the Federal Government represented Canada as an international personality, but the imperial Parliament in London retained the power to conclude treaties under Article 132 of the Act.[21] Pursuant to the Statute of Westminster of 1931, this prerogative of the British Crown was transferred to the Canadian Governor-General in Council – in other words, to the federal executive.[22] In theory, therefore, Canada's constitutional arrangements should have resembled those of the United States in matters of foreign affairs;[23] however, in the controversial *Labour Conventions* cases, the UK Privy Council – which granted leave to appeal from Canada's Supreme Court for cases begun before 1949 – decided that although the federal government may legally negotiate and conclude treaties on all subject matters, it could only pass implementing legislation on subjects covered by Section 91. See especially the Privy Council's oft-quoted interpretations of sections 91 and 92 of the Constitution Act 1867 in *Attorney General for Canada* v. *Attorney General for Ontario* ([1937] AC 326 ('*Labour Conventions*'), 354):

> ... if ... Canada incurs obligations they must, so far as legislation be concerned, when they deal with Provincial classes of subjects, be dealt with by the totality of powers, in other words by co-operation between

2000, Missouri concluded a Memorandum of Agreement with Manitoba on water issues without Congressional authorisation: see the letter from William H. Taft IV, the Legal Adviser to the US Department of State, to Senator Byron Dorgan of North Dakota, 'Capacity to Make: Role of Individual States of the United States: Analysis of Memorandum of Understanding between Missouri and Manitoba', 2001 Digest A (United States), pp. 179–98. Duchacek, 'Perforated Sovereignties', p. 20, also mentions the jointly financed water development in the Souris River Basin, linking Saskatchewan, North Dakota and Manitoba.

[20] British North America Act 1867, 30 & 31 Vict., ch. 3 (also 'Constitution Act 1867', name changed by the Constitution Act 1982, itself Sch. B to the Canada Act 1982 (UK), ch. 11), s. 91 (enumerating federal powers) and s. 92 (enumerating provincial powers).

[21] S. 132 of the British North America Act 1867 assigns to the federal Parliament 'all powers necessary or proper for performing the obligations of Canada or of any Province thereof, *as part of the British Empire*, towards Foreign Countries arising under Treaties between the Empire and such Foreign Countries' (emphasis added).

[22] The Statute of Westminster 1931 (22 & 23 Geo. V), ch. 4, corroborated on this point by Letters Patent of 1947, *reprinted in* (1947–8) *University of Toronto Law Journal* 475.

[23] For a detailed comparison of the Canadian and American treaty-implementing powers, see generally, Friesen, 'The Distribution of Treaty-Implementing Powers in Constitutional Federations: Thoughts on the American and Canadian Models'.

the Dominion and the Provinces. While the ship of state now sails on larger ventures and into foreign waters she still retains the watertight compartments which are an essential part of her original structure.[24]

Although harshly criticised,[25] *Labour Conventions* remains good law, and the effect of its holding has been to subordinate concerns over international obligations to the domestic separation of legislative competences.[26] Although the federal government has maintained that its consent remains an imperative condition for the validity of agreements concluded by the provinces,[27] a mechanism has been found whereby the

---

[24] See, generally, G. V. La Forest, 'The Labour Conventions Case Revisited' (1974) 12 *Canadian Year Book of International Law* 137, and Friesen, 'Treaty-Implementing Powers in Constitutional Federations', 1434–9, for Canadian judicial decisions after 1937 on the question. In particular, see the *Re: Offshore Mineral Rights of British Columbia* decision [1967] SCR 792 (Canada). In this reference, the Supreme Court of Canada was asked by the Federal Government whether the Province of British Columbia or Canada was sovereign over offshore resources in the territorial sea. Deciding that the rights in the territorial sea formerly asserted by the British Crown in respect of the Colony of British Columbia had passed to Canada in 1871, the Court expressly linked subjecthood to international responsibility, *ibid.*, 821:

> Canada is the sovereign State which will be recognized by international law as having the rights stated in the Convention of 1958 [on the Territorial Sea], and it is Canada, not the Province of British Columbia, that will have to answer the claims of other members of the international community for breach of the obligations and responsibilities imposed by the Convention.

The High Court of Australia referred expressly to this reasoning in *Bonsor v. La Macchia* [1970] 43 ALJR 275 (Australia), 294, where it held that legislative power over the territorial sea accrued to the Commonwealth, and not to New South Wales, by virtue of the international sovereignty of the former.

[25] See, e.g., B. Laskin, 'Some International Legal Aspects of Federalism: The Experience of Canada', in D. P. Currie (ed.), *Federalism and the New Nations of Africa* (University of Chicago Press, 1964), p. 389; G. J. Szablowski, 'Creation and Implementation of Treaties in Canada, (1956) 34 *Canadian Bar Review* 28, 30–2; G. L. Morris, 'The Treaty-Making Power: A Canadian Dilemma' (1967) 45 *Canadian Bar Review* 478, 482–92; Wildhaber, *Treaty-Making Power and Constitution*, pp. 293–5.

[26] Friesen, 'Treaty-Implementing Powers in Constitutional Federations', 1433. At 1436–40, he gives several examples of difficulties faced by Canada in acceding to and implementing its international obligations.

[27] See, e.g., the intervention by the Secretary of State for External Relations, Paul Martin, in the Canadian House of Commons, HC Deb. (1964–65), vol. XI, col. 11818:

> On the international plane, the federal government represents all of Canada and under international law only sovereign states are recognized as members of the international community ... The procedure followed on the occasion of the agreements cited above between France and Quebec is a reflection of and accords with the Canadian government's status under international law and the constitutional position in Canada. Standing

federal authorities of Canada can 'delegate' their treaty-making powers to other entities if necessary.[28] A good example of this is the 1983 agreement between Quebec and the United States on social security.[29]

The province most often asserting its rights to engage on the international plane is Quebec: since its first 'entente' on cultural questions with France, it has signed some 230 agreements with foreign governments.[30] In fact, Quebec has long argued that since the provinces must implement certain treaties, it is only logical under Section 92 that they should have an international power to negotiate and conclude them in the first place.[31] It should also be noted that the Quebec government is not the only provincial government to have sought enhanced treaty-making powers: Alberta has notably suggested that 'a revised constitution should include provisions relating to international affairs and should recognize the need for provincial involvement in those areas of foreign affairs of concern to them'.[32] Other provinces, primarily British Columbia, but also Ontario, Nova Scotia and New Brunswick, have also engaged in

      alone these agreements between France and Quebec could not have been regarded as agreements subject to international law.

[28] Quebec's first international agreement with France, on technical cooperation, was concluded in 1963 by an exchange of letters between two of their subordinate agencies. By an exchange of letters dated 23 and 27 December 1963 between the French Ambassador in Ottawa and the Department of External Affairs of Canada, the Canadian Government consented to the ententes. Similarly, in 1965, an entente on cultural and educational cooperation was signed by the ministers of education of Quebec and the ministers of foreign affairs and of national education of France, the first more formal arrangement of its kind; the Canadian Government again insisted on an exchange of letters with France, and even entered into a subsequent framework cultural agreement (*accord cadre*) with France allowing for any province, by referring to the *accord cadre*, to enter into such agreements with that State in matters of cultural affairs and scientific and technical exchanges: see Franco-Canadian Cultural Agreement (France-Canada), 17 November 1965, (1965) 17 *External Affairs* (Canada) 514.

[29] Understanding and Administrative Arrangement with the Government of Quebec (United States-Quebec), 30 March 1983, US-Quebec), *Treaties and Other International Agreements* (United States), No. 10,863. However, Quebec's agreement with the United States was a separate subsidiary agreement falling under a framework agreement which authorised Canadian provinces so to act: see Agreement with respect to Social Security (Canada-United States), 11 March 1981, 35 UST 3403, 3417, Art. XX.

[30] D. B. Hollis, 'Why State Consent Still Matters – Non-State Actors, Treaties, and the Changing Sources of International Law', (2005) 23 *Berkeley Journal of International Law* 137, 150. Nearly 60% of these agreements are with foreign States.

[31] See, e.g., the statement of Paul Gerain-Lajoie, Minister of Education of Quebec in 1965, reprinted in L. L. La Pierre, 'Quebec and Treaty-making', (1965) 20 *International Journal* 362, 364. See also, L. Sabourin, 'La participation des provinces canadiennes aux organisations internationales', (1965) 3 *Canadian Year Book of International Law* 73, 83.

[32] Government of Alberta, *Harmony in Diversity: A New Federalism for Canada* (Edmonton: Government of Alberta Publications, 1978), p. 8.

international affairs, primarily with states of the United States; but the agreements concluded by these provinces, sometimes known as 'international compacts' or 'understandings', fell short of treaty agreements, and have sometimes been regarded as purely political agreements,[33] based as they are on the goodwill of the parties and the reciprocal benefit derived therefrom. Again, Canadian practice has consistently asserted an involvement of the federal government to transform agreements between Canadian provinces and foreign States or federated entities into binding obligations.[34] Until this is done, agreements between Canadian provinces and foreign States are said to be governed by municipal, rather than international, law.[35]

The Canadian constitutional system, with its protection of the prerogatives of its federated entities,[36] shares some resemblance to the federal States which expressly confer treaty-making powers on federated entities, which will be discussed below (Section III, *infra*.). It has also come to have an influence on Australia, a fellow Commonwealth federation, to which we now turn.

3. Australia

The 'external affairs' power found in Section 51, paragraph xxix of the Australian Constitution of 1900, gives the Commonwealth Parliament

---

[33] The Canadian Government has consistently maintained that such agreements are extra-legal and do not properly belong to the sphere of international law: see, e.g., the position taken in the Comment of the Canadian Department of External Affairs Legal Bureau (25 January 1979), in (1980) 18 *Canadian Year Book of International Law* 316–17. For long-standing examples of the international engagement of these provinces, see M. C. Rand, 'International Agreements between Canadian Provinces and Foreign States' (1967) 25 *University of Toronto Faculty of Law Review* 75, 76 ss.

[34] See, *supra.*, n. 28, for a summary of Quebec's practice; see also how the United States and Canada stepped in to 'consent' to and indemnify an agreement between the city of Seattle and the province of British Columbia: Treaty between the United States of America and Canada relating to the Skagit River and Ross Lake, and the Seven Mile Reservoir on the Pend d'Oreille River (Canada-United States), 2 April 1984, *Treaties and Other International Agreements* (United States), No. 11,088.

[35] E. McWhinney, 'Canadian Federalism and the Foreign Affairs and Treaty Powers: the Impact of Quebec's "Quiet Revolution" (1969) 7 *Canadian Year Book of International Law* 3, 14, who argued that non-binding agreements concluded by sub-State entities 'afford none of the international law protections of a treaty apart perhaps from the limited *parens patriae* protection that any one nation-state might choose to invoke on behalf of its own citizens'.

[36] Friesen, 'Treaty-Implementing Powers in Constitutional Federations', 1440–1, has gone so far as to distinguish Canada from the United States by describing it as a 'compact of provinces' rather than a 'union'.

competence over external relations. Thus, as with Canada, treaty-making by virtue of the common law is a prerogative of the Crown, and hence exercisable by the Commonwealth Parliament.

In the leading case on treaty enforcement power, *The King* v. *Burgess*,[37] the High Court of Australia found that even when the federal Parliament had no competence over specified subject matters, the Commonwealth was nonetheless capable of undertaking an external commitment of an international character in those areas of reserved competence. They concluded that although legislation implementing those international commitments was a constitutionally valid exercise of the external affairs power under the constitution, the regulations made under the act would be invalid if they were not strictly necessary for ensuring the execution of a convention signed by the federal government.[38] In *Commonwealth* v. *Tasmania*, many decades later, it was held that the result of this was that no formal power sharing between levels of government would be required, even if the subject matter of a treaty falls within an area of concern for the component states.[39] Nevertheless, a certain restraint has permeated the federal government's exercise of its constitutional power to implement treaties, as, in some cases, it has relied on state legislation enacted for that purpose.[40] This restraint culminated in the policy of 'cooperative federalism' formally adopted by Australia in the late 1970s, which has resulted in a reluctance by it to ratify certain normative or standard-setting conventions.[41]

---

[37] *The King* v. *Burgess, ex parte Henry* [1936] 55 CLR 608 (Australia).

[38] *Ibid.*, p. 696. A concise description of the individual judgments in *The King* v. *Burgess* is given by Wildhaber, *Treaty-Making Power and Constitution*, pp. 298–300. The judgment in *The King* v. *Burgess* was confirmed as holding true after the *Labour Conventions* case in *Frost* v. *Stevenson* [1937] 59 CLR 528 (Australia), p. 599 (Evatt J).

[39] [1983] 158 CLR 1 (Australia). A. Byrnes and H. Charlesworth, 'Federalism and International Law in Australia' (1985) 79 *American Journal of International Law* 622, 635, suggest that the majority took 'an internationalist view of Australia's view in the world by rejecting a fragmented power to implement treaties. The demands of the international order are preferred to those of state autonomy: the only guarantees of federalism provided are the states' continued existence and capacity to function and freedom from discriminatory federal legislation.'

[40] See Wildhaber, *Treaty-Making Power and Constitution*, pp. 301–2, for a description of Australia's policies with regard to labour and human rights conventions between 1928 and 1947. In sum, the federal government had a policy of consultation and deferral to the policies of the State Parliaments when matters within their competence fell within the respective convention.

[41] B. R. Opeskin, 'Federal States in the International Legal Order' (1996) XLIII *Netherlands International Law Review* 353, 373. See, e.g., Australia's practice in implementing its obligations under the International Convention on the Elimination of All Forms of

III.   Federations which grant an actual treaty-making power to sub-national entities

1.   Germany

Article 32 of the Basic Law of the Federal Republic of Germany, whilst stipulating that the conduct of relations with other countries is the concern of the federation (the '*Bund*'),[42] grants the constituent entities (the '*Länder*') a right to be consulted 'in sufficient time' before a treaty which affects their specific circumstances is concluded.[43] Moreover, Article 32 provides that the *Länder*, in so far as it is within their competence, and after having secured permission from the federal government, may conclude treaties with foreign States.[44] Although the federal government can conclude treaties with respect to subjects falling within its field of exclusive legislative competence,[45] it may also enter into treaties concerning subjects over which it has concurrent legislative powers,[46] or where it possesses the right to enact general rules.[47] Provision is also made for the participation of the *Länder* in treaty negotiations conducted by the *Bund*.[48] In matters where concurrent powers are exercised, the *Länder* may conclude treaties in so far as the

Racial Discrimination, New York, signed 7 March 1966, in force 4 January 1969, 1037 UNTS 151. Australian state legislation was specifically preserved as a result of an amendment to the domestic Racial Discrimination Act 1975 (Cth. No. 52) (Australia), which prevented federal legislation in this field from overriding relevant state legislation. See also, B. R. Opeskin and D. R. Rothwell, 'The Impact of Treaties on Australian Federalism' (1995) 27 *Case Western Reserve Journal of International Law* 1, 17–19.

[42]   Art. 32, para. 1 of the Basic Law. For more extensive discussion of the German system, see W. Rudolf, 'Bundesstaat und Völkerrecht' (1989) 27 *Archiv des Völkerrechts* 1. Wildhaber, *Treaty-Making Power and Constitution*, pp. 302–10, describes the various theoretical schools which seek to reconcile the different interpretations of the German constitutional system.

[43]   Art. 32, para. 2 of the Basic Law.

[44]   Art. 32, para. 3 of the Basic Law. Arts. 73 and 87, *inter alia*, of the Basic Law reserve certain issues (foreign affairs and defence, citizenship and freedom of movement, passport matters, immigration, emigration and extradition) to the Federation. Art. 87 stipulates that the foreign service is a matter for direct federal administration: see Wildhaber, *Treaty-Making Power and Constitution*.

[45]   Art. 73 of the Basic Law.

[46]   So-called '*konkurriende Gesetzgebungszuständigkeit*': Art. 74 of the Basic Law.

[47]   So-called '*Rahmengesetzgebungszuständigkeit*': Art. 75 of the Basic Law.

[48]   The 'Kramer-Heubl-Papier' of 5 July 1968: it is not published, but see *Richlinien fur die Behandlung völkerrechtlicher Verträge*, Anlage D, mentioned in H. Beemelmans and H. D. Treviranus, 'Germany', in D. B. Hollis, M. R. Blakeslee and L. B. Ederington (eds.), *National Treaty Law and Practice: Dedicated to the Memory of Monroe Leigh* (Leiden and Boston: Brill, 2005) pp. 317, 329.

Bund has not yet done so; however, they must yield where the federation has concluded or wishes to conclude agreements relating to subjects over which it has concurrent legislative powers or the right to enact 'general rules'.[49]

This complex constitutional arrangement could have led to much deadlock and confusion. In practice, however, much treaty practice in Germany is conducted in accordance with the *Lindauer Abkommen* (Lindau Agreement), a 'gentlemen's agreement' according to which the *Länder* agreed to delegate their agreement-making powers to allow the federal government to conclude treaties in its own name on subjects deemed to be of predominantly federal concern. The *Bund* government, for its part, committed itself, on treaties of predominantly *Länder* concern, to seek their approval before any federal agreement would become constitutionally binding.[50] The Lindau Agreement, the basis of modern German treaty-making, survived reunification and continues to the present day.

2. Switzerland

Thoroughly revised in 2000, Switzerland's Federal Constitution contains several far-reaching changes to Swiss foreign policy, enshrining one of the purposes of the Swiss Confederation 'to strive to secure the long-term preservation of natural resources, and to promote a just and peaceful international order'[51] as well as the obligation of all Swiss authorities to respect international law.[52]

What is relevant for our purposes is the partition of competencies between the Federal Council and the cantons, which continues to be shared in so far as the conduct of external affairs is concerned. Although

---

[49] Art. 72, para. 1 of the Basic Law. The *Länder* have been rather active, concluding at least 79 treaties, not including concordats, from 1949 to 1994: see ibid., p. 328.

[50] See *Lindauer Abkommen* (Lindau Agreement) of 14 November 1957 between the federal government and the *Länder* governments, reprinted in H. Dreier (ed.), *Grundgesetz Kommentar*, 2nd edn (Tübingen: Mohr, 2006), vol. II, pp. 794–5. The Lindau Agreement affirms the federal government's leading role in foreign policy, but requires it to seek the consent of the *Länder* if the treaty under negotiation touches upon their areas of competence, for instance in culture or education. A similar provision can be found in Art. 10, para. 3 of the Constitution of Austria.

[51] Art. 2, para. 4 of the Swiss Constitution of 1 January 2000. See also Art. 54, para. 2, mentioning as a goal of Swiss foreign policy, to 'contribute to alleviate need and poverty in the world, and to promote respect for human rights, democracy, the peaceful coexistence of nations, and the preservation of natural resources'.

[52] This obligation applies to the Federal Council and the cantons (Art. 5, para. 4 of the Swiss Constitution), and also binds the Federal Tribunal and all other authorities (Art. 191).

the Confederation has the power to conclude any treaty on any subject, even if it falls within the domain of cantonal legislative or administrative powers,[53] the cantons have the formal right to 'participate in the preparation of decisions of foreign policy which concern their powers or their essential interests',[54] which, broadly speaking, gives them rights of participation and of negotiation in foreign policy, and requires that a consensus between the different levels of government be sought.[55] In practice, this suggests extensive information exchange between the levels of government, and the direct participation of cantonal representatives in certain negotiations involving Switzerland and foreign States.[56]

For their part, the cantons may conclude agreements with foreign States 'within the scope of their powers', subject to the caveat that such agreements may not be contrary to the law, nor to the interest of the Confederation or the laws of other cantons.[57] Active agreement-makers

---

[53] Art. 54, para. 1. See also L. Wildhaber, A. Scheidegger and M.D. Schinzel, 'Switzerland', in Hollis, Blakeslee and Ederington (eds.), *National Treaty Law and Practice*, pp. 627, 635. The 2000 Constitution appears to codify previous practice as to the full federal treaty-making power, even in matters within cantonal competence: see Wildhaber, *Treaty-Making Power and Constitution*, pp. 310–15, who, prior to 2000, recalled a Swiss debate over 'federalist' and 'centralist' interpretations of what was then Art. 8. See also *X* v. *Eidgenössische Steuerverwaltung*, BGE 96 (1970), vol. I, 737 (Switzerland), 747; *In re: Leuthardt*, BGE 9 (1883) 175 (Switzerland), at 178; J.-F. Aubert, *Traité de droit constitutionnel suisse* (Neuchâtel: Ides et Calendes, 1967), pp. 256–9; and W. Burckhardt, *Kommentar der Schweizerischen Bundesverfassung* (3rd edn, Bern: Stampfli, 1931), pp. 81–9.

[54] Art. 55, para. 1 of the Swiss Constitution.

[55] Art. 55, paras. 2–3. Wildhaber, Scheidegger and Schinzel, 'Switzerland', p. 665, suggest that the term 'take into consideration' contained in para. 3 is not as strong as it could have been, but that it suggests that the limitations on the federal power to act unilaterally seem to counterbalance the expansion of the federal treaty-making power to encroach on cantonal competencies.

[56] To regulate cantonal participation, Switzerland has enacted a Federal Statute on the Participation of the Cantons in the Foreign Policy of the Confederation, SR 138.1 (22 December 1999), found in Wildhaber, Scheidegger and Schinzel, 'Switzerland', Annex E, pp. 680–1.

[57] Art. 56, paras. 1–2. Wildhaber, *Treaty-Making Power and Constitution*, p. 315; and VEB 24 (1954) No. 5 (Switzerland). In Switzerland, the cantons have a limited international legal personality (*petite personnalité*); the Swiss Constitution thus leaves some limited room for the cantons to appear as subjects of rights and duties under international law. Austrian *Länder* now also possess an international treaty-making power, although it is limited to matters falling within their exclusive competence and only with neighbouring States: see Article 16(1–2) of the Constitution of Austria; and M. Thaler, *Die Vertragabschlußkompetenz der österreichischen Bundesländer* (Vienna: Braumüller, 1990). The pre-1992 Constitution of the Socialist Federal Republic of Yugoslavia, at Art. 271(2), provided for a similar competence for the federal republics.

prior to World War I, the cantons have rarely exercised their powers subsequently,[58] and when reviewing the subject matter of earlier cantonal agreements, many of these would fall under federal competence today.[59]

Interestingly, official intercourse between cantons and governments of foreign States or their representatives only takes place through the intermediacy of the Federal Council, which acts as an agent of the cantons.[60] Agreements negotiated in this manner must be notified to the Confederation; although they do not require permission,[61] they may be reviewed for compliance with federal law and the interests of the Confederation and of other cantons.[62] This appears reasonable: even if the cantons enter into an agreement, the Federal Council has long considered itself responsible for any cantonal breach of a federal or cantonal treaty.[63]

Cantons may also engage directly with 'lower ranking foreign authorities',[64] although in practice, this is commonly interpreted as extending to administrative and judicial officials operating on a non-political

---

[58] Wildhaber, *Treaty-Making Power and Constitution*, p. 317, identified only seven cantonal agreements between 1932 and 1972. See also, L. Di Marzo, *Component Units of Federal States and International Agreements* (Alphen aan der Rijn: Sijthoff and Noordhoff, 1980), pp. 123–6, who summarises Swiss cantonal practice in this regard.

[59] Swiss cantons have concluded some 140 international agreements, although it is difficult to gather all valid cantonal agreements in force, as many of these are neither published in the cantonal series of statutes, nor submitted to the federal government; see Wildhaber, Scheidegger, and Schinzel, 'Switzerland', pp. 667–8.

[60] *Ibid.*, p. 669. This practice is in line with the pre-2000 constitution, where cantonal agreements with foreign States are negotiated, signed and ratified in the name of the cantons, or both the federation and the cantons, by the Federal Council: see L. Wildhaber, 'Switzerland', in Michelmann and Soldatos (eds.), *Federalism and International Relations*, pp. 250–3.

[61] Art. 56, para. 2 of the Swiss Constitution.

[62] See Art. 62 of the Swiss Federal Statute on the Organisation of the Government and the Administration, SR 172.010, in Wildhaber, Scheidegger and Schinzel, 'Switzerland', Annex C, p. 677. Occasionally, the cantons 'forget' the requirement for federal approval: see Wildhaber, 'Switzerland', p. 260. In the normal course of affairs, however, such cases do not lead to conflict, as most of the agreements in fact comply with the substantive requirements of Article 102. Moreover, the Federal Council is often reluctant to intervene and generally turns a blind eye to the cantons' failure to submit their treaties.

[63] E. His, 'De la compétence des cantons suisse de conclure des traités', (1929) 10 *Revue de droit international et de legislation comparée*, 466, argued that this was the case even during the League era, when Switzerland, represented by the Federal Council, declared that '*[l]a responsabilité de l'Etat fédéral est de même ordre et de même étendue que celle de l'Etat unitaire*': see LN Doc C.75.M.69.1929.V.3, 243.

[64] Art. 56, para. 3.

level;[65] but it does not embrace state secretaries or ministers, which means that the cantons cannot directly negotiate even on plainly local or administrative agreements.[66] Yet, cantonal – and even municipal – participation in various transfrontier organisations is substantial,[67] and should not be underestimated.[68]

3. Belgium

The case of Belgium is unique, as there is no hierarchical relationship between the linguistic communities, the geographic regions and the federal institutions with respect to their spheres of competence, in particular as regards *jus tractati* (the treaty-making power).[69] The Belgian model is based on the objective of having as many exclusive spheres of competence as possible, based on the principle *in foro interno, in foro externo*, according to which competences on the domestic level are also brought into the arena of international relations.[70] In practice, this presumes that internal legislation enacted by the federated entities is

---

[65] Burckhardt, *Kommentar der Schweizerischen Bundesverfassung*, pp. 93, 678.

[66] Wildhaber, *Treaty-Making Power and Constitution*, p. 317.

[67] See Report on the Transfrontier Cooperation and the Participation of the Cantons in Foreign Policy (7 March 1994) BBl 1994 II 641, pp. 644, 659.

[68] See, in particular, Swiss cantonal and municipal participation pursuant to the European Outline Convention on Transfrontier Cooperation between Territorial Communities and Authorities, signed on 21 May 1980, entered into force for Switzerland on 4 June 1982 (see SR 0.131.1), ETS 159, and Protocol No. 2 thereto, ETS 169; and the so-called 'Agreement of Karlsruhe' between several frontier cantons of Switzerland, Germany, France and Luxembourg (23 January 1996), recalled in Wildhaber, Scheidegger and Schinzel, 'Switzerland', p. 668.

[69] Art. 167, para. 1 of the Coordinated Constitution of Belgium, coordinated on 17 February 1994, assigns the king, as the head of the federal executive power, 'the leadership of foreign affairs', but immediately following is added that this is only the case 'notwithstanding the competence of the Communities and Regions to regulate international cooperation, including the treaty-making power for the matters for which they are competent according to the Constitution'. Arts. 127 and 128 of the constitution confer *jus tractati* on the Flemish and French-speaking communities, and Article 130 on the German-speaking community. So far as the regions are concerned, only Art. 167, para. 3 of the Coordinated Constitution makes reference to their *jus tractati*. See generally, P. Gautier, 'Le regime des traités dans l'Etat fédéral – la conclusion des traités' (1994) 27 *Revue belge de droit international* 31, and R. Senelle, 'Federalizing a Divided State' in J. J. Hesse and V. Wright (eds.), *Federalizing Europe* (Oxford University Press, 1996), pp. 267, 307–11.

[70] The division of foreign policy matters in Belgium since 1993 has been laid down in Arts. 167–9 of the Coordinated Constitution. In particular, Art. 167, para. 1 states that '[t]he King manages international relations *without prejudice to* the ability of the Communities and Regions to engage in international cooperation, including the

equal in power to that of the federal level, and the allocation of the exclusive powers *ratione materiae* between the different orders of government is thus transposed at the international level.[71] Thus, if a Belgian regional government is competent internally for a given domain, in relation to the said domain it is automatically competent externally.[72] Perhaps unparalleled in other States, the federal executive does not have an implied power of supervision over the communities or regions in the exercise of their powers for international cooperation; in fact, this was expressly excluded.[73]

The complete parallelism between Belgium's governmental orders in treaty-making entails that the component entities of its federal structure possess a substantial treaty-making power,[74] one which far exceeds that of the federated entities in the other States surveyed above. The combined effect of the principle of fundamental equality of the various Belgian governments coupled with the principle *in foro interno, in foro externo* is without precedent in the constitutional arrangements of States, and the Belgian federal model also contains further innovations. If multiple layers of government are competent, a consensus is required to be reached for so-called 'mixed treaties'.[75] Given the non-subordination of either the federal or federated entities, a special statute lays down the procedure for

signature of treaties, for those matters within their respective responsibilities as established by the Constitution and in virtue thereof' (emphasis added). In foreign policy matters, all Belgian governments are thus jointly responsible for determining the federation's foreign policy.

[71] A. Alen and P. Peeters, 'Federal Belgium within the International Legal Order' in Wellens (ed.), *International Law*, pp. 123, 124.

[72] See, e.g., the citation of the agreements of the three Belgian regional governments with France and the Netherlands for the protection of the Scheldt: Belgium (Brussels–Capital, Flanders, Wallonia Regional Governments)–France–Netherlands: Agreements on the Protection of the Rivers Meuse and Scheldt, Charleville Mezières (France), 26 April 1994, (1995) 34 ILM 854 (Scheldt); (1995) 34 ILM 859 (Meuse). Art. 9 of each of the agreements requires each of the regional governments separately to notify France upon the completion of their required domestic procedures for entry into force, *ibid.*, p. 858.

[73] See Belgian Council of State, Legislation Section, opinion L. 22.506/8 (9 June 1993), Parliamentary Documents, Senate, 1993–1994, no. 956/1, p. 6.

[74] Some have even suggested that the federated entities of Belgium possess international legal personality: see Alen and Peeters, 'Federal Belgium within the International Legal Order', p. 135; W. J. Ganshof van der Meersch and R. Ergec, 'Les relations extérieures des Etats à système constitutionnel regional ou fédéral' [1986] *Revue de droit international et de droit comparé* 303; J. Wouters, and L. de Smet, 'The Legal Position of Federal States and Their Federated Entities in International Relations – The Case of Belgium' (Catholic University of Leuven, Institute for International Law, Working Paper No. 7 (June 2001)).

[75] Alen and Peeters, 'Federal Belgium within the International Legal Order', pp. 125–6, give several examples where mixed treaties came to be ratified by all the levels of government competent *ratione materiae*.

concluding mixed treaties in a mandatory *cooperation agreement* between the federal authority and the federated governments.[76]

In some cases, the federal authorities can substitute for a community or a region in order to comply with a ruling against the Belgian State by an international or supranational court or tribunal.[77] Strict conditions attach to this *power of substitution*, which have been characterised as 'so extremely severe that they can be considered as being rather symbolic';[78] yet they remain operational as a last resort, to ensure that Belgium meets its international obligations. As the Belgian Council of State has opined, 'even if the attribution of (constitutional treaty-making power) is a necessary condition for the federated entities to dispose of the treaty-making power, foreign States and especially international organisations must prove that they are willing to negotiate with the political sub-entities of a federal State'.[79] The power of substitution thus provides a valuable safeguard to ensure the effectiveness of the Belgian constitutional framework in relation to third States.

4.   *Other recent examples: Austria, Bosnia and Herzegovina, and the treaty-making power of Hong Kong and Macau*

A few other States have recently made constitutional arrangements worth mentioning. Since 1988, the Austrian Constitution allows the *Länder* to

---

[76] Art. 167, para. 4 of the Belgian Coordinated Constitution provided that a Special Majority Act would determine the rules for the conclusion of such 'mixed treaties'. Art. 92*bis*, para. 4*ter* of the Special Majority Act on Institutional Reform provided that the federal Government, the Communities and the Regions should determine these rules in a cooperation agreement, which was concluded on 8 March 1994: see Alen and Peeters, 'Federal Belgium within the International Legal Order', p. 26. See also 'Statement of the Kingdom of Belgium regarding the conclusion of international agreements alongside the other members of the European Community', OJ 1995 No. C157 (23 June 1995), p. 1, reprinted in Alen and Peeters, 'Federal Belgium within the International Legal Order', p. 127.

[77] Art. 169 of the Coordinated Constitution and Art. 16, para. 3 of the Special Majority Act on Institutional Reform.

[78] Alen and Peeters, 'Federal Belgium within the International Legal Order', p. 135.

[79] Belgian Council of State, Legislation Section, opinion of 16 September 1992, Parliamentary Documents, Senate, Extraordinary Session 1991–1992, no. 457/2, 15–17. Even those opposed to the constitutive theory of recognition in international law as a matter of principle, suggest that it applies with regard to sub-State entities: see I. Bernier, *International Legal Aspects of Federalism* (London: Longman & Sons, 1973), pp. 79–81. *Cf.* Van den Brande, 'The International Legal Position of Flanders', p. 152, who suggests instead that the role of international community should be seen in terms of *efficacy*; a refusal to enter into direct relationship with sub-State entities renders these entities' treaty-making power meaningless, but not non-existent.

conclude treaties, within their constitutional sphere of competence, with other States or their constituent entities, if these share borders with Austria. Unlike in Switzerland, federal approval *must* be obtained before their conclusion; and treaties concluded by a *Land* shall be revoked upon request by the federal government. Failure to respect these obligations means that competence in the matter passes to the federation.[80] In Bosnia and Herzegovina, the Muslim–Croat Federation of Bosnia and Herzegovina and the Republika Srpska may enter into agreements with States and international organisations with the consent of the federal parliamentary assembly.[81] Finally, although not a federal State, a special case is China, in relation to Hong Kong and Macau. Since 1997 and 1999, respectively, these two entities are Special Administrative Regions, and they not only possess a limited treaty-making power, but Hong Kong has joined international organisations, most prominently the World Trade Organization (WTO).[82]

IV.   Some observations: future avenues of research

Whatever the diversity of constitutional arrangements found above, the basic feature of a federation remains that it seeks to provide a unity – a federal State – with some room for diversity, for example in the form of multi-ethnic pluralism. So to do could conceivably grant federated entities an opportunity to assert their distinctiveness internationally. In fact, as has been shown above, certain constitutional arrangements can confer upon federated entities a considerable degree of independence in conducting foreign relations in matters coming within the ambit of their competence.[83]

---

[80]   Federal Constitutional Law of Austria, Art. 16(3). See F. Koja, 'Zur Auslegung des Art 16 Abs. 1 B-VG' (1990) 41 ÖzöR 1; Thaler, *Die Vertragsschlußkompetenz*; and F. Cede and G. Hafner, 'Austria', in Hollis, Blakeslee and Ederington (eds.), *National Treaty Law and Practice*, pp. 59, 70.

[81]   Art. III(2)(d) of the Constitution of Bosnia and Herzegovina; and both entities are parties to a number of international agreements which form the annexes to the Dayton Agreement (General Framework Agreement for Peace in Bosnia and Herzegovina), signed and entered into force 14 December 1995, (1996) 35 ILM 89.

[82]   Under Art. 151 of the Basic Law of Hong Kong, the region, using the name 'Hong Kong, China', may conclude international agreements in certain fields, including trade and air service agreements (Arts 116, 133–4, 152, and 155 of the Basic Law of the Hong Kong Special Administration Region of the People's Republic of China). Prior to being retroceded to China, Hong Kong concluded several international agreements as a separate international legal person, which have continued to this day.

[83]   Di Marzo, *Component Units of Federal States*, pp. 172–3, advances a theory of cumulative or shared responsibility, according to which both the component unit and the

1. Separate international legal personality?

Whatever the heterogeneity of practice described above, the question remains whether federated entities with the power to contract internationally binding legal obligations in the form of treaty-making powers – perhaps the quintessential requirement for international legal personality, however limited – can qualify as legal persons under international law.[84]

Such an argument has met with some resistance, due partly to the fear that such status for federated entities could lead to the fragmentation of the legal personality of the federal State.[85] Yet, if one considers the argument carefully, it neither suggests that federated entities are different and new legal persons, to the exclusion of the federal State, nor that they are the same legal person. On the contrary, a federal State remains vested with plenary or universal legal personality, whereas the legal personality of a federated entity remains limited, confined under international law as a corollary to constitutionally defined prerogatives to enter into treaties. What this overlapping conception of international legal personality would suggest is that the personality of the federal State and that of the federated entity never exist concurrently, in the sense that, through the constitutional mode of allocating competences, each level of personality operates within a different network of legal relations.

2. Reconciling the treaty-making power with the sovereignty of the State

Whatever the practice of States might suggest, it behoves international lawyers to resist the temptation to declare that federated entities, whatever their treaty-making prerogatives, have become separate subjects of international law. A first concern is primarily evidentiary: many of these 'agreements' are rarely published or consolidated in a manner that would

federal government would be simultaneously responsible for the same breach of international law. His argument is expressly policy-based, and does not rely on actual practice.

[84] Ago defines international legal personality in a functional manner: it 'is merely a concise way of describing the situation of an entity to which the international legal order attributes subjective legal situations, that is, subjective rights, faculties, powers and legal obligations': see R. Ago, 'Second Report on State Responsibility', *Yearbook of the International Law Commission*, 1970, vol. II, UN Doc. A/CN.4/233, p. 19, fn. 106.

[85] This is most apparent in the case of Belgium, where the federated entities' international competences are particularly strong: see Alen and Peeters, 'Federal Belgium within the International Legal Order', pp. 135–6; and Van den Brande, 'The International Legal Position of Flanders', pp. 150–1.

allow for an evaluation of their legal character.[86] Furthermore, in practice the federal governments have invariably stepped in, either during the
negotiating process or *post hoc*, to ratify the acts of their component
entities, and to assume international responsibility for them.[87] This
weakens the claim of such federated entities to act independently.

International law itself has developed techniques to ignore or interpret
away alternatives to a State-centric approach. As regards sub-State
actors, for example, their activities are simply projected back to the
national level.[88] Currently, as a matter of international law, the federal
State comes to be bound as a matter of international law when the acts by
sub-State units or federated entities have international legal consequences.[89] This is so regardless of the allocation of competences on the
constitutional level of a State and the degree of control by the federal
State over a given act.[90] It seems generally accepted that holding the

---

[86] Hollis, 'Why State Consent Still Matters', p. 150. Di Marzo, *Component Units of Federal
States*, Ch 2, attempts to systematise and catalogue the practice of some States, but
readily concedes, *ibid.*, p. 59, that 'a correct estimate of the practice is exceptionally
difficult to obtain'.

[87] See, e.g., Wildhaber, Scheidegger and Schinzel, 'Switzerland', p. 669, with respect to the
Canton of Jura, where the Swiss Federal Council authorised the Swiss Ambassador to act for
the canton of Jura in signing an agreement on cultural and technical cooperation with the
Republic of the Seychelles. For the practice of Canada and the United States, see, *supra.*, n. 34.

[88] This is the general approach taken by the International Law Commission in Article 4 of
the Articles on the Responsibility of States for Internationally Wrongful Acts, in Report
of the International Law Commission on the Work of its Fifty-Third Session, UN Doc.
A/56/10, chap. V (2001), GAOR 56th Sess. Supp. 10. See also, C. Schreuer, 'The Waning
of the Sovereign State: Towards a New Paradigm for International Law?' (1993) 4
European Journal of International Law 447, 455.

[89] This rule is confirmed in Article 7 of the Articles on State Responsibility, which states that
'the conduct of an organ of a territorial government within a State shall also be considered as
an act of that State under international law, *provided that organ was acting in that capacity in
the case in question*' (emphasis added). There is divergence as to the reasons for this
attribution. On the one hand, the federated entity can simply be seen as an organ of the
federal State. On the other hand, where an organ of a component state engages in conduct
which amounts to a specific breach of an obligation incumbent upon the component state as
a separate subject of international law, the international responsibility of the federal State
could be invoked, but only for direct responsibility: see Report of the International Law
Commission on the Work of its Twenty-Sixth Session, *Yearbook of the International Law
Commission*, 1974, vol. II, pt. I, UN Doc. A/9610/Rev.1, 157, p. 280.

[90] But *cf. ibid.*, p. 281, where the International Law Commission foresaw the possibility
of separate responsibility for sub-State entities in certain, extremely limited
circumstances:

> [w]here an organ of a component State of a federal State acts in a sphere in
> which the component State has international obligations that are incumbent
> on it and not on the federal State, that component State clearly emerges at the

federation bound is consistent with the idea that the internationally acknowledged treaty-making power of federated entities does not come into being by the federal constitution's conferral thereof upon the constituent units, but only if it is accepted by the contracting partners.[91] This suggests that there must be international recognition of the domestic constitutional arrangements for them to have legal effect in international law. States contracting with a federated entity are thus reassured that the federation will be ultimately responsible should that entity fail to meet its international legal obligations.[92] It seems that the perspective of international law remains that parent States are the ultimate addressees of both the primary and the secondary obligations arising from a treaty concluded by a federated entity, even if the two levels of obligation need not necessarily have identical addressees.[93]

There is also a conceptual argument as regards the international legal subjecthood of sub-State entities, which goes beyond Kelsen's claim that

> international level as a subject of international law separate from the federal State, and not merely as a territorial government entity subordinate to the federal State. *It stands to reason that in this case the conduct of the organ in question is, in virtue of article 5 of the present draft, the act of the component state; the problem of attributing the conduct in question to the federal State does not even arise in this hypothetical case, which thus falls automatically outside the scope of those covered by this article* [emphasis added].

However, the Commission was careful to explain, *ibid.*, that it is 'another matter to determine in such a case, not to what subject of international law the act is to be attributed, but what subject is to be held internationally responsible for that act'.

[91] C. Tomuschat, 'Component Territorial Units of States under International Law' in L. Daniele (ed.), *Regioni ed autonomie territoriale nel diritto internazionale ed europeo* (Naples: Scientifica Napoli, 2006), pp. 31, 48, a federation 'makes an offer which can be accepted by other States, without any obligation for any of them to do so'.

[92] As is pointed out in A. Aust, *Modern Treaty Law and Practice*, 2nd edn (Cambridge University Press, 2007), pp. 63–71, sovereign States frequently assume international legal responsibility for the agreements of sub-State actors, referring to the practice of Germany, Switzerland, Belgium, the United Kingdom, Bosnia and Herzegovina and China (although strictly in relation to Hong Kong and Macau, so-called 'Special Administrative Regions). *Cf.* the case of Mexico, which at Art. 117, para. 1 of its constitution expressly denies the binding nature of agreements concluded by its federated states: L. M. Díaz, 'Mexico', in Hollis, Blakeslee and Ederington (eds.), *National Treaty Law and Practice*, pp. 439, 450.

[93] See A. Peters, 'Treaty-Making Power', in Wolfrum (ed.), *Max Planck Encyclopaedia of Public International Law* Oxford: Oxford University Press, 2012), vol. X, p. 56, para. 32. This accords with the view expressed in O. J. Lissitzyn, 'Territorial Entities other than Independent States in the Law of Treaties' (1968-III) 125 *Recueil des Cours* 1, p. 84, that international law imposes only two prerequisites on sub-State entity treaty-making: (1) the consent of the federal State responsible for the sub-State actor; and (2) the willingness of the sub-State actor's treaty partners to regard it as capable of entering into treaties.

such entities are merely agents or designees of the State,[94] or that the federal State acts indirectly through its component units.[95] Independent treaty-making powers need not necessarily entail independent international personality, but in fact can be reconciled with the principle of State sovereignty, of which the power to enter into treaties is an essential attribute. Even if a State wishes, within its own constitutional arrangements, to allow its component units to exercise the sovereign prerogative of entering into treaties, the treaty-making power of such units derives from the basic competence of the sovereign State, as a whole, to conclude treaties. So goes this argument, the sovereignty of the State will stand behind any treaty concluded by a competent level of that State, be it the federal level or the federated level; any obligations thus contracted will bind the State as a whole, which will be responsible at international law for their breach. Accordingly, reference by international law to a State's domestic constitutional arrangements[96] would serve to reinforce its sovereignty in international law, rather than to disperse it.

In the final analysis, treaty-making by federated entities remains for now a consequence of the constitutional arrangements of a State; and the conclusion drawn here is that international law indeed takes its starting point in the domestic law of the State concerned. If so, future enquiry will be needed to understand whether such reference to domestic law incorporates the rules and norms of the latter into international law itself, and to gauge the effects at international law of such reference or incorporation.

---

[94] Lissitzyn, 'Territorial Entities in the Law of Treaties', p. 15, claims that while treaty conclusion by a dependent entity may lead to the determination that the sub-State entity is an international person possessing its own treaty-making capacity, whether or not it is a 'State, a second juridical explanation is also possible where the sub-State actor may be regarded as having no distinct international personality or capacity of its own, but merely the authority to act as an agent or organ of the dominant State which retains the requisite capacity. See also Hollis, 'Why State Consent Still Matters', 155; and with regard to Canada, see A. E. Gotlieb, *Canadian Treaty-Making* (Toronto: Butterworths, 1968), p. 31.

[95] Kelsen, *General Principles*, pp. 260–1.

[96] Van den Brande, 'The International Legal Position of Flanders', 151, fn. 31, suggests such reference to domestic law constitutes '*renvoi*', citing J. P. Rougeaux, 'Les renvois du droit international au droit interne' (1977) 81(1) *Revue générale de droit international public* 167, 362: 'un procédé technique par lequel un ordre juridique déclare applicable, pour régler une question dont la solution lui incombe, une norme d'un autre ordre juridique et non l'une de ces normes'.

INDEX